Merrill
Algebra Two
with Trigonometry

Foster · Rath · Winters

Charles E. Merrill Publishing Co.
A Bell & Howell Company
Columbus, Ohio

Toronto · London · Sydney

Alan G. Foster is chairman of the Mathematics Department at Addison Trail High School, Addison, Illinois. He has taught mathematics courses at every level of the high school curriculum. Mr. Foster obtained his B.S. from Illinois State University and his M.A. in mathematics from the University of Illinois, with additional work at Northern Illinois University, Purdue, Northwestern, and Princeton. Mr. Foster is active in professional organizations at local, state, and national levels, frequently speaking and conducting workshops. He is a past president of the Illinois Council of Teachers of Mathematics. Mr. Foster is a co-author of *Merrill Geometry*.

James N. Rath has 25 years of classroom experience in teaching mathematics at every level of the high school curriculum. He has also taught calculus at the college level. Mr. Rath is a former head of the Mathematics Department at Darien High School, Darien, Connecticut. He earned his B.A. in Philosophy from the Catholic University of America. He obtained both his M. Ed. and his M.A. in mathematics from Boston College. He developed a minicourse in BASIC for the Darien Public Schools. Mr. Rath is a member of various professional organizations in which he is active at local, state, and national levels. He is a co-author of *Merrill Pre-Algebra*.

Leslie J. Winters is chairperson of the Mathematics Department at John F. Kennedy High School, Granada Hills, California. He has taught mathematics at every level from junior high to college. He received his B.A. in mathematics from Pepperdine University, his B.S. in secondary education from the University of Dayton, his M.S. in secondary education from the University of Southern California, and his M.A. in mathematics from Boston College. Mr. Winters is a frequent speaker at local, state, and national conferences. He is a past president of the California Mathematics Council–Southern Section. Mr. Winters was one of two recipients of the 1983 Presidential Award for Excellence in Mathematics Teaching in the state of California.

ISBN 0-675-05485-0
Published by
Charles E. Merrill Publishing Co.
A Bell & Howell Company
Columbus, Ohio 43216

Printed in the United States of America

Consultants

Dr. F. Joe Crosswhite
Professor Emeritus of
  Mathematics Education
Ohio State University
Columbus, Ohio

Margaret J. Kenney
Assistant to the Director
Mathematics Institute
Boston College
Chestnut Hill, Massachusetts

Reviewers

Diane M. Fite
Mathematics Teacher
Temple High School
Temple, Texas

Farris Joe Love
Mathematics Teacher
Memphis City Schools
Memphis, Tennessee

Carroll K. Melnyk
Instructional Program
  Administrator, Computers
Lubbock Independent School District
Lubbock, Texas

Michael A. Torrelli
Mathematics Department Chairperson
Maple Heights High School
Maple Heights, Ohio

Alfred M. Galante, Jr.
Mathematics Coordinator
Randolph Public Schools
Randolph, Massachusetts

Neil D. McBeth
Mathematics Department Chairperson
Eldorado High School
Albuquerque, New Mexico

Leo Armando Ramirez
Mathematics Teacher
McAllen High School
McAllen, Texas

Thomas Willard
Mathematics Department Chairperson
Burlingame High School
Burlingame, California

Staff

Editorial
Series Editor: Evangeline Seltzer; *Editors:* Jane Seliga, Angela Stovall;
Photo Editor: Barbara Buchholz; *Production Editor:* Joy Dickerson

Art
Book Designer: Larry W. Collins; Project Artist: Lewis H. Bolen

Preface

This third edition of *Merrill Algebra Two with Trigonometry* is designed for use by students in second-year high school algebra courses. The text, which was developed in the classroom by experienced high school teachers, is based on the successful prior editions of *Merrill Algebra Two with Trigonometry*. The goals of the text are to develop proficiency with mathematical skills, to expand understanding of mathematical concepts, to improve logical thinking, and to promote success. To achieve these goals, the following strategies are used.

Build upon a Solid Foundation. This program develops and utilizes the learning spiral. Students first review those concepts basic to the understanding of algebra. Students' understanding is thus solidified before the introduction of more difficult concepts.

Utilize Sound Pedagogy. *Merrill Algebra Two with Trigonometry* covers in logical sequence all topics generally presented at this level. Concepts are introduced when they are needed. Each concept presented is then used within that lesson and in later lessons.

Gear Presentation for Learning. An appropriate reading level has been maintained throughout the text. Furthermore, many photographs, illustrations, charts, graphs, and tables provide visual aids for the concepts and skills presented. Hence, students are able to read and learn with increased understanding.

Use Relevant Real-Life Applications. Applications are provided not only for practice but also to aid understanding of how concepts are used.

The text offers a variety of aids for the students.

Student Annotations	Help students identify important concepts as they study.
Selected Answers	Allow students to check their progress as they work. These answers are provided at the back of the text.
Mini-Review	Provides students with a quick review of skills and concepts taught previously.
Vocabulary	Enables students to focus on increasing their mathematical vocabulary.
Chapter Summary	Provides students with a compact listing of major concepts presented within each chapter.
Chapter Review	Permits students to review each chapter by working sample problems from each lesson.
Chapter Test	Enables students to check their own progress.
Cumulative Review	Helps students to maintain their skills in applying algebraic concepts.
Standardized Test Practice Questions	Help students to become familiar with types of questions that appear on standardized tests.

The following special features, which appear periodically throughout the text, provide interesting and useful extra topics.

Using Calculators   Instructs students in using a calculator. The use of the calculator is related to concepts taught within the chapter.

Reading Algebra   Provides students with the instruction needed to read and interpret mathematical symbolism.

Problem Solving   Illustrates several helpful strategies for solving mathematical problems.

Applications   Provide insights into the uses of mathematics in everyday life from a variety of disciplines.

Using Computers   Provides a computer program and exercises related to the objectives of the chapter.

Excursions in Algebra   Enliven and help maintain student interest by providing interesting side trips. Topics are varied and include history, glimpses into development of algebra, enrichment concepts, and puzzles.

The textbook contains an appendix on **BASIC** which provides instruction in writing programs using the BASIC computer language.

Teachers and students familiar with the earlier editions of this text will be pleased to see that the text has been updated in keeping with current trends. The clarity of explanations has been retained and the sequencing of topics improved in this new edition of *Merrill Algebra Two with Trigonometry*.

Table of Contents

1   Equations and Inequalities

2   Linear Relations and Functions

3 Systems of Equations and Inequalities

4 More Systems of Equations

5 Polynomials

6 Roots

7 Quadratic Equations

8 Quadratic Relations and Functions

9 Conics

Lessons

Distance, Parabolas, and Circles

Ellipses and Hyperbolas

Quadratic Systems

Review and Testing

Applications and Extensions

Technology

10 Polynomial Functions

Lessons

Functions and Factors

Zeros

Graphing, Composition, and Inverses

Review and Testing

Applications and Extensions

Technology

11 Rational Polynomial Expressions

Lessons

Review and Testing

Applications and Extensions

Technology

12 Exponential and Logarithmic Functions

Lessons

Review and Testing

Applications and Extensions

Technology

13   Sequences and Series

14   Probability

15 Statistics

16 Trigonometric Functions and Identities

17 Triangle Trigonometry

Appendix: BASIC

CHAPTER 1

Equations and Inequalities

Equations can be used in many areas of our everyday lives. For example, suppose an investment of $7500 in solar heating equipment results in a yearly savings of $450 on heating bills. In addition to this, the owner receives a $2100 tax credit from the government the first year only. How many years will it take for the savings to equal the investment? This problem can be solved using the equation $450y + 2100 = 7500$.

1-1 Expressions and Formulas

We often use mathematical expressions such as $4(x + 2y) - 5x^3$. This expression contains the following kinds of symbols.

constants: 4 2 5 3	
variables: x y	represent unknown quantities
operation symbols: + −	tell which operations are involved
grouping symbols: ( )	tell order for doing operations

The following numerical expressions all represent the number sixteen. Sixteen is called the **value** of each expression.

$$4^2 \qquad 9 + 7 \qquad (12 \div 2) + 10$$

In the expression 4^2, the **base** is 4 and the **exponent** is 2. An exponent indicates the number of times the base is used as a factor.

4^2 means $4 \cdot 4$. $\qquad$ 10^1 means 10. $\qquad$ x^5 means $x \cdot x \cdot x \cdot x \cdot x$.

What is the value of $4 + 3 \cdot 2$? You might evaluate the expression in one of the ways below.

Multiply 3 and 2. Then add 4.

$$4 + 3 \cdot 2 = 4 + 6$$
$$= 10$$

Add 4 and 3. Then multiply by 2.

$$4 + 3 \cdot 2 = 7 \cdot 2$$
$$= 14$$

Which answer is correct?

A numerical expression should have a unique value. To find this value, you must know the order for performing operations.

1. **Evaluate all powers.** 2. **Do all multiplications and divisions from left to right.** 3. **Do all additions and subtractions from left to right.**	*Order of Operations*

Thus, the value of $4 + 3 \cdot 2$ is 10.

Example

1 **Find the value of $4 + 8^2 \div 4 \cdot 2$.**

$$4 + 8^2 \div 4 \cdot 2 = 4 + 64 \div 4 \cdot 2 \quad \textit{Evaluate all powers.}$$
$$= 4 + 16 \cdot 2 \quad \textit{Do all multiplications and divisions left to right.}$$
$$= 4 + 32 \quad \textit{Do all additions and subtractions left to right.}$$
$$= 36$$

The value is 36.

Grouping symbols are used to clarify or change the order of operations. Two kinds of grouping symbols are parentheses ( ) and brackets [ ]. Start with the operations inside the innermost grouping symbols.

Example

2 **Find the value of $[(4 + 8)^2 \div 3] \cdot 2$.**

$$\begin{aligned}[(4 + 8)^2 \div 3] \cdot 2 &= [(12)^2 \div 3] \cdot 2 & \textit{First add 4 and 8.}\\ &= [144 \div 3] \cdot 2 & \textit{Then find } 12^2.\\ &= [48] \cdot 2 & \textit{Now divide 144 by 3.}\\ &= 96 & \textit{Multiply 48 by 2.}\end{aligned}$$

The value is 96.

Mathematical expressions that contain at least one variable are called **algebraic expressions.** You can evaluate an algebraic expression by replacing each variable with a value. The same variable may occur more than once in an expression. Replace each occurance of the variable with the same value.

Example

3 **Evaluate $5x^2 + 3xy$ if $x = -5$ and $y = 3$.**

$$\begin{aligned}5x^2 + 3xy &= 5(-5)^2 + 3(-5)(3) & \textit{Replace x by } -5 \textit{ and y by 3.}\\ &= 5(25) + 3(-5)(3) & \textit{Find } (-5)^2.\\ &= 125 + (-45) & \textit{Multiply left to right.}\\ &= 80 & \textit{Add.}\end{aligned}$$

The value is 80.

A **formula** is a mathematical sentence about the relationships among certain quantities. For example, $A = l \cdot w$ relates the area of a rectangle to its length and width.

In a formula, if you know replacements for every variable except one, you can find a replacement for that variable.

Example

4 **The relationship between Celsius temperature *(C)* and Fahrenheit temperature *(F)* is given by $C = \dfrac{5(F - 32)}{9}$. Find *C* if $F = 68$.**

$$C = \frac{5(F - 32)}{9} \qquad \textit{Write the formula.}$$

$$C = \frac{5(68 - 32)}{9} \qquad \textit{Replace F by 68.}$$

$$C = \frac{180}{9} \qquad \textit{Subtract 32 from 68. Multiply 5 by 36.}$$

$$C = 20 \qquad \textit{Divide 180 by 9.}$$

The Celsius temperature is 20°.

Example

5 Simple interest is calculated by using the formula $I = prt$. In the formula, p represents the principal in dollars, r represents the interest rate (in hundredths), and t represents the time in years. Find the amount of interest for two years if the principal is \$6000 and the rate is 12%.

$$I = prt$$
$$I = 6000(0.12)(2)$$
$$I = 1440$$

The interest on \$6000 at 12% for 2 years is \$1440.

Exploratory Exercises

Find the value of each expression.

1. $2 + 8 - 3$
2. $5 - 3 \cdot 2$
3. $5 - (4 + 3)^2$
4. $2(6 + 1)$
5. $2 \cdot 6 + 1$
6. $3^3 - 2^3$
7. $3(2^2 + 3)$
8. $2 + 5^2$
9. $2(3 + 8) - 1$
10. $2(8) - 8 \div 4$
11. $5^2 - (3 + 2)^2$
12. $3 + (3 - 3)^3 - 3$

Written Exercises

Find the value of each expression.

1. $(6 + 5) \cdot 4 - 3$
2. $(6 + 5)(4 - 3)$
3. $12 + 8 \div 4$
4. $12 + (8 \div 4)$
5. $12 \div 8 \cdot 4$
6. $12 \div (8 \cdot 4)$
7. $(5 + 3)^2 - 16 \div 4$
8. $5 + 3^2 - 16 \div 4$
9. $2 \cdot 9 \div 6 + 7$
10. $8 - 2 \cdot 3 - 3$
11. $12 + 18 \div 6 + 7$
12. $4 + 8 \cdot 4 \div 2 - 10$
13. $[19 - (8 - 1)] \div 3$
14. $-8 \div [20 \div (16 - 11)]$
15. $[(-8 + 3) \times 4 - 2] \div 6$
16. $3 + [8 \div (9 - 2 \times 4)]$

Evaluate if $a = 3$, $b = 7$, $c = -2$, $d = \frac{1}{2}$, and $e = 0.3$.

17. $6a^3 - 2b$
18. $3ab - 6bc$
19. $3ad + bc$
20. $c^2 - 5d$
21. $5c + be$
22. $8e - 3bc$
23. $(a + c)^3 + d^2$
24. $(a + b - d)^2$
25. $12a^2 + bc$
26. $4a \div 12cd$
27. $\dfrac{6ac}{d}$
28. $\dfrac{3ab}{cd}$
29. $\dfrac{3ce}{d^2}$
30. $\dfrac{10e^2}{3d}$
31. $\dfrac{5a + 3c}{3b}$
32. $\dfrac{3ab^2 - c^3}{a + c}$
33. $(5a + 3d)^2 - e^2$
34. $(3b - 21d)^2$

Find the interest, I, given the following values for the principal, rate, and time.

35. $p = \$1000$, $r = 6\%$, and $t = 3$ years
36. $p = \$2500$, $r = 9\%$, and $t = 30$ months
37. $p = \$5000$, $r = 8\%$, and $t = 9$ months
38. $p = \$2000$, $r = 8\%$, and $t = 9$ months
39. $p = \$20,000$, $r = 14\frac{1}{2}\%$, and $t = 6$ years
40. $p = \$65,000$, $r = 16\%$, and $t = 63$ months

The formula for the area of a trapezoid is $A = \frac{h}{2}(b_1 + b_2)$. A represents the measure of the area, h represents the measure of the altitude, and b_1 and b_2 represent the measures of the bases. Calculate the measure of the area of each trapezoid given the following values.

41. $b_1 = 12$, $b_2 = 20$, and $h = 8$

42. $b_1 = 4$, $b_2 = 11$, and $h = 7$

43. $h = 10$, $b_1 = 6$, and $b_2 = 14$

44. $h = 8$, $b_2 = 16$, and $b_1 = 12$

45. $h = 8$, $b_1 = 8.6$, and $b_2 = 14.8$

46. $h = 12$, $b_2 = 9.7$, and $b_1 = 6.2$

47. $h = 9$, $b_2 = 7\frac{2}{3}$, and $b_1 = 4\frac{1}{6}$

48. $h = 6\frac{1}{2}$, $b_1 = 8\frac{1}{3}$, and $b_2 = 12$

Challenge

> **Example:** Use five 5's to write an expression that has a value of 10.
>
> $$\frac{55}{5} - \frac{5}{5} = 10 \quad \text{or} \quad 5 \cdot 5 - (5 + 5 + 5) = 10$$

49. Use nine 8's to write an expression that has a value of 14.

50. Use six 7's to write an expression that has a value of 110.

51. Use four 3's to write an expression for each integer from 1 to 10.

Using Calculators _____ Evaluating Expressions

A calculator can be used to evaluate expressions. It is best to use a calculator that evaluates expressions in the algebraic mode. That is, the algebraic order of operations should hold when the calculator performs any sequence of operations.

Example: Evaluate $-3 + 5 \div 2 + 5^2$.

ENTER: 3 $\boxed{+/-}$ $\boxed{+}$ 5 $\boxed{\div}$ 2 $\boxed{+}$ 5 $\boxed{x^2}$ $\boxed{=}$

DISPLAY: 3 -3 5   2 -0.5 5 25 24.5

The value is 24.5.

The $\boxed{+/-}$ key changes the sign of the number in the display. What does the $\boxed{x^2}$ key do?

If your calculator does not use the algebraic order of operations, your answer will be different. In such cases, read the manual for your calculator and adapt the order of entry accordingly.

Exercises
Use a calculator to evaluate each expression.

1. $6^2 \cdot 2 - 4 \cdot 2$

2. $42 - 54 \div 6$

3. $-24 \div 6 - 3^2 \div 3$

4. $8 + 5^2 + 6 \div 3$

5. $13 - 4(17)^2$

6. $32(81 - 16)$

Understanding algebra depends largely on understanding the symbols used in algebra. The symbols of language are the letters of the alphabet. In English, there are just 26 letters, and most letters have one or two sounds. On the other hand, there are many symbols used in mathematics, and the meaning of these symbols frequently depends on how they are used. Notice how the symbol 4 is used in each expression.

Expression	Translation
4	four
40	forty
0.04	four hundredths
4^2	four squared
2^4	two to the fourth power
$\dfrac{1}{4}$	one-fourth

In like manner, the symbol — may be used in several ways.

Expression	Translation
$9 - 4$	nine minus four
-4	negative four
$\dfrac{3}{4}$	three-fourths

Exercises

Match each expression with the correct translation.

1. $3a$
2. a^3
3. $3a^2 + 1$
4. $(3a + 1)^2$
5. $(3a)^2 + 1$
6. $\dfrac{a}{3}$

a. three times a squared plus one
b. three times a
c. three times a plus one, quantity squared
d. a divided by three
e. a to the third power
f. three times a, quantity squared, plus one

Write each algebraic expression in words.

7. $3ad + bc$
8. $6a^3 - 2b$
9. $(a + b - c)^2$
10. $(a + c)^3 + d^2$
11. $\dfrac{6ac}{d}$
12. $\dfrac{5a + 3c}{3b}$

1-2 Sets of Numbers

You should be familiar with the following sets of numbers and their graphs.

- The set of **whole numbers, W**

  W = {0, 1, 2, 3, 4, . . .}

- The set of **integers, Z**

  Z = {. . . , −2, −1, 0, 1, 2, . . .}

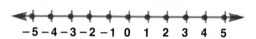

- The set of **rational numbers, Q**

$$Q = \left\{ \begin{array}{l} \text{all numbers that can be expressed} \\ \text{in the form } \dfrac{m}{n}, \text{ where } m \text{ and } n \\ \text{are integers and } n \text{ is } not \text{ zero} \end{array} \right\}$$

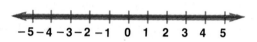

Q = {all numbers that can be expressed as either terminating or repeating decimals.}

Repeating decimals such as 8.34̄ and 1.2121 . . . are rational numbers.

Examples of rational numbers are $-\dfrac{2}{3}$, 5.8, −7, and 0. Even if all the rational numbers could be graphed on the number line, there would still be "holes" in the number line.

- The set of **irrational numbers, I**

  I = {all nonterminating, nonrepeating decimals}

Examples of irrational numbers are $\sqrt{2}$, π, and $-\sqrt{7}$. Irrational numbers combined with the rational numbers form the set of **real numbers.** The graph of all real numbers is the entire number line.

Here are some examples of nonrepeating decimals:
1.010010001 . . .
0.1234567 . . .

- The set of **real numbers, R**

  R = {all rationals and irrationals}

> **Each real number corresponds to exactly one point on the number line. Each point on the number line corresponds to exactly one real number.**

Completeness Property of Real numbers

Examples

Name the sets of numbers to which each number belongs.

1 $\sqrt{5}$

irrationals (I)
reals (R)

2 $\dfrac{3}{2}$

rationals (Q)
reals (R)

3 −7

integers (Z)
rationals (Q)
reals (R)

Examples

Evaluate each numerical expression. Then name the sets of numbers to which each number belongs.

4 $\sqrt{9}$

$\sqrt{9} = 3$
whole numbers (W), integers (Z), rationals (Q), reals (R)

5 $6 \div 10$

$6 \div 10 = 0.6$ or $\frac{3}{5}$
rationals (Q)
reals (R)

Exploratory Exercises

Name the sets of numbers to which each number belongs.

1. -8 2. $\frac{4}{3}$ 3. -2.6 4. π 5. $-\frac{7}{2}$ 6. 10

7. $\sqrt{10}$ 8. 5.11   9. 0   10. $-\frac{12}{3}$ 11. -1.0 12. $\sqrt{16}$

Written Exercises

Evaluate each numerical expression. Then name the sets of numbers to which each number belongs.

1. $8 - 7$ 2. $7 - 8$ 3. $-54 \div 6$ 4. $68 \div 100$
5. -2.4×10 6. $3.9 + 2.6$ 7. $9.2 - 8.2$ 8. $6 \div 2^2$
9. $\sqrt{25}$ 10. $\sqrt{36 + 5}$ 11. $\sqrt{100} - 100$ 12. $0 - \sqrt{4}$
13. $\sqrt{2} - \sqrt{2}$ 14. $\sqrt{9} \div \sqrt{4}$ 15. $\sqrt{9 \div 3}$ 16. $\sqrt{6}(\sqrt{9} - 3)$

Write *true* or *false*. If false, give a counterexample.

17. Every whole number is an integer.
18. Every integer is a whole number.
19. Every rational number is an integer.
20. Every real number is irrational.
21. Every irrational number is a real number.
22. Every integer is a rational number.
23. Every real number is either a rational number or an irrational number.
24. Every rational number is either an integer or a whole number.

mini-review

Simplify.
1. $15 - 3 \cdot 4$ 2. $8 \div 4 \cdot 2$
3. $5^2 \div [14 - (7 + 2)]$

Evaluate if $a = -4$ and $b = 2.5$.
4. a^2b 5. $2a + 3b - 7$

Using Calculators ———————— Irrational Numbers

If n is a whole number that is not a perfect square, then $\sqrt{n}$ is irrational. The square root key on a calculator can be used to approximate values of irrational numbers of the form $\sqrt{n}$. For example, $\sqrt{17} \approx 4.1231056$.

Exercises

Find an irrational number of the form $\sqrt{n}$ between each pair of given numbers.

1. 2 and 3   2. 6 and 7   3. 4.6 and 4.8   4. 10.1 and 10.2

1-3 Properties of Addition and Multiplication

Operations with real numbers have several important properties. One of the basic properties of addition and multiplication is **commutativity.** The order in which two real numbers are added or multiplied does not change their sum or their product.

$$8 + 3 = 3 + 8 \qquad 24 \cdot 9 = 9 \cdot 24$$

Another basic property of addition and multiplication is **associativity.** The way three or more real numbers are grouped, or associated, does not change their sum or their product.

$$(8 + 6) + 4 = 8 + (6 + 4) \qquad (11 \cdot 4) \cdot 3 = 11 \cdot (4 \cdot 3)$$

The sum of any real number and zero is identical to the original number. So, for real numbers the **additive identity** is zero.

$$9.2 + 0 = 9.2 \qquad 0 + \sqrt{5} = \sqrt{5}$$

The product of any real number and one is identical to the original number. So, for real numbers the **multiplicative identity** is one.

$$\frac{7}{9} \cdot 1 = \frac{7}{9} \qquad (1)(6.5) = 6.5$$

Each real number has a unique **additive inverse.** The sum of a number and its additive inverse is zero.

$$2 + (-2) = 0 \qquad -4.3 + 4.3 = 0$$

Each nonzero real number has a unique **multiplicative inverse,** or **reciprocal.** The product of a number and its reciprocal is one.

$$3\left(\frac{1}{3}\right) = 1 \qquad (-0.1)(-10) = 1$$

The following chart summarizes the properties for addition and multiplication.

For any real numbers a, b, and c		
	Addition	*Multiplication*
Commutative	$a + b = b + a$	$a \cdot b = b \cdot a$
Associative	$(a + b) + c = a + (b + c)$	$(a \cdot b) \cdot c = a \cdot (B \cdot c)$
Identity	$a + 0 = a = 0 + a$	$a \cdot 1 = a = 1 \cdot a$
Inverse	$a + (-a) = 0 = (-a) + a$	If a is *not* zero, then $a \cdot \dfrac{1}{a} = 1 = \dfrac{1}{a} \cdot a.$

Property of Real Numbers

The **distributive property** relates the operations of addition and multiplication.

> **For all real numbers a, b, and c,**
> $$a(b + c) = ab + ac \text{ and } (b + c)a = ba + ca.$$

Distributive Property

$$5(8 + 3) = 5(8) + 5(3)$$
$$5(11) = 40 + 15$$
$$55 = 55$$

$$\frac{1}{2}\left(6 + (-2)\right) = \frac{1}{2}(6) + \frac{1}{2}(-2)$$
$$\frac{1}{2}(4) = 3 + (-1)$$
$$2 = 2$$

The distributive property can be used to simplify expressions containing like terms. **Like terms** are identical except for their numerical factors. In $5y + 3x + 7y + 2y^2$, for example, $5y$ and $7y$ are like terms. Notice that $5y$, $3x$, and $2y^2$ are unlike terms.

Examples

1 **Simplify $5y + 3x + 7y + 2y^2$.**

$$\begin{aligned}
5y + 3x + 7y + 2y^2 &= 5y + (3x + 7y) + 2y^2 & \text{\textit{Associative Property for Addition}} \\
&= 5y + (7y + 3x) + 2y^2 & \text{\textit{Commutative Property for Addition}} \\
&= (5y + 7y) + 3x + 2y^2 & \text{\textit{Associative Property for Addition}} \\
&= (5 + 7)y + 3x + 2y^2 & \text{\textit{Distributive Property}} \\
&= 12y + 3x + 2y^2
\end{aligned}$$

2 **Simplify $\left(\frac{1}{2}a\right)(2b) + ab$.**

$$\begin{aligned}
\left(\frac{1}{2}a\right)(2b) + ab &= \frac{1}{2}(a \cdot 2)b + ab & \text{\textit{Associative Property for Multiplication}} \\
&= \frac{1}{2}(2 \cdot a)b + ab & \text{\textit{Commutative Property for Multiplication}} \\
&= \left(\frac{1}{2} \cdot 2\right)(ab) + ab & \text{\textit{Associative Property for Multiplication}} \\
&= 1ab + 1ab & \text{\textit{Multiplicative Inverse and Multiplicative Identity}} \\
&= (1 + 1)ab & \text{\textit{Distributive Property}} \\
&= 2ab
\end{aligned}$$

Exploratory Exercises

State the property shown in each of the following.

1. $8 + (6 + 4) = (8 + 6) + 4$

2. $7(5) = 5(7)$

3. $a(3 - 2) = a \cdot 3 - a \cdot 2$

4. $8 + (1 + 6) = 8 + (6 + 1)$

5. $3 + (-3) = 0$

6. $2(3 + 6) = 2(3) + 2(6)$

7. $3 + 6 = 6 + 3$

8. $8(6 - 7) = (6 - 7)8$

9. $8\left(\frac{1}{8}\right) = 1$

10. $3(47) = 3(40) + 3(7)$

Written Exercises

State the property shown in each of the following.

1. $3(9) = 9(3)$
2. $(5 + 6) + 3 = 5 + (6 + 3)$
3. $(4 + 11) \cdot 6 = 4(6) + 11(6)$
4. $(a + b) + [-(a + b)] = 0$
5. $11 + a = a + 11$
6. $(3 + 9) + 14 = 14 + (3 + 9)$
7. $3 + (a + b) = (a + b) + 3$
8. $7 \cdot 1 = 7$
9. $8(5 + 3) = 40 + 24$
10. $3a + 6 = 3(a + 2)$
11. $(11a + 3b) + 0 = 11a + 3b$
12. $8(4) = 4(8)$
13. $3\left(\dfrac{1}{3}\right) = 1$
14. $(4 + 9a)2b = 2b(4 + 9a).$
15. $a + b + 0 = a + b$
16. $\left(\dfrac{1}{m}\right)m = 1$
17. $11(3a + 2b) = 11(2b + 3a)$
18. $5a + (-5a) = 0$
19. $1 = ax^2 \cdot \dfrac{1}{ax^2}$
20. $0 + 7 = 7$

Simplify. Combine like terms.

21. $8 + 15 - 3$
22. $5(13 + 25)$
23. $7x + 8y + 9y - 5x$
24. $3a + 5b + 7a - 3b$
25. $3(5a + 6b) + 8(2a - b)$
26. $2(7c - 5d) - 3(d + 2c)$
27. $\dfrac{1}{4}(12 + 20a) + \dfrac{3}{4}(12 + 20a)$
28. $\dfrac{1}{2}(17 - 4x) - \dfrac{3}{4}(6 - 16x)$
29. $\dfrac{2}{3}\left(\dfrac{1}{2}a + 3b\right) + \dfrac{1}{2}\left(\dfrac{2}{3}a + b\right)$
30. $\dfrac{3}{4}(2x - 5y) + \dfrac{1}{2}\left(\dfrac{2}{3}x + 4y\right)$
31. $7(0.2m + 0.3n) + 5(0.6m - n)$
32. $9(0.6a - 0.2c) + 3(0.2a + 1.1c)$

33. If $a + b = a$, what is the value of b? What is b called?
34. If $ab = 1$, what is the value of a? What is a called?
35. If $ab = a$, what is the value of b? What is b called?
36. If $a + b = 0$, what is the value of a? What is a called?

Challenge

A set is *closed with respect to addition* if the sum of any two elements is also in the set. A set is *closed with respect to multiplication* if the product of any two elements is also in the set.

Decide whether each set is closed with respect to the given operation.

Examples: R, addition	I, multiplication
Yes, since the sum of any two real numbers is also a real number.	No, since the product of two irrational numbers is not always irrational.
	$\sqrt{5} \cdot \sqrt{5} = 5$ *This product is rational.*

37. R, multiplication
38. W, addition
39. I, addition
40. Q, multiplication
41. Z, addition
42. Z, multiplication

1-4 Solving Equations

Some relations have three important properties. In your study of arithmetic, you have assumed these properties for equality.

For any real number a, $a = a$.	*Reflexive Property of Equality*
For all real numbers a and b, **if $a = b$, then $b = a$.**	*Symmetric Property of Equality*
For all real numbers a, b, and c, **if $a = b$ and $b = c$, then $a = c$.**	*Transitive Property of Equality*

Example 1

State the property of equality shown in each of the following.

  a. $21.4 = 21.4$ **a.** reflexive property

  b. If $36 \cdot 2 = 72$, then $72 = 36 \cdot 2$.   **b.** symmetric property

  c. If $8 = 6 + 2$ and $6 + 2 = 5 + 3$,
     then $8 = 5 + 3$.   **c.** transitive property

Sentences with variables to be replaced, such as $5 = x + 4$, are called *open sentences*. Finding the replacements for the variable that make a sentence true is called *solving* the open sentence. Each of these is called a **solution** of the open sentence. The **solution set** of an open sentence is the set of *all* replacements for variables that make the sentence true.

An **equation** is a statement of equality between two mathematical expressions. Some equations may be solved by substitution. Recall that the **substitution property** allows you to replace an expression with an equivalent expression.

Example 2

Solve $y = 8(0.3) + 1.2$.

$y = 8(0.3) + 1.2$
$y = 2.4 + 1.2$ *Substitute 2.4 for 8(0.3).*
$y = 3.6$ *Substitute 3.6 for 2.4 + 1.2.*

The solution is 3.6

Sometimes an equation can be solved by adding the same number to both sides of the equation. The following example shows how to solve an equation and check the result.

Example

3 **Solve $x + 28.3 = 56.0$.**

$$x + 28.3 = 56.0$$
$$x + 28.3 + (-28.3) = 56.0 + (-28.3)$$
$$x = 27.7$$

Add -28.3 to both sides.
Substitution.

Check:
$$x + 28.3 = 56.0$$
$$27.7 + 28.3 \overset{?}{=} 56.0$$
$$56.0 = 56.0 \ ✔$$

The solution is 27.7.

The solution is correct.

The equation in example 3 could also have been solved by subtracting 28.3 from both sides.

> **For any real numbers a, b, and c, if $a = b$,**
> **then $a + c = b + c$**
> **and $a - c = b - c$.**

Addition and Subtraction Properties of Equality

Sometimes an equation can be solved by multiplying both sides by the same number. Study how this is done below.

Examples

4 **Solve $7x = 42$.**

$$7x = 42$$
$$\frac{1}{7} \cdot 7x = \frac{1}{7} \cdot 42$$
$$x = 6$$

Multiply both sides by $\frac{1}{7}$.
Substitution.

Check: $7x = 42$
$$7(6) \overset{?}{=} 42$$
$$42 = 42 \ ✔$$

The solution is 6.

5 **Solve $-\frac{2}{3}k = 14$.**

$$-\frac{3}{2}\left(-\frac{2}{3}\right)k = \left(-\frac{3}{2}\right)(14)$$
$$k = -21$$

Multiply both sides by $-\frac{3}{2}$.
Substitution.

The solution is -21. *Check this result.*

The equation in Example 4 could also have been solved by dividing both sides by 7.

> **For any real numbers a, b, and c, if $a = b$,**
> **then $a \cdot c = b \cdot c$ and, if c is not zero, $\dfrac{a}{c} = \dfrac{b}{c}$.**

Multiplication and Division Properties of Equality

Some equations involve more than one operation. You may combine steps when solving equations.

Examples

6 Solve $5x - 7 = 23$.

$$5x - 7 = 23$$
$$5x - 7 + 7 = 23 + 7 \qquad \text{Addition Property}$$
$$5x = 30 \qquad \text{Substitution}$$
$$\frac{5x}{5} = \frac{30}{5} \qquad \text{Division Property}$$
$$x = 6 \qquad \text{Substitution}$$

Check:
$$5x - 7 = 23$$
$$5(6) - 7 \stackrel{?}{=} 23$$
$$30 - 7 \stackrel{?}{=} 23$$
$$23 = 23 \quad ✔$$

The solution is 6.

7 Solve $\frac{3}{4}(8a + 20) - 2a = \frac{2}{3} + 1\frac{1}{3}$.

$$\frac{3}{4}(8a + 20) - 2a = \frac{2}{3} + 1\frac{1}{3}$$
$$6a + 15 - 2a = 2 \qquad \text{Distributive and Substitution Properties}$$
$$4a + 15 = 2 \qquad \text{Commutative, Distributive and Substitution Properties}$$
$$4a = -13 \qquad \text{Subtraction and Substitution Properties}$$
$$a = -\frac{13}{4} \qquad \text{Division and Substitution Properties}$$

The solution is $-\frac{13}{4}$.   *Check this result.*

Exploratory Exercises

State the property shown in each of the following.

1. $3 + (2 + 3) = 3 + (2 + 3)$
2. $3 + (2 + 3) = 3 + 5$
3. If $x + 3 = 7$, then $x = 4$.
4. If $5x = 40$, then $x = 8$.
5. If $7 = 2 + 5$, and $2 + 5 = \sqrt{49}$, then $7 = \sqrt{49}$.
6. If $8 + 1 = 9$ and $9 = 3 + 6$, then $8 + 1 = 3 + 6$.
7. If $3 = 2 + 1$, then $2 + 1 = 3$.
8. If $5 + 7 = 12$, then $12 = 7 + 5$.
9. If $2 + 1 = 3$, then $6 + (2 + 1) = 6 + 3$.
10. If $8 = 6 + 2$ and $6 + 2 = 5 + 3$, then $8 = 5 + 3$.
11. If $7 = n$, then $n = 7$.
12. If $\frac{2}{3}x = 6$, then $x = 9$.
13. $81 = 81$
14. $9 + 5 = (6 + 3) + 5$

Written Exercises

State the property shown in each of the following.

1. If $8 + 1 = x$, then $x = 8 + 1$.
2. If $6 + 9 = 5 + 10$ and $5 + 10 = 15$, then $6 + 9 = 15$.
3. If $7 + 4 = 7 + 3 + 1$ and $7 + 3 + 1 = 10 + 1$, then $7 + 4 = 10 + 1$.
4. $9 + (2 + 10) = 9 + 12$
5. $6 + a = 6 + a$
6. If $11 - 5 = 4 + 2$, then $4 + 2 = 11 - 5$.

7. $4 + 7 + 9 = 11 + 9$

8. $4 + 7 + 9 = 4 + 7 + 9$

9. If $5x + 7x = 4$, then $(5 + 7)x = 4$.

10. If $\frac{3}{4}x = \frac{2}{3}$, then $9x = 8$.

11. If $7x = 21$, then $x = 3$.

12. If $7b + 3 = 10$, then $7b = 7$.

13. $5x + 8x = 30 - 4$
    a. $(5 + 8)x = 30 - 4$
    b. $13x = 26$
    c. $x = 2$

14. $8a - 3 = 22$
    a. $8a = 22 + 3$
    b. $8a = 25$
    c. $a = \frac{25}{8}$

Solve each equation.

15. $4x = 30$

16. $15 = -3y$

17. $a + 17 = 31$

18. $12 = 8 - r$

19. $\frac{3}{4}x = \frac{5}{7}$

20. $5q = \frac{2}{5}$

21. $\frac{2}{5}m = 1\frac{3}{4}$

22. $\frac{3}{7}x = 4\frac{1}{2}$

23. $3x + 8 = 29$

24. $4 - 8x = 36$

25. $2 + 12x = -142$

26. $3 - 2x = 18$

27. $\frac{3}{4}r + 1 = 10$

28. $1 + \frac{2}{3}y = 27$

29. $9x + 4 = 2\frac{1}{2}$

30. $4x + \frac{3}{5} = 1\frac{7}{10}$

31. $\frac{8e}{9} + \frac{1}{3} = \frac{3}{5}$

32. $\frac{3}{8} - \frac{1}{4}x = \frac{1}{16}$

33. $1.2x + 3.7 = 13.3$

34. $4.5 - 3.9m = 20.1$

35. $1.1x - 0.09 = 2.22$

36. $9 = 16d + 51$

37. $5t + 4 = 2t + 13$

38. $2y - 8 = 14 - 9y$

39. $3x + 5 = 9x + 2$

40. $3x - 4 = 7x - 11$

41. $\frac{3}{4}s - \frac{1}{2} = \frac{1}{4}s + 5$

42. $\frac{2}{3} - \frac{3}{5}x = \frac{2}{5}x + \frac{4}{3}$

43. $8 - x = 5x + 32$

44. $4 + 3p = p - 12$

45. $2(3d - 10) = 40$

46. $3 = -3(y + 5)$

47. $5(3x + 5) = 4x - 8$

48. $2(6 - 7k) = 2k - 4$

49. $8x - 3 = 5(2x + 1)$

50. $2x - 4(x + 2) = -2x - 8$

Using Calculators

Solving Equations

A calculator can help you solve equations. First rewrite the equation so the variable is isolated on one side. Then use the calculator to do the arithmetic.

Example: Solve $6.8x + 37.25 = 80.2$.

$$x = \frac{80.2 - 37.25}{6.8}$$ *Isolate the variable.*

ENTER: 80.2 $\boxed{-}$ 37.25 $\boxed{=}$ $\boxed{\div}$ 6.8 $\boxed{=}$ *The result was rounded*

DISPLAY: 80.2   37.25 42.95 6.8 6.316   *to 3 decimal places.*

The solution is about 6.316.

Exercises

Use your calculator to solve each equation. Check each solution by substitution.

1. $285 - 38x = 2033$

2. $2467 - 897b = 10{,}091.5$

3. $8061 = 295a - 1084$

4. $847.6k - 3269.5 = 610.1k + 2406.75$

Example

3 The sum of Laurie's and Peggy's ages is 34 years. In 5 years, twice Laurie's age increased by Peggy's age will be 67 years. How old is each now?

Explore
Let n = Laurie's age now.
Then, $34 - n$ = Peggy's age now.
$n + 5$ = Laurie's age in 5 years.
$(34 - n) + 5$ = Peggy's age in 5 years.

Plan
$2(n + 5) + [(34 - n) + 5] = 67$

Solve
$$2n + 10 + 34 - n + 5 = 67$$
$$n + 49 = 67$$
$$n = 18$$

Examine
Laurie is 18 years old and Peggy is $34 - 18$ or 16 years old.
In 5 years, Laurie will be $18 + 5$ or 23. Peggy will be $16 + 5$ or 21. Will twice Laurie's age plus Peggy's age equal 67?
$$2(23) + 21 \stackrel{?}{=} 67$$
$$67 = 67 \; ✔$$

Exploratory Exercises

State an algebraic expression for each of the following. Use any variable.

1. four times a number.
2. one third of a number
3. twice a number increased by 11
4. eight increased by the square of a number
5. twice the sum of a number and 7
6. five times a number decreased by 4
7. the sum of twice a number and 7
8. three decreased by twice a number
9. twelve decreased by the square of a number
10. the product of the square of a number and six
11. one-fifth the sum of 4 and a number
12. four times the sum of 8 and a number
13. eight times the sum of a number and its square
14. the sum of 8 and four times a number
15. the square of the sum of a number and 11
16. the sum of the square of a number and 11

Written Exercises

Solve each problem.

1. A number decreased by 89 is 29. Find the number.
2. The sum of twice a number and 3 is 49. Find the number.
3. Eighty-seven increased by three times a number is 165. Find the number
4. Thirty-two decreased by twice a number is 18. Find the number.
5. Julia Blackford wants to pay about $6800 for a new car. The dealer says the car costs $8000. Julia's price is what percent of the dealer's price?
6. John Colston got $2000 trade-in on his car. The dealer is selling John's car for $1800. The dealer's selling price is what percent of the trade-in value?

7. Gunta's dad is 25 years older than Gunta. The sum of their ages is 61. How old is Gunta?

8. The sum of two consecutive odd integers is 124. What are the integers?

9. Mrs. Shieh was 24 years old when Ingrid was born. In three years the sum of their ages will be 68 years. How old is each now?

10. The sum of Paul and Beth Taulman's ages now is 67 years. Eight years ago Paul was twice as old as Beth. How old is each now?

11. Mary took five English tests. Her scores were 78%, 89%, 98%, 67%, and 90%. What must she score on the sixth test so that her average will be 85%?

12. Ben Jackson bought a microwave oven for $60 more than half its original price. He paid $274 for the oven. What was the original price?

13. Felipe Vasquez bought some 14¢ stamps and the same number of 22¢ stamps. He paid a total of $1.80 for all the stamps. How many of each kind did he buy?

14. Jenny Johnston bought some apples for 79¢ per pound and twice as many pounds of bananas for 39¢ per pound. If her total bill was $7.85, how many pounds of bananas did she buy?

15. Neva Fannin ordered concert tickets which cost $3.50 for adults and $2.50 for students. She ordered 4 more student tickets than adult tickets. Her total bill was $58. How many of each did she order?

16. The Drama Club sold 320 adult tickets and 153 student tickets for their last performance. Adult tickets were 75¢ more than student tickets. If the total receipts were $949.50, what was the price of each ticket?

17. The perimeter of a square is 12 meters greater than the perimeter of another square. Its area is 45 square meters greater than the area of the smaller square. Find the perimeter of each square.

18. The width of a rectangle is 12 units less than its length. If you add 30 units to both the length and width, you double the perimeter. Find the length and width of the original rectangle.

19. Ron Dorris is on his way to San Diego, 300 miles away. He drives 45 miles per hour for 3 hours. He drives 55 miles per hour for the rest of the trip. How long does Ron drive at 55 miles per hour?

20. Two hours after a truck leaves Phoenix traveling at 45 miles per hour, a car leaves to overtake the truck. If it takes the car ten hours to catch the truck, what was the car's speed?

21. Lita Vance is driving to Lake Tahoe, a distance of 662 miles. If she drives 55 miles per hour for 5 hours, at what speed must she travel to complete the total trip in 14 hours?

22. San Francisco and Los Angeles are 470 miles apart by train. An express train leaves Los Angeles at the same time a passenger train leaves San Francisco. The express train travels 10 miles per hour faster than the passenger train. The two trains pass each other in 2.5 hours. How fast is each train traveling?

Challenge

23. Two pieces of land have one side in common. One piece is in the shape of an equilateral triangle. The other piece is in the shape of a square. It takes 3125 feet of fence to go around the perimeter of the combined pieces of land. What is the length of each side of the square?

1-6 Solving Absolute Value Equations

Certainly -5 and 5 are quite different, but they do have something in common. They are the same distance from 0 on the number line, but in opposite directions.

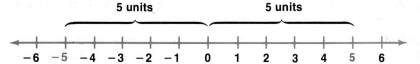

We say that -5 and 5 have the same **absolute value**. The absolute value of a number is the number of units it is from 0 on the number line.

The absolute value of -5 is 5.   The absolute value of 5 is 5.
$$|-5| = 5 \qquad\qquad\qquad |5| = 5$$

We can also define absolute value in the following way.

> **For any real number a:**
> **If $a \geq 0$, then $|a| = a$.**
> **If $a < 0$, then $|a| = -a$.**

*Definition of
Absolute Value*

Examples

1 **Find the absolute value of 3 and of -7.**

$|3| = 3$
$|-7| = -(-7)$ or 7

2 **Find the absolute value of $x - 5$.**

If x is 5 or greater, then $|x - 5| = x - 5$.
If x is less than 5, then $|x - 5| = -(x - 5)$.

3 **Find $|3x - 2| + 7.2$ if $x = -3$.**

$$
\begin{aligned}
|3x - 2| + 7.2 &= |3(-3) - 2| + 7.2 \\
&= |-9 - 2| + 7.2 \\
&= |-11| + 7.2 \\
&= 11 + 7.2 \\
&= 18.2
\end{aligned}
$$

The value is 18.2.

Some equations contain absolute value expressions. You can use the definition of absolute value to solve the equations.

Examples

4 **Solve $|x - 7| = 12$. Check each solution.**

$$|x - 7| = 12$$

If x − 7 is positive or zero $\quad x - 7 = 12 \quad$ or $\quad x - 7 = -12 \quad$ *If x − 7 is negative*

$$x = 19 \qquad\qquad x = -5$$

Check: $\quad |x - 7| = 12$

$$|19 - 7| \overset{?}{=} 12 \quad \text{or} \quad |-5 - 7| \overset{?}{=} 12$$
$$|12| \overset{?}{=} 12 \qquad\qquad |-12| \overset{?}{=} 12$$
$$12 = 12 \ ✔ \qquad\qquad 12 = 12 \ ✔$$

The solutions are 19 and -5.

5 **Solve $5|2x + 3| = 30$. Check each solution.**

$$5|2x + 3| = 30$$
$$|2x + 3| = 6$$

If 2x + 3 is positive or zero $\quad 2x + 3 = 6 \quad$ or $\quad 2x + 3 = -6 \quad$ *If 2x + 3 is negative*

$$2x = 3 \qquad\qquad 2x = -9$$
$$x = \frac{3}{2} \qquad\qquad x = -\frac{9}{2}$$

Check: $\quad 5|2x + 3| = 30$

$$5\left|2\left(\frac{3}{2}\right) + 3\right| \overset{?}{=} 30 \quad \text{or} \quad 5\left|2\left(-\frac{9}{2}\right) + 3\right| \overset{?}{=} 30$$
$$5|3 + 3| \overset{?}{=} 30 \qquad\qquad 5|-9 + 3| \overset{?}{=} 30$$
$$5|6| \overset{?}{=} 30 \qquad\qquad 5|-6| \overset{?}{=} 30$$
$$30 = 30 \ ✔ \qquad\qquad 5(6) \overset{?}{=} 30$$
$$\qquad\qquad\qquad\qquad 30 = 30 \ ✔$$

The solutions are $\frac{3}{2}$ and $-\frac{9}{2}$.

Some absolute value equations have *no solutions*. For example, $|x| = -3$ is *never* true. Since the absolute value of a number is always positive or zero, there is *no* replacement for x that will make the sentence true. The equation $|x| = -3$ has no solutions. The solution set has no members at all. It is called the empty set, $\{ \ \}$ or $\emptyset$.

Another name for $\emptyset$ is the null set.

Example

6 **Solve $|3x + 7| + 4 = 0$.**

$$|3x + 7| + 4 = 0$$
$$|3x + 7| = -4$$

This sentence is *never* true, so the equation has *no solutions*. The solution set is $\emptyset$.

It is important to check your answers when solving absolute value equations. Even if the correct procedure was used, the answers may not be actual solutions to the original equation. Study the following example.

Be especially careful when equations have variables on both sides.

Example

7   Solve $|2x + 12| = 7x - 3$.

$$2x + 12 = 7x - 3 \qquad \text{or} \qquad 2x + 12 = -(7x - 3)$$
$$15 = 5x \qquad\qquad\qquad\qquad 9x = -9$$
$$3 = x \qquad\qquad\qquad\qquad\quad x = -1$$

Check: $|2x + 12| = 7x - 3$

$$|2(3) + 12| \overset{?}{=} 7(3) - 3 \qquad\qquad |2(-1) + 12| \overset{?}{=} 7(-1) - 3$$
$$18 = 18 \; \checkmark \qquad\qquad\qquad\qquad 10 \overset{?}{=} -10 \qquad \text{no}$$

The only solution is 3.

Exploratory Exercises

Evaluate if $x = -5$.

1. $|x|$
2. $|4x|$
3. $|-2x|$
4. $|x + 6|$
5. $|7x - 1|$
6. $|-x|$
7. $|2x + 5|$
8. $|-2x + 5|$
9. $5 - |x|$
10. $5 - |-x|$
11. $|x| + x$
12. $|x - 7| - 8$
13. $|3x + 10| - 7$
14. $7 - |3x + 10|$
15. $|x + 4| + |2x|$

For each equation, determine which numbers in $\{-2, -1, 0, 1, 2\}$ are solutions.

16. $|-x| = 2$
17. $|x - 2| = 1$
18. $|x| = x$
19. $|x| = -x$
20. $|x| = |x - 4|$
21. $-x = |x + 2|$

Written Exercises

Solve.

1. $|x + 11| = 42$
2. $|x + 6| = 19$
3. $|x - 5| = 11$
4. $|x - 3| = 17$
5. $3|x + 7| = 36$
6. $5|x + 4| = 45$
7. $8|x - 3| = 88$
8. $11|x - 9| = 121$
9. $|2x + 7| = 19$
10. $\left|\frac{1}{2}x + 2\right| = 8$
11. $\left|x - \frac{7}{3}\right| = 6$
12. $|5x + 30| = 65$
13. $|2x + 5| = 16$
14. $|2x + 9| = 30$
15. $|2x - 37| = 15$
16. $|4x - 3| = -27$
17. $\frac{1}{3}|6x + 5| = 7$
18. $|2x + 7| = 0$
19. $3|5x + 2| = 51$
20. $8|4x - 3| = 64$
21. $-6|2x - 14| = -42$
22. $\frac{1}{2}|3x - 4| = 3$
23. $7|3x + 5| = 25$
24. $4|6x - 1| = 29$

25. $3|5x - 29| = -3$ **26.** $2|6 - 5x| = 26$ **27.** $9|3 - 2x| = 15$

28. $2|7 - 3x| = 3$ **29.** $|2a + 7| = a - 4$ **30.** $|7 + 3a| = 11 - a$

31. $3|x + 6| = 9x - 6$ **32.** $|x - 4| = 3x$ **33.** $|3t - 5| = 2t$

34. $5|3x - 4| = x + 1$ **35.** $|x - 3| + 7 = 2$ **36.** $3|2x - 5| = -1$

Challenge

Solve.

37. $|x + 3| = |5x - 9|$

38. $|x - 2| = |7x + 22|$

39. $|2x - 3| = |x + 7|$

40. $|3x + 2| = |5x - 12|$

41. $|3x - 1| = |5x - 2| - 4$

42. $|2x - 3| = |5x + 1| + 3$

mini-review

Simplify.

1. $8c - 3 - 2c + 2$

2. $\frac{1}{2}x + \frac{3}{2}x - 5$

3. $-(-x + 2y)$

4. $2(3y - 5) - 7y + 4$

5. $5(2 - 3x) - 2(4x - 2)$

Using Calculators _____ Absolute Value

The $\boxed{+/-}$ key on your calculator is helpful when evaluating absolute value expressions.

Example 1: Evaluate $7|6y - 8|$ when $y = 1$.

First evaluate $6y - 8$.

ENTER: 6 $\boxed{\times}$ 1 $\boxed{-}$ 8 $\boxed{=}$
DISPLAY: 6   1 6   8 -2

Absolute value cannot be negative, so change the sign of the number in the display. Then, multiply by 7.

ENTER: $\boxed{+/-}$ $\boxed{\times}$ 7 $\boxed{=}$
DISPLAY: -2 2   7 14   The value is 14.

Example 2: Evaluate $7|6y - 8|$ when $y = 2$.

ENTER: 6 $\boxed{\times}$ 2 $\boxed{-}$ 8 $\boxed{=}$ $\boxed{\times}$ 7 $\boxed{=}$
DISPLAY: 6   2 12 8 4   7 28   The value is 28.

In this case, the expression within the absolute value symbols had a positive value.

Exercises

Use your calculator to evaluate each expression.

1. $|7(-3) + 10|$

2. $|7(-3)| + 10$

3. $3|4x - 9|$ if $x = 3$

4. $3|4x - 9|$ if $x = 2$

5. $48|7k - 30|$ if $k = 14$

6. $3.5 - |4n - 10|$ if $n = 2.9$

1-7 Solving Inequalities

Jim and Karen are cyclists. Suppose you compare their weights. You can make only one of the following statements.

Jim's weight *is less than* Karen's weight.	Jim's weight *is the same as* Karen's weight.	Jim's weight *is more than* Karen's weight.

Let j stand for Jim's weight and k stand for Karen's weight. Then you can use inequalities and an equation to compare their weights.

$$j < k \qquad j = k \qquad j > k$$

This is an illustration of the **trichotomy property**.

For any two real numbers a and b, exactly one of the following statements is true. $$a < b \qquad a = b \qquad a > b$$	*Trichotomy Property*

Adding the same number to both sides of an inequality does *not* change the truth of the inequality.

For any real numbers, a, b, and c: **1. If $a > b$, then $a + c > b + c$ and $a - c > b - c$.** **2. If $a < b$, then $a + c < b + c$ and $a - c < b - c$.**	*Addition and Subtraction Properties for Inequalities*

You can use these properties to solve inequalities. The solution sets can be graphed on the number line.

Example

1 Solve $9x + 7 < 8x - 2$. Graph the solution set.

$$9x + 7 < 8x - 2$$
$$-8x + 9x + 7 < -8x + 8x - 2 \qquad \text{Add } -8x \text{ to both sides.}$$
$$x + 7 < -2$$
$$x + 7 + (-7) < -2 + (-7) \qquad \text{Add } -7 \text{ to both sides.}$$
$$x < -9$$

A circle means this point is not included.

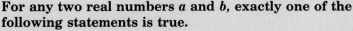

$-11 \;-10 \;-9 \;-8 \;-7 \;-6 \;-5 \;-4 \;-3 \;-2 \;-1 \quad 0 \quad 1$

The solutions are any real numbers less than -9.

To check, substitute -9 for x in $9x + 7 < 8x - 2$. The two sides should be equal. Then substitute a number less than -9. The inequality should be true.

You know that $18 > -11$ is a true inequality. If you multiply both sides of this inequality by a positive number, the result is a true inequality.

$$18 > -11 \qquad \textit{A true inequality}$$
$$18(3) > -11(3) \qquad \textit{Multiply both sides by 3.}$$
$$54 > -33 \qquad \textit{Another true inequality}$$

Suppose you multiply both sides of a true inequality by a negative number. Try -2.

$$18 > -11 \qquad \textit{A true inequality}$$
$$18(-2) > -11(-2) \qquad \textit{Multiply both sides by } -2.$$
$$-36 > 22 \qquad \textit{False!!!}$$

But, *reverse the inequality sign,* and the result is true.

$$-36 < 22 \qquad \textit{True.}$$

These examples suggest the following properties.

For any real numbers a, b, and c:

1. **If c is positive and $a < b$, then $ac < bc$ and $\dfrac{a}{c} < \dfrac{b}{c}$.**

2. **If c is positive and $a > b$, then $ac > bc$ and $\dfrac{a}{c} > \dfrac{b}{c}$.**

3. **If c is negative and $a < b$, then $ac > bc$ and $\dfrac{a}{c} > \dfrac{b}{c}$.**

4. **If c is negative and $a > b$, then $ac < bc$ and $\dfrac{a}{c} < \dfrac{b}{c}$.**

Multiplication and Division Properties for Inequalities

Examples 2 and 3 show how this property is used to solve inequalities.

Example

2   **Solve $-\dfrac{y}{3} < 4$. Graph the solution set.**

$$-\frac{y}{3} < 4$$

$$(-3)\left(-\frac{y}{3}\right) > (-3)(4) \qquad \textit{Reverse the inequality sign since each side is multiplied by } -3.$$

$$y > -12$$

The solutions are any real numbers greater than -12.
The solution set can be written $\{y \mid y > -12\}$. It is read *the set of all numbers y such that y is greater than -12.*

The symbols $\neq$, $\leq$, and $\geq$ can also be used when comparing numbers. The symbol $\neq$ means *is not equal to.* The symbol $\leq$ means *is less than or equal to.* The symbol $\geq$ means *is greater than or equal to.*

Example

3 Solve $-x \geq \dfrac{x - 11}{3}$. Graph the solution set.

$$-x \geq \frac{x - 11}{3}$$
$$-3x \geq x - 11 \qquad \textit{Multiply both sides by 3.}$$
$$-4x \geq -11 \qquad \textit{Add } -x \textit{ to both sides.}$$
$$x \leq \frac{11}{4} \qquad \textit{Reverse the inequality sign.}$$

A dot means this point is included.

The solution set is $\left\{ x \middle| x \leq \dfrac{11}{4} \right\}$.

Exploratory Exercises

Graph the solution set of each inequality.

1. $x > -3$ **2.** $a \leq 0$ **3.** $p \geq 4\frac{1}{2}$ **4.** $x < -7.5$ **5.** $\frac{5}{6}k \leq 10$ **6.** $-3n > 6$

Written Exercises

Solve each inequality. Graph the solution set.

1. $3x + 7 > 43$ **2.** $2t - 9 < 21$ **3.** $7n - 5 \geq 44$

4. $5x + 4 \geq 34$ **5.** $5r + 8 > 24$ **6.** $6s - 7 < 29$

7. $8 - 3x < 44$ **8.** $15 - 2t \geq 55$ **9.** $11 - 5y < -77$

10. $29 - 7y < 24$ **11.** $5(x - 3) \geq 15$ **12.** $9(x + 2) < 72$

Solve each inequality.

13. $5(2x - 7) > 10$ **14.** $3(4x + 7) < 21$ **15.** $3(3w + 1) \geq 48$

16. $25 \leq -5(4 - p)$ **17.** $5(5z - 3) \leq 60$ **18.** $-42 > 7(2x + 3)$

19. $-4(13 - 6t) < 26$ **20.** $40 \leq -6(5r - 7)$ **21.** $7x - 5 > 3x + 4$

22. $3x + 1 < x + 5$ **23.** $1 - 2x \leq 5x - 2$ **24.** $3 - 2x \geq 0$

25. $2(r - 3) + 5 \geq 9$ **26.** $3(3x + 2) > 7x - 2$ **27.** $1 + 2(x + 4) \geq 1 + 3(x + 2)$

28. $4(4z + 5) - 5 > 3(4z - 1)$ **29.** $2(3m + 4) - 2 \leq 3(1 + 3m)$

30. $2(m - 5) - 3(2m - 5) < 5m + 1$ **31.** $3b - 2(b - 5) < 2(b + 4)$

32. $7 + 3y > 2(y + 3) - 2(-1 - y)$ **33.** $0.01x - 2.32 \geq 0$

34. $x - 5 < 0.1$ **35.** $\dfrac{3x}{4} - \dfrac{1}{2} < 0$ **36.** $\dfrac{3x - 5}{2} \leq 0$

37. $\dfrac{2x + 3}{5} \leq 0.03$ **38.** $\dfrac{2x + 3}{5} \geq -0.03$ **39.** $20\left(\dfrac{1}{5} - \dfrac{w}{4}\right) \geq -2w$

40. $\dfrac{3x - 3}{5} < \dfrac{4x - 2}{6}$ **41.** $\dfrac{x + 8}{16} - 1 > \dfrac{4 - x}{12}$ **42.** $\dfrac{2 - 3b}{4} \leq 2\left(\dfrac{2b}{3} - 4b\right)$

Challenge

Find the set of all numbers x satisfying the given conditions.

43. $x + 1 > 0$ and $x - 3 < 0$ **44.** $x - 1 < 0$ and $x + 2 > 0$

45. $3x - 2 \geq 0$ and $5x - 1 \leq 0$ **46.** $2x + 1 > 0$ and $x - 1 > 0$

1-8 Problem Solving: Using Inequalities

The symbols of inequality may be used to represent different types of verbal sentences. Study the verbal sentences for each inequality below.

$x < 14$

x is less than 14.
x is fewer than 14.

$x > 14$

x is greater than 14.
x is more than 14.

$x \leq 14$

x is less than or equal to 14.
x is at most 14.
x is no more than 14.
The greatest value of x is 14.
The maximum value of x is 14.

$x \geq 14$

x is greater than or equal to 14.
x is at least 14.
x is no less than 14.
The least value of x is 14.
The minimum value of x is 14.

Inequalities can be used to solve many verbal problems. The procedure used to solve problems with equations can also be used to solve problems with inequalities.

Example

1 **Corbie Cochran wants to invest $10,000, some in bonds at 6% interest annually and the rest in stocks at 9% interest annually. If he wishes to earn at least $720 in interest this year, what is the minimum he should invest in stocks?**

The phrase <u>*at least 720*</u> *means greater than or equal to 720.*

Explore Let n = amount invested in stocks.
Then $10,000 - n$ = amount invested in bonds.

Plan (rate)(amount) + (rate)(amount) $\geq$ minimum desired
    $(0.09)(n)$ $+ (0.06)(10,000 - n) \geq$ 720

Solve $0.09n + 600 - 0.06n \geq 720$
$0.03n \geq 120$
$n \geq 4000$

Corbie must invest at least $4000 in stocks.

Examine If Corbie invests $4000 in stocks, then he will invest $6000 in bonds. Find the amount he will earn from each investment. Is the total at least $720?

6% of $6000 = $360
9% of $4000 = $360
      $720   total

Now check an amount greater than $4000 for stocks. Make sure the total is greater than $720.

2 **Kym Sutherland has 6 quarts of a 90% antifreeze solution. How much 40% antifreeze must she add to make a solution that is at most 70% antifreeze?**

Explore Let x = number of quarts of 40% antifreeze to be added.
Write an expression for the amount of antifreeze in each solution.

90% of 6 qt   ▶ 0.90(6)

40% of x qt   ▶ 0.40(x)

70% of (6 + x) qt ▶ 0.70(6 + x)

Plan 90% of 6 qt + 40% of x qt is at most 70% of (6 + x) qt
   0.90(6)   +   0.40(x)   ≤   0.70(6 + x)

Solve $0.90(6) + 0.40(x) \leq 0.70(6 + x)$
   $5.4 + 0.4x \leq 4.2 + 0.7x$
   $1.2 \leq 0.3x$
   $4 \leq x$

Therefore, Kym must add at least 4 quarts of 40% antifreeze solution.

Examine Check whether adding 4 or more quarts of 40% solution to 6 quarts of 90% solution produces at most a 70% solution. Replace x by 4 in the expression below. Then try a number greater than 4.

$$\frac{0.90(6) + 0.40(x)}{6 + x}$$ This expression represents the strength of the antifreeze solution.

Try 4. $\dfrac{0.90(6) + 0.40(4)}{6 + 4} = 0.7$ or 70%   *Adding 4 quarts produces a 70% solution.*

Try 5. $\dfrac{0.90(6) + 0.40(5)}{6 + 5} \approx 0.67$ or 67%   *Adding 5 quarts produces a 67% solution.*

The answer is reasonable.

The table at the right is for state income tax. Corinne figured her tax to be $37.41. According to the table, this means her taxable income is at least $3925, but less than $3950.

Let c stand for Corinne's taxable income. Then two inequalities, $c \geq 3925$ and $c < 3950$, describe her taxable income. The sentence, $c \geq 3925$ and $c < 3950$, is called a **compound sentence.** A compound sentence containing **and** is true only if both parts of it are true. A compound sentence containing **or** is true if at least one part of it is true.

If Ohio taxable income (Line 6) is:		
At least	**But less than**	**The tax is:**
3,900	3,925	37.17
3,925	3,950	37.41
3,950	3,975	37.64
3,975	4,000	37.88
4,000	4,025	38.12
4,025	4,050	38.36
4,050	4,075	38.59
4,075	4,100	38.83
4,100	4,125	39.07
4,125	4,150	39.31
4,150	4,175	39.54
4,175	4,200	39.78
4,200	4,225	40.02

Another way of writing $c \geq 3925$ and $c < 3950$ is as follows.

$$3925 \leq c < 3950$$

The sentence is read, "c is greater than or equal to 3925 *and* less than 3950." (Inequality sentences containing **or** *cannot* be combined in this way.)

To solve a compound sentence, solve each part of the compound sentence.

Example

3 **Solve $3 < 2x - 1 < 9$.**

First, write the compound sentence using the word *and*. Then solve each part of the sentence.

$3 < 2x - 1$ and $2x - 1 < 9$
$4 < 2x$ and $2x < 10$
$2 < x$ and $x < 5$
The solution set is $\{x \mid 2 < x < 5\}$.

Or both parts may be solved at the same time.
$3 < 2x - 1 < 9$
$4 < 2x < 10$ *Add 1 to each part of the compound sentence.*
$2 < x < 5$ *Divide each part by 2.*

Exploratory Exercises

State whether each compound sentence is *true* or *false*.

1. $9 > 8$ and $9 > 7$
2. $15 \geq 14$ and $5 < 4$
3. $-2 < 1$ and $1 > 2$
4. $5 < 10$ and $-5 > -10$
5. $-5 < -6$ or $3 > 0$
6. $-3 \leq -3$ or $8 > 11$

State a mathematical expression for each verbal expression.

7. The number of students, c, in the class is at least 30.
8. The number of students, m, in the math club is more than 50.
9. The number of students, s, that can ride the bus is no more than 48.
10. The maximum price, p, is \$250.
11. The minimum value, v, is 99¢.
12. The number of people, p, that can attend the show is no more than 400.

Rewrite each compound sentence using the word *and*.

13. $-3 < x < 2$
14. $-1 \leq b < 3$
15. $1 < 3y \leq 13$
16. $-12 < t \leq 4$
17. $5 \leq 3 - 2g < 1$
18. $-2 < 3(k + 2) < 6$

Rewrite each compound sentence without using the word *and*.

19. $-2 < x$ and $x < 10$
20. $0 \leq b$ and $b < 5$
21. $x \geq -2$ and $x \leq 10$
22. $y > 4$ and $y \leq 9$
23. $m \leq 5$ and $-5 \leq m$
24. $n > -15$ and $n < 7$

Written Exercises

Solve each problem.

1. Diencha has $110.37 in her checking account. The bank does not charge for checks if $50 or more is in the account. For how much can she write a check and not be charged?

2. The Municipal Parking Garage charges $1.50 for the first hour and $0.50 for each additional hour. For how many hours can you park your car if the most you can pay is $4.50?

3. One number is twice another number. Twice the lesser number increased by the greater number is at least 85. Find the *least* possible value for the lesser number.

4. Dave Sharp has $10 to buy stamps. He wants to buy twice as many 22¢ stamps as 14¢ stamps. What is the greatest number of 22¢ stamps he can buy?

5. Donna Pennycuff invested part of $8000 in stock that lost 2%. She invested the balance at 8% interest annually. If her total gain for the year was at least $400, what was the greatest amount of money that she could have invested in stock?

6. Apples cost 10¢ per pound more than grapefruit. Carleton Foushee buys 6 pounds of grapefruit and 8 pounds of apples and pays less than $10.50. What is the highest possible price per pound he paid for apples?

7. The Speedy Car Rental Company rents a car for $12.95 per day plus 15 cents per mile. Your company has limited you to a daily budget of $90. What is the maximum number of miles that you can drive each day?

8. A factory can produce a table in 30 minutes and a chair in 12 minutes. It plans to produce dining sets with 4 chairs for each table. What is the maximum number of sets that can be produced in an 8-hour shift?

9. You are enrolled in an algebra course where five tests will be given in the first quarter. You need 450 points to get an A. Your scores on the first four tests were 89, 87, 95, and 98. What is the minimum score that you can earn on the last test and still get an A for the quarter?

10. Harry Smith left an estate which was estimated to be worth at most $300,000. His will stated that one-fourth of the estate be given to his church and the remainder be divided equally among his four children. What are the maximum amounts to be paid to the church and to each child?

11. Susan's softball team has won 11 games and has lost 8 games. They have 11 more games to play. To win at least 50% of *all* games, how many more games must they win?

12. The Raiders play 84 games this season. At midseason they had won 30 games. To win at least 60% of *all* games, how many of the remaining games must they win?

13. Roy has 8 gallons of 40% antifreeze solution. How much 100% antifreeze must be added to make a solution that is at least 60% antifreeze?

14. A 20 gallon salt solution is 30% salt. What is the greatest number of gallons of water that can be evaporated so the solution is still less than 45% salt?

Solve each compound sentence.

15. $2 < y + 4 < 11$

16. $1 < x - 2 < 7$

17. $x - 4 < 1$ or $x + 2 > 1$

18. $y + 6 > -1$ or $y - 2 < 4$

19. $4 < 2x - 2 < 10$

20. $-1 < 3m + 2 < 14$

21. $2x - 1 < -5$ or $3x + 2 \geq 5$

22. $5b < 9 + 2b$ or $9 - 2b > 11$

Applications in Energy BTU's

Energy is often measured in BTU's. BTU stands for British Thermal Unit. A BTU is the amount of heat required to raise the temperature of one pound of water 1° Fahrenheit.

Example 1: **How much energy (in BTU's) is required to heat 50 gallons of water from 40°F to 98°F? A gallon of water weighs about 8 pounds.**

energy required = weight × specific heat × temperature change
= 50(8 lb) × 1 BTU/lb°F × (98 − 40)°F
= 23,200 BTU

The chart below shows the number of BTU's provided by various energy sources, if the heating system is 100% efficient.

1 pound of coal = 15,000 BTU
1 cubic foot of natural gas = 1000 BTU
1 gallon of gasoline = 150,000 BTU

Example 2: **How much natural gas is needed to produce 23,200 BTU of heat if the heating system is 60% efficient?**

Since the system is 60% efficient, each cubic foot of natural gas provides 60% of 1000 or 600 BTU. Divide 23,200 by 600.

$23{,}200 \div 600 = 38\frac{2}{3}$ About 39 ft³ of natural gas is needed.

Exercises
Solve.

1. How much energy is required to heat 100 pounds of water from 40°F to 100°F?

2. How much energy is required to heat 25 gallons of water from 45°F to 103°F?

3. How much energy is required for 4 hot showers? Each shower uses 10 gallons of water heated from 50°F to 110°F.

4. A water heater holds 50 gallons of water. If it is 60% efficient, how much natural gas is needed to heat the water from 50°F to 130°F?

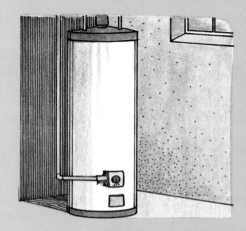

5. A coal stove is 20% efficient. How many pounds of coal are needed to heat 40 gallons of water from 50°F to 200°F?

6. A gasoline heater is 30% efficient. How many pounds of water can be heated from 40°F to 140°F with 4 gallons of gasoline?

32 *Equations and Inequalities*

1-9 Absolute Value Inequalities

The absolute value of a number represents its distance from zero on the number line. You can use this idea to help solve absolute value inequalities.

Examples

1 **Solve $|x| < 3$.**

$|x| < 3$ means the distance between x and 0 is less than 3 units. To make $|x| < 3$ true, you must substitute values for x that are less than 3 units from 0.

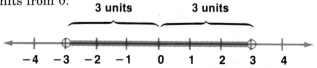

3 units　　　**3 units**

All the numbers between -3 and 3 are less than three units from zero. The solution set is $\{x \mid -3 < x < 3\}$.

2 **Solve $|x| \geq 2$.**

To make this true, you must substitute values for x that are 2 or more units from 0.

The solution set is $\{x \mid x \geq 2 \text{ or } x \leq -2\}$

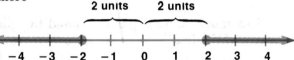

2 units　　　**2 units**

3 **Solve $|2x - 5| > 9$. Graph the solution set.**

The inequality $|2x - 5| > 9$ says that $2x - 5$ is more than 9 units from 0.

$$\textit{If } 2x - 5 \geq 0 \quad 2x - 5 > 9 \qquad \text{or} \qquad 2x - 5 < -9 \quad \textit{If } 2x - 5 < 0$$
$$2x > 14 \qquad\qquad\qquad 2x < -4$$
$$x > 7 \qquad\qquad\qquad x < -2$$

The solution set is $\{x \mid x < -2 \text{ or } x > 7\}$.

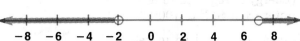

4 **Solve $|2x + 3| + 4 < 5$. Graph the solution set.**

$|2x + 3| + 4 < 5$
　$|2x + 3| < 1$　　*Add -4 to each side to isolate the absolute value expression.*

The inequality $|2x + 3| < 1$ says that $2x + 3$ is less than 1 unit from 0. Thus, it can be written as follows.

$$-1 < 2x + 3 < 1$$
$$-4 < 2x < -2$$
$$-2 < x < -1$$

The solution set is $\{x \mid -2 < x < -1\}$.

Some absolute value inequalities have *no solutions*. For example, $|4x - 9| < -7$ is *never* true. Since the absolute value of a number is always positive or zero, there is *no* replacement for x that will make the sentence true. The inequality $|4x - 9| < -7$ has no solutions.

Some absolute value inequalities are *always* true. For example, $|10x + 3| > -5$ is *always* true. Since the absolute value of a number is always positive or zero, any replacement for x will make the sentence true. The solution set for $|10x + 3| > -5$ is the set of real numbers.

Exploratory Exercises

Write an absolute value inequality for each sentence. Then graph each inequality on a number line.

1. All numbers between -3 and 3.
2. All numbers less than 8 and greater than -8.
3. All numbers greater than 6 or less than -6.
4. All numbers less than or equal to 5, and greater than or equal to -5.
5. $x > 3$ or $x < -3$
6. $x < 6$ and $x > -6$
7. $x \le 4$ and $x \ge -4$
8. $x \ge 7$ or $x \le -7$
9. $-6 < x < 6$
10. $-3 < x < 3$
11. $x > -2$ and $x < 2$
12. $x < 10$ and $x > -10$

Written Exercises

Solve each inequality. Graph each solution set.

1. $|x| < 9$
2. $|x| \ge 2$
3. $|x + 1| > 3$
4. $|x + 1| \le 3$
5. $|x - 4| \le 8$
6. $|3x| < 6$
7. $|7x| \ge 21$
8. $|x - 9| > 5$
9. $|x| > 7$
10. $|5x| < 35$
11. $|2x| \le 26$
12. $|2x| \ge -64$
13. $|3x| < -15$
14. $|5x| < 15$
15. $|x + 3| > 17$
16. $|x - 4| \le -12$
17. $|x - 12| < 42$
18. $|x + 9| \ge 17$
19. $|2x - 9| \le 27$
20. $|3x + 11| > 1$
21. $|4x - 3| \ge 12$
22. $|3x + 7| \le 26$
23. $|5x + 7| < 81$
24. $|3x + 11| > 42$
25. $|6x + 25| + 14 < 6$
26. $6 + |3x| > 0$
27. $|2x - 5| \le 7$
28. $|4x| + 3 \le 0$
29. $|x| \le x$
30. $|x| > x$
31. $|x + 2| - x \ge 0$
32. $2 + |3 - 2x| > 0$

Challenge _____

Solve each inequality.

33. $|x + 1| + |x - 1| \le 2$
34. $|x + 3| + |x - 3| > 8$
35. $|x + 2| + |x - 2| \le 4$
36. $|x + 2| + |x - 2| > 16$

mini-review▮▮▮

Write *true* or *false*.

1. $4(5 + 7) = 4(5) + 7$
2. $|-x| = x$ when $x = -2$
3. 0 is a rational number.
4. All integers are real numbers.
5. If $-2x < 18$ then $x < -9$.

Solving Inequalities

Trial-and-error can be used to find solutions to an inequality. Consider $|x - 3| \le 4$.

Try -5.	*Try 0.*	*Try 5.*
$|-5 - 3| \overset{?}{\le} 4$	$|0 - 3| \overset{?}{\le} 4$	$|5 - 3| \overset{?}{\le} 4$
$|-8| \overset{?}{\le} 4$	$|-3| \overset{?}{\le} 4$	$|2| \overset{?}{\le} 4$
$8 \overset{?}{\le} 4$ no	$3 \overset{?}{\le} 4$ yes	$2 \overset{?}{\le} 4$ yes

So, two solutions are 0 and 5. There are many other solutions. Finding solutions by trial-and-error is time consuming unless you use a computer. A computer can test many values quickly and easily. The following program can be used to find all integer solutions between -10 and 10.

```
10  FOR X = -10 TO 10
20  IF ABS(X - 3) <= 4 THEN PRINT X
30  NEXT X
40  END
```

ABS means absolute value.
< = means ≤.
Lines 10 to 30 form a loop in the program.

Enter the program and type RUN.
The computer will print these solutions: -1, 0, 1, 2, 3, 4, 5, 6, 7

Exercises

For each inequality, write a new statement for line 20 of the program above. Then run the new program and list the integer solutions between -10 and 10.

1. $|x + 1| > 3$
2. $|x + 2| < 6$
3. $|2x - 3| \le 5$
4. $|3x + 4| \le 10$
5. $|8 - x| \le 7$
6. $|4 - x| > 3$

Vocabulary

variable (3)
value (3)
base (3)
exponent (3)
algebraic expression (4)
formula (4)
whole numbers, W (8)
integers, Z (8)
rational numbers, Q (8)
irrational numbers, I (8)
real numbers, R (8)
commutativity (10)

associativity (10)
additive identity (10)
multiplicative identity (10)
additive inverse (10)
multiplicative inverse (10)
reciprocal (10)
distributive property (11)
like terms (11)
solution (13)
equation (13)
absolute value (21)
trichotomy property (25)
compound sentence (29)

Chapter Summary

1. **Order of Operations:** 1. Evaluate all powers. 2. Do all multiplications and divisions from left to right. 3. Do all additions and subtractions from left to right. (3)

2. In a formula, if you know replacements for every variable except one, you can find a replacement for that variable. (4)

3. **Completeness Property:** Each real number corresponds to exactly one point on the number line. Each point on the number line corresponds to exactly one real number. (8)

4. **Properties of Operations:** (11)

For any real numbers a, b, and c		
	Addition	Multiplication
Commutative	$a + b = b + a$	$a \cdot b = b \cdot a$
Associative	$(a + b) + c = a + (b + c)$	$(a \cdot b) \cdot c = a \cdot (b \cdot c)$
Identity	$a + 0 = a = 0 + a$	$a \cdot 1 = a = 1 \cdot a$
Inverse	$a + (-a) = 0 = -a + a$	If a is *not* zero, then $a \cdot \dfrac{1}{a} = 1 = \dfrac{1}{a} \cdot a.$
Distributive of multiplication over addition: $a(b + c) = ab + ac$ and $(b + c)a = ba + ca$		

5. **Properties of Equality:** (13–14)

For any real numbers a, b, and c	
Reflexive:	$a = a$
Symmetric:	If $a = b$, then $b = a$.
Transitive:	If $a = b$ and $b = c$, then $a = c$.
Addition and Subtraction:	If $a = b$, then $a + c = b + c$, and $a - c = b - c$.
Multiplication and Division:	If $a = b$, then $a \cdot c = b \cdot c$, and if c is not zero, $\dfrac{a}{c} = \dfrac{b}{c}$.

6. **Problem-Solving Plan:** 1. Explore the problem. 2. Plan the solution. 3. Solve the problem. 4. Examine the solution. (18)

7. The absolute value of a number is the number of units it is from zero on the number line. For any number a, if $a \geq 0$, then $|a| = a$. If $a < 0$, then $|a| = -a$. (21)

8. **Trichotomy Property:** For any two numbers a and b, exactly one of the following statements is true. $a < b$, $a = b$, or $a > b$. (25)

9. Properties of Inequalities: (25–26)

	For any real numbers a, b, and c
Addition and Subtraction	1. If $a > b$, then $a + c > b + c$ and $a - c > b - c$. 2. If $a < b$, then $a + c < b + c$ and $a - c < b - c$.
Multiplication and Division	1. If c is positive and $a < b$, then $ac < bc$ and $\dfrac{a}{c} < \dfrac{b}{c}$. 2. If c is positive and $a > b$, then $ac > bc$ and $\dfrac{a}{c} > \dfrac{b}{c}$. 3. If c is negative and $a < b$, then $ac > bc$ and $\dfrac{a}{c} > \dfrac{b}{c}$. 4. If c is negative and $a > b$, then $ac < bc$ and $\dfrac{a}{c} < \dfrac{b}{c}$.

Chapter Review

1–1 Find the value of each expression.

1. $(4 + 6)^2 - 24 \div 3$ **2.** $4 + 6^2 - 24 \div 3$ **3.** $(3 - 9)^2 \times 2 - 10 \div 6$

Evaluate if $a = -\dfrac{1}{2}$, $b = 4$, $c = 5$, and $d = -3$.

4. $\dfrac{3ab}{cd}$ **5.** $\dfrac{4a + 3c}{3b}$ **6.** $\dfrac{3ab^2 - d^3}{a}$

1–2 Name the sets of numbers to which each number belongs. (Use W, Z, Q, I, and R.)

7. -25.8 **8.** $\sqrt{13}$ **9.** $\dfrac{64}{8}$ **10.** -9.0

1–3 State the property shown in each of the following.

11. $3 + (a + b) = (a + b) + 3$ **12.** $(3 + a) + b = 3 + (a + b)$

13. $(a + b) + 0 = (a + b)$ **14.** $(a + b) + [-(a + b)] = 0$

Simplify.

15. $(9 + 48)7 + 3$ **16.** $15r + 18s + 16r - 8s$

17. $7p + 9q - 10p + 4q$ **18.** $(14y + 7z)\dfrac{1}{7} - (7z + 14y)\dfrac{2}{7}$

1–4   State the property shown in each of the following.

19. $3r + (7 - 1)s = 3r + 6s$

20. $5x + 3y = 5x + 3y$

21. If $12 - 7 = 3 + 2$, then
$3 + 2 = 12 - 7.$

22. If $12 - 7 = 10 - 5$ and
$10 - 5 = 5$, then $12 - 7 = 5.$

Solve each equation.

23. $15x + 25 = 2(x - 4)$

24. $3(6 - 4x) = 4x + 2$

25. $2(3x - 1) = 3(x + 2)$

26. $9 = \dfrac{3y - 6}{2}$

27. $\dfrac{2}{7}a = \dfrac{16}{5}$

28. $\dfrac{3}{4}y + \dfrac{3}{4} = \dfrac{5}{2}$

1–5   Solve each problem.

29. The width of a rectangle is 4 meters more than one-third its length. The perimeter is 64 meters. Find the length and width.

30. Maureen's dad is 32 years older than Maureen. Six years ago, the sum of their ages was 52. How old is Maureen now?

31. To estimate when to harvest his snap bean crop, a South Carolina farmer counts heat units. As of May 1, he has counted 1022 heat units. There are usually 19 heat units per day in May. Snap beans require 1250 heat units to mature. The farmer can plan to harvest his crop in how many more days?

32. Rockford and Chicago are 126 miles apart by train. An express train leaves Chicago at the same time that a passenger train leaves Rockford. The express train travels 15 miles per hour faster than the passenger train. The two trains pass each other in 0.7 hours. How fast is each train traveling?

1–6   Solve each equation.

33. $|2x - 37| = 15$

34. $|p - 3| + 7 = 2$

35. $8|2a - 3| = 64$

1–7   Solve each inequality. Graph the solution set.

36. $8(2x - 1) > 11x + 31$

37. $3 - 4x \le 6x + 5$

38. $4(3x + 2) + 6 \ge 7x - 9$

1–8   Solve each problem.

39. Tania has 10 gallons of a 50% antifreeze solution. How much 100% antifreeze must she add to make a solution that is at least 80% antifreeze?

40. Roxie has $8.40 to spend on gasoline. Where Roxie lives gasoline costs between $1.40 and $1.60 per gallon. How many gallons of gasoline can Roxie buy?

Solve each compound sentence.

41. $-1 < 3(y - 2) \le 9$

42. $2x - 5 < -5$ or $3x + 2 \ge 5$

1–9   Solve each inequality. Graph the solution set.

43. $7 + |9 - 2x| > 4$

45. $|2x + 5| \le 4$

44. $|6 + 7x| + 11 \le 2$

46. $|3x + 7| \ge 26$

Chapter Test

State the property shown in each of the following.

1. $(5 \cdot r) \cdot s = 5 \cdot (r \cdot s)$

2. $(5 \cdot r) \cdot s = s \cdot (5 \cdot r)$

3. $\left(4 \cdot \frac{1}{4}\right) \cdot 3 = \left(4 \cdot \frac{1}{4}\right) \cdot 3$

4. $(6 - 2)a - 3b = 4a - 3b$

5. If $2(7) + 3 = 14 + 3$ and $14 + 3 = 17$, then $2(7) + 3 = 17$.

6. If $(a + b)c = ac + bc$, then $ac + bc = (a + b)c$.

Evaluate.

7. $(2 + 3)^3 - 4 \div 2$

8. $[2 + 3^3 - 4] \div 2$

9. $(2^5 - 2^3) + 2^3$

10. $[5(19 - 4) \div 3] - 4^2$

Evaluate if $a = -9$, $b = \frac{2}{3}$, $c = 8$, and $d = -6$.

11. $\frac{a}{b^2} + c$

12. $\frac{db + 4c}{a}$

13. $2b(4a + d^2)$

14. $\frac{4a + 3c}{3b}$

Name the sets of numbers to which each number belongs. (Use W, Z, Q, I, and R.)

15. $\sqrt{13}$

16. 0.68

17. $\frac{-10}{2}$

18. $\sqrt{49}$

Solve each equation.

19. $2x - 7 - (x - 5) = 0$

20. $5y - 3 = -2y + 10$

21. $\frac{a}{4} + 3 = \frac{5}{2}$

22. $5t + 7 = 5t + 3$

23. $5r - (5 + 4r) = (3 + r) - 8$

24. $|5x + 10| - 3 = 0$

25. $|5x + 10| + 3 = 0$

26. $|4x - 5| + 4 = 7x + 8$

Solve each inequality. Graph the solution set.

27. $4 > m + 1$

28. $4p + 8 \geq 12$

29. $3(2 + 3r) + r < 2(9 - r)$

30. $-12 < 7x - 5 \leq 9$

31. $|5 + t| \leq 8$

32. $|9x - 4| + 8 > 4$

Solve each problem.

33. Mary scored 87, 89, 76, and 77 on her first four English tests. She needs 400 points to earn a grade of B for the course. What must be the minimum score on her next test in order for her to have a B average?

34. Gloria's softball team has won 13 games and lost 7 games. They have 12 more games to play. To win at least 50% of all games, how many more games must they win?

35. The formula $A = 180(n - 2)/n$ relates the measure of one interior angle, A, of a regular polygon to the number of sides, n. If an interior angle of a regular polygon measures 150 degrees, find the number of sides.

CHAPTER 2

Linear Relations and Functions

There is a relation between the number of trees processed by a sawmill and the amount of lumber produced. Since trees vary in size, the same number of trees may yield different amounts of lumber. So, the relation is *not* a function.

2-1 The Coordinate Plane

The graph of all **ordered pairs** of real numbers is the entire plane.

Two perpendicular number lines separate the plane into four parts, called **quadrants.** The horizontal number line usually is called the *x*-axis. The vertical number line usually is called the *y*-axis. The plane determined by the perpendicular axes is called a **coordinate plane.**

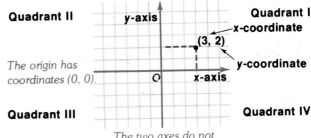

Quadrant II   y-axis   Quadrant I
x-coordinate
(3, 2)
The origin has coordinates (0, 0).
O   x-axis   y-coordinate
Quadrant III   Quadrant IV
The two axes do not lie in any quadrant.

Each point in the coordinate plane corresponds to exactly one ordered pair of numbers. These numbers are called the **coordinates** of the point. The coordinates of a point are given in a particular order. For example, $(-2, 3)$ and $(3, -2)$ do *not* represent the same point.

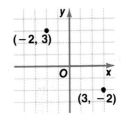

$(-2, 3)$
O   x
$(3, -2)$

Each ordered pair of numbers corresponds to exactly one point in the coordinate plane. The point is the **graph** for the ordered pair.

When you graph a set of ordered pairs, make sure all points can be shown on the same grid. When there are no labels on the axes, each unit is understood to represent an increment of one. Occasionally, you may need to label the axes using increments other than one.

Example

1 **Graph the set of ordered pairs.**

$\{(8, -6), (4, -2), (1, 1), (-3, 5), (-6, 8)\}$

Label the axes by twos.
Then graph each ordered pair.

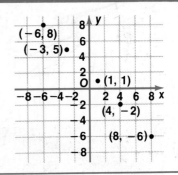

$(-6, 8)$
$(-3, 5)$
$(1, 1)$
$(4, -2)$
$(8, -6)$

Exploratory Exercises

In which quadrant will (*x*, *y*) lie given the following conditions?

1. *x* is positive and *y* is positive
2. *x* is positive and *y* is negative
3. *x* is negative and *y* is negative
4. *x* is negative and *y* is positive
5. *x* is negative and *y* is 0
6. *x* is 0 and *y* is positive.

Graph each ordered pair on the same coordinate plane.

7. $(7, 4)$
8. $(-7, 4)$
9. $(7, -4)$
10. $(-7, -4)$
11. $(2.5, 0)$
12. $(0, 2.5)$
13. $(1.5, 3)$
14. $(3, 1.5)$

Written Exercises

Graph each set of ordered pairs on the same coordinate plane. Remember to choose appropriate labels for the coordinate axes.

1. $\{(-8, 8), (-8, -8), (0, 4), (0, -4), (8, 0)\}$

2. $\{(-6, 12), (-3, 6), (0, 0), (6, -3), (12, -6)\}$

3. $\left\{(-1, 1), \left(-\frac{1}{4}, \frac{1}{2}\right), \left(\frac{1}{2}, 1\right), \left(1, -\frac{3}{4}\right)\right\}$

4. $\left\{\left(-2, \frac{1}{2}\right), \left(-1, 1\frac{1}{2}\right), \left(0, \frac{3}{4}\right), \left(1\frac{1}{2}, -2\right)\right\}$

5. $\{(3, 4), (9, 21), (15, 15), (21, 13), (25, 3)\}$

6. $\{(2, 12), (4, 3), (8, 11), (11, 3), (14, 12)\}$

7. $\{(0, -15), (5, -20), (10, -10), (12, 12)\}$

8. $\{(-40, 40), (20, 10), (10, -30), (-25, -25)\}$

9. $\{(0, -3), (3, 6), (6, 9), (9, 6), (12, -3)\}$

10. $\{(0.8, 0.6), (0.2, 0), (-0.2, -0.4), (-0.6, -0.6)\}$

11. $\{(-1.75, -2), (-1, -1.5), (0, -0.75), (1, 0), (2, 1.5)\}$

12. $\{(-9, 15), (-6, 0), (-3, -9), (0, -12), (3, -9), (6, 0), (9, 15)\}$

Each of the following are the coordinates of three vertices of a rectangle. Graph them. Then, find each fourth vertex.

13. $(3, 1), (3, -3), (-5, -3)$

14. $(2, 0), (0, 2), (-4, -2)$

15. $(1, 0), (3, 0), (3, 3)$

16. $(-1, 0), (1, 1), (0, 3)$

17. $(-3, 4), (5, 4), (5, -3)$

18. $(4, -1), (1, -4), (0, -3)$

mini-review

Solve.

1. $5(x + 3) = 2x - 3$

2. $4|k - 3| = -8$

3. $|m - 5| - 3 = 4$

4. $-3(x - 2) + 1 \geq 4x$

5. If you add 17 to a certain number and multiply the sum by 5, the result is 155. Find the number.

Excursions in Algebra _____ History

René Descartes (1596–1650) was a French mathematician and philosopher. He is credited with the invention of a branch of mathematics called analytic geometry. Analytic geometry is a combination of ideas from algebra and geometry. Analytic geometry uses the following.

1. The coordinate plane
2. The correspondence of ordered pairs of numbers to points in the coordinate plane
3. Graphs of expressions like $f(x) = 2x + 1$

Descartes, in 1637, became the first mathematician to put the three steps together.

Sometimes, ordered pairs are referred to as Cartesian coordinates. The word Cartesian is taken from the name Descartes.

2-2 Relations and Functions

The amount of electricity produced in recent years in the U.S. can be shown using ordered pairs. The first number is the year, and the second number is the amount in billions of kilowatt hours.

Year	Kilowatt Hours (billions)
1974	1870
1976	2040
1978	2200
1980	2290
1982	2240
1984	2300

{(1974, 1870), (1976, 2040), (1978, 2200),
(1980, 2290), (1982, 2240), (1984, 2300)}

A set of ordered pairs is called a **relation.** The set of first coordinates, in this case years, is called the **domain** of the relation. The set of second coordinates, kilowatt hours (in billions), is called the **range** of the relation.

> **A relation is a set of ordered pairs. The domain is the set of all first coordinates of the ordered pairs. The range is the set of all second coordinates of the ordered pairs.**

Definition of Relation, Domain, and Range

A **mapping** illustrates how each element in the domain of a relation is paired with an element in the range. The following diagrams are mappings of the given relations.

{(3, 2), (2, 7), (5, 8)}

domain   range

{(8, 4), (3, 9), (1, 2), (7, 4)}

domain   range

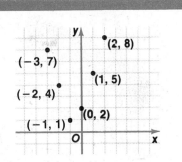

Example

1 State a relation shown by the graph. Then state the domain and range of the relation.

The relation is
{(−3, 7), (−2, 4), (−1, 1), (0, 2), (1, 5), (2, 8)}.

The domain is {−3, −2, −1, 0, 1, 2}.

The range is {7, 4, 1, 2, 5, 8}.

The graph on the left shows how the amount of electricity consumed compares with the cost of the electricity. The graph on the right shows the amount of electricity used in a certain area at different hours in an average weekday.

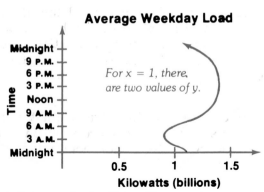

The first graph shows a special type of relation called a **function**.

Examples

2 **Is {(2, 3), (3, −4), (4, 1), (1, 3)} a function?**

This relation is a function since each element of the domain is paired with exactly one element of the range.

3 **Is {(4, 4), (−2, 3), (4, 2), (3, 4), (1, 1)} a function?**

This relation is *not* a function. The element 4 of the domain is paired with two different elements of the range, 4 and 2.

4 **Which of the following mappings represent functions?**

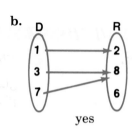

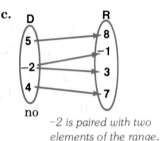

5 **Does $y = 4x$ represent a function?**

Suppose the value of x is 3. What is the corresponding value of y? Is there more than one value for y? When x is 3, y is 12. There is only one value for y. If you try other values of x you will see that they are always paired with exactly one value of y. The equation $y = 4x$ does represent a function.

The graph on the right represents the following relation.

$$\{(-2, 3), (-1, 1), (1, 2), (1, -1), (3, 1)\}$$

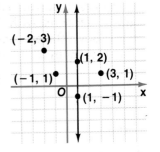

Suppose you drew a vertical line through each point on the graph. The vertical line through (1, 2) would also pass through (1, -1). This shows that the relation is *not* a function. There are two elements of the range, 2 and -1, that pair with one element of the domain, 1.

If any vertical line drawn on the graph of a relation passes through no more than one point of that graph, then the relation is a function.

Vertical Line Test for a Function

Example

6 **Use the vertical line test to determine if the relation graphed is a function.**

The vertical line whose equation is $x = 2$ intersects the graph at (2, 2) and (2, -2). Therefore, the relation is *not* a function.

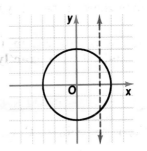

Equations that represent functions often are written in a special way. The equation $y = 2x + 1$ can be written $f(x) = 2x + 1$. The symbol $f(x)$ is read "*f* of *x*." Likewise, the symbol $f(3)$ is read "*f* of 3." If 3 is an element of the domain of the function, then $f(3)$ is the corresponding element of the range. To show that the value of $f(3)$ is 7, you write $f(3) = 7$.

Letters other than f can be used to represent a function. For example, the equation $y = 4x + 3$ can be written $g(x) = 4x + 3$.

Examples

7 **Find $f(15)$ if $f(x) = 100x - 5x^2$.**

$$f(x) = 100x - 5x^2$$
$$f(15) = 100(15) - 5(15)^2 \quad \textit{Substitute 15 for x.}$$
$$= 1500 - 5(225)$$
$$= 375$$

Therefore, $f(15) = 375$.

8 **Find $g(a + 2)$ if $g(x) = x^2 - 7$**

$$g(x) = x^2 - 7$$
$$g(a + 2) = (a + 2)^2 - 7$$
$$= a^2 + 4a + 4 - 7$$
$$= a^2 + 4a - 3$$

Therefore, $g(a + 2) = a^2 + 4a - 3$.

In this book, sometimes the equation for a function is given without a specified domain. In such cases, the domain is understood to be all real numbers for which the function is defined. The corresponding range values are also real numbers.

Exploratory Exercises

State the domain and range of each relation. Then state if the relation is a function.

1. {(4, 4), (1, 1), (3, 3)}
2. {(6, 4)}
3. {(4, 3), (8, −2), (−17, 4), (−17, 8)}
4. {(1, 5), (5, 1)}
5. {(−3, −3), (−2, −2), (2, 2), (4, 4)}
6. {(−3, 3), (−2, 2), (2, −2), (4, −4)}
7. {(5, −3), (−3, 5)}
8. {(−3, 3), (−2, 3), (2, 3), (4, 3)}

State the relation shown by each of the following mappings. Then state if the relation is a function.

9.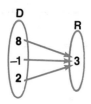
10.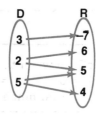
11.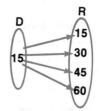
12.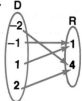

Written Exercises

State a relation shown by the graph. Then state the domain and range of the relation.

1.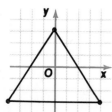
2.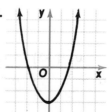
3.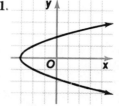
4.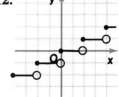

Use the vertical line test to determine if each relation is a function. Write *yes* or *no*.

5.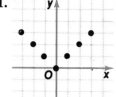
6.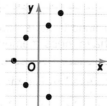
7.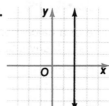
8.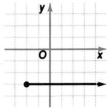

9.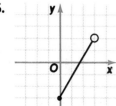
10.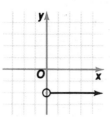
11.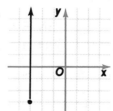
12.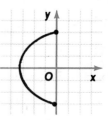

Given $f(x) = \dfrac{7}{x - 2}$, find each value.

13. $f(12)$ **14.** $f(3)$ **15.** $f(-1)$ **16.** $f(5.5)$ **17.** $f(0)$ **18.** $f(1.3)$

19. $f\left(\dfrac{1}{2}\right)$ **20.** $f\left(\dfrac{2}{3}\right)$ **21.** $f(a)$ **22.** $f(u + 2)$ **23.** $f(3a)$ **24.** $f(2)$

Given $g(x) = 4x^3 + 2x^2 + x - 7$, find each value.

25. $g(1)$ **26.** $g(-4)$ **27.** $g\left(-\dfrac{1}{2}\right)$ **28.** $g\left(\dfrac{1}{2}\right)$ **29.** $g(t)$ **30.** $g(2s)$

Given $h(x) = \dfrac{x^2 + 5x - 6}{x + 3}$, find each value.

31. $h(6)$ **32.** $h(-4)$ **33.** $h\left(\dfrac{1}{3}\right)$ **34.** $h\left(\dfrac{1}{2}\right)$ **35.** $h(a + 1)$ **36.** $h(2m + 3)$

Challenge

State the domain of each relation.

> **Sample:** $f(x) = \dfrac{14}{x + 4}$ The relation is undefined when the denominator is 0.
> $$x + 4 = 0 \quad \text{or} \quad x = -4$$
> Thus, the domain is all real numbers except -4.

37. $f(x) = \dfrac{3}{x - 5}$ **38.** $f(x) = \dfrac{8}{|2x - 7|}$ **39.** $g(x) = \dfrac{3}{x^2}$ **40.** $g(x) = \dfrac{2x + 3}{2x - 1}$

41. $x = |y|$ **42.** $y = |x| - 1$ **43.** $x = |-y|$ **44.** $x = -|y + 4|$

Using Calculators _____ Memory

The memory feature of a calculator can be used to store numbers that will be used over and over again. Many calculators have these memory keys:

STO	Store	Stores the number displayed in the memory.
RCL	Recall	Retrieves the stored number from the memory to the display.

Example: Given $f(x) = 3x^2 - 4x + 5$, find $f\left(\dfrac{1}{3}\right)$.

First, store $\dfrac{1}{3}$ in memory.   ENTER: 1 $\boxed{\div}$ 3 $\boxed{=}$ $\boxed{\text{STO}}$ *Only the first three digits*
                 DISPLAY: 1   3 .333 .333   *of the display are shown.*

Then, press the recall key each time x appears.

     ENTER: 3 $\boxed{\times}$ $\boxed{\text{RCL}}$ $\boxed{x^2}$ $\boxed{-}$ 4 $\boxed{\times}$ $\boxed{\text{RCL}}$ $\boxed{+}$ 5 $\boxed{=}$ *The x^2 key squares the*
     DISPLAY: 3   .333 .111 .333 4   .333   -1 5 4   *number in the display.*

The answer is 4.

Exercises

1. Given $f(x) = 4x^2 - 3x + 8$, find   **a.** $f(6)$ **b.** $f(-5)$ **c.** $f\left(\dfrac{11}{9}\right)$

2. Given $g(x) = \dfrac{2x - 1}{x + 3}$, find   **a.** $g(-2)$ **b.** $g\left(\dfrac{5}{9}\right)$ **c.** $g(7)$
     Hint: Use parentheses. $g(x) = (2x - 1)/(x + 3)$.

2-3 Linear Functions

You can write the solutions to open sentences in two variables as sets of ordered pairs. These solutions can be graphed in the coordinate plane. The following graph represents the solutions to $3x - y = 1$.

An infinite number of ordered pairs will satisfy $3x - y = 1$. The graph of these ordered pairs is a straight line. An equation whose graph is a straight line is called a **linear equation.**

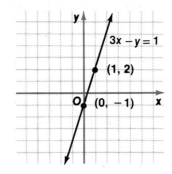

When variables other than x and y are used, assume that the letter coming first in the alphabet represents the domain or horizontal coordinate.

In a linear equation each term is a constant, like 7, or a constant times a variable to the first power, like $7x$. Thus, $4x + 3y = 7$, $y = 8$, $5m - n = 1$, and $y = 7 + 2x$ are linear equations. But $3x + y^2 = y$ and $\frac{1}{x} + y = 4$ are *not.* *Why?*

Any linear equation can be written in **standard form.**

> The standard form of a linear equation is
> $$Ax + By = C$$
> where A, B, and C are real numbers, and A and B are *not both* zero.

Standard Form of a Linear Equation

Usually A, B, and C are given as integers that have greatest common factor 1.

Example

1 **Write the equation $x = \frac{2}{3}y - 1$ in standard form.**

$$x = \frac{2}{3}y - 1$$

$3x = 2y - 3$ *Multiply both sides by 3 to eliminate the fraction.*
$3x - 2y = -3$ *Add $-2y$ to both sides.*

To graph a linear equation, it is helpful to make a table of ordered pairs that satisfy the equation. These ordered pairs can then be graphed and connected with a straight line. Since two points determine a line, you need only two points to graph a linear equation in two variables. In checking your work it is helpful to use a third point.

Examples

2 **Graph $3y = -2x - 6$.**

First, solve the equation for y.
$$3y = -2x - 6$$
$$y = -\frac{2}{3}x - 2$$

Next, find three ordered pairs that satisfy the equation. Then, graph the ordered pairs and connect the points with a line.

x	$-\frac{2}{3}x - 2$	y	(x, y)
-3	$-\frac{2}{3}(-3) - 2$	0	$(-3, 0)$
0	$-\frac{2}{3}(0) - 2$	-2	$(0, -2)$
3	$-\frac{2}{3}(3) - 2$	-4	$(3, -4)$

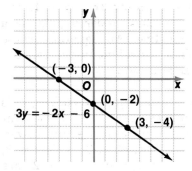

3 **Graph $2a = 3b - 4$.**

First, solve the equation for b.
$$2a = 3b - 4$$
$$-3b = -2a - 4$$
$$b = \frac{2}{3}a + \frac{4}{3}$$

Next, find three ordered pairs that satisfy the equation. Then graph the ordered pairs and connect the points with a line.

a	$\frac{2}{3}a + \frac{4}{3}$	b	(a, b)
-2	$\frac{2}{3}(-2) + \frac{4}{3}$	0	$(-2, 0)$
1	$\frac{2}{3}(1) + \frac{4}{3}$	2	$(1, 2)$
4	$\frac{2}{3}(4) + \frac{4}{3}$	4	$(4, 4)$

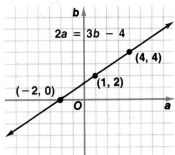

Not all linear equations represent functions. For example, consider the equation $x = 3$. Its graph is a vertical line. Any vertical line drawn on the graph of the equation passes through every point of that graph. The relation is *not* a function.

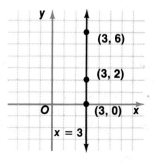

The equation $x = 3$ means that y can have any value as long as x is 3.

Any function whose ordered pairs satisfy a linear equation is called a **linear function**.

> **A linear function can be defined by** $f(x) = mx + b$ **where** m **and** b **are real numbers.**

Definition of Linear Function

In the definition of a linear function, m or b may be zero.

If $m = 0$, then $f(x) = b$. The graph is a horizontal line. This function is called a **constant function**.

Examples

4 **Which of the following are linear functions?**

a. $f(x) = x^3 + 4$

This cannot be written in the form $f(x) = mx + b$. Thus, it is *not* a linear function.

b. $g(x) = 4 - x$

This can be written in the form $f(x) = mx + b$ where $m = -1$ and $b = 4$. Thus, it is a linear function.

Exploratory Exercises

State whether each equation is a linear equation.

1. $x^2 + y^2 = 7$ **2.** $x + y = 4$ **3.** $x - 2y = 5$ **4.** $x^2 = 9$

5. $a + 3b = 7$ **6.** $5m^2 = n^2$ **7.** $y = -4x$ **8.** $7 = 2y$

State whether each of the following is a linear function.

9. $f(x) = x^2 + 3$ **10.** $g(x) = 7$ **11.** $3[g(x)] = x$ **12.** $g(x) = x - 4$

13. $5[f(x)] = 5x^2 - 5$ **14.** $4[f(b)] = 2 - b$ **15.** $f(x) = \frac{2}{3}(6 - 9x)$ **16.** $g(x) = x(2 - x)$

Written Exercises

Write each equation in standard form.

1. $y = 2x - 6$ **2.** $y = -4x + 1$ **3.** $x = 5$ **4.** $y - 7 = 0$

5. $y = \frac{5}{8}x + 1$ **6.** $x = \frac{1}{3}y - 4$ **7.** $y = 3x$ **8.** $x = \frac{3}{5} + \frac{y}{4}$

Graph each equation.

9. $y = x$ **10.** $y = x + 1$ **11.** $y = 2x + 3$ **12.** $y = 5x - 4$

13. $b = 2a - 3$ **14.** $p = 5q + 1$ **15.** $x + y = 7$ **16.** $x - y = 4$

17. $4x + 3y = 12$ **18.** $2x - 5y = 10$ **19.** $2a + 3b = 6$ **20.** $5 = 5x$

21. $f(x) = 2x + 1$ **22.** $f(x) = 3x - 1$ **23.** $3s - 2t = 6$ **24.** $2r - 3s = 6$

25. $5x = 4$ **26.** $3y = 5$ **27.** $x + 1 = 2y$ **28.** $3x - 4 = 2y$

29. $\frac{1}{3}x + \frac{1}{2}y = 1$ **30.** $\frac{2}{3}x + \frac{1}{4}y = 2$ **31.** $\frac{x}{4} - \frac{y}{3} = 2$ **32.** $\frac{x}{3} + \frac{y}{2} = 3$

Challenge

33. $3[f(a)] = 2$ **34.** $4[g(x)] = 4$ **35.** $-[h(y)] = 2y - 3$ **36.** $3[p(x)] = x - 6$

Simulation games are games that resemble real life processes. The game called LIFE, created by John Horton Conway, is one example. It shows, in a simple way, the evolution of a society of living organisms as it ages with time.

You can play LIFE using a grid of squares and counters in two different colors, say black and red. The counters are placed on the grid, one to a square. Then you change the positions of the counters according to the following *genetic laws,* or rules for births, deaths, and survivals.

SURVIVALS   Every counter with 2 or 3 neighboring counters survives for the next generation.   *Neighboring counters have common sides or corners.*

DEATH   Every counter with 4 or more neighbors dies from overpopulation. Every counter with only one neighbor or none dies from isolation.

BIRTHS   Every empty cell with exactly 3 neighbors is a birth cell. A counter is placed on the cell for the next generation.

To help eliminate mistakes in play, the following procedure is suggested.

1. Start with a pattern of black counters.
2. Put a red counter where each birth cell will occur.
3. Put a second black counter on top of each death cell. Ignore the red counters when determining death cells.
4. Check the new pattern. Then, remove all dead counters, and replace the newborn red counters with black counters.

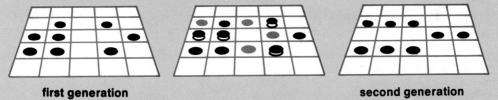

first generation   **second generation**

Notice that births and deaths occur simultaneously. Together, they are a move to the next generation.

When you play this game, you will find that many patterns either die, reach a stable repeating pattern or become blinkers, alternating between two patterns.

Computers are very helpful in simulations because they can display the changes, and a number of patterns can be observed in a short period of time.

Exercises
Find the next six generations for each of the following.

1.   2.   3.   4.   5.

2-4   Slopes and Intercepts

A ramp installed to give handicapped people access to a certain building has a base 12 meters long and an elevation of 2 meters. The steepness or **slope** of the ramp is found by using the following ratio.

$$\text{slope} = \frac{\text{change in vertical units}}{\text{change in horizontal units}}$$

Thus, the slope of the ramp is $\frac{2}{12}$ or $\frac{1}{6}$.

Slope is also defined for the graphs of linear functions. In the graph of $f(x) = 4x$ shown at the right, the y-coordinates increase 8 units for each 2 units increase in the corresponding x-coordinates. The slope of the line whose equation is $f(x) = 4x$ is $\frac{8}{2}$ or 4. The vertical change is the difference of the y-coordinates. The horizontal change is the difference of the corresponding x-coordinates.

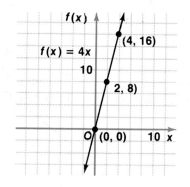

x	$4x$
0	0
2	8
4	16

The slope, m, of a line passing through points (x_1, y_1) and (x_2, y_2) is given by the following equation.	
$$m = \frac{y_2 - y_1}{x_2 - x_1}$$	*Definition of Slope*

Example

1   Determine the slope of the line that passes through $(1, -3)$ and $(0, -5)$.

$$\begin{aligned}
\text{slope} &= \frac{y_2 - y_1}{x_2 - x_1} \\
&= \frac{-5 - (-3)}{0 - 1} \\
&= \frac{-2}{-1} \\
&= 2 \qquad \text{The slope of the line is 2.}
\end{aligned}$$

Examples

2 **Determine the slope of each of the following lines.**

a.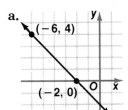

b.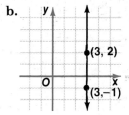

c.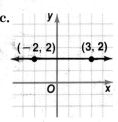

a. slope $= \dfrac{4 - 0}{-6 - (-2)}$

$= \dfrac{4}{-4}$ or -1

The slope is -1.

b. slope $= \dfrac{2 - (-1)}{3 - 3}$

$= \dfrac{3}{0}$

The slope is undefined.

c. slope $= \dfrac{2 - 2}{-2 - 3}$

$= \dfrac{0}{-5}$ or 0

The line has a slope of 0.

3 **Graph the line that passes through $(-1, -2)$ and whose slope is $\dfrac{3}{4}$.**

First graph the ordered pair $(-1, -2)$. Since the slope is $\dfrac{3}{4}$, the vertical change is 3 and the horizontal change is 4. From $(-1, -2)$ move 3 units up and 4 units to the right. This point is $(3, 1)$. Connect these two points with a straight line.

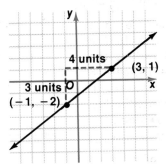

The previous examples suggest the following statements about the slope of a line.

| If the line rises to the right, then the slope is positive. | If the line is horizontal, then the slope is zero. | If the line falls to the right, then the slope is negative. | If the line is vertical, then the slope is *undefined*. |

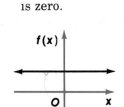

positive slope

zero slope

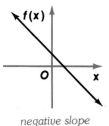

negative slope

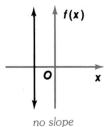

no slope

The graphs of $f(x) = 3x + 2$, $g(x) = 3x$, and $h(x) = 3x - 5$ are lines with the same slope. But, these lines do *not* pass through the same points.

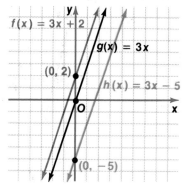

The slope of each line is 3. Note that 3 is also the coefficient of x in each equation. In general, the slope of a line is the coefficient of x when its equation is solved for y.

Consider the points where each line crosses the *y*-axis.

$f(x) = 3x + 2$ crosses at $(0, 2)$.
$g(x) = 3x$ crosses at $(0, 0)$.
$h(x) = 3x - 5$ crosses at $(0, -5)$.

The x-coordinate of each point is 0.

The *y*-coordinates at these points are called the **y-intercepts** of the lines. The *y*-intercept is the value of *y* when *x* is zero.

$f(x) = 3x + 2$ has *y*-intercept 2.
$g(x) = 3x$ or $g(x) = 3x + 0$ has *y*-intercept 0.
$h(x) = 3x - 5$ or $h(x) = 3x + (-5)$ has *y*-intercept -5.

The **x-intercept** of a line is the value of *x* when *y* is zero. What are the *x*-intercepts of the lines described above?

Example

4   **Find the *y*-intercept and *x*-intercept of the line whose equation is $5x + 3y = 9$.**

To find the *y*-intercept, let $x = 0$ and solve for *y*.

$$5(0) + 3y = 9$$
$$3y = 9$$
$$y = 3 \qquad \text{The } y\text{-intercept is 3.}$$

To find the *x*-intercept, let $y = 0$ and solve for *x*.

$$5x + 3(0) = 9$$
$$5x = 9$$
$$x = \frac{9}{5} \qquad \text{The } x\text{-intercept is } \frac{9}{5}.$$

Exploratory Exercises

State the slope, y-intercept, and x-intercept for each graph.

1.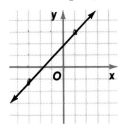

2.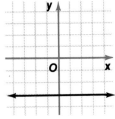

3.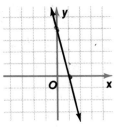

4.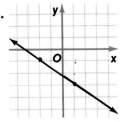

5.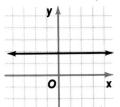

6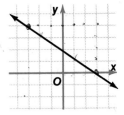

7.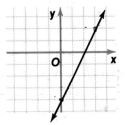

8.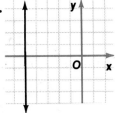

Written Exercises

Determine the slope of the line passing through each pair of points.

1. $(6, 1)$ and $(8, -4)$

2. $(5, 7)$ and $(4, -6)$

3. $(-3, 0)$ and $(8, 2)$

4. $(-6, -3)$ and $(4, 1)$

5. $(-8, -2)$ and $(-4, 8)$

6. $(6, 1)$ and $(6, 7)$

7. $(2.5, 3)$ and $(1, -9)$

8. $(0, 0)$ and $\left(\frac{3}{2}, \frac{1}{4}\right)$

9. $\left(1\frac{3}{4}, \frac{1}{3}\right)$ and $\left(2, \frac{1}{3}\right)$

10. $(1.8, 6)$ and $(-1, 3.2)$

11. $(a, 2)$ and $(a, -2)$

12. $(5, k)$ and $(k + 1, k)$

Find the y-intercept and x-intercept of each line whose equation is given below.

13. $y = 5x - 9$

14. $y = -3x - 5$

15. $y - 1 = 7x$

16. $y + 6 = 5x$

17. $3y = -2x - 15$

18. $3y = x + 4$

19. $y = -2$

20. $x = 4$

21. $f(x) = x - 2$

22. $g(x) = 4x - 1$

23. $x + 2y = 5$

24. $2x + 3y = 6$

25. $3x - 2y = 12$

26. $5x + 3y = 30$

27. $x + 2y = 7$

28. $3x + y = 6$

29. $2x - 3y = 12$

30. $5x - 2y = 20$

Graph the equation of the line that passes through the given point and has the given slope.

31. $(-3, 2)$, $m = -2$

32. $(0, 0)$, $m = 3$

33. $(3, 4)$, $m = -1$

34. $(-1, 1)$, $m = \frac{1}{4}$

35. $(2, -1)$, $m = 0$

36. $(-4, 1)$, $m = -\frac{5}{3}$

37. $(2, -3)$, $m = \frac{3}{5}$

38. $(-3, -1)$, no slope

39. $(2, 5)$, $m = -\frac{2}{3}$

40. $\left(4, 3\frac{1}{2}\right)$, $m = 0$

41. $(5, -2)$, no slope

42. $\left(\frac{1}{4}, 1\right)$, $m = 4$

Find the missing coordinate if the line through the two points has the given slope.

43. $(0, 0)$ and $(x, 7)$, $m = 7$

44. $(6, y)$ and $(2, -13)$, $m = 3$

45. $(-2, -7)$ and $(0, y)$, $m = -\dfrac{1}{2}$

46. $(x, -1)$ and $(3, 6)$, $m = 1$

47. $(5, 3)$ and $(3, y)$, $m = -3$

48. $\left(-17\dfrac{1}{2}, -35\right)$ and $(x, 0)$, $m = 2$

49. $\left(-10\dfrac{2}{3}, y\right)$ and $\left(-8\dfrac{1}{3}, 16\right)$, $m = -3$

50. $\left(4\dfrac{1}{2}, -3\right)$ and $\left(x, \dfrac{1}{2}\right)$, $m = -\dfrac{5}{7}$

mini-review

1. Evaluate $(5x^2)(11 - 2^3)$ if $x = 9$.
2. Is $\sqrt{16}$ a rational number?
3. Simplify $\dfrac{3}{4}\left(x + \dfrac{1}{3}x\right)$.
4. Solve $|3x - 1| \le 2$.
5. John's test scores so far are 76, 90, 82, and 95. What must he score on the next test to have an average of at least 85?

Using Calculators _____ Slope

You can use your calculator to determine the slope of a line. Remember to insert parentheses when necessary.

Example: Determine the slope of the line passing through $(3, 2)$ and $(1, -6)$.

Recall that $\dfrac{y_2 - y_1}{x_2 - x_1} = (y_2 - y_1)/(x_2 - x_1)$.

ENTER: (2 − 6 +/−) ÷ (3 − 1) =

DISPLAY: 2   6   −6   8   3   1   2   4

The slope is 4.

Exercises

Determine the slope of the line passing through each pair of points.

1. $(6, 7)$ and $(-2, 5)$
2. $(-7, 3)$ and $(-4, -6)$
3. $(4, 9)$ and $(-10, 5)$
4. $(8, 5)$ and $(0, 9)$
5. $(7, 2)$ and $(-9, 3)$
6. $(3, 24)$ and $(5, 64)$

Excursions in Algebra _____ Age of Diophantus

The solution to this riddle is the age of the ancient Greek mathematician, Diophantus.

His youth lasted one-sixth of his life. He grew a beard after one-twelfth more. He married after one-seventh more. He had a son 5 years later. His son lived half as long as his father. Diophantus died 4 years after his son died.

2-5 Finding Linear Equations

In the figure at the right, $\overleftrightarrow{AB}$ passes through points $A(0, b)$ and $B(x, y)$. Notice that b is the y-intercept of $\overleftrightarrow{AB}$.

Suppose you want to find an equation for $\overleftrightarrow{AB}$. Let m represent the slope of the line.

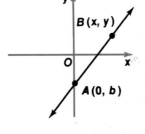

$m = \dfrac{y - b}{x - 0}$ *Definition of slope*

$m = \dfrac{y - b}{x}$ *Solve for y.*

$mx = y - b$

$y = mx + b$

This equation of a line, $y = mx + b$, is called the **slope-intercept form.**

The slope-intercept form of the equation of a line is $y = mx + b$. The slope is m and the y-intercept is b.	*Slope-Intercept Form of a Linear Equation*

Suppose you are given the slope and y-intercept of a line. You can find the slope-intercept form of the equation of the line by substitution. For example, if the slope of a line is $-\dfrac{2}{3}$ and its y-intercept is 14, an equation of the line is $y = -\dfrac{2}{3}x + 14$. The standard form of this equation is $2x + 3y = 42$.

The form $y = mx + b$ is often written as $f(x) = mx + b$.

Example

1 **Find the slope-intercept form of the equation of a line with slope $\dfrac{2}{3}$ passing through (4, 7).**

First, substitute the slope and coordinates of the point into the slope-intercept form and solve for b.

$y = mx + b$

$7 = \left(\dfrac{2}{3}\right)(4) + b$ *Substitute 7 for y, $\dfrac{2}{3}$ for m, and 4 for x.*

$7 = \dfrac{8}{3} + b$

$\dfrac{13}{3} = b$

Write the equation in slope-intercept form.

$y = \dfrac{2}{3}x + \dfrac{13}{3}$ *Substitute $\dfrac{2}{3}$ for m and $\dfrac{13}{3}$ for b.*

Examples

2 **Find the slope-intercept form of the equation of a line passing through $(-2, 5)$ and $(3, 0)$.**

First find the slope.

$$\text{slope} = \frac{5 - 0}{-2 - 3}$$
$$= \frac{5}{-5}$$
$$= -1$$

Next, substitute the slope and coordinates of one point in the slope-intercept form and solve for b.

$y = mx + b$
$5 = (-1)(-2) + b$ *Substitute 5 for y, -1 for m, and -2 for x. Using the other*
$5 = 2 + b$ *point would give the same results.*
$3 = b$

The slope-intercept form of the equation of the line is $y = -x + 3$.

3 **Find the slope and y-intercept of a line with equation in standard form.**

Recall that the standard form of the equation of a line is $Ax + By = C$. If B is not zero, the slope and y-intercept are found by solving the equation for y.

$Ax + By = C$
$By = -Ax + C$
$y = -\dfrac{A}{B}x + \dfrac{C}{B}$ The slope is $-\dfrac{A}{B}$ and the y-intercept is $\dfrac{C}{B}$.

Consider the line with equation $y = -2x + 4$. The standard form of this equation is $2x + y = 4$. The following calculations use the information from Example 3 to find the slope and y-intercept.

$$\text{slope} = -\frac{A}{B} \qquad\qquad y\text{-intercept} = \frac{C}{B}$$
$$= -\frac{2}{1} \text{ or } -2 \qquad\qquad = \frac{4}{1} \text{ or } 4$$

Notice that these values are the same as the values you would obtain from the slope-intercept form of the equation.

Exploratory Exercises

Find the slope-intercept form of the equation of each line which has slope m and y-intercept b.

1. $m = 5, b = -3$
2. $m = -1, b = 3$
3. $m = -1, b = 4$
4. $m = 8, b = 1$
5. $m = \frac{2}{3}, b = -7$
6. $m = \frac{1}{4}, b = 6$
7. $m = 2.5, b = 0$
8. $m = -4.1, b = -9$
9. $m = 0, b = 0$

State the slope and y-intercept of the graph of each equation.

10. $y = -2x + 5$ **11.** $y = -4x + 6$ **12.** $\frac{1}{2}y = 7x - 1$

13. $y = x - 8$ **14.** $y = -\frac{3}{4}x - 3$ **15.** $y = \frac{1}{3}x$

16. $-y = 0.2x + 6$ **17.** $-y = x$ **18.** $y = cx + t$

Find the slope-intercept form of each equation.

19. $2x + 5y = 10$ **20.** $3x - y = 6$ **21.** $2x + 3y = 4$

22. $4x + 8y = 11$ **23.** $2x - 2y = 4$ **24.** $2x = 11$

Written Exercises

State the slope and y-intercept of the graph of each equation.

1. $-2x + y = 15$ **2.** $0.4x - 0.4y = 0.4$ **3.** $5x - 3y = 0.6$

4. $3x - 4y = 1$ **5.** $8x = 1$ **6.** $8x - y = -1$

7. $x - \frac{1}{2}y = 2$ **8.** $2x - \frac{1}{3}y = -5$ **9.** $\frac{1}{5}x - \frac{1}{3}y = \frac{1}{7}$

Find the slope-intercept form of the equation of the line that satisfies the given conditions.

10. slope $= \frac{1}{2}$, passes through $(6, 4)$ **11.** slope $= \frac{3}{4}$, passes through $(8, -1)$

12. slope $= \frac{2}{3}$, passes through $(6, -2)$ **13.** slope $= -\frac{4}{5}$, passes through $(2, -3)$

14. slope $= 4$, passes through $(2, -3)$ **15.** slope $= 5$, passes through the origin

16. passes through $(6, 1)$ and $(8, -4)$ **17.** passes through $(-6, -3)$ and $(4, 1)$

18. passes through $(-3, 0)$ and $(8, 2)$ **19.** passes through $(6, 1)$ and $(6, 7)$

20. passes through $(-8, -2)$ and $(-4, 8)$ **21.** passes through $(4, 6)$ and $(0, 0)$

22. x-intercept $= -3$, y-intercept $= 6$ **23.** x-intercept $= 6$, y-intercept $= 4$

24. x-intercept $= \frac{3}{5}$, y-intercept $= 6$ **25.** x-intercept $= \frac{1}{3}$, y-intercept $= -\frac{1}{4}$

26. x-intercept $= 0$, y-intercept $= 2$ **27.** x-intercept $= -7$, y-intercept $= 0$

Find the standard form of the equation of the line that satisfies the given conditions.

28. slope $= 1$, passes through $(2, 3)$ **29.** slope $= 2$, passes through $(4, 6)$

30. slope $= -2$, passes through $(-1, 4)$ **31.** slope $= -3$, passes through $(2, 5)$

32. slope $= \frac{4}{3}$, passes through $(4, 3)$ **33.** slope $= -\frac{2}{3}$, passes through $(-3, 5)$

34. passes through $(2, 3)$ and $(1, 5)$ **35.** passes through $(2, 5)$ and $(3, 6)$

36. passes through $(1, -2)$ and $(3, 7)$ **37.** passes through $(1, 0)$ and $(2, -5)$

38. passes through $(-1, 5)$ and $(2, 3)$ **39.** passes through $(-1, -1)$ and $(-1, 8)$

40. x-intercept $= 4$, y-intercept $= 3$ **41.** x-intercept $= 9$, y-intercept $= 1$

42. x-intercept $= -6$, y-intercept $= 5$ **43.** x-intercept $= -1$, y-intercept $= 1$

44. x-intercept $= 0$, y-intercept $= -5$ **45.** x-intercept $= 0$, y-intercept $= 7$

Challenge

Find k in each equation if the given ordered pair is a solution.

46. $5x + ky = 8$, $(3, -1)$ **47.** $4x - ky = 7$, $(4, 3)$

48. $2x - 3y = k$, $(-1, -4)$ **49.** $3x + 8y = k$, $\left(0, -\frac{1}{2}\right)$

50. $kx + 3y = 11$, $(7, 2)$ **51.** $kx - 5y = 21$, $(3, -2)$

2-6 Special Functions

Recall that a linear function can be described by $y = mx + b$ or $f(x) = mx + b$ where m and b are real numbers. Some linear functions have special names.

If $m = 0$, the function is called a **constant function.** Its graph is a horizontal line.

If $b = 0$ and $m = 1$, the function is called the **identity function.** Its graph passes through the origin and forms congruent angles with the axes.

If $b = 0$ and $m \neq 0$, the function is called a **direct variation.** Its graph passes through the origin.

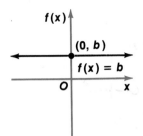

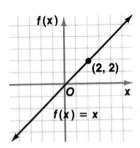

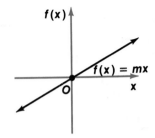

A linear function described by $y = b$ or $f(x) = b$ is called a **constant function.**

Definition of Constant Function

A linear function described by $y = x$ or $f(x) = x$ is called the **identity function.**

Definition of Identity Function

A linear function described by $y = mx$ or $f(x) = mx$ where $m \neq 0$ is called a **direct variation.** The constant m is called the **constant of variation** or **constant of proportionality.**

Definition of Direct Variation

A special language is often used with direct variation. The equation $y = mx$ means y varies directly with x, or y is *directly proportional* to x.

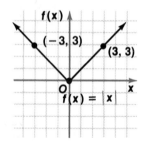

Several other functions are closely related to linear functions. Absolute value functions are one example.

Consider $f(x) = |x|$ or $y = |x|$. When x is positive or zero the function is like $y = x$. When x is negative the function is like $y = -x$. The graph of $f(x) = |x|$ is shown on the right.

All of the following graphs represent absolute value functions.

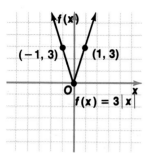

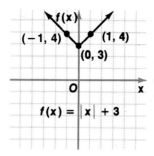

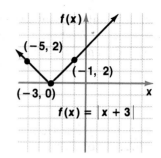

The domain is $\{x \mid x \text{ is real}\}$.
The range is $\{y \mid y \geq 0\}$.

The domain is $\{x \mid x \text{ is real}\}$.
The range is $\{y \mid y \geq 3\}$.

The domain is $\{x \mid x \text{ is real}\}$.
The range is $\{y \mid y \geq 0\}$.

Step functions like the ones graphed below are also related to linear functions.

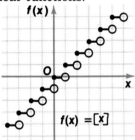

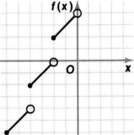

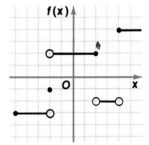

One type of step function is the **greatest integer function.** The *greatest integer of x* is written $[x]$ and means the greatest integer *not* greater than x. For example, $[6.2]$ is 6 and $[-1.8]$ is -2. The greatest integer function is given by $f(x) = [x]$ and is graphed above on the left.

Example

1   **Graph $f(x) = [x] + 1$.**

x	$[x]$	$[x] + 1$
0	0	1
0.2	0	1
0.6	0	1
1.0	1	2
1.5	1	2
2.0	2	3
-1.0	-1	0
-1.5	-2	-1
-2.0	-2	-1

The domain is all real numbers.

The range is all integers.

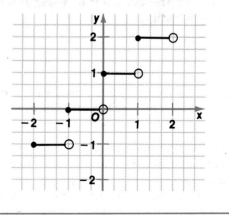

Exploratory Exercises

Identify each function as C for *constant,* **as I for** *identity,* **as D for** *direct variation,* **as A for** *absolute value,* **or as G for** *greatest integer function.*

1. $f(x) = |3x - 2|$ **2.** $f(x) = [-x]$ **3.** $g(x) = 3x$

4. $g(x) = [2x]$ **5.** $y = |2x|$ **6.** $f(x) = |2x + 1|$

7. $f(x) = \left| x - \dfrac{2}{3} \right|$ **8.** $g(x) = 19$ **9.** $g(x) = [2x + 1]$

10. $h(x) = -2x$ **11.** $f(x) = \dfrac{1}{2}x$ **12.** $p(x) = x$

13. $h(x) = [x - 3]$ **14.** $f(x) = -3x$ **15.** $g(x) = |x + 3|$

16. $h(x) = -7$ **17.** $m(x) = |-3x|$ **18.** $f(x) = \left[x - \dfrac{1}{2} \right]$

19. $f(x) = \left[x - 2\dfrac{1}{2} \right]$ **20.** $f(x) = [3x - 5]$ **21.** $m(x) = \dfrac{2}{3}$

22. $g(x) = -x$ **23.** $k(x) = |x - 8|$ **24.** $f(x) = 0$

Written Exercises

Graph each function.

1. $f(x) = x$ **2.** $g(x) = 3x$ **3.** $h(x) = -2x$

4. $f(x) = \dfrac{1}{2}x$ **5.** $p(x) = |x|$ **6.** $r(x) = |2x|$

7. $g(x) = |-3x|$ **8.** $f(x) = |x + 3|$ **9.** $f(x) = \left| x - \dfrac{2}{3} \right|$

10. $f(x) = |2x + 1|$ **11.** $g(x) = [-x]$ **12.** $h(x) = -[x]$

13. $p(x) = [2x]$ **14.** $f(x) = 2[x]$ **15.** $r(x) = [x] - 3$

16. $p(x) = 3 - [x]$ **17.** $h(x) = |3x| - 2$ **18.** $g(x) = -|x| + 3$

19. $r(x) = 2|x| - 3$ **20.** $f(x) = |x - 3| + 2$ **21.** $f(x) = \left[x - \dfrac{1}{2} \right]$

22. $f(x) = -[x - 2]$ **23.** $m(x) = [3x - 5]$ **24.** $g(x) = [2x + 7]$

Explain how the graphs of each pair of equations differ.

25. $y = 2[x]$ and $y = [2x]$

26. $y = [x + 5]$ and $y = [x] + 5$

27. $y = |x - 3|$ and $y = |x| - 3$

28. $y = |3x|$ and $y = 3|x|$

29. $y = |2x + 5|$ and $y = |2x| + 5$

30. $y = [2x + 5]$ and $y = [2x] + 5$

31. $y = |ax|$ and $y = a|x|$

32. $y = |x + b|$ and $y = |x| + b$

33. $y = -3[x]$ and $y = [-3x]$

34. $y = -2|x|$ and $y = |-2x|$

Challenge

Graph each function.

35. $y = |[x]|$ **36.** $y = [|x|]$

mini-review

1. Solve $0.5y - 7.5 = -7.1$.
2. Mr. Wiekart bought a dinette set for $53 more than 50% of its original price. He paid $382. What was the original price?
3. Find $f(2)$ if $f(x) = x^2 - 3x$.
4. Is the following relation a function? $\{(2, 3), (3, -2), (4, 2), (3, 4)\}$
5. Find the slope of the line through $(3, 0)$ and $(-7, 3)$.

Problem Solving

An important strategy for solving problems is to look for a pattern. Sometimes a pattern may be obvious, but many times it is not. You may have to "play" with the facts and figures until you arrive at a pattern. Then you can solve the problem by generalizing and applying the pattern.

Example: **Write an equation showing the relationship between the variables in the chart below.**

x	1	2	3	4	5
y	17	21	25	29	33

Look for a pattern by finding differences between successive values of x and successive values of y.

$$+1 \quad +1 \quad +1 \quad +1$$

x	1	2	3	4	5
y	17	21	25	29	33

$$+4 \quad +4 \quad +4 \quad +4$$

Notice that the changes are in x are 1 while the changes in y are 4. This suggests that $y = 4x$ since the changes in y are 4 times the changes in x. Try $x = 1$ in $y = 4x$.

$$y = 4 \cdot 1 \text{ or } 4$$

But when x is 1, y is 17, not 4. To make y equal to 17 when x is equal to 1, you need to add 13. The equation becomes $y = 4x + 13$. This equation checks for each value of x.

Exercises

Write an equation showing the relationship between the variables in each chart. Then complete the chart.

1.

x	1	2	3			6
y	8	16		32	40	

2.

a	1	2	3	4	5	6
b	5	7	9			

3. The Worthington City Council has 12 members. After their last session, each member shook hands with each other member. How many handshakes were there in all?

4. At Dublin High School, there are 500 students and 500 lockers, numbered 1 through 500. Suppose the first student opens each locker. Then the second student closes every second locker. The third student changes the state of every third locker (the student closes the open lockers and opens the closed lockers). The fourth student changes the state of every fourth locker. This process continues until the five-hundredth student changes the state of the five-hundredth locker. After this process is completed, state which lockers are open.

2-7 Problem Solving: Linear Functions

Geothermal energy is generated wherever water comes into contact with heated underground rocks. This heat turns the water into steam which is used to make electricity.

The underground temperature of rocks varies with their depth below the surface. The temperature at the surface is about 20°C. At a depth of 2 km, the temperature is about 90°C. This information can be used to find an equation for the relationship, assuming the relationship is linear.

/Explore/ Read the problem carefully.
Let d represent the depth given in kilometers.
Let t represent the temperature in degrees Celsius.
Use ordered pairs of the form (d, t) to show the relationship between depth and temperature.

- *When the depth is 0, the temperature is 20°C.* ♦ (0, 20)
- *When the depth is 2 km, the temperature is 90°C.* ♦ (2, 90)

/Plan/ Write a linear equation from the ordered pairs.

/Solve/ A line through (0, 20) and (2, 90) has a slope of $\dfrac{90 - 20}{2 - 0}$ or 35. The line intersects the vertical axis at 20. So, the equation is $t = 35d + 20$.

/Examine/ Check whether the solution makes sense. Compute $35d + 20$ when d is 0 and when d is 2.

When d is 0, t is 35(0) + 20, or 20. ✔
When d is 2, t is 35(2) + 20, or 90. ✔

So, the equation $t = 35d + 20$ is correct.
This equation gives a good approximation for depths less than 4 kilometers.

Examples

1 **Find the underground temperature 3600 meters below the surface.**

$t = 35d + 20$
$t = 35(3.6) + 20$ *3600 m = 3.6 km*
$t = 146$ The temperature is about 146°C.

2 **Ace Repair Shop has the following chart for its employees to use in computing customers' bills. Write an equation to describe the relationship between the number of labor hours and the charge. (Assume the relationship is linear.)**

Labor Hours	0.5	0.75	1	1.25	1.5	2
Charge	$29	$33.50	$38	$42.50	$47	$56

First draw a graph to show the relationship.

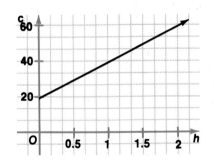

Using two points on the line, (2, 56) and (1, 38), find the slope of the line.

$$m = \frac{56 - 38}{2 - 1}$$

$$= \frac{18}{1} \text{ or } 18$$

Then, substitute the slope and coordinates of one point in the general slope-intercept form and solve for b.

$$y = mx + b$$
$$38 = (18)(1) + b$$
$$20 = b$$

Thus, the equation that describes the relationship is $c = 18h + 20$.

Exploratory Exercises

Solve each problem.

1. Inches of snowfall varies directly with inches of rainfall. Thirty-five inches of snow is about the same as 3.5 inches of rain. Write an equation to describe the relationship between inches of snowfall and inches of rainfall.

2. Twelve inches of snowfall is equivalent to how much rainfall?

3. Forty-eight inches of snowfall is equivalent to how much rainfall?

4. Eleven inches of rainfall is equivalent to how much snowfall?

5. Four and one-half inches of rainfall is equivalent to how much snowfall?

6. Frontier Auto Shop has a standard $12 shop charge for every job it takes. In addition, the mechanic working on the job charges $20 per hour. Write an equation to describe the relationship between time spent on a job and total charge for the job.

7. Cindy Baker is a mechanic at Frontier Auto Shop. She spent 4 hours on a job. How much will the customer be charged?

8. Joshua Levy is a mechanic at Frontier Auto Shop. He spent 2.5 hours on a job. How much will the customer be charged?

9. Frontier Auto Shop charges $47 for a job. How much time did the mechanic spend on the job?

10. Frontier Auto Shop charged $100 for a job. How much time did the mechanic spend on the job?

11. Light travels faster than sound. If you count the number of seconds between when you see lightning and when you hear it, you can estimate how far away it is. The distance d in kilometers between you and the lightning is estimated by $d = \frac{1}{3}s$ where s is the number of seconds. Complete the chart for estimating the distance.

Time (seconds)	2	3	4	5	10	15	20	25	30	40	50	60
Distance (kilometers)												

12. Crickets vary their number of chirps with the temperature. If you count the number of chirps in a minute, you can tell the temperature. The temperature t in degrees Celsius is estimated by $t = 0.2(n + 32)$ where n is the number of chirps in one minute. Complete the chart for estimating the temperature.

Chirps	50	60	70	80	90	100	110	120	130
Temperature (Celsius)									

Written Exercises

Write an equation to describe the relationship in each of the following.

1. The present population of Whitehall is 47,000. The population increases by 550 each year. What will be the population in y years?

2. A telephone company charges $12 per month plus 10¢ for each local call. What is the monthly bill if c local calls are made?

3. A ranger calculates there are 6,000 deer in a preserve. She also estimates that 75 more deer die than are born each year. How many deer will be in the preserve x years from now?

4. The RD Rug Company produced 600 oriental rugs its first year of business. Each year after that, production increased by 100. What will be the annual production of oriental rugs after y years?

5. The ABC Car Rental Agency rents cars for $23 a day plus 18¢ a mile. How much does it cost to rent a car for a week and drive it t miles?

6. Emilio earns a flat salary of $150 per week for selling records. He receives an extra 30¢ for each record over 100 that he sells. How much will he make if he sells r records?

For each of the following, write an equation to describe the relationship. Then, use the equation to complete each table. Assume each relationship is linear.

7. Cost of Bowling at Bingo's Bowling Lanes

Number of Games	1	2	3	4	5	6
Cost	$1.25	$2.50	$3.75			

8. Cost of Repair Work at Acme Auto Repair

Hours of Labor	1	2	3	4	6	8	12	15	20	25	30
Total Bill	$44	$56	$68	$80							

9. Cost of Long Distance Phone Call

Minutes	3	4	5	6	8	10	15	20	30	45	60
Cost	$1.38	$1.72	$2.06								

10. Number of Luncheon Specials Sold at Open Hearth Restaurant

Number of Customers	20	30	40	50	75	100	150	200
Number of Luncheon Specials	10	16	22	28				

2-8 Graphing Linear Inequalities in Two Variables

The graph of $y = -\frac{2}{3}x + \frac{5}{3}$ is a line which separates the coordinate plane into two regions.

The graph of $y > -\frac{2}{3}x + \frac{5}{3}$ is the region *above* the line. In that region the value of y is greater than the value of $-\frac{2}{3}x + \frac{5}{3}$.

The graph of $y < -\frac{2}{3}x + \frac{5}{3}$ is the region *below* the line. In that region the value of y is less than the value of $-\frac{2}{3}x + \frac{5}{3}$.

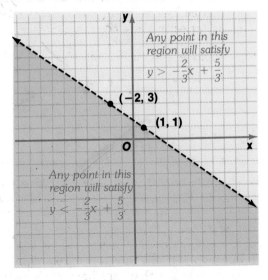

The line described by $y = -\frac{2}{3}x + \frac{5}{3}$ is called the *boundary* of each region. If the boundary is part of a graph, it is drawn as a solid line. If the boundary is *not* part of a graph, it is drawn as a broken line.

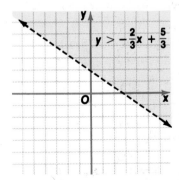

Note that $>$ tells you the boundary is *not* included.

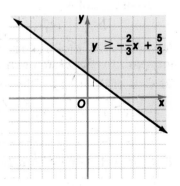

Note that $\geq$ tells you the boundary is included.

Example

1 Graph $2y - 5x \leq 1$.

$$2y - 5x \leq 1$$
$$2y \leq 5x + 1$$
$$y \leq \frac{5}{2}x + \frac{1}{2}$$

The slope is $\frac{5}{2}$.

The y-intercept is $\frac{1}{2}$.

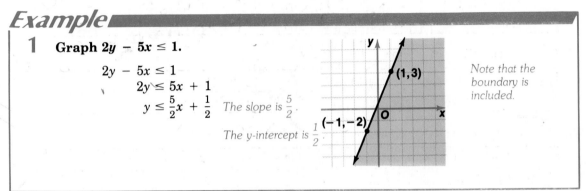

Note that the boundary is included.

Example

2 **Graph $y > |x| - 1$.**

To determine which region should be shaded, test two points, one on each side of the graph. Substitute these values into the inequality.

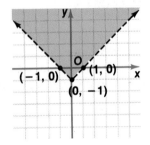

Note that the boundary is not included.

$$\begin{array}{ll} (1, 1) & (1, -1) \\ y \overset{?}{>} |x| - 1 & y \overset{?}{>} |x| - 1 \\ 1 \overset{?}{>} |1| - 1 & -1 \overset{?}{>} |1| - 1 \\ 1 \overset{?}{>} 0 \ \checkmark & -1 \overset{?}{>} 0 \ \ No \end{array}$$

The shaded region should include $(1, 1)$.

Exploratory Exercises

Name which points, $(0, 0)$, $(2, -3)$, or $(-1, 2)$, satisfy each inequality.

1. $x + 2y < 7$ 2. $3x - y \geq 2$ 3. $3x + 2y \leq 0$ 4. $x + y \geq 7$

5. $4x + 2y \geq 7$ 6. $5x - y > 2$ 7. $y < 0$ 8. $4x \geq -12$

Written Exercises

Draw the graph of each inequality.

1. $y < 3$ 2. $x < 1$ 3. $y > 5x - 3$ 4. $y \geq x - 7$

5. $y \leq -3x + 1$ 6. $y < 2x + 3$ 7. $2x - 5y \geq 4$ 8. $2x + 5y \geq 3$

9. $y > \frac{1}{3}x + 7$ 10. $y > \frac{1}{2}x - 3$ 11. $x - 2y \leq 2$ 12. $-2x + 5 \leq 3y$

13. $y \geq |x|$ 14. $y \geq |x| - 3$ 15. $|x| + y \geq 3$ 16. $y + |x| < 2$

17. $y < |x| + 2$ 18. $y < |x| - 2$ 19. $y > |2x|$ 20. $y \geq |3x|$

21. $|y| < x$ 22. $|y| \geq 2x$ 23. $|x| \leq |y|$ 24. $|x| > |y|$

25. Graph all points to the right of $x = 4$.

26. Graph all points in the second quadrant between $x = -2$, $x = -5$, and $y = 3$.

27. Graph all points in the first quadrant bounded by the two axes and the line $x + 2y = 4$.

28. Graph all points in the fourth quadrant bounded by the two axes and the lines $3x - y = 4$ and $x - y = 5$.

Challenge

Draw the graph of each of the following.

29. $|x| + |y| = 1$ 30. $|x| - |y| = 1$

31. $|x| + |y| \leq 1$ 32. $|x| + |y| > 1$

mini-review

1. Solve $\left|\frac{1}{2}x + 3\right| = 0$.

2. Solve $6x + 1 > x + 21$ and graph the solution set.

3. Find the x-intercept and y-intercept of the graph of $5y = x - 2$.

4. Find the slope and y-intercept of the graph of $3x - 4y = -10$.

5. Graph $f(x) = |2x| + 1$.

Slope and Y-Intercept

The computer program at the right can be used to find the slope and y-intercept of the line through any two points. The program uses the formula for slope.

$$m = \frac{y_2 - y_1}{x_2 - x_1} \qquad \text{See line 40.}$$

To find a formula for y-intercept, substitute the coordinates of a specific point (x_1, y_1) into the slope-intercept form. Then solve for b.

$$y_1 = m_1x + b$$
$$b = y_1 - mx_1 \qquad \text{See line 60.}$$

```
10  PRINT "ENTER THE
       COORDINATES"
15  PRINT "OF TWO POINTS."
20  INPUT X1, Y1, X2, Y2
30  IF X1 = X2 THEN 90
40  LET M = (Y2 - Y1) /
       (X2 - X1)
44  PRINT
50  PRINT "SLOPE = ";M
60  LET B = Y1 - M * X1
70  PRINT "Y-INTERCEPT = ";B
80  GOTO 110
90  PRINT "UNDEFINED SLOPE."
100 PRINT "NO Y-INTERCEPT."
110 END
```

When you run the program, the computer will ask for the coordinates of two points and print a question mark. Suppose the points are (3, 5) and (7, −2). The coordinates should be entered as shown at the right. Study the output. Notice that the slope and y-intercept are expressed as decimals.

```
RUN
ENTER THE COORDINATES
OF TWO POINTS.
?  3,5,7,-2
SLOPE  =  -1.75
Y-INTERCEPT  =  10.25
```

Exercises

Use the program to find the slope and y-intercept of the line through each pair of points named. Then write the equation of the line in slope-intercept form.

1. (2, −7), (−2, −9)   **2.** (4, 9), (−1, 12)   **3.** (−2, 7), (−2, 2)   **4.** (−6, 3), (0, 3)

Three or more points that lie on the same line are *collinear*. Decide if points A, B, and C are collinear. (Hint: Use the program to see if $\overleftrightarrow{AB}$ has the same slope as $\overleftrightarrow{BC}$.) Then write the equations for $\overleftrightarrow{AB}$, $\overleftrightarrow{BC}$, and $\overleftrightarrow{AC}$.

5. A(1, 29), B(3, 61), C(7, 125)

7. A(−1, 4), B(−2, 0), C(−3, −2)

9. A(9, −3), B(0, 0), C(18, 6)

6. A(0, 1), B(5, 2), C(6, 3)

8. A(3, −7), B(6, −6), C(15, −3)

10. A(6, −5), B(6, −1), C(4, −5)

Vocabulary

ordered pairs (41)
quadrants (41)
x-axis (41)
y-axis (41)
origin (41)
coordinate plane (41)
coordinate (41)
graph (41)
relation (43)
domain (43)
range (43)
mapping (43)
function (44)

vertical line test (45)
linear equation (48)
standard form (48)
linear function (50)
slope (52)
y-intercept (54)
x-intercept (54)
slope-intercept form (57)
constant function (60)
identity function (60)
direct variation (60)
greatest integer function (61)
linear inequalities (67)

Chapter Summary

1. Each point in a coordinate plane corresponds to exactly one ordered pair of numbers. Each ordered pair of numbers corresponds to exactly one point in a coordinate plane. (41)

2. Definition of Relation, Domain, and Range: A relation is a set of ordered pairs. The domain is the set of all first coordinates of the ordered pairs. The range is the set of all second coordinates of the ordered pairs. (43)

3. Definition of Function: A function is a relation in which each element of the domain is paired with exactly one element of the range. (44)

4. Vertical Line Test for a Function: If any vertical line drawn on the graph of a relation passes through no more than one point of that graph, then the relation is a function. (45)

5. An equation whose graph is a straight line is called a linear equation in two variables. (48)

6. Standard Form of a Linear Equation: The standard form of a linear equation is $Ax + By = C$, where A, B, and C are real numbers, and A and B are *not both* zero. (48)

7. Definition of Linear Function: A linear function can be defined by $f(x) = mx + b$ where m and b are real numbers. (50)

8. Definition of Slope: The slope, m, of a line passing through points (x_1, y_1) and (x_2, y_2) is given by the following equation.

$$m = \frac{y_2 - y_1}{x_2 - x_1} \quad (52)$$

9. The *y*-intercept is the value of a function when *x* is zero. The *x*-intercept is the value of a function when *y* is zero.   (54)

10. Slope-Intercept Form of a Linear Equation: The slope-intercept form of the equation of a line is $y = mx + b$. The slope is *m* and the *y*-intercept is *b*.   (57)

11. Definition of Constant Function: A linear function described by $y = b$ or $f(x) = b$ is called a constant function.   (60)

12. Definition of Identity Function: A linear function described by $y = x$ or $f(x) = x$ is called the identity function.   (60)

13. Definition of Direct Variation: A linear function described by $y = mx$ or $f(x) = mx$ where $m \neq 0$ is called a direct variation. The constant *m* is called the constant of variation or constant of proportionality.   (60)

14. The greatest integer of *x* is written [*x*] and means the greatest integer not greater than *x*.   (61)

15. An inequality describes the set of points above or below the boundary line.   (67)

Chapter Review ▄▄▄▄▄▄▄▄▄▄▄▄▄▄▄▄▄▄

2–1 **Graph each set of ordered pairs. Use appropriate labels on the axes.**

1. $\left\{ (4, 2), (3, 1), (0, 5), \left(-5, \frac{1}{2} \right), \left(-2, -1\frac{1}{2} \right) \right\}$

2. $\{(0, 40), (25, 10), (-30, 15), (-20, 30), (10, 20)\}$

3. $\{(-9, -12), (4, -8), (3, -3), (6, 10)\}$

2–2 **State the domain and range of each relation. Then state if the relation is a function.**

4. $\{(4.5, 1), (-4.5, 2), (4.5, 3), (-3.5, 4)\}$

5. $\{(1, 4.5), (2, -4.5), (3, 4.5), (4, -3.5), (5, -3.5)\}$

6. $\{(13, -8), (14, -9), (15, -9), (16, -8)\}$

Use the vertical line test to determine if each relation is a function.

7.
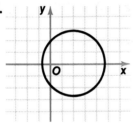

8.
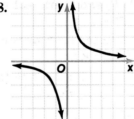

9.
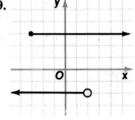

Given $f(x) = 2x^3 + 4x^2 + 4x + 1$, find each value.

10. $f(0)$ **11.** $f(-3)$ **12.** $f(a)$

2–3   **State whether each equation is a linear equation.**

13. $x^2 + y^2 = 4$ **14.** $xy = 12$ **15.** $y = 5$ **16.** $x + y = 9$

Graph each equation.

17. $y = \frac{1}{3}x$ **18.** $y = 3x$ **19.** $y = 2x - 1$ **20.** $3y = 2x + 1$

2–4   **Find the slope, y-intercept and x-intercept of the graph of each of the following.**

21. $3x + 7y = 2$ **22.** $4x - 3y = 7$

23. $\frac{1}{3}x - \frac{2}{3}y = 5$ **24.** $\frac{1}{2}x + \frac{3}{4}y = 1$

Determine the slope of the line passing through each pair of points.

25. (5, 1) and (3, 7)   **26.** $(-4, 2)$ and $(-4, 0)$ **27.** $(-3, -2)$ and (0, 4)

A line has slope $\frac{2}{3}$. For each pair of points on the line, find the missing coordinate.

28. (0, 6) and $(-6, y)$ **29.** $(-9, 0)$ and $(x, 10)$

Graph the line that passes through the given point and has the given slope.

30. $(-3, 2)$, $m = 3$ **31.** (3, 4), $m = \frac{1}{4}$ **32.** $(2, -1)$, $m = -\frac{5}{3}$

2–5   **Find the slope-intercept form of the equation of the line that satisfies the given conditions.**

33. slope $= 5$, y-intercept $= -7$ **34.** slope $= \frac{2}{3}$, passes through $(1, -4)$

35. passes through $(-3, 0)$ and $(4, -6)$ **36.** x-intercept $= -2$, y-intercept $= 5$

Find the standard form of the equation of the line that satisfies the given conditions.

37. slope $= 4$, passes through $(5, -2)$ **38.** slope $= -\frac{3}{2}$, y-intercept $= 7$

39. x-intercept $= 2$, y-intercept $= -6$ **40.** passes through (5, 3) and $(-2, 1)$

2–6   **Graph each function.**

41. $g(x) = |-x|$ **42.** $q(x) = |x - 3|$ **43.** $f(x) = |2x| - 1$

44. $p(x) = [-x]$ **45.** $f(x) = -[x]$ **46.** $f(x) = [3x]$

2–7   **47.** The Thomas Parcel Service charges $2.50 per pound for the first three pounds and $1.00 for each pound thereafter. Write an equation to find the cost of sending a package that weighs p pounds. Assume $p \geq 3$.

         48. Use the equation in exercise 55 to find the cost of sending packages which weigh 6 lb, 8 lb, 15 lb, and 42 lb.

2–8   **Graph each inequality.**

49. $3x + 4y < 9$ **50.** $2x - 5y > 4$

51. $y \geq |x| + 5$ **52.** $y \leq |x + 5|$

Chapter Test

Graph each set of ordered pairs. Use appropriate labels on the axes.

1. $\{(-8, 1), (-4, 8), (3, 0), (8, -6), (0, -5)\}$ **2.** $\left\{\left(\frac{1}{5}, \frac{3}{5}\right), \left(\frac{2}{5}, \frac{4}{5}\right), \left(-\frac{3}{5}, 0\right), \left(0, \frac{2}{5}\right), \left(-\frac{1}{5}, -\frac{2}{5}\right)\right\}$

State the domain and range of each relation. Then state if the relation is a function.

3. $\{(1, 2), (7, 2), (9, -3), (2, 7)\}$ **4.** $\{(1.4, 1.4), (1.4, 1.5)\}$ **5.** $\{(3, -2), (5, 4), (7, -2)\}$

Use the vertical line test to determine if each relation is a function.

6.
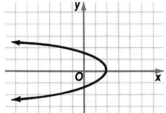

7.
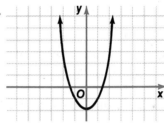

8.
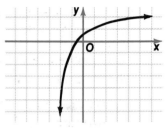

Given $f(x) = 2x^3 + 3x^2 - 5x - 4$, find each value.

9. $f(-3)$ **10.** $f\left(\frac{2}{3}\right)$ **11.** $f(2c)$

Graph each equation or inequality.

12. $y = \frac{12}{5}x$ **13.** $y = 7$ **14.** $y = -7x + 3$ **15.** $y = 3x - \frac{1}{2}$

16. $5x + 2y = 12$ **17.** $3y - 3x = 10$ **18.** $5y + 3x - 10 = 0$ **19.** $4x + 12y = -15$

20. $2x + 3y > 7$ **21.** $4x + 6y \leq 9$ **22.** $f(x) = |x + 2|$ **23.** $f(x) = -[x]$

24. $y < 3|x| - 1$ **25.** $y \geq |3x - 1|$ **26.** $y = |4x + 3| + 2$ **27.** $y = 2[x] - 7$

Determine the slope of the line passing through each pair of points.

28. $(7, 4)$ and $(-2, 5)$ **29.** $(0, 6)$ and $(1, -1)$

Find the slope-intercept form of the equation of the line that satisfies the given conditions.

30. slope $= 4$, passes through $\left(\frac{2}{3}, \frac{2}{3}\right)$ **31.** passes through $(0, 7)$ and $(5, 2)$

Find the standard form of the equation of the line that satisfies the given conditions.

32. slope $= \frac{1}{3}$, y-intercept $= 7$ **33.** x-intercept $= -6$, y-intercept $= -6$

A line has a slope $-\frac{2}{5}$. For each pair of points on the line, find the missing coordinate.

34. $(5, 1)$ and $(15, y)$ **35.** $(x, 2)$ and $(-5, 5)$

36. As a waiter, Ryan earns an average of $28.00 a day in tips. If he also earns $3.00 per hour, write an equation to determine the total amount he earns in an h hour day.

Evaluate if $a = 4$, $b = -7$, $c = \frac{1}{3}$, and $d = -3$.

1. $\dfrac{a}{c^2}$

2. $\dfrac{ab + 4c}{d}$

3. $2a(4c + b^2) + |d|$

Write *true* or *false*. If false, give a counter example.

4. Every rational number is an integer.

5. Every irrational number is a real number.

Simplify.

6. $(9 - 29)7 - 12$

7. $\dfrac{2}{3}(15 - 9a) - (6a - 21)\left(\dfrac{1}{3}\right)$

Solve each open sentence.

8. $4 - 7a = 25$

9. $2(6 - 7x) = 2x - 4$

10. $|2r - 9| = 0$

11. $5x + 8 > 24$

12. $1 - 2y \le 5y - 2$

13. $|x - 4| \le -8$

14. $|7 + 3x| = 11 - x$

Graph each equation or inequality on the number line.

15. $x + 5 = 5(x + 5)$

16. $5(n - 3) \le 6(n - 3)$

17. $3(a - 3) - a = a + 1$

18. $5(y - 1) - (2y + 1) < 5(y + 2)$

Graph each set of ordered pairs.

19. $\{(2, 26), (1.5, 30), (1, 20), (0, 16)\}$

20. $\{(-2.2, 0), (-2.6, 1.8), (2, 3.2)\}$

Given $f(x) = 2x^3 + 4x^2 - x + 2$, find each value.

21. $f(3)$ 22. $f(-4)$ 23. $f\left(\dfrac{1}{2}\right)$

Graph each equation.

24. $y - 3x = 2$ 25. $y = -5$

26. $y = \dfrac{1}{2}x$ 27. $y = [2x]$

28. $y = 3|x| - 2$ 29. $y = -[x - 1]$

Find the x-intercept and y-intercept for the graph of each of the following.

30. $3x + 5y = 10$ 31. $\dfrac{1}{2}x + 4y = -4$

Find the slope-intercept form of lines satisfying the following conditions.

32. x-intercept $= 5$, y-intercept $= 4$

33. slope $= \dfrac{4}{5}$, passes through $(6, -2)$

34. passes through $(6, 1)$ and $(-4, 8)$

Graph each inequality.

35. $y < |x + 2|$ 36. $y < |x| + 2$

Problem Solving

37. Sam is driving a distance of 662 miles. If he drives 55 miles per hour for 5 hours, at what speed must he travel to complete the total trip in 14 hours?

38. The length of a garden is 3 yards more than twice the width. The perimeter is at most 84 yards. What is the maximum length of the garden?

39. Emilio earns a flat salary of $150 per week selling records. He receives an extra 20¢ for each record over 100 that he sells. How much will he make if he sells r records, if $r > 100$.

40. The ABC Car Rental Agency rents cars for $15 a day plus 13¢ a mile. How much would it cost to rent a car for five days, if the car will be driven 250 miles?

The test questions on this page deal with a variety of concepts from arithmetic and algebra.

Directions: Choose the one best answer. Write A, B, C, or D.

1.

   Figure is not drawn to scale.

   Suppose numbers $\frac{5}{6}$, 1, $\frac{1}{3}$, $\frac{3}{2}$, and $\frac{6}{5}$ are arranged from least to greatest on the number line above, with each number corresponding to a letter. If the greatest number corresponds to E, which letter corresponds to $\frac{5}{6}$?

   (A) A   (B) B   (C) C   (D) D

2. If $8x + 10y$ represents the perimeter of a rectangle, and $x + 3y$ represents its width, the length is

   (A) $3x + 2y$ (B) $7x + 7y$
   (C) $6x + 4y$ (D) $3.5x + 3.5y$

3. In the series 2, 6, 11, 17, 24, 32, 41, 51 the eighth term is

   (A) 41   (B) 45   (C) 51   (D) 62

4. If 9 less than the product of a number and -4 is greater than 7, which of the following could be that number?

   (A) -5 (B) -3 (C) 4   (D) 5

5. Which of the following is *not* equivalent to $-\frac{6}{8}$?

   (A) $-\frac{3}{4}$ (B) $\frac{3}{-4}$ (C) $-\frac{-12}{-16}$ (D) $-\frac{6}{-8}$

6. Which of the following is the least?

   (A) $\frac{1}{2}$ (B) $\frac{7}{13}$ (C) $\frac{4}{9}$ (D) $\frac{8}{15}$

7. If the radius of a circle is tripled, then the area is multiplied by

   (A) 3   (B) 6   (C) 9   (D) 27

8. A point on the graph of $x + 3y = 13$ is

   (A) (4, 4)   (B) $(-5, 6)$
   (C) $(-2, 3)$ (D) $(4, -3)$

9. Which represents an irrational number?

   (A) $-\frac{2}{3}$ (B) $\sqrt{4}$ (C) π (D) 0

10. For what values of y will $2y - 4$ be equal to $2y + 6$?

    (A) all negative values   (B) 0
    (C) all positive values   (D) no values

11. If a number is increased by 5 and the result is multiplied by 8, the product is 168. What is the original number?

    (A) 16   (B) 42   (C) 46   (D) 128

12. The average of 7, 5, 9, 3, and $2x$ is x. What is the value of x?

    (A) 2.4   (B) 4   (C) 6   (D) 8

13. The radius of a wheel is 4 cm. How many revolutions will it make if it is rolled a distance of 400π?

    (A) 25π (B) 25   (C) 50   (D) 100π

14. Which of the following is the difference of two consecutive prime numbers less than 40?

    (A) 1   (B) 5   (C) 8   (D) 11

15. How many integers between 199 and 301 are divisible by 4 or 10?

    (A) 26   (B) 31   (C) 35   (D) 37

16. A patient must be given medication every 7 hours starting at 7 A.M. Monday. On what day will the patient first receive medication at 6 P.M.?

    (A) Monday   (B) Tuesday
    (C) Wednesday   (D) Friday

CHAPTER 3

Systems of Equations and Inequalities

One of the most practical applications of mathematics to business is the branch of mathematics called linear programming. A company can use it to schedule production to meet sales requirements at a minimum cost to the company. Linear programming depends on the graphs of linear equations and inequalities.

3-1　Parallel and Perpendicular Lines

The graphs of $y = -\frac{3}{4}x - 3$, $y = -\frac{3}{4}x$, and $y = -\frac{3}{4}x + 3$ are

straight lines that have the same slope. They are **parallel lines.**

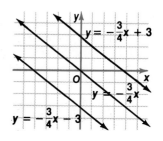

In a plane, lines with the same slope are parallel lines.
Also, vertical lines are parallel.

Definition of Parallel Lines

Examples

1　**Find the slope of a line *parallel* to the line whose equation is $3y - 5x = 15$.**

Parallel lines have the same slope.
Find the slope of the line whose equation is $3y - 5x = 15$. To do so, write the equation in slope-intercept form.　$y = mx + b$

$$3y - 5x = 15$$
$$3y = 5x + 15$$
$$y = \frac{5}{3}x + 5 \qquad \text{The slope of any line parallel to the given line is } \frac{5}{3}.$$

2　**Find an equation of the line that passes through (4, 6) and is *parallel* to the line whose equation is $y = \frac{2}{3}x + 5$.**

The slope is $\frac{2}{3}$.　*Notice that $y = \frac{2}{3}x + 5$ is in slope-intercept form.*

Use (4, 6) and the slope $\frac{2}{3}$ to find the y-intercept.

$$y = mx + b$$
$$6 = \left(\frac{2}{3}\right)(4) + b \qquad \text{Substitution.}$$
$$6 = \frac{8}{3} + b$$
$$\frac{10}{3} = b \qquad \qquad \text{The y-intercept is } \frac{10}{3}.$$

An equation of the line is $y = \frac{2}{3}x + \frac{10}{3}$.

The graphs of $y = \frac{5}{3}x + 2$ and $y = -\frac{3}{5}x + 6$ are straight lines that are **perpendicular.** Notice how their slopes are related.

$$\left(\frac{5}{3}\right)\left(-\frac{3}{5}\right) = -1$$

The product of their slopes is -1.

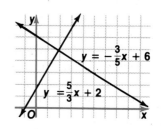

> **In a plane, two nonvertical lines are perpendicular if and only if the product of their slopes is -1. Any vertical line is perpendicular to any horizontal line.**

Definition of Perpendicular Lines

Consider any two nonvertical perpendicular lines in a plane. Here is a way to show that their slopes have a product of -1. Consider a line that is neither vertical nor horizontal, with slope $\frac{r}{s}$. This is shown by the black line at the right. Now consider rotating the line 90°. Notice that the slope of the new line (shown in red) is $-\frac{s}{r}$. The product of the slopes of the two lines is $\left(\frac{r}{s}\right)\left(-\frac{s}{r}\right)$ or -1.

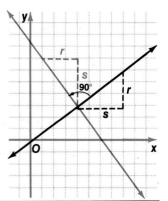

Examples

3 **Find the slope of a line perpendicular to the line whose equation is $3y - x = 2$.**

$$3y - x = 2$$
$$-x + 3y = 2 \qquad \textit{This equation is in standard form, } Ax + By = C.$$

Recall that the slope of a line whose equation is in standard form is $-\frac{A}{B}$.

The slope of the given line is $-\left(\frac{-1}{3}\right)$ or $\frac{1}{3}$.

$\frac{1}{3} \cdot m = -1 \qquad$ *Let m stand for the slope of the perpendicular line.*

$\qquad m = -3 \qquad$ The slope of any line perpendicular to the given line is -3.

4 **Find an equation of the line that passes through $(4, 6)$ and is perpendicular to the line whose equation is $y = \frac{2}{3}x + 5$.**

The slope of the given line is $\frac{2}{3}$. $\qquad y = \frac{2}{3}x + 5$ *is in slope-intercept form.*

$\frac{2}{3} \cdot m = -1 \qquad$ *Let m stand for the slope of the perpendicular line.*

$\qquad m = -\frac{3}{2}$

The slope of the perpendicular line is $-\frac{3}{2}$.

$y = mx + b \qquad$ *Let b stand for the y-intercept of the perpendicular line.*

$6 = \left(-\frac{3}{2}\right)(4) + b \qquad$ *The line passes through (4, 6) and has slope $-\frac{3}{2}$.*

$12 = b \qquad$ *The y-intercept is 12.*

An equation of the line is $y = -\frac{3}{2}x + 12$. *This could be written $3x + 2y = 24$.*

Exploratory Exercises

Find the slope of a line that is parallel to each line whose equation is given.

1. $y = 4x + 2$

2. $y = 5 - 2x$

3. $2y = 3x - 8$

4. $6y - 5x = 0$

5. $\frac{1}{3}x - \frac{3}{8}y = 11$

6. $x = 4y + 7$

Find the slope of a line that is perpendicular to each line whose equation is given.

7. $y = 2x + 4$

8. $y = 2 - 5x$

9. $3y = 8x - 2$

10. $5y - 6x = 0$

11. $3x - 8y = 11$

12. $4x = 7y + 1$

Written Exercises

State whether the graphs of the following equations are parallel, perpendicular or neither.

1. $x + y = 5$
$x + y = -10$

2. $x + y = 5$
$x - y = 5$

3. $y = 2x$
$y = 2x - 4$

4. $2y + 3x = 5$
$3y - 2x = 5$

5. $\frac{1}{3}x + \frac{2}{3}y = \frac{3}{5}$
$2x + 4y = 7$

6. $2y + 3x = 5$
$3y + 3x = 5$

7. $3x - 8y = 11$
$3x - 6y = 10$

8. $\frac{1}{2}x + \frac{1}{3}y = 2$
$2x - 3y = 4$

9. $7x - 5y = 2$
$\frac{1}{7}x - \frac{1}{5}y = 2$

Find an equation of the line that passes through each given point and is parallel to the line with the given equation.

10. $(4, 2)$; $y = 2x - 4$

11. $(3, 1)$; $y = \frac{1}{3}x + 6$

12. $\left(\frac{1}{2}, \frac{1}{3}\right)$; $x + 2y = 5$

13. $(0, 0)$; $3x - y = 4$

14. $(4, -2)$; $\frac{x}{3} - \frac{y}{5} = 2$

15. $\left(\frac{1}{2}, \frac{1}{3}\right)$; $x + y = 4$

16. $(-3, -1)$; $y + x = 6$

17. $(7, -1)$; $2y - 3x = 1$

18. $(3, 7)$; $\frac{2}{3}x = \frac{1}{2}y$

Find an equation of the line that passes through each given point and is perpendicular to the line with the given equation.

19. $(-2, 0)$; $y = -3x + 7$

20. $(-3, 4)$; $y = \frac{2}{3}x + 1$

21. $(2, 5)$; $3x + 5y = 7$

22. $(3, 6)$; $4x - y = 2$

23. $(0, -4)$; $6x - 3y = 5$

24. $(5, -3)$; $4x + 7y = 11$

25. $(12, 6)$; $\frac{3}{4}x + \frac{1}{2}y = 2$

26. $(-10, 3)$; $\frac{2}{3}x + y = 6$

27. $(6, -5)$; $3x - \frac{1}{5}y = 3$

Find the value of a for which the graph of the first equation is perpendicular to the graph of the second equation.

28. $y = ax - 5$; $2y = 3x$

29. $y = ax + 2$; $3y - 4x = 7$

30. $y = \frac{a}{3}x - 6$; $4x + 2y = 6$

31. $3y + ax = 8$; $y = \frac{3}{4}x + 2$

32. Show that $(1, 3)$, $(4, 1)$, and $(5, 9)$ are vertices of a right triangle.

33. Show that $(-6, 5)$, $(-2, 7)$, $(5, 3)$, and $(1, 1)$ are vertices of a parallelogram.

Challenge

34. Three vertices of a parallelogram are $(10, 3)$, $(-1, 2)$ and $(1, -1)$. Find the fourth vertex.

35. Two vertices of a square are $(3, 3)$ and $(11, 7)$. Find the other two vertices of the square.

3-2 Solving Systems of Equations Graphically

The cost of renting a car from ACE is $18 per day plus 30¢ per mile driven. The cost of renting a similar car from QUALITY is $20 per day plus 25¢ per mile driven. Caroline needs to rent a car for one day. Should she rent from ACE or QUALITY?

Let d = cost of renting car for one day.
Let m = number of miles driven in one day.

You can write the following equations.

$d = 18 + 0.30m$ *Cost of renting car from ACE for one day.*

$d = 20 + 0.25m$ *Cost of renting car from QUALITY for one day.*

Graphing these two equations shows how the costs compare. The graphs show that the QUALITY car costs more if less than 40 miles are driven. The QUALITY and ACE cars cost the same if 40 miles are driven. The ACE car costs more if more than 40 miles are driven.

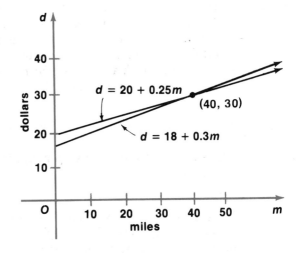

Each point on a line satisfies the equation of the line. Since (40, 30) is on both lines graphed above, it satisfies both equations.

Together the equations $d = 18 + 0.30m$ and $d = 20 + 0.25m$ are called a **system of equations.** The solution of the system is (40, 30).

Example

1   **Solve the system of equations by graphing.**

$3x - y = 1$
$2x + y = 4$

The slope-intercept form of $3x - y = 1$ is $y = 3x - 1$.
The slope-intercept form of $2x + y = 4$ is $y = -2x + 4$.
The two lines have different slopes. The graphs of the equations are intersecting lines.

The solution of the system is (1, 2).

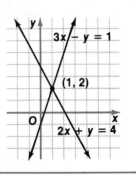

Example 2

Solve the system of equations by graphing.

$2y + 3x = 6$
$4y + 6x = 12$

The slope-intercept form of $2y + 3x = 6$ is $y = -\dfrac{3}{2}x + 3$.

The slope-intercept form of $4y + 6x = 12$ is $y = -\dfrac{3}{2}x + 3$.

Both lines have the same slope and the same y-intercept. The graphs of the equations are the same line. Any ordered pair on the graph satisfies both equations. So, there is an *infinite number* of solutions to this system of equations.

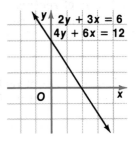

The solution set is
$\{(x, y)|2y + 3x = 6\}$.

A **consistent** system of equations has at least one solution. For example, the systems of equations in Examples 1 and 2 are consistent. If there is exactly one solution, the system is **independent.** If there are infinitely many solutions, the system is **dependent.** So, the system of equations in Example 1 is *consistent and independent.* The system of equations in Example 2 is *consistent and dependent.*

Example 3

Solve the system of equations by graphing.

$y = -3x - 2$
$y = -3x + 3$

Both lines have the same slope but different y-intercepts. The graphs of the equations are parallel lines. Since they do not intersect, there is *no solution* to this system of equations. Such a system is said to be **inconsistent.**

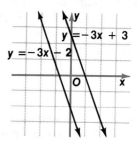

The solution set is empty. $\emptyset$.

The following chart gives a summary of the possibilities for the graphs of two linear equations in two variables.

Graphs of Equations	Slopes of Lines	Name of System of Equations	Number of Solutions
lines intersect	different slopes	consistent and independent	one
lines coincide	same slope, same intercepts	consistent and dependent	infinitely many
lines parallel	same slope, different intercepts	inconsistent	none

Exploratory Exercises

State the ordered pair which is the intersection of each pair of lines.

1. a, b
2. a, e
3. a, d
4. b, c
5. c, d
6. e, d
7. b, f
8. f, d

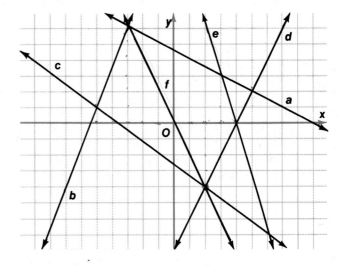

Written Exercises

Graph each system of equations and state its solution. Then state whether the system is *consistent and independent, consistent and dependent,* or *inconsistent.*

1. $x + y = 4$
   $2x + 3y = 9$

2. $x + y = 6$
   $x - y = 2$

3. $x + y = 6$
   $3x + 3y = 3$

4. $x + 1 = y$
   $2x - 2y = 8$

5. $x + 2y = 5$
   $3x - 15 = -6y$

6. $2x + 4y = 8$
   $x + 2y = 4$

7. $y = -3x$
   $6y - x = -38$

8. $\frac{1}{2}x + \frac{1}{3}y = 2$
   $x - y = -1$

9. $\frac{3}{4}x - y = 0$
   $\frac{y}{3} + \frac{x}{2} = 6$

10. $x + y = 1$
    $3x + 5y = 7$

11. $x + 5y = 10$
    $x + 5y = 15$

12. $3x - 8y = 4$
    $6x - 42 = 16y$

13. $x + y = -6$
    $2x - y = 2$

14. $3x + 6 = 7y$
    $x + 2y = 11$

15. $2x + 3y = 5$
    $-6x - 9y = -15$

16. $\frac{2}{3}x = \frac{5}{3}y$
    $2x - 5y = 0$

17. $y = \frac{x}{2}$
    $2y = x + 4$

18. $9x + 8y = 8$
    $\frac{3}{4}x + \frac{2}{3}y = 8$

19. $2x + 3y = -4$
    $-3x + y = -5$

20. $-2x + 5y = -14$
    $x - y = 1$

21. $9x - 5 = 7y$
    $4\frac{1}{2}x - 3\frac{1}{2}y = 2\frac{1}{2}$

22. Write an equation of the line passing through $(5, -1)$ that is inconsistent with $5x - 3y = 2$.

23. Find a and b so that $ax + 5y = b$ and $6x + 10y = 16$ will be consistent and dependent equations.

Write a system of equations for each problem and solve by graphing.

24. George bought 7 quarts of cleaning fluid: x quarts at \$3.00 per quart and y quarts at \$2.00 per quart. Find x and y if the total cost was \$16.00.

25. Kenneth mixes r cups of cashews with s cups of peanuts. This yields 12 cups of a mixture having one part cashews to three parts peanuts. Find r and s.

The cost of driving a car is affected by the rate at which it uses gasoline. The graph at the right shows the cost of gasoline, based on the number of miles driven and the usage rate in miles per gallon (mpg). (The cost of gasoline was $1.50 per gallon.)

Suppose Car A gets an average of 20 miles per gallon and Car B gets 30 miles per gallon. Each car is driven 600 miles. From the graph, you can see that the gasoline cost for Car A is $45 and for Car B is $30.

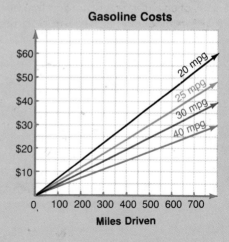

Gasoline Costs

There are also fixed expenses for operating a car, such as loan repayment and insurance. The weekly fixed expenses are $40 for Car A, and $55 for Car B. This information can be used to draw a graph which shows the total weekly operating costs for the two cars.

Each line on the graph at the right has the same slope as the corresponding line on the graph above. However, the intercept of each line is the fixed cost per week.

Study the graph. The operating cost for Car A is less when a person drives less than 600 miles per week. When is the operating cost for Car B less than for Car A?

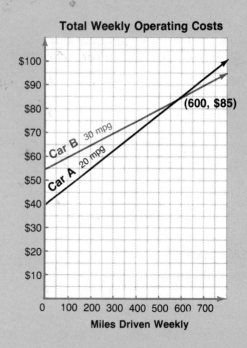

Total Weekly Operating Costs

Exercises

1. Make a graph to compare the total costs of operating Cars C and D. Car C gets 40 mpg and has fixed costs of $50 per week. Car D gets 25 mpg and has fixed costs of $40 per week.

2. Make a graph to compare the total costs of operating Cars Q and R. Car Q gets 25 mpg and has fixed costs of $35 per week. Car R gets 20 mpg and has fixed costs of $45 per week.

3-3 Solving Systems of Equations Algebraically

Usually a system of equations is easier to solve by algebraic methods rather than by graphing. Two such methods are the **substitution method** and the **elimination method**.

Examples

1 **Use the substitution method to solve the system of equations.**

$y = 3x - 1$
$3x + 2y = 16$

The first equation indicates that y is equal to $3x - 1$. Therefore, $3x - 1$ can be *substituted* for y in the second equation.

$$3x + 2y = 16$$
$$3x + 2(3x - 1) = 16 \qquad \text{Substitute } 3x - 1 \text{ for } y. \quad .$$
$$3x + 6x - 2 = 16 \qquad \text{The resulting equation now has only one variable, } x.$$
$$9x - 2 = 16$$
$$9x = 18$$
$$x = 2$$

Now find y by substituting 2 for x in the equation $y = 3x - 1$.

$$y = 3x - 1$$
$$y = 3(2) - 1 \qquad \text{Substitute 2 for } x.$$
$$y = 5$$

The solution is (2, 5).

2 **Use the elimination method to solve the system of equations.**

$4x + 2y = -8$
$x - 2y = -7$

Add the second equation to the first equation.

$$4x + 2y = -8$$
$$\underline{x - 2y = -7} \qquad \text{Add.}$$
$$5x \qquad = -15 \qquad \text{The variable } y \text{ is eliminated.}$$
$$x = -3 \qquad \text{Solve for } x.$$

To find y, substitute -3 for x in $x - 2y = -7$.

$$x - 2y = -7$$
$$(-3) - 2y = -7 \qquad \text{Substitute 3 for } x.$$
$$-2y = -4$$
$$y = 2$$

The solution is $(-3, 2)$.

Example

3 Use the elimination method to solve the system of equations.

$2x + 3y = 2$
$3x - 4y = -14$

Adding the two equations does *not* eliminate either of the variables. However, if the first equation is multiplied by 4 and the second equation is multiplied by 3, the variable y can be eliminated by addition.

| $2x + 3y = 2$ | Multiply by 4. | $8x + 12y = 8$ |
| $3x - 4y = -14$ | Multiply by 3. | $9x - 12y = -42$ |

Now add to eliminate y. Then solve for x.

$8x + 12y = 8$
$\underline{9x - 12y = -42}$ Add.
$17x \qquad = -34$ The variable y is eliminated.
$\quad x \qquad = -2$ Solve for x.

Finally, substitute -2 for x and solve for y.
Use the original first equation.

$2(-2) + 3y = 2$
$-4 + 3y = 2$
$3y = 6$
$y = 2$

The solution is $(-2, 2)$.

An alternate method is to eliminate x first. Multiply the first equation by 3 and the second equation by -2.

$6x + 9y = 6$
$\underline{-6x + 8y = 28}$
$17y = 34$
$y = 2$

Then solve for x.

$2x + 3(2) = 2$
$2x = -4$
$x = -2$

Exploratory Exercises

For each system, state the multipliers you would use to eliminate each of the variables by addition.

1. $2x + 3y = 7$
   $3x - 4y = 2$

2. $x - y = 1$
   $3x - y = 3$

3. $6x - 4y = 20$
   $4x + y = 6$

4. $x + 2y = 3$
   $5x - 3y = 2$

5. $3x + 4y = 6$
   $2x + 5y = 11$

6. $x + 8y = 12$
   $-3x + 7y = -5$

7. $3x + 4y = 7$
   $4x - 3y = 1$

8. $2x - 3y = 0$
   $6x + 5y = 7$

9. $x + y = 6$
   $-2x + y = -3$

Written Exercises

Solve each system of equations by the substitution method.

1. $y = 3x$
   $x + 2y = -21$

2. $6x - 4y = -6$
   $3x + y = 3$

3. $2x + 2y = 4$
   $x - 2y = 0$

4. $2m + n = 1$
   $m - n = 8$

5. $x - 2y = 5$
   $3x - 5y = 8$

6. $3x + 4y = -7$
   $2x + y = -3$

Solve each system of equations by the elimination method.

7. $4x + y = 9$
$3x - 2y = 4$

8. $x - y = 4$
$x + 2y = 1$

9. $2x + y = 0$
$5x + 3y = 1$

10. $3x + 2y = 9$
$2x - 3y = 19$

11. $4x - 3y = -4$
$3x - 2y = -4$

12. $8x + 3y = 4$
$4x - 9y = -5$

Solve each system of equations. (Use either method.)

13. $3x + 2y = 40$
$x - 7y = -2$

14. $2x + 3y = 8$
$x - y = 2$

15. $x + y = 6$
$x - y = 4.5$

16. $2x - y = 36$
$3x - \frac{1}{2}y = 26$

17. $3y - 2x = 4$
$\frac{1}{6}(3y - 4x) = 1$

18. $3x + \frac{1}{3}y = 10$
$2x - 5 = \frac{1}{3}y$

19. $5m + 2n = -8$
$4m + 3n = 2$

20. $2a + 2b = -3$
$5a + 3b = 6$

21. $3x - 5y = -13$
$4x + 3y = 2$

22. $-9x - 6y = -15$
$13x + 7y = 18\frac{1}{3}$

23. $3m + 7n = 5$
$2m = -7 - 3n$

24. $2y - 3x = 0$
$x - y + 2 = 0$

25. $\frac{2x + y}{3} = 15$
$\frac{3x - y}{5} = 1$

26. $\frac{1}{4}x + y = \frac{7}{2}$
$\frac{1}{2}x - \frac{1}{4}y = 1$

27. $\frac{x}{2} - \frac{2y}{3} = 2\frac{1}{3}$
$\frac{3x}{2} + 2y = -25$

28. $2x + 3y - 8 = 0$
$3x + 2y - 17 = 0$

29. $0.2a = 0.3b$
$0.4a - 0.2b = 0.2$

30. $\frac{1}{3}x + \frac{1}{3}y = 5$
$\frac{1}{6}x - \frac{1}{9}y = 0$

31. $\frac{1}{3}x + 5 = \frac{2}{3}y$
$\frac{1}{2}x + \frac{1}{3}y = \frac{1}{2}$

32. $\frac{a}{2} + \frac{b}{3} = 4$
$\frac{2a}{3} + \frac{3b}{2} = \frac{35}{3}$

33. $\frac{m}{3} + \frac{n}{5} = -\frac{1}{5}$
$\frac{2m}{3} - \frac{3n}{4} = -5$

34. $34x - 63y = -1063$
$14x + 43y = 2251$

35. $108x + 537y = -1395$
$-214x - 321y = 535$

36. $93a + 17b = -157.1$
$74a - 75b = -4392$

37. $4.3a + 6.4b = -2.85$
$5.2a - 6.5b = 42.12$

38. $3.2a + 3.5b = -6.365$
$-2.3a + 5.3b = 44.669$

39. $6.7a + 9.3b = -38.99$
$-7.2a - 3.1b = 18.46$

40. $6a + 7b = -10.15$
$9.2a - 6b = 69.944$

Solve each problem.

41. The sum of two numbers is 42. Their difference is 12. What are the two numbers?

42. The sum of Kari's age and her mother's age is 52. Kari's mother is 20 years older than Kari. How old is each?

43. The perimeter of a rectangle is 86 cm. Twice the width exceeds the length by 2 cm. Find the dimensions of the rectangle.

mini-review

1. Evaluate $-2b^2$ if $b = -3$.

2. Is $\sqrt{9}$ an irrational number?

3. Is $r^2 + s^2 = 16$ a linear equation?

4. Find the standard form of the equation of the line that has x-intercept -2 and y-intercept 5.

5. Graph $y \leq |x| - 2$.

3-4 Cramer's Rule

A square array of numbers or variables enclosed between vertical lines is called a **determinant.** The following determinant has 2 rows and 2 columns and is called a second order determinant.

rows $\swarrow \searrow$ $\begin{vmatrix} a & b \\ c & d \end{vmatrix}$ *The quantities in a determinant are called elements.*

$\uparrow \uparrow$
columns

The value of a second order determinant is defined as follows.

$$\begin{vmatrix} a & b \\ c & d \end{vmatrix} = ad - bc$$

Value of a Second Order Determinant

Note that the value of a second order determinant is found using products along the diagonals. Subtract the value of bc from ad.

$ad - bc$

Examples

1 **Find the value of** $\begin{vmatrix} 2 & 1 \\ 3 & 4 \end{vmatrix}.$

$\begin{vmatrix} 2 & 1 \\ 3 & 4 \end{vmatrix} = 2 \cdot 4 - 3 \cdot 1$

$= 5$

2 **Find the value of** $\begin{vmatrix} -6 & 7 \\ 0 & -2 \end{vmatrix}.$

$\begin{vmatrix} -6 & 7 \\ 0 & -2 \end{vmatrix} = -6(-2) - 0(7)$

$= 12$

Determinants can be used to solve a system of linear equations. Consider solving the following system of two equations in two variables.

$$ax + by = c$$
$$dx + ey = f$$

Solve for y using the elimination method.

$$
\begin{array}{ll}
adx + bdy = cd & \text{Multiply the first equation by } d. \\
\underline{-adx - aey = -af} & \text{Multiply the second equation by } -a. \\
bdy - aey = cd - af & \text{Add.} \\
(bd - ae)y = cd - af & \text{Factor.}
\end{array}
$$

$$y = \frac{cd - af}{bd - ae} \text{ or } y = \frac{af - cd}{ae - bd}$$ Notice that $bd - ae$ cannot be zero.

Then solve for x in the same manner.

$$x = \frac{ce - bf}{ae - bd}$$

Thus, the solution to the system is $\left(\dfrac{ce - bf}{ae - bd}, \dfrac{af - cd}{ae - bd}\right)$.

Notice that the denominator of each fraction is the same. It can be written as a determinant. Also, each numerator may be written as a determinant.

$$ae - bd = \begin{vmatrix} a & b \\ d & e \end{vmatrix} \qquad ce - bf = \begin{vmatrix} c & b \\ f & e \end{vmatrix} \qquad af - cd = \begin{vmatrix} a & c \\ d & f \end{vmatrix}$$

Therefore, the solution to a system of two linear equations in two variables can be found using determinants. This method is known as **Cramer's Rule.**

The solution to the system of equations $\begin{array}{l} ax + by = c \\ dx + ey = f \end{array}$ is (x, y)

where $x = \dfrac{\begin{vmatrix} c & b \\ f & e \end{vmatrix}}{\begin{vmatrix} a & b \\ d & e \end{vmatrix}}$, $y = \dfrac{\begin{vmatrix} a & c \\ d & f \end{vmatrix}}{\begin{vmatrix} a & b \\ d & e \end{vmatrix}}$ and $\begin{vmatrix} a & b \\ d & e \end{vmatrix} \neq 0$.

Cramer's Rule

Example

3 Use Cramer's rule to solve the following system: $\begin{array}{l} 3x - 5y = -7 \\ x + 2y = 16 \end{array}$

$$x = \frac{\begin{vmatrix} -7 & -5 \\ 16 & 2 \end{vmatrix}}{\begin{vmatrix} 3 & -5 \\ 1 & 2 \end{vmatrix}} \qquad\qquad y = \frac{\begin{vmatrix} 3 & -7 \\ 1 & 16 \end{vmatrix}}{\begin{vmatrix} 3 & -5 \\ 1 & 2 \end{vmatrix}}$$

$$= \frac{-7(2) - 16(-5)}{3(2) - 1(-5)} \qquad\qquad = \frac{3(16) - 1(-7)}{3(2) - 1(-5)}$$

$$= \frac{66}{11} \qquad\qquad\qquad\qquad = \frac{55}{11}$$

$$= 6 \qquad\qquad\qquad\qquad = 5 \qquad \text{The solution is } (6, 5).$$

Exploratory Exercises

Find the value of each determinant.

1. $\begin{vmatrix} 3 & 1 \\ 4 & 6 \end{vmatrix}$

2. $\begin{vmatrix} 7 & -3 \\ 0 & 1 \end{vmatrix}$

3. $\begin{vmatrix} 0 & 1 \\ 0 & 1 \end{vmatrix}$

4. $\begin{vmatrix} 11 & -2 \\ -3 & -5 \end{vmatrix}$

5. $\begin{vmatrix} 1 & 0 \\ 0 & 1 \end{vmatrix}$

6. $\begin{vmatrix} -8 & -7 \\ -4 & -6 \end{vmatrix}$

7. $\begin{vmatrix} 2 & 4 \\ -3 & 1 \end{vmatrix}$

8. $\begin{vmatrix} -5 & 3 \\ 1 & 2 \end{vmatrix}$

Write the determinants you would use to solve each system by Cramer's Rule.

9. $3x + 2y = 5$
$4x - y = 3$

10. $4x + 2y = 8$
$6x - 3y = 0$

11. $2a - 4b = 16$
$3a - 5b = 21$

12. $r - s = 0$
$2r + 5s = -3$

13. $3x + y = -8$
$4x - 2y = -14$

14. $x + y = 6$
$x - y = 2$

Written Exercises

Find the value of each determinant.

1. $\begin{vmatrix} 7 & 8 \\ -9 & 0 \end{vmatrix}$

2. $\begin{vmatrix} 5 & 5 \\ 5 & 5 \end{vmatrix}$

3. $\begin{vmatrix} -6 & -2 \\ 2 & 6 \end{vmatrix}$

4. $\begin{vmatrix} 8 & -1 \\ 13 & 0 \end{vmatrix}$

5. $\begin{vmatrix} 24 & 6 \\ -13 & -4 \end{vmatrix}$

6. $\begin{vmatrix} 18 & -5 \\ -9 & 11 \end{vmatrix}$

7. $\begin{vmatrix} -13 & -11 \\ 17 & -12 \end{vmatrix}$

8. $\begin{vmatrix} -6 & 7 \\ -9 & 10 \end{vmatrix}$

Solve by using Cramer's Rule.

9. $5x + 4y = -1$
$2x - y = 10$

10. $x - 4y = 1$
$2x + 3y = 13$

11. $3m - n = 2$
$m + n = 5$

12. $3x + 2y = 5$
$5x - 6y = 11$

13. $x + 11 = 8y$
$8(x - y) = 3$

14. $2x - y = 7$
$x + 3y = 7$

15. $x - y = 0$
$2x + 5y = -3$

16. $3a + 8 = -b$
$4a - 2b = -14$

17. $6a + 5b = -7$
$2a - 3b = 7$

18. $7y + 4x = 22$
$8x - 2y = -5$

19. $3x - 4y = 23$
$9x + 2y = -15$

20. $2x - 3y = 19$
$6x + 6y = -3$

21. Explain why Cramer's Rule will not work if a system of equations is dependent or inconsistent.

22. How do you determine if a system of equations is dependent by using Cramer's Rule?

23. How do you determine if a system of equations is inconsistent by using Cramer's Rule?

Excursions in Algebra _____ History

Gabriel Cramer was a Swiss mathematician of the 18th century. He was a professor of mathematics at the University of Geneva at the age of twenty. Although Cramer's Rule is named after him, he was not the first person to originate that result. Colin Maclaurin, a British mathematician, wrote the rule for solving systems of equations by determinants in his *Treatise of Algebra*. It was published in 1748, two years before Cramer published Cramer's Rule. Often in mathematics, the person who popularized a result had his name attached to it, although later it was learned that someone else had originally discovered the same result.

3-5 Graphing Systems of Inequalities

Consider the following system of inequalities.

$$y \geq 2x - 1$$
$$y \leq -2x - 2$$

To solve this system, find the ordered pairs that satisfy *both* inequalities. One way is to graph each inequality and find the intersection of the two graphs.

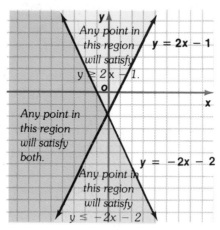

Some systems of inequalities have *no* solutions.

Example

1 Solve the following system by graphing.

$$y > x + 1$$
$$y < x - 4$$

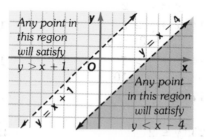

The broken lines indicate that the boundaries are not part of the graphs.

The graphs of the two inequalities have *no* points in common. So *no* ordered pair will satisfy both inequalities.

Systems of more than two inequalities can also be graphed.

Example

2 Solve the following system by graphing.

$y \leq 3$
$x \geq -2$
$y > x$

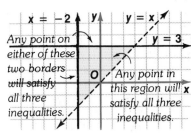

x = -2

y = x

y = 3

Any point on either of these two borders will satisfy all three inequalities.

Any point in this region will satisfy all three inequalities.

Exploratory Exercises

Does the point given in color satisfy the system of inequalities?

1. $y < \frac{1}{2}x + 2$ $(0, 0)$
  $y > 3x - 2$

2. $y < x - 2$ $(1, 2)$
  $y > -x$

3. $y > -2$ $(1, 1)$
  $x \leq 1$

4. $y < 3$ $(4, 4)$
  $x \geq -1$

Written Exercises

Solve each system of inequalities by graphing.

1. $y > 3$
  $x \leq 1$

2. $y \leq 5$
  $x \geq -1$

3. $y > 3$
  $y + x > 2$

4. $y < -2$
  $y - x > 1$

5. $y \geq 2x - 2$
  $y \leq -x + 2$

6. $y \geq x - 3$
  $y \geq -x + 1$

7. $y > x + 1$
  $y < x - 3$

8. $y - x \leq 3$
  $y \geq x + 2$

9. $y < -x - 3$
  $x + 2 > y$

10. $x + y > 5$
  $x - y \leq 3$

11. $x + y \geq 3$
  $2x - 3y \leq 6$

12. $x + 2y \geq 7$
  $3x - 4y < 12$

13. $y > x + 2$
  $2y < x - 3$

14. $x + y > 7$
  $x + y < 10$

15. $x - 2y < 12$
  $2x + 3y > 12$

16. $-4y - 3x > 10$
  $2y - 3x < 5$

17. $|x| > 5$
  $x + y < 6$

18. $|x + 2| < 3$
  $x + y \geq 1$

19. $x \geq 1$
  $y < -1$
  $y > x$

20. $y \leq 2$
  $y \geq 2x$
  $y \geq x + 1$

21. $x \geq -1$
  $x \leq 1$
  $y > 2$

22. $x \geq -2$
  $2y \geq 3$
  $x - y \leq -5$

23. $2y \leq x$
  $3x + 5y \leq 10$
  $x \leq 3$

24. $y < 2x + 1$
  $y > 2x - 2$
  $3x + y > 8$

25. $y > x + 3$
  $y < x - 4$
  $2y + 3x > 4$

26. $x + y < 9$
  $x - y > 3$
  $y - x > 4$

27. $x + y < 8$
  $2x - 3y > 12$
  $2x + 3y < 12$

Problem Solving

To solve many problems in mathematics, you can write an equation. Then you solve the equation and answer the problem. However, this procedure may not always be the best one to use.

There are other strategies which may be more suitable than writing an equation. One of these strategies is to solve a simpler problem. This strategy involves setting aside the original problem and solving a simpler or more familiar case of the problem. The same concepts and relationships that were used to solve the simpler problem can then be used to solve the original problem.

Example: **Find the sum of the numbers 1 through 1000.**

Obviously, this problem could be solved by actually adding all the numbers. But this process would be very tedious even if you used a calculator.

Consider a simpler problem. Find the sum of the numbers 1 through 10.

$$
\begin{array}{ccccc}
1 & 2 & 3 & 4 & 5 \\
+\,10 & +\,9 & +\,8 & +\,7 & +\,6 \\
\hline
11 & 11 & 11 & 11 & 11
\end{array}
$$

The sum is $5 \cdot 11$ or 55.

Now extend this concept to the original problem.

$$
\begin{array}{cccccc}
1 & 2 & 3 & & 499 & 500 \\
+\,1000 & +\,999 & +\,998 & \ldots & +\,502 & +\,501 \\
\hline
1001 & 1001 & 1001 & & 1001 & 1001
\end{array}
$$

The sum of 1 through 1000 is 500×1001 or 500,500.

This strategy may also involve breaking a complicated problem down into several easier problems. After these problems are solved, their solutions may be used to solve the original problem.

Exercises
Solve each problem.

1. A drain pipe is 750 cm long. A spider climbs up 100 cm during the day but falls back 80 cm during the night. If the spider begins at the bottom of the pipe, on what day will it get to the top?

2. Find the total number of squares in the checkerboard shown at the right.

3. Find the sum of the first n positive integers.

4. A total of 3001 digits were used to print the page numbers of the Northern College annual. How many pages are in the annual?

3-6 Linear Programming

Linear programming is a procedure for finding the maximum or the minimum value of a function in two variables, subject to given conditions on the variables. The conditions are often expressed as linear inequalities.

Suppose you want to find the maximum or minimum value for the function $f(x, y) = 5x - 3y$. The values of x and y have the following conditions.

$$x \geq 0 \qquad 0 \leq y \leq 5$$
$$x + y \leq 7 \qquad 3y \geq x - 3$$

By graphing each inequality and finding the solution set for the system, you can determine the set of ordered pairs that satisfy all of the given conditions. The polygonal region shown below is the set of points which are common solutions to the above inequalities.

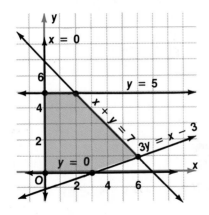

Every point in the shaded region has coordinates that satisfy each of the inequalities given above.

The region includes infinitely many points. It would be impossible to evaluate the function for all points within the region. Mathematicians have shown that the maximum and minimum values are always represented by vertices of the region. In this case there are five vertices. So, you need to find the value of $5x - 3y$ for $(0, 0)$, $(3, 0)$, $(6, 1)$, $(2, 5)$, and $(0, 5)$.

$$f(x, y) = 5x - 3y \qquad\qquad f(6, 1) = 5(6) - 3(1)$$
$$= 27$$

$$f(0, 0) = 5(0) - 3(0) \qquad\qquad f(2, 5) = 5(2) - 3(5)$$
$$= 0 \qquad\qquad\qquad\qquad\qquad = -5$$

$$f(3, 0) = 5(3) - 3(0) \qquad\qquad f(0, 5) = 5(0) - 3(5)$$
$$= 15 \qquad\qquad\qquad\qquad\qquad = -15$$

Thus, the maximum value is 27 at $(6, 1)$ and the minimum value is -15 at $(0, 5)$.

Example

1 Find the maximum and minimum values of $f(x, y) = x + 2y$ for the polygonal region determined by the following inequalities.

$$x \geq 0 \qquad y \geq 0 \qquad 2x - y \leq 4 \qquad x + 3y \leq 9$$

First, graph the inequalities and find the coordinates of the vertices of the resulting polygon.

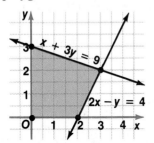

The coordinates of the vertices are $(0, 0)$, $(2, 0)$, $(3, 2)$, and $(0, 3)$.

Then evaluate the function $f(x, y) = x + 2y$ at each vertex.

$$f(0, 0) = 0 + 2(0) = 0 \qquad f(3, 2) = 3 + 2(2) = 7$$
$$f(2, 0) = 2 + 2(0) = 2 \qquad f(0, 3) = 0 + 2(3) = 6$$

The maximum value of the function is 7 at $(3, 2)$ and the minimum value is 0 at $(0, 0)$.

Exploratory Exercises

Given $f(x, y) = 3x + 2y$, find each value.

1. $f(3, 2)$ **2.** $f(4, 1)$ **3.** $f(-2, 1)$ **4.** $f(5, -2)$

5. $f(0, -5)$ **6.** $f(6, 0)$ **7.** $f(0.5, 1.2)$ **8.** $f(-1, 0.25)$

Given $f(x, y) = 5x - 2y$, find each value.

9. $f(4, 1)$ **10.** $f(0, 0)$ **11.** $f(-5, 4)$ **12.** $f(-2, -6)$

13. $f(5, -3)$ **14.** $f(3, 1.5)$ **15.** $f(0, -0.3)$ **16.** $f(-0.2, -1)$

Find the maximum and minimum values of each function defined for the polygonal region having vertices $(0, 0)$, $(5, 0)$, $(4, 6)$, and $(0, 6)$.

17. $f(x, y) = x + y$ **18.** $f(x, y) = y - x$ **19.** $f(x, y) = \frac{1}{2}x - y$

20. $f(x, y) = x + 3y$ **21.** $f(x, y) = -x - 3y$ **22.** $f(x, y) = 0.5x - 1.5y$

Written Exercises

Graph each system of inequalities. Name the vertices of the polygon formed.

1. $1 \leq y \leq 3$
$y \leq 2x + 1$
$y \leq -\frac{1}{2}x + 6$

2. $x \geq 0$
$y \geq 3$
$y \geq 2x + 1$
$y \leq -\frac{1}{2}x + 6$

3. $y \geq 1$
$y \leq 2x + 1$
$x \leq 6$

4. $0 \leq x \leq 50$
$0 \leq y \leq 70$
$60 \leq x + y \leq 80$

Graph each system of inequalities. Name the vertices of the polygon formed. Find the maximum and minimum values of the given function.

5. $y \geq 2$
  $1 \leq x \leq 5$
  $y \leq x + 3$
  $f(x, y) = 3x - 2y$

6. $x + y \geq 2$
  $4y \leq x + 8$
  $y \geq 2x - 5$
  $f(x, y) = 4x + 3y$

7. $y \leq 7$
  $y \leq x + 4$
  $y \geq -x + 6$
  $x \leq 5$
  $f(x, y) = 2x - 3y$

8. $y \leq x + 5$
  $y \geq x$
  $x \geq -3$
  $y + 2x \leq 5$
  $f(x, y) = x - 2y$

9. $y \leq x + 6$
  $y + 2x \geq 6$
  $2 \leq x \leq 6$
  $f(x, y) = 3x + y$

10. $x + y \geq 2$
  $4y \leq x + 8$
  $2y \geq 3x - 6$
  $f(x, y) = 3y + x$

11. $y \geq 0$
  $0 \leq x \leq 5$
  $-x + y \leq 2$
  $x + y \leq 6$
  $f(x, y) = 5x - 3y$

12. $x \geq 0$
  $y \geq 0$
  $x + 2y \leq 6$
  $2y - x \leq 2$
  $x + y \leq 5$
  $f(x, y) = 3x - 5y$

mini-review

1. Simplify $\frac{1}{6}(3x - 18) - \frac{1}{3}(x - 9)$.
2. The length of a rectangle is 35 meters more than three times its width. Its perimeter is 390 meters. Find its dimensions.
3. Solve $|2x - 5| \geq 7$. Graph the solution set.
4. Graph $g(x) = [2x] + 1$.
5. The cost for renting a canoe is $3.50 for the first hour and $1.25 for each successive half-hour. Write an equation to describe the relationship between hours and cost. Then find the cost for renting a canoe for $3\frac{1}{2}$ hours.

Using Calculators —————————————— **Multiple Storage**

Some calculators can store several values at once. This feature is helpful if you need to evaluate the same function for several ordered pairs.

Example: Evaluate $f(5, 8)$ and $f(9, 3)$ if $f(x, y) = 35x + 41y$.

First, store the coefficients, 35 and 41.

ENTER: 35 $\boxed{\text{STO}}$ 1	41 $\boxed{\text{STO}}$ 2
DISPLAY: 35	41

Storage and recall procedures may vary. Consult the manual for your calculator.

Then, evaluate $f(5, 8)$.

ENTER: $\boxed{\text{RCL}}$ 1 $\boxed{\times}$ 5 $\boxed{+}$ $\boxed{\text{RCL}}$ 2 $\boxed{\times}$ 8 $\boxed{=}$
DISPLAY: 35   5 175   41   8 503   So, $f(5, 8) = 503$.

In a similar manner, evaluate $f(9, 3)$.

ENTER: $\boxed{\text{RCL}}$ 1 $\boxed{\times}$ 9 $\boxed{+}$ $\boxed{\text{RCL}}$ 2 $\boxed{\times}$ 3 $\boxed{=}$
DISPLAY: 35   9 315   41   3 438   So, $f(9, 3) = 438$.

Exercises

Given $f(x, y) = 0.08x + 0.93y$, find each value.

1. $f(58, 17)$ **2.** $f(36, 25)$ **3.** $f(30, 30)$ **4.** $f(6.8, 10.2)$

Given $f(x, y) = 164x - 47y$, find each value.

5. $f(14, 6)$ **6.** $f(20, 14.3)$ **7.** $f(8.2, 5.9)$ **8.** $f(0.07, 0.12)$

3-7   Problem Solving: Linear Programming

Many practical problems can be solved by linear programming. These problems are of such a nature that certain conditions exist for the variables, and some function of these variables must be maximized or minimized. Use the following method to solve linear programming problems.

1. **Define variables.**
2. **Write a system of inequalities.**
3. **Graph the system. Find vertices of the polygon formed.**
4. **Write an expression to be maximized or minimized.**
5. **Substitute values from the vertices into the expression.**
6. **Select the greatest or least result. Answer the problem.**

Linear Programming Procedure

Examples

1 The Blair company make two types of pianos: spinets and consoles. The equipment in the factory allows for making at most 450 spinets and 200 consoles in one month. The chart shows the cost of making each type of piano and the profit. During the month of June, the company can spend $360,000 to make these pianos. To make the greatest profit, how many of each type should be made in June?

Piano	Cost per Unit	Profit per Unit
Spinet	$600	$125
Console	$900	$200

Define variables.

Let s = the number of spinets made.
Let c = the number of consoles made.

Write inequalities.

$0 \le s \le 450$ The number of spinets made is between 0 and 450 inclusive.

$0 \le c \le 200$ The number of consoles made is between 0 and 200 inclusive.

$600s + 900c \le 360,000$ The cost of spinets plus the cost of consoles does not exceed $360,000.

Graph the system.

Any point in the shaded region will satisfy the conditions of the problem. The vertices of the polygon are (0, 0), (0, 200), (300, 200), (450, 100), and (450, 0).

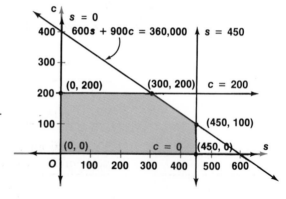

	Write expression to be maximized.	Profit = Profit on Spinets + Profit on Consoles		Recall that the maximum or minimum value is always at one of the vertices.

Write expression to be maximized.

$$\text{Profit} = \text{Profit on Spinets} + \text{Profit on Consoles}$$
$$P(s, c) = \quad\quad 125s \quad + \quad\quad 200c$$

Recall that the maximum or minimum value is always at one of the vertices.

Substitute values from the vertices into the expression.

(s, c)	$(0, 0)$	$(0, 200)$	$(300, 200)$	$(450, 100)$	$(450, 0)$
$125s + 200c$	$0	$40,000	$77,500	$76,250	$56,250

Answer the problem.

The Blair Company will make the greatest profit by building 300 spinets and 200 consoles. This produces a profit of $77,500.

2 **Raw Materials A and B are used to make one of the Target Company's products. The product must contain no more than 9 units of A and at least 18 units of B. It must cost no more than $300. The following chart shows how much each unit of raw material costs and weighs.**

Material	Cost per Unit	Weight per Unit
A	$4	10 pounds
B	$12	20 pounds

How much of each raw material should be used to maximize the weight?

Define variables.

Let a stand for amount of material A used.
Let b stand for amount of material B used.

Write inequalities.

$0 \le a \le 9$ The product contains no more than 9 units of A.
$b \ge 18$ The product contains at least 18 units of B.
$4a + 12b \le 300$ The cost can be no more than $300.

Graph the system.

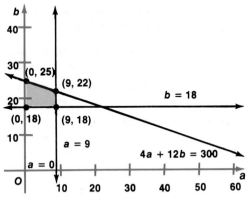

The vertices are $(0, 18)$, $(0, 25)$, $(9, 22)$, and $(9, 18)$.

Write expression to be maximized.

$$\text{Weight} = \text{Weight material A} + \text{Weight material B}$$
$$P(a, b) = \quad\quad 10a \quad + \quad\quad 20b$$

Substitute values into the expression.

(a, b)	$(0, 18)$	$(0, 25)$	$(9, 22)$	$(9, 18)$
$10a + 20b$	360	500	530	450

Answer the problem.

The Target Company should use 9 units of material A and 22 units of material B for each unit of product.

Exploratory Exercises

The area of a parking lot is 600 square meters. A car requires 6 square meters and a bus requires 30 square meters of space. The attendant can handle no more than 60 vehicles. If a car is charged $2.50 and a bus $7.50, how many of each should be accepted to maximize income? Let c = the number of cars accepted. Let b = the number of buses accepted.

1. Write an expression to represent the total income.
2. Write an inequality to represent the total number of cars and buses.
3. Write an inequality to represent the amount of space required for the cars and buses.
4. Graph the system of inequalities. (Show only the first quadrant since b and c cannot be negative.)
5. Name the vertices of the polygon.
6. Evaluate the expression from Exercise 1 for each vertex.
7. To maximize income, how many cars and how many buses should be accepted?
8. What is the maximum income?

Written Exercises

Solve.

1. A painter has exactly 32 units of yellow dye and 54 units of green dye. He plans to mix as many gallons as possible of color A and color B. Each gallon of color A requires 4 units of yellow dye and 1 unit of green dye. Each gallon of color B requires 1 unit of yellow dye and 6 units of green dye.
   a. Let x be the number of gallons of color A and let y be the number of gallons of color B. Write the inequalities.
   b. Graph the system of inequalities and name the vertices of the polygon formed.
   c. Find the maximum number of gallons, $x + y$, possible.

2. A farmer has 20 days in which to plant corn and beans. The corn can be planted at a rate of 10 acres per day and the beans at a rate of 15 acres per day. The farm has 250 acres available.
   a. Let x be the number of acres of corn and let y be the number of acres of beans. Write the inequalities that represent the situation.
   b. Graph the system of inequalities and name the vertices of the polygon formed.
   c. If corn profits $30 per acre and beans profit $25 per acre, find the values of x and y that maximize the profit.
   d. If corn profits $29 per acre and beans profit $30 per acre, find the values of x and y that maximize the profit.

3. A dressmaking shop makes dresses and pantsuits. The equipment in the shop allows for making at most 30 dresses and 20 pantsuits in a week. It takes 10 worker-hours to make a dress and 20 worker-hours to make a pantsuit. There are 500 worker-hours available per week in the shop.
   a. If the profit on a dress and the profit on a pantsuit are the same, how many of each should be made to maximize the profit?
   b. If the profit on a pantsuit is three times the profit on a dress, how many of each should be made to maximize the profit?

4. Fashion Furniture makes two kinds of chairs, rockers and swivels. Two operations, A and B, are used. Operation A is limited to 20 hours a day. Operation B is limited to 15 hours per day. The following chart shows the amount of time each operation takes for one chair. It also shows the profit made on each chair.

Chair	Operation A	Operation B	Profit
Rocker	2 h	3 h	$12
Swivel	4 h	1 h	$10

How many chairs of each kind should Fashion Furniture make each day to maximize profit?

5. Recreation Unlimited produces footballs and basketballs. Producing a football requires 4 hours on machine A and 2 hours on machine B. Producing a basketball requires 6 hours on machine A, 6 hours on machine B, and 1 hour on machine C. Machine A is available 120 hours per week, machine B is available 72 hours per week, and machine C is available 10 hours per week. If the company profits $3 on each football and $2 on each basketball, how many of each should be produced to maximize the company's profit?

6. The table gives the amounts of ingredient A and ingredient B in two types of dog foods: X and Y.

Food Type	Amount of Ingredient A	Amount of Ingredient B
X	1 unit per pound	$\frac{1}{2}$ unit per pound
Y	$\frac{1}{3}$ unit per pound	1 unit per pound

The dogs in a kennel must get *at least* 40 pounds of food per day. The food may be a mixture of type X and type Y. The daily diet must contain at least 20 units of ingredient A and at least 30 units of ingredient B. The dogs must not get more than 100 pounds of food per day.
a. Type X costs $0.80 per pound and type Y costs $0.40 per pound. What is the least possible cost per day for feeding the dogs?
b. If the price on type X is raised to $1.00 per pound and the price on type Y remains the same, should the mixture be changed?

⏤⁄🔲✳⏤⁄🔲✳ Using Computers ⏤⁄🔲✳⏤⁄🔲✳

Parallel and Perpendicular Lines

The standard form of a linear equation is $Ax + By = C$, and the slope is $-\frac{A}{B}$.
Suppose you are given the equation of a line, and the coordinates of a point that is not on the line. The slope of a parallel line that passes through the given point is $-\frac{A}{B}$.

The slope of a perpendicular line that passes through the given point is $\frac{B}{A}$.

The following computer program can be used to find the equations of lines parallel and perpendicular to the given line, that pass through the given point.

Run the program below for the linear equation $x + y = 5$ and the ordered pair (4, 5).

```
RUN
ENTER A, B, AND C OF A
LINEAR EQUATION IN
STANDARD FORM: 1, 1, 5
ENTER THE COORDINATES OF
A POINT THAT IS NOT ON
THE LINE: 4, 5

Y = -1X + 9 IS A LINE
PARALLEL TO 1X + 1Y = 5
THAT PASSES THROUGH (4, 5).
Y = 1X + 1 IS A LINE
PERPENDICULAR TO
1X + 1Y = 5
THAT PASSES THROUGH (4, 5).
```

Exercises

Run the program for each linear equation and ordered pair. Write the equation of the parallel line and the equation of the perpendicular line.

1. $5x + y = -1$; (3, 5)
2. $-x + y = 6$; (5, 2)
3. $6x - 3y = 5$; (1, 4)
4. $-2x + 4y = 3$; (3, 4)

```
10  PRINT "ENTER A,B, AND C OF A
    LINEAR EQUATION"
20  INPUT "IN STANDARD FORM: ";A,
    B,C
30  PRINT "ENTER THE COORDINATES
    OF A POINT"
40  INPUT "THAT IS NOT ON THE
    LINE: ";P,Q
50  PRINT : PRINT "Y = "; - (A /
    B);"X + "; (Q + (A / B) * P);
60  PRINT " IS A LINE PARALLEL TO ";
70  PRINT A; "X + ";B;"Y = ";C;
    "THAT PASSES THROUGH (";P;",
    ";Q;")."
80  PRINT "Y = ";(B / A);"X + ";
    (Q - (B / A) * P);
90  PRINT " IS A LINE
    PERPENDICULAR TO ";
100 PRINT A;"X + ";B;"Y = ";C;"
    THAT PASSES THROUGH (";P;","
    ;Q;")."
110 END
```

Lines that are parallel to the same line are parallel to each other. Lines that are perpendicular to the same line are also parallel to each other. A set of parallel lines is called a **family of lines.** Run the program several times to find equations of lines perpendicular to $x + 4y = 8$. Use the ordered pairs (2, 3), (4, 1), (6, 2), and (5, 5). Then complete the following exercises.

5. List equations for a family of lines that are parallel to $x + 4y = 8$.

6. List equations for a family of lines that are perpendicular to $x + 4y = 8$.

7. Do the four ordered pairs given above determine four distinct lines parallel to $x + 4y = 8$?

8. Do the four ordered pairs given above determine four distinct lines perpendicular to $x + 4y = 8$?

9. Write equations for four lines that are parallel to $x - 2y = 3$.

10. Write equations for four lines that are perpendicular to $x - 2y = 3$.

Vocabulary

parallel lines (77)	independent system (81)	substitution method (84)
perpendicular lines (78)	dependent system (81)	determinant (87)
system of equations (80)	inconsistent system (81)	Cramer's Rule (88)
consistent system (81)	elimination method (84)	linear programming (93)

Chapter Summary

1. **Definition of Parallel Lines:** In a plane, lines with the same slope are parallel lines. Also, vertical lines are parallel. (77)

2. **Definition of Perpendicular Lines:** In a plane, two nonvertical lines are perpendicular if and only if the product of their slopes is -1. Any vertical line is perpendicular to any horizontal line. (78)

3. Possibilities for the graphs of two linear equations in two variables. (81)

Graphs of Equations	Slopes of Lines	Name of System of Equations	Number of Solutions
lines intersect	different slopes	consistent and independent	one
lines coincide	same slope, same intercepts	consistent and dependent	infinitely many
lines parallel	same slope, different intercepts	inconsistent	none

4. The substitution method and the elimination method can be used to solve systems of equations. (84)

5. A square array of numbers enclosed between vertical lines is called a determinant. (87)

6. The value of a second order determinant is defined as

$$\begin{vmatrix} a & b \\ c & d \end{vmatrix} = ad - bc. \quad (87)$$

7. **Cramer's Rule:** The solution to the system $\begin{matrix} ax + by = c \\ dx + ey = f \end{matrix}$ is (x, y)

$$\text{where } x = \dfrac{\begin{vmatrix} c & b \\ f & e \end{vmatrix}}{\begin{vmatrix} a & b \\ d & e \end{vmatrix}},\ y = \dfrac{\begin{vmatrix} a & c \\ d & f \end{vmatrix}}{\begin{vmatrix} a & b \\ d & e \end{vmatrix}} \text{ and } \begin{vmatrix} a & b \\ d & e \end{vmatrix} \neq 0. \quad (88)$$

8. To solve a system of inequalities, find the ordered pairs that satisfy both inequalities. (90)

9. **Linear Programming Procedure:**
   1. Define variables.
   2. Write a system of inequalities.
   3. Graph the system. Find vertices of the polygon formed.
   4. Write an expression to be maximized or minimized.
   5. Substitute values from vertices into the expression.
   6. Select the greatest or least result. Answer the problem. (96)

Chapter Review

3–1 Find an equation of the line that passes through each given point and is parallel to the line with the given equation.

1. $(4, 6)$; $y = 3x - 2$

2. $(1, 1)$; $y = -3x - 1$

3. $(-1, -1)$; $y = 6x - 8$

4. $(7, 7)$; $2x + 3y = 6$

Find an equation of the line that passes through each given point and is perpendicular to the line with the given equation.

5. $(3, 5)$; $y = 2x - 5$

6. $(1, 4)$; $y = 3x - 1$

7. $(-1, -1)$; $2y + 3x = 10$

8. $(0, 10)$; $y = 4x$

3–2 Graph each system of equations and state its solution. Then, state whether the system is *consistent and independent, consistent and dependent,* or *inconsistent.*

9. $x + y = -8$
$2x - y = 2$

10. $x + y = 6$
$x - y = 2$

11. $x + y = 11$
$3x - 3y = 3$

12. $x + y = 6$
$2x + 2y = 12$

3–3 Solve each system of equations algebraically.

13. $x + y = 6$
$x - y = 4\frac{1}{2}$

14. $3x - 5y = -13$
$4x + 3y = 2$

15. $2x + 3y = 8$
$x - y = 2$

16. $\frac{1}{3}x + \frac{1}{3}y = 5$
$\frac{1}{6}x - \frac{1}{9}y = 0$

3–4 Find the value of each determinant.

17. $\begin{vmatrix} 2 & 3 \\ 4 & 5 \end{vmatrix}$

18. $\begin{vmatrix} 6 & -1 \\ 3 & -2 \end{vmatrix}$

Solve each system of equations using Cramer's rule.

19. $7x - 8y = 11$
$9x - 2y = 3$

20. $x + 2y = 5$
$x - y = 6$

3–5 Solve each system of inequalities by graphing.

21. $x + y < 2$
$x + 2y > -3$

22. $y < -2$
$y - x > 1$

23. $y \geq x - 3$
$y \geq -x + 1$

24. $x + y < 4$
$y \geq -3x + 1$

3–6 Graph each system of inequalities. Name the vertices of the polygon formed. Find the maximum and minimum values of the given function.

25. $x \geq 0$
$y \geq 0$
$x + y \leq 3$ $f(x, y) = 2x + 4y$
$3x + y \leq 6$

26. $0 \leq x \leq 5$
$0 \leq y \leq 6$ $f(x, y) = 2x + 3y$
$x + y \leq 9$

3–7 Solve.

27. A farmer has 90 acres on which he may raise peanuts and corn. He has accepted orders requiring at least 10 acres of peanuts and 5 acres of corn. He also must follow a regulation that the acreage for corn must be at least twice the acreage for peanuts. If the profit is $100 per acre of corn and $200 per acre of peanuts, how many acres of each will give him the greatest profit?

Chapter Test

Find an equation of the line that passes through each given point and is parallel to the line with the given equation.

1. $(2, 4); y = 3x - 5$

2. $(7, -4); y = -x + 6$

Find an equation of the line that passes through each given point and is perpendicular to the line with the given equation.

3. $(3, 4); y = 2x + 1$

4. $(6, -1); y + 2x = 5$

Graph each system of equations. Then state the solution to the system.

5. $x + y = 7$
   $x - y = 1$

6. $2x + 3y = 5$
   $-3x + 6y = 12$

Solve each system of equations algebraically.

7. $3x + 8y = -6$
   $4x - 2y = 11$

8. $7x + 2y = 11$
   $3x + 16 = -8y$

Find the value of each determinant.

9. $\begin{vmatrix} 3 & 1 \\ -2 & 4 \end{vmatrix}$

10. $\begin{vmatrix} 9 & 0 \\ 5 & -6 \end{vmatrix}$

Solve each system of equations using Cramer's rule.

11. $-2x + 3y = 5$
    $x + 4y = 14$

12. $4x + y = 5$
    $-8x + 3y = 10$

Solve each system of inequalities by graphing.

13. $y > 2x + 1$
    $y \le -3x + 4$

14. $x + y \le 6$
    $x - y \ge 4$

Graph each system of inequalities. Name the vertices of the polygon formed. Find the maximum and minimum values of the given function.

15. $0 \le x \le 6$
    $0 \le y \le 2$ $\quad f(x, y) = 2x + y$
    $x + y \le 4$

16. $0 \le x \le 4$
    $y + x \le 6$ $\quad f(x, y) = 3x - 2y$
    $y \ge 0$

Solve.

17. A builder has 60 lots on which he can build houses with one house on each lot. He builds two types of houses, colonial and ranch. Sales experience has taught him that he should plan to build at least 3 times as many ranch-style houses as colonial. If he makes a profit of $5000 on each colonial and $4500 on each ranch, how many of each kind should he build to maximize profit?

CHAPTER 4

More Systems of Equations

A computer can be programmed to make drawings such as the one shown above. The program involves many variables and many systems of equations. Arrays of numbers called matrices can represent systems of equations and are also used with three-dimensional computer graphics. By using multiplication of matrices, the size or perspective of a drawing can be changed.

4-1 Solving Systems of Equations in Three Variables

The equation $2x + 3y + z = 10$ is an equation in three variables, x, y, and z. The solution to such an equation is an **ordered triple.**

The system below has three equations and three variables.

$$2x + 3y + z = 10$$
$$4x + 2y - z = 13$$
$$x + y + z = 5$$

Each equation is satisfied when x is 3, y is 1, and z is 1.

$$2(3) + 3(1) + (1) = 6 + 3 + 1 = 10$$
$$4(3) + 2(1) - (1) = 12 + 2 - 1 = 13$$
$$(3) + (1) + (1) = 3 + 1 + 1 = 5$$

Thus, the solution to this system is the ordered triple $(3, 1, 1)$.

Systems of equations for three variables are solved using the same methods as those for equations in two variables.

Example

1 Solve the following system of equations.

$$2x + y + z = 11$$
$$3y - z = -1$$
$$2z = 8$$

Solve the third equation for z.

$$2z = 8$$
$$z = 4$$

Substitute 4 for z in the second equation.

$$3y - (4) = -1$$
$$3y = 3$$
$$y = 1$$

Substitute 4 for z and 1 for y in the first equation.

$$2x + (1) + (4) = 11$$
$$2x = 6$$
$$x = 3$$

The solution is $(3, 1, 4)$.

Check: *First equation* $2(3) + 1 + 4 = 11$
         Second equation $3(1) - 4 = -1$
         Third equation $2(4) = 8$

Example

2 **Solve the following system of equations.**

$$2x + 3y + 2z = 14$$
$$4x + 2y - z = 15$$
$$x + y + 3z = 8$$

Use elimination to make a system of two equations in two variables.

$$\begin{array}{l} 2x + 3y + 2z = 14 \\ 4x + 2y - z = 15 \end{array}$$ **Multiply by 2.**
$$\begin{array}{l} 2x + 3y + 2z = 14 \\ \underline{8x + 4y - 2z = 30} \\ 10x + 7y \qquad = 44 \end{array}$$ *Add to eliminate z.*

$$\begin{array}{l} 4x + 2y - z = 15 \\ x + y + 3z = 8 \end{array}$$ **Multiply by 3.**
$$\begin{array}{l} 12x + 6y - 3z = 45 \\ \underline{x + y + 3z = 8} \\ 13x + 7y \qquad = 53 \end{array}$$ *Add to eliminate z.*

The result is two equations with the same two variables.

$$10x + 7y = 44$$
$$13x + 7y = 53$$

Solve this system for x and y.

$$\begin{array}{l} 10x + 7y = 44 \\ 13x + 7y = 53 \end{array}$$ **Multiply by −1.**
$$\begin{array}{l} -10x - 7y = -44 \\ \underline{13x + 7y = 53} \\ 3x \qquad = 9 \\ x \qquad = 3 \end{array}$$ *Add to eliminate y.*

Now substitute 3 for x in $10x + 7y = 44$ to find y.

$$10(3) + 7y = 44 \qquad \textit{Substitute 3 for x.}$$
$$30 + 7y = 44$$
$$7y = 14$$
$$y = 2$$

Then substitute the values for x and y in one of the original equations. Solve the equation for z.

$$x + y + 3z = 8$$
$$(3) + (2) + 3z = 8$$
$$3z = 3$$
$$z = 1$$

The solution is (3, 2, 1).

Exploratory Exercises

A possible solution for each system of equations is given in color. Check to see if it is the correct solution.

1. $x + y + z = 6$
$x - 3y + 2z = 1$
$2x - y + 2z = 0$ (2, 2, 2)

2. $2x + 3y - z = 0$
$x + 2y + z = 0$
$x - y + z = 0$ (0, 0, 0)

3. $x + y + z = 3$
$x - z = 1$
$y - z = -4$ (3, −2, 2)

4. $4x + y - 2z = 0$
$-2x + y + z = 0$
$x - 2y = 0$ (3, 0, 6)

5. $3x + 2y + z = 5$
$2x + y - z = 2$
$x + y + z = 0$ (8, −11, 3)

6. $x + y = -6$
$x + z = -2$
$y + z = 2$ (−4, −2, 2)

Written Exercises

Solve each system of equations.

1. $a - 2b + c = -9$
   $2b + 3c = 16$
   $4b = 8$

2. $x + y + z = -1$
   $2x + y = 2$
   $-3x = -9$

3. $2x + 4y - z = -3$
   $y + z = 4$
   $2y = -2$

4. $x + y - z = -1$
   $x + y + z = 3$
   $3x - 2y - z = -4$

5. $a + b + c = 0$
   $2a + b - c = 2$
   $2a + 2b + c = 5$

6. $x + y + z = 15$
   $x + z = 12$
   $y + z = 10$

7. $x - 2y + z = 3$
   $2x + y - 2z = 31$
   $-x + 2y + 3z = -23$

8. $x + y + z = 4$
   $x - y + z = 0$
   $x - y - z = -2$

9. $a + b - 2c = 4$
   $2a + b + 2c = 0$
   $a - 3b - 4c = -2$

10. $2x + 3y + z = 7$
    $x + y + z = 4$
    $3x + 4y - 2z = 6$

11. $x + y + z = -1$
    $2x - y + z = 19$
    $3x - 2y - 4z = 16$

12. $2x - y + 4z = 7$
    $x - 3y + z = -2$
    $3x - 2y + 2z = -2$

13. $x + 2y - 3z = 10$
    $-4x + y - z = -10$
    $3x - 7y + 2z = 5$

14. $x + 8y + 2z = -24$
    $3x + y + 7z = -3$
    $4x - 3y + 6z = 9$

15. $2a + b + c = 7$
    $12a - 2b - 2c = 2$
    $\dfrac{2a}{3} - b + \dfrac{c}{3} = -\dfrac{1}{3}$

Solve each problem.

16. The sum of three numbers is 20. The first number is the sum of the second and the third, and the third number is three times the first. Find the numbers.

17. The sum of three numbers is 16. One of the numbers is the sum of the other two numbers. It is also four times the difference of the other two numbers. Find the numbers.

18. The perimeter of a triangle is 18 feet. The longest side is twice as long as the shortest side. The length of the remaining side is the average of the lengths of the longest and shortest sides. Find the lengths of the three sides.

Challenge

Solve each system of equations.

19. $w + x + y + z = 2$
    $2w - x - y + 2z = 7$
    $2w + 3x + 2y - z = -2$
    $3w - 2x - y - 3z = -2$

20. $4a + 6b + 2c + 4d = -12$
    $-2a + 3b + c + d = -3$
    $6a - 3b + c - d = 9$
    $-10a - 6b - c - 2d = 1$

mini-review

Solve.

1. A bookstore makes a profit of $6.50 on a certain cookbook. How many of these cookbooks must the store sell to make a profit of at least $150.00?

2. Find $f(6)$ if $f(x) = x^2 - 4x + 3$.

3. Find the slope, y-intercept, and x-intercept of the graph of $7x - 3y = 14$.

4. Graph this system of equations and state its solution.
   $$3x - 5y = 4$$
   $$4x - y = 11$$

5. Graph this system of inequalities and name the vertices of the polygon formed. Then find the maximum and minimum values of $3x + 2y$ for the region.
   $$x + y \leq 5$$
   $$x \geq 1$$
   $$y \geq 2$$

4-2　Equations of Planes

To draw the graph of a linear equation in three variables, it is necessary to use three dimensions. The graph of an equation of the form $Ax + By + Cz = D$ is a plane.

The graph of all ordered triples of real numbers is space.

> **If A, B, and C are real numbers and not all zero, then the graph of $Ax + By + Cz = D$ is a plane.**

Equation of a Plane

To graph a plane it is necessary to divide space into 8 regions, each called an **octant.** Think of three coordinate planes intersecting at right angles as shown below.

The octants are numbered as shown below. Any point lying in a coordinate plane is not in any octant. The signs of x, y, and z for each octant are shown as an ordered triple.

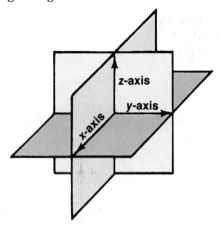

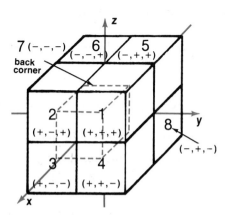

Example

1 **Locate the point (2, 4, 3).**

First, locate 2 on the positive x-axis, 4 on the positive y-axis, and 3 on the positive z-axis. Complete a "box" by drawing lines parallel to the axes through each intercept.

The point is in the first octant.

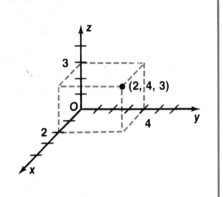

When graphing an ordered triple, it is not necessary to show the entire "box". Simply indicate the corner of the box. The desired point will always be the corner farthest from the origin.

If one of the coordinates is zero, the sketch will be a rectangle instead of a box.

Example

2 **Locate the point $(-2, -3, 1)$.**

First, locate -2 on the x-axis. Then draw a segment 3 units long in the negative direction, parallel to the y-axis. From that point, draw a segment 1 unit long in the positive direction, parallel to the z-axis.
The desired point is in octant 6.

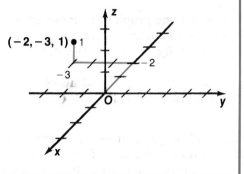

To graph a linear equation in three variables, first find the intercepts of the graph. Connect the intercepts on each axis. This forms the portion of a plane that lies in a single octant. Study the following example.

Example

3 **Graph $2x + 4y + 3z = 12$.**

To find the x-intercept, let $y = 0$ and $z = 0$.
$$2x = 12$$
$$x = 6$$

To find the y-intercept, let $x = 0$ and $z = 0$.
$$4y = 12$$
$$y = 3$$

To find the z-intercept, let $x = 0$ and $y = 0$.
$$3z = 12$$
$$z = 4$$

To indicate the plane, connect the intercepts. Remember, a plane extends infinitely in two dimensions.

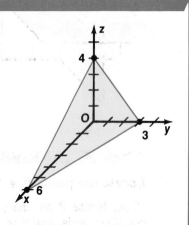

The portion in octant 1 is shown.

The intersection of a plane with one of the coordinate planes is a line called a **trace**. The xy-trace is the line formed by the intersection of a plane with the xy-plane. Since all points in the xy-trace have a z-coordinate of zero, the equation can be found by letting $z = 0$ in the equation of the plane. Equations for the other two traces can be found in a similar manner.

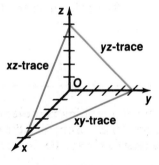

Example

4

Graph $10x - 5y + 4z = 20$ and find the trace in each coordinate plane.

The x-, y-, and z-intercepts are 2, -4, and 5.

To find the equation of the xy-trace, let $z = 0$.

$$10x - 5y = 20$$
$$2x - y = 4 \quad \text{\textit{Simplify.}}$$

To find the equation of the xz-trace, let $y = 0$.

$$10x + 4z = 20$$
$$5x + 2z = 10 \quad \text{\textit{Simplify.}}$$

To find the equation of the yz-trace, let $x = 0$.

$$-5y + 4z = 20$$

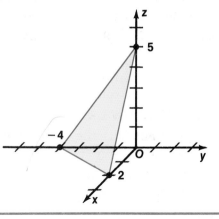

If you know the equations of two traces, you can write the equation of the plane containing the two traces.

Example

5

The equations for two traces of a plane are $3x + 2y = -12$ and $3x - 4z = -12$. Find the equation of the plane.

First, find the intercepts of the two traces.
The xy-trace is $3x + 2y = -12$.
The x-intercept is -4 and the y-intercept is -6.
The xz-trace is $3x - 4z = -12$.
The x-intercept is -4 and the z-intercept is 3.

Use the intercepts to write the equation of the plane. The x-, y-, and z-intercepts are -4, -6, and 3. The least common multiple is 12. So, use 12 as the constant in the equation. Divide 12 by each intercept to obtain the coefficients.

$$\frac{12}{-4} = -3 \qquad \frac{12}{-6} = -2 \qquad \frac{12}{3} = 4$$

The equation of the plane is $-3x - 2y + 4z = 12$.

Exploratory Exercises

In which octant does each point lie?

1. $(6, 4, 1)$ **2.** $(7, 5, -6)$ **3.** $(4, 0, 3)$

4. $(3, -7, 2)$ **5.** $(-3, 8, 2)$ **6.** $(0, -2, -4)$

7. $(-5, -6, 4)$ **8.** $(2, -5, -9)$ **9.** $(-3, -6, -1)$

10. $(-5, 8, 0)$ **11.** $(-5, 2, -3)$ **12.** $(-3, -2, 5)$

Find the x-, y-, and z-intercepts for each equation.

13. $10x - 2y + 5z = 10$

14. $2x + y - z = 12$

15. $3x + 5y + 2z = 30$

16. $x - y - z = 1$

17. $3x + 6y - 8z = 24$

18. $5x + y - 3z = 15$

19. $2x + 5y + z = 6$

20. $2x + 4y - z = 5$

21. $5x - 2y = 8$

22. $5x - 7y + 2z = 9$

23. $3y + 2z = 12$

24. $2x + y - 3z = 10$

Written Exercises

In which octant does the point (x, y, z) lie given the following conditions?

1. $x = 2, y = 3, z < 0$

2. $x < 0, y = 2, z > 0$

3. $x < 0, y > 0, z = -3$

4. $x = 3, y < 0, z > 0$

5. $x = -3, y > 0, z = 5$

6. $x < 0, y < 0, z < 0$

7. $x > 2, y < -1, z < -2$

8. $x > 3, y < -1, z = 4$

9. $x > 3, y > 0, z = 2$

10. $x < -2, y = -3, z > 1$

Graph each equation. Find the x-, y-, and z-intercepts and the traces in the coordinate planes.

11. $2x - 3y + z = 12$

12. $4x - 2y - 3z = 24$

13. $2x + 8y - z = 8$

14. $-3x + 6y - 4z = 24$

15. $3x + 6y + 2z = 9$

16. $4x - y + 2z = 10$

17. $3x - y = 3$

18. $5y + 2z = 20$

19. $4x - 3y + 2z = 15$

20. $3x + 8y - 5z = 12$

21. $3z - 2x = 5$

22. $5x - 8y = -12$

23. $3x = 8$

24. $y = 5$

Write the equation of the plane with the following x-, y-, and z-intercepts.

25. $4, -2, 3$

26. $2, -2, 5$

27. $-3, 1, 6$

28. $1, 3, 2$

29. $-1, -3, -4$

30. $7, 1, 4$

31. $\frac{1}{2}, 3, -2$

32. $-4, \frac{2}{3}, 1$

33. $4, \frac{1}{3}, \frac{1}{4}$

34. $\frac{3}{4}, -2, \frac{1}{3}$

35. $\frac{2}{3}, \frac{7}{3}, -\frac{1}{2}$

36. $-\frac{1}{2}, -\frac{4}{3}, -\frac{5}{8}$

Write the equation of the plane given two of its traces in the coordinate planes.

37. $3x - 5y = 8, 5y - 2z = -8$

38. $4x + 3y = 12, 3y - z = 12$

39. $2x - y = 6, 2y + 3z = -12$

40. $5x + 3z = 15, y + z = 5$

41. $5x - 4y = 20, 4y - 7z = -20$

42. $2x - 5z = 6, 3y - 5z = 6$

43. $x + 5y = 1, x + 3z = 1$

44. $x - 4y = 1, 8y + z = -2$

45. $2x + y = 4, x = 2$

46. $3y - 4z = 6, y = 2$

47. $x = 4, y = -3$

48. $x = -2, z = 5$

4-3 Determinants and Cramer's Rule

A third-order determinant has three rows and three columns. In a determinant, the **minor** of an element is the determinant formed when the row and column containing the element are deleted. Study the determinant at the right.

$$\begin{vmatrix} 1 & 3 & 7 \\ 4 & 8 & 2 \\ 9 & 5 & 6 \end{vmatrix}$$

The minor of 1 is $\begin{vmatrix} 8 & 2 \\ 5 & 6 \end{vmatrix}$.

The minor of 5 is $\begin{vmatrix} 1 & 7 \\ 4 & 2 \end{vmatrix}$.

A method called **expansion by minors** may be used to find the value of any third order determinant, as shown below. Each element in a row is multiplied by its minor. Notice that the signs of the terms alternate, with the first term being positive.

$$\begin{vmatrix} a & b & c \\ d & e & f \\ g & h & i \end{vmatrix} = a\begin{vmatrix} e & f \\ h & i \end{vmatrix} - b\begin{vmatrix} d & f \\ g & i \end{vmatrix} + c\begin{vmatrix} d & e \\ g & h \end{vmatrix}$$

Expansion of a Third Order Determinant

Example

1 Find the value of $\begin{vmatrix} 2 & 3 & 4 \\ 6 & 5 & 7 \\ 1 & 2 & 8 \end{vmatrix}$ using expansion by minors.

$$\begin{vmatrix} 2 & 3 & 4 \\ 6 & 5 & 7 \\ 1 & 2 & 8 \end{vmatrix} = 2\begin{vmatrix} 5 & 7 \\ 2 & 8 \end{vmatrix} - 3\begin{vmatrix} 6 & 7 \\ 1 & 8 \end{vmatrix} + 4\begin{vmatrix} 6 & 5 \\ 1 & 2 \end{vmatrix}$$
$$= 2(40 - 14) - 3(48 - 7) + 4(12 - 5)$$
$$= 52 - 123 + 28$$
$$= -43$$

Another method for evaluating a third-order determinant is to use diagonals. Write the first two columns on the right side of the determinant. Then find the product of the three elements in each diagonal. Add the products for the diagonals that extend from upper left to lower right. Then subtract the products for the other diagonals. The result is the value of the determinant. This is shown in the diagram below.

Subtract: *gec   hfa   idb*

$$= aei + bfg + cdh - gec - hfa - idb$$

Add: *aei   bfg   cdh*

Examples

Find the value of each determinant by using diagonals.

2
$$\begin{vmatrix} 2 & 3 & 4 \\ 6 & 5 & 7 \\ 1 & 2 & 8 \end{vmatrix}$$

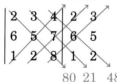

20 28 144

Find the products of the diagonals.

80 21 48

$= 80 + 21 + 48 - 20 - 28 - 144$
$= -43$

3
$$\begin{vmatrix} -1 & 4 & 0 \\ 3 & -2 & -5 \\ -3 & 1 & 2 \end{vmatrix}$$

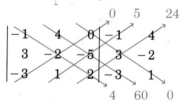

0 5 24

4 60 0

$= 4 + 60 + 0 - 0 - 5 - 24$
$= 35$

Cramer's Rule may be extended to solve a system of three linear equations in three variables. The determinant in each denominator contains the coefficients of the variables. The determinant in each numerator is the same determinant except for the column of the coefficients of the variable to be found. This column is replaced by the column of constants.

Example

4 **Use Cramer's Rule to solve the following system of equations.**

$$a + 2b - c = -7$$
$$2a + 3b + 2c = -3$$
$$a - 2b - 2c = 3$$

$$a = \frac{\begin{vmatrix} -7 & 2 & -1 \\ -3 & 3 & 2 \\ 3 & -2 & -2 \end{vmatrix}}{\begin{vmatrix} 1 & 2 & -1 \\ 2 & 3 & 2 \\ 1 & -2 & -2 \end{vmatrix}}$$

$$b = \frac{\begin{vmatrix} 1 & -7 & -1 \\ 2 & -3 & 2 \\ 1 & 3 & -2 \end{vmatrix}}{\begin{vmatrix} 1 & 2 & -1 \\ 2 & 3 & 2 \\ 1 & -2 & -2 \end{vmatrix}}$$

$$c = \frac{\begin{vmatrix} 1 & 2 & -7 \\ 2 & 3 & -3 \\ 1 & -2 & 3 \end{vmatrix}}{\begin{vmatrix} 1 & 2 & -1 \\ 2 & 3 & 2 \\ 1 & -2 & -2 \end{vmatrix}}$$

$$= \frac{17}{17} \text{ or } 1$$

$$= \frac{-51}{17} \text{ or } -3$$

$$= \frac{34}{17} \text{ or } 2$$

The solution is $(1, -3, 2)$. *Check this solution.*

A system of three equations in three variables does not always have a solution that is a unique ordered triple. The graph of each equation is a plane. Depending on the constants involved, one of the following possibilities occurs.

The three planes intersect at one point. So, the system has a unique solution.

The three planes intersect at a line. There are an infinite number of solutions to the system.

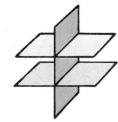

Each diagram below shows three planes that have no points in common. These systems of equations have no solutions.

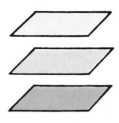

For a system of linear equations in two variables, a unique solution exists if the determinant is not zero. This test can also be used for a system of three equations in three variables.

Consider this system: $a_1x + b_1y + c_1z = d_1$
$$a_2x + b_2y + c_2z = d_2$$
$$a_3x + b_3y + c_3z = d_3$$

Test for Unique Solutions

A unique solution exists if $\begin{vmatrix} a_1 & b_1 & c_1 \\ a_2 & b_2 & c_2 \\ a_3 & b_3 & c_3 \end{vmatrix} \neq 0.$

Example

5 **If a unique solution exists, find the solution.**

$$2a - b + 3c = 5$$
$$3a + 2b - 5c = 7$$
$$a - 4b + 11c = 3$$

$$\begin{vmatrix} 2 & -1 & 3 \\ 3 & 2 & -5 \\ 1 & -4 & 11 \end{vmatrix} = 2\begin{vmatrix} 2 & -5 \\ -4 & 11 \end{vmatrix} + 1\begin{vmatrix} 3 & -5 \\ 1 & 11 \end{vmatrix} + 3\begin{vmatrix} 3 & 2 \\ 1 & -4 \end{vmatrix}$$

$$= 2(22 - 20) + (33 + 5) + 3(-12 - 2)$$

$$= 4 + 38 - 42 \text{ or } 0$$

No unique solution exists.

Example

6 If a unique solution exists, find the solution.

$$4x - 3y + z = -1$$
$$2x + 9y + 5z = 2$$
$$2x - 6y - 3z = 0$$

$$\begin{vmatrix} 4 & -3 & 1 \\ 2 & 9 & 5 \\ 2 & -6 & -3 \end{vmatrix} = -66 \qquad \text{The value of the determinant is } -66.$$

$$x = \frac{\begin{vmatrix} -1 & -3 & 1 \\ 2 & 9 & 5 \\ 0 & -6 & -3 \end{vmatrix}}{-66} = \frac{-33}{-66} = \frac{1}{2} \qquad y = \frac{\begin{vmatrix} 4 & -1 & 1 \\ 2 & 2 & 5 \\ 2 & 0 & -3 \end{vmatrix}}{-66} = \frac{-44}{-66} = \frac{2}{3}$$

$$z = \frac{\begin{vmatrix} 4 & -3 & -1 \\ 2 & 9 & 2 \\ 2 & -6 & 0 \end{vmatrix}}{-66} = \frac{66}{-66} = -1$$

The solution is $\left(\frac{1}{2}, \frac{2}{3}, -1\right)$. *Check this solution.*

Exploratory Exercises

Find the value of each determinant.

1. $\begin{vmatrix} 5 & 7 \\ -3 & 2 \end{vmatrix}$
2. $\begin{vmatrix} 6 & 0 \\ 9 & -1 \end{vmatrix}$
3. $\begin{vmatrix} 2 & 0 & 2 \\ 0 & 3 & -3 \\ -3 & -2 & 0 \end{vmatrix}$
4. $\begin{vmatrix} 2 & 3 & 4 \\ 3 & 2 & -1 \\ 4 & 3 & 7 \end{vmatrix}$

Name the determinants you would use to solve each system by Cramer's Rule.

5. $a - 2b + 3c = -4$
$2a - b + 4c = -1$
$2a + 3b + 5c = 1$

6. $2x + 4y - z = -6$
$x - 2y + 3z = 2$
$x + 2y - 4z = -10$

Written Exercises

Find the value of each determinant.

1. $\begin{vmatrix} 1 & 3 & -2 \\ 2 & -1 & 1 \\ -2 & 2 & 3 \end{vmatrix}$
2. $\begin{vmatrix} -1 & 1 & 2 \\ 2 & 1 & 0 \\ 3 & 6 & -2 \end{vmatrix}$
3. $\begin{vmatrix} 1 & -1 & 1 \\ 4 & 3 & 1 \\ 0 & 5 & 2 \end{vmatrix}$
4. $\begin{vmatrix} 3 & -1 & 2 \\ 0 & 4 & 1 \\ 5 & -2 & -3 \end{vmatrix}$

5. $\begin{vmatrix} 1 & 2 & -3 \\ 3 & -5 & -1 \\ 4 & 4 & 1 \end{vmatrix}$
6. $\begin{vmatrix} 3 & 2 & 5 \\ -1 & 1 & 1 \\ 4 & 3 & 3 \end{vmatrix}$
7. $\begin{vmatrix} 40 & 20 & -25 \\ 10 & 15 & 55 \\ -5 & -10 & -30 \end{vmatrix}$
8. $\begin{vmatrix} 44 & 41 & 46 \\ 32 & -59 & 36 \\ 72 & -61 & 84 \end{vmatrix}$

Check whether each system of equations has a unique solution. If a unique solution exists, solve by using Cramer's Rule.

9. $2x - y + z = -2$
   $x + 2y + 6z = 3$
   $3x - y + 2z = -1$

10. $4a + b + 3c = 1$
    $2a + c = 3$
    $4a - 6b = 8$

11. $a + 2b - 3c = -13$
    $2a - b + 3c = 23$
    $3a + b - 3c = -8$

12. $3x - y + 2z = 11$
    $6x - 3y + z = -1$
    $-3x - 2y + 2z = 11$

13. $2x - y + 3z = 4$
    $3x + 2y + z = 7$
    $x + 3y - 2z = 3$

14. $x + 9y - 2z = 2$
    $-x - 3y + 4z = 1$
    $2x + 3y - 6z = -5$

15. $x + 4y + 3z = 10$
    $2x - 2y + z = 15$
    $x + 2y - 3z = -1$

16. $5x - y + 2z = 5$
    $2x - 3y + 5z = 1$
    $3x + 2y - 3z = 4$

17. $3x + 2y - 2z = 5$
    $6x - 5y + 2z = 7$
    $3x - 4y + 8z = 0$

18. $x + 5y = -1$
    $2x - 5y + 3z = 11$
    $x + 10y - 6z = -7$

19. $2x + 3y + 4z = 4$
    $2x - 8z = -1$
    $4x - 6y + 4z = -1$

20. $3x + 4y + z = 10$
    $6x - 2y - z = 6$
    $3x + 6y - 2z = 2$

Write a system of equations for each problem and solve using Cramer's Rule.

21. Floyd has 16 coins in pennies, nickels, and dimes. The number of dimes is equal to the sum of the number of pennies and number of nickels. If the total value of the coins is $1.08, how many of each kind does he have?

22. Meiko bought 97 cans of soft drink. The number of root beers exceeded the number of colas by 15. The total number of colas and orange drinks was 23 less than twice the number of root beers. How many cans of each did she buy?

Using Calculators _____ **Storing a Sum**

Many calculators have a key which can be used to add a number to a previously stored value. This key is often labeled M+ or SUM. For a problem that requires many steps, this key may help you minimize errors. Find the value of the determinant below. Use diagonals.

$$\begin{vmatrix} 4 & 2 & -1 \\ 5 & 7 & 8 \\ -3 & 6 & -2 \end{vmatrix}$$

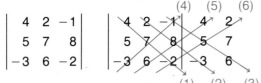

Find the product of the diagonals in the order shown. Use the M+ or SUM key to add the products.

ENTER: (1) 4 × 7 × 2 +/− = M+ −56

(2) 2 × 8 × 3 +/− = M+ −48

(3) 1 +/− × 5 × 6 = M+ −30

(4) 3 +/− × 7 × 1 +/− = +/− M+ −21

(5) 6 × 8 × 4 = +/− M+ −192

(6) 2 +/− × 5 × 2 = +/− M+ 20

The display for the value of each diagonal is shown in blue.

For diagonals (4), (5), and (6), find the additive inverse of each product before using the M+ key.

Finally, press the recall key to obtain the final answer, −327.

Exercises
Use a calculator to find the value of each determinant in Written Exercises 7–8.

4-4 Augmented Matrix Solutions

A rectangular arrangement of terms in rows and columns enclosed in brackets or large parentheses is called a **matrix.** Unlike determinants, a matrix does not have a numerical value. The matrix at the right has two rows and four columns.

$$\text{rows} \begin{array}{c} \text{columns} \\ \begin{bmatrix} 1 & 9 & 5 & 7 \\ 6 & 4 & 12 & 2 \end{bmatrix} \end{array}$$

A system of equations may be represented by a matrix called an **augmented matrix.**

<table>
<tr><th>System of Equations</th><th>Matrix</th></tr>
<tr><td>

$3x + 4y - 2z = 5$

$2x + y - z = 1$

$-x - y - 2z = -9$

</td><td>

$$\begin{bmatrix} 3 & 4 & -2 & 5 \\ 2 & 1 & -1 & 1 \\ -1 & -1 & -2 & -9 \end{bmatrix}$$

</td></tr>
</table>

Each row in the matrix corresponds to an equation. Each column corresponds to the coefficient of a given variable or the constant term.

The system of equations can be solved by using the matrix rather than the equations themselves. Each change of the matrix represents a corresponding change of the system.

$$\begin{bmatrix} 3 & 4 & -2 & 5 \\ -4 & -2 & 2 & -2 \\ -1 & -1 & -2 & -9 \end{bmatrix}$$ *Multiply Row 2 by -2.*

$$\begin{bmatrix} -1 & 2 & 0 & 3 \\ -5 & -3 & 0 & -11 \\ -1 & -1 & -2 & -9 \end{bmatrix}$$ *Replace Row 1 by sum of Row 1 and Row 2.*
Replace Row 2 by sum of Row 2 and Row 3.

$$\begin{bmatrix} -3 & 6 & 0 & 9 \\ -10 & -6 & 0 & -22 \\ -1 & -1 & -2 & -9 \end{bmatrix}$$ *Multiply Row 1 by 3.*
Multiply Row 2 by 2.

$$\begin{bmatrix} -13 & 0 & 0 & -13 \\ -10 & -6 & 0 & -22 \\ -1 & -1 & -2 & -9 \end{bmatrix}$$ *Replace by sum of Row 1 and Row 2.*

The last matrix represents the following system.

$$\begin{aligned} -13x &= -13 \\ -10x - 6y &= -22 \\ -x - y - 2z &= -9 \end{aligned}$$

This system has the same solution as the original system. Use algebra to solve the system.

$$\begin{aligned} -13x &= -13 \\ x &= 1 \end{aligned}$$ *Solve for x.*

To find y, substitute 1 for x in the second equation.

$$-10(1) - 6y = -22$$
$$-6y = -12$$
$$y = 2$$

To find z, substitute the values for x and y in the third equation.

$$-(1) - (2) - 2z = -9$$
$$-2z = -6$$
$$z = 3 \qquad \text{The solution is } (1, 2, 3).$$

In general, you may use any of the following row operations on a matrix. The resulting matrix yields the same solution as the original matrix.

1. **Interchange any two rows.**
2. **Replace any row with a nonzero multiple of that row.**
3. **Replace any row with the sum of that row and another row.**

Row Operations on Matrices

The goal of the augmented matrix method is to obtain all zeros in both of the following "triangles," and ones in place of a, f, and k.

$$\begin{vmatrix} a & b & c & d \\ e & f & g & h \\ i & j & k & l \end{vmatrix}$$

Example

1 **Use an augmented matrix to solve this system:**

$$x + 2y + z = 0$$
$$2x + 5y + 4z = -1$$
$$x - y - 9z = -5$$

Write the augmented matrix.
$$\begin{bmatrix} 1 & 2 & 1 & 0 \\ 2 & 5 & 4 & -1 \\ 1 & -1 & -9 & -5 \end{bmatrix}$$

Multiply row 1 by -1 and add to row 3.
$$\begin{bmatrix} 1 & 2 & 1 & 0 \\ 2 & 5 & 4 & -1 \\ 0 & -3 & -10 & -5 \end{bmatrix}$$
The first element in row 3 is 0.

Multiply row 1 by -2 and add to row 2.
$$\begin{bmatrix} 1 & 2 & 1 & 0 \\ 0 & 1 & 2 & -1 \\ 0 & -3 & -10 & -5 \end{bmatrix}$$
The first element in row 2 is 0.

Multiply row 2 by -2 and add to row 1.
$$\begin{bmatrix} 1 & 0 & -3 & 2 \\ 0 & 1 & 2 & -1 \\ 0 & -3 & -10 & -5 \end{bmatrix}$$
The second element in row 1 is 0.

Multiply row 2 by 3 and add to row 3.
$$\begin{bmatrix} 1 & 0 & -3 & 2 \\ 0 & 1 & 2 & -1 \\ 0 & 0 & -4 & -8 \end{bmatrix}$$
The second element in row 3 is 0.

Multiply row 3 by $-\frac{1}{4}$.
$$\begin{bmatrix} 1 & 0 & -3 & 2 \\ 0 & 1 & 2 & -1 \\ 0 & 0 & 1 & 2 \end{bmatrix}$$
This system could now be solved algebraically.

Multiply row 3 by 3 and add to row 1.
$$\begin{bmatrix} 1 & 0 & 0 & 8 \\ 0 & 1 & 2 & -1 \\ 0 & 0 & 1 & 2 \end{bmatrix}$$

Multiply row 3 by -2 and add to row 2.
$$\begin{bmatrix} 1 & 0 & 0 & 8 \\ 0 & 1 & 0 & -5 \\ 0 & 0 & 1 & 2 \end{bmatrix}$$
This matrix has zeros in both "triangles," so the solution is obvious.

The last augmented matrix represents $x = 8$, $y = -5$, and $z = 2$.
The solution is $(8, -5, 2)$.

Exploratory Exercises

State the row operations you would use so that a zero occurs in the second column of row one.

1. $\begin{bmatrix} -3 & 2 & 1 \\ 4 & 2 & 6 \end{bmatrix}$

2. $\begin{bmatrix} 2 & 4 & 3 \\ -2 & -3 & 1 \end{bmatrix}$

3. $\begin{bmatrix} -6 & -2 & -3 \\ 4 & 3 & 11 \end{bmatrix}$

4. $\begin{bmatrix} 2 & -1 & 3 \\ 4 & 2 & -6 \end{bmatrix}$

5. $\begin{bmatrix} -9 & -1 & 6 \\ 0 & -4 & -8 \end{bmatrix}$

6. $\begin{bmatrix} 1 & -6 & 0 \\ -2 & 4 & -3 \end{bmatrix}$

Written Exercises

Solve each system of equations. Use the augmented matrix method.

1. $6x + y = 9$
$3x + 2y = 0$

2. $-2x - 3y = -11$
$3x + y = -1$

3. $3x + 2y = 5$
$4x - 3y = 1$

4. $2a - 3b = 19$
$3a + 2b = 9$

5. $8x - 2y = 3$
$4x + 12y = -5$

6. $4m + 6n = 7$
$8m - 3n = 4$

7. $x + y + z = -2$
$2x - 3y + z = -11$
$-x + 2y - z = 8$

8. $x + y + z = 6$
$2x - 3y + 4z = 3$
$4x - 8y + 4z = 12$

9. $x + 2y + z = 24$
$2x - 3y + z = -1$
$x - 2y + 2z = 7$

10. $x - 2y - 4z = -3$
$2x + 3y + 7z = 13$
$3x - 2y + 5z = -15$

11. $a + b + c = 0$
$3a - 2b + 5c = 1$
$2a + b + 2c = -1$

12. $2x + y + z = 0$
$3x - 2y - 3z = -21$
$4x + 5y + 3z = -2$

13. $4x + 3y + z = -10$
$x - 12y + 2z = -5$
$x + 18y + z = 4$

14. $2x + 6y + 8z = 5$
$-2x + 9y - 12z = -1$
$4x + 6y - 4z = 3$

15. $8m - 3n - 4p = 6$
$4m + 9n - 2p = -4$
$6m + 12n + 5p = -1$

16. $4x + 2y + 3z = 6$
$2x + 7y - 3z = 0$
$-3x - 9y + 2z = -13$

17. $x + y + z + w = 10$
$2x - y + 3z - w = 5$
$3x + y + z + w = 12$
$-x - y + z + w = 4$

18. $x + y + z + w = 0$
$2x + 3y - z + w = 7$
$3x + 2y - 3z + 2w = 9$
$4x - y - z - w = -5$

4-5   Operations with Matrices

The matrix $\begin{bmatrix} 3 & 1 & 4 \\ 8 & -2 & 5 \end{bmatrix}$ has two rows and three columns.

It is therefore called a 2×3 matrix (read "2 by 3"). This is called the **dimension** of the matrix.

A matrix containing only one row is called a <u>row matrix</u>. A matrix containing only one column is called a <u>column matrix</u>.

> **Two matrices are equal if and only if they have the same dimension and their corresponding elements are equal.**

Definition of Equal Matrices

Example

1   **Find the values of x and y for which the following is true.**

$$\begin{bmatrix} 3x \\ y \end{bmatrix} = \begin{bmatrix} 31 + 4y \\ 6 - 2x \end{bmatrix}$$

Since matrices are equal if and only if the corresponding elements are equal, the following equations may be written.

$$3x = 31 + 4y$$
$$y = 6 - 2x$$

Substitute $6 - 2x$ for y in the first equation. Solve for x and then find y.

$$3x = 31 + 4(6 - 2x)$$
$$3x = 31 + 24 - 8x \qquad\qquad y = 6 - 2x$$
$$11x = 55 \qquad\qquad\qquad y = 6 - 2(5) \quad \textit{Substitute 5 for x.}$$
$$x = 5 \qquad\qquad\qquad\quad y = -4$$

Therefore the matrices are equal if $x = 5$ and $y = -4$.

Multiplication of a matrix by a constant is performed according to the following rule.

> **The product of a matrix and a constant, k, is a matrix of the same dimension with each element multiplied by k.**

Multiplying a Matrix by a Constant

Example

2   **Find $5 \begin{bmatrix} -1 & 3 & 5 \\ 2 & 8 & -4 \end{bmatrix}$.**

Multiply each element of the matrix by 5.

$$5 \begin{bmatrix} -1 & 3 & 5 \\ 2 & 8 & -4 \end{bmatrix} = \begin{bmatrix} 5(-1) & 5(3) & 5(5) \\ 5(2) & 5(8) & 5(-4) \end{bmatrix} = \begin{bmatrix} -5 & 15 & 25 \\ 10 & 40 & -20 \end{bmatrix}$$

Addition of matrices is defined under certain conditions.

> **If A and B are two $m \times n$ matrices, then $A + B$ is an $m \times n$ matrix where each element is the sum of the corresponding elements of A and B.**   *Addition of Matrices*

Addition of matrices is not defined for matrices of different dimensions.

Examples

3 Find $\begin{bmatrix} 5 & 4 \\ 3 & -1 \\ 2 & 7 \end{bmatrix} + \begin{bmatrix} -8 & 3 \\ -2 & 5 \\ 2 & 3 \end{bmatrix}$.

Add the corresponding elements.

$$\begin{bmatrix} 5 & 4 \\ 3 & -1 \\ 2 & 7 \end{bmatrix} + \begin{bmatrix} -8 & 3 \\ -2 & 5 \\ 2 & 3 \end{bmatrix} = \begin{bmatrix} 5 + (-8) & 4 + 3 \\ 3 + (-2) & -1 + 5 \\ 2 + 2 & 7 + 3 \end{bmatrix} = \begin{bmatrix} -3 & 7 \\ 1 & 4 \\ 4 & 10 \end{bmatrix}$$

4 Find $3\begin{bmatrix} 4 & -7 \\ 3 & 8 \end{bmatrix} - 5\begin{bmatrix} -3 & 6 \\ 5 & -2 \end{bmatrix}$.

$$3\begin{bmatrix} 4 & -7 \\ 3 & 8 \end{bmatrix} - 5\begin{bmatrix} -3 & 6 \\ 5 & -2 \end{bmatrix} = \begin{bmatrix} 12 & -21 \\ 9 & 24 \end{bmatrix} - \begin{bmatrix} -15 & 30 \\ 25 & -10 \end{bmatrix} = \begin{bmatrix} 27 & -51 \\ -16 & 34 \end{bmatrix}$$

Under special circumstances, multiplication of matrices can be performed. The number of columns in the first matrix must be the same as the number of rows in the second matrix.

> **The product of an $m \times n$ matrix, A, and an $n \times r$ matrix, B, is the $m \times r$ matrix AB. The ij^{th} element of AB is the sum of the products of the elements of the ith row of A and the jth column of B.**   *Product of Two Matrices*

Example

5 If $A = \begin{bmatrix} 2 & -1 \\ 3 & 4 \end{bmatrix}$ and $B = \begin{bmatrix} 3 & -9 & 2 \\ 5 & 7 & -6 \end{bmatrix}$, find AB.   *Matrix BA is not defined.*

$$AB = \begin{bmatrix} 2(3) + (-1)(5) & 2(-9) + (-1)(7) & (2)(2) + (-1)(-6) \\ 3(3) + 4(5) & 3(-9) + 4(7) & (3)(2) + 4(-6) \end{bmatrix}$$

$$AB = \begin{bmatrix} 6 - 5 & -18 - 7 & 4 + 6 \\ 9 + 20 & -27 + 28 & 6 - 24 \end{bmatrix} = \begin{bmatrix} 1 & -25 & 10 \\ 29 & 1 & -18 \end{bmatrix}$$

Examples

6 If $A = \begin{bmatrix} 2 & 1 & -3 \\ 5 & -4 & 1 \end{bmatrix}$ and $B = \begin{bmatrix} 2 & 5 & 2 \\ 3 & -6 & -3 \end{bmatrix}$, find AB.

The dimension of A is 2×3 and the dimension of B is 2×3. Since the number of columns of A, 3, does not equal the number of rows of B, 2, multiplication of A and B is not defined.

7 Find the dimension of matrix M, if $A_{3 \times 2} \cdot B_{2 \times 4} = M$.

According to the definition of the product of two matrices, the dimension of M would be 3×4.

Exploratory Exercises

Find each product.

1. $3 \begin{bmatrix} 4 & 1 \\ -2 & 3 \end{bmatrix}$

2. $5 \begin{bmatrix} -3 & 4 & 1 \\ 2 & 7 & 0 \end{bmatrix}$

3. $\frac{1}{2}[5 \quad -4 \quad \sqrt{2}]$

4. $-4 \begin{bmatrix} 2 & 5 \\ -3 & 2 \\ 6 & -4 \end{bmatrix}$

5. $\frac{2}{3} \begin{bmatrix} 9 \\ -12 \\ 3 \end{bmatrix}$

6. $\frac{4}{5} \begin{bmatrix} 10 & -3 \\ 20 & 5 \end{bmatrix}$

Perform the indicated operations.

7. $\begin{bmatrix} 2 & -1 \\ 3 & 5 \end{bmatrix} + \begin{bmatrix} 4 & -1 \\ -3 & 2 \end{bmatrix}$

8. $\begin{bmatrix} 4 & 1 \\ 3 & 8 \\ -2 & 9 \end{bmatrix} + \begin{bmatrix} 3 & -7 \\ -4 & 2 \\ 0 & -5 \end{bmatrix}$

9. $[4 \quad 0 \quad 2 \quad -7] - [2 \quad 5 \quad -4 \quad 6]$

10. $\begin{bmatrix} 4 & 1 \\ -9 & 3 \end{bmatrix} - \begin{bmatrix} 8 & -4 \\ 2 & 3 \end{bmatrix}$

Find the dimension of matrix M. The dimensions of matrix A and matrix B are given as subscripts.

11. $A_{3 \times 2} \cdot B_{2 \times 3} = M$

12. $A_{4 \times 1} \cdot B_{1 \times 3} = M$

13. $A_{3 \times 4} \cdot M = B_{3 \times 5}$

14. $A_{3 \times 1} \cdot M = B_{3 \times 4}$

15. $M \cdot A_{2 \times 3} = B_{3 \times 3}$

16. $M \cdot A_{4 \times 2} = B_{4 \times 2}$

Written Exercises

Find the dimension of matrix M. The dimensions of matrix A and matrix B are given as subscripts.

1. $A_{5 \times 1} \cdot B_{1 \times 7} = M$

2. $A_{5 \times 2} \cdot M = B_{5 \times 4}$

3. $M \cdot A_{4 \times 1} = B_{4 \times 1}$

4. $A_{4 \times 3} \cdot B_{3 \times 1} = M$

5. $A_{3 \times 2} \cdot M = B_{3 \times 3}$

6. $M \cdot A_{3 \times 5} = B_{5 \times 5}$

Use matrices A, B, C, and D to find each of the following.

$$A = \begin{bmatrix} 3 & -1 \\ 2 & 4 \end{bmatrix} \qquad B = \begin{bmatrix} 4 & 0 & -3 \\ 7 & -5 & 9 \end{bmatrix} \qquad C = \begin{bmatrix} -6 & 4 \\ -2 & 8 \\ 3 & 0 \end{bmatrix} \qquad D = \begin{bmatrix} -1 & 0 \\ 3 & 7 \end{bmatrix}$$

7. $2A$

8. $3D$

9. $\frac{1}{3}C$

10. $\frac{1}{2}B$

11. $A + D$

12. $D - A$

13. $2A + 3D$

14. $4D - 3A$

15. AB

16. BC

17. CB

18. AA

19. $AB + B$

20. DD

21. AD

22. DA

Find the values of x, y, and z that make the following true.

23. $y\begin{bmatrix} 3 & -4 \\ 2 & x \end{bmatrix} = \begin{bmatrix} 15 & -20 \\ z & 5 \end{bmatrix}$

24. $\begin{bmatrix} 2x \\ y + 1 \end{bmatrix} = \begin{bmatrix} 8 \\ 3 \end{bmatrix}$

25. $4\begin{bmatrix} x & y - 1 \\ 3 & z \end{bmatrix} = \begin{bmatrix} 20 & 8 \\ 6z & x + y \end{bmatrix}$

26. $3\begin{bmatrix} x + y & z \\ y & 0 \end{bmatrix} = \begin{bmatrix} 15 & 3 \\ z - x & 0 \end{bmatrix}$

27. $3\begin{bmatrix} x \\ 3x \end{bmatrix} + 2\begin{bmatrix} 3y \\ 5y - 1 \end{bmatrix} = \begin{bmatrix} -6 \\ 4 \end{bmatrix}$

28. $4\begin{bmatrix} x \\ 2y \end{bmatrix} - 3\begin{bmatrix} 2y \\ 3x \end{bmatrix} = \begin{bmatrix} 26 \\ -53 \end{bmatrix}$

Challenge _____

29. Show that the sum of two matrices is commutative.

30. Show that the product of two matrices is *not* commutative.

mini-review

1. Solve $4(x + 5) = x + 11$.
2. Graph $g(x) = |x + 3|$.
3. Find an equation of the line that passes through $(1, 3)$ and is parallel to the line $y = 4x - 5$.
4. Solve this system: $\quad 6a - b = 4$
$\qquad\qquad\qquad\qquad -2a + 3b = -4$
5. Use Cramer's rule to solve this system: $\quad 5x + 3y = -20$
$\qquad\qquad\qquad\qquad\qquad 2x + y = -8$

Excursions in Algebra _____ **Mathematics Contests**

A number of mathematics contests are available to high school students. One of the best known contests is the Annual High School Mathematics Contest. Another contest is the U.S. Mathematical Olympiad, which is patterned after the International Mathematical Olympiad.

In one contest the following question appeared. The time limit for this question and another paired with it was 11 minutes. Eighty-six percent of the contestants answered the question correctly. Time yourself as you work the problem.

A club found that it could achieve a membership ratio of 2 adults for each minor either by inducting 24 adults or by expelling x minors. Find x.

The elements of an $m \times n$ matrix can be represented using double subscript notation. An $m \times n$ matrix has m rows and n columns.

$$\begin{bmatrix} e_{11} & e_{12} & e_{13} \cdots e_{1n} \\ e_{21} & e_{22} & e_{23} \cdots e_{2n} \\ \cdot & \cdot & \cdot & \cdot \\ \cdot & \cdot & \cdot & \cdot \\ \cdot & \cdot & \cdot & \cdot \\ e_{m1} & e_{m1} & e_{m3} \cdots e_{mn} \end{bmatrix}$$

e_{ij} represents the element in row i and column j.

For example, the element in the third row and fourth column is e_{34}. A matrix can be multiplied by another matrix if the first matrix has the same number of columns as the second matrix has rows. Consider the two matrices, A and B, shown below. The product, AB, will have the same number of rows as A and the same number of columns as B.

$A_{2 \times 3}$ $\qquad\qquad$ $B_{3 \times 4}$ $\qquad\qquad$ $AB_{\ 2 \times 4}$

$$\begin{bmatrix} -3 & 9 & 4 \\ 8 & 5 & -7 \end{bmatrix} \times \begin{bmatrix} 5 & 8 & 1 & 7 \\ 9 & 2 & -6 & -4 \\ -1 & 3 & 0 & 6 \end{bmatrix} = \begin{bmatrix} e_{11} & e_{12} & e_{13} & e_{14} \\ e_{21} & e_{22} & e_{23} & e_{24} \end{bmatrix}$$

Element e_{ij} can be obtained by multiplying row i of matrix A times column j of matrix B. The product of a row and a column is a real number, as shown in the following example.

Example: **Find e_{23} of matrix AB. Use matrices A and B shown above.**

Multiply the second row of A by the third column of B.

$$[8 \quad 5 \quad -7] \cdot \begin{bmatrix} 1 \\ -6 \\ 0 \end{bmatrix} = 8(1) + 5(-6) + (-7)(0)$$

Find the sum of the products of the corresponding elements.

$$= 8 - 30 + 0$$
$$= -22$$

Exercises

Multiply a row of A by a column of B to obtain the indicated element of matrix AB.

1. e_{11} $\qquad$ **2.** e_{21} $\qquad$ **3.** e_{12} $\qquad$ **4.** e_{22} $\qquad$ **5.** e_{14} $\qquad$ **6.** e_{24} $\qquad$ **7.** e_{13}

8. Show the complete product matrix, AB.

4-6 Identities and Inverses

Since $\begin{bmatrix} a & b \\ c & d \end{bmatrix} \cdot \begin{bmatrix} 1 & 0 \\ 0 & 1 \end{bmatrix} = \begin{bmatrix} a & b \\ c & d \end{bmatrix}$ and $\begin{bmatrix} 1 & 0 \\ 0 & 1 \end{bmatrix} \cdot \begin{bmatrix} a & b \\ c & d \end{bmatrix} =$ $\begin{bmatrix} a & b \\ c & d \end{bmatrix}$, then $\begin{bmatrix} 1 & 0 \\ 0 & 1 \end{bmatrix}$ is the **identity matrix** for multiplication of 2×2 matrices. This concept can be extended to the general case.

> **The identity matrix, *I*, for multiplication is a square matrix with a 1 for every element of the principal diagonal and a 0 in all other positions. The principal diagonal extends from upper left to lower right.**

Identity Matrix for Multiplication

Recall that 1 is the multiplicative identity for real numbers. Any nonzero number a has a multiplicative inverse, $\frac{1}{a}$, since $a\left(\frac{1}{a}\right) = \left(\frac{1}{a}\right)a = 1$.

Similarly, $\begin{bmatrix} 1 & 0 \\ 0 & 1 \end{bmatrix}$ is the multiplicative identity for 2×2 matrices, called $I_{2 \times 2}$. We want to find for a matrix A an inverse matrix A^{-1} such that $A \cdot A^{-1} = A^{-1} \cdot A = I$.

Example

1 **Given** $A = \begin{bmatrix} 5 & 3 \\ 2 & 1 \end{bmatrix}$, **find** A^{-1}.

Let $A^{-1} = \begin{bmatrix} x & y \\ z & w \end{bmatrix}$, then $\begin{bmatrix} 5 & 3 \\ 2 & 1 \end{bmatrix} \cdot \begin{bmatrix} x & y \\ z & w \end{bmatrix} = \begin{bmatrix} 1 & 0 \\ 0 & 1 \end{bmatrix}$.

Expanding yields the following equations.
(1) $5x + 3z = 1$
(2) $5y + 3w = 0$
(3) $2x + z = 0$
(4) $2y + w = 1$

Use equations (1) and (3) to find x and z.

$$\begin{array}{l} 5x + 3z = 1 \\ 2x + z = 0 \end{array} \Rightarrow \begin{array}{ll} 5x + 3z = 1 & \\ -6x - 3z = 0 & \text{Add.} \\ \hline -x = 1 & \end{array}$$

$$x = -1$$
$$z = 2$$

Use equations (2) and (4) to find y and w.

$$\begin{array}{l} 5y + 3w = 0 \\ 2y + w = 1 \end{array} \Rightarrow \begin{array}{ll} 5y + 3w = 0 & \\ -6y - 3w = -3 & \text{Add.} \\ \hline -y = -3 & \end{array}$$

$$y = 3$$
$$w = -5$$

Thus, $A^{-1} = \begin{bmatrix} -1 & 3 \\ 2 & -5 \end{bmatrix}$.   **Check:** $\begin{bmatrix} 5 & 3 \\ 2 & 1 \end{bmatrix} \cdot \begin{bmatrix} -1 & 3 \\ 2 & -5 \end{bmatrix} = \begin{bmatrix} 1 & 0 \\ 0 & 1 \end{bmatrix}$

2 **Find the inverse of** $\begin{bmatrix} a & b \\ c & d \end{bmatrix}$.

Let $\begin{bmatrix} x & y \\ z & w \end{bmatrix}$ be the inverse.

$\begin{bmatrix} a & b \\ c & d \end{bmatrix}\begin{bmatrix} x & y \\ z & w \end{bmatrix} = \begin{bmatrix} 1 & 0 \\ 0 & 1 \end{bmatrix}$ ▶ (1) $ax + bz = 1$
(2) $ay + bw = 0$
(3) $cx + dz = 0$
(4) $cy + dw = 1$

Use equations (1) and (3) to find x.

$ax + bz = 1$ ▶ $adx + bdz = d$
$cx + dz = 0$ $bcx + bdz = 0$
$\overline{(ad - bc)x = d}$

$$x = \frac{d}{ad - bc}$$

Now, find z.

$acx + bcz = c$
$acx + adz = 0$
$\overline{(bc - ad)z = c}$

$$z = \frac{c}{bc - ad} \text{ or } \frac{-c}{ad - bc}$$

Use equations (2) and (4) to find y.

$ay + bw = 0$ ▶ $ady + bdw = 0$
$cy + dw = 1$ $bcy + bdw = b$
$\overline{(ad - bc)y = -b}$

$$y = \frac{-b}{ad - bc}$$

Now, find w.

$acy + bcw = 0$
$acy + adw = a$
$\overline{(bc - ad)w = -a}$

$$w = \frac{-a}{bc - ad} \text{ or } \frac{a}{ad - bc}$$

Thus, the inverse of $\begin{bmatrix} a & b \\ c & d \end{bmatrix}$ is $\begin{bmatrix} \dfrac{d}{ad - bc} & \dfrac{-b}{ad - bc} \\ \dfrac{-c}{ad - bc} & \dfrac{a}{ad - bc} \end{bmatrix}$ or $\dfrac{1}{ad - bc}\begin{bmatrix} d & -b \\ -c & a \end{bmatrix}$.

Notice that $ad - bc$ is the value of the determinant of the matrix. Since $\dfrac{1}{ad - bc}$ is not defined when $ad - bc = 0$, the value of the determinant of the matrix must not be zero for the matrix to have an inverse.

Any matrix M, $\begin{bmatrix} a & b \\ c & d \end{bmatrix}$, will have an inverse M^{-1} if and only if $\begin{vmatrix} a & b \\ c & d \end{vmatrix} \neq 0$. Then $M^{-1} = \dfrac{1}{ad - bc}\begin{bmatrix} d & -b \\ -c & a \end{bmatrix}$.

Inverse of a 2 × 2 Matrix

Example

3 For $A = \begin{bmatrix} -3 & 5 \\ 1 & -4 \end{bmatrix}$, find A^{-1} and check.

$\begin{vmatrix} -3 & 5 \\ 1 & -4 \end{vmatrix} = 12 - 5 = 7$ *Since the value is not zero, matrix A has an inverse.*

$A^{-1} = \frac{1}{7}\begin{bmatrix} -4 & -5 \\ -1 & -3 \end{bmatrix}$

Check: $\frac{1}{7}\begin{bmatrix} -4 & -5 \\ -1 & -3 \end{bmatrix} \cdot \begin{bmatrix} -3 & 5 \\ 1 & -4 \end{bmatrix} = \frac{1}{7}\begin{bmatrix} 7 & 0 \\ 0 & 7 \end{bmatrix} = \begin{bmatrix} 1 & 0 \\ 0 & 1 \end{bmatrix}$.

The **transpose** of any matrix is the matrix formed by interchanging the rows and the columns. If the matrix is square, the transpose is square. A matrix with dimension $m \times n$ has a transpose with dimension $n \times m$. The transpose of matrix A is written A^T.

Examples

Find the transpose for each matrix.

4 $M = \begin{bmatrix} 2 & -1 \\ 3 & 5 \end{bmatrix}$

$M^T = \begin{bmatrix} 2 & 3 \\ -1 & 5 \end{bmatrix}$

5 $A = \begin{bmatrix} 5 & 0 & -3 \\ -2 & 1 & 7 \end{bmatrix}$

$A^T = \begin{bmatrix} 5 & -2 \\ 0 & 1 \\ -3 & 7 \end{bmatrix}$

Recall that a minor of an element of a determinant is the determinant obtained by removing the row and column containing the element. Each element of a square matrix also has a minor.

$X = \begin{bmatrix} 5 & 1 & 3 \\ 2 & 3 & -7 \\ 4 & 9 & 3 \end{bmatrix}$.

The minor of 9 in matrix X at the right is $\begin{vmatrix} 5 & 3 \\ 2 & -7 \end{vmatrix}$.

A positive or negative sign is associated with each minor, depending on the position of the element in the matrix. Study the diagram below. Consider an element e_{rc} in row r and column c.

$\begin{bmatrix} + & - & + \\ - & + & - \\ + & - & + \end{bmatrix}$ The sign is positive if $r + c$ is even. The sign is negative if $r + c$ is odd.

The **signed minor** of an element is the minor multiplied by its sign. The element 9 in matrix X occupies a negative position. So, its signed minor is $-\begin{vmatrix} 5 & 3 \\ 2 & -7 \end{vmatrix}$. The value is $-(-41)$ or 41.

Example

6 Find the signed minor of each element in the second row of the matrix. Evaluate each signed minor.

$$\begin{bmatrix} 5 & -2 & 6 \\ -3 & 4 & 5 \\ 8 & 2 & 0 \end{bmatrix}$$

The signed minor of e_{21} is $-\begin{vmatrix} -2 & 6 \\ 2 & 0 \end{vmatrix}$.

$$-\begin{vmatrix} -2 & 6 \\ 2 & 0 \end{vmatrix} = -(0 - 12) = 12$$

The signed minor of e_{22} is $+\begin{vmatrix} 5 & 6 \\ 8 & 0 \end{vmatrix}$.

$$+\begin{vmatrix} 5 & 6 \\ 8 & 0 \end{vmatrix} = 0 - 48 = -48$$

The signed minor of e_{23} is $-\begin{vmatrix} 5 & -2 \\ 8 & 2 \end{vmatrix}$.

$$-\begin{vmatrix} 5 & -2 \\ 8 & 2 \end{vmatrix} = -(10 + 16) = -26$$

Several steps are needed to find the inverse of a 3×3 matrix. An inverse exists if the determinant of the matrix does *not* equal zero.

To find the inverse of a 3×3 matrix with a nonzero determinant, *D*:
1. **Replace each element by the value of its signed minor.**
2. **Find the transpose for the new matrix.**
3. **Multiply this transpose by the reciprocal of the determinant, *D*.**

Finding the Inverse of a 3×3 Matrix

Example

7 Find the inverse of the following matrix.

$$\begin{bmatrix} 2 & 3 & -1 \\ 2 & 4 & 5 \\ 0 & -3 & 7 \end{bmatrix}$$

To be sure an inverse exists, evaluate the determinant, D.

$$D = 2(43) - 3(14) - 1(-6) = 50$$

Replace each element by the value of its signed minor.

$$\begin{bmatrix} 43 & -14 & -6 \\ -18 & 14 & 6 \\ 19 & -12 & 2 \end{bmatrix}$$

Find the transpose for the new matrix.

$$\begin{bmatrix} 43 & -18 & 19 \\ -14 & 14 & -12 \\ -6 & 6 & 2 \end{bmatrix}$$

Multiply by the reciprocal of the determinant, D.

$$\frac{1}{50}\begin{bmatrix} 43 & -18 & 19 \\ -14 & 14 & -12 \\ -6 & 6 & 2 \end{bmatrix}$$

Exploratory Exercises

What is the sign of the element in each of the following positions?

1. e_{31}
2. e_{43}
3. e_{22}
4. e_{11}
5. e_{33}
6. e_{14}

7. Write a 2×2 identity matrix.
8. Write a 3×3 identity matrix.
9. Can a matrix have a transpose and not an inverse?
10. Can a matrix have an inverse and not a transpose?
11. Why can't a non-square matrix have an inverse?

Find the transpose and inverse for each matrix.

12. $\begin{bmatrix} 24 & 4 \\ -3 & 7 \end{bmatrix}$
13. $\begin{bmatrix} 0 & 1 \\ 1 & 0 \end{bmatrix}$
14. $\begin{bmatrix} 4 & -3 \\ 3 & 8 \end{bmatrix}$
15. $\begin{bmatrix} 2 & -5 \\ 6 & 1 \end{bmatrix}$

State the signed minor for each indicated element of the determinant at the right.

$\begin{vmatrix} 1 & 4 & -2 \\ 3 & -2 & 6 \\ 8 & 0 & -6 \end{vmatrix}$

16. e_{21}
17. e_{11}
18. e_{33}
19. e_{12}
20. e_{13}
21. e_{22}

Written Exercises

Find the signed minor for each indicated element of the determinant at the right.

$\begin{vmatrix} 1 & -3 & 2 \\ 5 & -6 & -4 \\ 9 & 3 & 7 \end{vmatrix}$

1. e_{11}
2. e_{32}
3. e_{33}
4. e_{23}
5. e_{13}
6. e_{21}

Evaluate each determinant.

7. $\begin{vmatrix} 2 & 3 \\ 4 & -2 \end{vmatrix}$
8. $\begin{vmatrix} 5 & 4 \\ -3 & 0 \end{vmatrix}$
9. $\begin{vmatrix} 2 & -3 & 1 \\ 4 & 0 & -2 \\ 4 & 6 & -3 \end{vmatrix}$
10. $\begin{vmatrix} 1 & -6 & 5 \\ 3 & 3 & 7 \\ -4 & 1 & -2 \end{vmatrix}$

Find the transpose and the inverse (if one exists) for each matrix.

11. $\begin{bmatrix} 4 & 3 \\ -2 & 8 \end{bmatrix}$
12. $\begin{bmatrix} 2 & 1 & 5 \\ -3 & 4 & 7 \end{bmatrix}$
13. $\begin{bmatrix} -2 & 5 \\ 3 & 1 \end{bmatrix}$

14. $\begin{bmatrix} 9 & 3 \\ 1 & 4 \end{bmatrix}$
15. $[3 \quad 2]$
16. $\begin{bmatrix} 2 & -4 \\ -1 & 2 \end{bmatrix}$

17. $\begin{bmatrix} 3 & 1 & 2 \\ -2 & 0 & 4 \\ 3 & 5 & 2 \end{bmatrix}$
18. $\begin{bmatrix} 1 & 0 & 2 \\ 0 & 4 & 2 \\ 3 & 5 & 0 \end{bmatrix}$
19. $\begin{bmatrix} 1 & 0 & 0 \\ 0 & 1 & 0 \\ 0 & 0 & 1 \end{bmatrix}$

20. $\begin{bmatrix} 1 & -4 & 3 \\ 2 & 3 & -7 \\ 3 & -1 & -4 \end{bmatrix}$
21. $\begin{bmatrix} 4 & -2 & 5 \\ 0 & 6 & 1 \\ 5 & -2 & 3 \end{bmatrix}$
22. $\begin{bmatrix} 7 & 4 & 2 \\ 0 & 2 & 3 \\ 1 & 5 & -2 \end{bmatrix}$

4-7 Using Inverse Matrices to Solve Systems

Consider the following matrices:

$$A = \begin{bmatrix} 5 & 3 \\ 7 & 5 \end{bmatrix} \quad X = \begin{bmatrix} x \\ y \end{bmatrix} \quad C = \begin{bmatrix} -5 \\ -11 \end{bmatrix}$$

If $AX = C$, then $\begin{bmatrix} 5 & 3 \\ 7 & 5 \end{bmatrix} \cdot \begin{bmatrix} x \\ y \end{bmatrix} = \begin{bmatrix} -5 \\ -11 \end{bmatrix}$.

By multiplying the matrices, you can obtain a system of equations.

$$\begin{bmatrix} 5x + 3y \\ 7x + 5y \end{bmatrix} = \begin{bmatrix} -5 \\ -11 \end{bmatrix} \quad \blacktriangleright \quad \begin{array}{l} 5x + 3y = -5 \\ 7x + 5y = -11 \end{array}$$

The equation $\begin{bmatrix} 5 & 3 \\ 7 & 5 \end{bmatrix} \cdot \begin{bmatrix} x \\ y \end{bmatrix} = \begin{bmatrix} -5 \\ -11 \end{bmatrix}$ is called the *matrix equation*

form of the system $\begin{cases} 5x + 3y = -5 \\ 7x + 5y = -11 \end{cases}$.

Examples

1 Write the following system of equations in matrix equation form.

$$5x + 2y = 8$$
$$3x - y = 7$$

The matrix equation is $\begin{bmatrix} 5 & 2 \\ 3 & -1 \end{bmatrix} \cdot \begin{bmatrix} x \\ y \end{bmatrix} = \begin{bmatrix} 8 \\ 7 \end{bmatrix}$.

2 Write the following system of linear equations as a matrix equation.

$$2x + y - z = 9$$
$$x - 3y + 2z = 16$$
$$3x + 2y - z = 5$$

The matrix equation is $\begin{bmatrix} 2 & 1 & -1 \\ 1 & -3 & 2 \\ 3 & 2 & -1 \end{bmatrix} \cdot \begin{bmatrix} x \\ y \\ z \end{bmatrix} = \begin{bmatrix} 9 \\ 16 \\ 5 \end{bmatrix}$.

The matrix equation $\begin{bmatrix} 1 & 0 \\ 0 & 1 \end{bmatrix} \cdot \begin{bmatrix} x \\ y \end{bmatrix} = \begin{bmatrix} a \\ b \end{bmatrix}$ represents the linear system $\begin{cases} x = a \\ y = b \end{cases}$. A logical method of solution would suggest making the coefficient matrix into an identity matrix, thereby making the solution obvious. This can be done by multiplying both sides of the matrix equation by the inverse matrix.

Examples

3 **Solve** $\begin{bmatrix} 5 & 3 \\ 7 & 5 \end{bmatrix} \cdot \begin{bmatrix} x \\ y \end{bmatrix} = \begin{bmatrix} -5 \\ -11 \end{bmatrix}.$

First, find the inverse of $\begin{bmatrix} 5 & 3 \\ 7 & 5 \end{bmatrix}$. The inverse is $\dfrac{1}{4} \begin{bmatrix} 5 & -3 \\ -7 & 5 \end{bmatrix}$.

Multiply both sides of the equation by this inverse.

$$\frac{1}{4} \begin{bmatrix} 5 & -3 \\ -7 & 5 \end{bmatrix} \cdot \begin{bmatrix} 5 & 3 \\ 7 & 5 \end{bmatrix} \cdot \begin{bmatrix} x \\ y \end{bmatrix} = \frac{1}{4} \begin{bmatrix} 5 & -3 \\ -7 & 5 \end{bmatrix} \cdot \begin{bmatrix} -5 \\ -11 \end{bmatrix}$$

$$\frac{1}{4} \begin{bmatrix} 4 & 0 \\ 0 & 4 \end{bmatrix} \cdot \begin{bmatrix} x \\ y \end{bmatrix} = \frac{1}{4} \begin{bmatrix} 8 \\ -20 \end{bmatrix}$$

$$\begin{bmatrix} 1 & 0 \\ 0 & 1 \end{bmatrix} \cdot \begin{bmatrix} x \\ y \end{bmatrix} = \begin{bmatrix} 2 \\ -5 \end{bmatrix}$$

$$\begin{bmatrix} x \\ y \end{bmatrix} = \begin{bmatrix} 2 \\ -5 \end{bmatrix}$$ Thus, the solution is $(2, -5)$.

4 **Solve by using matrices:** $3x - 2y + z = 0$
$\qquad\qquad\qquad\qquad\qquad\; 2x + 3y = 12$
$\qquad\qquad\qquad\qquad\qquad\;\; y + 4z = -18$

The matrix equation for this system is $\begin{bmatrix} 3 & -2 & 1 \\ 2 & 3 & 0 \\ 0 & 1 & 4 \end{bmatrix} \cdot \begin{bmatrix} x \\ y \\ z \end{bmatrix} = \begin{bmatrix} 0 \\ 12 \\ -18 \end{bmatrix}.$

The inverse of $\begin{bmatrix} 3 & -2 & 1 \\ 2 & 3 & 0 \\ 0 & 1 & 4 \end{bmatrix}$ is $\dfrac{1}{54} \begin{bmatrix} 12 & 9 & -3 \\ -8 & 12 & 2 \\ 2 & -3 & 13 \end{bmatrix}.$

Multiply both sides by the inverse.

$$\frac{1}{54} \begin{bmatrix} 12 & 9 & -3 \\ -8 & 12 & 2 \\ 2 & -3 & 13 \end{bmatrix} \begin{bmatrix} 3 & -2 & 1 \\ 2 & 3 & 0 \\ 0 & 1 & 4 \end{bmatrix} \begin{bmatrix} x \\ y \\ z \end{bmatrix} = \frac{1}{54} \begin{bmatrix} 12 & 9 & -3 \\ -8 & 12 & 2 \\ 2 & -3 & 13 \end{bmatrix} \begin{bmatrix} 0 \\ 12 \\ -18 \end{bmatrix}$$

$$\frac{1}{54} \begin{bmatrix} 54 & 0 & 0 \\ 0 & 54 & 0 \\ 0 & 0 & 54 \end{bmatrix} \begin{bmatrix} x \\ y \\ z \end{bmatrix} = \frac{1}{54} \begin{bmatrix} 162 \\ 108 \\ -270 \end{bmatrix}$$

$$\begin{bmatrix} 1 & 0 & 0 \\ 0 & 1 & 0 \\ 0 & 0 & 1 \end{bmatrix} \begin{bmatrix} x \\ y \\ z \end{bmatrix} = \begin{bmatrix} 3 \\ 2 \\ -5 \end{bmatrix}$$

$$\begin{bmatrix} x \\ y \\ z \end{bmatrix} = \begin{bmatrix} 3 \\ 2 \\ -5 \end{bmatrix}$$ The solution is $(3, 2, -5)$.

Exploratory Exercises

State the system of linear equations represented by each matrix equation.

1. $\begin{bmatrix} 3 & 1 \\ 4 & -2 \end{bmatrix} \begin{bmatrix} x \\ y \end{bmatrix} = \begin{bmatrix} 13 \\ 24 \end{bmatrix}$

2. $\begin{bmatrix} 5 & 4 \\ 3 & -5 \end{bmatrix} \begin{bmatrix} x \\ y \end{bmatrix} = \begin{bmatrix} -3 \\ -24 \end{bmatrix}$

3. $\begin{bmatrix} 2 & -11 \\ 1 & 2 \end{bmatrix} \begin{bmatrix} x \\ y \end{bmatrix} = \begin{bmatrix} 3 \\ 9 \end{bmatrix}$

4. $\begin{bmatrix} 2 & 3 \\ 0 & 1 \end{bmatrix} \begin{bmatrix} x \\ y \end{bmatrix} = \begin{bmatrix} -16 \\ 0 \end{bmatrix}$

5. $\begin{bmatrix} 1 & -2 & 0 \\ 3 & 1 & 2 \\ 4 & -3 & 3 \end{bmatrix} \begin{bmatrix} x \\ y \\ z \end{bmatrix} = \begin{bmatrix} -8 \\ 9 \\ 1 \end{bmatrix}$

6. $\begin{bmatrix} 2 & 0 & 5 \\ 1 & 8 & 2 \\ 3 & -5 & 7 \end{bmatrix} \begin{bmatrix} x \\ y \\ z \end{bmatrix} = \begin{bmatrix} 1 \\ 2 \\ 3 \end{bmatrix}$

7. $\begin{bmatrix} 1 & 1 & 2 \\ 3 & -6 & 4 \\ 4 & -5 & -2 \end{bmatrix} \begin{bmatrix} x \\ y \\ z \end{bmatrix} = \begin{bmatrix} 5 \\ -17 \\ 4 \end{bmatrix}$

8. $\begin{bmatrix} 5 & 3 & -2 \\ 2 & 3 & 2 \\ 1 & -2 & -6 \end{bmatrix} \begin{bmatrix} x \\ y \\ z \end{bmatrix} = \begin{bmatrix} 0 \\ -5 \\ 1 \end{bmatrix}$

State a matrix equation for each system of linear equations.

9. $2x - y = 11$
$3x + 2y = -1$

10. $3x - y = 5$
$2x + 3y = 29$

11. $2x + 5y = 1$
$3x + 4y = 12$

12. $x + 7y = 1$
$2x + 5y = -7$

13. $x + y - z = 2$
$2x + 3y - 4z = -1$
$x - 6y + z = 1$

14. $2x + 5y + 6z = -2$
$x - 3y + 2z = 1$
$5x + 2y + 8z = 9$

Written Exercises

1–14. Solve each system of equations in Exploratory Exercises 1-14.

Solve.

15. $\begin{bmatrix} 4 & 8 \\ 2 & -3 \end{bmatrix} \begin{bmatrix} x \\ y \end{bmatrix} = \begin{bmatrix} 7 \\ 0 \end{bmatrix}$

16. $\begin{bmatrix} 5 & 1 \\ 9 & 3 \end{bmatrix} \begin{bmatrix} x \\ y \end{bmatrix} = \begin{bmatrix} 1 \\ 1 \end{bmatrix}$

17. $\begin{bmatrix} 3 & 1 & 1 \\ -6 & 5 & 3 \\ 9 & -2 & -1 \end{bmatrix} \begin{bmatrix} x \\ y \\ z \end{bmatrix} = \begin{bmatrix} -1 \\ -2 \\ 2 \end{bmatrix}$

18. $\begin{bmatrix} 1 & 4 & 2 \\ 2 & -4 & 6 \\ -1 & 8 & -4 \end{bmatrix} \begin{bmatrix} x \\ y \\ z \end{bmatrix} = \begin{bmatrix} 3 \\ 1 \\ 2 \end{bmatrix}$

19. $\begin{bmatrix} 2 & 4 & -1 \\ 6 & 2 & 3 \\ 7 & 2 & -2 \end{bmatrix} \begin{bmatrix} x \\ y \\ z \end{bmatrix} = \begin{bmatrix} -2 \\ 3 \\ 0 \end{bmatrix}$

20. $\begin{bmatrix} 1 & 2 & 2 \\ 2 & -1 & 1 \\ 3 & -2 & 3 \end{bmatrix} \begin{bmatrix} x \\ y \\ z \end{bmatrix} = \begin{bmatrix} 5 \\ 1 \\ 0 \end{bmatrix}$

Solve each system of equations.

21. $4x + 3y = 5$
$8x - 9y = 0$

22. $6a + 2b = 11$
$3a - 8b = 1$

23. $4x - 2y + 3z = -5$
$2x + y + 5z = 2$
$8x - 3y + z = -1$

24. $2m + 2n + 3p = 3$
$5m - 4n + 6p = -3$
$m - 2n = 0$

25. $3a + 6b + 2c = -5$
$6a - 6b + 4c = 5$
$9a - 12b = -5$

26. $x - y + 3z = 4$
$5x + 3y - 6z = 10$
$3x - y + 3z = 9$

For a fund raising project the members of the classes of Mrs. Clef and Mr. Steele sold cookies as shown in the chart below.

	Chocolate Chips	Peanut Creams	Mint Wafers
Mrs. Clef's Class	32 boxes	20 boxes	30 boxes
Mr. Steele's Class	28 boxes	22 boxes	34 boxes

The profit per box is shown below.

Chocolate Chips　$0.40
Peanut Creams　　0.20
Mint Wafers　　　0.50

The profit for each class is found as follows.

　　　　　　　　　　　　　　　　　　　　　　　Profit

Mrs. Clef's class:　$32(0.40) + 20(0.20) + 30(0.50) = 31.80$　◆　$31.80

Mr. Steele's class:　$28(0.40) + 22(0.20) + 34(0.50) = 32.60$　◆　$32.60

Another way to find the profit for each class is to use multiplication of matrices.

Sales per Class × *Profit per Box* = *Profit per Class* ($)

$$\begin{bmatrix} 32 & 20 & 30 \\ 28 & 22 & 34 \end{bmatrix} \times \begin{bmatrix} 0.40 \\ 0.20 \\ 0.50 \end{bmatrix} = \begin{bmatrix} 31.80 \\ 32.60 \end{bmatrix}$$

Exercises

For each exercise, copy the two matrices above (Sales per Class and Profit per Box), changing the appropriate elements. Then multiply to find the profit for each class.

1. The profit on each box of Peanut Creams is 45¢ instead of 20¢.

2. The profit on each type of box is 15¢ more.

3. Boxes of Peanut Creams Sold:
　　Mrs. Clef's Class　　42
　　Mr. Steele's Class　　35

4. Boxes of Chocolate Chips Sold:
　　Mrs. Clef's Class　　25
　　Mr. Steele's Class　　30

4-8 Problem Solving: Using Three Variables

A system of three linear equations in three variables can be used to solve many types of problems.

Example

1 A year ago Kathie Faught inherited $48,000. She invested the total amount, part in stocks, part in bonds, and the remainder in a term account. She earned 6% on the stocks, 8% on the bonds and 12% on the term account. For the year, she earned a total of $4240. She earned three times as much from the term account as she did from the stocks. How much was invested in each?

Explore Let s = amount in stocks. Let b = amount in bonds. Let t = amount in the term account.

Plan Write a system of equations.
(1) $s + b + t = 48,000$
(2) $0.06s + 0.08b + 0.12t = 4240$
(3) $0.12t = 3(0.06s)$

Solve Solve the system.

$$12t = 18s \qquad \textit{Multiply (3) by 100.}$$

$$t = \frac{3}{2}s \qquad \textit{Solve for t in terms of s.}$$

$$s + b + \frac{3}{2}s = 48,000 \qquad \textit{Substitute } \frac{3}{2}s \textit{ for t in (1).}$$

$$\frac{5}{2}s + b = 48,000 \qquad \textit{Simplify.}$$

$$b = 48,000 - \frac{5}{2}s \qquad \textit{Solve for b in terms of s.}$$

$$6s + 8b + 12t = 424,000 \qquad \textit{Multiply (2) by 100.}$$

$$6s + 8\left(48,000 - \frac{5}{2}s\right) + 12\left(\frac{3}{2}s\right) = 424,000 \qquad \textit{Substitute } \frac{3}{2}s \textit{ for t}$$

$$6s + 384,000 - 20 + 18s = 424,000 \qquad \textit{and } 48,000 - \frac{5}{2}s \textit{ for b.}$$

$$4s = 40,000$$

$$s = 10,000$$

$$t = 15,000 \qquad \textit{Find t using } t = \frac{3}{2}s.$$

$$10,000 + b + 15,000 = 48,000 \qquad \textit{Find b using } s + b + t = 48,000.$$

$$b = 23,000 \qquad \textit{Simplify.}$$

Examine Kathie invested $10,000 in stocks, $23,000 in bonds, and $15,000 in a term account.
Find the earnings for stocks, bonds, and the term account.
Stocks: 6% of $10,000 = $ 600
Bonds: 8% of $23,000 = $1840
Term: 12% of $15,000 = $1800
　　　　　　　　Total $4240 ✔

Three times the amount earned in stocks is 3($600) or $1800.

The total is correct.

Example

2 The sum of the digits of a three digit number is 10. When the digits are reversed, the new number formed is 99 less than the original. The hundreds digit equals the sum of the tens digit and the units digit. Find the number.

Explore Let h = the hundreds digit
Let t = the tens digit
Let u = the units digit
The number is $100h + 10t + u$.

Plan Write a system of equations.
(1) $h + t + u = 10$
(2) $100u + 10t + h = (100h + 10t + u) - 99$
(3) $h = t + u$

Solve Solve the system.

$(t + u) + t + u = 10$ *Replace h by t + u in (1).*
$\qquad\quad 2t + 2u = 10$
$\qquad\qquad t + u = 5$ *Recall h = t + u.*
$\qquad\qquad\quad h = 5$ *Find h.*

$\qquad 99h - 99u = 99$ *Simplify (2).*
$\qquad\qquad h - u = 1$

$\qquad\qquad 5 - u = 1$ *Substitute 5 for h in h − u = 1.*
$\qquad\qquad\quad u = 4$ *Find u.*

$\qquad 5 + t + 4 = 10$ *Find t using h + t + u = 10.*
$\qquad\qquad\quad t = 1$ *The number is 514.*

Examine
$$\begin{array}{r} 514 \\ -415 \\ \hline 99 \end{array}$$
When the digits are reversed, the new number is 99 less than the original.

Exploratory Exercises

State an equation using three variables to illustrate each sentence.

1. The sum of Rose's and Bill's ages exceeds twice Maggie's age by 14 years.
2. The sum of the angles of a triangle is 180°.
3. Annie's weight increased by twice Betty's weight is 80 pounds greater than Colleen's weight.
4. The perimeter of a triangle is 42 inches.
5. The sum of two angles of a triangle exceeds the third by 62°.

Written Exercises

Write three equations in three variables for each problem. Then solve.

1. The sum of the digits of a three digit number is 15. The hundreds digit exceeds the sum of the tens digit and the units digit by 1. When the digits are reversed, the new number is 495 less than the original number. Find the number.

2. The sum of the digits of a three digit number is 17. The tens digit is three times the hundreds digit. The sum of the hundreds and the tens digits is one less than the units digit. Find the number.

3. Martha Sheff sells three models of sports cars, the *Streak,* the *Cruiser,* and the *Dreamette.* One week she sold 55 sports cars. The sum of the number of Streaks and Dreamettes sold was 4 times the number of Cruisers sold. The number of Dreamettes sold was two less than the number of Streaks sold. How many of each model were sold?

4. Jim Hunts sells appliances. He had a three-day sale on three models of toasters. On the first day, he sold 8 of model *A,* 3 of model *B,* and 6 of model *C.* On the second day, he sold 6 of *A,* 4 of *B,* and 10 of *C.* On the final day, he sold 10 of *A,* 7 of *B,* and 6 of *C.* His total sales for these three days were $400, $488, and $568, respectively. Find the cost of each model of toaster.

5. The perimeter of a triangle is 45 cm. The two shorter sides differ by 2 cm. The longest is 7 cm less than the sum of the other two. Find the length of each side.

6. The measure of one angle of a triangle is twice the measure of another. The measure of the third angle exceeds four times the measure of the smaller by 12 degrees. Find the measure of each angle.

7. The sum of the ages of Mark, Laurie, and Peggy is 79 years. The sum of Mark's and Peggy's ages exceeds twice Laurie's age by one year. Five years ago, Mark was the same age as Peggy is now. Find their ages now.

8. The sum of the ages of Arturo, Benny, and Carlos is 41 years. Twice Arturo's age exceeds the sum of Benny's and Carlos's age by one year. Five years ago, Benny was 2 years more than twice as old as Carlos. Find their ages now.

9. If Agnes buys six apples, five bananas, and two oranges, the cost will be $2.85. If she buys three apples, seven bananas, and four oranges, the cost will be $2.70. If apples are one cent less than twice as expensive as oranges, what is the cost of each?

10. The Dairy Dream Ice Cream Parlor sells the following sizes of ice cream cones: singles, 49¢; doubles, 79¢; triples, 99¢. One afternoon Kyong Mae sold 52 ice cream cones. She sold two more than twice as many doubles as triples. In all she sold $38.18 in cones. How many of each size did she sell?

11. The sum of the digits of a three digit number is 14. The tens digit exceeds twice the hundreds digit by one. If 3 were added to the number, the units and hundreds digit would be the same. Find the number.

12. In a three digit number, twice the hundreds digit exceeds the sum of the tens and units digit by 3. When the digits are reversed, the new number formed is 198 greater than the original number. The sum of the digits of the new number is 12. Find the original number.

13. The largest angle of a triangle is 15 degrees greater than the smallest. The sum of the two larger angles exceeds twice the smaller by 24°. Find the measure of each angle.

14. The longest side of a triangle is three times the length of the smallest side and the perimeter is 83 inches. Twice the longest side exceeds the sum of the other two sides by 34 inches. Find the lengths of the three sides.

⊟⊉⊘❋⊟⊉⊘❋ *Using Computers* ⊟⊉⊘❋⊟⊉⊘❋

Cramer's Rule

The computer program below can be used to solve a system of three equations in three variables. The DATA lines in the program show the coefficients of the system at the right.

$$x + 2y - z = -7$$
$$2x + 3y + 2z = -3$$
$$x - 2y - 2z = 3$$

```
10   FOR I = 1 TO 3
20   FOR J = 1 TO 4
30   READ A(I,J)
40   NEXT J
50   NEXT I
55   DATA      1,2,-1,-7
56   DATA      2,3,2,-3
57   DATA      1,-2,-2,3
60   FOR K = 0 TO 3
70   FOR J = 1 TO 3
80   FOR I = 1 TO 3
90   IF J = K THEN 120
100  LET B(I,J) = A(I,J)
110  GOTO 130
120  LET B(I,J) = A(I,4)
130  NEXT I
140  NEXT J
150  LET M1 = B(2,2) * B(3,3)
        - B(3,2) * B(2,3)
160  LET M2 = B(2,1) * B(3,3)
        - B(3,1) * B(2,3)
170  LET M3 = B(2,1) * B(3,2)
        - B(3,1) * B(2,2)
180  LET D(K) = B(1,1) * M1 -
        B(1,2) * M2 + B(1,3) * M3
190  NEXT K
200  IF D(0) = 0 THEN 250
210  PRINT "X = ";D(1);"/";D(0);
        " OR ";D(1) / D(0)
220  PRINT "Y = ";D(2);"/";D(0);
        " OR ";D(2) / D(0)
230  PRINT "Z = ";D(3);"/";D(0);
        " OR ";D(3) / D(0)
240  GOTO 260
250  PRINT "NO UNIQUE
        SOLUTION"
260  END
```

In lines 10-50, the computer interprets the data as an augmented matrix.

$$\begin{bmatrix} 1 & 2 & -1 & -7 \\ 2 & 3 & 2 & -3 \\ 1 & -2 & -2 & 3 \end{bmatrix}$$

$A(I, J)$ is the element in row I and column J.

Lines 60-190 form a loop for evaluating four different 3×3 determinants. For each determinant, three columns of the augmented matrix are used. The four values are stored as D(0), D(1), D(2), and D(3).

Line 200 checks whether the determinant of the system, D(0), is 0. If so, the computer will print "NO SOLUTION". Otherwise, the computer will read lines 210-230 and print the solution of the system.

The output for the program is shown below.

```
]RUN
X = 17/17 OR 1
Y = -51/17 OR -3
Z = 34/17 OR 2
```

Exercises

Use the computer program to check your solutions for Written Exercises 9 to 20 on page 116.

Vocabulary

ordered triple (105)
octant (108)
trace (109)
minor (112, 126)
expansion by minors (112)
matrix (117)
augmented matrix (117)

dimension (120)
identity matrix (125)
inverse (126)
transpose (127)
signed minor (128)
matrix equation (130)

Chapter Summary

1. If A, B, and C are real numbers and not all zero, then the graph of $Ax + By + Cz = D$ is a plane. (108)

2. Given the equation of a plane as $Ax + By + Cz = D$, the x-intercept is $\dfrac{D}{A}$, the y-intercept is $\dfrac{D}{B}$, and the z-intercept is $\dfrac{D}{C}$. The trace in the xy-plane is $Ax + By = D$, the trace in the xz-plane is $Ax + Cz = D$, and the trace in the yz-plane is $By + Cz = D$. (109, 110)

3. Expansion by minors can be used to find the value of a third order determinant.
$$\begin{vmatrix} a & b & c \\ d & e & f \\ g & h & i \end{vmatrix} = a\begin{vmatrix} e & f \\ h & i \end{vmatrix} - b\begin{vmatrix} d & f \\ g & i \end{vmatrix} + c\begin{vmatrix} d & e \\ g & h \end{vmatrix} \quad (112)$$

4. Cramer's Rule may be extended to solve a system of three linear equations in three variables. The determinant in each denominator contains the coefficients of the variables. The determinant in each numerator is the same determinant except for the column of the coefficients of the variable to be found. This column is replaced by the column of constants. (113)

5. Consider this system:
$$a_1x + b_1y + c_1z = d_1$$
$$a_2x + b_2y + c_2z = d_2$$
$$a_3x + b_3y + c_3z = d_3$$

A unique solution exists if $\begin{vmatrix} a_1 & b_1 & c_1 \\ a_2 & b_2 & c_2 \\ a_3 & b_3 & c_3 \end{vmatrix} \neq 0.$ (114)

6. Row Operations on Matrices:
   1. Interchange any two rows.
   2. Replace any row with a nonzero multiple of that row.
   3. Replace any row with the sum of that row and another row. (118)

7. Two matrices are equal if and only if they have the same dimension and their corresponding elements are equal. (120)

8. The product of a matrix, A, and a constant, k, is a matrix of the same dimension with each element multiplied by k. (120)

9. If A and B are two $m \times n$ matrices, then $A + B$ is an $m \times n$ matrix where each element is the sum of the corresponding elements of A and B. (121)

10. The product of an $m \times n$ matrix, A, and an $n \times r$ matrix, B, is the $m \times r$ matrix AB. The ij^{th} element of AB is the sum of the products of the ith row of A and the jth column of B. (121)

11. The identity matrix, I, for multiplication is a square matrix with a 1 for every element of the principal diagonal and 0 in all other positions. (125)

12. Any matrix M, $\begin{bmatrix} a & b \\ c & d \end{bmatrix}$, will have an inverse M^{-1} if and only if $\begin{vmatrix} a & b \\ c & d \end{vmatrix} \neq 0$. Then $M^{-1} = \dfrac{1}{ad - bc} \begin{bmatrix} d & -b \\ -c & a \end{bmatrix}$. (126)

13. The transpose of any matrix is the matrix formed by interchanging the rows and the columns. (127)

14. A signed minor of an element of a matrix is the minor of that element multiplied by the sign of the position that element occupies. (128)

15. To find the inverse of a 3×3 matrix with a nonzero determinant, D:
1. Replace each element by the value of its signed minor.
2. Find the transpose for the new matrix.
3. Multiply this transpose by the reciprocal of the determinant, D.
(128)

16. The following matrix equation is equivalent to the linear system.

$$\begin{bmatrix} a & b \\ d & e \end{bmatrix} \cdot \begin{bmatrix} x \\ y \end{bmatrix} = \begin{bmatrix} c \\ f \end{bmatrix} \qquad \begin{array}{c} ax + by = c \\ dx + ey = f \end{array}$$

Inverse matrices can be used to solve systems of linear equations in matrix equation form. (130)

Chapter Review

4–1 Solve each system of equations.

1. $x + y + z = -1$
  $2x + 4y + z = 1$
  $3x - y - z = -15$

2. $x + y + 2z = 3$
  $2x - 2y - 3z = 2$
  $3x - y - 2z = 1$

4–2 In which octant does each point lie?

3. $(8, -2, 3)$　　　**4.** $(4, 2, -1)$　　　**5.** $(-3, -6, -1)$　　　**6.** $(-2, 1, -3)$

Graph each equation. Find the x-, y-, and z-intercepts and the traces in the coordinate plane.

7. $2x - 3y + 4z = 12$

8. $x + y - 2z = 4$

9. $5x - 2y + 3z = 6$

10. $3x + 4y - 7z = 11$

4–3 **Find the value of each determinant.**

11. $\begin{vmatrix} 7 & 1 & 6 \\ 3 & -1 & 4 \\ -2 & 3 & 0 \end{vmatrix}$

12. $\begin{vmatrix} 5 & 8 & -3 \\ -2 & -1 & 4 \\ 3 & 2 & -4 \end{vmatrix}$

Check whether a unique solution exists. If so, solve by using Cramer's Rule.

13. $x + y - z = -5$
$\quad 2x - 2y - 3z = -2$
$\quad 2x + y + 2z = 9$

14. $4x - 2y + z = 4$
$\quad 3x + y - 2z = 1$
$\quad x - 3y + 3z = 3$

4–4 **Solve by the augmented matrix method.**

15. $x + y = 1$
$\quad 2x - 3y = 17$

16. $2x + 3y + 2z = -5$
$\quad 3x - y + 6z = -6$
$\quad x - 4y + 2z = -2$

4–5 **Perform the indicated operations.**

17. $3\begin{bmatrix} 4 & 1 & -2 \\ 2 & -3 & 4 \end{bmatrix}$

18. $\begin{bmatrix} 4 & -2 & -1 \\ 2 & -3 & 5 \end{bmatrix} + \begin{bmatrix} 7 & 0 & -9 \\ -5 & 4 & 1 \end{bmatrix}$

19. $\begin{bmatrix} 3 & -1 \\ 4 & 2 \end{bmatrix}\begin{bmatrix} 3 \\ -1 \end{bmatrix}$

20. $[4 \quad 1 \quad 3]\begin{bmatrix} 3 & -2 \\ -1 & 4 \\ -2 & 0 \end{bmatrix}$

4–6 **21.** Find the inverse of $\begin{bmatrix} 3 & -2 \\ 4 & 1 \end{bmatrix}$.

22. Find the transpose of $\begin{bmatrix} 4 & -3 & 5 \\ 7 & 0 & -2 \end{bmatrix}$.

23. Find the inverse of $\begin{bmatrix} 1 & 3 & 0 \\ 1 & 4 & -2 \\ 2 & 1 & 2 \end{bmatrix}$.

4–7 **Write each system of linear equations in matrix equation form, then solve using matrices.**

24. $2x - 9y = 5$
$\quad x + 2y = 9$

25. $2x + 3y - z = -2$
$\quad 3x + y + z = 9$
$\quad 2x - 4y - 3z = 8$

4–8 **Solve each problem. Use a system of equations in three variables.**

26. The sum of the digits of a three digit number is 18. If the digits are reversed, the new number is the same as the original number. The units digit is one less than twice the tens digit. Find the number.

27. The sum of the ages of Alan, Jim, and Les is 157 years. Twenty years ago, six times Jim's age was equal to seven times Alan's age. In eight years, Les will be three times as old as Alan was 30 years ago. Find their ages now.

Chapter Test

Solve each system of equations.

1. $2x - 3y + z = 7$
   $3x - y + 2z = 1$
   $x + 2y - 3z = -14$

2. $x + 3y + z = 5$
   $2x + y - 5z = 4$
   $3x - y - 4z = -11$

In which octant does each point lie?

3. $(-5, -4, 3)$

4. $(8, 2, -1)$

5. $(6, -4, 2)$

6. Graph the plane represented by $4x - 2y + 3z = 6$.

7. Find the x-, y-, and z-intercepts for $5x - 7y + 8z = 20$.

8. Find the traces in the coordinate planes for $3x - 5y + 6z = 10$.

Use Cramer's Rule to solve each system.

9. $r + s + t = 7$
   $3r - 7s + 2t = 11$
   $-9r + 21s + 3t = -3$

10. $2x + 4y - 3z = -8$
    $x - 2y + 6z = -1$
    $x + 4y - 9z = -8$

Solve each system by the augmented matrix method.

11. $6x - y = -15$
    $5x + 2y = -4$

12. $x + 3y - z = 0$
    $3x + 5y + 2z = 9$
    $2x - y - 8z = 1$

Perform the indicated operations.

13. $\begin{bmatrix} 2 & -4 & 1 \\ 3 & 8 & -2 \end{bmatrix} - 2\begin{bmatrix} 1 & 2 & -4 \\ -2 & 3 & 7 \end{bmatrix}$

14. $\begin{bmatrix} 1 & 2 \\ -4 & 3 \\ 5 & 2 \end{bmatrix}\begin{bmatrix} 5 \\ 4 \end{bmatrix}$

Find the inverse of each matrix.

15. $\begin{bmatrix} 5 & -2 \\ 6 & 3 \end{bmatrix}$

16. $\begin{bmatrix} 1 & 0 & 2 \\ 1 & 2 & -3 \\ 2 & 0 & 3 \end{bmatrix}$

Write each system of linear equations in matrix equation form, then solve using matrices.

17. $x + 8y = -3$
    $2x - 6y = -17$

18. $3x + y + 2z = 4$
    $4x + 2y - z = -4$
    $x - 3y - 4z = 2$

Solve each problem. Use a system of equations in three variables.

19. Maria is 18 pounds heavier than Larisa and 12 pounds heavier then Heather. Their combined weight is 342 pounds. Find each of their weights.

20. The sum of the digits of a three digit number is 12. The units digit is twice the hundreds digit. Three times the sum of the units and the hundreds digit equals the tens digit. Find the number.

Solve each open sentence.

1. $\frac{2}{3}(x + 1) = -\frac{4}{5}$ 2. $|3 + 2r| = 3$

3. $2x \leq 5(x - 3)$ 4. $|b + 1| > 3$

Graph each equation.

5. $2x + y = 4$ 6. $2x - y \geq 4$

7. $y = |x - 2| + 3$

8. $x - y < 4$

9. Given $a = -4$ and $b = 7$, evaluate $3b - a^2$.

10. Is $-\sqrt{9}$ a rational number or an irrational number?

11. Simplify $7x + 18y - 10x + 3y$.

12. Given $f(x) = x^2 - 6x$, find $f\left(\frac{1}{2}\right)$.

13. Find the standard form of the line with x-intercept -3 and y-intercept 8.

14. Find the slope of a line perpendicular to the graph of $y = \frac{4}{5}x + 3$.

15. Graph the system and state its solution. Then state whether the system is consistent and independent, consistent and dependent, or inconsistent.

$$9x + 8y = 8$$
$$\frac{3}{4}x + \frac{2}{3}y = 8$$

Solve each system.

16. $2x - 5y = 1$ 17. $3x - 6y + 2z = -11$
    $3x - 4y = -2$ $x + 5y - 4z = -6$
                        $-2x - 15y + 2z = 9$

Solve each system of inequalities by graphing. For exercise 19, name the vertices of the polygonal region.

18. $y > x$ 19. $y \geq x - 4$
    $y < x - 3$ $y \geq -3x$
                    $y \leq \frac{1}{2}x + \frac{7}{2}$
                    $x \leq 5$

Find the value of each determinant.

20. $\begin{vmatrix} 3 & 1 \\ 4 & 7 \end{vmatrix}$ 21. $\begin{vmatrix} 1 & 2 & -2 \\ 2 & -1 & 1 \\ 3 & -3 & 4 \end{vmatrix}$

22. Solve using row operations on matrices.

$$x + y + z = 6$$
$$2x - 3y + 4z = 3$$
$$4x - 8y + 4z = 12$$

23. Write the equation of a plane with x-intercept 1, y-intercept 3, and z-intercept 2.

24. Simplify $\begin{bmatrix} 3 & -7 \\ 6 & -2 \end{bmatrix} + \begin{bmatrix} -3 & 5 \\ 6 & 0 \end{bmatrix}$.

25. Find the inverse of $\begin{bmatrix} 3 & -4 \\ 2 & -6 \end{bmatrix}$.

26. Solve the matrix equation.

$$\begin{bmatrix} 2 & 4 & -1 \\ 6 & 2 & 3 \\ -7 & 2 & -2 \end{bmatrix} \begin{bmatrix} x \\ y \\ z \end{bmatrix} = \begin{bmatrix} -2 \\ 3 \\ 0 \end{bmatrix}$$

Problem Solving

27. Leon bought a 10-speed bicycle on sale for 75% of its original price. The sale price was $41 less than the original price. Find the original price and the sale price.

28. A certain telephone call costs $1.38 for the first three minutes and $0.34 for each minute thereafter. Write an equation to describe the relationship between the length of the telephone call and the cost of the telephone call.

29. A number decreased by 54 is 32. Find the number.

30. One angle of a triangle is twice another. The third angle exceeds four times the smaller by 12 degrees. Find the size of each.

The test questions on this page deal with ratios, proportions, and percents.

Directions: Choose the one best answer. Write A, B, C, or D.

1. 40% of 10 inches is how many sixths of 2 feet?

    (A) $\frac{1}{3}$ (B) 1   (C) 2   (D) 4

2. For nonzero numbers a, b, c, and d, $\frac{a}{b} = \frac{c}{d}$. Which of the following must be true?

    (A) $\frac{a}{b} = \frac{b}{c}$ (B) $\frac{a+b}{b} = \frac{c+b}{d}$

    (C) $\frac{d}{b} = \frac{c}{a}$ (D) $\frac{b}{c+d} = \frac{d}{a+b}$

3. Find the percent of increase if your salary increases from $250 a week to $300 a week.

    (A) $16\frac{2}{3}\%$ (B) 20%

    (C) 22%   (D) 25%

4. If your grade was 90 and is now 75, find the percent of decrease.

    (A) $16\frac{2}{3}\%$ (B) 18%

    (C) 20%   (D) 22%

5. 9 is 6% of what number?

    (A) 110   (B) 120   (C) 130   (D) 150

6. If $\frac{x}{y} = \frac{5}{6}$, then $18x =$

    (A) $\frac{5}{3}y$ (B) $90y$ (C) $15y$ (D) $\frac{5y}{6}$

7. The price of an item was reduced by 20% then later reduced by 5%. The two reductions were equivalent to the single reduction of

    (A) 15%   (B) 24%   (C) 25%   (D) 75%

8. Ten gallons of gas was added to a tank that had been $\frac{1}{4}$ full. If it is now $\frac{7}{8}$ full, how many gallons does the tank hold?

    (A) 16   (B) 18   (C) 20   (D) 24

9. The ratio of Jean's weight to Jim's weight is 3:4. If Jean gains 30 pounds and Jim does not gain any, the ratio will be 7:8. How much does Jim weigh?

    (A) 60   (B) 170   (C) 180   (D) 240

10. Last year Joe attended $\frac{1}{2}$ the number of sporting events that Jan did. George attended $\frac{1}{3}$ the number that Jan did. If George attended 8 sporting events, how many did Joe attend?

    (A) 1   (B) 4   (C) 8   (D) 12

11. If $\frac{1}{9} = \frac{x}{.45}$, what is the value of x?

    (A) .05   (B) .5   (C) 5   (D) 6

12. In a class of 54 students, 12 are honor students. What part of the class are *not* honor students?

    (A) $\frac{21}{33}$ (B) $\frac{7}{9}$ (C) $\frac{2}{7}$ (D) $\frac{2}{9}$

13. 22% of 440 is 4.4% of

    (A) 96.8   (B) 425.92
    (C) 220   (D) 2200

14. 75% of $10a$ is b. What percent of $2b$ is a?

    (A) $13\frac{1}{3}$ (B) $6\frac{2}{3}$ (C) $7\frac{1}{2}$ (D) 15

15. John spent $\frac{1}{4}$ of his money on a book and then spent $\frac{2}{5}$ of the remaining money for lunch. What fractional part of the original amount is left?

    (A) $\frac{3}{20}$ (B) $\frac{3}{8}$ (C) $\frac{9}{20}$ (D) $\frac{4}{9}$

CHAPTER 5

Polynomials

"Slugger Les" has a batting average of 0.250. What are his chances of getting exactly 2 hits in the next 3 times at bat?

In order to find the answer, it is necessary to expand $(H + N)^3$ by multiplication of binomials. The terms of the binomial expansion can be used to express the different probabilities. Since $(H + N)^3 = H^3 + 3H^2N + 3HN^2 + N^3$ and two hits are desired, the term with H^2 or $3H^2N$ is used. The probability of a hit, $H = 0.25$, and the probability of not getting a hit, $N = 0.75$, are substituted in $3H^2N$. The rounded answer is 0.141.

In this chapter you will learn about addition, subtraction, multiplication, and division of binomials and polynomials.

5-1 Monomials

A **monomial** is an expression that is a number, a variable, or the product of a number and one or more variables. Expressions like -3, y, m^7, $-4x^2$, and $\frac{3}{5}ab^3$ are monomials. Expressions like $2x + 1$, $\frac{3}{x}$, and $\sqrt{x}$ are *not* monomials.

A monomial that contains no variable is called a **constant.** The numerical factor of a monomial is called the **coefficient.** For example, the coefficient of $-4x^2$ is -4. The **degree** of a monomial is the sum of the exponents of its variables. The degree of a nonzero constant is 0. The constant 0 has no degree.

Monomial	Coefficient	Variables	Exponent(s)	Degree
y	1	y	1	1
$-4x^2$	-4	x	2	2
m^7	1	m	7	7
$\frac{3}{5}ab^3$	$\frac{3}{5}$	a and b	1 and 3	4

Recall that $y = 1 \cdot y^1$.

If two monomials are the same or differ only by their coefficients, they are called **like terms.**

Like $6x^3y$ and $17x^3y$ Unlike $3a^2b$ and $4ab^2$

Examples

1 **Simplify $6x^3y - 17x^3y$.**

$6x^3y - 17x^3y = (6 - 17)x^3y$ *Distributive Property*
$\qquad\qquad\quad = -11x^3y$

2 **Simplify $3n^4p^5 - 7n^4p^5 + 8n^4p^5$.**

$3n^4p^5 - 7n^4p^5 + 8n^4p^5 = (3 - 7 + 8)n^4p^5$ *Distributive Property*
$\qquad\qquad\qquad\qquad\quad = 4n^4p^5$

The expression x^3 means $x \cdot x \cdot x$. You can use the meaning of exponents to discover how to multiply powers.

Example

3 **Simplify $(s^2t^3)(s^4t^5)$.**

$(s^2t^3)(s^4t^5) = (s \cdot s \cdot t \cdot t \cdot t)(s \cdot s \cdot s \cdot s \cdot t \cdot t \cdot t \cdot t \cdot t)$
$\qquad\qquad\quad = s \cdot s \cdot s \cdot s \cdot s \cdot s \cdot t \cdot t \cdot t \cdot t \cdot t \cdot t \cdot t \cdot t$
$\qquad\qquad\quad = s^6t^8$ *Notice that $2 + 4 = 6$ and $3 + 5 = 8$. Also, $s^2 \cdot s^4 = s^6$ and $t^3 \cdot t^5 = t^8$.*

Example 3 suggests the following property.

> **For any real number a, and positive integers m and n,**
> $$a^m \cdot a^n = a^{m+n}.$$

Multiplying Powers

Examples

4   **Simplify $(4^2)^3$.**

$$(4^2)^3 = 4^2 \cdot 4^2 \cdot 4^2$$
$$= 4^{2+2+2}$$
$$= 4^6$$

5   **Simplify $(h^4)^5$.**

$$(h^4)^5 = h^4 \cdot h^4 \cdot h^4 \cdot h^4 \cdot h^4$$
$$= h^{4+4+4+4+4}$$
$$= h^{20}$$

Examples 4 and 5 suggest the following property.

> **For any real number a, and positive integers m and n,**
> $$(a^m)^n = a^{mn}.$$

Raising a Power to a Power

Example 6 shows how to raise a power to a power. Example 7 shows one way to find the power of a product.

Examples

6   **Simplify $(r^5)^6$.**

$$(r^5)^6 = r^{5 \cdot 6}$$
$$= r^{30}$$

7   **Simplify $(ab)^4$.**

$$(ab)^4 = a \cdot b \cdot a \cdot b \cdot a \cdot b \cdot a \cdot b$$
$$= a \cdot a \cdot a \cdot a \cdot b \cdot b \cdot b \cdot b$$
$$= a^4 b^4$$

The power of a product is the product of the powers.

> **For any real numbers a, b, and positive integer m,**
> $$(ab)^m = a^m b^m.$$

Finding a Power of a Product

You can simplify many kinds of expressions using the properties of exponents along with the commutative and associative properties.

Examples

8   **Simplify $(4x^2y)(-3x^3y^4)$.**

$$(4x^2y)(-3x^3y^4) = 4 \cdot (-3) \cdot x^2 \cdot x^3 \cdot y \cdot y^4$$
$$= -12 \cdot x^{2+3} \cdot y^{1+4}$$
$$= -12x^5y^5$$

9   **Simplify $(-2r^2s^3)^3$.**

$$(-2r^2s^3)^3 = (-2)^3(r^2)^3(s^3)^3$$
$$= -8 \cdot r^{(2 \cdot 3)} \cdot s^{(3 \cdot 3)}$$
$$= -8r^6s^9$$

Example

10 **Simplify** $\left(\frac{1}{2}x^2\right)^3$.

$$\left(\frac{1}{2}x^2\right)^3 = \frac{1}{2}\cdot x^2 \cdot \frac{1}{2}\cdot x^2 \cdot \frac{1}{2}\cdot x^2$$

$$= \left(\frac{1}{2}\right)^3 (x^2)^3$$

$$= \frac{1}{8}x^6$$

Exploratory Exercises

State whether each expression is a monomial. If it is, name its coefficient.

1. $7x$
2. y^2
3. $3xy + y$
4. $-5ab$
5. $\frac{11xy}{7}$
6. $\sqrt{cd}$
7. $\frac{3}{x}$
8. -8

State the degree of each monomial.

9. $5x^3$
10. $11m$
11. $5x^3y^2z^4$
12. $4xy$
13. 17
14. 0
15. $-24p^4q$
16. $-b$

Written Exercises

Simplify.

1. $4m + 7m + (-3m)$
2. $2x^3 + 3x^3 + (-6x^3)$
3. $4d^3 - d^3 + 2d^3$
4. $4ab^2 - 3ab^2$
5. $27x^2 - 3y^2 + 12x^2$
6. $3x^2y + 4 - 3x^2y$
7. $y^5 \cdot y^7$
8. $n^4 \cdot n^3 \cdot n^2$
9. $2^3 \cdot 2^4$
10. $t^{13} \cdot t^{15} \cdot t^{18}$
11. $8^6 \cdot 8^4 \cdot (8^2)^2$
12. $(m^3)^2$
13. $(y^5)^2$
14. $(2a)^3$
15. $(3a)^4$
16. $(rs^3)(-5r^2s^3)$
17. $(5m^2k^2)(4mk^3)$
18. $(x^2y^2)^2x^3y^3$
19. $(3x^2y)^2(5xy^2z)^4$
20. $(-2ab^2)^3(6a^2)^4$
21. $\left(\frac{3}{5}c^2f\right)\left(\frac{4}{3}cd\right)^2$
22. $\left(-\frac{3}{4}x^2y^3\right)^2\left(\frac{8}{9}xy^4\right)$
23. $(4rs^2t)^2\left(-\frac{1}{2}r^2t\right)^3(3st^3)^4$
24. $(-4a)(a^2)(-a^3) + 3a^2a^4$

25. $-2r(rk^2)(-5rm^2) + (-r^2)(2rk)(4km^2)$
26. $(5a)(6a^2b)(3ab^3) + (4a^2)(3b^3)(2a^2b)$
27. $(5mn^2)(m^3n)(-3p^2) + (8np)(3mp)(m^3n^2)$
28. $(2xy^2)^3 + (2xy^2)^2(6xy^2)$
29. $(3a)(a^2b)^3 + (2a)^2(-a^5b^3)$

Challenge

Solve for a or x.

30. $(k^4)^a = k^{20}$
31. $k^4k^x = k^{10}$
32. $(m^3)^{3a} = m^{36}$
33. $(b^2)^xb^3 = b^{11}$

mini-review

Graph the inequality.

1. $y < 3x - 4$.

Graph each system.

2. $x + y = 8$
   $x - y = 4$
3. $x + y < 5$
   $x + 2y > -4$

Simplify.

4. $(2a)(3a^3b)^2 + (3a)^2(-a^5b^2)$
5. $\dfrac{-4a^3b^2c^3}{16a^2b}$

5-2 Dividing Monomials

If you add exponents when you multiply powers, then it seems reasonable to subtract exponents when you divide powers.

$$\frac{x^5}{x^3} = \frac{x \cdot x \cdot x \cdot x \cdot x}{x \cdot x \cdot x} \qquad \begin{array}{l} \leftarrow 5 \text{ factors} \\ \leftarrow 3 \text{ factors} \end{array}$$

$$= x \cdot x \qquad \leftarrow 2 \text{ or } (5 - 3) \text{ factors}$$

$$= x^{5-3} \text{ or } x^2$$

This and other similar examples suggest the following property.

For any real number a, and integers m and n, $$\frac{a^m}{a^n} = a^{m-n} \text{ if } a \neq 0.$$

Dividing Powers

Why is 0 not an acceptable value for a?

Examples

1 Simplify $\frac{p^9}{p^4}$.

$$\frac{p^9}{p^4} = p^{9-4} \qquad \textit{To divide powers,}$$
$$\textit{subtract the exponents.}$$

$$= p^5$$

2 Simplify $\frac{(2xy)^5}{(x^2y)^2}$.

$$\frac{(2xy)^5}{(x^2y)^2} = \frac{(2)^5(x)^5(y)^5}{(x^2)^2(y)^2}$$

$$= \frac{32x^5y^5}{x^4y^2}$$

$$= 32x^{(5-4)}y^{(5-2)}$$

$$= 32x^1y^3 \text{ or } 32xy^3$$

Study the two ways to simplify $\frac{x^4}{x^4}$ shown below.

$$\frac{x^4}{x^4} = \frac{x \cdot x \cdot x \cdot x}{x \cdot x \cdot x \cdot x} \qquad\qquad \frac{x^4}{x^4} = x^{4-4} \qquad \textit{Use the rule for}$$
$$= 1 \qquad\qquad\qquad\qquad = x^0 \qquad \textit{dividing powers.}$$

Since $\frac{x^4}{x^4}$ cannot have two different values, you can conclude that x^0 is equal to 1. In general, *any* nonzero number raised to the zero power is equal to 1.

For any real number a, except $a = 0$, $$a^0 = 1.$$

Zero Exponent

Let's examine why 0^0 is not defined. Logically 0^0 could stand for 0^{m-m} or $\frac{0^m}{0^m}$. The expression $\frac{0^m}{0^m}$ would imply division by zero since $0^m = 0$. Division by zero is not defined. Thus, 0^0 is not defined.

Study the two ways to simplify $\dfrac{x^3}{x^7}$ shown below. Assume x is a nonzero real number.

$$\dfrac{x^3}{x^7} = \dfrac{x \cdot x \cdot x}{x \cdot x \cdot x \cdot x \cdot x \cdot x \cdot x}$$

$$= \dfrac{1}{x \cdot x \cdot x \cdot x}$$

$$= \dfrac{1}{x^4}$$

$$\dfrac{x^3}{x^7} = x^{3-7}$$

$$= x^{-4}$$

Use the property for dividing powers.

Since $\dfrac{x^3}{x^7}$ cannot have two different values, you can conclude that x^{-4} is equal to $\dfrac{1}{x^4}$. By taking the reciprocal of each expression, you can also conclude that $\dfrac{1}{x^{-4}}$ is equal to x^4. These and many similar examples suggest the following properties.

> **For any real number a, except $a = 0$, and any integer n,**
> $$a^{-n} = \dfrac{1}{a^n} \text{ and } \dfrac{1}{a^{-n}} = a^n.$$

Negative Integer Exponents

To simplify a quotient of monomials, write an equivalent form that uses only positive exponents and no parentheses. Also, each base should appear only once and all fractions should be in simplest form. The rules for positive integral exponents can be extended to include negative exponents.

Examples

3 Simplify $\dfrac{xy^4}{x^6y^4z^{-2}}$.

$$\dfrac{xy^4}{x^6y^4z^{-2}} = \dfrac{x}{x^6} \cdot \dfrac{y^4}{y^4} \cdot \dfrac{1}{z^{-2}}$$

$$= x^{1-6} \cdot y^{4-4} \cdot z^2$$

$$= x^{-5} \cdot y^0 \cdot z^2$$

$$= \dfrac{z^2}{x^5}$$

4 Simplify $\dfrac{(2ab)^2(a^3c)^2}{10b^2c^3}$.

$$\dfrac{(2ab)^2(a^3c)^2}{10b^2c^3} = \dfrac{(4a^2b^2)(a^6c^2)}{10b^2c^3}$$

$$= \dfrac{4}{10}\left(\dfrac{a^8}{1}\right)\left(\dfrac{b^2}{b^2}\right)\left(\dfrac{c^2}{c^3}\right)$$

$$= \dfrac{2}{5}a^8b^0c^{-1}$$

$$= \dfrac{2a^8}{5c}$$

Use the properties for multiplying powers.

Use the property for dividing powers.

The properties of exponents may be used to simplify many different types of expressions.

Examples

5 Simplify $\dfrac{5^{2k}}{5^{2k-3}}$.

$$\dfrac{5^{2k}}{5^{2k-3}} = 5^{2k-(2k-3)}$$
$$= 5^3$$
$$= 125$$

6 Simplify $(a^2 + 2ab + b^2)(a + b)^{-1}$.

$$(a^2 + 2ab + b^2)(a + b)^{-1} = \dfrac{a^2 + 2ab + b^2}{a + b}$$
$$= \dfrac{(a + b)^2}{a + b}$$
$$= a + b$$

Exploratory Exercises

Simplify.

1. $\dfrac{r^4}{r}$

2. $\dfrac{m^{10}}{m^7}$

3. $\dfrac{n^5}{n^5}$

4. $\dfrac{x^6}{x^8}$

5. $\dfrac{5y^{10}}{y^{13}}$

6. $\dfrac{3m^6}{m^6}$

7. 2^{-3}

8. 6^{-2}

9. $\dfrac{1}{y^{-4}}$

10. $\dfrac{1}{m^{-2}}$

11. $\dfrac{6^{-2}}{6^{-4}}$

12. $\dfrac{3^{-3}}{3^{-2}}$

Written Exercises

Simplify.

1. $m^{-8}m^3$

2. $r^{-2}r^4$

3. $\dfrac{12n^8}{4n^3}$

4. $\dfrac{-24s^8}{2s^5}$

5. $\dfrac{6mn^2}{3m}$

6. $\dfrac{an^6}{n^5}$

7. $\dfrac{xy^7}{x^4}$

8. $\dfrac{48a^8}{12a^{11}}$

9. $\dfrac{15b^9}{3b^{12}}$

10. $\dfrac{4x^3}{28x^5}$

11. $\dfrac{12b^4}{60b^6}$

12. $\dfrac{-20y^5}{40y^2}$

13. $\dfrac{2x^{-3}}{6(x^2)^2}$

14. $\dfrac{8(m^{-2})^2}{4m^{-2}}$

15. $\dfrac{16b^6c^5}{4b^4c^2}$

16. $\dfrac{1}{m^0 + n^0}$

17. $\dfrac{4}{x^0 + y^0}$

18. $\dfrac{-15r^5s^2}{5r^5s^{-4}}$

19. $\dfrac{-27w^3t^7}{-3w^3t^{12}}$

20. $\dfrac{-2a^3b^6}{24a^2b^2}$

21. $\dfrac{(3c^2)^2(-d^5)}{-45c^7d^3}$

22. $\dfrac{-66p^3(mp)^{10}}{33(mp)^2}$

23. $\dfrac{20n^5m^9}{20nm^7}$

24. $\dfrac{5^{2x}}{5^{2x+2}}$

25. $\dfrac{3^{xy+5}}{3^{xy}}$

26. $\dfrac{r^{2a}}{r^{2a-3}}$

27. $\dfrac{x^{3a}}{x^{3a-2}}$

28. $\dfrac{16b^6c^5}{(2b^2c)^2}$

29. $\dfrac{(x + 4)^3}{(x + 4)^7}$

30. $\dfrac{3(x - 7)^6}{(x - 7)^{10}}$

31. $\dfrac{2(x + 3)^4}{10(x + 3)^2}$

32. $\dfrac{2(y^2 - 5)^3}{8(y^2 - 5)^5}$

33. $(x^3y^2)^{-1}$

34. $(m^4n^5)^{-2}$

35. $5^{-3}b^3x^4y^{-1}$

36. $\left(\dfrac{2}{3}\right)^{-1}x^3y^0z^{-4}$

37. $\dfrac{2m}{n^{-1}}$

38. $\dfrac{5x}{y^{-1}}$

39. $\dfrac{3m^{-4}}{4^{-1}m^{-2}}$

40. $\dfrac{2^{-1}x^5}{3x^{-2}}$

41. $\dfrac{-15r^5s^8(r^3s^2)}{45r^4s}$

42. $\dfrac{-3w^6t^7}{(-27w^3t^2)(wt)^2}$

43. $\dfrac{(-2r^3)^2(r^{-2})^{-1}}{(r^2)^{-3}}$

44. $\dfrac{(4x^3y)(4^2x^{-1}y)}{4^3xy^2}$

45. $m^{-3}(m^2 + m^4 - m^{-1})$

46. $a^3(a^{-2} + a^{-5} + a)$

47. $(18 - 12x)(9 - 6x)^{-1}$

48. $(2a^2b - 4ab^2)(a - 2b)^{-1}$

49. $(c^2 - c^3)(c^2 - 1)^{-1}$

50. $(a^3 - b^3)(a - b)^{-2}$

Challenge

Show why each statement is, or is not, true.

51. $2^5 + 2^5 = 2^6$

52. $3^5 + 3^5 = 3^6$

53. $3^5 + 3^5 + 3^5 = 3^6$

5-3　Exponents and Scientific Notation

The properties of exponents may be used to simplify and evaluate powers of rational numbers. Study the following examples.

Examples

1 Evaluate $\left(\dfrac{3}{5}\right)^4$.

$$\left(\frac{3}{5}\right)^4 = \frac{3}{5} \cdot \frac{3}{5} \cdot \frac{3}{5} \cdot \frac{3}{5}$$

$$= \frac{3^4}{5^4}$$

$$= \frac{27}{625}$$

2 Evaluate $\left(\dfrac{2}{3}\right)^{-5}$.

$$\left(\frac{2}{3}\right)^{-5} = \left[\left(\frac{2}{3}\right)^{-1}\right]^5$$

Use the power property.

$$= \left(\frac{3}{2}\right)^5 \qquad \left(\frac{2}{3}\right)^{-1} = \frac{1}{\frac{2}{3}} = \frac{3}{2}$$

$$= \frac{3}{2} \cdot \frac{3}{2} \cdot \frac{3}{2} \cdot \frac{3}{2} \cdot \frac{3}{2}$$

$$= \frac{3^5}{2^5} \quad \text{or} \quad \frac{243}{32}$$

These and other similar examples suggest the following properties.

> **For any nonzero real numbers a and b, and integer n,**
> $$\left(\frac{a}{b}\right)^n = \frac{a^n}{b^n} \quad \text{and} \quad \left(\frac{a}{b}\right)^{-n} = \left(\frac{b}{a}\right)^n \quad \text{or} \quad \frac{b^n}{a^n}.$$

Powers of Quotients

Examples

3 Simplify $\left(\dfrac{1}{k}\right)^{-3}$.

$$\left(\frac{1}{k}\right)^{-3} = k^3$$

4 Simplify $\left(\dfrac{3y^2}{2x}\right)^{-2}$.

$$\left(\frac{3y^2}{2x}\right)^{-2} = \frac{(2x)^2}{(3y^2)^2} = \frac{4x^2}{9y^4}$$

An important application of exponents is **scientific notation.** Recall that very large or very small numbers are often written in scientific notation.

> **A number is expressed in scientific notation when it is in the form**
> $$a \times 10^n$$
> **where $1 \le a < 10$ and n is an integer.**

Definition of Scientific Notation

Study these examples.

139,000,000,000
= 1.39 × 100,000,000,000
= 1.39 × 10^{11}　　*The decimal point was moved 11 places to the left and placed after the first nonzero digit.*

0.0000000106
= 1.06 × 0.00000001
= 1.06 × $\dfrac{1}{10^8}$　　*The decimal point was moved 8 places to the right and placed after the first nonzero digit.*
= 1.06 × 10^{-8}

Examples

5 **Multiply 0.543 by 617,000.**

$$0.543 \times 617,000 = (5.43 \times 10^{-1})(6.17 \times 10^5) \quad \text{Express 0.543 and 617,000 in scientific}$$
$$= 5.43 \times 6.17 \times 10^{-1} \times 10^5 \quad \text{notation.}$$
$$= 33.5031 \times 10^4$$
$$= 335,031$$

6 **Divide 0.00086 by 0.031.**

$$\frac{0.00086}{0.031} = \frac{8.6 \times 10^{-4}}{3.1 \times 10^{-2}} \quad \text{Express 0.00086 and 0.031 in scientific notation.}$$
$$= \frac{8.6}{3.1} \times 10^{-4-(-2)}$$
$$\approx 2.8 \times 10^{-2}$$
$$\approx 0.028$$

Exploratory Exercises

Simplify.

1. $\left(\frac{1}{2}\right)^{-2}$ 2. $\left(\frac{1}{4}\right)^4$ 3. $\left(\frac{3}{b}\right)^6$ 4. $\left(\frac{7}{b}\right)^{-5}$ 5. $\left(\frac{1}{10}\right)^{-4}$ 6. $\left(\frac{1}{10}\right)^6$

7. $\left(\frac{1}{5}\right)^3$ 8. $\left(\frac{1}{3}\right)^{-3}$ 9. $\left(\frac{2}{3}\right)^0$ 10. $\left(\frac{3}{5}\right)^{-2}$ 11. $\left(\frac{k}{4}\right)^{-3}$ 12. $\left(\frac{1}{k}\right)^0$

Express each of the following in scientific notation.

13. 0.0021   14. 0.0692   15. 810.4   16. 482.09
17. 9,000,000,000   18. 786,500,000   19. 0.000000721   20. 0.0000528

Express each of the following in decimal notation.

21. 6×10^3 22. 9.8×10^4 23. 5.7×10^{-4} 24. 5.4×10^{-3}
25. 3.21×10^6 26. 7.2×10^{-5} 27. 4.27×10^{-2} 28. 6.7×10^6

Written Exercises

Simplify.

1. $\left(\frac{2}{b}\right)^{-7}$ 2. $\left(\frac{3}{a}\right)^{-5}$ 3. $\left(\frac{x}{k^{-1}}\right)^{-1}$ 4. $\left(\frac{1}{d^{-1}}\right)^{-2}$

5. $\left(\frac{-3y^4}{2y^2}\right)^{-2}$ 6. $\left(\frac{3}{2x^{-2}}\right)^{-1}$ 7. $\left(\frac{3}{2}\right)^{-4}\left(\frac{3}{2}\right)^2$ 8. $\left(\frac{7}{8}\right)^4\left(\frac{7}{8}\right)^{-3}$

9. $\left(\frac{1}{a+b}\right)^{-2}$ 10. $\left(\frac{1}{x^2y^3}\right)^3$ 11. $\left(\frac{2}{d^3f}\right)^5$ 12. $\left(\frac{2}{2s+t}\right)^{-2}$

13. $\left(\frac{1}{5}\right)^{-2} + \left(\frac{1}{4}\right)^{-1}$ 14. $\left(\frac{1}{2}\right)^{-2} + \left(\frac{1}{3}\right)^2$ 15. $\left(\frac{x}{y^{-1}z^2}\right)^{-1}$ 16. $\left(\frac{k}{(k+1)^{-1}}\right)^{-2}$

Evaluate. Express each answer both in scientific and in decimal notation.

17. $(7.2 \times 10^5)(8.1 \times 10^3)$ 18. $(9.5 \times 10^3)^2$ 19. $\dfrac{8 \times 10^{-1}}{16 \times 10^{-2}}$ 20. $\dfrac{15 \times 10^4}{6 \times 10^{-2}}$

21. $(4,300)(0.02)$

22. $(34,000)(0.0056)$

23. $\dfrac{0.000000036}{0.00011}$

24. $\dfrac{5,600,000,000}{60,000}$

25. $\dfrac{(93,000,000)(0.0005)}{0.0015}$

26. $\dfrac{(84,000,000)(0.00004)}{0.0016}$

Solve each problem.

27. Light from a laser travels about 300,000 km per second. How many kilometers can this light travel in a day?

28. In astronomy, a light year is the distance light travels in one year. If light travels about 186,000 miles per second, how many miles are in a light year?

29. Wavelengths of light are measured in Angstrom units. An Angstrom unit is 10^{-8} cm. The wavelength of cadmium's green line is 5085.8 Angstrom units. How many wavelengths of cadmium's green line are there in one meter?

30. The mass of a proton is 1.672×10^{-24} grams. If the mass of the earth's moon is 7.35×10^{22} kilograms, how many times larger is its mass than that of a proton?

31. Metal expands and contracts with changes in temperature. The change in the length of steel per degree Celsius is given by the constant 11×10^{-6}. A steel bridge 200 meters long varies in temperature 70° Celsius. What is the change in the length of the bridge in centimeters?

32. Newton's law of gravitation can be used to compute the mass of the earth in grams. His formula applied is:

$$908 = \frac{6.67 \times 10^{-8} \times 1 \times M}{(6.37 \times 10^{8})^2}$$

If M represents mass, what is the mass of the earth in grams?

Challenge

Simplify.

33. $\left(\dfrac{y^2 + 2y - 15}{y^2 + 3y - 10}\right)\left(\dfrac{y^2 - 9}{y^2 - 9y + 14}\right)^{-1}$

34. $\left(\dfrac{x^3 - y^3}{x^2 + xy + y^2}\right)\left(\dfrac{(x - y)^2}{4x + 4y}\right)^{-1}$

Using Calculators ————— The Exponential Shift Key

Many calculators have an exponential shift key $\boxed{\text{EE} \downarrow}$ This key is used to enter numbers in scientific notation. Enter 7158×10^{19} as follows.

ENTER: 7158 $\boxed{\text{EE} \downarrow}$ 19 $\boxed{=}$ *Any operation key can be used.*

DISPLAY: 7158.   7158. 00   7158. 19   7.158 22

The display 7.158   22 means 7.158×10^{22}. The number 7158×10^{19} expressed in scientific notation is 7.158×10^{22}.

Exercises

Use the exponential shift key to enter each of the following in scientific notation.

1. 80.01×10^7 **2.** -25.38×10^{10} **3.** -0.00891×10^{16} **4.** 6504×10^{-11}

Compute each of the following.

5. $(0.65 \times 10^6) + (2.99 \times 10^7)$ **6.** $(75.21 \times 10^8) - (20.08 \times 10^6)$

7. $(21.5 \times 10^{-4})(150.2 \times 10^{-3})$ **8.** $(0.008 \times 10^{-2}) \div (54.6 \times 10^{-15})$

5-4 Polynomials

A **polynomial** is either a monomial or the sum of monomials. For example, $8x + y$, $3x^2 + 2x + 4$, and $5 - 3y + 5xy^2$ are polynomials. The expression $x^2 + \dfrac{2}{x}$ is *not* a polynomial since $\dfrac{2}{x}$ is not a monomial.

Recall that $5 - 3y + 5xy^2$ can be written as $5 + (-3y) + 5xy^2$.

Each monomial in a polynomial is called a **term** of the polynomial. A polynomial with two unlike terms is called a *binomial*. A polynomial with three unlike terms is called a *trinomial*.

The degree of a polynomial is the degree of the monomial of greatest degree.

Example

1 **Find the degree of $5x^3 + 3x^2y^2 + 4xy^2 + 3x - 2$.**

$5x^3$ has degree 3
$3x^2y^2$ has degree 4
$4xy^2$ has degree 3
$3x$ has degree 1
-2 has degree 0

The terms of polynomials are usually arranged so that the powers of a variable are in ascending or descending order.

The degree of the polynomial is 4.

You can simplify polynomials by adding like terms as in Example 2. Examples 3 and 4 show how to add or subtract polynomials by adding or subtracting like terms.

Examples

2 **Simplify $6x^2y + 3xy^4 + 7y + 5xy^4 - 9x^2y + 8y$.**

$$6x^2y + 3xy^4 + 7y + 5xy^4 - 9x^2y + 8y = (6x^2y - 9x^2y) + (3xy^4 + 5xy^4) + (7y + 8y)$$
$$= (6 - 9)x^2y + (3 + 5)xy^4 + (7 + 8)y$$
$$= -3x^2y + 8xy^4 + 15y$$

3 **Simplify $(7m^2k - 8mk^2 + 19k) + (18mk^2 - 3k)$.**

$$(7m^2k - 8mk^2 + 19k) + (18mk^2 - 3k) = \underbrace{7m^2k}_{} \underbrace{- 8mk^2 + 18mk^2}_{} + \underbrace{19k - 3k}_{}$$
$$= 7m^2k + 10mk^2 + 16k$$

4 **Simplify $(2x^2 - 3xy + 5y^2) - (4x^2 - 3xy - 2y^2)$.**

$$(2x^2 - 3xy + 5y^2) - (4x^2 - 3xy - 2y^2) = \underbrace{2x^2 - 4x^2}_{} \underbrace{- 3xy + 3xy}_{} + \underbrace{5y^2 + 2y^2}_{}$$
$$= -2x^2 + 0xy + 7y^2$$
$$= -2x^2 + 7y^2$$

Use the distributive property to multiply polynomials.

Examples

5 **Find $3x(4xy^3 - 7x^2y - 3y)$.**

$$3x(4xy^3 - 7x^2y - 3y) = 3x \cdot 4xy^3 - 3x \cdot 7x^2y - 3x \cdot 3y$$
$$= 12x^2y^3 - 21x^3y - 9xy$$

6 **Find $(2a - 3b)(3a + 4ab + b)$.**

$(2a - 3b)(3a + 4ab + b)$
$= 2a(3a + 4ab + b) - 3b(3a + 4ab + b)$
$= 2a(3a) + 2a(4ab) + 2a(b) - 3b(3a) - 3b(4ab) - 3b(b)$
$= 6a^2 + 8a^2b + 2ab - 9ab - 12ab^2 - 3b^2$
$= 6a^2 + 8a^2b - 7ab - 12ab^2 - 3b^2$

7 **Find $(x + 4)(x + 11)$.**

$(x + 4)(x + 11) = (x + 4) \cdot x + (x + 4) \cdot 11$
$= (x \cdot x) + (4 \cdot x) + (x \cdot 11) + (4 \cdot 11)$
$= x^2 + 4x + 11x + 44$
$= x^2 + 15x + 44$

The following process can be used to multiply binomials.

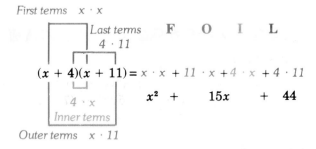

This process is called the **FOIL** method.

The product of two binomials is the sum of the products of

> **F**   the *first* terms,
> **O**   the *outer* terms,
> **I**   the *inner* terms, and
> **L**   the *last* terms.

FOIL Method for Multiplying Binomials

Examples

8 Find $(2x + 3)(x - 5)$.

$$\begin{array}{ccccccccc} & \text{F} & & \text{O} & & \text{I} & & \text{L} \\ (2x + 3)(x - 5) = & 2x \cdot x & + & 2x \cdot (-5) & + & 3 \cdot x & + & 3 \cdot (-5) \end{array}$$
$$\begin{array}{rcccl} = & 2x^2 & - & 10x & + & 3x & - & 15 \\ = & 2x^2 & - & & 7x & & - & 15 \end{array}$$

9 Find $(5x - 3)(2x - 7)$.

$$\begin{array}{ccccccccc} & \text{F} & & \text{O} & & \text{I} & & \text{L} \\ (5x - 3)(2x - 7) = & 5x \cdot 2x & + & 5x \cdot (-7) & + & (-3) \cdot 2x & + & (-3) \cdot (-7) \end{array}$$
$$\begin{array}{rcccl} = & 10x^2 & - & 35x & - & 6x & + & 21 \\ = & 10x^2 & - & & 41x & & + & 21 \end{array}$$

Exploratory Exercises

Find the degree of each polynomial.

1. $3x^2 + 27xy$
2. $x^2 + 2x + 3$
3. $a^8 + a^7b + a^6b^2 - a^2b^6 - ab^7 - b^8$
4. $3x^4y^2 - 5x^2y + 3$
5. $3r^5 - 3r^4 - 7r - 5$
6. $z^5 + 5z^4 + 9z^3 + 9z^2$
7. $m^3 + 2mn^2 + 4n^3$
8. $5xy - 2x^2 - 3y^2$
9. $13xy^7 + 36x^3y^5 - 2x^4y^5 - xy$
10. $16x^4yz + 12x^2y^3z - 24x^3y^2z - 18xy^4z$

Verify the following products. Use the FOIL method.

11. $(a + b)^2 = a^2 + 2ab + b^2$
12. $(a - b)^2 = a^2 - 2ab + b^2$
13. $(a + b)(a - b) = a^2 - b^2$

Written Exercises

Simplify.

1. $(7x - 2y) + (9x + 4y)$
2. $(-12y - 6y^2) + (-7y + 6y^2)$
3. $(-3x + 5y - 10z) + (-6x + 8z - 6y)$
4. $(7t + 4m + a) + (-3a - 7t + m)$
5. $(7m^2 + 9m + 3) - (3m^2 + 8m + 2)$
6. $(3a^2 - 5d + 17) - (-a^2 + 5d - 3)$
7. $(2x^2 + x + 5) + (3x^2 - x - 4)$
8. $(3y^2 + 5y - 7) + (2y^2 - 7y + 10)$
9. $-4(a + 2b) + 7(a + b)$
10. $4(a^2 - b^2) + 3(a^2 + b^2)$
11. $(8r^2 + 5r + 14) - (7r^2 + 6r + 8)$
12. $(4k^2 + 10k - 14) - (3k^2 + 7k - 5)$
13. $(4x + 11) - (3x^2 + 7x - 3)$
14. $(10n^2 - 3nt + 4t^2) - (3n^2 + 5nt)$
15. $(4x^4 + 3x^3 + x - 7) + (3x^4 - 5x^3 + 7x^2 - 3x + 8)$
16. $(8b^5 + 4b^3 + 7b^2 - 15) + (3b^5 + 7b^3 - b + 14)$
17. $(2m^7 + 3m^5 + 2m^3 - 18) - (m^7 + 3m^4 + m^3 + 2m^2)$
18. $-7a^2(a^3 - ab)$
19. $4f(gf^2 - bh)$
20. $3a^3b^2(-2ab^2 + 4a^2b - 7a)$
21. $-5mn^2(-3m^2n + 6m^3n - 3m^4n^4)$
22. $4ax^2(-9a^3x^2 + 8a^2x^3 + 6a^4x^4)$
23. $17b^3d^2(-4b^2d^2 - 11b^3d^3 - 5bd^4)$
24. $m^{-3}(m^2 + m^4 - m^{-1})$
25. $a^3(a^{-2} + a^{-5} + a)$
26. $4a^{-1}b^2(a^2b^{-1} + 3a^3b^{-2} + 4^{-2}ab^{-1})$
27. $y^2x^{-3}(yx^4 + y^{-1}x^3 + y^{-2}x^2)$

28. $(x + 7)(x + 2)$ **29.** $(m - 7)(m + 5)$ **30.** $(m^2 + 5)(m^2 - 4)$

31. $(y^2 + y)(y^2 + 5)$ **32.** $(3y - 8)(2y + 7)$ **33.** $(2x + 7)(3x + 5)$

34. $(2r^2 + 3)(r^2 - 5)$ **35.** $(2x + 3y)(3x - 5y)$ **36.** $(6a - 5)(7a - 9)$

Use the FOIL method to find each product.

37. $(m + 4)^2$ **38.** $(x - 8)^2$ **39.** $(y - 2)^2$

40. $(k + 6)^2$ **41.** $(y - 5)(y + 5)$ **42.** $(2p + q^3)^2$

43. $(x - 3y)^2$ **44.** $(a + 6b)(a - 6b)$ **45.** $(4m - 3n)^2$

46. $(5r - 2)^2$ **47.** $(1 + 4r)^2$ **48.** $(6a + 2)^2$

49. $(4a - 2b)(4a + 2b)$ **50.** $(5x + 12)(5x - 12)$ **51.** $(x^3 - y)(x^3 + y)$

Find each product.

52. $(a - 1)(a^2 - 2a - 1)$ **53.** $(2x - 3)(x^2 - 3x - 8)$ **54.** $(x - y)(x^2 + xy + y^3)$

55. $(a + b)(a^2 - ab + b^2)$ **56.** $(m - 4)(3m^2 + 5m - 4)$ **57.** $(2t - 5)(t^2 + 7t + 8)$

58. $r(r - 2)(r - 3)$ **59.** $p(p + 5)(p - 1)$ **60.** $(b + 1)(b - 2)(b + 3)$

61. $(2x - 3)(x + 1)(3x - 2)$ **62.** $(2a + 1)(a - 2)^2$ **63.** $(a - 2b)^2(2a + 3b)$

64. $(a - b)(a^2 + ab + b^2)$ **65.** $(2k + 3)(k^2 - 7k + 21)$ **66.** $(x^2 + y)(x^2 + xy + y^2)$

67. $(z^2 + r)(z + zr + r^2)$ **68.** $(a - 2)(a^2 + 6a + 9)$ **69.** $(y + 4)(y^2 - 7y + 12)$

Challenge

Find each product.

70. $(x^2 + 2x - 3)(5x^2 + 3x - 7)$ **71.** $(3r^2 + 2d + 1)(5r^2 - 2r - 6)$

72. $(a^2 - ab + b^2)(a^2 + ab + b^2)$ **73.** $(4m^2 - m + 8)(m^3 + 2m^2 + 3m + 4)$

Excursions in Algebra _____ Special Products

You know that $(x - y)(x + y) = x^2 - y^2$. This fact can be used to multiply numbers mentally. Suppose you want to find $36 \cdot 44$. Notice that $36 = 40 - 4$ and $44 = 40 + 4$.

$$36 \cdot 44 = (40 - 4)(40 + 44)$$

Let x = 40 and y = 4 in $(x - y)(x + y) = x^2 - y^2$.

$$= 40^2 - 4^2$$
$$= 1600 - 16$$
$$= 1584$$

Try this method to calculate $27 \cdot 33$, $19 \cdot 21$, and $53 \cdot 67$ mentally.

Here is another method to find some products mentally. You know the following.

$$(x + 1)^2 = x^2 + 2x + 1$$

Suppose you want to find $(101)^2$.

$$(101)^2 = (100)^2 + 2(100) + 1$$

Let x = 100 in the expression $(x + 1)^2 = x^2 + 2x + 1$. *Here 2x + 1 = 201 and 100^2 = 10000 can be calculated mentally.*

$$= 10000 + 200 + 1$$
$$= 10,201$$

Use this method to find the square of a number $(x + 1)$ when you already know the square of x. Can you find 31^2, 13^2, and 201^2 mentally?

Every reproductive cell contains genes in pairs. When genes split and recombine, the combinations may be dominant hybrid or recessive. The following diagram shows the genes splitting to form the three genotypes.

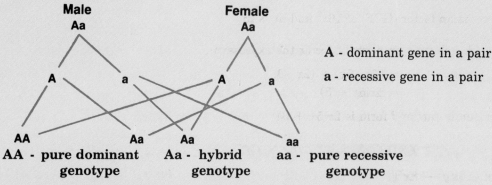

A - dominant gene in a pair

a - recessive gene in a pair

AA - pure dominant genotype   Aa - hybrid genotype   aa - pure recessive genotype

The Hardy-Weinberg Law is used to study dominant and recessive traits in a population. The frequency of the members of a pair of genes for a specific trait in a population is described by the expansion of a binomial expression, $(p\,\mathbf{A} + q\,\mathbf{a})^2$.

$$(p\,\mathbf{A} + q\,\mathbf{a})(p\,\mathbf{A} + q\,\mathbf{a}) = p^2\,\mathbf{AA} + 2pq\,\mathbf{Aa} + q^2\,\mathbf{aa}$$
p is proportion of dominant "A" gene in population.
q is proportion of recessive "a" gene in population.

$p + q = 1$ The sum of the proportions must equal the whole population.

Example: In the original population on a remote island, the recessive blue-eyed gene had a frequency of $1:4$ while the dominant brown-eyed gene had a frequency of $3:4$. After several generations, what would be the expected proportion of genotypes in the population?

Brown-eyed, pure dominant

$$p^2\,\mathbf{AA} = \left(\frac{3}{4}\right)^2 \mathbf{AA}$$
$$= \frac{9}{16}\,\mathbf{AA}$$

9 out of 16

Brown-eyed, blue recessive

$$2pq\,\mathbf{Aa} = 2\left(\frac{3}{4}\right)\left(\frac{1}{4}\right)\mathbf{Aa}$$
$$= \frac{3}{8}\,\mathbf{Aa}$$

6 out of 16

Blue-eyed, pure recessive

$$q^2\,\mathbf{aa} = \left(\frac{1}{4}\right)^2 \mathbf{aa}$$
$$= \frac{1}{16}\,\mathbf{aa}$$

1 out of 16

Exercises   **Solve.**

1. Assume that a certain recessive trait occurs in $\frac{1}{25}$ of the population. That is, $q^2 = \frac{1}{25}$. What proportion of the population is pure dominant genotype and what proportion carries the hybrid genotype?

2. Assume that a hybrid genotype occurs in $\frac{12}{25}$ of the population. That is, $2pq = \frac{12}{25}$. Since $p + q = 1$, or $p = 1 - q$, substitute for p and determine the pure dominant and pure recessive proportions of the population.

5-5 Factoring

Suppose you wish to write $10x^2 + 6x$ in factored form. First find the greatest common factor (GCF) of $10x^2$ and $6x$.

GCF is the greatest factor that a set of terms has in common.

$$10x^2 = 2 \cdot 5 \cdot x \cdot x$$
$$\updownarrow \quad\quad \updownarrow$$
$$6x = 2 \cdot 3 \cdot x$$

The greatest common factor (GCF) of $10x^2$ and $6x$ is $2x$.

Now use the distributive property to factor the expression.

$$10x^2 + 6x = (2x \cdot 5x) + (2x \cdot 3)$$
$$= 2x(5x + 3)$$

$10x^2 + 6x$ written in factored form is $2x(5x + 3)$.

Examples

1 **Factor $12xy^2 - 8x^2y$.**

$$12xy^2 - 8x^2y = (2 \cdot 2 \cdot 3 \cdot x \cdot y \cdot y) - (2 \cdot 2 \cdot 2 \cdot x \cdot x \cdot y)$$
$$= (4xy \cdot 3y) - (4xy \cdot 2x) \quad \text{\textit{4xy is the GCF.}}$$
$$= 4xy(3y - 2x)$$

2 **Factor $2n^2y + 3ny^2 - 5n^2y^2 + 7ny^3$.**

$$2n^2y + 3ny^2 - 5n^2y^2 + 7ny^3$$
$$= (2 \cdot n \cdot n \cdot y) + (3 \cdot n \cdot y \cdot y) - (5 \cdot n \cdot n \cdot y \cdot y) + (7 \cdot n \cdot y \cdot y \cdot y)$$
$$= (ny \cdot 2n) + (ny \cdot 3y) - (ny \cdot 5ny) + (ny \cdot 7y^2) \quad \text{\textit{ny is the GCF.}}$$
$$= ny(2n + 3y - 5ny + 7y^2)$$

You have found products like $(x - 7)(x + 7)$.

$$(x - 7)(x + 7) = x \cdot x + 7 \cdot x - 7 \cdot x - 7 \cdot 7$$
$$= x^2 \quad\quad\quad\quad - 7^2$$
$$= x^2 - 49$$

To factor $x^2 - 49$, reverse the steps.

$$x^2 - 49 = x^2 - 7^2$$
$$= x^2 + 7x - 7x - 7^2$$
$$= x(x + 7) - 7(x + 7)$$
$$= (x - 7)(x + 7)$$

Factoring $x^2 - 49$ shows the following pattern.

For any numbers a and b, $a^2 - b^2 = (a - b)(a + b)$.

Factoring Difference of Two Squares

3 **Factor $16a^2 - 4$.**

$$16a^2 - 4 = 4(4a^2 - 1) \qquad \text{\textit{4 is the GCF.}}$$
$$= 4[(2a)^2 - (1)^2]$$
$$= 4(2a - 1)(2a + 1)$$

4 **Factor $4x^2 - \frac{1}{9}$.**

$$4x^2 - \frac{1}{9} = (2x)^2 - \left(\frac{1}{3}\right)^2$$
$$= \left(2x - \frac{1}{3}\right)\left(2x + \frac{1}{3}\right)$$

You know how to factor the difference of two squares. Can you factor the difference of two cubes? Consider $a^3 - b^3$.

$$a^3 - b^3 = a^3 - a^2b + a^2b - b^3 \qquad \text{\textit{Notice that } } -a^2b + a^2b = 0.$$
$$= a^2(a - b) + b(a^2 - b^2) \qquad \text{\textit{Distributive Property}}$$
$$= a^2(a - b) + b(a - b)(a + b) \qquad \text{\textit{Factor.}}$$
$$= (a - b)[a^2 + b(a + b)] \qquad \text{\textit{Distributive Property}}$$
$$= (a - b)(a^2 + ab + b^2) \qquad \text{\textit{Multiply.}}$$

A similar method can be used to show how to factor the sum of two cubes. That is, $a^3 + b^3 = (a + b)(a^2 - ab + b^2)$.

For any numbers a and b, $$a^3 + b^3 = (a + b)(a^2 - ab + b^2), \text{ and}$$ $$a^3 - b^3 = (a - b)(a^2 + ab + b^2).$$	*Factoring Sum or Difference of Cubes*

5 **Factor $m^3 + 27$.** *This is the sum of cubes. The GCF is 1.*

$$m^3 + 27 = m^3 + 3^3$$
$$= (m + 3)(m^2 - m \cdot 3 + 3^2)$$
$$= (m + 3)(m^2 - 3m + 9)$$

6 **Factor $27y^3 - 8x^3$.** *This is the difference of cubes. The GCF is 1.*

$$27y^3 - 8x^3 = (3y)^3 - (2x)^3$$
$$= (3y - 2x)[(3y)^2 + 3y \cdot 2x + (2x)^2]$$
$$= (3y - 2x)(9y^2 + 6xy + 4x^2)$$

Exploratory Exercises

Factor.

1. $6a + 6b$
2. $8m - 2n$
3. $ab + ac$
4. $y^3 - y^2$
5. $r^2 - 9$
6. $x^2 - 49$
7. $100 - m^2$
8. $y^2 - 81z^2$
9. $2x^2 + 6y + 8b$
10. $x^2 + xy + 3x$
11. $3a^2 + 6a + 9y$
12. $r^4 + r^3s + r^2s^2$
13. $25a^2 - b^2$
14. $36s^2 - 100$
15. $5x^2y - 10xy^2$
16. $-15x^2 - 5x$
17. $8m^2 + 4am + 16my$
18. $7pm + 2p^2 - 14px$
19. $x^3 + 8$
20. $b^3 - 27$
21. $r^3 - 1$

Written Exercises

Factor.

1. $b^2 - 144$
2. $y^3 - 1$
3. $1 + r^3$
4. $m^2 - 121$
5. $8 - x^3$
6. $8a^3 + 1$
7. $3d^2 - 48$
8. $b^3 - 8a^3$
9. $27 + x^3$
10. $2y^3 - 98y$
11. $8 + x^3$
12. $a^3b^3 - 27$
13. $4a^2 - 9$
14. $2r^3 - 16s^3$
15. $9y^2 - 64$
16. $3m^3 + 24p^3$
17. $8b^3 - 27x^3$
18. $9p^2 - 4q^2$
19. $ab - a^4b$
20. $16s^2 - 81r^2$
21. $r^4 - s^4$
22. $r^3s^3 - 8s^3$
23. $64y^3 - 1$
24. $m^6 - 27$
25. $y^6 + 125$
26. $16y^4 - k^4$
27. $1 - 8m^6$
28. $16x^4 - 196y^4$
29. $(a + b)^2 - m^2$
30. $(x - y)^2 - z^2$

Using Calculators _____ The Power Key

Many calculators have a key that can be used to find the powers of a number other than 2. This key, $\boxed{y^x}$, is called the *y to the x power key*. To use this key, first enter *y*, press the key, and then enter *x*.

Example: If $f(x) = 4x^4 - 3x^3$, find $f(2.6)$.

ENTER: 4 $\boxed{\times}$ 2.6 $\boxed{y^x}$ 4 $\boxed{-}$ 3 $\boxed{\times}$ 2.6 $\boxed{y^x}$ 3 $\boxed{=}$

DISPLAY: 4   2.6   4 182.7904 3   2.6   3 130.0624

Exercises

Use the *y to the x* power key to find each of the following.

1. 4.9^5
2. $91.6^3 - 13.5^4$
3. $\left(\dfrac{1}{219}\right)^2 - \left(\dfrac{7}{68}\right)^4$
4. If $f(x) = 3x^3 + 7x^2 - 13x + 5$, find $f(2)$.
5. If $f(x) = 2x^3 + 9x^2 - 3x - 5$, find $f(3.1)$.
6. If $f(x) = 7x^4 - 21x^3 + 16x^2 + 31x - 27$, find $f(2.3)$.
7. If $f(x) = 7.9x^3 - 3.2x^2 + 6.8x + 71.2$, find $f(-2.7)$.
8. If $f(x) = x^5 - 3x^4 + 2x^3 - 1$, find $f\left(1\dfrac{213}{365}\right)$.   *Hint: Store $1\dfrac{213}{365}$ in memory.*

5-6 Factoring Trinomials

When factoring trinomials, first look for the common monomial factors.

$$18x^3 - 48x^2y + 32xy^2 = 2x \cdot 9x^2 - 2x \cdot 24xy + 2x \cdot 16y^2$$
$$= 2x(9x^2 - 24xy + 16y^2)$$

The trinomial $9x^2 - 24xy + 16y^2$ can be factored further. Use one of the following patterns.

> **For any numbers a and b,**
> $$a^2 + 2ab + b^2 = (a + b)^2, \text{ and}$$
> $$a^2 - 2ab + b^2 = (a - b)^2$$

Factoring Perfect Squares

Example

1 **Factor $9x^2 - 24xy + 16y^2$.**

$$9x^2 - 24xy + 16y^2 = (3x)^2 - 2(12xy) + (4y)^2 \qquad \text{\textit{Use the pattern}}$$
$$= (3x)^2 - 2(3x)(4y) + (4y)^2 \qquad a^2 - 2ab + b^2 = (a - b)^2$$
$$= (3x - 4y)^2$$

Thus, $9x^2 - 24xy + 16y^2$ in factored form is $(3x - 4y)^2$.

The factored form of the original trinomial, $18x^3 - 48x^2y + 32xy^2$, is $2x(3x - 4y)^2$.

Many trinomials like $x^2 - 5x + 6$ are *not* perfect squares. They can be factored by reversing the following pattern.

$$(x + r)(x + s) = x \cdot x + x \cdot s + r \cdot x + r \cdot s$$
$$= x^2 + (r + s)x + rs$$

For $x^2 - 5x + 6$, the middle coefficient -5 corresponds to $r + s$. The 6 corresponds to rs. You must find two numbers, r and s, whose sum is -5 and whose product is 6.

Factors of 6	Sum of Factors
1, 6	7
$-1, -6$	-7
2, 3	5
$-2, -3$	-5

The two numbers are -2 and -3.   *Check this using the FOIL method.*

$$x^2 - 5x + 6 = (x - 2)(x - 3)$$

2 Factor $x^2 - 3x - 18$.

Factors of -18	Sum of Factors
$-1, 18$	17
$1, -18$	-17
$-3, 6$	3
$3, -6$	-3
$-2, 9$	7
$2, -9$	-7

The two numbers are 3 and -6. The product of 3 and -6 is -18 and the sum of 3 and -6 is -3.

$$x^2 - 3x - 18 = (x + 3)(x - 6)$$

Consider $2x^2 + 7x + 6$. The coefficient of x^2 is *not* 1. The factors of $2x^2 + 7x + 6$ can be found by reversing the following pattern.

$$\begin{aligned}
(ax + b)(cx + d) &= (ax + b)cx + (ax + b)d \\
&= acx^2 + bcx + adx + bd \\
&= acx^2 + (bc + ad)x + bd
\end{aligned}$$

Notice that the product of the *coefficient* of the x^2 term and the *constant* term is $abcd$. The product of the two coefficients of the x term, bc and ad, is also $abcd$.

For $2x^2 + 7x + 6$, the product of the x^2 *coefficient* and the *constant* is 12.

$$2x^2 + 7x + 6$$

The two coefficients of x must have a sum of 7 and a product of 12. The only possibility is 3 and 4 because $3 + 4 = 7$ and $3 \cdot 4 = 12$.

$$2x^2 + (4x + 3x) + 6 \qquad \text{\textit{Consider the factors of 12 which have a sum of 7.}}$$

$$\begin{aligned}
2x^2 + 7x + 6 &= 2x^2 + (4x + 3x) + 6 \\
&= (2x^2 + 4x) + (3x + 6) \qquad &&\text{\textit{Associative Property}} \\
&= 2x(x + 2) + 3(x + 2) \qquad &&\text{\textit{Distributive Property \ (x + 2 is a common binomial factor.)}} \\
&= (2x + 3)(x + 2) \qquad &&\text{\textit{Distributive Property}}
\end{aligned}$$

The following checklist can be used to help you factor a given polynomial.

1. Check for the greatest common monomial factor.

2. Check for special products.
   a. If there are *two terms,* look for difference of squares, sum of cubes, difference of cubes.
   b. If there are *three terms,* look for perfect squares.

3. Try other factoring methods.
   a. If there are *three terms,* try the trinomial pattern.
   b. If there are *four or more terms,* try grouping.

Examples

4 **Factor $14aby + 14amy + 7b^2y - 7m^2y$.**

$$14aby + 14amy + 7b^2y - 7m^2y = 7y[2ab + 2am + b^2 - m^2] \quad \text{7y is the GCF.}$$
$$= 7y[2a(b + m) + (b - m)(b + m)]$$
$$= 7y(2a + b - m)(b + m)$$

5 **Factor $m^3 - 3m^2a + 3ma^2 - a^3$.**

$$m^3 - 3m^2a + 3ma^2 - a^3 = (m^3 - a^3) - (3m^2a - 3ma^2)$$
$$= (m^2 + ma + a^2)(m - a) - 3ma(m - a)$$
$$= (m^2 + ma + a^2 - 3ma)(m - a)$$
$$= (m^2 - 2ma + a^2)(m - a)$$
$$= (m - a)^2(m - a)$$
$$= (m - a)^3$$

6 **Factor $6a^2 + 27a - 15$.**

$$6a^2 + 27a - 15 = 3(2a^2 + 9a - 5) \quad \text{3 is the GCF.}$$
$$= 3(2a - 1)(a + 5)$$

7 **Factor $r^3 - r^2 - 30r$.**

$$r^3 - r^2 - 30r = r(r^2 - r - 30) \quad \text{r is the GCF.}$$
$$= r(r - 6)(r + 5)$$

8 **Factor $5y^6 - 5y^2$.**

$$5y^6 - 5y^2 = 5y^2(y^4 - 1)$$
$$= 5y^2(y^2 + 1)(y^2 - 1)$$
$$= 5y^2(y^2 + 1)(y + 1)(y - 1)$$

Exploratory Exercises

Complete each factorization.

1. $y(3y - 2) + 4k(3y - 2)$
2. $3x(a - 2b) - 4(a - 2b)$
3. $a(y - b) - c(y - b)$
4. $3m(m - 7) + k(m - 7)$
5. $a(a + b) - 2(a + b)$
6. $r(r - 4) - p(r - 4)$
7. $2x^2(x - 3) + (x - 3)$
8. $b(3b - 2y) - (3b - 2y)$
9. $(x + y)^2 - \frac{1}{4}$
10. $(2a + b)^2 - \frac{1}{16}$
11. $m^2 - (k - 3)^2$
12. $4a^2 - (3b + 1)^2$
13. $k^2(k + 4) - 9(k + 4)$
14. $a^2(x + y) - b^2(x + y)$
15. $(x + y)(x - y) - 4(x - y)$
16. $(a + b) + 3(a - b)(a + b)$

Written Exercises

Factor.

1. $3y^2 + 12yk - 2y - 8k$
2. $3ax - 6bx - 4a + 8b$
3. $ay - ab - cy + cb$
4. $3m^2 - 21m + mk - 7k$
5. $a^2 + ab - 2a - 2b$
6. $r^2 - 4r - rp + 4p$
7. $2x^3 - 6x^2 + x - 3$
8. $3b^2 - 2by - 3b + 2y$
9. $x^2 + 2xy + y^2 - r^2$
10. $4a^2 + 4ab - y^2 + b^2$
11. $m^2 - k^2 + 6k - 9$
12. $4a^2 - 6b - 9b^2 - 1$
13. $k^3 + 4k^2 - 9k - 36$
14. $a^2x - b^2x + a^2y - b^2y$
15. $x^2 - y^2 + 4y - 4x$
16. $a + b + 3a^2 - 3b^2$
17. $a^2 - b^2 + 8b - 16$
18. $a^2 - 4a + 4 - 25x^2$
19. $2ab + 2am - b - m$
20. $y^3 + y^2 - y - 1$
21. $x^2 + 6x + 9 - a^2$
22. $n^2 + 2nx - 1 + x^2$
23. $a^2 - a + \frac{1}{4} - y^2$
24. $\frac{1}{16} - 9x^2 + 12xy - 4y^2$
25. $x^3 + x^2y - xyz - x^2z$
26. $p^2 - q^2 - 2p - 2q$
27. $18x^2 - 21x - 9$
28. $2y^3 - 10y^2 - 72y$
29. $b^2 - y^2 - 2yp - p^2$
30. $a^2 + 2ab + b^2 - 9$
31. $2ab + 2am + b^2 - m^2$
32. $3pq + 3ps + q^2 - s^2$
33. $8a^3 + 27$
34. $16m^3 - 2$
35. $3r - 81r^4$
36. $7p^3 + 56s^3$
37. $x^3 + y^3 - x^2y - xy^2$
38. $t^3 + 125 + 5t^2 + 25t$
39. $x^4 - 13x^2 + 36$
40. $y^4 - 14y^2 + 45$
41. $(r - p)^3 + 4rp(r - p)$
42. $a(a + 1)(a + 2) - 3a(a + 1)$
43. $4ax + 14ay - 10bx - 35by$
44. $r^2 - rt - rt^2 + t^3$
45. $8ax - 6x - 12a + 9$
46. $10x^2 - 14xy - 15x + 21y$

Challenge

Factor.

47. $a^4 - 12a^3b + 24a^2b^2 - 8ab^3$
48. $a^4 - 16a^2 + 3a^3 - 48a$
49. $x^3y - 3x^2y - 6xy + 8y$
50. $m^3n + m^2n - mn^3 - mn^2$
51. $4x^2 + 12xy + 9y^2 - z^2$
52. $m^2 - 8m + 16 - 4a^2 + 28ab - 49b^2$

mini-review

1. Write a linear equation to show the relationship.

   Cost of Long Distance Calls

Minutes	3	4	5
Cost	$1.15	$1.35	$1.55

2. Find the slope of the line perpendicular to $\frac{1}{2}x + \frac{1}{3}y = 2$.

3. Factor $y^2 - 16$.

4. Factor $x^2 - 10x + 21$.

5. Factor $2y^3 - 10y^2 - 72y$.

Some problems may provide more information than that which is actually necessary to solve the problem. Other problems may not provide enough information to solve the problem. And yet other problems may be misleading because they lead to unwarranted assumptions. Consider the following example.

Example: Suppose two trains, each traveling uniformly, start towards each other at the same time along a straight track. One train is traveling at 60 mph and the other at 90 mph. At the start, with the trains 300 miles apart, a bee travels from one train to the other at the rate of 200 mph. When the bee reaches the second train, it immediately returns to the first train. This continues until the trains meet.. How many miles did the bee travel?

A first reaction may be to try to track the path of the bee. Instead, simply calculate the bee's distance by multiplying its rate of speed by the time it traveled.

To find the time it traveled, calculate the time it took the trains to meet.

Let t = the number of hours the trains traveled before meeting.
$$60t + 90t = 300$$
$$150t = 300$$
$$t = 2$$

The bee was traveling 200 mph. In two hours, the bee traveled a total distance of 400 miles.

Exercises

Solve each problem.

1. Samuel went into a hardware store and asked the clerk how much 1 cost. The clerk said, "25¢." Then he asked how much 10 cost, and the clerk said, "50¢." "Good," he replied, "I'll take 1025," and then paid the clerk $1.00. What did he buy?

2. Kandy and Mark are both chess players. They have completed 7 games. Each has won the same number of games and there were no ties. How did this happen?

3. How much will it cost to cut a log into eight equal pieces, if cutting it into four equal pieces costs 90¢?

4. Find the digit that each letter represents so that the following equation is true.
$$(HE)^2 = SHE$$

5-8 Dividing Polynomials

You can use the properties of exponents to divide a monomial by a monomial. You also use these properties to divide a polynomial by a monomial.

Examples

1 **Divide $16x^4$ by $8x^3$.**

$$16x^4 \div 8x^3 = \frac{16x^4}{8x^3} \qquad \textit{The denominator cannot have a value of 0. } (x \neq 0)$$

$$= \frac{16}{8} \cdot x^{4-3}$$

$$= 2x$$

2 **Simplify $-49r^3s^5(7rs^2)^{-1}$**

$$-49r^3s^5(7rs^2)^{-1} = -49r^3s^5\left(\frac{1}{7rs^2}\right)$$

$$= \frac{-49r^3s^5}{7rs^2} \qquad r \neq 0, s \neq 0$$

$$= -7r^2s^3$$

3 **Simplify $\dfrac{36m^4y^4 - 18m^3y}{6m^2y}$.** $\qquad m \neq 0, y \neq 0$

$$\frac{36m^4y^4 - 18m^3y}{6m^2y} = \frac{36m^4y^4}{6m^2y} - \frac{18m^3y}{6m^2y}$$

$$= \frac{36}{6} \cdot m^{4-2}y^{4-1} - \frac{18}{6} \cdot m^{3-2}y^{1-1}$$

$$= 6m^2y^3 - 3m \qquad y^{1-1} = y^0 \text{ or } 1.$$

$$= 3m(2my^3 - 1)$$

Dividing a polynomial by a polynomial is similar to long division. The example at the right reviews long division with numbers.

You use a similar process to divide polynomials. Remember, you must have like terms to add or subtract.

Divide 883 by 21.

$$\begin{array}{r} 42 \\ 21\overline{)883} \\ \underline{840} \quad \textit{Subtract } 40 \cdot 21. \\ 43 \\ \underline{42} \quad \textit{Subtract } 2 \cdot 21. \\ 1 \quad \textit{Stop when remainder is less than 21.} \end{array}$$

$$\frac{883}{21} = 42\frac{1}{21}$$

Examples

4 **Divide $8y^2 + 8y + 3$ by $2y + 1$.**

$$
\begin{array}{r}
4y + 2 \\
2y + 1 \overline{)\, 8y^2 + 8y + 3} \\
\underline{8y^2 + 4y} \\
4y + 3 \\
\underline{4y + 2} \\
1
\end{array}
$$

Subtract $4y(2y + 1)$.

Subtract $2(2y + 1)$.

Stop when degree of remainder is less than degree of $2y + 1$.

Before dividing one polynomial by another, it is helpful to arrange the terms in descending powers of the variable.

$$\frac{8y^2 + 8y + 3}{2y + 1} = 4y + 2 + \frac{1}{2y + 1} \qquad y \neq -\frac{1}{2}$$

5 **Simplify $(x^3 + 5x^2 + 5x + 16)(x^2 + 3)^{-1}$**

$$(x^3 + 5x^2 + 5x + 16)(x^2 + 3)^{-1} = (x^3 + 5x^2 + 5x + 16) \div (x^2 + 3)$$

$$
\begin{array}{r}
x + 5 \\
x^2 + 3 \overline{)\, x^3 + 5x^2 + 5x + 16} \\
\underline{x^3 + 3x} \\
5x^2 + 2x + 16 \\
\underline{5x^2 + 15} \\
2x + 1
\end{array}
$$

$$(x^3 + 5x^2 + 5x + 16)(x^2 + 3)^{-1} = x + 5 + \frac{2x + 1}{x^2 + 3}$$

If the remainder upon division is zero, then the divisor is a factor of the polynomial.

Example

6 **Show that $a + 2$ is a factor of $a^3 + 3a^2 - 2a - 8$.**

$$
\begin{array}{r}
a^2 + a - 4 \\
a + 2 \overline{)\, a^3 + 3a^2 - 2a - 8} \\
\underline{a^3 + 2a^2} \\
a^2 - 2a \\
\underline{a^2 + 2a} \\
-4a - 8 \\
\underline{-4a - 8} \\
0
\end{array}
$$

Thus, $a^3 + 3a^2 - 2a - 8 = (a + 2)(a^2 + a - 4)$.

Exploratory Exercises

Use division to simplify each expression.

1. $\dfrac{7^4}{7^5}$

2. $\dfrac{12^6}{12^4}$

3. $\dfrac{g^6}{g^3}$

4. $\dfrac{h^{16}}{h^2}$

5. $\dfrac{a^{10}}{a^{10}}$

6. $\dfrac{14r^{11}}{2r^{10}}$

7. $\dfrac{8a^2b^4}{2b}$

8. $\dfrac{3^3r^3s^3}{9r^2}$

9. $36x^3y^5(12x^2y^2)^{-1}$

10. $\dfrac{6xy^2 - 3xy + 2x^2y}{xy}$

11. $\dfrac{a^3b^2 - a^2b + 2a}{-ab}$

12. $\dfrac{6r^2s^2 + 3rs^2 - 9r^2s}{3rs}$

Written Exercises

Simplify.

1. $\dfrac{6p^4q^2 + 4p^2q + 5pq^3}{pq}$

2. $\dfrac{12mz^3 + 9m^2z^2 - 15m^2z}{-3mz}$

3. $\dfrac{28k^3py - 42kp^2y^2 + 56kp^3y^2}{14kpy}$

4. $\dfrac{18k^3lm^2 + 27k^2lm + 45k^2l^2m^2}{9klm}$

5. $\dfrac{15r^2s + 23rs^2 + 6s^3}{3rs}$

6. $\dfrac{4a^2b^3c^4 + 13ab - 12a^4b^2c}{2abc}$

7. $(x^2 - 12x - 45) \div (x + 3)$

8. $(a^2 + 7a - 60) \div (a + 12)$

9. $(6y^2 + 7y - 3) \div (2y + 3)$

10. $(15b^2 + 14b - 8) \div (5b - 2)$

11. $(8a^2 + 34a + 19) \div (2a + 7)$

12. $(20b^2 - 17b - 61) \div (5b + 7)$

13. $(28y^2 + 23y - 12) \div (7y - 3)$

14. $(80x^2 + 6x - 4) \div (10x - 3)$

15. $(a^2 - 5a - 84)(a + 7)^{-1}$

16. $(x^2 + 20x + 91)(x + 7)^{-1}$

17. $(a^2 - 5ab + 6b^2) \div (a - 3b)$

18. $(12x^2 - 4xy - y^2) \div (2x - y)$

19. $(6z^2 + 2z - 28) \div (3z + 7)$

20. $(3b^2 - 7ba - 20a^2) \div (3b + 5a)$

21. $(a^2 + 4a - 16) \div (6 - a)$

22. $(y^2 + y - 8) \div (3 - y)$

23. $(8x^2 - 4x + 11)(x + 5)^{-1}$

24. $(126k^2 + 113k - 26)(14k - 3)^{-1}$

25. $(56m^2 - 113m + 59) \div (8m - 7)$

26. $(20r^2 + 7r - 10) \div (5r - 2)$

27. $(6y^3 + 11y^2 - 4y - 4)(3y - 2)^{-1}$

28. $(8x^3 - 22x^2 - 5x + 12)(4x + 3)^{-1}$

29. $(6a^3 + 5a^2 + 9) \div (2a + 3)$

30. $(8b^2 - 4b + 1) \div (2b - 1)$

31. $(m^3 - 1) \div (m - 1)$

32. $(a^3 - 8) \div (a - 2)$

33. $(y^3 - 9y^2 + 27y - 28) \div (y - 3)$

34. $(x^3 + 6x^2 + 12x + 12) \div (x + 2)$

35. $(6a^3 - 5a^2 - 12a - 4) \div (3a + 2)$

36. $(2p^3 + 7p^2 - 29p + 29) \div (2p - 3)$

37. $(m^3 - 7m + 3m^2 - 21)(m^2 - 7)^{-1}$

38. $(48p^3 - 15 + 6p^2 - 40p)(6p^2 - 5)^{-1}$

39. $(x^3 + 4x - 4) \div (x + 2)$

40. $(2t^3 - 2t - 3) \div (t - 1)$

41. $(x^4 + 4) \div (x^2 - 2x + 2)$

42. $(y^4 + 4y^3 + 10y^2 + 12y + 9) \div (y^2 + 2y + 3)$

43. $(a^4 - 3a^2 + 1) \div (a^2 + a - 1)$

44. $(x^4 - 4x^2 + 12x - 9) \div (x^2 + 2x - 3)$

45. Is $3y - 2$ a factor of $6y^3 - y^2 - 5y + 2$? Write *yes* or *no*.

46. Is $4x + 5$ a factor of $4x^3 + x^2 + 10$? Write *yes* or *no*.

47. One factor of $a^3 - 2a^2 - a + 2$ is $a - 2$. Find the other factors.

48. One factor of $2m^3 - 11m^2 + 18m - 9$ is $m - 3$. Find the other factors.

49. Find the remainder when dividing $x^2 + 3x + 5$ by $x - 2$.
    If $f(x) = x^2 + 3x + 5$, find $f(2)$.
    Compare the answers.

50. Find the remainder when dividing $x^3 - 5x^2 + 6x - 4$ by $x - 3$.
    If $f(x) = x^3 - 5x^2 + 6x - 4$, find $f(3)$.
    Compare the answers.

5-9   Synthetic Division

There is another method for dividing a polynomial by a binomial of the form $x - r$, called **synthetic division**. To divide the polynomial $3x^3 - 4x^2 - 3x - 2$ by $x - 3$, follow the steps below.

Step 1   Write the terms of the polynomial in descending order. Then write the coefficients as shown.

$$3 \quad -4 \quad -3 \quad -2$$

Step 2   Write the constant, r, of the divisor $x - r$ to the left. For the divisor $x - 3$, r is 3.

$$\underline{3} \ | \ 3 \quad -4 \quad -3 \quad -2$$

Step 3   Bring down the first coefficient.

$$
\begin{array}{r|rrrr}
\underline{3} & 3 & -4 & -3 & -2 \\
\hline
& 3 & & &
\end{array}
$$

Step 4   Multiply the first coefficient by r. Then write the product under the second coefficient.

$$
\begin{array}{r|rrrr}
\underline{3} & 3 & -4 & -3 & -2 \\
& & 9 & & \\
\hline
& 3 & & &
\end{array}
$$

Step 5   Add. $-4 + 9 = 5$

$$
\begin{array}{r|rrrr}
\underline{3} & 3 & -4 & -3 & -2 \\
& & 9 & & \\
\hline
& 3 & 5 & &
\end{array}
$$

Step 6   Multiply the sum, 5, by r. Write the product under the next coefficient.

$$
\begin{array}{r|rrrr}
\underline{3} & 3 & -4 & -3 & -2 \\
& & 9 & 15 & \\
\hline
& 3 & 5 & &
\end{array}
$$

Step 7   Add. $-3 + 15 = 12$

$$
\begin{array}{r|rrrr}
\underline{3} & 3 & -4 & -3 & -2 \\
& & 9 & 15 & \\
\hline
& 3 & 5 & 12 &
\end{array}
$$

Step 8   Again multiply the sum, 12, by r. Write the product under the next coefficient.

$$
\begin{array}{r|rrrr}
\underline{3} & 3 & -4 & -3 & -2 \\
& & 9 & 15 & 36 \\
\hline
& 3 & 5 & 12 &
\end{array}
$$

Step 9   Add. $-2 + 36 = 34$

$$
\begin{array}{r|rrrr}
\underline{3} & 3 & -4 & -3 & -2 \\
& & 9 & 15 & 36 \\
\hline
& 3 & 5 & 12 & 34
\end{array}
$$

Step 10   Write the result. $3x^2 + 5x + 12 + \dfrac{34}{x - 3}$

Compare this process to the long division process.

$$
\begin{array}{r|rrrr}
\underline{3} & 3 & -4 & -3 & -2 \\
& & 9 & 15 & 36 \\
\hline
& 3 & 5 & 12 & 34
\end{array}
$$

$$
\require{enclose}
\begin{array}{r}
3x^2 + 5x + 12 \\
x - 3 \enclose{longdiv}{3x^3 - 4x^2 - 3x - 2} \\
\underline{3x^3 - 9x^2} \\
5x^2 - 3x \\
\underline{5x^2 - 15x} \\
12x - 2 \\
\underline{12x - 36} \\
34
\end{array}
$$

Examples

1 Find $(2y^3 - 3y^2 - 8y + 4) \div (y + 2)$.

$$\underline{-2}\,\big|\;\begin{array}{rrrr} 2 & -3 & -8 & 4 \\ & -4 & 14 & -12 \\ \hline 2 & -7 & 6 & -8 \end{array}$$

$y + 2$ is the same as $y - (-2)$.

The result is $2y^2 - 7y + 6 - \dfrac{8}{y + 2}$.

2 Find $(2a^3 + a^2 + 12) \div (a + 2)$.

$$\underline{-2}\,\big|\;\begin{array}{rrrr} 2 & 1 & 0 & 12 \\ & -4 & 6 & -12 \\ \hline 2 & -3 & 6 & 0 \end{array}$$

The coefficient of a is zero in $2a^3 + a^2 + 12$. Zero coefficients must be included when you do synthetic division.

The result is $2a^2 - 3a + 6$.

Check: $(a + 2)(2a^2 - 3a + 6)$
$= 2a^3 - 3a^2 + 6a + 4a^2 - 6a + 12$
$= 2a^3 + a^2 + 12$ ✔

3 Find $(2t^5 - 13t^3 - 70t^2 - 23t - 4) \div (t - 4)$.

$$\underline{4}\,\big|\;\begin{array}{rrrrrr} 2 & 0 & -13 & -70 & -23 & -4 \\ & 8 & 32 & 76 & 24 & 4 \\ \hline 2 & 8 & 19 & 6 & 1 & 0 \end{array}$$

The result is $2t^4 + 8t^3 + 19t^2 + 6t + 1$.

Check: $(t - 4)(2t^4 + 8t^3 + 19t^2 + 6t + 1)$
$= 2t^5 + 8t^4 + 19t^3 + 6t^2 + t - 8t^4 - 32t^3 - 76t^2 - 24t - 4$
$= 2t^5 - 13t^3 - 70t^2 - 23t - 4$ ✔

Some divisors, such as $2x - 1$, have leading coefficients other than one. For example, suppose you want to divide $4x^3 + x - 1$ by $2x - 1$. You can display the intended division in the following manner, factoring the leading coefficient of the divisor from the divisor and dividend.

$$\frac{4x^3 + x - 1}{2x - 1} = \frac{2\left(2x^3 + \frac{1}{2}x - \frac{1}{2}\right)}{2\left(x - \frac{1}{2}\right)}$$

Factor 2 from both the divisor and the dividend.

$$= \frac{2x^3 + \frac{1}{2}x - \frac{1}{2}}{x - \frac{1}{2}}$$

Now, use synthetic division to divide $2x^3 + \frac{1}{2}x - \frac{1}{2}$ by $x - \frac{1}{2}$.

Examples

4 **Divide $4x^3 + x - 1$ by $2x - 1$.**

$$\frac{4x^3 + x - 1}{2x - 1} = \frac{2x^3 + \frac{1}{2}x - \frac{1}{2}}{x - \frac{1}{2}}$$

$$\begin{array}{r|rrrr}
\frac{1}{2} & 2 & 0 & \frac{1}{2} & -\frac{1}{2} \\
 & & 1 & \frac{1}{2} & \frac{1}{2} \\
\hline
 & 2 & 1 & 1 & 0
\end{array}$$

The result is $2x^2 + x + 1$.

Check the solution.
Does $(2x - 1)(2x^2 + x + 1) = 4x^3 + x - 1$?

5 **Divide $3a^4 - 2a^3 + 5a^2 - 4a - 2$ by $3a + 1$.**

$$\frac{3a^4 - 2a^3 + 5a^2 - 4a - 2}{3a + 1} = \frac{3\left(a^4 - \frac{2}{3}a^3 + \frac{5}{3}a^2 - \frac{4}{3}a - \frac{2}{3}\right)}{3\left(a + \frac{1}{3}\right)}$$

$$= \frac{a^4 - \frac{2}{3}a^3 + \frac{5}{3}a^2 - \frac{4}{3}a - \frac{2}{3}}{a + \frac{1}{3}}$$

$$\begin{array}{r|rrrrr}
-\frac{1}{3} & 1 & -\frac{2}{3} & \frac{5}{3} & -\frac{4}{3} & -\frac{2}{3} \\
 & & -\frac{1}{3} & \frac{1}{3} & -\frac{2}{3} & \frac{2}{3} \\
\hline
 & 1 & -1 & 2 & -2 & 0
\end{array}$$

The result is $a^3 - a^2 + 2a - 2$.

Exploratory Exercises

Match the division problem with the correct synthetic division.

1. $(a^3 + 6a^2 + 3a + 1) \div (a - 2) = a^2 + 8a + 19 + \dfrac{39}{a - 2}$

a. $\begin{array}{r|rrrr}
2 & 3 & 0 & -5 & 10 \\
 & & 6 & 12 & 14 \\
\hline
 & 3 & 6 & 7 & 24
\end{array}$

2. $(z^3 + 2z^2 - 3z + 4) \div (z - 5) = z^2 + 7z + 32 + \dfrac{164}{z - 5}$

b. $\begin{array}{r|rrrr}
2 & 1 & 6 & 3 & 1 \\
 & & 2 & 16 & 38 \\
\hline
 & 1 & 8 & 19 & 39
\end{array}$

3. $(2y^3 - 5y + 1) \div (y + 1) = 2y^2 - 2y - 3 + \dfrac{4}{y + 1}$

c. $\begin{array}{r|rrrr}
-1 & 2 & 0 & -5 & 1 \\
 & & -2 & 2 & 3 \\
\hline
 & 2 & -2 & -3 & 4
\end{array}$

4. $(3y^3 - 5y + 10) \div (y - 2) = 3y^2 + 6y + 7 + \dfrac{24}{y - 2}$

d. $\begin{array}{r|rrrr}
5 & 1 & 2 & -3 & 4 \\
 & & 5 & 35 & 160 \\
\hline
 & 1 & 7 & 32 & 164
\end{array}$

Written Exercises

Divide using synthetic division.

1. $(2x^3 - 3x^2 + 3x - 4) \div (x - 2)$
2. $(3y^3 + 2y^2 - 32y + 2) \div (y - 3)$
3. $(2a^3 + a^2 - 2a + 3) \div (a + 1)$
4. $(3m^3 - 2m^2 + 2m - 1) \div (m - 1)$
5. $(x^4 - 2x^3 + x^2 - 3x + 2) \div (x - 2)$
6. $(3y^4 - 6y^3 - 2y^2 + y - 6) \div (y + 1)$
7. $(6k^3 - 19k^2 + k + 6) \div (k - 3)$
8. $(z^4 - 3z^3 - z^2 - 11z - 4) \div (z - 4)$
9. $(2b^3 - 11b^2 + 12b + 9) \div (b - 3)$
10. $(x^3 + 2x^2 - 5x - 6) \div (x - 2)$
11. $(y^4 - 16y^3 + 86y^2 - 176y + 105) \div (y - 5)$
12. $(a^4 - 5a^3 - 13a^2 + 53a + 60) \div (a + 1)$
13. $(2x^4 - 5x^3 - 10x + 8) \div (x - 3)$
14. $(2a^4 - 5a^3 + 2a - 3) \div (a - 1)$
15. $(y^4 + 6y^3 - 7y^2 + 7y - 1) \div (y + 3)$
16. $(h^5 - 6h^3 + 4h^2 - 3) \div (h - 2)$
17. $(4x^4 - 5x^2 + 2x + 3) \div (2x - 1)$
18. $(2b^3 - 3b^2 - 8b + 4) \div (2b + 1)$
19. $(6x^3 - 28x^2 + 19x + 3) \div (3x - 2)$
20. $(4y^4 - 5y^2 - 8y - 10) \div (2y - 3)$
21. $(x^5 + 32) \div (x + 2)$
22. $(x^5 - 3x^2 - 20) \div (x - 2)$

Challenge

Divide using synthetic division.

23. $(x^4 - 2x^3 - 34x^2 + 41x - 12) \div (x^2 + 5x - 3)$
24. $(x^5 + 3x^4 - 7x^3 + 11x^2 - 14x + 3) \div (x^3 - x^2 + 2x - 2)$

Using Calculators _____ Synthetic Division

To divide $x^3 + 13x^2 - 12x - 8$ by $x + 2$, you can use synthetic division as shown.

$$
\begin{array}{r|rrrr}
-2 & 1 & 13 & -12 & -8 \\
   &   & -2 & -22 & 68 \\
\hline
   & 1 & 11 & -34 & 60 \\
\end{array}
$$

The process can quickly be done by calculator. Write out the coefficients and bring down the leading coefficient as usual. Then procede as follows.

ENTER: 2 $\boxed{+/-}$ $\boxed{\times}$ 1 $\boxed{=}$ -2 $\boxed{+}$ 13 $\boxed{=}$ 11   *The display shows the second coefficient of the quotient.*

$\boxed{\times}$ 2 $\boxed{+/-}$ $\boxed{=}$ -22 $\boxed{+}$ 12 $\boxed{+/-}$ $\boxed{=}$ -34 *The display shows the third coefficient of the quotient.*

$\boxed{\times}$ 2 $\boxed{+/-}$ $\boxed{=}$ 68 $\boxed{+}$ 8 $\boxed{+/-}$ $\boxed{=}$ 60   *The display shows the remainder.*

Solution: $x^2 + 11x - 34 + \dfrac{60}{x + 2}$

Exercises Divide the following using synthetic division and your calculator.

1. $(3x^4 + 0.6x^3 - 3.7x^2 + 0.5x + 4) \div (x - 3)$
2. $(4x^3 + 6.7x^2 - 7.3x + 1.45) \div (x - 0.2)$
3. $(5x^5 + 7.7x^4 - x^2 + 7.59) \div (x - 0.5)$

Synthetic Division

The following is a simple program in BASIC to compute the coefficients of the quotient and the remainder with synthetic division.

```
10    INPUT "DEGREE OF POLYNOMIAL:  ";N
20    INPUT "CONSTANT R: ";R
30    PRINT "ENTER COEFFICIENTS:"
40    FOR X = 1 TO N + 1
50    INPUT A(X)
60    NEXT X
70    LET B(1) = A(1)
80    PRINT "COEFFICIENTS OF QUOTIENT
         ARE:"
90    PRINT B(1);"    ";
100   FOR X = 1 TO N - 1
110   B(X + 1) = A(X + 1) + R * B(X)
120   PRINT B(X + 1);"    ";
130   NEXT X
134   PRINT
140   PRINT "REMAINDER: ";A(N + 1) +
         R * B(N)
150   END
```

*R is the constant in the divisor $X - R$.
For example, in exercise 1
the divisor is $x - 3$, so $R = 3$.*

Input loop (brace for lines 40–60)

Computation and Print loop (brace for lines 100–130)

Exercises

Enter the program on your computer and use it to execute the following divisions.

1. $(x^4 + 2x^3 - 7x^2 + 2x - 8) \div (x - 3)$ (Hint: Let $R = 3$.)
2. $(x^4 + 8x^3 + 22x^2 + 24x + 9) \div (x + 1)$
3. $(2x^5 + 3x^4 - 6x^3 + 6x^2 - 8x + 3) \div (x + 1)$
4. $(x^5 - 15x^3 - 10x^2 + 60x + 72) \div (x + 3)$
5. $(x^5 - 3x^2 - 20) \div (x - 2)$
6. $(2y^4 - 2.5y^2 - 4y + 1.5) \div (y - 1.5)$
7. $(x^4 - 6x^2 + 8) \div (x - 2)$

This program will work up to the 10th degree. For a degree greater than 10, the statement 5 DIM A(n), B(n) is required. The value of n must be at least one greater than the degree of the equation. Add the DIM statement to the program and execute the following divisions.

8. $(x^{12} - 16x^8 - 256x^4 + 4096) \div (x - 2)$
9. $(x^{12} - 10) \div (x + 2)$

Vocabulary

monomial (145)
constant (145)
coefficient (145)
degree of monomial (145)
like terms (145)
negative integer exponents (149)

scientific notation (151)
polynomial (154)
binomial, trinomial (154)
degree of polynomial (154)
FOIL (155)
synthetic division (172)

Chapter Summary

1. Properties of Exponents: For any nonzero numbers a and b, and integers m and n, the following hold.

   1. $a^m \cdot a^n = a^{m+n}$ (146)

   2. $(a^m)^n = a^{mn}$ (146)

   3. $(ab)^m = a^m b^m$ (146)

   4. $\dfrac{a^m}{a^n} = a^{m-n}$ (148)

   5. $a^0 = 1$ (148)

   6. $\left(\dfrac{a}{b}\right)^n = \dfrac{a^n}{b^n}$ (151)

   7. $\left(\dfrac{a}{b}\right)^{-n} = \left(\dfrac{b}{a}\right)^n = \dfrac{b^n}{a^n}$ (151)

2. Definition of Scientific Notation: A number is expressed in scientific notation when it is in the form $a \times 10^n$. Here $1 \le a < 10$ and n is an integer. (151)

3. The degree of a monomial is the sum of the exponents of its variables. The degree of a polynomial is the degree of the monomial of greatest degree. (145, 154)

4. The product of two binomials is the sum of the product of
   - F the first terms,
   - O the outer terms,
   - I the inner terms, and
   - L the last terms. (155)

5. Factoring Difference of Two Squares: For any numbers a and b,
   $a^2 - b^2 = (a - b)(a + b)$ (159)

6. Factoring Sum or Difference of Cubes: For any numbers a and b,
   $a^3 + b^3 = (a + b)(a^2 - ab + b^2)$, and
   $a^3 - b^3 = (a - b)(a^2 + ab + b^2)$. (160)

7. Factoring Perfect Squares: For any numbers a and b,
   $a^2 + 2ab + b^2 = (a + b)^2$, and
   $a^2 - 2ab + b^2 = (a - b)^2$ (162)

8. Checklist for factoring polynomials.
   1. Check for the greatest common monomial factor.
   2. Check for special products.
      a. If there are *two terms,* look for difference of squares, sum of cubes, difference of cubes.
      b. If there are *three terms,* look for perfect squares.
   3. Try other factoring methods.
      a. If there are *three terms,* try the trinomial pattern.
      b. If there are *four or more terms,* try grouping. (166)

Chapter Review

5–1 **Simplify each expression.**

1. $y^9 \cdot y^2$ **2.** $(xy^4)(-5x^2y^3)$ **3.** $(x^3)^2$ **4.** $(4a^2)^3$

5. $(5a)(6a^2b)(3ab^3) + (4a^2)(3b^3)(2a^2b)$ **6.** $(3a)(a^2b)^3 + (2a)^2(-a^5b^3)$

5–2 **Simplify each expression.**

7. $\dfrac{a^6}{a^2}$ **8.** $\dfrac{14a^4b^3}{(7ab)^{-2}}$ **9.** $\dfrac{m^3n^2}{2m^3n}$

10. $3x^0$ **11.** $(3x)^0$ **12.** $\dfrac{-3x^3yz^4}{12x^2y^{-1}}$

5–3 **Simplify each expression.**

13. $\left(\dfrac{2}{x}\right)^{-2}$ **14.** $\left(\dfrac{1}{m}\right)^{-6}$ **15.** $\left(\dfrac{2}{3x^2}\right)^{-1}$

16. Change to scientific notation: 3,176,000,000

17. Change to decimal notation: 1.592×10^{-4}

18. Express the answer in scientific notation: $\dfrac{72,000,000 \times 0.005}{0.0015}$

5–4 **Simplify each expression by performing the indicated operations.**

19. $(4b^3 + 7b^2 - 3b + 5) + (-3b^3 + 8b^2 - 7)$

20. $(p^4 + 5p^2 - 3p + 7) - (p^3 + p^2 - 3p + 5)$

21. $(4a - 5)(a + 7)$ **22.** $(3m - 7)^2$

23. $(y + 7)(y^2 - 3y + 5)$ **24.** $(2x - 5)(x^2 + 8x - 7)$

25. $(m + 1)(2m + 7)(m + 3)$ **26.** $(2z - 5)(2z + 5)(z - 6)$

5–5 **Factor.**

27. $y^2 - 25$ **28.** $3a^2s - 6as^2 + 3s^3$ **29.** $m^3 + 8$

30. $x^4 - y^4$ **31.** $8m^3 - 27$ **32.** $p^3q^3 - 27q^3$

5–6 **Factor.**

33. $x^2 - 7x + 10$ **34.** $2x^2 + 7xy + 3y^2$ **35.** $9p^2 - 30pt + 25t^2$

36. $r^3 + 6r^2s + 8rs^2$ **37.** $5b^2 - 19ab - 4a^2$ **38.** $6x^2 + 11xy + 4y^2$

39. $21b^2 + 13b - 20$ **40.** $10m^2 + 19m + 6$

5–7 **Factor.**

41. $x^2 - 2xy + x - 2y$ **42.** $3a^2 + 12ab - 2a - 8b$

43. $-b^2 + 8b + a^2 - 16$ **44.** $4a^2 + 4ab - a^2 + b^2$

5–8 **Find each solution using long division. Show your work.**

45. $(8y^3 - 22y^2 - 5y + 15) \div (4y + 3)$

46. $(2r^3 + 11r^2 - 9r - 18) \div (2r + 3)$

47. Show that $x + 1$ is *not* a factor of $2x^3 + x^2 - 11x - 30$.

48. Show that $x - 3$ is a factor of $2x^3 - 11x^2 + 12x + 9$.

5–9 Find each solution using synthetic division. Show your work.

49. $(2m^3 - 3m^2 - 8m + 1) \div (m - 4)$

50. $(2r^3 + r^2 - 13r + 6) \div (2r - 1)$

51. Show that $2x + 1$ is a factor of $2x^3 - 11x^2 + 12x + 9$.

Chapter Test

Simplify each expression.

1. $(m^2)^5$

2. $\dfrac{16b^7}{2b^5}$

3. $\left(\dfrac{m}{4}\right)^{-2}$

4. $\dfrac{x^3}{x^{-4}}$

5. $\dfrac{7m}{m^{-3}} + \dfrac{3m^3}{m^{-1}}$

6. $\left(\dfrac{2y^{-2}}{2}\right)^{-1}\left(\dfrac{m^2n}{y}\right)$

7. $(4a^2b^2)(5ab^3)$

8. $(5x)(6x^2y^3) + (2xy)^3 - x^2y^0$

9. $3x^2y + 4 - 3x^2y$

10. $(3y^4 + 5y^3 + y - 7) + (4y^4 - 3y^3 + 7y^2 - 3y + 8)$

11. $(4b^3 + 7b^2 - 3b + 5) - (2b^3 - 5b^2 + 2b + 7)$

12. $(2y + 7)(y - 3)$

13. $(3m + 5)^2$

14. $(y - 4)(3y^2 - 5y + 4)$

15. $(x + 3)(2x - 5)(3x + 4)$

Factor.

16. $a^2 - 121$

17. $k^2 + 3k - 40$

18. $a^2 + 6am + 9m^2$

19. $y^3 + 125$

20. $3y^2 + 15y + 18$

21. $64a^3 - 1$

22. $8a^3 - 12a^2b + 6ab^2 - b^3$

23. $6y^2 + 17y + 10$

24. $2m^3 - 6m^2 + m - 3$

25. $8m^2 - 14m - 15$

26. $r^2 + 4rs + 4s^2 - 9y^2$

27. $3y^2 - 19y + 28$

28. Change to scientific notation: 5,906,000,000

29. Change to decimal notation: 1.672×10^{-3}

30. Express the answer in scientific notation: $\dfrac{84{,}000{,}000 \times 0.0013}{0.021}$

31. Use long division to find $(6y^3 - 5y^2 - 12y - 17) \div (3y + 2)$. Show your work.

32. Use synthetic division to find $(5m^3 - 3m^2 + 2m - 5) \div (m + 2)$. Show your work.

33. Show that $a - 3$ is a factor of $a^4 - a^3 + a^2 - 25a + 12$.

34. One factor of $2y^3 + y^2 - 13y + 6$ is $y + 3$. Find the other factors.

35. One factor of $4b^3 + 6b^2 + 40b - 22$ is $2b - 1$. Find the other factors.

CHAPTER 6

Roots

How long will the thunderstorm last? If the diameter of the storm system is known, weather forecasters can calculate an answer. The time, t, in hours is found using the formula $t^2 = \dfrac{d^3}{216}$, where d is the diameter in miles. Solving this equation for t involves finding roots. That is, $t = \sqrt{\dfrac{d^3}{216}}$. In this chapter, you will learn more about roots.

6-1 Roots

Squaring a number means using that number as a factor two times. *Cubing* a number means using that number as a factor three times.

$6^2 = 6 \cdot 6$ or 36 *6 is used as a factor two times.*
$6^3 = 6 \cdot 6 \cdot 6$ or 216 *6 is used as a factor three times.*

Raising a number to the nth power means using that number as a factor n times.

$5^4 = 5 \cdot 5 \cdot 5 \cdot 5$ or 625 *5 is used as a factor four times. n = 4*

$2^8 = 2 \cdot 2 \cdot 2 \cdot 2 \cdot 2 \cdot 2 \cdot 2 \cdot 2$ *2 is used as a factor eight times. n = 8*

$6^n = \underbrace{6 \cdot 6 \cdot 6 \cdot \ldots \cdot 6}_{n \text{ factors}}$ *6 is used as a factor n times.*

The inverse of raising a number to the nth power is finding the **nth root** of that number. For example, the inverse of squaring is finding a **square root.**

To find a square root of 36, you must find two equal factors whose product is 36.

$$x^2 = 36 \qquad x \cdot x = 36$$

Since 6 times 6 is 36, one square root of 36 is 6. Since -6 times -6 is 36, another square root of 36 is -6.

Any number which is the square of an integer is called a perfect square.

> **For any real numbers a and b,**
> **if $a^2 = b$, then a is a square root of b.**

Definition of Square Root

To find the cube root of 125, you must find three equal factors whose product is 125.

$$x^3 = 125 \qquad x \cdot x \cdot x = 125$$

Since 5 times 5 times 5 is 125, the cube root of 125 is 5.

> **For any real numbers a and b, and any positive integer n, if $a^n = b$, then a is an nth root of b.**

Definition of nth Root

The symbol $\sqrt[n]{}$ indicates an nth root.

index ⟶ ↓   ↓ ⟵ *radical sign*
$$\sqrt[n]{256} \longleftarrow \text{radicand}$$

When *no* index appears, the **radical** sign $\sqrt{}$ indicates a nonnegative square root.

Some numbers have more than one real root. For example, 36 has two real square roots, 6 and -6.

The symbol $\sqrt[n]{b}$ indicates the principal nth root of b. The principal nth root of b is a positive number *unless* n is odd and b is negative. In this case the principal root is negative.

$\sqrt{36} = 6$	$\sqrt{36}$ indicates the principal square root of 36.
$-\sqrt{36} = -6$	$-\sqrt{36}$ indicates the negative of the principal square root of 36.
$\pm\sqrt{36} = \pm 6$	$\pm\sqrt{36}$ indicates both square roots of 36 $\pm$ *means positive or negative.*
$\sqrt[3]{-27} = -3$	$\sqrt[3]{-27}$ indicates the principal cube root of -27.
$-\sqrt[4]{16} = -2$	$-\sqrt[4]{16}$ indicates the negative of the principal fourth root of 16.

The following chart gives a summary of the real nth roots of a number b.

The Real nth Roots of b, $\sqrt[n]{b}$

	$b > 0$	$b < 0$	$b = 0$
n even	one positive root one negative root	no real roots	one real root, 0
n odd	one positive root no negative roots	no positive roots one negative root	one real root, 0

Examples

1 Find $\pm\sqrt{64b^2}$.

$\pm\sqrt{64b^2} = \pm\sqrt{(8b)^2}$

$= \pm 8b$ *The square roots of $64b^2$ are $\pm 8b$.*

2 Find $-\sqrt{(x + 3)^4}$.

$-\sqrt{(x + 3)^4} = -\sqrt{[(x + 3)^2]^2}$

$= -(x + 3)^2$ *The principal square root of $(x + 3)^4$ is $(x + 3)^2$.*

3 Find $\sqrt[3]{27x^6}$.

$\sqrt[3]{27x^6} = \sqrt[3]{(3x^2)^3}$

$= 3x^2$ *The principal cube root of $27x^6$ is $3x^2$.*

4 Find $\sqrt[6]{c^6}$.

Since $(c)^6 = c^6$, c is a sixth root of c^6.   *6 is an even number, so the principal sixth root of*
Thus, $\sqrt[6]{c^6} = |c|$.   *c^6 is a positive number.*

From similar examples, you can make this generalization.

For any real number a, and any integer n greater than one:

    1. If n is even, then $\sqrt[n]{a^n} = |a|$.

    2. If n is odd, then $\sqrt[n]{a^n} = a$.

Property of nth Roots

Expressions such as $\sqrt{64}$ and $\sqrt[3]{-\frac{1}{8}}$ name rational numbers.

$$\sqrt{64} = 8 \qquad\qquad \sqrt[3]{-\frac{1}{8}} = -\frac{1}{2}$$

Real numbers that cannot be written as terminating or repeating decimals are **irrational numbers**. Numbers such as $\sqrt{2}$ and $\sqrt{3}$ are irrational. To compute with irrational numbers, decimal approximations are often used. The tables of roots and powers on pages 611 and 612 give approximations.

Example

5 **Find a decimal approximation for $\sqrt[3]{28}$.**

Cubes and Cube Roots

n	n^3	$\sqrt[3]{n}$	$\sqrt[3]{10n}$	$\sqrt[3]{100n}$
1.0	1.000	1.000	2.154	4.642
1.1	1.331	1.032	2.224	4.791
1.2	1.728	1.063	2.289	4.932
1.3	2.197	1.091	2.351	5.066
2.5	15.625	1.357	2.924	6.300
2.6	17.576	1.375	2.962	6.383
2.7	19.683	1.392	3.000	6.463
2.8	21.952	1.409	3.037	6.542
2.9	24.389	1.426	3.072	6.619

Let $n = 2.8$.
Then $10n = 10(2.8)$ or 28.

So $\sqrt[3]{28} = \sqrt[3]{10(2.8)}$
$\qquad\quad = 3.037$

Check: $(3.037)^3 = 28.01137165$

Exploratory Exercises

Find the value of each expression.

1. 7^2
2. 11^2
3. 3^3
4. 4^3
5. 2^4
6. 3^4
7. 13^2
8. 5^3
9. 10^5

Simplify.

10. $\sqrt{121}$
11. $-\sqrt{144}$
12. $\sqrt[3]{8}$
13. $\sqrt[4]{16}$
14. $\sqrt[3]{y^3}$
15. $-\sqrt[4]{y^4}$
16. $\sqrt[4]{y^8}$
17. $\sqrt[3]{-64}$
18. $\sqrt[5]{32n^5}$
19. $\sqrt{16a^2b^4}$
20. $\sqrt{(x-2)^2}$
21. $\sqrt{x^2 + 6x + 9}$

Use the tables of powers and roots or a calculator to find each value.

22. $\sqrt{47}$
23. 51^2
24. 19^3
25. $\sqrt[3]{18}$
26. $\sqrt[3]{30}$
27. 53^3

Written Exercises

Simplify.

1. $-\sqrt{81}$
2. $\sqrt{169}$
3. $\sqrt{225}$
4. $-\sqrt[3]{27}$
5. $\sqrt[4]{81}$
6. $\sqrt[3]{64}$
7. $\sqrt[5]{-1}$
8. $\sqrt[3]{-1000}$
9. $\sqrt{0.49}$
10. $\sqrt[3]{0.125}$
11. $\sqrt{121n^2}$
12. $\sqrt{144x^6}$
13. $\sqrt{(3s)^4}$
14. $\sqrt{(5b)^4}$
15. $\sqrt{576}$
16. $\sqrt{676}$
17. $\sqrt{64a^2b^4}$
18. $-\sqrt{121b^2c^6}$
19. $\sqrt[3]{-8b^3m^3}$
20. $\sqrt[3]{-27r^3s^3}$
21. $\sqrt[3]{64a^6b^3}$
22. $\sqrt{(x+y)^2}$
23. $\sqrt{(3p+q)^2}$
24. $\sqrt[3]{(2m+n)^3}$
25. $\sqrt[3]{(z+a)^3}$
26. $\sqrt[4]{(r+s)^4}$
27. $\sqrt[5]{(2m-3)^5}$
28. $\sqrt{x^2+10x+25}$
29. $\sqrt{x^2+6x+9}$
30. $\sqrt{4r^2+12r+9}$
31. $\sqrt{9x^2+6x+1}$
32. $\sqrt{x^2-6xy+9y^2}$
33. $\sqrt{4x^2+12xy+9y^2}$

Use the tables of powers and roots or a calculator to find each value.

34. 64^2
35. $\sqrt{83}$
36. $\sqrt{9.5}$
37. 4.9^2
38. $\sqrt[3]{23}$
39. $\sqrt[3]{8.1}$
40. 9.8^3
41. 48^3
42. $\sqrt[3]{300}$

Challenge

43. Does $\sqrt[4]{(-x)^4} = x$ no matter what value x represents? Explain.
44. Does $\sqrt[5]{(-x)^5} = x$ no matter what value x represents? Explain.
45. Under what circumstances is $\sqrt[n]{(-x)^n} = x$?

Using Calculators _____ Roots

Some calculators have a key labeled $\sqrt[x]{y}$ for finding roots. Other calculators require the use of the inverse and power keys, $\boxed{\text{INV}}$ and $\boxed{y^x}$. The following example shows how to evaluate $\sqrt[3]{682}$ on either type of calculator.

Use the root key.	or	Use the inverse and power keys.

ENTER: 682 $\boxed{\sqrt[x]{y}}$ 3 $\boxed{=}$ ENTER: 682 $\boxed{\text{INV}}$ $\boxed{y^x}$ 3 $\boxed{=}$

Using either method, the final display is 8.8022721.

To check, enter the following: 8.8022721 $\boxed{y^x}$ 3 $\boxed{=}$ The result should be about 682.

Exercises

Use a calculator to find a decimal approximation to three places for each of the following. Check your approximations by using the power key.

1. $\sqrt[4]{70}$ 2. $\sqrt[5]{413}$ 3. $\sqrt[4]{21}$ 4. $\sqrt[7]{16,384}$ 5. $\sqrt[8]{6581}$ 6. $\sqrt[6]{8549}$

6-2   Multiplying Radicals

The following examples show an important property of radicals.

$$\sqrt{4} \cdot \sqrt{9} = 2 \cdot 3 \text{ or } 6 \qquad\qquad \sqrt[3]{-8} \cdot \sqrt[3]{27} = -2 \cdot 3 \text{ or } -6$$

$$\sqrt{4 \cdot 9} = \sqrt{36} \text{ or } 6 \qquad\qquad \sqrt[3]{-8 \cdot 27} = \sqrt[3]{-216} \text{ or } -6$$

For any real numbers a and b, and any integer n greater than one:
1. **If n is even, then $\sqrt[n]{ab} = \sqrt[n]{a} \cdot \sqrt[n]{b}$ as long as a and b are both positive.**
2. **If n is odd, then $\sqrt[n]{ab} = \sqrt[n]{a} \cdot \sqrt[n]{b}$.**

Product Property of Radicals

To simplify a square root, first write the prime factorization of the radicand. Then use the product property of radicals to isolate perfect squares. Finally, simplify each radical.

Examples

1 **Simplify $\sqrt{63}$.**

$$\begin{aligned} \sqrt{63} &= \sqrt{3^2 \cdot 7} \qquad && \textit{The prime factorization of 63 is } 3^2 \cdot 7. \\ &= \sqrt{3^2} \cdot \sqrt{7} \qquad && \textit{Product Property of Radicals} \\ &= 3\sqrt{7} \end{aligned}$$

2 **Simplify $\sqrt{45x^3y^2}$.**

$$\begin{aligned} \sqrt{45x^3y^2} &= \sqrt{3^2 \cdot 5 \cdot x^2 \cdot x \cdot y^2} \\ &= \sqrt{3^2} \cdot \sqrt{5} \cdot \sqrt{x^2} \cdot \sqrt{x} \cdot \sqrt{y^2} \\ &= 3x|y|\sqrt{5x} \qquad \textit{If } x < 0, \textit{ then } \sqrt{x^3} \textit{ has no real roots. Therefore, you must} \\ & \qquad\qquad\qquad\quad \textit{assume that } x \geq 0. \textit{ Thus, it is not necessary to write } \sqrt{x^3} = \\ & \qquad\qquad\qquad\quad |x|\sqrt{x}. \end{aligned}$$

To simplify nth roots, find the factors that are nth powers and use the product property.

Examples

3 **Simplify $\sqrt[4]{2m} \cdot \sqrt[4]{5m^3}$.**

$$\begin{aligned} \sqrt[4]{2m} \cdot \sqrt[4]{5m^3} &= \sqrt[4]{2m \cdot 5m^3} \\ &= \sqrt[4]{10m^4} \\ &= \sqrt[4]{10} \cdot \sqrt[4]{m^4} \\ &= m\sqrt[4]{10} \end{aligned}$$

4 **Simplify $\sqrt[3]{54x^3y^5}$.**

$$\begin{aligned} \sqrt[3]{54x^3y^5} &= \sqrt[3]{3^3 \cdot 2 \cdot x^3 \cdot y^3 \cdot y^2} \\ &= \sqrt[3]{3^3} \cdot \sqrt[3]{2} \cdot \sqrt[3]{x^3} \cdot \sqrt[3]{y^3} \cdot \sqrt[3]{y^2} \\ &= 3 \cdot \sqrt[3]{2} \cdot x \cdot y \cdot \sqrt[3]{y^2} \\ &= 3xy\sqrt[3]{2y^2} \end{aligned}$$

When multiplying rational numbers and radicals, multiply each separately and then simplify.

$$2\sqrt{2} \cdot 4\sqrt{6} = 2 \cdot 4 \cdot \sqrt{2} \cdot \sqrt{6}$$
$$= 8\sqrt{12}$$
$$= 8 \cdot 2 \cdot \sqrt{3} \text{ or } 16\sqrt{3}$$

You can use the distributive property to help simplify radicals.

Examples

5 Simplify $\sqrt{6}(\sqrt{3} + 2\sqrt{15})$.
$\sqrt{6}(\sqrt{3} + 2\sqrt{15})$
$= \sqrt{6} \cdot \sqrt{3} + \sqrt{6} \cdot 2\sqrt{15}$
$= \sqrt{18} + 2\sqrt{90}$
$= 3\sqrt{2} + 2 \cdot 3\sqrt{10}$
$= 3\sqrt{2} + 6\sqrt{10}$

6 Simplify $\sqrt{a}(\sqrt{a} + a\sqrt{b})$.
$\sqrt{a}(\sqrt{a} + a\sqrt{b})$
$= \sqrt{a} \cdot \sqrt{a} + \sqrt{a} \cdot a\sqrt{b}$
$= a + a\sqrt{ab}$

Exploratory Exercises

Simplify.

1. $\sqrt{8}$
2. $\sqrt{32}$
3. $\sqrt{50x^2}$
4. $\sqrt{98y^4}$
5. $\sqrt[3]{16}$
6. $\sqrt[3]{54}$
7. $\sqrt[4]{48}$
8. $\sqrt[4]{32}$
9. $\sqrt{b^3}$
10. $\sqrt{y^5}$
11. $\sqrt[4]{a^5}$
12. $\sqrt[3]{m^4}$
13. $\sqrt[5]{r^7}$
14. $\sqrt[4]{k^6}$
15. $\sqrt{3} \cdot \sqrt{15}$
16. $\sqrt{6} \cdot \sqrt{3}$
17. $\sqrt[4]{3} \cdot \sqrt[4]{54}$
18. $\sqrt[3]{9} \cdot \sqrt[3]{6}$
19. $\sqrt{5}(\sqrt{5} - \sqrt{3})$
20. $\sqrt{5}(\sqrt{7} + \sqrt{5})$

Written Exercises

Simplify.

1. $5\sqrt{54}$
2. $4\sqrt{50}$
3. $\sqrt[3]{24}$
4. $\sqrt[3]{56}$
5. $\sqrt{162}$
6. $\sqrt{450}$
7. $\sqrt[3]{-192}$
8. $\sqrt[3]{88}$
9. $3\sqrt{242}$
10. $6\sqrt{216}$
11. $\sqrt[4]{112}$
12. $\sqrt[4]{405}$
13. $(4\sqrt{18})(2\sqrt{14})$
14. $(-3\sqrt{24})(5\sqrt{20})$
15. $\sqrt[3]{121}\sqrt[3]{88}$
16. $(7\sqrt[3]{16})(5\sqrt[3]{20})$
17. $\sqrt{3}(\sqrt{6} - 2)$
18. $\sqrt{7}(3 + \sqrt{7})$
19. $\sqrt{7}(\sqrt{14} + \sqrt{21})$
20. $-\sqrt{2}(\sqrt{3} + \sqrt{2})$
21. $\sqrt[3]{2}(3\sqrt[3]{4} + 2\sqrt[3]{32})$
22. $\sqrt[3]{9}(4\sqrt[3]{9} + 2\sqrt[3]{6})$
23. $\sqrt[3]{8a^4b^7}$
24. $\sqrt{8m^2b^3}$
25. $\sqrt{50r^3p^4}$
26. $\sqrt[4]{81m^4p^5}$
27. $\sqrt[3]{3x^4y^4}$
28. $\sqrt{8x^2y} \cdot \sqrt{2xy}$
29. $\sqrt{3x^2z^3} \cdot \sqrt{15x^2z}$
30. $\sqrt[3]{3ab^5} \cdot \sqrt[3]{24a^2b^2}$
31. $\sqrt[4]{5m^3b^5} \cdot \sqrt[4]{125m^2b^3}$
32. $\sqrt[4]{3b^6r^7} \cdot \sqrt[4]{81b^2r^2}$
33. $\sqrt[3]{54r^4s^3} \cdot \sqrt[3]{16rs}$
34. $\sqrt{125m^2n} \cdot \sqrt{32m^4n^6}$
35. $\sqrt[4]{32a^5b^3} \cdot \sqrt[4]{162a^3b^2}$
36. $\sqrt{r}(\sqrt{r} + r\sqrt{s})$
37. $\sqrt{b}(b + a\sqrt{b})$
38. $\sqrt{m}(\sqrt{p} + \sqrt{mq})$

mini-review

1. Evaluate $\begin{vmatrix} 6 & -4 \\ 3 & 1 \end{vmatrix}$.

2. In which octant does $(4, -2, 2)$ lie?

3. Find the inverse of $\begin{bmatrix} -2 & -3 \\ 4 & 7 \end{bmatrix}$.

4. Express 0.000368 in scientific notation.

5. Factor $b^3 - 27a^3$.

6-3 Computing with Radicals

Two radical expressions are called **like radical expressions** if the indexes are alike and the radicands are alike.

$7\sqrt[3]{2}$ and $6\sqrt[3]{2}$ are like expressions. *Both the indexes and radicands are alike.*

$\sqrt[4]{9}$ and $\sqrt[5]{9}$ are *not* like expressions. *The indexes are not alike.*

$5\sqrt{3x}$ and $-5\sqrt{3y}$ are *not* like expressions. *The radicands are not alike.*

$\sqrt[3]{2a}$ and $\sqrt[4]{2b}$ are *not* like expressions. *Neither the indexes nor the radicands are alike.*

Radicals are added or subtracted the same way monomials are added or subtracted.

Combine like terms.

$$3x + 2x + 4y = (3 + 2)x + 4y$$
$$= 5x + 4y$$

Combine like radicals.

$$3\sqrt{6} + 2\sqrt{6} + 4\sqrt{7} = (3 + 2)\sqrt{6} + 4\sqrt{7}$$
$$= 5\sqrt{6} + 4\sqrt{7}$$

Examples

1 Simplify $3 + 4\sqrt{7} + 5 + 6\sqrt{7}$.

$3 + 4\sqrt{7} + 5 + 6\sqrt{7}$
$= 3 + 5 + 4\sqrt{7} + 6\sqrt{7}$
$= (8) + (4 + 6)\sqrt{7}$
$= 8 + 10\sqrt{7}$

2 Simplify $3 + 4\sqrt{a} + 6\sqrt{a}$.

$3 + 4\sqrt{a} + 6\sqrt{a}$
$= 3 + (4 + 6)\sqrt{a}$
$= 3 + 10\sqrt{a}$

3 Simplify $5\sqrt{27} + 2\sqrt{3} - 7\sqrt{48}$.

Simplify each radical. Then add or subtract.

$5\sqrt{27} + 2\sqrt{3} - 7\sqrt{48} = 5\sqrt{3^2 \cdot 3} + 2\sqrt{3} - 7\sqrt{4^2 \cdot 3}$
$= 5\sqrt{3^2}\sqrt{3} + 2\sqrt{3} - 7\sqrt{4^2}\sqrt{3}$
$= 5 \cdot 3\sqrt{3} + 2\sqrt{3} - 7 \cdot 4\sqrt{3}$
$= 15\sqrt{3} + 2\sqrt{3} - 28\sqrt{3}$ or $-11\sqrt{3}$

4 Simplify $\sqrt[3]{40a} + \sqrt[3]{135a}$.

$\sqrt[3]{40a} + \sqrt[3]{135a} = \sqrt[3]{2^3 \cdot 5a} + \sqrt[3]{3^3 \cdot 5a}$
$= \sqrt[3]{2^3} \cdot \sqrt[3]{5a} + \sqrt[3]{3^3} \cdot \sqrt[3]{5a}$
$= 2\sqrt[3]{5a} + 3\sqrt[3]{5a}$
$= 5\sqrt[3]{5a}$

Expressions such as $(5 + 3\sqrt{2})(3 + \sqrt{2})$ can be simplified using the FOIL method.

$$
\begin{array}{ccccc}
& \text{F} & \text{O} & \text{I} & \text{L} \\
(5 + 3\sqrt{2})(3 + \sqrt{2}) = & 5 \cdot 3 + & 5 \cdot \sqrt{2} + & 3\sqrt{2} \cdot 3 + & 3\sqrt{2} \cdot \sqrt{2} \\
= & 15 \ + & 5\sqrt{2} \ + & 9\sqrt{2} \ + & 6 \\
= & 21 \ + & 14\sqrt{2} & &
\end{array}
$$

Example

5 Simplify $(6 + \sqrt{2})(\sqrt{10} + \sqrt{5})$.

$$\begin{aligned}
& \qquad\qquad\qquad\qquad \textbf{F} \qquad\quad \textbf{O} \qquad\quad \textbf{I} \qquad\qquad \textbf{L}\\
(6 + \sqrt{2})(\sqrt{10} + \sqrt{5}) &= 6\sqrt{10} + 6\sqrt{5} + \sqrt{2}\sqrt{10} + \sqrt{2}\sqrt{5}\\
&= 6\sqrt{10} + 6\sqrt{5} + \sqrt{20} + \sqrt{10}\\
&= 6\sqrt{10} + 6\sqrt{5} + 2\sqrt{5} + \sqrt{10}\\
&= 6\sqrt{10} + \sqrt{10} + 6\sqrt{5} + 2\sqrt{5}\\
&= 7\sqrt{10} + 8\sqrt{5}
\end{aligned}$$

Binomials that are of the form $a\sqrt{b} + c\sqrt{d}$ and $a\sqrt{b} - c\sqrt{d}$ are called **conjugates** of each other. Notice that the product of conjugates is a rational number.

Examples

6 Simplify $(7 + \sqrt{2})(7 - \sqrt{2})$.

$$\begin{aligned}
& \qquad\qquad\qquad\qquad \textbf{F} \qquad\quad\; \textbf{O} \qquad\quad \textbf{I} \qquad\qquad \textbf{L}\\
(7 + \sqrt{2})(7 - \sqrt{2}) &= 7 \cdot 7 - 7\sqrt{2} + 7\sqrt{2} - \sqrt{2} \cdot \sqrt{2}\\
&= 49 - \sqrt{2^2}\\
&= 49 - 2\\
&= 47
\end{aligned}$$

7 Simplify $(2a + 7\sqrt{b})(2a - 7\sqrt{b})$.

$$\begin{aligned}
& \qquad\qquad\qquad\qquad\qquad \textbf{F} \qquad\quad \textbf{O} \qquad\qquad \textbf{I} \qquad\qquad \textbf{L}\\
(2a + 7\sqrt{b})(2a - 7\sqrt{b}) &= 4a^2 - 14a\sqrt{b} + 14a\sqrt{b} - 49(\sqrt{b})^2\\
&= 4a^2 - 49b
\end{aligned}$$

Exploratory Exercises

Simplify.

1. $3\sqrt{7} - 4\sqrt{7}$
2. $8\sqrt[3]{6} + 3\sqrt[3]{6}$
3. $3\sqrt[4]{5} - 10\sqrt[4]{5}$
4. $7\sqrt{y} + 4\sqrt{y}$
5. $5\sqrt[3]{x} + 4\sqrt[3]{x} - 6\sqrt[3]{x}$
6. $7\sqrt[3]{2} - 3\sqrt[3]{2}$
7. $\sqrt[5]{3} + 4\sqrt[5]{3}$
8. $2\sqrt{2} + \sqrt{8}$
9. $6\sqrt{3} - \sqrt{27}$
10. $8\sqrt{5} + \sqrt{75}$
11. $\sqrt[3]{40} - 2\sqrt[3]{5}$
12. $7\sqrt[3]{3} - \sqrt[3]{24}$

Multiply.

13. $(3 + \sqrt{5})(4 + \sqrt{5})$
14. $(5 + \sqrt{3})(3 - \sqrt{3})$
15. $(b - \sqrt{2a})(b - \sqrt{2a})$
16. $(3a + \sqrt{5b})(3a - \sqrt{5b})$
17. $(6 + \sqrt{2})(6 - \sqrt{2})$
18. $(2 + \sqrt{7})(2 - \sqrt{7})$
19. $(4 + \sqrt{3})^2$
20. $(1 - \sqrt{5})^2$
21. $(m + \sqrt{y})^2$

Written Exercises

Simplify.

1. $5\sqrt{2} + 3\sqrt{2} - 8$
2. $-4\sqrt{2} + 6 + 10\sqrt{2}$
3. $-3\sqrt{5} + 5\sqrt{2} + 4\sqrt{20} - 3\sqrt{50}$
4. $8\sqrt{3} - 3\sqrt{75}$
5. $3\sqrt{7} - 5\sqrt{28}$
6. $5\sqrt{20} + \sqrt{24} - \sqrt{180} + 7\sqrt{54}$
7. $7\sqrt[3]{5b} + 4\sqrt[3]{5b}$
8. $\sqrt[3]{48} - \sqrt[3]{6}$
9. $8\sqrt[3]{2a} + 3\sqrt[3]{2a} - 8\sqrt[3]{2a}$
10. $\sqrt[3]{54} - \sqrt[3]{128}$
11. $7\sqrt[3]{2} + 6\sqrt[3]{150}$
12. $5\sqrt[3]{135} - 2\sqrt[3]{81}$
13. $7\sqrt{24} + \sqrt[3]{24}$
14. $\sqrt[3]{16} - \sqrt{32}$
15. $\sqrt{98} - \sqrt{72} + \sqrt{32}$
16. $\sqrt{108} - \sqrt{48} + (\sqrt{3})^3$
17. $7\sqrt[4]{2} + 8\sqrt[4]{2}$
18. $\sqrt[4]{5} + 6\sqrt[4]{5} - 2\sqrt[4]{5}$
19. $\sqrt[4]{x^2} + \sqrt[4]{x^6}$
20. $-\sqrt{2x^2y^4} + \sqrt{8x^2y^4}$
21. $\sqrt[4]{y^4z^6} + \sqrt[4]{16y^4z^6}$
22. $\sqrt[3]{27m^5n^6} + \sqrt[3]{8m^8n^3}$
23. $\sqrt[4]{z^4} + \sqrt[3]{z^6} + \sqrt{z^8}$
24. $\sqrt{100m^3n} - \sqrt{64mn^3}$
25. $(5 + \sqrt{2})(3 + \sqrt{2})$
26. $(4 + \sqrt{3})(3 + \sqrt{6})$
27. $(5 + \sqrt{6})(5 - \sqrt{2})$
28. $(8 - \sqrt{3})(6 + \sqrt{3})$
29. $(7 + \sqrt{11p})(7 - \sqrt{11p})$
30. $(5 - 3\sqrt{5})(3 + \sqrt{5})$
31. $(\sqrt{3} + \sqrt{5})(\sqrt{12} - \sqrt{5})$
32. $(4 + \sqrt{5})^2$
33. $(1 - \sqrt{3})^2$
34. $(4\sqrt{5} - 3\sqrt{2})(2\sqrt{5} + 2\sqrt{2})$
35. $(\sqrt{3a} + \sqrt{2b})(\sqrt{15a} - \sqrt{3b})$
36. $(3 - \sqrt[3]{4})(\sqrt[3]{2} + \sqrt[3]{16})$
37. $(4 - \sqrt[3]{9})(\sqrt[3]{3} + \sqrt[3]{81})$
38. $(y + \sqrt[3]{4})(y^2 - y\sqrt[3]{4} + \sqrt[3]{16})$
39. $(x - \sqrt[3]{3})(x^2 + x\sqrt[3]{3} + \sqrt[3]{9})$
40. $(m + \sqrt[3]{a})(m^2 - m\sqrt[3]{a} + \sqrt[3]{a^2})$
41. $(2 + \sqrt[3]{k})(4 - 2\sqrt[3]{k} + \sqrt[3]{k^2})$

Factor over the real numbers.

42. $x^2 - 5$
43. $a^2 + 4a\sqrt{5} + 20$
44. $b^2 - 10b\sqrt{2} + 50$
45. $r^3 - 2r$

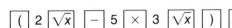

Using Calculators _____ Radical Expressions

The calculator can be used to show that two radical expressions have the same value. For example, the expression $(\sqrt{3} - 2\sqrt{2})(\sqrt{2} - 5\sqrt{3})$ can be simplified to $-19 + 11\sqrt{6}$. Here is how to show that the two expressions have the same value. First evaluate $(\sqrt{3} - 2\sqrt{2})(\sqrt{2} - 5\sqrt{3})$.

ENTER: (3 $\sqrt{x}$ − 2 × 2 $\sqrt{x}$) ×

(2 $\sqrt{x}$ − 5 × 3 $\sqrt{x}$) =

DISPLAY: 7.9443872

Then evaluate $-19 + 11\sqrt{6}$.

ENTER: 19 $+/-$ + 11 × 6 $\sqrt{x}$ =

DISPLAY: 7.9443872

Exercises Show that the given expressions have the same value.

1. $8\sqrt{24} - 3\sqrt{54} + 5\sqrt{25}$; $7\sqrt{6} + 25$
2. $(2\sqrt{6} - 5\sqrt{3})(3\sqrt{3} + 4\sqrt{6})$; $3 - 42\sqrt{2}$
3. $(2\sqrt{5} - 8\sqrt{32})(6\sqrt{2} - 11\sqrt{5})$; $-494 + 364\sqrt{10}$

6-4   Dividing Radicals

The following examples show an important property of radicals.

$$\frac{\sqrt{100}}{\sqrt{4}} = \frac{10}{2} \text{ or } 5 \qquad\qquad \frac{\sqrt[3]{216}}{\sqrt[3]{-27}} = \frac{6}{-3} \text{ or } -2$$

$$\sqrt{\frac{100}{4}} = \sqrt{25} \text{ or } 5 \qquad\qquad \sqrt[3]{\frac{216}{-27}} = \sqrt[3]{-8} \text{ or } -2$$

> **For any real numbers a and b, $b \neq 0$, and any n greater than one,**
> $$\sqrt[n]{\frac{a}{b}} = \frac{\sqrt[n]{a}}{\sqrt[n]{b}}$$
> **as long as all roots are defined.**

Quotient Property of Radicals

The quotient property can be used in simplifying radicals.

Examples

1 **Simplify** $\sqrt[3]{\dfrac{3}{8}}$.

$$\sqrt[3]{\frac{3}{8}} = \frac{\sqrt[3]{3}}{\sqrt[3]{8}} \qquad \textit{Quotient Property of Radicals}$$

$$= \frac{\sqrt[3]{3}}{2}$$

2 **Simplify** $\dfrac{6\sqrt{15}}{2\sqrt{3}}$.

$$\frac{6\sqrt{15}}{2\sqrt{3}} = \frac{6}{2}\sqrt{\frac{15}{3}} \qquad \textit{Quotient Property of Radicals}$$

$$= 3\sqrt{5}$$

Fractions are usually written without radicals in the denominator. Similarly, radicands are not left in fraction form. The process of eliminating radicals from the denominator or fractions from the radicand is called **rationalizing the denominator**.

Examples

3 **Simplify** $\dfrac{3}{2\sqrt{5}}$.

$$\frac{3}{2\sqrt{5}} = \frac{3}{2\sqrt{5}} \cdot \frac{\sqrt{5}}{\sqrt{5}} \qquad \textit{Why is } \frac{\sqrt{5}}{\sqrt{5}} \textit{ used?}$$

$$= \frac{3\sqrt{5}}{2\sqrt{5 \cdot 5}}$$

$$= \frac{3\sqrt{5}}{10}$$

4 **Simplify** $\sqrt{\dfrac{5}{a}}$.

$$\sqrt{\frac{5}{a}} = \frac{\sqrt{5}}{\sqrt{a}} \cdot \frac{\sqrt{a}}{\sqrt{a}} \qquad \textit{Why is } \frac{\sqrt{a}}{\sqrt{a}} \textit{ used?}$$

$$= \frac{\sqrt{5 \cdot a}}{\sqrt{a \cdot a}}$$

$$= \frac{\sqrt{5a}}{a}$$

In general, a radical expression is simplified when the following conditions are met.

1. The index n is as small as possible.
2. The radicand contains no factor (other than one) which is the nth power of an integer or polynomial.
3. The radicand contains no fractions.
4. No radicals appear in the denominator.

Conditions for Simplified Radicals

Examples

5 Simplify $\sqrt[3]{\dfrac{5}{3b}}$.

$$\sqrt[3]{\frac{5}{3b}} = \frac{\sqrt[3]{5}}{\sqrt[3]{3b}} \cdot \frac{\sqrt[3]{3^2b^2}}{\sqrt[3]{3^2b^2}}$$

Why is $\dfrac{\sqrt[3]{3^2b^2}}{\sqrt[3]{3^2b^2}}$ used?

$$= \frac{\sqrt[3]{5 \cdot 3^2 b^2}}{\sqrt[3]{3^3 b^3}}$$

$$= \frac{\sqrt[3]{45b^2}}{3b}$$

6 Simplify $\dfrac{1 - \sqrt{3}}{5 + 2\sqrt{3}}$.

Conjugates can be used to rationalize the denominator.

$$\frac{1 - \sqrt{3}}{5 + 2\sqrt{3}} = \frac{1 - \sqrt{3}}{5 + 2\sqrt{3}} \cdot \frac{5 - 2\sqrt{3}}{5 - 2\sqrt{3}}$$

$$= \frac{5 - 2\sqrt{3} - 5\sqrt{3} + 2\sqrt{3}^2}{25 - (2\sqrt{3})^2}$$

$$= \frac{5 - 2\sqrt{3} - 5\sqrt{3} + 6}{25 - 4(3)}$$

$$= \frac{11 - 7\sqrt{3}}{13}$$

Exploratory Exercises

Simplify.

1. $\dfrac{\sqrt{6}}{\sqrt{3}}$

2. $\dfrac{\sqrt{10}}{\sqrt{2}}$

3. $\dfrac{\sqrt[3]{18y}}{\sqrt[3]{6}}$

4. $\dfrac{\sqrt[4]{35x^5}}{\sqrt[4]{7}}$

5. $\sqrt{\dfrac{5}{4}}$

6. $\sqrt{\dfrac{7}{9}}$

7. $\sqrt[3]{\dfrac{5}{8}}$

8. $\sqrt[3]{\dfrac{4}{27}}$

State the fraction that each of the following expressions should be multiplied by to rationalize the denominator.

9. $\dfrac{2}{\sqrt{3}}$

10. $\dfrac{4}{\sqrt{2}}$

11. $\dfrac{1}{\sqrt{a}}$

12. $\dfrac{3}{\sqrt{b}}$

13. $\dfrac{3}{\sqrt[3]{4}}$

14. $\dfrac{4}{\sqrt[3]{2}}$

15. $\dfrac{7}{\sqrt[3]{9}}$

16. $\dfrac{4}{\sqrt[3]{16}}$

Name the conjugate of each expression.

17. $1 + \sqrt{3}$

18. $4 - \sqrt{5}$

19. $1 - \sqrt{2}$

20. $4 + \sqrt{3}$

21. $3 + \sqrt{5}$

22. $5 - \sqrt{2}$

23. $5 + 3\sqrt{3}$

24. $5 + 2\sqrt{5}$

25. $2\sqrt{2} - 3$

26. $2\sqrt{7} - 5$

27. $\sqrt{2} - 5\sqrt{3}$

28. $\sqrt{7} + \sqrt{2}$

Written Exercises

Simplify.

1. $\dfrac{\sqrt{10}}{\sqrt{2}}$

2. $\dfrac{\sqrt{12}}{\sqrt{3}}$

3. $\dfrac{\sqrt{14}}{\sqrt{2}}$

4. $\dfrac{\sqrt{21}}{\sqrt{7}}$

5. $\dfrac{\sqrt[3]{81}}{\sqrt[3]{9}}$

6. $\dfrac{\sqrt[3]{54}}{\sqrt[3]{6}}$

7. $\sqrt{\dfrac{5}{4}}$

8. $\sqrt{\dfrac{7}{16}}$

9. $\sqrt{\dfrac{8}{9}}$

10. $\sqrt{\dfrac{21}{12}}$

11. $\sqrt[3]{\dfrac{5}{8}}$

12. $\sqrt[3]{\dfrac{2}{27}}$

13. $\sqrt[3]{\dfrac{54}{125}}$

14. $\sqrt[3]{\dfrac{16}{27}}$

15. $\sqrt[4]{\dfrac{5}{16}}$

16. $\sqrt[4]{\dfrac{7}{81}}$

17. $\sqrt{\dfrac{1}{3}}$

18. $\sqrt{\dfrac{1}{5}}$

19. $\sqrt{\dfrac{2}{m}}$

20. $\sqrt{\dfrac{3}{r}}$

21. $\sqrt{\dfrac{5}{12a}}$

22. $\sqrt{\dfrac{5}{32b}}$

23. $\sqrt[3]{\dfrac{5}{9p^2}}$

24. $\sqrt[3]{\dfrac{9}{4m^2}}$

25. $\sqrt[4]{\dfrac{2}{3}}$

26. $\sqrt[4]{\dfrac{3}{2}}$

27. $\dfrac{1}{3 + \sqrt{5}}$

28. $\dfrac{3}{5 - \sqrt{2}}$

29. $\dfrac{2}{3 - \sqrt{5}}$

30. $\dfrac{7}{4 - \sqrt{3}}$

31. $\dfrac{1 + \sqrt{2}}{3 - \sqrt{2}}$

32. $\dfrac{2 + \sqrt{6}}{2 - \sqrt{6}}$

33. $\dfrac{2 - \sqrt{3}}{5 + 3\sqrt{3}}$

34. $\dfrac{3 + 4\sqrt{5}}{5 + 2\sqrt{5}}$

35. $\dfrac{\sqrt{x + 1}}{\sqrt{x - 1}}$

36. $\dfrac{m + \sqrt{a}}{2\sqrt{a} - p}$

37. $\sqrt{\dfrac{2}{5}} + \sqrt{40} + \sqrt{10}$

38. $\sqrt[3]{\dfrac{1}{4}} + \sqrt[3]{54} - \sqrt[3]{16}$

Solve each problem. Round all answers to the nearest hundredth.

39. Find the time, T, in seconds for a complete swing (back and forth) of a pendulum whose length is 6 feet.

Let $T = 2\pi \sqrt{\dfrac{L}{32}}$, where $\pi \approx 3.14$.

40. Find the time, T, in seconds for a complete swing of a pendulum whose length is 98 centimeters.

Let $T = 2\pi \sqrt{\dfrac{L}{980}}$, where $\pi \approx 3.14$.

41. Find the radius, r, of a sphere whose surface area S is 616 square inches.

Let $r = \dfrac{1}{2}\sqrt{\dfrac{S}{\pi}}$, where $\pi \approx \dfrac{22}{7}$.

42. Find the time, t, in seconds required for a freely falling body to fall a distance s of 150 feet. Let $t = \dfrac{1}{4}\sqrt{s}$.

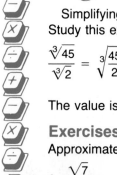

Using Calculators _____ Radicals

Simplifying radicals may make it easier to approximate the value of an expression. Study this example.

$$\dfrac{\sqrt[3]{45}}{\sqrt[3]{2}} = \sqrt[3]{\dfrac{45}{2}}$$

ENTER: 45 $\div$ 2 $=$ $\boxed{\text{INV}}$ $\boxed{y^x}$ 3 $=$

DISPLAY: $45 \qquad 2\ 22.5 \qquad\qquad 3\ 2.8231081$

The value is about 2.8231.

Exercises

Approximate the value of each expression to four decimal places.

1. $\dfrac{\sqrt{7}}{\sqrt{16}}$

2. $\sqrt[3]{\dfrac{5}{8}}$

3. $\dfrac{\sqrt[3]{54}}{\sqrt[3]{125}}$

4. $\dfrac{\sqrt[3]{4923}}{462.7}$

5. $\sqrt[3]{\dfrac{(3.29)(63)^2}{5236}}$

Reading Algebra

In mathematics, many words have specific definitions. However, when these words are used in everyday language, they frequently have a different meaning. Study each pair of sentences. How does the meaning of the word in boldface differ?

A. Plants receive nourishment and water from their **roots.**
B. The square **roots** of 36 are 6 and -6.

A. The United States is a major world **power.**
B. Raising a number to the nth **power** means using that number as a factor n times.

A. I am **positive** I left my homework in my locker.
B. For any numbers a and b, and any **positive** integer n, if $a^n = b$, then a is an nth root of b.

A. The **principal** will speak at the school assembly.
B. The symbol $\sqrt[n]{b}$ indicates the **principal** nth root of b.

A. The soup tastes a little **odd.**
B. For any number a and any integer n greater than one, if n is **odd,** then $\sqrt[n]{a^n} = a$.

Read the following property and the paragraph below. Which words are mathematical words? Which words are ordinary words? Which mathematical words have another meaning in everyday language?

For any nonnegative real numbers a and b and any integer n greater than one, $\sqrt[n]{ab} = \sqrt[n]{a} \cdot \sqrt[n]{b}$.	*Product Property of Radicals*

Simplifying a square root means finding the square root of the greatest perfect square factor of the radicand. You use the product property of radicals to simplify square roots.

Exercises

Write two sentences for each word. First, use the word in everyday language. Then use the word in a mathematical context.

1. index	2. negative	3. even	4. rational
5. irrational	6. like	7. rationalize	8. coordinates
9. real	10. degree	11. absolute	12. identity

6-5 Rational Exponents

The properties of exponents can also be extended to include rational number exponents. Study the examples below.

$$5^{\frac{1}{2}} \cdot 5^{\frac{1}{2}} = 5^{\frac{1}{2}+\frac{1}{2}}$$
$$= 5$$

But, it is also true that $\sqrt{5} \cdot \sqrt{5} = 5$. Therefore, the values of $5^{\frac{1}{2}}$ and $\sqrt{5}$ must be the same.

$$4^{\frac{1}{3}} \cdot 4^{\frac{1}{3}} \cdot 4^{\frac{1}{3}} = 4^{\frac{1}{3}+\frac{1}{3}+\frac{1}{3}}$$
$$= 4$$

But, it is also true that $\sqrt[3]{4} \cdot \sqrt[3]{4} \cdot \sqrt[3]{4} = 4$. Therefore, the values of $4^{\frac{1}{3}}$ and $\sqrt[3]{4}$ must be the same.

These examples and other similar examples suggest the following definition.

> **For any real number b and for any integer n, with n greater than one, $b^{\frac{1}{n}} = \sqrt[n]{b}$, except when $b < 0$ and n is even.**

Rational Numbers as Exponents

From the definition you can conclude that $7^{\frac{1}{2}} = \sqrt{7}$ and $(-8)^{\frac{1}{3}} = \sqrt[3]{-8}$ or -2. Since $-16 < 0$, the expression $(-16)^{\frac{1}{4}}$ is not defined.

Examples

1 Evaluate $27^{\frac{1}{3}}$.

$$27^{\frac{1}{3}} = \sqrt[3]{27} \text{ or } 3 \qquad \textit{Recall that } 3^3 = 3 \cdot 3 \cdot 3 \text{ or } 27.$$

2 Evaluate $1000^{-\frac{1}{3}}$.

$$1000^{-\frac{1}{3}} = \frac{1}{1000^{\frac{1}{3}}}$$

$$= \frac{1}{\sqrt[3]{1000}} \text{ or } \frac{1}{10} \qquad \textit{Recall that } 10^3 = 10 \cdot 10 \cdot 10 \text{ or } 1000.$$

3 Evaluate $16^{\frac{1}{4}}$.

$$16^{\frac{1}{4}} = (2^4)^{\frac{1}{4}} \qquad \textit{Rewrite 16 as } 2^4.$$
$$= 2^1 \text{ or } 2 \qquad \textit{Recall that } (a^m)^n = a^{mn}.$$

The following results show how the properties of exponents can be extended even further.

$$5^{\frac{3}{2}} = (5^{\frac{1}{2}})^3 \text{ or } (\sqrt{5})^3$$
$$5^{\frac{3}{2}} = (5^3)^{\frac{1}{2}} \text{ or } \sqrt{5^3}$$

Therefore, the values of $(\sqrt{5})^3$ and $\sqrt{5^3}$ must be the same.

$$7^{\frac{2}{3}} = (7^{\frac{1}{3}})^2 \text{ or } (\sqrt[3]{7})^2$$
$$7^{\frac{2}{3}} = (7^2)^{\frac{1}{3}} \text{ or } \sqrt[3]{7^2}$$

Therefore, the values of $(\sqrt[3]{7})^2$ and $\sqrt[3]{7^2}$ must be the same. These and other similar examples suggest the following definition.

For any nonzero real number b, and any integers m and n, with $n > 1$ $$b^{\frac{m}{n}} = \sqrt[n]{b^m} = (\sqrt[n]{b})^m$$ **except when $b < 0$ and n is even.**

Definition of Rational Exponents

Examples

4 **Evaluate $27^{\frac{2}{3}}$.**

$$27^{\frac{2}{3}} = (\sqrt[3]{27})^2$$
$$= (3)^2$$
$$= 9$$

5 **Evaluate $8^{\frac{1}{3}} \cdot 8^{\frac{4}{3}}$.**

$$8^{\frac{1}{3}} \cdot 8^{\frac{4}{3}} = 8^{\frac{5}{3}}$$
$$8^{\frac{5}{3}} = (\sqrt[3]{8})^5$$
$$= (2)^5 \quad \text{or} \quad 32$$

When a radical is in simplest form, its index is as small as possible.

Examples

6 **Express $\sqrt[6]{25}$ in simplest radical form.**

$$\sqrt[6]{25} = 25^{\frac{1}{6}}$$ *The index is 6. Is it possible to find a smaller index?*
$$= (25^{\frac{1}{2}})^{\frac{1}{3}}$$
$$= (\sqrt{25})^{\frac{1}{3}}$$ *Note that $25^{\frac{1}{2}} = \sqrt{25}$.*
$$= 5^{\frac{1}{3}} \quad \text{or} \quad \sqrt[3]{5}$$

7 **Express $3^{\frac{1}{2}}x^{\frac{2}{3}}y^{\frac{1}{6}}$ in simplest radical form.**

$$3^{\frac{1}{2}}x^{\frac{2}{3}}y^{\frac{1}{6}} = 3^{\frac{3}{6}}x^{\frac{4}{6}}y^{\frac{1}{6}}$$
$$= (3^3x^4y^1)^{\frac{1}{6}}$$
$$= \sqrt[6]{27x^4y}$$

Rewrite all exponents using the same denominator.

8 **Express $\sqrt[5]{(32x)^2}$ using rational exponents.**

$$\sqrt[5]{(32x)^2} = (32x)^{\frac{2}{5}}$$
$$= 32^{\frac{2}{5}} \cdot x^{\frac{2}{5}}$$
$$= (32^{\frac{1}{5}})^2 \cdot x^{\frac{2}{5}}$$
$$= 2^2x^{\frac{2}{5}} \quad \text{or} \quad 4x^{\frac{2}{5}}$$

Exploratory Exercises

Evaluate.

1. $4^{\frac{3}{2}}$
2. $9^{\frac{3}{2}}$
3. $8^{-\frac{1}{3}}$
4. $16^{-\frac{3}{4}}$
5. $(16^{\frac{1}{2}})^{-\frac{1}{2}}$
6. $27^{-\frac{2}{3}}$
7. $64^{\frac{5}{6}}$
8. $64^{-\frac{1}{3}}$
9. $\sqrt[3]{8^2}$
10. $16^{-\frac{1}{4}}$
11. $\sqrt[4]{81}$
12. $\sqrt[3]{216}$
13. $(6^{\frac{2}{3}})^3$
14. $9^{\frac{1}{3}} \cdot 9^{\frac{5}{3}}$
15. $\dfrac{36^{\frac{3}{4}}}{36^{\frac{1}{4}}}$
16. $16^{-\frac{3}{2}}$

Express each of the following in simplest radical form.

17. $\sqrt[4]{36}$
18. $\sqrt[6]{49}$
19. $\sqrt[6]{81}$
20. $\sqrt[4]{25}$

Written Exercises

Express each of the following using exponents.

1. $\sqrt{21}$
2. $\sqrt[3]{30}$
3. $\sqrt[6]{32}$
4. $\sqrt[4]{x}$
5. $\sqrt[3]{y}$
6. $\sqrt{25x^3y^4}$
7. $\sqrt[3]{8m^3r^6}$
8. $\sqrt[4]{8x^3y^5}$
9. $\sqrt[4]{27}$
10. $\sqrt[3]{16a^5b^7}$
11. $\sqrt[3]{n^2}$
12. $\sqrt[6]{b^3}$

Express each of the following in simplest radical form.

13. $64^{\frac{1}{6}}$
14. $5^{\frac{1}{2}}$
15. $6^{\frac{1}{3}}$
16. $x^{\frac{3}{4}}$
17. $a^{\frac{3}{2}}b^{\frac{5}{2}}$
18. $4^{\frac{1}{3}}x^{\frac{2}{3}}y^{\frac{4}{3}}$
19. $2^{\frac{5}{3}}x^{\frac{7}{3}}$
20. $(2x)^{\frac{1}{2}}x^{\frac{1}{2}}$
21. $5^{\frac{2}{3}}p^{\frac{2}{3}}q^{\frac{1}{3}}$
22. $(3m)^{\frac{2}{5}}n^{\frac{3}{5}}$
23. $r^{\frac{5}{2}}q^{\frac{3}{4}}$
24. $w^{\frac{4}{7}}y^{\frac{3}{7}}$
25. $x^{\frac{1}{3}}y^{\frac{1}{2}}$
26. $a^{\frac{5}{6}}b^{\frac{3}{2}}x^{\frac{7}{3}}$
27. $5^2b^{\frac{1}{2}}c^{\frac{1}{4}}$
28. $x^{\frac{3}{4}}y^{\frac{1}{3}}z^{\frac{5}{6}}$
29. $\sqrt[4]{9}$
30. $\sqrt[4]{49}$
31. $\sqrt[6]{8}$
32. $\sqrt[8]{16}$

Evaluate each expression.

33. $121^{\frac{1}{2}}$
34. $\left(\dfrac{1}{32}\right)^{\frac{1}{5}}$
35. $\sqrt[3]{12^3}$
36. $\sqrt[4]{256}$
37. $\left(\dfrac{343}{64}\right)^{\frac{1}{3}}$
38. $\left(\dfrac{216}{729}\right)^{\frac{2}{3}}$
39. $(6^{\frac{2}{3}})^3$
40. $(9^{\frac{3}{4}})^{\frac{2}{3}}$
41. $(0.125)^{\frac{2}{3}}$
42. $(0.008)^{\frac{1}{3}}$
43. $(0.027)^{\frac{1}{3}}$
44. $(0.0016)^{\frac{1}{4}}$

Challenge

Express each of the following in simplest radical form.

45. $\sqrt[3]{2^5} \cdot \sqrt[4]{2}$
46. $\sqrt[3]{2^2} \cdot \sqrt[6]{2^7}$
47. $\sqrt{3} \cdot \sqrt[3]{3^2}$
48. $\sqrt[3]{5^2} \cdot \sqrt{5}$
49. $\sqrt[5]{16} \cdot \sqrt[5]{2}$
50. $\sqrt[3]{32} \cdot \sqrt[3]{2}$
51. $\sqrt[3]{\sqrt{27}}$
52. $\sqrt{\sqrt[3]{36}}$

Using Calculators —————————————— Rational Exponents

Here are two ways to evaluate $4^{\frac{2}{3}}$.

$$4^{\frac{2}{3}} = (\sqrt[3]{4})^2$$

ENTER: 4 [INV] [y^x] 3 [=] [x^2]
DISPLAY: 4   3 1.5874 2.5198

$$4^{\frac{2}{3}} = \sqrt[3]{4^2}$$

ENTER: 4 [x^2] [INV] [y^x] 3 [=]
DISPLAY: 4 16   3 2.5198

Exercises Evaluate.

1. $7^{\frac{2}{3}}$
2. $12^{\frac{3}{5}}$
3. $32^{\frac{6}{5}}$
4. $38^{\frac{3}{7}}$
5. $15^{\frac{4}{3}}$
6. $68^{\frac{8}{5}}$

6-6 Simplifying Expressions with Rational Exponents

A rational expression that contains a fractional exponent in the denominator must also be rationalized.

Examples

1 Simplify $\dfrac{1}{3^{\frac{1}{2}}}$.

$\dfrac{1}{3^{\frac{1}{2}}} = \dfrac{1}{3^{\frac{1}{2}}} \cdot 1$

$\qquad = \dfrac{1}{3^{\frac{1}{2}}} \cdot \dfrac{3^{\frac{1}{2}}}{3^{\frac{1}{2}}}$ *Why is $\dfrac{3^{\frac{1}{2}}}{3^{\frac{1}{2}}}$ chosen?*

$\qquad = \dfrac{3^{\frac{1}{2}}}{3}$

2 Simplify $\dfrac{1}{4^{\frac{1}{3}}}$.

$\dfrac{1}{4^{\frac{1}{3}}} = \dfrac{1}{4^{\frac{1}{3}}} \cdot 1$

$\qquad = \dfrac{1}{4^{\frac{1}{3}}} \cdot \dfrac{4^{\frac{2}{3}}}{4^{\frac{2}{3}}}$ *Why is $\dfrac{4^{\frac{2}{3}}}{4^{\frac{2}{3}}}$ chosen?*

$\qquad = \dfrac{4^{\frac{2}{3}}}{4}$

It is important to choose a multiplier carefully. Study the following ways to simplify $\dfrac{1}{5^{\frac{3}{2}}}$.

$\dfrac{1}{5^{\frac{3}{2}}} = \dfrac{1}{5^{\frac{3}{2}}}\left(\dfrac{5^{\frac{3}{2}}}{5^{\frac{3}{2}}}\right)$

$\qquad = \dfrac{5^{\frac{3}{2}}}{5^3}$

$\qquad = \dfrac{5 \cdot 5^{\frac{1}{2}}}{5 \cdot 5^2}$ or $\dfrac{5^{\frac{1}{2}}}{5^2}$

$\dfrac{1}{5^{\frac{3}{2}}} = \dfrac{1}{5^{\frac{3}{2}}}\left(\dfrac{5^{\frac{1}{2}}}{5^{\frac{1}{2}}}\right)$

$\qquad = \dfrac{5^{\frac{1}{2}}}{5^2}$

Notice that there are fewer steps in simplifying $\dfrac{1}{5^{\frac{3}{2}}}$ when 1 is written in the form $\dfrac{5^{\frac{1}{2}}}{5^{\frac{1}{2}}}$.

An expression is simplified when it meets these conditions.

1. **It has no negative exponents.**
2. **It has no fractional exponents in the denominator.**
3. **It is not a complex fraction.**
4. **The index of any remaining radical is as small as possible.**

Conditions for Simplified Expressions

When you simplify an expression, be sure your answer meets all of the above conditions. In some problems, the simplest form may not always be the most convenient to use. Sometimes the content of a problem determines the most appropriate form for the answer.

Examples

3 Simplify $r^{-\frac{1}{9}}$.

$$r^{-\frac{1}{9}} = \frac{1}{r^{\frac{1}{9}}}$$

$$= \frac{1}{r^{\frac{1}{9}}}\left(\frac{r^{\frac{8}{9}}}{r^{\frac{8}{9}}}\right)$$

Why choose to multiply by $\dfrac{r^{\frac{8}{9}}}{r^{\frac{8}{9}}}$?

$$= \frac{r^{\frac{8}{9}}}{r}$$

4 Simplify $\dfrac{a^{\frac{1}{2}} - b^{\frac{1}{2}}}{a^{\frac{1}{2}} + b^{\frac{1}{2}}}$.

$$\frac{a^{\frac{1}{2}} - b^{\frac{1}{2}}}{a^{\frac{1}{2}} + b^{\frac{1}{2}}} = \frac{a^{\frac{1}{2}} - b^{\frac{1}{2}}}{a^{\frac{1}{2}} + b^{\frac{1}{2}}} \cdot \frac{a^{\frac{1}{2}} - b^{\frac{1}{2}}}{a^{\frac{1}{2}} - b^{\frac{1}{2}}}$$

$$= \frac{a - 2a^{\frac{1}{2}}b^{\frac{1}{2}} + b}{a - b}$$

Exploratory Exercises

State a factor that can be used to rationalize each expression.

1. $\dfrac{6}{3^{\frac{1}{2}}}$
2. $\dfrac{10}{5^{\frac{2}{3}}}$
3. $\dfrac{16}{4^{\frac{1}{2}}}$
4. $\dfrac{1}{x^{\frac{1}{3}}}$
5. $\dfrac{1}{y^{\frac{2}{3}}}$
6. $a^{-\frac{1}{5}}$

7. $p^{-\frac{3}{2}}$
8. $\dfrac{1}{x^{\frac{1}{2}} + 1}$
9. $\dfrac{m + p}{m^{\frac{1}{2}} + p}$
10. $\dfrac{r}{r^{\frac{1}{2}} - s^{\frac{1}{2}}}$
11. $\dfrac{2}{t^{\frac{3}{2}} + s^{\frac{1}{2}}}$
12. $\dfrac{1}{b^{\frac{3}{2}} + b^{\frac{1}{2}}}$

Written Exercises

1–12. Simplify each expression in Exploratory Exercises 1–12.
Simplify each expression.

13. $\dfrac{1}{y^{\frac{2}{5}}}$
14. $\dfrac{3}{r^{\frac{4}{5}}}$
15. $b^{-\frac{1}{4}}$
16. $m^{-\frac{5}{6}}$

17. $\dfrac{15}{5^{\frac{2}{3}}}$
18. $\dfrac{24}{6^{\frac{2}{3}}}$
19. $\dfrac{rm^{\frac{1}{2}}}{b^{\frac{3}{2}}}$
20. $\dfrac{pq}{\sqrt[3]{a}}$

21. $\dfrac{b^{\frac{3}{2}} + 3b^{-\frac{1}{2}}}{b^{\frac{1}{2}}}$
22. $\dfrac{a^{\frac{1}{3}}m + 3a^{-\frac{1}{3}}}{a^{\frac{2}{3}}}$
23. $\dfrac{3x + 4x^2}{x^{-\frac{2}{3}}}$
24. $\dfrac{3m}{b^{-\frac{3}{2}} \cdot \sqrt[3]{a}}$

25. $\left(r^{-\frac{1}{6}}\right)^{-\frac{2}{3}}$
26. $\left(y^{\frac{1}{3}}\right)^{-\frac{3}{4}}$
27. $\dfrac{r^{\frac{3}{2}}}{r^{\frac{1}{2}} + 2}$
28. $\dfrac{x^{\frac{1}{2}} + y^{\frac{1}{2}}}{x^{\frac{1}{2}} - y^{\frac{1}{2}}}$

29. $\dfrac{a^{\frac{1}{2}} - b^{\frac{1}{2}}}{a^{\frac{1}{2}} + b^{\frac{1}{2}}}$
30. $\dfrac{x^{\frac{1}{2}} + 1}{x^{\frac{1}{2}} - 1}$
31. $\dfrac{rs}{r^{\frac{1}{2}} + r^{\frac{3}{2}}}$
32. $\dfrac{x^{\frac{1}{3}}}{x^{\frac{2}{3}} - x^{-\frac{1}{3}}}$

33. $\dfrac{b^{\frac{1}{2}}}{b^{\frac{3}{2}} - b^{\frac{1}{2}}}$
34. $\dfrac{a^{-\frac{2}{3}}b^{\frac{1}{2}}}{b^{-\frac{3}{2}} \cdot \sqrt[3]{a}}$
35. $\left(\dfrac{x^{-2}y^{-6}}{9}\right)^{-\frac{1}{2}}$
36. $\left(\dfrac{z^{-\frac{2}{3}}}{5^{-1}z^{\frac{1}{3}}}\right)^{-2}$

37. $\left(\sqrt[6]{5}x^{\frac{7}{4}}y^{-\frac{2}{3}}\right)^{12}$
38. $\dfrac{8^{\frac{1}{6}} - 9^{\frac{1}{4}}}{\sqrt{3} + \sqrt{2}}$
39. $\dfrac{9x^{-\frac{4}{3}} - 4y^{-2}}{3x^{-\frac{2}{3}} + 2y^{-1}}$
40. $\dfrac{a^{\frac{5}{3}} - a^{\frac{1}{3}}b^{\frac{4}{3}}}{a^{\frac{2}{3}} + b^{\frac{2}{3}}}$

41. Evaluate $-\dfrac{4}{9}x^9\left(\dfrac{3}{x^2} - \dfrac{1}{\sqrt[3]{2}}\right)$ when $x = \sqrt[6]{2}$.

42. Evaluate $\dfrac{3^0y + 4y^{-1}}{y^{-\frac{2}{3}}}$ when $y = 8$.

Challenge

Simplify.

43. $\dfrac{1}{x^{\frac{1}{3}} - y^{\frac{1}{3}}}$
44. $\dfrac{a}{a^{\frac{1}{3}} - b^{\frac{2}{3}}}$
45. $\dfrac{1}{a^{\frac{2}{3}} - b^{\frac{2}{3}}}$
46. $\dfrac{z^{\frac{1}{3}}}{z^{\frac{2}{3}} - z^{\frac{1}{3}}}$

6-7 Equations with Radicals

The properties of radicals can be used to solve equations.

Example

1 Solve $x + 2 = x\sqrt{3}$.

$$x + 2 = x\sqrt{3}$$
$$x - x\sqrt{3} = -2$$
$$x(1 - \sqrt{3}) = -2 \qquad \textit{Distributive Property}$$
$$x = \frac{-2}{1 - \sqrt{3}}$$
$$x = \frac{-2}{1 - \sqrt{3}} \cdot \frac{1 + \sqrt{3}}{1 + \sqrt{3}} \qquad \textit{The conjugate of } 1 - \sqrt{3} \textit{ is } 1 + \sqrt{3}.$$
$$x = \frac{-2(1 + \sqrt{3})}{1^2 - (\sqrt{3})^2}$$
$$x = \frac{-2(1 + \sqrt{3})}{-2}$$
$$x = 1 + \sqrt{3}$$

Check:
$$x + 2 = x\sqrt{3}$$
$$(1 + \sqrt{3}) + 2 \stackrel{?}{=} (1 + \sqrt{3})\sqrt{3}$$
$$\sqrt{3} + 3 = \sqrt{3} + 3$$

The solution is $1 + \sqrt{3}$.

Variables may appear in the radicand of a radical. Equations containing such radicals are called **radical equations.**

Squaring both sides of an equation may produce results that do *not* satisfy the equation.

You must check all possible solutions in the original equation.

$$x = 2 \qquad \text{This equation has } one \text{ solution, 2.}$$
$$(x)^2 = (2)^2 \qquad \text{Square both sides.}$$
$$x^2 = 4 \qquad \text{This equation has } two \text{ solutions, 2 and } -2.$$

Examples

2 Solve $7 + \sqrt{a - 3} = 1$.

$$7 + \sqrt{a - 3} = 1$$
$$\sqrt{a - 3} = -6 \qquad \textit{Isolate the radical.}$$
$$(\sqrt{a - 3})^2 = (-6)^2 \qquad \textit{Square both sides.}$$
$$a - 3 = 36$$
$$a = 39$$

Check:
$$7 + \sqrt{a - 3} = 1$$
$$7 + \sqrt{39 - 3} \stackrel{?}{=} 1$$
$$7 + \sqrt{36} \stackrel{?}{=} 1$$
$$13 \neq 1$$

The answer does *not* check.
The equation has *no* solutions.

3 Solve $3 - \sqrt{x - 2} = 0$.

$$3 - \sqrt{x - 2} = 0$$
$$3 = \sqrt{x - 2}$$
$$3^2 = (\sqrt{x - 2})^2$$
$$9 = x - 2$$
$$11 = x$$

Check:
$$3 - \sqrt{x - 2} = 0$$
$$3 - \sqrt{11 - 2} \stackrel{?}{=} 0$$
$$3 - \sqrt{9} \stackrel{?}{=} 0$$
$$3 - 3 \stackrel{?}{=} 0$$
$$0 = 0$$

The solution is 11.

Examples

4 **Solve** $\sqrt{2y - 3} - \sqrt{2y + 3} = -1.$

$$\sqrt{2y - 3} - \sqrt{2y + 3} = -1$$

$$\sqrt{2y - 3} = \sqrt{2y + 3} - 1 \qquad \textit{Isolate one radical.}$$

$$2y - 3 = 2y + 3 - 2\sqrt{2y + 3} + 1 \qquad \textit{Square each side.}$$

$$-7 = -2\sqrt{2y + 3} \qquad \textit{Note middle term from expansion.}$$

$$\frac{7}{2} = \sqrt{2y + 3} \qquad \textit{Isolate the remaining radical.}$$

$$\frac{49}{4} = 2y + 3 \qquad \textit{Square each side.}$$

$$\frac{37}{4} = 2y$$

$$y = \frac{37}{8}$$

The solution is $\frac{37}{8}$ or $4\frac{5}{8}$.

Check: $\quad \sqrt{2y - 3} - \sqrt{2y + 3} = -1$

$$\sqrt{2\left(\frac{37}{8}\right) - 3} - \sqrt{2\left(\frac{37}{8}\right) + 3} \overset{?}{=} -1$$

$$\sqrt{\frac{25}{4}} - \sqrt{\frac{49}{4}} \overset{?}{=} -1$$

$$\frac{5}{2} - \frac{7}{2} \overset{?}{=} -1$$

$$-1 = -1$$

5 **Solve** $\sqrt[3]{3y - 1} - 2 = 0.$

$$\sqrt[3]{3y - 1} - 2 = 0$$

$$\sqrt[3]{3y - 1} = 2$$

$$(\sqrt[3]{3y - 1})^3 = 2^3$$

$$3y - 1 = 8$$

$$3y = 9$$

$$y = 3$$

Check: $\quad \sqrt[3]{3y - 1} - 2 = 0$

$$\sqrt[3]{3(3) - 1} - 2 \overset{?}{=} 0$$

$$\sqrt[3]{8} - 2 \overset{?}{=} 0$$

$$2 - 2 \overset{?}{=} 0$$

$$0 = 0$$

The solution is 3.

6 **Solve** $r = \sqrt[3]{\dfrac{3w}{4\pi d}}$ **for** $d.$

$$r = \sqrt[3]{\frac{3w}{4\pi d}}$$

$$r^3 = \frac{3w}{4\pi d} \qquad \textit{Cube both sides.}$$

$$r^3 \cdot d = \frac{3w}{4\pi d} \cdot d \qquad \textit{Multiply both sides by d.}$$

$$\frac{r^3 d}{r^3} = \frac{3w}{4\pi r^3} \qquad \textit{Divide both sides by } r^3.$$

$$d = \frac{3w}{4\pi r^3}$$

Exploratory Exercises

Solve each equation.

1. $\sqrt{x} = 2$
2. $\sqrt{y} = 3$
3. $\sqrt{m} - 8 = 0$
4. $\sqrt{t} - 4 = 0$
5. $\sqrt{2x + 7} = 3$
6. $\sqrt{3x + 7} = 7$
7. $\sqrt[3]{x - 2} = 3$
8. $\sqrt[4]{2x + 7} = 2$
9. $x\sqrt{3} - x = 7$
10. $x\sqrt{5} + x = 3$
11. $x\sqrt{3} + 4 = 7 + \sqrt{3}$
12. $2z\sqrt{7} + 3 = 5 + 6\sqrt{7}$

Written Exercises

Solve each equation.

1. $6 + 2x\sqrt{3} = 0$
2. $2 + 5n\sqrt{10} = 0$
3. $x\sqrt{2} + 3x = 4$
4. $x - x\sqrt{5} = 2$
5. $3x + 5 = x\sqrt{3}$
6. $2x + 7 = -x\sqrt{2}$
7. $2x - x\sqrt{11} = 13$
8. $13 - 3x = x\sqrt{5}$
9. $\sqrt{y - 5} - 7 = 0$
10. $\sqrt{x - 4} - 3 = 0$
11. $\sqrt[3]{y + 1} = 2$
12. $\sqrt[3]{m - 1} = 3$
13. $\sqrt[5]{2a} = 3$
14. $\sqrt[4]{3p} - 2 = 0$
15. $\sqrt{2x + 3} - 7 = 0$
16. $\sqrt{3y - 5} - 3 = 1$
17. $\sqrt{5y + 1} + 6 = 10$
18. $\sqrt{1 + 2r} - 4 = -1$
19. $\sqrt{2x + 3} + 3 = 10$
20. $\sqrt{4a + 8} + 5 = 7$
21. $\sqrt[3]{m + 5} + 6 = 4$
22. $\sqrt[4]{2x + 3} + 5 = 4$
23. $\sqrt{x + 5} = \sqrt{2x - 3}$
24. $\sqrt{x - 4} = \sqrt{2x - 3}$
25. $\sqrt{x - 5} - \sqrt{x} = 1$
26. $\sqrt{m + 12} - \sqrt{m} = 2$
27. $\sqrt{b + 4} = \sqrt{b + 20} - 2$
28. $\sqrt{y + 6} - \sqrt{y} = \sqrt{2}$
29. $\sqrt{x - 1} + \sqrt{x + 3} = 5$
30. $\sqrt{x + 1} + \sqrt{x - 3} - 5 = 0$
31. $\sqrt{y^2 + 5y} + y + 10 = 0$
32. $\sqrt{4x + 1} - \sqrt{4x - 2} = 3$
33. $\sqrt{5x^2 + 7x - 2} - x\sqrt{5} + 4 = 0$
34. $\sqrt{3x^2 + 11x - 5} = x\sqrt{3} + 1$
35. $\sqrt{x + 8} + 3 = \sqrt{x + 35}$
36. $\sqrt{y + 12} + 1 = \sqrt{y + 21}$
37. $\sqrt{x - 4} - 6 = \sqrt{x + 20}$
38. $\sqrt{3x - 5} = 2 - \sqrt{x - 1}$

Solve each equation for the variable indicated.

39. $y = \sqrt{r^2 + s^2}$ for r
40. $t = \sqrt{\dfrac{2s}{g}}$ for s
41. $r = \sqrt[3]{\dfrac{2mM}{c}}$ for c
42. $T = \dfrac{1}{2}\sqrt{\dfrac{u}{g}}$ for g
43. $v = \dfrac{1}{2}\sqrt{1 + \dfrac{T}{\ell}}$ for ℓ
44. $m^2 = \sqrt[3]{\dfrac{rp}{g^2}}$ for p

mini-review

1. Solve this system by graphing.

$$y \le x + 1$$
$$2y > x - 2$$

2. Evaluate $\begin{vmatrix} 1 & 4 & -1 \\ 6 & 2 & 5 \\ 0 & -8 & 3 \end{vmatrix}$.

3. Find the product.

$$\begin{bmatrix} 3 & 4 \\ -1 & 2 \end{bmatrix} \cdot \begin{bmatrix} 5 & -2 \\ 1 & 0 \end{bmatrix}$$

4. Simplify $4(b^2c)^3$.

5. Factor $3x^4 - 4ax^3 + 4a^2x^2$.

6-8   Pure Imaginary Numbers

Some equations have irrational solutions. For example, the solutions to $x^2 - 5 = 0$ are $\sqrt{5}$ and $-\sqrt{5}$.

Numbers like $\sqrt{5}$ and π are irrational.

The equation $x^2 = -1$ has *no* solution among the real numbers. This is because the square of a real number is nonnegative.

The number i is defined to be a solution to $x^2 = -1$ and is *not* a real number. It is called the **imaginary unit.**

Using i as you would any constant, you can define square roots of negative numbers.

$$i^2 = -1 \quad \text{so} \quad \sqrt{-1} = i$$
$$(2i)^2 = 2^2 i^2 \text{ or } -4 \quad \text{so} \quad \sqrt{-4} = \sqrt{4} \cdot \sqrt{-1} \text{ or } 2i$$
$$(i\sqrt{3})^2 = i^2(\sqrt{3})^2 \text{ or } -3 \quad \text{so} \quad \sqrt{-3} = \sqrt{3} \cdot \sqrt{-1} \text{ or } i\sqrt{3}$$

To avoid confusion between $\sqrt{3}i$ and $\sqrt{3i}$, express $\sqrt{3}i$ as $i\sqrt{3}$.

> **For any positive real number b,**
> $$\sqrt{-(b^2)} = \sqrt{b^2} \cdot \sqrt{-1} \text{ or } bi$$
> **where i is a number whose square is -1. The number i is called the imaginary unit, and bi is called a pure imaginary number.**

Definition of Pure Imaginary Number

Pure imaginary numbers are simplified by rewriting them as the product of i and a real number. For example, $3i$, $-i\sqrt{3}$, and $5i\sqrt{10}$ are in simplest form.

Examples

1 **Simplify $\sqrt{-16}$.**

$$\sqrt{-16} = \sqrt{16} \cdot \sqrt{-1}$$
$$= 4 \cdot i$$
$$= 4i$$

2 **Simplify $\sqrt{-24}$.**

$$\sqrt{-24} = \sqrt{24} \cdot \sqrt{-1}$$
$$= i\sqrt{24}$$
$$= i\sqrt{4 \cdot 6}$$
$$= 2i\sqrt{6}$$

Pure imaginary numbers can be multiplied by using the commutative and associative properties for multiplication.

Examples

3 **Simplify $3i \cdot 5i$.**

$$3i \cdot 5i = (3 \cdot 5)(i \cdot i)$$
$$= 15i^2$$
$$= 15(-1) \qquad i^2 = -1$$
$$= -15$$

4 **Simplify $\sqrt{-3} \cdot \sqrt{-12}$.**

Change $\sqrt{-3}$ and $\sqrt{-12}$ to imaginary form before multiplying.

$$\sqrt{-3} \cdot \sqrt{-12} = i\sqrt{3} \cdot i\sqrt{12}$$
$$= i^2\sqrt{36}$$
$$= -1 \cdot 6$$
$$= -6$$

Simplifying powers of i reveals an interesting pattern.

$$i^1 = i \qquad\qquad i^5 = i^4 \cdot i = 1 \cdot i \quad = i$$
$$i^2 = -1 \qquad\qquad i^6 = i^4 \cdot i^2 = 1 \cdot (-1) = -1$$
$$i^3 = i^2 \cdot i \; = -1 \cdot i \quad = -i \qquad i^7 = i^4 \cdot i^3 = 1 \cdot (-i) = -i$$
$$i^4 = i^2 \cdot i^2 = -1 \cdot (-1) = 1 \qquad i^8 = i^4 \cdot i^4 = 1 \cdot 1 \quad = 1$$

The values $i,\ -1,\ -i,$ and 1 repeat in cycles of four.

Examples

5 **Simplify i^{15}.**

$$i^{15} = i^4 \cdot i^4 \cdot i^4 \cdot i^3$$
$$= 1 \cdot 1 \cdot 1 \cdot (-i)$$
$$= -i$$

6 **Simplify i^{86}.**

$$i^{86} = (i^2)^{43} \qquad \text{Remember } i^2 = -1.$$
$$= (-1)^{43}$$
$$= -1 \qquad -1 \text{ raised to an odd power is } -1.$$

7 **Solve $x^2 + 5 = 0$**

$$x^2 + 5 = 0$$
$$x^2 = -5$$
$$x^2 = -1 \cdot 5$$
$$x = \pm i\sqrt{5} \quad \text{The solutions, both pure imaginary numbers, are } i\sqrt{5} \text{ and } -i\sqrt{5}.$$

Exploratory Exercises

Simplify.

1. $\sqrt{-36}$ 2. $\sqrt{-64}$ 3. $4\sqrt{-2}$ 4. $6\sqrt{-4}$
5. $\sqrt{-3} \cdot \sqrt{-3}$ 6. $\sqrt{-2} \cdot \sqrt{-2}$ 7. $\sqrt{-5} \cdot \sqrt{5}$ 8. $\sqrt{-7} \cdot \sqrt{7}$
9. $3 \cdot 2i$ 10. $5 \cdot 7i$ 11. i^6 12. i^{91}

Written Exercises

Simplify.

1. $\sqrt{-81}$ 2. $\sqrt{-121}$ 3. $\sqrt{-50}$ 4. $\sqrt{-98}$
5. $\sqrt{\dfrac{-4}{9}}$ 6. $\sqrt{\dfrac{-9}{16}}$ 7. $\sqrt{\dfrac{-1}{3}}$ 8. $\sqrt{\dfrac{-1}{2}}$
9. i^5 10. i^{10} 11. i^{11} 12. i^{43} 13. i^{71} 14. i^{112} 15. i^{82} 16. i^{243}
17. $\sqrt{-8} \cdot \sqrt{-2}$ 18. $\sqrt{-15} \cdot \sqrt{-5}$ 19. $\sqrt{-14} \cdot \sqrt{-7}$ 20. $\sqrt{-3} \cdot \sqrt{-18}$
21. $(\sqrt{-3})^2$ 22. $(\sqrt{-12})^2$ 23. $(\sqrt{-3})^3$ 24. $(\sqrt{-4})^3$
25. $(-2\sqrt{-8})(3\sqrt{-2})$ 26. $(4\sqrt{-12})(-2\sqrt{-3})$ 27. $(6\sqrt{-24})(-3\sqrt{6})$
28. $(2\sqrt{15})(-3\sqrt{-15})$ 29. $(2i)(3i)^2$ 30. $5i(-2i)^2$

Solve each equation.

31. $x^2 + 16 = 0$ 32. $a^2 + 49 = 0$ 33. $z^2 + 169 = 0$ 34. $c^2 + 144 = 0$
35. $n^2 + 3 = 0$ 36. $t^2 + 12 = 0$ 37. $2y^2 + 8 = 0$ 38. $3b^2 + 18 = 0$
39. $5x^2 + 125 = 0$ 40. $3z^2 + 24 = 0$ 41. $4m^2 + 5 = 0$ 42. $9k^2 + 32 = 0$

6-9   Complex Numbers

Numbers such as $5i$, $6 - i$, and $27 + 2i$ are imaginary numbers since they contain the imaginary unit, i. The real numbers together with the imaginary numbers form the set of **complex numbers**.

> **A complex number is any number that can be written in the form $a + bi$ where a and b are real numbers and i is the imaginary unit.**

Definition of Complex Number

> a is called the real part. bi is called the imaginary part.

Any real number is also a complex number. For example, $\sqrt{2}$ can be written as $\sqrt{2} + 0i$. Its imaginary part is $0i$ or 0. A complex number is a real number *only if its imaginary part is 0*.

Any two complex numbers denoted by $a + bi$ and $c + di$, are equal if and only if their real parts are equal and their imaginary parts are equal. That is,

$$a + bi = c + di \text{ if and only if } a = c \text{ and } b = d.$$

As long as $b \neq 0$, the complex number $a + bi$ is also called an imaginary number.

Example

1   **Find values for x and y such that $2x + 3yi = 6 + 2i$.**

$2x + 3yi = 6 + 2i$
$2x = 6$ and $3y = 2$

$x = 3$ $y = \dfrac{2}{3}$

Check: $2(3) + 3\left(\dfrac{2}{3}\right)i \stackrel{?}{=} 6 + 2i$

$6 + 2i = 6 + 2i$

To add or subtract complex numbers, you combine their real parts and combine their imaginary parts. This is done by using the commutative, associative, and distributive properties. The FOIL method can be used to multiply complex numbers.

Examples

2   **Find $(3 + 6i) + (7 - 2i)$.**

$(3 + 6i) + (7 - 2i)$
$= (3 + 7) + (6i - 2i)$
$= 10 + 4i$

3   **Find $(6 - 5i) - (3 - 2i)$.**

$(6 - 5i) - (3 - 2i)$
$= (6 - 3) + (-5i - (-2i))$
$= 3 - 3i$

4   **Find $(6 - 7i)(4 + 3i)$.**

$$ \overset{\text{F}}{} \qquad \overset{\text{O}}{} \qquad \overset{\text{I}}{} \qquad \overset{\text{L}}{}$$

$(6 - 7i)(4 + 3i) = 6 \cdot 4 + 6 \cdot 3i + (-7i) \cdot 4 + (-7i) \cdot 3i$
$= 24 + 18i - 28i - 21i^2$
$= (24 + 21) + (18i - 28i) \qquad -21i^2 = 21$
$= 45 - 10i$

This chart summarizes addition, subtraction, and multiplication of complex numbers.

For any complex numbers $a + bi$ and $c + di$:
$(a + bi) + (c + di) = (a + c) + (b + d)i$
$(a + bi) - (c + di) = (a - c) + (b - d)i$
$(a + bi)(c + di) = (ac - bd) + (ad + bc)i$

Exploratory Exercises

Simplify.

1. $(6 + 3i) + (2 + 8i)$
2. $(4 - i) + (3 + 3i)$
3. $(5 + 2i) - (2 + 2i)$
4. $(7 - 6i) - (5 - 6i)$
5. $(7 + 3i) + (3 - 3i)$
6. $(2 + 4i) + (2 - 4i)$
7. $4(5 + 3i)$
8. $-6(2 - 3i)$
9. $(1 + 3i)(2 + 4i)$
10. $(2 - 3i)(1 - 4i)$
11. $(3 + 2i)(4 - i)$
12. $(6 + i)(6 - i)$

Find values of x and y for which each equation is true.

13. $x - yi = 5 + 6i$
14. $x + yi = 2 - 3i$
15. $x - yi = 7 - 2i$
16. $x - yi = 4 + 5i$
17. $x + 2yi = 3$
18. $2x + yi = 5i$

Written Exercises

2-28 even

Simplify.

1. $(3 + 2i) + (4 + 5i)$
2. $(2 + 6i) + (4 + 3i)$
3. $(9 + 6i) - (3 + 2i)$
4. $(11 - \sqrt{-3}) - (-4 + \sqrt{-5})$
5. $(5 + \sqrt{-7}) + (-3 + \sqrt{-2})$
6. $(8 - 7i) + (-5 - i)$
7. $(3 - 11i) - (-5 + 4i)$
8. $(-6 - 2i) - (-8 - 3i)$
9. $(4 + 2i\sqrt{3}) + (1 - 5i\sqrt{3})$
10. $(8 - 3i\sqrt{5}) + (-3 + 2i\sqrt{5})$
11. $2(-3 + 2i) + 3(-5 - 2i)$
12. $-6(2 - i) + 3(4 - 5i)$
13. $(2 - 3i)(5 + i)$
14. $(5 + 3i)(6 - i)$
15. $(6 - 2i)^2$
16. $(2 + i\sqrt{3})^2$
17. $(7 - i\sqrt{2})(5 + i\sqrt{2})$
18. $(4 - 3i)(7 - 2i)$
19. $(3 + 2i)^2$
20. $(3 + 4i)^2$
21. $(\sqrt{2} + i)(\sqrt{2} - i)$
22. $(3 + 2i)(3 - 2i)$
23. $(2 - \sqrt{-3})(2 + \sqrt{-3})$
24. $(3 + \sqrt{-2})(3 - \sqrt{-2})$
25. $(2 + i)(3 - 4i)(1 + 2i)$
26. $(6 - i)(5 + 2i)(3 + 3i)$
27. $(7 - 5i)(2 - 3i)(7 + 5i)$
28. $(9 + 2i)(5 + i)(9 - 2i)$
29. $(4 + 3i)(2 - 7i)(3 + i)$
30. $(7 - i)(4 + 2i)(5 + 2i)$

Find values of x and y for which each sentence is true.

31. $2x + 5yi = 4 + 15i$
32. $3x + 2yi = 18 + 7i$
33. $(x - y) + (x + y)i = 2 - 4i$
34. $(2x + y) + (x - y)i = 7 - i$
35. $(x + 2y) + (2x - y)i = 5 + 5i$
36. $(x + 4y) + (2x - 3y)i = 13 + 7i$

37. Write an expression for the additive inverse of the complex number $a + bi$.
38. Show that 0 is the additive identity for complex numbers.
39. Show that 1 is the multiplicative identity for complex numbers.

Applications in Electronics

Electrical Circuits

In a simplified electrical circuit there are three basic things to be considered: flow of electric current, I, resistance to that flow, Z, called impedance, and electromotive force, E, called voltage. All three are related in the formula $E = I \cdot Z$. This basic formula can be expressed in several ways.

Current is measured in amps. Impedance is measured in ohms. Voltage is measured in volts.

$$E = I \cdot Z \qquad \frac{E}{Z} = I \qquad \frac{E}{I} = Z$$

The current, impedance, and voltage are often expressed as complex numbers. Electrical engineers use j instead of i to represent an imaginary number. For electrical engineers, $j = \sqrt{-1}$ and $j^2 = -1$.

Example: **Compute the voltage, E, when $I = (35 - j40)$ amps and $Z = (10 + j2)$ ohms.**

$E = I \cdot Z$

$\quad = (35 - j40)(10 + j2)$

$\quad = 350 + j70 - j400 - j^2 80$

$\quad = 350 - j330 + 80$

$\quad = 430 - j330$

The voltage is $(430 - j330)$ volts.

Exercises

Find E given the following values.

1. $I = (4 + j3)$ amps, $Z = (16 - j28)$ ohms

2. $I = (6 - j8)$ amps, $Z = (14 + j8)$ ohms

Find I given the following values.

3. $E = (70 + j226)$ volts, $Z = (6 + j8)$ ohms

4. $E = (85 + j110)$ volts, $Z = (3 - j4)$ ohms

Find Z given the following values.

5. $E = (-50 + j100)$ volts, $I = (-6 - j2)$ amps

6. $E = (100 + j10)$ volts, $I = (-8 + j3)$ amps

6-10　More about Complex Numbers

Complex numbers of the form $a + bi$ and $a - bi$ are called **conjugates** of each other. Notice that the product of complex conjugates is always a real number.

Examples

1 Find $(3 + 5i)(3 - 5i)$.

$(3 + 5i)(3 - 5i)$

$= 9 - 25i^2$

$= 9 - (-25)$

$= 34$

2 Find $(a + bi)(a - bi)$.

$(a + bi)(a - bi)$

$= a^2 - b^2i^2$

$= a^2 - (-b^2)$

$= a^2 + b^2$

Sometimes rational expressions contain complex numbers. Since i represents a radical, rational expressions are usually written without imaginary numbers in the denominator. As with radicals, the denominator should be rationalized.

Examples

3 Simplify $\dfrac{3 + 7i}{2i}$.

$\dfrac{3 + 7i}{2i} = \dfrac{3 + 7i}{2i} \cdot \dfrac{i}{i}$

$= \dfrac{3i + 7i^2}{2i^2}$

$= \dfrac{-7 + 3i}{-2}$

$= \dfrac{7 - 3i}{2}$

4 Simplify $\dfrac{4 + 3i}{1 - 2i}$.

$\dfrac{4 + 3i}{1 - 2i} = \dfrac{4 + 3i}{1 - 2i} \cdot \dfrac{1 + 2i}{1 + 2i}$

Conjugates are used to rationalize the denominator.

$= \dfrac{4 \cdot 1 + 4 \cdot 2i + 3i \cdot 1 + 3i \cdot 2i}{1 \cdot 1 + 1 \cdot 2i + -2i \cdot 1 + -2i \cdot 2i}$

$= \dfrac{4 + 8i + 3i - 6}{1 + 2i - 2i + 4}$

$= \dfrac{-2 + 11i}{5}$

5 Find the multiplicative inverse of $3 - 5i$.

The multiplicative inverse of $3 - 5i$ is $\dfrac{1}{3 - 5i}$. Now simplify.

$\dfrac{1}{3 - 5i} = \dfrac{1}{3 - 5i} \cdot \dfrac{3 + 5i}{3 + 5i}$

$= \dfrac{3 + 5i}{9 - 25i^2}$

$= \dfrac{3 + 5i}{34}$

The inverse is $\dfrac{3 + 5i}{34}$.

Check: $3 - 5i \cdot \dfrac{3 + 5i}{34} = \dfrac{9 + 25}{34}$

$= 1$

The product of a number and its multiplicative inverse is 1.

Exploratory Exercises

Find the conjugate of each complex number.

1. $2 + i$
2. $1 + 3i$
3. $5 - 4i$
4. $3 - 2i$
5. $4i$
6. $7i$
7. $-5i$
8. $-3i$
9. 6
10. 8
11. $5 - 6i$
12. $12 + i$

Show that each of the following are multiplicative inverses of one another.

13. $3 + 2i; \dfrac{3 - 2i}{13}$
14. $5 - 4i; \dfrac{5 + 4i}{41}$
15. $6 + 8i; \dfrac{3 - 4i}{50}$

Written Exercises

Find the product of each complex number and its conjugate.

1. $3 - 7i$
2. $6 + 5i$
3. $2 + 9i$
4. $17 - i$
5. $2 - 3i$
6. $7 - 7i$
7. $-2i$
8. $-10i$

Simplify.

9. $\dfrac{3 - 2i}{1 - i}$
10. $\dfrac{4 + 5i}{1 + i}$
11. $\dfrac{1 + i}{3 + 2i}$
12. $\dfrac{1 - i}{4 - 5i}$
13. $\dfrac{3 + 5i}{2i}$

14. $\dfrac{4 - 7i}{-3i}$
15. $\dfrac{5 - 6i}{-3i}$
16. $\dfrac{2 + i}{5i}$
17. $\dfrac{3}{4 - i}$
18. $\dfrac{2}{6 + 5i}$

19. $\dfrac{4}{\sqrt{3} + 2i}$
20. $\dfrac{7}{\sqrt{2} - 3i}$
21. $\dfrac{2 + i\sqrt{3}}{2 - i\sqrt{3}}$
22. $\dfrac{1 + i\sqrt{2}}{1 - i\sqrt{2}}$
23. $\dfrac{3 - i\sqrt{5}}{3 + i\sqrt{5}}$

24. $\dfrac{2 - i\sqrt{7}}{2 + i\sqrt{7}}$
25. $\dfrac{(2 + 3i)^2}{(3 + i)^2}$
26. $\dfrac{(3 + 3i)^2}{(1 + i)^2}$
27. $\dfrac{1 - i}{(1 + i)^2}$
28. $\dfrac{(4 + 3i)^2}{(3 - i)^2}$

Find the multiplicative inverse of each complex number.

29. $3 + i$
30. $2 - 5i$
31. $7 - 3i$
32. $3 + 7i$
33. $\dfrac{4i}{3 + i}$
34. $\dfrac{2i}{5 - i}$
35. $\dfrac{-i}{2 - 3i}$
36. $\dfrac{-3i}{3 + 4i}$

37. Write an expression for the multiplicative inverse of $a + bi$.

Challenge

38. Show that $-\dfrac{1}{2} + \dfrac{1}{2}i\sqrt{3}$ is a cube root of 1. (Hint: Find the cube of the number.)

39. Show that $-\dfrac{1}{2} - \dfrac{1}{2}i\sqrt{3}$ is another cube root of 1.

40. Show that $1 + i\sqrt{3}$ is a cube root of -8.

41. Show that $1 - i\sqrt{3}$ is another cube root of -8.

mini-review

Patty makes woodcarvings of ducks and owls. A craft shop pays her $10 for each duck and $14 for each owl. The shop will accept at most 12 ducks and 8 owls per week. Patty has at most 30 hours per week to make the woodcarvings. A duck can be carved in 2 hours and an owl in 3 hours. How many of each should she make per week to maximize her earnings?

1. Define variables and write a system of inequalities.
2. Graph the system.
3. Find the vertices of the region.
4. Write an expression for her earnings.
5. Evaluate the expression for each vertex. Then state the answer to the problem.

A **field** is a mathematical system consisting of a set of numbers, S, together with the operations of addition and multiplication. The following properties must hold for all elements a, b, and c in S.

Field Properties	Addition	Multiplication
closure	$a + b$ is in S.	ab is in S.
commutative	$a + b = b + a$	$a \cdot b = b \cdot a$
associative	$(a + b) + c = a + (b + c)$	$(a \cdot b) \cdot c = a \cdot (b \cdot c)$
identity	0 is in S. $a + 0 = a = 0 + a$	1 is in S. $a \cdot 1 = a = 1 \cdot a$
inverse	$-a$ is in S. $a + -a = 0 = -a + a$	$\frac{1}{a}$ is in S. $a \cdot \frac{1}{a} = 1 = \frac{1}{a} \cdot a$ if $a \neq 0$
distributive of multiplication over addition	$a(b + c) = ab + ac$ and $(b + c)a = ba + ca$	

You know that these properties hold for all real numbers. So, the real number system is a field.

To determine if a number system is a field, decide whether the closure property holds for addition and multiplication. Then check to see if the commutative, associative, and distributive properties hold. (These three properties are always true for subsets of the real numbers.) Also, check whether identity elements and inverses exist. If you can find a counterexample, the system is *not* a field.

Example: Is the whole number system a field?

The additive inverse of 5 is -5. Since -5 is not a whole number, the whole number system is not a field.

Exercises

Show that each property holds for the set of complex numbers.
1. commutative property of addition
2. commutative property of multiplication
   (Hint: Let $a + bi$ and $c + di$ be two complex numbers.)

3. associative property of addition
4. associative property of multiplication
5. distributive property of multiplication over addition
6. Show that the set of complex numbers is closed under addition.
7. Show that the set of complex numbers is closed under multiplication.

Decide whether each number system is a field. If the system is not a field, give a counterexample for each field property that is not satisfied.

8. complex numbers
9. natural numbers
10. integers
11. positive real numbers
12. irrational numbers
13. rational numbers
14. imaginary numbers
15. negative rational numbers

Iteration

Computers and calculators do not store tables. They use *iteration* to find roots. An iteration method involves a repeated series of operations. Each repetition produces a more precise result. One iteration method for finding square roots is the divide-and-average method. The following program can be used to find $\sqrt{N}$, given N and an approximate value, A.

```
10 PRINT "WHAT IS THE RADICAND?"
20 INPUT N
30 PRINT "CHOOSE A FIRST
   APPROXIMATION:"
40 INPUT A
50 PRINT "SUCCESSIVE APPROXIMATIONS
   ARE: "
60 LET L = (N / A + A) / 2
70 PRINT L
80 IF ABS (L - A) < 0.00001 THEN
   110
90 LET A = L
100 GOTO 60
110 END
```

Enter positive numbers for N and A.

The computer will find the average of $\dfrac{N}{A}$ and A, and print it. If L is close to A, the computer will go to line 110. If not, the computer will replace A by L and return to line 60.

This method works even if the first approximation is poor. Suppose the program is used to find $\sqrt{875}$. The first column below shows the output when 30 is used as the first approximation. The second column shows the output when a poor choice, 9, is used. Compare the results.

```
]RUN                                ]RUN
WHAT IS THE RADICAND?               WHAT IS THE RADICAND?
?875                                ?875
CHOOSE A FIRST APPROXIMATION.       CHOOSE A FIRST APPROXIMATION.
?30                                 ?9
SUCCESSIVE APPROXIMATIONS ARE:      SUCCESSIVE APPROXIMATIONS ARE:
29.5833334                         53.1111111
29.5803991                         34.7930033
29.5803989                         29.9708689
                                   29.5829425
                                   29.580399
                                   29.5803989
```

Exercises

Use the program to approximate each square root.

1. $\sqrt{68}$ **2.** $\sqrt{947}$ **3.** $\sqrt{2050}$ **4.** $\sqrt{413}$ **5.** $\sqrt{1794}$ **6.** $\sqrt{4608}$

7. How can you change the program so that only the final approximation will be printed?

Vocabulary

square root (181)
nth root (181)
radical sign (181)
index (181)
radicand (181)

conjugates (188)
rational exponents (195)
radical equations (199)
imaginary units (202)
pure imaginary number (202)

complex number (204)
real part (204)
imaginary part (204)
complex conjugates (204)

Chapter Summary

1. **Definition of Square Root:** For any real numbers a and b, if $a^2 = b$, then a is a square root of b. (181)

2. **Definition of nth Root:** For any real numbers a and b, and any positive integer n, if $a^n = b$, then a is an nth root of b. (181)

3. The Real nth Roots of b, $\sqrt[n]{b}$ (182)

	$b > 0$	$b < 0$	$b = 0$
n even	one positive root one negative root	no real roots	one real root, 0
n odd	one positive root no negative roots	no positive roots one negative root	one real root, 0

4. **Property of nth Roots:** For any real number a, and any integer n greater than one: **1.** If n is even, then $\sqrt[n]{a^n} = |a|$. **2.** If n is odd, then $\sqrt[n]{a^n} = a$. (182)

5. **Product Property of Radicals:** For any real numbers a and b, and any integer n greater than one:
   1. If n is even, then $\sqrt[n]{ab} = \sqrt[n]{a} \cdot \sqrt[n]{b}$ as long as a and b are both positive.
   2. If n is odd, then $\sqrt[n]{ab} = \sqrt[n]{a} \cdot \sqrt[n]{b}$. (185)

6. **Quotient Property of Radicals:** For any real numbers a and b, $b \neq 0$, and any integer n greater than one, $\sqrt[n]{\dfrac{a}{b}} = \dfrac{\sqrt[n]{a}}{\sqrt[n]{b}}$ as long as all roots are defined. (190)

7. **Conditions for Simplified Radicals:** **1.** The index n is as small as possible. **2.** The radicand contains no factor (other than one) which is the nth power of an integer or polynomial. **3.** The radicand contains no fractions. **4.** No radicals appear in the denominator. (191)

8. **Rational Numbers as Exponents:** For any real number b and for any integer n, with n greater than one, $b^{\frac{1}{n}} = \sqrt[n]{b}$ except for $b < 0$ and n even. (194)

9. **Definition of Rational Exponents:** For any nonzero real number b, and any integers m and n, with $n > 1$,
   $b^{\frac{m}{n}} = \sqrt[n]{b^m} = (\sqrt[n]{b})^m$ except when $b < 0$ and n is even. (195)

10. Conditions for Simplified Expressions:
   1. It has no negative exponents.
   2. It has no fractional exponents in the denominator.
   3. It is not a complex fraction.
   4. The index of any remaining radical is as small as possible.   (197)

11. These steps are usually used to solve a radical equation.
   1. Isolate the radical.   4. Solve for the variable.
   2. Raise both sides to a power.   5. Check each solution.   (199)
   3. Combine terms.

12. Definition of Pure Imaginary Number: For any positive real number b, $\sqrt{-(b^2)} = bi$ where i is a number whose square is -1.   (202)

13. Definition of a Complex Number: A complex number is any number that can be written in the form $a + bi$ where a and b are real numbers and i is the imaginary unit.   (204)

Chapter Review

6–1 **Find the principal roots of each expression.**

   1. $\sqrt{49a^2}$
   2. $\sqrt[3]{-27}$
   3. $\sqrt[3]{8x^3y^6}$
   4. $\sqrt[4]{16}$

Use the table of powers and roots to find each value.

   5. $\sqrt[3]{39}$
   6. $\sqrt[3]{290}$
   7. $(9.8)^3$
   8. $(1.5)^3$

6–2 **Simplify.**

   9. $\sqrt[3]{48a^2}$
   10. $\sqrt[4]{32m^5}$
   11. $-3\sqrt{18} \cdot 5\sqrt{15}$
   12. $2\sqrt[3]{54} \cdot 4\sqrt[3]{16}$
   13. $\sqrt{5}(\sqrt{10} + 2)$
   14. $\sqrt{3}(\sqrt{6} + \sqrt{12})$
   15. $\sqrt[3]{3}(\sqrt[3]{16} + \sqrt[3]{9})$
   16. $\sqrt{3m^3n^4} \cdot \sqrt{24m^6n}$
   17. $\sqrt[3]{2xy^4} \cdot \sqrt[3]{36x^2y^2}$

6–3 **Simplify.**

   18. $3\sqrt{12} - 4\sqrt{75} + 4$
   19. $(6 + \sqrt{2})(10 + \sqrt{5})$
   20. $(3 + \sqrt{5})(3 - \sqrt{5})$

6–4 **Simplify.**

   21. $\sqrt{\dfrac{10}{2}}$
   22. $\dfrac{\sqrt[3]{80}}{\sqrt[3]{2}}$
   23. $\dfrac{4}{\sqrt[3]{16}}$
   24. $\dfrac{\sqrt{3} + \sqrt{2}}{4 + \sqrt{3}}$

6–5 **For each of the following evaluate or express using exponents.**

   25. $6^{\frac{1}{2}} \cdot 6^{\frac{3}{2}}$
   26. $125^{\frac{1}{3}}$
   27. $(0.008)^{\frac{2}{3}}$
   28. $(25^{\frac{3}{4}})^{\frac{2}{3}}$
   29. $\sqrt[4]{x^4y^3}$
   30. $\sqrt[3]{27m^3n^2}$
   31. $\sqrt[5]{32w^{10}r^5}$

Write in simplest radical form.

   32. $r^2s^{\frac{1}{3}}y^{\frac{1}{2}}$
   33. $\sqrt[6]{27}$
   34. $(3x)^{\frac{1}{2}}x^{\frac{1}{4}}$

6–6 **Simplify each expression.**

   35. $\dfrac{1}{z^{\frac{3}{5}}}$
   36. $\dfrac{w^{-\frac{2}{3}}r^{\frac{1}{2}}}{wr^2}$
   37. $\dfrac{z^{\frac{1}{3}}}{z^{\frac{2}{3}} - z^{-\frac{1}{3}}}$
   38. $\dfrac{x^{\frac{1}{2}} - y^{\frac{1}{2}}}{x^{\frac{1}{2}} + y^{\frac{1}{2}}}$

6–7 Solve each equation.

39. $\sqrt{2x + 7} = 3$

40. $\sqrt[3]{y + 2} = 4$

41. $\sqrt{r + 12} - \sqrt{r} = 2$

6–8 Simplify.

42. $\sqrt{-24}$

43. i^7

44. $\sqrt{-3} \cdot \sqrt{-3}$

45. $(2\sqrt{5})(-3\sqrt{-5})$

6–9 Find the sum, difference, and product for each pair of complex numbers.

46. $7 + 2i, 5 - 3i$

47. $3 + 8i, 3 - 8i$

6–10 Simplify.

48. $\dfrac{4 + 3i}{1 - 2i}$

49. $\dfrac{7 - 3i}{2i}$

50. $\dfrac{(4 - 3i)^2}{(3 + i)^2}$

Chapter Test

Find the principal root of each expression.

1. $\sqrt{81x^2}$

2. $\sqrt[3]{-27y^3}$

3. $\sqrt{x^2 - 8xy + 16y^2}$

Simplify.

4. $\sqrt[3]{108m^4}$

5. $7\sqrt[3]{16} \cdot 5\sqrt[3]{20}$

6. $\sqrt{125x^2y} \cdot 3\sqrt{81x^2y^2}$

7. $2\sqrt{27} + 2\sqrt{3} - 7\sqrt{48}$

8. $(4 - \sqrt{3})(4 + \sqrt{3})$

9. $(\sqrt{3} - \sqrt{5})(\sqrt{15} + 3)$

10. $\dfrac{3}{\sqrt[3]{4}}$

11. $\dfrac{3}{\sqrt[4]{8}}$

12. $\dfrac{2 + \sqrt{2}}{1 - \sqrt{2}}$

13. $\sqrt[3]{2}(\sqrt[3]{24} - \sqrt[3]{4})$

14. $\sqrt[3]{16x^3} + 5\sqrt[3]{54x^3} - 3\sqrt[3]{128x^3}$

15. $\sqrt{\dfrac{5}{32}} + \sqrt{90} + \dfrac{\sqrt{30}}{\sqrt{3}} - \sqrt{\dfrac{2}{5}}$

16. $\dfrac{1}{y^{\frac{2}{3}}}$

17. $\dfrac{15}{5^{\frac{3}{3}}}$

18. $\dfrac{r + s}{r^{\frac{1}{2}} + s^{\frac{1}{2}}}$

19. $\dfrac{x^{\frac{5}{3}}y + 3x^{-\frac{1}{3}}}{x^{\frac{2}{3}}}$

Evaluate.

20. $27^{-\frac{4}{3}}$

21. $(\sqrt[3]{27})^2$

22. $\dfrac{16}{4^{\frac{3}{2}}}$

23. $\left(\dfrac{1}{64}\right)^{-\frac{2}{3}}$

Express each of the following using exponents.

24. $\sqrt[3]{n^2}$

25. $\sqrt{a^6}$

26. $\sqrt[3]{8m^2r^7}$

27. $\sqrt[4]{x^4y^6b^2}$

Solve each equation.

28. $\sqrt{2x - 5} = 9$

29. $\sqrt[3]{a + 3} - 1 = 2$

Simplify.

30. $\sqrt{-50}$

31. $3i + \sqrt{-4}$

32. $(7 - 3i) + (4 + 5i)$

33. $\sqrt{-3} \cdot \sqrt{-24}$

34. $\dfrac{4 - 5i}{3 + 7i}$

35. $(4 - 6i) - (4 + 6i)$

36. $\dfrac{4 - 7i}{2i}$

37. $(6 + i)(7 - 3i)$

38. $\dfrac{(2 + 3i)^2}{(1 - i)^2}$

Solve.

1. $\frac{8}{9}x + \frac{1}{3} = \frac{3}{5}$ 2. $5|b + 4| = 45$

3. $3(4m + 7) < 21$ 4. $|z - 3| > 5$

Graph each equation.

5. $y + 6 = -x$ 6. $y = |x - 7|$

7. $4x + 5y \le 10$

8. Simplify $(2m + 3n) + (8m - 2n)$.

9. Find the x-intercept and y-intercept of the graph of $3y = x + 4$.

10. Find the standard form of the equation of the line that passes through $(-6, -3)$ and $(4, -6)$.

Solve each system of equations.

11. $3x - 2y = 8$ 12. $2y - 3x = 0$
    $4x + y = 7$ $x - y = -2$

Solve each system of inequalities by graphing. For exercise 14, name the vertices of the polygonal region.

13. $2x + 3y < 6$ 14. $x \ge 0$
    $y > -x + 4$ $y \ge 1$
                            $x + y \le 4$

Find the value of each determinant.

15. $\begin{vmatrix} 4 & -2 \\ 3 & 2 \end{vmatrix}$ 16. $\begin{vmatrix} 1 & 2 & -1 \\ 2 & -1 & 3 \\ -3 & -4 & 5 \end{vmatrix}$

Find the dimensions of matrix M. The dimensions of matrix A and matrix B are given as subscripts.

17. $A_{3 \times 2} \cdot B_{2 \times 4} = M$

18. $M \cdot A_{3 \times 5} = B_{5 \times 5}$

Solve the system by elimination.

19. $x + y + z = 15$
    $x + z = 12$
    $y + z = 10$

Simplify.

20. $\left(\frac{2}{3}c^2 f\right)\left(\frac{3}{8}cd\right)$ 21. $\frac{20n^5 m^9}{20nm^{10}}$

22. $\left(\frac{3}{2x^{-2}}\right)^{-1}$ 23. $(r + s)^3$

24. $(4x + 11) - (3x^2 + 7x - 3)$

25. $\sqrt[3]{27x^6 y^3}$ 26. $\sqrt[3]{135r^7 s^5}$

27. $(\sqrt{3})(\sqrt{8})$ 28. $\sqrt{-2} \cdot \sqrt{-24}$

29. $\frac{x^{\frac{1}{2}} - y^{\frac{1}{2}}}{x^{\frac{1}{2}} + y^{\frac{1}{2}}}$ 30. $\frac{5 + 6i}{2i}$

31. $(4 - 7i) - (2 - 8i)$

32. $\frac{1 + \sqrt{3}}{2 - \sqrt{3}}$

Factor.

33. $9a^3 b^2 + 12ab^3$ 34. $z^2 + 10z + 16$

35. $2r + 2s + rt + st$

36. Divide $(6a^2 + 11a - 10)$ by $(3a - 2)$.

37. Divide $(x^5 + 32)$ by $(x + 2)$ using synthetic division.

38. Express $\sqrt[3]{x^2}$ using exponents.

39. Solve $3 + 2x\sqrt{3} = 5$.

Problem Solving

40. Graph the set of ordered pairs. State whether the points are vertices of a rectangle.
    $$\{(-4, 6), (1, 1), (5, 5), (0, 10)\}$$

41. How many pounds of cashews costing $5.75 a pound should be mixed with 4 pounds of walnuts costing $3.50 a pound to obtain a mixture costing $5.00 a pound?

42. The Marinacci family has invested $10,000. Part of the money is invested at 5% and part at 7%. If the total income from these investments is $540, how much is invested at each rate?

The questions on this page involve comparing two quantities, one in Column A and one in Column B. In certain questions, information related to one or both quantities is centered above them. All variables used stand for real numbers

Directions:
Write A if the quantity in Column A is greater.
Write B if the quantity in Column B is greater.
Write C if the quantities are equal.
Write D if there is not enough information to determine the relationship

	Examples	
	Column A	**Column B**

I.

$$\frac{x}{y} \qquad\qquad \frac{y}{x}$$

The answer is D because it is not known whether x and y are positive or negative. The values of $\frac{x}{y}$ and $\frac{y}{x}$ depend on the choices for x and y.

II. $\qquad\qquad a > 0$

$$4a - 3a \qquad\qquad 4 \cdot 3a$$

The answer is B because $12a$ is greater than a for all positive values of a.

	Column A	**Column B**
1.	$\dfrac{8a + 12}{2}$	$4a + 6$
2.	$(-9)^{72}$	$(-9)^{83}$
3.	$-3 < n < 0$	
	$-3(n + n)$	$(n)(n)(n)$
4.	$n + 11 > 12$	
	$3n + 8$	$16 - 2n$
5.	$a < 0 < b$	
	$\dfrac{a}{2}$	b^2
6.	a if $3a < 23$	b if $23 < 3b$
7.	$x^2 > y^2$	
	$(y + 1)^2$	$(x + 1)^2$
8.	$\frac{1}{2}\%$ of 400	0.5×400
9.	$\dfrac{.05}{x} = \dfrac{.2}{.06}$	
	x	0.2

	Column A	**Column B**
10.	$6 > b > -5$	
	$\dfrac{b}{5}$	$\dfrac{5}{b}$
11.	30% of r is 6	
	The percent that 60 is of r.	The percent that r is of 6.
12.	$.8 \times 6d$	$\frac{3}{5}$ of $8d$
13.	$23 - 4(2)0$	$6 + 10(3 - 2)$
14.	$\dfrac{x}{2} = z^2$	
	x	z
15.	Area of a circle with diameter 10.	Area of a right triangle with hypotenuse 10.
16.	$\frac{1}{3} < a < \frac{2}{3}$	
	$\frac{2}{3} < b < 1$	
	$a + b$	$a^2 + b^2$

CHAPTER 7

Quadratic Equations

Quadratic equations can be used in many situations. For example, Joel Bellman wants to build a swimming pool with a sidewalk of uniform width surrounding it. Joel wants the dimensions of the pool and sidewalk to be 15 meters by 20 meters. The pool must have an area of 150 square meters. To find out how wide the sidewalk must be, Joel uses a quadratic equation.

7-1 Quadratic Equations

Any equation that can be written in the form $ax^2 + bx + c = 0$, $a \neq 0$ is a **quadratic equation.** Equations such as $z^2 - 8 = 0$ and $x^2 - 2x - 15 = 0$ are quadratic equations. You have learned how to solve some types of quadratic equations.

Example

1 **Solve $x^2 - 8 = 0$.**

$x^2 - 8 = 0$ *In this quadratic equation, $b = 0$.*

$x^2 = 8$

$x = \pm\sqrt{8}$ or $\pm2\sqrt{2}$ The solutions are $2\sqrt{2}$ and $-2\sqrt{2}$.

Quadratic equations can be solved by factoring. The equation from Example 1, $x^2 - 8 = 0$, can be factored as the difference of two squares.

$(x - \sqrt{8})(x + \sqrt{8}) = 0$ *The solutions are the same as in Example 1.*

The factoring method depends on the **zero product property.**

For any numbers a and b, **if $ab = 0$, then $a = 0$ or $b = 0$.**	*Zero Product Property*

Examples

2 **Solve $x^2 - 2x - 15 = 0$.**

$x^2 - 2x - 15 = 0$

$(x - 5)(x + 3) = 0$ *Factor.*

$x - 5 = 0$ or $x + 3 = 0$ *Zero Product Property*

$x = 5$ or $x = -3$

Check: $x^2 - 2x - 15 = 0$

$(5)^2 - 2(5) - 15 \stackrel{?}{=} 0$ or $(-3)^2 - 2(-3) - 15 \stackrel{?}{=} 0$

$0 = 0$ $0 = 0$

The solutions are 5 and -3.

3 **Solve $9x^2 - 24x = -16$.**

$9x^2 - 24x = -16$ **Check:** $9x^2 - 24x = -16$

$9x^2 - 24x + 16 = 0$ $9\left(\frac{4}{3}\right)^2 - 24\left(\frac{4}{3}\right) \stackrel{?}{=} -16$

$(3x - 4)(3x - 4) = 0$

$3x - 4 = 0$ or $3x - 4 = 0$ $16 - 32 \stackrel{?}{=} -16$

$3x = 4$ $3x = 4$ $-16 = -16$

$x = \frac{4}{3}$ $x = \frac{4}{3}$ The solution is $\frac{4}{3}$.

Exploratory Exercises

Identify which of the following are quadratic equations.

1. $4x^2 + 7x - 3 = 0$

2. $5y^4 - 7y^2 = 0$

3. $2a^2 + 7a = 0$

4. $4x^2 - 2x + 11 = 0$

5. $3z^3 + 4 = 0$

6. $\frac{1}{2}y^2 + \frac{3}{4} = 0$

7. $\frac{2}{3}c^3 - 3c^2 + 2c = 0$

8. $z^2 + 7z - 3 = z^3$

9. $3d^2 - 9 = d$

Solve each equation.

10. $(x - 4)(x + 5) = 0$

11. $(y - 3)(y + 7) = 0$

12. $(a + 6)(a + 2) = 0$

13. $(m - 8)(m - 1) = 0$

14. $z(z - 1)^2 = 0$

15. $s(s + 4) = 0$

16. $(3y + 7)(y + 5) = 0$

17. $(2b + 5)(b - 1) = 0$

18. $(2x + 3)(3x - 1) = 0$

Written Exercises

Solve each equation.

1. $x^2 + 6x + 8 = 0$

2. $z^2 + 4z + 3 = 0$

3. $a^2 - 9a + 20 = 0$

4. $m^2 - 8m + 12 = 0$

5. $b^2 + 3b - 10 = 0$

6. $y^2 - 4y - 21 = 0$

7. $x^2 + 4x + 4 = 0$

8. $c^2 - 12c + 36 = 0$

9. $n^2 + 3n = 0$

10. $z^2 - 5z = 0$

11. $d^2 - 3d = 4$

12. $m^2 + 6m = 27$

13. $z^2 + z = 30$

14. $y^2 - y = 12$

15. $2x^2 + 5x + 3 = 0$

16. $2a^2 + 9a + 4 = 0$

17. $2z^2 - 3z - 9 = 0$

18. $3b^2 + 13b - 10 = 0$

19. $3c^2 = 5c$

20. $10y^2 = y$

21. $6d^2 + 13d + 6 = 0$

22. $12m^2 + 25m + 12 = 0$

23. $4s^2 - 11s - 3 = 0$

24. $4a^2 - 17a + 4 = 0$

25. $z^2 + 3z - 40 = 0$

26. $6m^2 + 7m - 3 = 0$

27. $3r^2 - 14r + 8 = 0$

28. $2y^2 + 11y - 21 = 0$

29. $12c^2 - 17c - 5 = 0$

30. $3t^2 + 4t - 15 = 0$

31. $12p^2 + 8p = 15$

32. $18n^2 - 3n = 1$

33. $4b^2 - 13b = 12$

34. $18m^2 - 3m = 15$

35. $4x^2 + 9 = 12x$

36. $9y^2 + 16 = -24y$

37. $121 = 16b^2$

38. $4t^2 = 25$

Challenge

Solve each equation.

39. $n^3 = 9n$

40. $a^3 = 81a$

41. $35z^3 + 16z^2 = 12z$

42. $18r^3 + 16r = 34r^2$

43. $25d^3 + 9d = 30d^2$

44. $16t^3 = 40t^2 - 25t$

45. $\frac{1}{4}x^2 - \frac{1}{5}x + 1 = 0$

46. $0.25y^2 = 0.6y - 0.36$

Problem Solving

Some problems may be solved by using a guess-and-check strategy. This procedure involves first making an educated guess for the solution to a problem. The next step is to check your guess in terms of the problem. Even though it may not be correct, it may give you an indication of how to improve your next guess. This procedure is repeated until you arrive at the correct answer.

Example: **Find the least prime number greater than 720.**

One way to solve this problem is to check each integer beginning with 721 for prime divisors until you find a prime number. However, if known information is used, time and effort in this guess-and-check method can be saved. Obviously, any even integer greater than 720 is not prime. Since 720 is divisible by 3, every third integer greater than 720 will not be prime. Any integer greater than 720 whose last digit is 5 or 0 is not prime. Thus, many possibilities are eliminated.

Try 721.   *Using a calculator is helpful.*

$721 \div 7 = 103$ *not prime*

Try 727.

$727 \div 7 \approx 103.9$	$727 \div 11 \approx 66.1$
$727 \div 13 \approx 55.9$	$727 \div 17 \approx 42.8$
$727 \div 19 \approx 38.3$	$727 \div 23 \approx 31.6$
$727 \div 29 \approx 25.1$	*Why can you stop after this division?*

Thus, 727 is the least prime number greater than 720.

Exercises
Solve each problem.

1. Find the least prime number greater than 840.

2. Rich and Peg raise cows and chickens. They counted all the heads and got 12. They counted all the feet and got 40. How many cows and chickens do they have?

3. Supply a digit for each letter so the multiplication problem is correct. Each letter represents a different digit.

$$\begin{array}{r} ABCDE \\ \times\,4 \\ \hline EDCBA \end{array}$$

4. Write an eight-digit number using the digits 1, 2, 3, and 4 each twice so that the 1's are separated by 1 digit, the 2's are separated by 2 digits, the 3's are separated by 3 digits, and the 4's are separated by 4 digits.

5. Copy the diagram below. In each block write a digit such that the digit in the first block indicates the total number of zeros in the entire ten-digit number, the digit in the block marked "1" indicates the total number of 1's in the number, and so on to the last block whose indicates the total number of 9's in the number.

0	1	2	3	4	5	6	7	8	9

7-2 Completing the Square

An equation like $(x - 4)^2 = 3$ can be solved by taking the square root of both sides.

$$(x - 4)^2 = 3$$
$$\left.\begin{array}{c} \sqrt{(x - 4)^2} = \sqrt{3} \\ |x - 4| = \sqrt{3} \end{array}\right]\quad \textit{These two steps may be omitted.}$$
$$x - 4 = \pm\sqrt{3}$$
$$x = 4 \pm \sqrt{3} \quad \text{The solutions are } 4 + \sqrt{3} \text{ and } 4 - \sqrt{3}.$$

The equation $x^2 - 6x + 9 = 2$ can be solved in a similar way.

$$x^2 - 6x + 9 = 2$$
$$(x - 3)^2 = 2$$
$$x - 3 = \pm\sqrt{2}$$
$$x = 3 \pm \sqrt{2} \quad\quad \text{The solutions are } 3 + \sqrt{2} \text{ and } 3 - \sqrt{2}.$$

To solve a quadratic equation by taking square roots you must have a perfect square equal to a constant. A method called **completing the square** is based on this concept.

Consider the following perfect squares.

$$(x + 7)^2 = x^2 + 14x + 49 \qquad\qquad (x + b)^2 = x^2 + 2bx + b^2$$
$$\left(\frac{14}{2}\right)^2 \rightarrow (7)^2 \qquad\qquad\qquad \left(\frac{2b}{2}\right)^2 \rightarrow (b)^2$$

Notice that the coefficient of the linear term is divided by 2, then squared.

The pattern shown above can be used to complete the square when two terms are known. Complete the square for $x^2 - 8x$.

$$x^2 - 8x + \rule{1cm}{0.3cm}$$
$$\left(\frac{8}{2}\right)^2 \rightarrow (4)^2 \text{ or } 16 \qquad \text{The answer is } x^2 - 8x + 16.$$

$x^2 - 8x + 16$ *is a perfect square trinomial.*

Example

1 **Solve $x^2 - 8x + 11 = 0$ by completing the square.**

$$x^2 - 8x + 11 = 0 \qquad\qquad \textit{The left side of the equation is not a perfect square.}$$
$$x^2 - 8x = -11 \qquad\qquad \textit{Subtract 11 from each side.}$$
$$x^2 - 8x + 16 = -11 + 16 \qquad \textit{Add } \left(\frac{-8}{2}\right)^2 \textit{ or 16 to each side. A perfect square}$$
$$\textit{trinomial is formed on the left side.}$$
$$(x - 4)^2 = 5 \qquad\qquad \textit{Factor.}$$
$$x - 4 = \pm\sqrt{5} \qquad\qquad \textit{Take the square root of each side.}$$
$$x = 4 \pm \sqrt{5} \qquad\qquad \textit{Solve for x.}$$

The solutions are $4 + \sqrt{5}$ and $4 - \sqrt{5}$.

When the coefficient of the second degree term is not 1, another step is required. In the following example, it is necessary to write an equivalent equation that has 1 as the coefficient of the second degree term.

Examples

2 **Solve $2m^2 - 8m + 3 = 0$.**

$$2m^2 - 8m + 3 = 0$$

$$m^2 - 4m + \frac{3}{2} = 0 \qquad \text{\textit{Divide each side by 2.}}$$

$$m^2 - 4m = -\frac{3}{2}$$

$$m^2 - 4m + 4 = -\frac{3}{2} + 4 \qquad \text{\textit{Add} } \left(\frac{-4}{2}\right)^2 \text{\textit{ or 4 to each side.}}$$

$$(m - 2)^2 = \frac{5}{2} \qquad \text{\textit{Factor.}}$$

$$m - 2 = \pm\sqrt{\frac{5}{2}} \qquad \text{\textit{Take the square root of each side.}}$$

$$m - 2 = \pm\frac{\sqrt{10}}{2} \qquad \text{\textit{Rationalize the denominator.}}$$

$$m = 2 \pm \frac{\sqrt{10}}{2} \qquad \text{\textit{Solve for m.}}$$

The solutions are $2 + \dfrac{\sqrt{10}}{2}$ and $2 - \dfrac{\sqrt{10}}{2}$.

3 **Solve $3x^2 - 11x - 4 = 0$.**

$$3x^2 - 11x - 4 = 0$$

$$x^2 - \frac{11}{3}x - \frac{4}{3} = 0 \qquad \text{\textit{Divide each side by 3.}}$$

$$x^2 - \frac{11}{3}x = \frac{4}{3}$$

$$x^2 - \frac{11}{3}x + \frac{121}{36} = \frac{4}{3} + \frac{121}{36} \qquad \text{\textit{Add} } \left(-\frac{11}{3} \div 2\right)^2 \text{\textit{ or } } \frac{121}{36} \text{\textit{ to each side.}}$$

$$\left(x - \frac{11}{6}\right)^2 = \frac{169}{36} \qquad \text{\textit{Factor.}}$$

$$x - \frac{11}{6} = \pm\frac{13}{6} \qquad \text{\textit{Take square root of each side.}}$$

$$x = \frac{11}{6} \pm \frac{13}{6} \qquad \text{\textit{Add} } \frac{11}{6} \text{\textit{ to each side.}}$$

$$x = 4 \text{ or } x = -\frac{1}{3}$$

The solutions are 4 and $-\dfrac{1}{3}$.

Exploratory Exercises

State whether or not each trinomial is a perfect square.

1. $x^2 + 4x + 4$

2. $a^2 + 14a + 28$

3. $b^2 - 6b - 9$

4. $x^2 - x + \frac{1}{4}$

5. $m^2 - 10m + 25$

6. $a^2 - 3a + \frac{9}{2}$

Find the value of c that makes each trinomial a perfect square.

7. $y^2 - 6y + c$ **8.** $x^2 + 2x + c$ **9.** $m^2 - 20m + c$

10. $t^2 + 40t + c$ **11.** $n^2 + 12n + c$ **12.** $x^2 + 18x + c$

13. $y^2 + 3y + c$ **14.** $r^2 - 9r + c$ **15.** $s^2 + 11s + c$

16. $a^2 - 100a + c$ **17.** $n^2 - n + c$ **18.** $x^2 + 15x + c$

Written Exercises

Find the value of c that makes each trinomial a perfect square.

1. $x^2 + 6x + c$ **2.** $x^2 - 10x + c$ **3.** $y^2 + \frac{1}{2}y + c$

4. $a^2 + 9a + c$ **5.** $r^2 + r + c$ **6.** $x^2 - 16x + c$

7. $y^2 - 3y + c$ **8.** $m^2 - \frac{2}{3}m + c$ **9.** $b^2 + 7b + c$

10. $a^2 - \frac{4}{5}a + c$ **11.** $r^2 + 50r + c$ **12.** $n^2 - 30n + c$

Solve each equation by completing the square.

13. $y^2 - 2y = 24$ **14.** $t^2 + 4t = 96$

15. $z^2 + 3z = 88$ **16.** $x^2 - 3x = 10$

17. $x^2 - 8x + 15 = 0$ **18.** $r^2 - 6r + 8 = 0$

19. $c^2 + 8c - 20 = 0$ **20.** $b^2 + 2b - 48 = 0$

21. $x^2 - 7x + 12 = 0$ **22.** $s^2 - 10s + 21 = 0$

23. $x^2 + 8x - 84 = 0$ **24.** $m^2 + 3m - 180 = 0$

25. $x^2 + 3x - 40 = 0$ **26.** $y^2 + 12y + 4 = 0$

27. $n^2 - 8n + 14 = 0$ **28.** $r^2 + 5r - 8 = 0$

29. $x^2 - 7x + 5 = 0$ **30.** $t^2 + 3t - 8 = 0$

31. $a^2 - 5a - 10 = 0$ **32.** $b^2 - \frac{3}{4}b + \frac{1}{8} = 0$

33. $y^2 + \frac{7}{3}y + \frac{2}{3} = 0$ **34.** $4x^2 + 19x - 5 = 0$

35. $6m^2 + 7m - 3 = 0$ **36.** $3c^2 - 14c + 8 = 0$

37. $2y^2 + 11y - 21 = 0$ **38.** $12r^2 - 17r - 5 = 0$

39. $3t^2 + 4t - 15 = 0$ **40.** $6s^2 + 2s + 3 = 0$

41. $3z^2 - 12z + 4 = 0$ **42.** $2x^2 - 3x + 4 = 0$

Challenge

Solve each equation by completing the square.

43. $x^2 + ax + a = 0$

44. $x^2 + ax + b = 0$

45. $ax^2 + bx + a = 0$

46. $ax^2 + bx + c = 0$

mini-review

1. Solve $|2x - 3| \geq 9$.
Graph the solution set.

2. Graph $y = 6x - 3$.

3. Find the value of $\begin{vmatrix} 4 & -2 \\ 1 & 7 \end{vmatrix}$.

4. Simplify $\dfrac{24b^2c^5}{18bc^6}$.

5. Solve $\sqrt{3x + 9} = 6$.

7-3 The Quadratic Formula

Completing the square can be used to develop a general formula for solving quadratic equations.

$$ax^2 + bx + c = 0 \qquad (a \neq 0)$$
Start with the general form of a quadratic equation.

$$x^2 + \frac{b}{a}x + \frac{c}{a} = 0$$
Divide by a so that the coefficient of x^2 is 1.

$$x^2 + \frac{b}{a}x = -\frac{c}{a}$$
Subtract $\frac{c}{a}$ from each side.

$$x^2 + \frac{b}{a}x + \left(\frac{b}{2a}\right)^2 = -\frac{c}{a} + \left(\frac{b}{2a}\right)^2$$
Complete the square by adding $\left(\frac{b}{a} \div 2\right)^2$ or $\left(\frac{b}{2a}\right)^2$ to each side.

$$\left(x + \frac{b}{2a}\right)^2 = -\frac{c}{a} + \frac{b^2}{4a^2}$$
Factor the left side.

$$\left(x + \frac{b}{2a}\right)^2 = \frac{b^2 - 4ac}{4a^2}$$
Add fractions on the right side.

$$\left|x + \frac{b}{2a}\right| = \sqrt{\frac{b^2 - 4ac}{4a^2}}$$
Take the square root of each side.

$$x + \frac{b}{2a} = \pm\frac{\sqrt{b^2 - 4ac}}{2a}$$
Simplify.

$$x = \frac{-b \pm \sqrt{b^2 - 4ac}}{2a}$$
Solve for x.

The result is called the **quadratic formula** and can be used to solve *any* quadratic equation.

> **The solutions of a quadratic equation of the form $ax^2 + bx + c = 0$ with $a \neq 0$ are given by this formula.**
> $$x = \frac{-b \pm \sqrt{b^2 - 4ac}}{2a}$$

Quadratic Formula

Example

1 **Solve $x^2 - 3x - 28 = 0$ using the quadratic formula.**

$$x = \frac{-b \pm \sqrt{b^2 - 4ac}}{2a}$$

$$= \frac{-(-3) \pm \sqrt{(-3)^2 - 4(1)(-28)}}{2(1)}$$
Substitute the following values into the formula. $a = 1$, $b = -3$, $c = -28$

$$= \frac{3 \pm \sqrt{121}}{2}$$

$$= \frac{3 \pm 11}{2}$$

The solutions are $\frac{3 + 11}{2}$ and $\frac{3 - 11}{2}$ or 7 and -4.

The quadratic formula yields *both* solutions to a quadratic equation, even if those solutions are imaginary.

Examples

2 **Solve $2x^2 + 3x - 7 = 0$.**

$$x = \frac{-b \pm \sqrt{b^2 - 4ac}}{2a}$$

$$= \frac{-3 \pm \sqrt{3^2 - 4(2)(-7)}}{2(2)} \qquad a = 2,\ b = 3,\ c = -7$$

$$= \frac{-3 \pm \sqrt{9 + 56}}{4}$$

$$= \frac{-3 \pm \sqrt{65}}{4}$$

The solutions are $\dfrac{-3 + \sqrt{65}}{4}$ and $\dfrac{-3 - \sqrt{65}}{4}$.

3 **Solve $3x^2 - 5x + 9 = 0$.**

$$x = \frac{-b \pm \sqrt{b^2 - 4ac}}{2a}$$

$$= \frac{-(-5) \pm \sqrt{(-5)^2 - 4(3)(9)}}{2(3)} \qquad a = 3,\ b = -5,\ c = 9$$

$$= \frac{5 \pm \sqrt{-83}}{6}$$

The solutions are $\dfrac{5 + i\sqrt{83}}{6}$ and $\dfrac{5 - i\sqrt{83}}{6}$.   *Notice that the imaginary solutions always appear as conjugate pairs.*

Some cubic equations can be solved using the quadratic formula. First, a binomial factor must be found.

Example

4 **Solve $x^3 - 27 = 0$.**

$$x^3 - 27 = 0 \qquad \text{\textit{The left side is the difference of two cubes.}}$$
$$(x - 3)(x^2 + 3x + 9) = 0 \qquad \text{\textit{Factor.}}$$
$$x - 3 = 0 \quad \text{or} \quad x^2 + 3x + 9 = 0 \qquad \text{\textit{Zero Product Property}}$$

$$x = 3 \quad \text{or} \qquad x = \frac{-3 \pm \sqrt{(3)^2 - 4(1)(9)}}{2(1)}$$

$$= \frac{-3 \pm \sqrt{-27}}{2}$$

$$= \frac{-3 \pm 3i\sqrt{3}}{2}$$

The solutions are 3, $\dfrac{-3 + 3i\sqrt{3}}{2}$ and $\dfrac{-3 - 3i\sqrt{3}}{2}$.

Exploratory Exercises

State the values of *a*, *b*, and *c* for each quadratic equation.

1. $5x^2 - 3x + 7 = 0$
2. $2y^2 + y - 3 = 0$
3. $z^2 + 2z - 1 = 0$
4. $3r^2 - 4r = -1$
5. $3z^2 = 2z - 7$
6. $x^2 = 1 - x$

Written Exercises

Solve each equation.

1. $x^2 - x - 30 = 0$
2. $x^2 + 10x + 16 = 0$
3. $y^2 + 2y - 15 = 0$
4. $r^2 + 13r + 42 = 0$
5. $t^2 - 10t + 24 = 0$
6. $s^2 + 5s - 24 = 0$
7. $x^2 - 5x + 4 = 0$
8. $5x^2 - x - 4 = 0$
9. $3x^2 - 7x - 20 = 0$
10. $4x^2 - 11x - 3 = 0$
11. $6m^2 - m - 15 = 0$
12. $24x^2 - 14x - 5 = 0$
13. $14r^2 + 33r - 5 = 0$
14. $6y^2 + 19y + 15 = 0$
15. $20a^2 + 3a - 2 = 0$
16. $2x^2 + 3x + 3 = 0$
17. $6y^2 + 8y + 5 = 0$
18. $5m^2 + 7m + 3 = 0$
19. $2x^2 - 5x + 4 = 0$
20. $x^2 - 9x + 21 = 0$
21. $2z^2 + 2z + 3 = 0$
22. $6t^2 = 2t - 1$
23. $7y^2 = y + 2$
24. $8a^2 = -2a$
25. $24t = 7t^2$
26. $8r^2 + 6r + 1 = 0$
27. $3x^2 - 6x + 8 = 0$
28. $x^3 - 8 = 0$
29. $x^3 + 8 = 0$
30. $x^3 + 64 = 0$
31. $x^3 - 64 = 0$
32. $a^3 = 125$
33. $a^3 = 1$

Using Calculators _____ Quadratic Equations

Example: Solve $5x^2 + 12x - 8 = 0$ using the quadratic formula.

$$x = \frac{-b \pm \sqrt{b^2 - 4ac}}{2a}$$

$$= \frac{-(12) \pm \sqrt{(12)^2 - 4(5)(-8)}}{2(5)}$$

First evaluate $\sqrt{b^2 - 4ac}$ and store the result in memory.

ENTER: 12 $\boxed{x^2}$ $\boxed{-}$ 4 $\boxed{\times}$ 5 $\boxed{\times}$ 8 $\boxed{+/-}$ $\boxed{=}$ $\boxed{\sqrt{x}}$ $\boxed{\text{STO}}$
DISPLAY: 17.435596

Then find the solutions.

ENTER: 12 $\boxed{+/-}$ $\boxed{+}$ $\boxed{\text{RCL}}$ $\boxed{=}$ $\boxed{\div}$ $\boxed{(}$ 2 $\boxed{\times}$ 5 $\boxed{)}$ $\boxed{=}$
DISPLAY: .54355958

ENTER: 12 $\boxed{+/-}$ $\boxed{-}$ $\boxed{\text{RCL}}$ $\boxed{=}$ $\boxed{\div}$ $\boxed{(}$ 2 $\boxed{\times}$ 5 $\boxed{)}$ $\boxed{=}$
DISPLAY: -2.9435596

The solutions are approximately 0.54 and -2.94.

Exercises

Solve each equation using the quadratic formula. Round to the nearest hundredth.

1. $3y^2 - 4y - 10 = 0$
2. $z^2 + 9z + 2 = 0$
3. $2x^2 + 5x - 9 = 0$
4. $11m^2 - 12m - 10 = 0$
5. $4a^2 + 3a - 2 = 0$
6. $t^2 - 16t + 4 = 0$

7-4 The Discriminant

In the quadratic formula the expression under the radical sign, $b^2 - 4ac$, is called the **discriminant.** For example, the discriminant of the equation $2x^2 + 6x - 7$ is $6^2 - 4(2)(-7)$, or 92.

The discriminant can give information about the solutions, or **roots**, of a quadratic equation.

A root of an equation is a number that satisfies the equation.

Equation	Value of the Discriminant	Roots
$4x^2 + 20x + 25 = 0$	0	$-\dfrac{5}{2}$
$a^2 + a - 12 = 0$	49	$-4, 3$
$x^2 + 5x - 3 = 0$	37	$\dfrac{-5 + \sqrt{37}}{2}, \dfrac{-5 - \sqrt{37}}{2}$
$3y^2 + 4y + 5 = 0$	-44	$\dfrac{-2 + i\sqrt{11}}{3}, \dfrac{-2 - i\sqrt{11}}{3}$

The chart below summarizes the information the discriminant of a quadratic equation gives about its solutions. The coefficients of the variables in the equation must be real numbers.

Discriminant	Nature of the Roots
zero	one real root
positive	two real roots
negative	two imaginary roots

A quadratic equation with *integral* coefficients has rational roots if and only if its discriminant is a perfect square or 0.

Examples

Describe the nature of the roots in the following equations.

1 $x^2 + 6x + 10 = 0$

$a = 1, b = 6, c = 10$

$$b^2 - 4ac = (6)^2 - 4(1)(10)$$
$$= 36 - 40$$
$$= -4$$

The value of the discriminant is negative, so $x^2 + 6x + 10 = 0$ has two imaginary roots.

2 $2x^2 + x - 3 = 0$

$a = 2, b = 1, c = -3$

$$b^2 - 4ac = (1)^2 - 4(2)(-3)$$
$$= 1 + 24$$
$$= 25$$

The value of the discriminant is a positive perfect square so $2x^2 + x - 3 = 0$ has two real roots and they are rational.

Exploratory Exercises

Find the value of the discriminant for each quadratic equation.

1. $x^2 + 5x - 2 = 0$
2. $y^2 + 6y + 9 = 0$
3. $2x^2 - 5x + 3 = 0$
4. $a^2 = 16$
5. $t^2 - 8t + 16 = 0$
6. $5x^2 + 16x + 3 = 0$
7. $2y^2 + y - 10 = 0$
8. $6a^2 + 2a + 1 = 0$
9. $12a^2 - 7a + 1 = 0$
10. $-3x^2 + x - 2 = 0$
11. $x^2 + 4 = 0$
12. $3a^2 - a + 3 = 0$

Written Exercises

Find the value of the discriminant for each quadratic equation. Describe the nature of the roots. If the roots are real, tell whether they are rational or irrational. Then solve each equation.

1. $x^2 - 2x - 35 = 0$
2. $a^2 + 12a + 32 = 0$
3. $y^2 - 4y + 4 = 0$
4. $x^2 - 10x + 25 = 0$
5. $x^2 - 4x + 1 = 0$
6. $m^2 - 6m + 4 = 0$
7. $4x^2 + 8x + 3 = 0$
8. $4y^2 + 16y + 15 = 0$
9. $3x^2 + 11x + 4 = 0$
10. $z^2 + 4z + 2 = 0$
11. $m^2 - 2m + 5 = 0$
12. $y^2 - 6y + 13 = 0$
13. $a^2 + 9a - 2 = 0$
14. $c^2 - 12c + 42 = 0$
15. $a^2 = 6a$
16. $3m^2 = 108m$
17. $4x^2 - 8x + 13 = 0$
18. $x^2 + 4x + 53 = 0$
19. $3n^2 - 19n = -6$
20. $2a^2 - 13a = 7$
21. $x^2 - x + 1 = 0$
22. $n^2 + 4n + 29 = 0$
23. $a^2 + a - 5 = 0$
24. $3b^2 + 7b + 3 = 0$

Challenge

Find a value of k so that each given equation will have (a) one real root, (b) two real roots, and (c) two imaginary roots.

25. $x^2 + 3x + k = 0$
26. $x^2 + kx + 6 = 0$
27. $kx^2 + 3x - 2 = 0$
28. $2x^2 - 5x - k = 0$

Excursions in Algebra _____ Perfect Numbers

Hrotsvitha (932–1002) was a nun who lived in a Benedictine Abbey in Saxony. She was one of the first persons to write about **perfect numbers**. A perfect number is one that is equal to the sum of its *aliquot* parts. That is, it is equal to the sum of all its factors including 1, but *not* including itself. Consider this example.

$$6 = \underbrace{1 + 2 + 3}$$

factors of 6, but not including 6

Hrotsvitha wrote about three perfect numbers other than 6, namely 28, 496, and 8128.

Exercises

Show that each of the following are perfect numbers.

1. 28
2. 496
3. 8128

7-5 Sum and Product of Roots

Sometimes an equation must be found to fit certain conditions. For example, suppose you know that the roots of a quadratic equation are 5 and -7. Find the quadratic equation.

Let x stand for a root of the equation.

Then $x = 5$ or $x = -7$.

If $x = 5$, then $x - 5 = 0$. If $x = -7$, then $x + 7 = 0$.

$$(x - 5)(x + 7) = 0 \qquad \textit{Why?}$$

$$x^2 + 2x - 35 = 0$$

The quadratic equation $x^2 + 2x - 35 = 0$ has roots 5 and -7. Solve that equation as a check.

Consider the sum and product of 5 and -7.

$$\text{sum} = 5 + (-7) = -2 \qquad \text{product} = 5 \cdot (-7) = -35$$

How are the sum and product related to $x^2 + 2x - 35 = 0$?

In general, the roots of $ax^2 + bx + c = 0$ are $\dfrac{-b + \sqrt{b^2 - 4ac}}{2a}$ and $\dfrac{-b - \sqrt{b^2 - 4ac}}{2a}$. If these roots are called s_1 and s_2 where $s_1 = \dfrac{-b + \sqrt{b^2 - 4ac}}{2a}$ and $s_2 = \dfrac{-b - \sqrt{b^2 - 4ac}}{2a}$, then the sum and product can be found.

$$s_1 + s_2 = \frac{-b + \sqrt{b^2 - 4ac}}{2a} + \frac{-b - \sqrt{b^2 - 4ac}}{2a}$$

$$= \frac{-2b}{2a}$$

$$= -\frac{b}{a}$$

$$s_1 s_2 = \frac{-b + \sqrt{b^2 - 4ac}}{2a} \cdot \frac{-b - \sqrt{b^2 - 4ac}}{2a}$$

$$= \frac{b^2 - (b^2 - 4ac)}{4a^2}$$

$$= \frac{c}{a}$$

The following conclusions can now be stated.

> If the roots of $ax^2 + bx + c = 0$ with $a \neq 0$ are s_1 and s_2, then
> $$s_1 + s_2 = -\frac{b}{a} \quad \text{and} \quad s_1 s_2 = \frac{c}{a}.$$

Sum and Product of Roots

Examples

1 **Find the sum and product of the roots of $3x^2 - 16x - 12 = 0$. Then solve the equation.**

$$s_1 + s_2 = -\frac{b}{a} \qquad\qquad s_1 s_2 = \frac{c}{a}$$

$$= -\frac{-16}{3} \text{ or } \frac{16}{3} \qquad\qquad = \frac{-12}{3} \text{ or } -4$$

$$x = \frac{-b \pm \sqrt{b^2 - 4ac}}{2a}$$

$$= \frac{-(-16) \pm \sqrt{(-16)^2 - 4(3)(-12)}}{2(3)}$$

$$= \frac{16 \pm \sqrt{256 + 144}}{6} \qquad\qquad \textit{In the equation } 3x^2 - 16x - 12 = 0, a = 3,$$
$$\textit{b = -16, and c = -12.}$$

$$= \frac{16 \pm \sqrt{400}}{6}$$

$$= \frac{16 \pm 20}{6} \qquad \text{The roots are } \frac{16 + 20}{6} \text{ and } \frac{16 - 20}{6} \text{ or 6 and } -\frac{2}{3}.$$

2 **Find a quadratic equation that has roots $-\dfrac{5}{4}$ and $\dfrac{16}{5}$.**

$$s_1 + s_2 = -\frac{5}{4} + \frac{16}{5} \qquad\qquad s_1 s_2 = \left(-\frac{5}{4}\right)\left(\frac{16}{5}\right)$$

$$= \frac{39}{20} \qquad -\frac{b}{a} = \frac{39}{20} \qquad\qquad = \frac{-80}{20} \qquad \frac{c}{a} = \frac{-80}{20}$$

Therefore, a = 20, b = -39, and c = -80.
The equation is $20x^2 - 39x - 80 = 0$.

3 **Find a quadratic equation that has roots $5 + 2i$ and $5 - 2i$.**

$$s_1 + s_2 = (5 + 2i) + (5 - 2i)$$
$$= 10 \qquad\qquad -\frac{b}{a} = 10 \text{ or } \frac{10}{1}$$

$$s_1 s_2 = (5 + 2i)(5 - 2i)$$
$$= 25 + 4 \qquad\qquad \frac{c}{a} = 29 \text{ or } \frac{29}{1}$$
$$= 29$$

Therefore, a = 1, b = -10, and c = 29.
The equation is $x^2 - 10x + 29 = 0$.

4 **Find k such that -3 is a root of $x^2 + kx - 24 = 0$.**

Let $s_1 = -3$.
Solve for s_2. \qquad\qquad Now solve for k.

$$s_1 s_2 = \frac{c}{a} \qquad\qquad s_1 + s_2 = -\frac{b}{a}$$

$$-3(s_2) = \frac{-24}{1} \qquad\qquad -3 + 8 = -\frac{k}{1} \qquad \textit{Substitute 8 for } s_2.$$

$$s_2 = 8 \qquad\qquad\qquad -5 = k \qquad \text{The value of } k \text{ is } -5.$$

Exploratory Exercises

State the sum and the product of the roots of each quadratic equation.

1. $x^2 + 7x - 4 = 0$
2. $x^2 + 8x + 7 = 0$
3. $x^2 - 3x + 5 = 0$
4. $2x^2 + 8x - 3 = 0$
5. $3x^2 + 7x - 9 = 0$
6. $2x^2 + 7 = 0$
7. $5x^2 - 3x = 0$
8. $4x^2 + 3x - 12 = 0$
9. $5x^2 = 3$
10. $2x^2 + 9x = 0$
11. $3x^2 - 2x + 11 = 0$
12. $7x^2 = 0$
13. $2x^2 - \frac{1}{2}x + \frac{2}{3} = 0$
14. $x^2 + 4x - \frac{5}{3} = 0$
15. $3x^2 - \frac{x}{5} - \frac{4}{5} = 0$

Written Exercises

Find the sum and the product of the roots of each quadratic equation. Then solve each equation.

1. $x^2 + 6x - 7 = 0$
2. $y^2 + 5y + 6 = 0$
3. $2z^2 - 5z - 3 = 0$
4. $6t^2 + 28t - 10 = 0$
5. $x^2 - 3x + 1 = 0$
6. $2c^2 - 5c + 1 = 0$
7. $4a^2 + 21a = 18$
8. $3b^2 - 8b = 35$
9. $2x^2 - 6x + 5 = 0$
10. $y^2 + 9y + 25 = 0$
11. $9n^2 - 1 = 0$
12. $s^2 - 16 = 0$
13. $2x^2 - 7x = 15$
14. $8m^2 + 6m = -1$
15. $15c^2 - 2c - 8 = 0$
16. $4k^2 + 27k - 7 = 0$
17. $a^2 + 25a + 156 = 0$
18. $x^2 + 4x - 77 = 0$
19. $3z^2 - 7z + 3 = 0$
20. $7s^2 + 5s - 1 = 0$
21. $12x^2 + 19x + 4 = 0$

Find a quadratic equation having the given roots.

22. $8, -2$
23. $5, -2$
24. $6, 4$
25. $-2, 3$
26. $6, -6$
27. $-9, -4$
28. $3, \frac{1}{2}$
29. $5, \frac{2}{3}$
30. $-\frac{3}{4}, 12$
31. $\frac{3}{4}, -4$
32. $-\frac{1}{2}, \frac{1}{2}$
33. $-\frac{2}{5}, \frac{2}{5}$
34. $\frac{5}{8}, \frac{1}{4}$
35. $\frac{1}{3}, \frac{1}{2}$
36. $\sqrt{3}, 2\sqrt{3}$
37. $\sqrt{2}, -5\sqrt{2}$
38. $2 + \sqrt{3}, 2 - \sqrt{3}$
39. $5 - \sqrt{2}, 5 + \sqrt{2}$
40. $3i, -3i$
41. $-6i, 6i$
42. $3 + 7i, 3 - 7i$
43. $5 + i\sqrt{3}, 5 - i\sqrt{3}$
44. $\frac{1 + \sqrt{7}}{2}, \frac{1 - \sqrt{7}}{2}$
45. $\frac{5 - 3i}{4}, \frac{5 + 3i}{4}$

Find k such that the number given is a root of the equation given.

46. $3; x^2 + kx - 21 = 0$
47. $1; x^2 + kx - 5 = 0$
48. $3; x^2 + 6x - k = 0$
49. $-\frac{3}{2}; 2x^2 + kx - 12 = 0$
50. $3; 6x^2 + kx - 5 = 0$
51. $-5; x^2 + 12x + k = 0$

Excursions in Algebra ———————— Contest Problem

The following problem appeared in a high school contest of the Mathematical Association of America.

Suppose s_1 and s_2 are roots of the equation $ax^2 + bx + c = 0$. Find the value of $\frac{s_1^2 + s_2^2}{s_1^2 s_2^2}$ in terms of a, b, and c. (Hint: $s_1^2 + s_2^2 = (s_1 + s_2)^2 - 2s_1 s_2$)

Gravity affects falling objects and objects propelled upwards, like rockets and baseballs. On earth, the acceleration due to gravity is about 32 ft/sec^2. The formula below can be used to compute an object's distance from the ground, s, after t seconds. The initial velocity, v_0, is given in feet per second.

$$s = v_0t - \frac{1}{2}gt^2 \quad \boxed{\text{Replace } g \text{ by 32.}} \quad s = v_0t - 16t^2$$

Example 1: **An object is propelled upwards from the ground with an initial velocity of 192 feet per second. How long will it take to return to ground level?**

$s = v_0t - 16t^2$

$0 = 192t - 16t^2$ *Replace s by 0 since the distance is 0 when the object returns to ground level. Replace v_0 by 192.*

$0 = t(192 - 16t)$ *Factor and use the zero product property.*

$t = 0 \quad \text{or} \quad 192 - 16t = 0$

$\qquad\qquad\qquad\quad -16t = -192$

$\qquad\qquad\qquad\qquad t = 12$

The object will return to the ground in 12 seconds.

Example 2: **A rocket is fired upwards from a platform 288 feet above ground with an initial velocity of 960 feet per second. Find the number of seconds it will take the rocket to return to ground level.**

$s = v_0t - 16t^2$

$-288 = 960t - 16t^2$ *Ground level is 288 feet below the platform, so replace s by -288. Replace v_0 by 960.*

$16t^2 - 960t - 288 = 0$ *Rewrite the equation so the coefficient of t^2 is positive.*

$t^2 - 60t - 18 = 0$ *This is not easily factorable, so use the quadratic formula.*

$t \approx -0.3 \quad \text{or} \quad t \approx 60.3$

Reject the negative root since time must be positive. The rocket will return to the ground in about 60 seconds.

Exercises

Given the height of the platform from which each rocket is launched and the initial velocity below, find the number of seconds it will take the rocket to return to ground level.

1. height: 96 ft
    velocity: 80 ft/s

2. height: 480 ft
    velocity: 112 ft/s

3. height: 288 ft
    velocity: 112 ft/s

7-6 Problem Solving: Quadratic Equations

Sometimes a drawing will help you write an equation to solve a problem. Consider the following problem.

> The Pinetown Recreation Bureau planned to build an ice-skating rink with dimensions 30 meters by 60 meters. Their budget has been cut, so they must reduce the area of the rink to 1000 square meters. A strip will be removed from one end, and a strip of the same width will be removed from one side. Find the width of the strips.

Explore The problem asks for the width of the strips. Let w stand for the width of the strips.

Make a drawing.

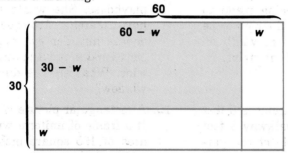

Plan The length of the blue rectangle is $60 - w$. The width of the blue rectangle is $30 - w$.

$$\text{length} \times \text{width} = \text{area}$$
$$(60 - w)(30 - w) = 1000$$

Solve
$$(60 - w)(30 - w) = 1000$$
$$1800 - 60w - 30w + w^2 = 1000$$
$$1800 - 90w + w^2 = 1000$$
$$800 - 90w + w^2 = 0$$
$$(10 - w)(80 - w) = 0$$

$$10 - w = 0 \quad \text{or} \quad 80 - w = 0$$
$$10 = w \quad \text{or} \quad 80 = w$$

Check all solutions to the problem. In this case, 80 is not a reasonable solution, so the strip will be 10 meters wide.

Examine If a 10 meter strip is removed from 30 meters, the width will be 20 meters. Likewise, the 60 meter length minus the 10 meters will leave a length of 50 meters.

$$20 \text{ m} \times 50 \text{ m} = 1000 \text{ m}^2$$

Written Exercises

Solve each problem.

1. Find two consecutive integers whose product is 702.

2. Find two consecutive even integers whose product is 288.

3. Find two consecutive odd integers whose product is 1443.

4. Find two consecutive integers whose product is 552.

5. If the product of two consecutive odd integers is decreased by one-third the lesser integer, the result is 250. Find the integers.

6. If the product of two consecutive integers is decreased by 20 times the greater integer, the result is 442. Find the integers.

7. The sum of the squares of two consecutive integers is 265. Find the integers.

8. The sum of the squares of two consecutive even integers is 244. Find the integers.

9. A local park is 30 meters long by 20 meters wide. Plans are being made to double the area by adding a strip at one end and another of the same width on one side. Find the width of the strips.

10. Jackie Ruben is building a children's playhouse. She wants each window to have an area of 315 square inches for adequate air. For eye appeal, she wants each window to be six inches higher than wide. What are the dimensions of each window?

11. The length of Hillcrest Garden is 6 feet more than its width. A walkway 3 feet wide surrounds the outside of the garden. The total area of the walkway is 288 square feet. Find the dimensions of the garden.

12. A rectangular picture is 12 by 16 inches. If a frame of uniform width contains an area of 165 square inches, what is the width of the frame?

13. The difference of the squares of two consecutive integers is 21. Find the integers.

14. The difference of the squares of two consecutive odd integers is 48. Find the integers.

15. If a number is increased by its square, the result is 72. Find the number.

16. The square of a number exceeds 11 times the number by 312. Find the number.

17. If a number is decreased by its square, the result is $\frac{2}{9}$. Find the number.

18. The square of a number decreased by the square of one-half the number is 108. Find the number.

19. The sum of a number and its reciprocal is $\frac{10}{3}$. Find the number.

20. A number increased by 4 times its reciprocal is $\frac{20}{3}$. Find the number.

21. The Hillside Garden Club wants to double the area of its rectangular display of roses. If it is now 6 meters by 4 meters, by what equal amount must each dimension be increased?

22. A rectangular garden 25 feet by 50 feet is increased on all sides by the same amount. Its area increases 400 square feet. By how much is each dimension increased?

23. If a number is decreased by its reciprocal, the result is $\frac{11}{30}$. Find the number.

24. The difference between a number and its reciprocal is $\frac{16}{15}$. Find the number.

25. Jim Finley is a professional photographer. He has a photo 8 centimeters long and 6 centimeters wide. A customer wants a print of the photo. The print is to have half the area of the original. Jim plans to reduce the length and width of the photo by the same amount. What are the dimensions of the print?

26. Gary and Jan's family room has a rug that is 9 feet by 12 feet. A strip of floor of equal width is uncovered along all edges of the rug. If the area of the uncovered floor is 270 square feet, how wide is the strip?

27. The square of a number increased by 21 is equal to 10 times the number. Find the number.

28. Two numbers differ by 9. The sum of their squares is 653. Find the numbers.

29. Three times the square of a number equals 21 times the number. Find the number.

30. Thirty decreased by one-half of a number is one-sixth of the square of the number. Find the number.

31. A rectangular flower bed in Lake Park is 20 by 28 meters. A walk of uniform width surrounds the flower bed. If the area of the flower bed and walk is 1008 square meters, what is the width of the walk?

32. Three boys are to mow a rectangular lawn with dimensions 100 by 120 feet. Bill is going to mow one-third of the lawn by mowing a strip of uniform width around the outer edge of the lawn. What is the width of the strip?

Challenge

33. In the diagram below, the rectangle shaded red and created by the dotted line is similar to the rectangle with dimensions 1 by x. The value of x represents the "golden ratio." Write a proportion and solve for x to find the golden ratio. Round to the nearest thousandth.

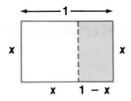

mini-review

1. What property is shown?
   $x + (y + z) = (x + y) + z$
2. Graph $y < |x - 2|$.
3. Solve the system of equations.
   $x + y = -2$
   $2x - 14 = y$
4. Add. $\begin{bmatrix} 2 & 1 \\ 0 & 6 \end{bmatrix} + \begin{bmatrix} -2 & 4 \\ 7 & -6 \end{bmatrix}$
5. Factor $m^3 + 5m^2 - 24m$.

Excursions in Algebra _____ Handshakes

At the conclusion of a committee meeting, a total of 28 handshakes were exchanged. Assuming each person was equally polite toward all the others, how many people were present? (Hint: Assume n persons were at the meeting. With how many persons did each person shake hands? Use a quadratic equation.)

7-7 Quadratic Form

The equation $x^4 - 20x^2 + 64 = 0$ is *not* a quadratic equation. But it looks very much like a quadratic equation. It is in **quadratic form** because it can be written as $(x^2)^2 - 20(x^2) + 64 = 0$.

> For any numbers a, b, and c, except $a = 0$, an equation that may be written as $a[f(x)]^2 + b[f(x)] + c = 0$, where $f(x)$ is some expression in x, is in quadratic form.

Definition of Quadratic Form

An equation in quadratic form can be solved by the same methods used for solving quadratic equations.

In an equation such as $x^2 + 2x + 1 = 0$, $f(x)$ is just x.

Example

1 **Solve $x^4 - 13x^2 + 36 = 0$.**

$$x^4 - 13x^2 + 36 = 0$$
$$(x^2)^2 - 13(x^2) + 36 = 0 \quad \text{The equation is in quadratic form. } f(x) \text{ is } x^2.$$
$$(x^2 - 9)(x^2 - 4) = 0$$
$$(x + 3)(x - 3)(x + 2)(x - 2) = 0$$

$$x + 3 = 0 \quad \text{or} \quad x - 3 = 0 \quad \text{or} \quad x + 2 = 0 \quad \text{or} \quad x - 2 = 0$$
$$x = -3 \quad \text{or} \quad x = 3 \quad \text{or} \quad x = -2 \quad \text{or} \quad x = 2$$

The solutions or roots are -3, 3, -2, and 2.

Recall that $(a^m)^n$ equals a^{mn} for any nonzero number a and any rational numbers n and m. This property of exponents is often used when solving equations.

Example

2 **Solve $x^{\frac{2}{3}} = 16$.**

$$x^{\frac{2}{3}} = 16$$
$$(x^{\frac{2}{3}})^{\frac{3}{2}} = \pm(16)^{\frac{3}{2}} \quad \text{Raise each side to the } \frac{3}{2} \text{ power. Why is } \pm \text{ necessary?}$$
$$x = \pm(16^{\frac{1}{2}})^3$$
$$x = \pm(4)^3$$
$$x = \pm 64$$

Check:

$$x^{\frac{2}{3}} = 16 \qquad\qquad x^{\frac{2}{3}} = 16$$
$$64^{\frac{2}{3}} \stackrel{?}{=} 16 \qquad\qquad (-64)^{\frac{2}{3}} \stackrel{?}{=} 16$$
$$(\sqrt[3]{64})^2 \stackrel{?}{=} 16 \qquad\qquad (\sqrt[3]{-64})^2 \stackrel{?}{=} 16$$
$$4^2 \stackrel{?}{=} 16 \qquad\qquad (-4)^2 \stackrel{?}{=} 16$$
$$16 = 16 \qquad\qquad 16 = 16$$

The solutions or roots are 64 and -64.

Examples

3 **Solve $y^{-2} - 64 = 0$.**

$$y^{-2} - 64 = 0$$
$$(y^{-1})^2 - 64 = 0$$
$$(y^{-1} + 8)(y^{-1} - 8) = 0$$
$$y^{-1} = -8 \quad \text{or} \quad y^{-1} = 8$$
$$y = -\frac{1}{8} \qquad\qquad y = \frac{1}{8}$$

The solutions are $-\frac{1}{8}$ and $\frac{1}{8}$.

The equation may also be solved as follows:

$$y^{-2} = 64$$
$$(y^{-2})^{-\frac{1}{2}} = 64^{-\frac{1}{2}}$$
$$y = \pm\frac{1}{8}$$

4 **Solve $x^{\frac{1}{2}} - 6x^{\frac{1}{4}} + 8 = 0$.**

$$x^{\frac{1}{2}} - 6x^{\frac{1}{4}} + 8 = 0$$
$$(x^{\frac{1}{4}})^2 - 6(x^{\frac{1}{4}}) + 8 = 0 \qquad \text{So } f(x) \text{ is } x^{\frac{1}{4}}.$$
$$(x^{\frac{1}{4}} - 2)(x^{\frac{1}{4}} - 4) = 0 \qquad \text{Factor to solve for } f(x).$$
$$x^{\frac{1}{4}} - 2 = 0 \quad \text{or} \quad x^{\frac{1}{4}} - 4 = 0$$
$$x^{\frac{1}{4}} = 2 \qquad\qquad x^{\frac{1}{4}} = 4$$

To solve for x, continue as shown.

$$x^{\frac{1}{4}} = 2 \qquad \text{or} \qquad x^{\frac{1}{4}} = 4$$
$$(x^{\frac{1}{4}})^4 = (2)^4 \qquad\qquad (x^{\frac{1}{4}})^4 = 4^4$$
$$x = 2^4 \text{ or } 16 \qquad\qquad x = 4^4 \text{ or } 256$$

The solutions are 16 and 256.

Check: $x^{\frac{1}{2}} - 6x^{\frac{1}{4}} + 8 = 0$

$$16^{\frac{1}{2}} - 6(16^{\frac{1}{4}}) + 8 \overset{?}{=} 0$$
$$4 - 6(2) + 8 \overset{?}{=} 0$$
$$0 = 0$$

$$256^{\frac{1}{2}} - 6(256^{\frac{1}{4}}) + 8 \overset{?}{=} 0$$
$$16 - 6(4) + 8 \overset{?}{=} 0$$
$$0 = 0$$

The quadratic formula can be used to solve equations that are expressed in quadratic form. Remember to check each solution carefully.

Example

5 **Solve $x - 7\sqrt{x} - 8 = 0$.**

$$x - 7\sqrt{x} - 8 = 0$$
$$(\sqrt{x})^2 - 7(\sqrt{x}) - 8 = 0 \qquad f(x) = \sqrt{x}$$
$$\sqrt{x} = \frac{-b \pm \sqrt{b^2 - 4ac}}{2a}$$
$$= \frac{-(-7) \pm \sqrt{(-7)^2 - 4(1)(-8)}}{2(1)} \qquad a = 1, b = -7, c = -8$$
$$= \frac{7 \pm \sqrt{81}}{2}$$
$$= \frac{7 \pm 9}{2}$$
$$\sqrt{x} = 8 \quad \text{or} \quad \sqrt{x} = -1$$
$$x = 64 \quad \text{or} \quad x = 1$$

Check:

$$x - 7\sqrt{x} - 8 = 0$$
$$64 - 7\sqrt{64} - 8 \overset{?}{=} 0$$
$$64 - 7 \cdot 8 - 8 \overset{?}{=} 0$$
$$0 = 0$$

$$x - 7\sqrt{x} - 8 = 0$$
$$1 - 7\sqrt{1} - 8 \overset{?}{=} 0$$
$$1 - 7 - 8 \overset{?}{=} 0$$
$$-14 \neq 0$$

The only solution is 64.

Exploratory Exercises

State whether each equation is in quadratic form.

1. $x^4 + 5x^2 + 3 = 0$
2. $4y^4 - 3y^2 + 2 = 0$
3. $6x^4 + 7x - 8 = 0$
4. $6x^4 + 8x^2 = 0$
5. $6x + 5\sqrt{x} - 2 = 0$
6. $2p + 5\sqrt{p} = 9$

Solve each equation.

7. $r^{\frac{1}{3}} = 2$
8. $x^{\frac{1}{3}} = 3$
9. $y^{\frac{1}{2}} = 5$
10. $x^{-\frac{1}{2}} = 4$
11. $z^{-2} = 25$
12. $r^{-3} = 27$
13. $y^{\frac{3}{2}} - 8 = 0$
14. $z^{-\frac{1}{3}} - 2 = 0$
15. $p^{-2} = 169$

Written Exercises

Express each equation in quadratic form.

1. $x^{\frac{4}{3}} - 7x^{\frac{2}{3}} + 12 = 0$
2. $x^{-6} - 8x^{-3} + 16 = 0$
3. $x - 10x^{\frac{1}{2}} + 25 = 0$
4. $x^{\frac{1}{2}} + 7x^{\frac{1}{4}} + 12 = 0$
5. $x^{\frac{1}{2}} - 8x^{\frac{1}{4}} + 15 = 0$
6. $y^{\frac{1}{2}} - 10y^{\frac{1}{4}} + 16 = 0$
7. $r^{\frac{2}{3}} - 5r^{\frac{1}{3}} + 6 = 0$
8. $s^{\frac{2}{3}} - 9s^{\frac{1}{3}} + 20 = 0$
9. $a^{-\frac{2}{3}} - 11a^{-\frac{1}{3}} + 28 = 0$
10. $k^{-\frac{4}{3}} - 10k^{-\frac{2}{3}} + 21 = 0$

Solve each equation.

11. $x^4 - 5x^2 + 4 = 0$
12. $y^4 - 3y^2 + 2 = 0$
13. $z^4 - 25z^2 + 144 = 0$
14. $m^4 - 40m^2 + 144 = 0$
15. $s^4 - 25 = 0$
16. $x^4 - 16 = 0$
17. $y^4 - 9 = 0$
18. $a^4 - 36 = 0$
19. $x^4 - 25x^2 = 0$
20. $z^4 - 9z^2 = 0$
21. $b^4 + 9b^2 + 18 = 0$
22. $c^4 - 2c^2 - 8 = 0$
23. $x^4 - 6x^2 + 8 = 0$
24. $y^4 - 11y^2 + 24 = 0$
25. $m - 9\sqrt{m} + 8 = 0$
26. $s - 13\sqrt{s} + 36 = 0$
27. $x - 2\sqrt{x} + 1 = 0$
28. $z - 16\sqrt{z} + 64 = 0$
29. $a^6 - 64a^3 = 0$
30. $m^6 - 64 = 0$
31. $z^6 - 7z^3 - 8 = 0$
32. $a^6 + 26a^3 - 27 = 0$
33. $y^6 - 10y^3 + 16 = 0$
34. $m^6 - 2m^3 + 1 = 0$
35. $x^{\frac{1}{2}} - 10x^{\frac{1}{4}} + 16 = 0$
36. $x^{\frac{2}{3}} - 8x^{\frac{1}{3}} + 15 = 0$
37. $r^{\frac{2}{3}} - 12r^{\frac{1}{3}} + 20 = 0$
38. $b^{\frac{2}{3}} - 7b^{\frac{1}{3}} + 10 = 0$
39. $m - 11m^{\frac{1}{2}} + 30 = 0$
40. $s - 5s^{\frac{1}{2}} + 6 = 0$
41. $x^{\frac{4}{3}} - 8x^{\frac{2}{3}} + 16 = 0$
42. $y^{\frac{4}{3}} - 13y^{\frac{2}{3}} + 36 = 0$
43. $a^{-\frac{2}{3}} - 10a^{-\frac{1}{3}} + 21 = 0$
44. $y^{-\frac{2}{5}} - 4y^{-\frac{1}{5}} + 4 = 0$
45. $y^{-1} - 5y^{-\frac{1}{2}} + 6 = 0$
46. $y^3 - 16y^{\frac{3}{2}} + 64 = 0$

Challenge

Solve each equation.

47. $3g^{\frac{2}{3}} - 10g^{\frac{1}{3}} + 8 = 0$
48. $2a^{\frac{1}{2}} - 13a^{\frac{1}{4}} + 20 = 0$
49. $6x - 19x^{\frac{1}{2}} + 15 = 0$
50. $3m + m^{\frac{1}{2}} - 2 = 0$
51. $2r^{\frac{1}{2}} + r^{\frac{1}{4}} - 15 = 0$
52. $2y^{\frac{2}{3}} - 5y^{\frac{1}{3}} - 12 = 0$
53. $|x + 1|^2 = 4$
54. $|y - 2|^2 - 9 = 0$
55. $|m + 3|^2 - 2|m + 3| = -1$
56. $|a - 4|^2 - 7|a - 4| = -6$

Discriminant and Roots

The computer program at the right can be used to find the roots of a quadratic equation in decimal form. The program also states whether the roots are real or imaginary and prints the discriminant.

A quadratic equation in the form $ax^2 + bx + c = 0$ provides the values for A, B, and C.

Example: $x^2 - 14x + 49 = 0$
$A = 1, B = -14, C = 49$

Enter and run this program on your computer using these values. You should get the following output.

```
ONE ROOT: 7
THE DISCRIMINANT IS 0
```

```
10 INPUT "ENTER A,B,C, OF
      QUADRATIC FORMULA: ";A,B,C
20 LET D = B * B - 4 * A * C
30 IF D < 0 THEN 110
40 IF D > 0 THEN 70
50 PRINT "ONE ROOT: "; - B / (2 *
      A)
60 GOTO 150
70 LET X = ( - B + SQR (D)) / ( 2
      * A)
80 LET Y = ( - B - SQR (D)) / ( 2
      * A)
90 PRINT "TWO REAL ROOTS: ";X;" "
      ;Y
100 GOTO 150
110 PRINT "TWO COMPLEX ROOTS: ";
120 PRINT - B / (2 * A);"+";SQR
      ( - D) / (2 * A);"I"
130 PRINT - B / (2 * A);"-";SQR
      ( - D) / (2 * A);"I"
150 PRINT "THE DISCRIMINANT IS "
      ;D
160 END
```

Exercises

Using the computer program above, find the values of the discriminant and roots of each quadratic equation. Describe the nature of the roots. If the roots are real, decide whether or not they are rational.

1. $10x^2 + 33x - 7 = 0$

2. $6n^2 + 8n + 1 = 0$

3. $3y^2 + 3y = -2$

4. $x^2 = 6x - 13$

Find the value of the discriminant and roots of each equation. What do you notice about the roots and discriminants of each group of equations?

5. $m^2 - 4m + 6 = 0$
$m^2 + 4m + 6 = 0$

6. $x^2 - 3x - 28 = 0$
$2x^2 - 6x - 56 = 0$
$5x^2 - 15x - 140 = 0$

7. $x^2 - 25 = 0$
$2x^2 - 10 = 0$
$16x^2 - 12 = 0$

8. $x^2 + 4x + 4 = 0$
$x^2 - 10x + 25 = 0$
$4x^2 + 32x + 64 = 0$

Vocabulary

quadratic equation   (217)
zero product property   (217)
completing the square   (220)

quadratic formula   (223)
discriminant   (226)
quadratic form   (235)

Chapter Summary

1. **Zero Product Property:**   For any numbers a and b, if $ab = 0$, then $a = 0$ or $b = 0$.   (217)

2. Completing the square can be used to solve quadratic equations.   (220)

3. **Quadratic Formula:**   The roots of a quadratic equation of the form $ax^2 + bx + c = 0$ with $a \neq 0$ are given by the following formula.

$$x = \frac{-b \pm \sqrt{b^2 - 4ac}}{2a} \quad (223)$$

4. The discriminant, $b^2 - 4ac$, gives information about the solutions or roots of a quadratic equation whose coefficients are real numbers.   (226)

Discriminant	Nature of the Roots
zero	one real root
positive	two real roots
negative	two imaginary roots

5. If the roots of $ax^2 + bx + c = 0$, with $a \neq 0$, are s_1 and s_2, then

$$s_1 + s_2 = -\frac{b}{a} \text{ and } s_1 s_2 = \frac{c}{a}. \quad (228)$$

6. **Definition of Quadratic Form:**   For any numbers a, b, and c, except $a = 0$, an equation that may be written as $a[f(x)]^2 + b[f(x)] + c = 0$, where $f(x)$ is some expression in x, is in quadratic form.   (235)

7. An equation in quadratic form can be solved by the same methods used for solving quadratic equations.   (235)

Chapter Review

7–1 **Solve each equation.**

    1. $(2x + 3)(3x - 1) = 0$ **2.** $(x + 7)(4x - 5) = 0$ **3.** $2x^2 + 5x + 3 = 0$

    4. $2x^2 + 9x + 4 = 0$ **5.** $15a^2 + 13a = 6$ **6.** $8b^2 + 10b = 3$

7–2 **Find the value of c that makes each trinomial a perfect square.**

    7. $x^2 + 14x + c$ **8.** $a^2 - 7a + c$

    Solve each equation by completing the square.

    9. $x^2 - 20x + 75 = 0$ **10.** $x^2 - 5x - 24 = 0$

    11. $2t^2 + t - 21 = 0$ **12.** $r^2 + 4r = 96$

7–3 **Solve each equation using the quadratic formula.**

    13. $3x^2 - 11x + 10 = 0$ **14.** $2x^2 - 8x = 0$

    15. $2p^2 - 9 = 0$ **16.** $2q^2 - 5q + 4 = 0$

7–4 **Find the value of the discriminant for each quadratic equation. Describe the nature of the roots. If the roots are real, tell whether they are rational or irrational. Then solve each equation.**

    17. $4x^2 - 40x + 25 = 0$ **18.** $2y^2 + 6y + 5 = 0$

    19. $n^2 = 8n - 16$ **20.** $7b^2 = 4b$

7–5 **Find the sum and the product of the roots for each quadratic equation. Then solve each equation.**

    21. $x^2 - 12x - 45 = 0$ **22.** $2m^2 - 10m + 9 = 0$

    23. $3s^2 - 11 = 0$ **24.** $2x^2 = 3 - 5x$

    Find a quadratic equation having the given roots.

    25. $4, -6$ **26.** $\dfrac{3}{4}, \dfrac{1}{3}$

    27. $5 - 3i, 5 + 3i$ **28.** $2 - \sqrt{3}, 2 + \sqrt{3}$

7–6 **Solve each problem.**

    29. The square of a number decreased by twenty times that number is 384. Find the number.

    30. Find five consecutive integers such that the sum of the squares of the smallest and largest is 208.

    31. A rectangular lawn has dimensions 24 feet by 32 feet. A sidewalk will be constructed along the inside edges of all four sides. The remaining lawn will have an area of 425 square feet. How wide will the walk be?

7–7 **Solve each equation.**

    32. $x^4 - 8x^2 + 16 = 0$ **33.** $x^4 - 12x^2 + 27 = 0$ **34.** $p - 4\sqrt{p} - 45 = 0$

    35. $r + 9\sqrt{r} = -8$ **36.** $x^{\frac{1}{2}} - 15x^{\frac{1}{4}} + 36 = 0$ **37.** $x^{\frac{2}{3}} - 9x^{\frac{1}{3}} + 20 = 0$

Chapter Test

Solve each equation.

1. $x^2 + 8x - 33 = 0$
2. $6y^2 - y - 15 = 0$
3. $x^2 - 6x + 8 = 0$
4. $y^2 + 7y - 18 = 0$
5. $3x^2 + x - 14 = 0$
6. $12x^2 - 5x = 3$
7. $5x^2 - 125 = 0$
8. $4x^2 = 324$
9. $x^2 + 6x - 216 = 0$
10. $3x^2 + 4x + 2 = 0$
11. $x^4 - 9x^2 + 20 = 0$
12. $x - 9\sqrt{x} + 8 = 0$
13. $2x + 3\sqrt{x} = 9$
14. $x^4 - 11x^2 - 80 = 0$
15. $x^{\frac{1}{2}} - 15x^{\frac{1}{4}} + 50 = 0$
16. $x - 11x^{\frac{1}{2}} + 30 = 0$
17. $3x + x^{\frac{1}{2}} - 2 = 0$
18. $2m^{\frac{2}{3}} - 5m^{\frac{1}{3}} - 12 = 0$

Find the value of c that makes each trinomial a perfect square.

19. $n^2 + 6n + c$
20. $x^2 - 5x + c$

State the value of the discriminant for each quadratic equation. Describe the nature of the roots. If the roots are real, tell whether they are rational or irrational.

21. $6x^2 + 7x - 5 = 0$
22. $2y^2 - 9y + 11 = 0$
23. $9a^2 - 30a + 25 = 0$
24. $7m^2 = 4m$

Find the sum and the product of the roots for each quadratic equation.

25. $x^2 - 15x + 56 = 0$
26. $2x^2 - 3x - 12 = 0$
27. $x + 7 = 4x^2$
28. $2x^2 = 3 - 5x$

Find a quadratic equation having the given roots.

29. $0, -3$
30. $8, -3$
31. $\dfrac{4}{3}, \dfrac{2}{3}$
32. $5 + 2i, 5 - 2i$

Solve each problem.

33. The sum of the squares of two consecutive odd integers is 1154. Find the integers.

34. The Dolphin Pool Company will build a pool for Sally Wadman having 600 square feet of surface. Ms. Wadman's pool, along with a deck of uniform width, will have dimensions 30 feet by 40 feet. What will be the width of the decking around the pool?

CHAPTER 8

Quadratic Relations and Functions

In physics, the path an object follows when thrown or dropped is called a *trajectory*. An object launched upward, like the fireworks in the photo, will have a trajectory in the shape of a parabola.

8-1 Quadratic Functions

A model rocket is launched with an initial velocity of 50 meters per second. The height of the rocket is a function of the time after blast off. The height, $h(t)$, of the rocket t seconds after blast off is given by the equation $h(t) = 50t - 5t^2$. This equation is an example of a **quadratic function**.

A quadratic function is a function described by an equation of the form $f(x) = ax^2 + bx + c$ where $a \neq 0$.	*Definition of Quadratic Function*

The term ax^2 is called the *quadratic term*, bx is the *linear term*, and c is the *constant term*.

$f(x) = bx + c$ describes a linear function. $f(x) = c$ describes a constant function.

Examples

1 Write $f(x) = (x + 3)^2 + 5$ in quadratic form. Identify the quadratic term, the linear term, and the constant term.

$$\begin{aligned} f(x) &= (x + 3)^2 + 5 \\ &= x^2 + 6x + 9 + 5 \\ &= x^2 + 6x + 14 \end{aligned}$$

The quadratic term is x^2.
The linear term is $6x$.
The constant term is 14.

2 A theater has seats for 500 people. It is filled to capacity for each show and tickets cost $3.00 per show. The owner wants to increase ticket prices. She estimates that for each $0.20 increase in price, 25 fewer people will attend. Write a quadratic equation to describe the owner's income after she increases her prices.

Let p = number of $0.20 price increases.
Then $3.00 + 0.20p$ = ticket price.
And $500 - 25p$ = number tickets sold.

Income = (number of tickets sold) × (ticket price)

$$\begin{aligned} I &= (500 - 25p) \cdot (3.00 + 0.20p) \\ &= 1500 + 100p - 75p - 5p^2 \\ &= 1500 + 25p - 5p^2 \end{aligned}$$

Exploratory Exercises

State whether each of the following is a quadratic equation.

1. $f(x) = x^2 + 3x + 5$
2. $f(x) = -3x^2 - 8x - 7$
3. $f(x) = 2x - 6$
4. $f(x) = (x - 4)^2$
5. $g(x) = -3(x - 4)^2 - 6$
6. $p(x) = x + 1$
7. $m(x) = 3x^2$
8. $r(s) = s^2 + 2s$
9. $f(x) = \dfrac{1}{x^2} + \dfrac{1}{x} + 1$
10. $g(x) = -\dfrac{1}{3}x + \dfrac{4}{5}$

For each equation identify the quadratic term, the linear term, and the constant term.

11. $f(x) = x^2 + 3x - \dfrac{1}{4}$
12. $f(x) = 4x^2 - 8x - 2$
13. $m(x) = x^2 - 3x - \dfrac{1}{4}$
14. $g(p) = \dfrac{1}{3}p + 4$
15. $g(a) = 3a^2 - 2$
16. $n(x) = -4x^2 - 8x - 9$
17. $z = x^2 + 3x$
18. $q = -4x^2 - 2x$
19. $h(x) = (x + 3)^2$
20. $h(x) = (2x - 5)^2$

Written Exercises

Write each equation in quadratic form. identify

1. $f(x) = (x - 2)^2$
2. $f(x) = (x + 4)^2$
3. $f(x) = (3x + 2)^2$
4. $f(x) = (2x - 5)^2$
5. $f(x) = 2(4x + 1)^2$
6. $f(x) = -4(2x - 4)^2$
7. $f(x) = 3(x - 4)^2 - 6$
8. $f(x) = 4(x + 1)^2 + 10$
9. $f(x) = 5(3x - 2)^2 + 4$
10. $f(x) = -3(2x + 2)^2 + 6$
11. $f(x) = \dfrac{1}{5}(10x - 5)^2 + 8$
12. $f(x) = \dfrac{1}{6}(6x + 12)^2 + 5$

13. Write a quadratic equation to describe the area of a circle in terms of its radius.

14. Write a quadratic equation to describe the area of an isosceles right triangle in terms of its legs.

Define a variable and write a quadratic equation for each of the following. Do *not* solve the equation.

15. the product of two numbers whose sum is 40

16. the product of two numbers whose sum is 36

17. the product of two numbers whose difference is 64

18. the product of two numbers whose difference is 25

19. the area of a rectangle whose perimeter is 20 centimeters

20. the area of a rectangle whose perimeter is 64 millimeters

21. The product of two consecutive integers is 9 less than the square of the second integer.

22. The square of an integer is 97 less than the square of the next consecutive integer.

23. A taxi service transports 300 passengers a day between two airports. The charge is $8.00. The owner estimates that for each $1 increase in fare, he will lose 20 passengers. Write a quadratic equation to describe the owner's income after he increases his prices.

25. Ms. Morrison has 120 meters of fence to make a rectangular pen for her ducks. She will use the side of a shed for one side of the pen. Write a quadratic equation to describe the area of the pen.

26. Last year 200 people came to see the fall play at Jones High School. The cost per ticket was $2.00. This year the drama teacher estimates that for each $0.25 increase in price, 10 fewer people will come to the play. Write a quadratic equation to describe the income after the price is increased.

24. Bill Taylor's garden has a fence along one side. He wishes to fence in the other three sides with 200 feet of fencing. Write a quadratic equation to describe the area of the garden.

mini-review

1. Solve this system: $2x - 3y = -1$
$\qquad\qquad\qquad\qquad x + 6y = 7$

2. Factor $5x^2 + 27x - 18$.

3. Divide $3x^2 + 10x - 1$ by $3x + 1$.

4. Simplify $\dfrac{6 - i}{2i + 5}$.

5. Solve by completing the square: $x^2 - 14x - 1 = 0$.

Using Calculators _____ **The Square Key**

The $\boxed{x^2}$ key, found on most calculators, squares the number on the display.

Example: Write $f(x) = 2(x - 3)^2 - 1$ in quadratic form. Then evaluate both functions for $x = 5$.

$$f(x) = 2(x - 3)^2 - 1$$
$$= 2(x^2 - 6x + 9) - 1$$
$$= 2x^2 - 12x + 17$$

Evaluate $2(x - 3)^2 - 1$ for $x = 5$.

ENTER: 2 $\boxed{\times}$ $\boxed{(}$ 5 $\boxed{-}$ 3 $\boxed{)}$ $\boxed{x^2}$ $\boxed{-}$ 1 $\boxed{=}$
DISPLAY: 2   5   3   2   4   8   1   7

Evaluate $2x^2 - 12x - 17$ for $x = 5$.

ENTER: 2 $\boxed{\times}$ 5 $\boxed{x^2}$ $\boxed{-}$ 12 $\boxed{\times}$ 5 $\boxed{+}$ 17 $\boxed{=}$
DISPLAY: 2   5   25   50   12   5   -10   17   7

Since the functions are equivalent, both functions have the same value for x = 5.

Exercises

Write each equation in quadratic form and evaluate each for the specified value.

1. $f(x) = (x - 5)^2 + 10$; $x = 7$

2. $f(x) = 3(x + 4)^2 - 18$; $x = 3$

3. $f(x) = -2(x + 1)^2 + 16$; $x = 5$

4. $f(x) = \frac{1}{4}(2x - 1)^2 - \frac{5}{4}$; $x = 6$
Hint: Convert fractions to decimals first.

Evaluate each equation below for $x = 5$ and $x = 2$. State whether the two equations are equivalent for these values of x.

5. $f(x) = (x + 2)^2 - 17$
$\quad g(x) = x^2 + 5x - 18$

6. $f(x) = x^2 - 2x - 17$
$\quad g(x) = (x - 1)^2 - 18$

8-2 Parabolas

Consider the following situation.

A rocket is launched with an initial velocity of 50 meters per second. The height, $h(t)$, of the rocket t seconds after blast-off is given by the equation $h(t) = 50t - 5t^2$.

A graph of this equation can be drawn by making a table of values, plotting points, and connecting the points with a smooth curve. The resulting graph is called **parabola.**

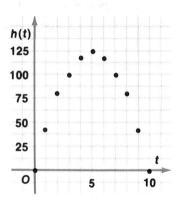

t	$50t - 5t^2$	$h(t)$
0	$50(0) - 5(0)^2$	0
1	$50(1) - 5(1)^2$	45
2	$50(2) - 5(2)^2$	80
3	$50(3) - 5(3)^2$	105
4	$50(4) - 5(4)^2$	120
5	$50(5) - 5(5)^2$	125
6	$50(6) - 5(6)^2$	120
7	$50(7) - 5(7)^2$	105
8	$50(8) - 5(8)^2$	80
9	$50(9) - 5(9)^2$	45
10	$50(10) - 5(10)^2$	0

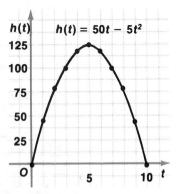

Notice that 10 seconds after blast-off, the height of the rocket is zero. This means that it has returned to earth. It appears to have reached its maximum height of 125 meters at 5 seconds after blast-off. Test some other values of t between 4 and 6 to check.

Test values of t like 4.9 and 5.1 to determine if the maximum height is reached at 5 seconds.

The graph of any quadratic function is a parabola. Parabolas have certain common characteristics. They all have an **axis of symmetry** and a **vertex.** The axis of symmetry is the line about which the parabola is symmetric. The vertex is the point of intersection of the parabola and the line of symmetry.

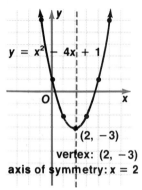

$y = x^2 - 4x + 1$

(2, −3)

vertex: (2, −3)
axis of symmetry: $x = 2$

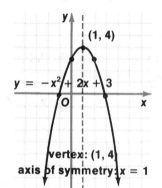

(1, 4)

$y = -x^2 + 2x + 3$

vertex: (1, 4)
axis of symmetry: $x = 1$

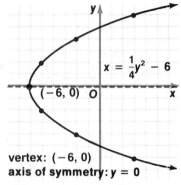

$x = \frac{1}{4}y^2 - 6$

(−6, 0)

vertex: (−6, 0)
axis of symmetry: $y = 0$

If the sketches are folded along the axis of symmetry, the two halves of the parabola coincide.

The graphs of $y = x^2$, $y = 2x^2$, and $y = \frac{1}{2}x^2$ are drawn on the same set of axes.

Each graph has vertex $(0, 0)$.

Each graph has axis of symmetry $x = 0$.

Each graph opens upward.

The greater the coefficient of x^2, the narrower the graph.

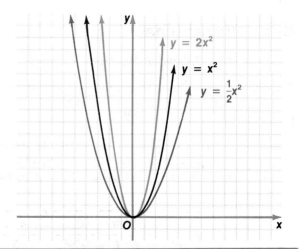

Example

1

Graph $y = -x^2$, $y = -2x^2$, and $y = -\frac{1}{2}x^2$ on the same set of axes. State the vertex, axis of symmetry, and direction of opening.

Find ordered pairs that satisfy the equation. Then graph the ordered pairs and sketch the graph of the equation.

x	-3	-2	-1	0	1	2	3
$-x^2$	-9	-4	-1	0	-1	-4	-9
$-2x^2$	-18	-8	-2	0	-2	-8	-18
$-\frac{1}{2}x^2$	$-\frac{9}{2}$	-2	$-\frac{1}{2}$	0	$-\frac{1}{2}$	-2	$-\frac{9}{2}$

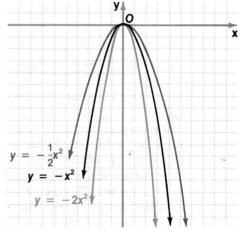

Each graph has vertex $(0, 0)$. Each graph has axis of symmetry $x = 0$. Each graph opens downward.

The greater the absolute value of the coefficient of x^2, the narrower the graph.

By studying these graphs, and many like them, the following conclusions can be made about the graph of $y = ax^2$.

$y = ax^2$	a is positive	a is negative
Vertex	$(0, 0)$	$(0, 0)$
Axis of symmetry	$x = 0$	$x = 0$
Direction of opening	upward	downward
As the value of $|a|$ increases, the graphs of $y = ax^2$ narrow.		

Exploratory Exercises

Complete each table of values.

1.

x	-6	-4	$-\frac{1}{2}$	$\frac{1}{2}$	4	6
$-4x^2$						

2.

x	-9	-3	$-\frac{1}{3}$	$\frac{1}{3}$	3	9
$\frac{1}{3}x^2$						

3. Plot each set of points in Exercise 1 and connect the points with a smooth curve.

4. Plot each set of points in Exercise 2 and connect the points with a smooth curve.

Written Exercises

For each problem, sketch the graphs of the equations on the same set of axes.

1. $y = x^2$, $y = 3x^2$, $y = \frac{1}{3}x^2$

2. $y = -x^2$, $y = -3x^2$, $y = -\frac{1}{3}x^2$

3. $y = x^2$, $y = -x^2$

4. $y = 4x^2$, $y = -4x^2$

5. $f(x) = 3x^2$, $f(x) = -2x^2$, $f(x) = \frac{1}{4}x^2$

6. $f(x) = -\frac{1}{4}x^2$, $f(x) = -\frac{1}{3}x^2$, $f(x) = -x^2$

For each equation, state the vertex, axis of symmetry, and direction of opening.

7. $f(x) = 2x^2$

8. $y = -x^2$

9. $y = -3x^2$

10. $f(x) = 4x^2$

11. $f(x) = -5x^2$

12. $f(x) = -\frac{1}{3}x^2$

13. $f(x) = -\frac{4}{3}x^2$

14. $y = \frac{3}{4}x^2$

15. $f(x) = \frac{1}{3}x^2$

16. $y = \frac{7}{9}x^2$

Determine a value of a so that each point named is on the graph of $f(x) = ax^2$.

> **Sample:** $(5, -4)$
>
> $f(x) = ax^2$
>
> $-4 = a(5)^2$ *Substitute 5 for x and -4 for f(x).*
>
> $-4 = a \cdot 25$
>
> $a = -\dfrac{4}{25}$

17. $(2, 2)$

18. $(4, -4)$

19. $(1, 1)$

20. $(6, 6)$

21. $(3, -18)$

22. $(-2, 5)$

23. $\left(\frac{1}{2}, -1\right)$

24. $(-3, 3)$

25. $(-1, 3)$

26. $(-1, 1)$

27. $(-3, 6)$

28. (x, y)

29. If the coordinates $(4, 4)$ satisfy the equation $f(x) = \frac{1}{4}x^2$, then what equation does $(4, -4)$ satisfy?

30. How does the graph of $f(x) = 4x^2$ compare to the graph of $f(x) = -3x^2$?

Communication in everyday life depends on a knowledge of English grammar. In the same manner, communication in algebra depends on a knowledge of mathematical grammar.

Arrangement of symbols is an important part of grammar and music. Examples in music, English, and mathematics are given below. In each case, the statement on the left communicates a thought. The statement on the right is nonsense.

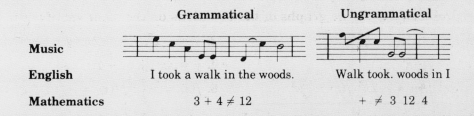

	Grammatical	**Ungrammatical**
Music		
English	I took a walk in the woods.	Walk took. woods in I
Mathematics	$3 + 4 \neq 12$	$+ \neq 3\ 12\ 4$

Punctuation also plays an important role in grammar. Study the two sentences.

My mother, my sister Carol, Andrew, and I went to the theater.

My mother, my sister, Carol, Andrew, and I went to the theater.

In the first sentence, four people, namely my mother, my sister Carol, Andrew, and I, went to the theater. In the second sentence, five people, namely my mother, my sister, Carol, Andrew, and I, went to the theater.

Now study the following mathematical sentences.

$$g(a) = 3a^2 - 2 \qquad G(a) = (3a)^2 - 2$$

In the first sentence, g of a is equal to three times a squared, minus two. In the second sentence, G of a is equal to three times a, quantity squared, minus two. In other words, in the first sentence, square a and then multiply by three. In the second sentence, multiply three times a and then square the product.

Exercises

For each pair of equations, explain how the first and second equation differ.

1. $f(x) = (x - 2)^2 \qquad F(x) = x^2 - 2$ **2.** $f(x) = 3(x + 4)^2 \qquad F(x) = (3x + 4)^2$

3. $f(x) = x^2 + 3x + 5 \qquad F(x) = x^2 + 3(x + 5)$ **4.** $f(x) = (x - 4)^2 \qquad F(x) = (4 - x)^2$

5. $h(x) = (2x - 5)^2 \qquad H(x) = (2x)^2 - 5^2$ **6.** $m(x) = (-2x)^2 + 3 \quad M(x) = -(2x)^2 + 3$

7. $g(x) = 4x^2 - 2 \qquad G(x) = 4(x^2 - 2)$ **8.** $n(x) = (x + 2)^2 \qquad N(x) = x^2 + 4x$

8-3 Graphing $y = a(x - h)^2$

You have studied parabolas with equations of the form $y = ax^2$. No matter what the value of a, the axis of symmetry for each parabola was $x = 0$ with the vertex at $(0, 0)$.

Below, the graphs of $y = x^2$, $y = (x - 3)^2$, and $y = (x + 3)^2$ are drawn on the same set of axes.

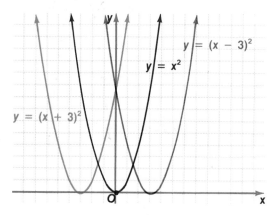

Notice that each graph has the same shape. The only difference is their horizontal position.

Below, the graphs of $y = (x - 3)^2$, $y = 2(x - 3)^2$, and $y = \frac{1}{2}(x - 3)^2$ are drawn on the same set of axes.

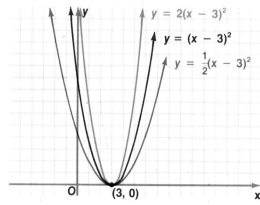

Notice that each graph has the same vertex and axis of symmetry. The only difference is their shape. Their widths vary.

In general, the graph of $f(x) = a(x - h)^2$ has the same shape and direction of opening as the graph of $f(x) = ax^2$. But its position is translated $|h|$ units to the left or right.

$y = a(x - h)^2$	a is positive	a is negative
Vertex	$(h, 0)$	$(h, 0)$
Axis of symmetry	$x = h$	$x = h$
Direction of opening	upward	downward
As the value of $|a|$ increases, the graphs of $y = a(x - h)^2$ narrow.		

Examples

1 Graph $f(x) = -2(x - 5)^2$.

Since h is 5, the vertex is $(5, 0)$ and the axis of symmetry is $x = 5$.

Since a is -2, the graph opens downward and is narrower than the graph of $f(x) = x^2$.

It is helpful to find several points on the graph other than the vertex.

$f(4) = -2(4 - 5)^2$ or -2
$f(6) = -2(6 - 5)^2$ or -2
$f(3) = -2(3 - 5)^2$ or -8
$f(7) = -2(7 - 5)^2$ or -8

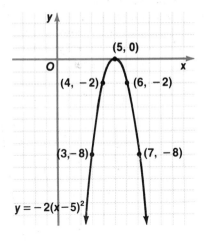

2 Graph $f(x) = 3x^2 + 12x + 12$.

First, write the equation in the form $f(x) = a(x - h)^2$, if possible.

$$f(x) = 3x^2 + 12x + 12$$
$$= 3(x^2 + 4x + 4)$$
$$= 3(x + 2)^2$$
$$= 3(x - (-2))^2$$

Therefore, a is 3 and h is -2.
The vertex is $(-2, 0)$.
The axis of symmetry is $x = -2$.
The graph opens upward and is narrower than the graph of $f(x) = x^2$.

$f(-1) = 3(-1 - (-2))^2$ or 3
$f(-3) = 3(-3 - (-2))^2$ or 3
$f(0) = 3(0 - (-2))^2$ or 12
$f(-4) = 3(-4 - (-2))^2$ or 12

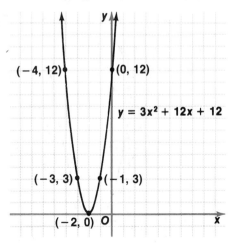

Exploratory Exercises

Name the vertex, axis of symmetry, and direction of opening for the graph of each of the following.

1. $f(x) = x^2$

2. $f(x) = -2x^2$

3. $f(x) = (x - 3)^2$

4. $f(x) = (x + 7)^2$

5. $f(x) = -2(x + 4)^2$

6. $f(x) = 4(x - 2)^2$

7. $y = 6(x + 3)^2$

8. $y = -5(x - 1)^2$

9. $y = -\frac{1}{3}(x + 2)^2$

10. $y = \frac{1}{6}(x - 4)^2$

11. $y = \frac{1}{4}(x - 2)^2$

12. $y = \frac{2}{3}\left(x - \frac{3}{4}\right)^2$

Written Exercises

Write each equation in the form $f(x) = a(x - h)^2$. Then name the vertex, axis of symmetry, and direction of opening for the graph of each equation.

1. $f(x) = x^2 - 2x + 1$
2. $f(x) = x^2 + 8x + 16$
3. $f(x) = \frac{2}{5}x^2 + \frac{8}{5}x + \frac{8}{5}$
4. $f(x) = -3x^2 - 18x - 27$
5. $f(x) = 6x^2 + 60x + 150$
6. $f(x) = 4x^2 - 8x + 4$
7. $f(x) = -9x^2 + 18x - 9$
8. $f(x) = \frac{3}{4}x^2 - 6x + 12$
9. $f(x) = 4x^2 - 44x + 121$
10. $f(x) = 4x^2 + 60x + 225$
11. $f(x) = 5x^2 - 30x + 45$
12. $f(x) = -3x^2 - 6x - 3$
13. $f(x) = 8x^2 + 24x + 18$
14. $f(x) = \frac{9}{2}x^2 - 3x + \frac{1}{2}$
15. $f(x) = 9x^2 - 60x + 100$
16. $f(x) = 9x^2 + 30x + 25$

Draw the graphs for each pair of equations on the same set of axes.

17. $y = 2x^2$ and $y = 2(x - 3)^2$
18. $y = -3x^2$ and $y = -3(x + 2)^2$
19. $f(x) = -3x^2$ and $g(x) = -3\left(x + \frac{1}{4}\right)^2$
20. $f(x) = 4x^2$ and $h(x) = 4(x - 6)^2$
21. $f(x) = -\frac{1}{4}x^2$ and $f(x) = -\frac{1}{4}(x + 2)^2$
22. $f(x) = -5x^2$ and $g(x) = -5(x - 10)^2$

23. Write the equation of a parabola with position 3 units to the right of the parabola with equation $f(x) = x^2$.

24. Write the equation of a parabola with position 4 units to the left of the parabola with equation $f(x) = -2x^2$.

25. Write the equation of a parabola with position $\frac{3}{4}$ unit to the left of the parabola with equation $f(x) = -\frac{1}{4}x^2$.

26. Write the equation of a parabola with position 6 units to the right of the parabola with equation $f(x) = 5x^2$.

Draw the graph for each of the following.

27. $f(x) = 3x^2 + 18x + 27$
28. $f(x) = 4x^2 - 16x + 16$
29. $f(x) = -2x^2 + 20x - 50$
30. $f(x) = -5x^2 - 40x - 80$

Challenge

Complete the following table.

	vertex	direction of opening	contains the point	axis of symmetry	equation of the parabola
31.	$(0, 0)$	up	$(4, 2)$		
32.	$(3, 0)$	down	$(-2, -4)$		
33.	$(-2, 0)$	up	$(0, 4)$		
34.	$(5, 0)$	down	$(6, -3)$		
35.	$(-4, 0)$	up	$(-6, 12)$		
36.	$(-1, 0)$	up	$(0, 7)$		

8-4　Graphing $y = a(x - h)^2 + k$

Below, the graphs of $y = x^2$, $y = x^2 + 3$, and $y = x^2 - 3$ are drawn on the same set of axes.

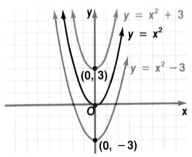

Notice that each graph has the same shape. The only difference is their vertical position.

Study the graphs of $y = x^2 - 3$, $y = (x - 2)^2 - 3$, and $y = (x + 2)^2 - 3$.

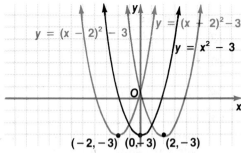

How do these graphs compare?

How do you think the graphs of $y = (x + 2)^2 - 3$, $y = 4(x + 2)^2 - 3$, and $y = \frac{1}{4}(x + 2)^2 - 3$ will compare?

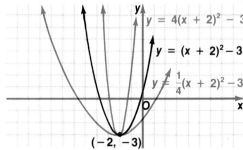

In general, as the value of k changes, the graph of $f(x) = a(x - h)^2 + k$ is translated $|k|$ units up or down.

$y = a(x - h)^2 + k$	a is positive	a is negative
Vertex	(h, k)	(h, k)
Axis of symmetry	$x = h$	$x = h$
Direction of opening	upward	downward
As the value of $|a|$ increases, the graphs of $y = a(x - h)^2 + k$ narrow.		

1 **Graph $f(x) = \frac{1}{2}(x - 2)^2 - 5$.**

The value of a is $\frac{1}{2}$, h is 2, and k is -5.

The vertex is $(2, -5)$

The axis of symmetry is $x = 2$.

The graph opens upward and is wider than the graph of $f(x) = x^2$.

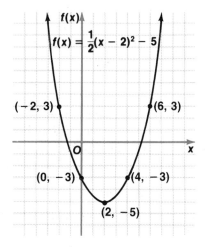

x	$\frac{1}{2}(x - 2)^2 - 5$	$f(x)$
4	$\frac{1}{2}(4 - 2)^2 - 5$	-3
0	$\frac{1}{2}(0 - 2)^2 - 5$	-3
6	$\frac{1}{2}(6 - 2)^2 - 5$	3
-2	$\frac{1}{2}(-2 - 2)^2 - 5$	3

2 **Graph $f(x) = 2x^2 - 12x + 19$.**

First, write the equation in the form $f(x) = a(x - h)^2 + k$. To do this, you must complete the square.

$$\begin{aligned} f(x) &= 2x^2 - 12x + 19 \\ &= 2(x^2 - 6x) + 19 \\ &= 2(x^2 - 6x + 9) + 19 - 2(9) \\ &= 2(x - 3)^2 + 1 \end{aligned}$$

Therefore, a is 2, h is 3, and k is 1.

The vertex is $(3, 1)$.

The axis of symmetry is $x = 3$.

The graph opens upward and is narrower than the graph of $f(x) = x^2$.

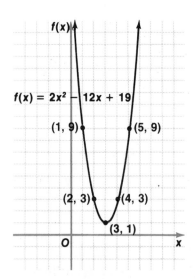

x	$2(x - 3)^2 + 1$	$f(x)$
2	$2(2 - 3)^2 + 1$	3
4	$2(4 - 3)^2 + 1$	3
1	$2(1 - 3)^2 + 1$	9
5	$2(5 - 3)^2 + 1$	9

Example

3 **Graph $f(x) = -2x^2 - 12x - 22$.**

First, write the equation in the form
$f(x) = a(x - h)^2 + k$.
To do this, you must complete the
square.

$$
\begin{aligned}
f(x) &= -2x^2 - 12x - 22 \\
&= -2(x^2 + 6x) - 22 \\
&= -2(x^2 + 6x + 9) - 22 + 2(9) \\
&= -2(x + 3)^2 - 4
\end{aligned}
$$

Therefore, a is -2, h is -3, and k is -4.
The vertex is $(-3, -4)$.
The axis of symmetry is $x = -3$.
The graph opens downward and is
narrower than the graph of $f(x) = x^2$.

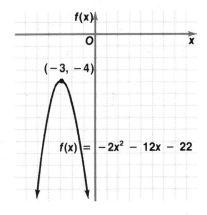

$f(x) = -2x^2 - 12x - 22$

Exploratory Exercises

Name the vertex, axis of symmetry, and direction of opening for the graph of each of the following.

1. $y = 2x^2$

2. $y = -\frac{1}{5}x^2$

3. $f(x) = 4(x - 8)^2$

4. $f(x) = -1(x + 2)^2$

5. $f(x) = -3x^2 + 6$

6. $g(x) = 5x^2 - 6$

7. $y = 5(x + 3)^2 - 1$

8. $y = -2(x - 2)^2 - 2$

9. $f(x) = 2(x - 1)^2 + \frac{1}{3}$

10. $f(x) = 4(x + 2)^2 - \frac{3}{2}$

11. $f(x) = -\frac{1}{3}(x + 2)^2 - \frac{4}{3}$

12. $g(x) = 3\left(x - \frac{1}{2}\right)^2 + \frac{1}{4}$

Written Exercises

Draw the graph for each of the following.

1. $f(x) = (x + 2)^2 - 3$

2. $f(x) = (x - 3)^2 + 4$

3. $f(x) = x^2 - 4$

4. $f(x) = 2x^2 + 3$

5. $f(x) = 2(x + 3)^2 - 5$

6. $f(x) = 3(x - 1)^2 + 2$

7. $f(x) = \frac{1}{2}(x + 3)^2 - 5$

8. $f(x) = \frac{1}{3}(x - 1)^2 + 2$

9. $f(x) = x^2 + 6x + 2$

10. $f(x) = x^2 - 2x + 7$

11. $f(x) = -2x^2 + 16x - 31$

12. $f(x) = -x^2 - 4x - 10$

13. $f(x) = 2x^2 + 8x + 10$

14. $f(x) = 3x^2 + 18x + 6$

15. $f(x) = -9x^2 - 18x - 6$

16. $f(x) = -4x^2 - 16x + 2$

17. $f(x) = -0.25x^2 - 2.5x - 0.25$

18. $f(x) = -\frac{2}{3}x^2 + 4x - 9$

Challenge

19. Given $f(x) = ax^2 + bx + c$ with $a \neq 0$, complete the square to rewrite the equation in the form $f(x) = a(x - h)^2 + k$. State an expression for h and k in terms of a, b, and c.

8-5   Problem Solving: Using Parabolas

A ball is thrown upward at an initial speed of 80 feet per second. The height it will reach after t seconds is given by the following equation.

$h(t) = 80t - 16t^2$ *This equation represents height in feet.*

At what time does the ball reach its maximum height?

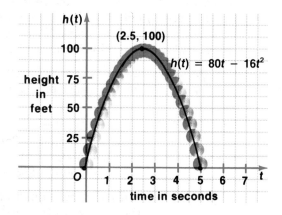

Compare the time-lapse photograph to the graph of $h(t) = 80t - 16t^2$. They both give a visual description of the height of the ball at a certain time.

The graph is a parabola. Its highest point is at the vertex (2.5, 100). This shows that the ball reaches a maximum height of 100 feet in 2.5 seconds.

Many problem situations involve finding a **maximum** or **minimum value.** If such a problem can be described by a quadratic equation, it often can be solved by finding the vertex of its graph.

Examples

1 **Find two numbers whose difference is 64 and whose product is a minimum.**

Explore Let x stand for the lesser number.
Then $64 + x$ stands for the other number.

Plan product $= (x) \cdot (64 + x)$
$= 64x + x^2$

Solve The equation above is a quadratic equation. Find the vertex by writing the equation in the form $y = a(x - h)^2 + k$. Then the vertex is (h, k). Let y stand for the product.

$y = 64x + x^2$
$= x^2 + 64x + \left(\dfrac{64}{2}\right)^2 - \left(\dfrac{64}{2}\right)^2$
$= (x + 32)^2 - 1024$

The vertex is $(-32, -1024)$.
The product is mimimized when x is -32.
So $64 + x$ is $64 + (-32)$ or 32.

The two numbers are -32 and 32.

Examine Check other pairs of numbers whose difference is 64 to see if their product is greater than $(-32)(32)$.

$$(-32)(32) = -1024$$
$$(-30)(34) = -1020$$
$$(53)(-11) = -583$$

2 **A theater has seats for 500 people. It is filled to capacity for each show and tickets cost \$3.00 per show. The owner wants to increase ticket prices. She estimates that for each \$0.20 increase in price, 25 fewer people will attend. What ticket price will maximize her income?**

Explore Let p = number of \$0.20 price increases. Then $3.00 + 0.20p$ stands for the ticket price and $500 - 25p$ stands for the number of tickets sold.

Plan Income = (number of tickets sold) × (ticket price)
$$= \quad (500 - 25p) \quad \cdot (3.00 + 0.20p)$$
$$= 1500 + 100p - 75p - 5p^2$$
$$= 1500 + 25p - 5p^2$$

Solve The equation is quadratic. Find the vertex by writing the equation in the form $y = a(x - h)^2 + k$. Let y stand for income.

$$y = 1500 + 25p - 5p^2$$
$$= -5(p^2 - 5p) + 1500$$
$$= -5\left[p^2 - 5p + \left(-\frac{5}{2}\right)^2\right] + 1500 + 5\left(-\frac{5}{2}\right)^2$$
$$= -5\left(p - \frac{5}{2}\right)^2 + \frac{6125}{4}$$

The vertex is $\left(\frac{5}{2}, \frac{6125}{4}\right)$.

The income is maximized when the owner makes $\frac{5}{2}$ or $2\frac{1}{2}$ price increases. Since each increase is to be \$0.20, the total increase is $2\frac{1}{2}(0.20)$ or \$0.50. A ticket price of \$3.50 will maximize the owner's income.

Examine The owner's income would be $\left(\frac{6125}{4}\right)$, or \$1531.25. Try other values for p to see whether her income could be greater.

Exploratory Exercises

A newsletter has a circulation of 50,000 and sells for 40¢ a copy. Due to increased labor and production costs the publisher will raise the price of the newsletter. A publisher's survey indicates that for each 10¢ increase in price, the circulation decreases by 5000.

1. Let x stand for the number of 10¢ price increases. Write an algebraic expression to describe the increased price per copy.

2. Write an algebraic expression to describe the reduced circulation after the price increase.

3. The publisher's income on the newsletter is the product of the price per copy and the circulation. It is also a function of the number of price increases. Write an equation to describe this function.

4. Draw a graph relating the publisher's income to the number of price increases. Use number of price increases for the x-axis and income in dollars for the y-axis.

5. What price per copy will maximize the publisher's income on the newsletter?

A manufacturer can sell x items per month at a price of $(300 - 2x)$ dollars per item. It costs the manufacturer $(20x + 1000)$ dollars to produce x items.

6. One item sells for $(300 - 2x)$ dollars. Write an algebraic expression to describe the price of x items.

7. The manufacturer's profit is the selling price minus the cost of producing the items. Write an algebraic expression to describe the manufacturer's profit on x items in one month.

8. The manufacturer's profit is a function of the number of items sold. Write an equation to describe this function.

9. Draw a graph relating the manufacturer's profit to the number of items produced. Use number of items for the x-axis and profit in dollars for the y-axis.

10. How many items should the manufacturer produce in one month to maximize profit?

Written Exercises

Solve each problem.

1. Find two numbers whose difference is 36 and whose product is a minimum.

2. Find two numbers whose sum is 36 and whose product is a maximum.

3. Find two numbers whose sum is 37 and whose product is a maximum.

4. Find two numbers whose difference is 25 and whose product is a minimum.

5. Find two numbers whose difference is -20 and whose product is a minimum.

6. Find two numbers whose sum is -16 and whose product is a maximum.

7. Find the dimensions and maximum area of a rectangle if its perimeter is 40 centimeters.

8. Find the dimensions and maximum area of a rectangle if its perimeter is 24 inches.

9. George Polo has 120 meters of fence to make a rectangular pen for rabbits. If a shed is used as one side of the pen, what would be the length and width for maximum area?

10. Sara Meyer has 150 feet of fence to put around a rectangular garden. If a 10 foot opening is left on one side for a gate, what would be the length and width for maximum area?

11. A taxi service operates between two airports, transporting 300 passengers a day. The charge is $8.00. The owner estimates that 20 passengers will be lost for each $1 increase in the fare. What charge would be most profitable for the service?

12. An airline transports 800 people a week between two cities. A round trip ticket costs $300. The company wants to increase the price. They estimate that for each $5 increase 10 passengers will be lost. What ticket price will maximize their income?

13. An object is fired upward from the top of a tower at a velocity of 80 feet per second. The tower is 200 feet high. The height of the object above the ground t seconds after firing is given by the formula $h(t) = -16t^2 + 80t + 200$. What is the maximum height reached by the object? How long after firing does it reach maximum height?

14. A ball is thrown upward into the air with an initial velocity of 64 feet per second. The formula $h(t) = 64t - 16t^2$ gives its height above the ground after t seconds. What is its height after 1.5 seconds? What is its maximum height? How many seconds will pass before it returns to the ground?

15. Ken Graham has 1200 meters of fence to put around two rectangular yards. If the yards are to be separated by part of the fence, what would be the length and width for maximum area?

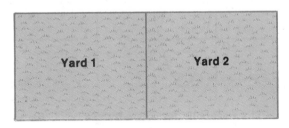

16. A square, which is 5 centimeters by 5 centimeters, is cut from each corner of a rectangular piece of cardboard and the sides are folded up to make a box. If the bottom of the box must have a perimeter of 50 centimeters, what would be the length, width, and height for maximum volume?

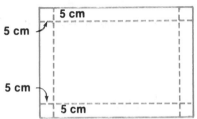

17. A wire 36 cm long is cut into 2 pieces and each piece is bent to form a square. How long should each piece be to minimize the sum of the areas of the two squares?

18. A wire 32 in. long is cut into 2 pieces. One piece is bent to form a square. The other piece is bent to form a rectangle which is 2 in. longer than it is wide. How long should each piece be to minimize the sum of the areas of the square and the rectangle?

19. Last year 200 people came to see the fall play at Jones High School. The cost per ticket was $2.00. This year the drama teacher wants to increase the ticket price. He estimates that for each $0.25 increase, 10 fewer people will come to the play. What ticket price will maximize the income?

20. The steamship, *The Golden Conifer,* is rented to take 100 campers to Pine Mountain. The fare is $5 per camper. The steamship company has agreed to reduce the fare by two cents per passenger for every camper over 100. How many passengers will produce a maximum rental for the company?

mini-review

1. Solve using row operations on matrices:
$$x + 2y = 2$$
$$x + 3y - z = -1$$
$$2x - 4y - 3z = 6$$

2. Factor $5x^7 - 80x^3$.

3. Divide using synthetic division:
$(2x^3 - 9x + 1) \div (x - 3)$

4. Simplify $\sqrt{576x^6y^3}$.

5. Simplify $\left(\dfrac{x^{-3}}{x^2y^{-1}}\right)^{-2}$.

Example

2 Use the algebraic method to solve $x^2 > 2x + 8$.

$x^2 - 2x - 8 > 0$ *The product of two factors is positive only if both*
$(x - 4)(x + 2) > 0$ *factors are positive or both factors are negative.*

$x - 4 > 0$ and $x + 2 > 0$ or $x - 4 < 0$ and $x + 2 < 0$ *Solve each compound*
     $x > 4$ and $x > -2$ or $x < 4$ and $x < -2$ *sentence shown in color.*
                                           In each case, the values
             $x > 4$ or $x < -2$ *of x must satisfy each*
                                             inequality.

The solution set is $\{x \mid x > 4 \text{ or } x < -2\}$.

Exploratory Exercises

Indicate if the factors must be positive or negative in each quadratic inequality.

1. $(x - 8)(x + 2) < 0$ **2.** $(x + 4)(x - 3) > 0$ **3.** $(x + 6)(x + 2) > 0$

4. $(x - 8)(x - 7) < 0$ **5.** $(x + 2)(x - 3) \geq 0$ **6.** $(x + 7)(x - 11) \leq 0$

7. $x^2 + 10x + 25 \leq 0$ **8.** $x^2 - 11x - 26 > 0$ **9.** $x^2 + 3x - 18 \geq 0$

Written Exercises

Solve each inequality.

1. $x^2 + x - 6 > 0$ **2.** $y^2 + 4y - 21 < 0$ **3.** $p^2 + 2p \geq 24$

4. $m^2 - 4m \leq 5$ **5.** $2b^2 - b < 6$ **6.** $6r^2 + 5r > 4$

7. $x^2 - 4x \leq 0$ **8.** $z^2 \geq 2z$ **9.** $t^2 \leq 36$

10. $b^2 \geq 3b + 28$ **11.** $r^2 + 12r \leq -27$ **12.** $a^2 - 10a + 25 \geq 0$

13. $5c - 2c^2 > -3$ **14.** $-5y - 3y^2 < -2$ **15.** $b^2 + 8b \geq -16$

16. $m^2 \leq 3$ **17.** $4t^2 - 9 < -4t$ **18.** $9s^2 - 2 > -6s$

Challenge

Solve each inequality.

19. $(x - 3)(x + 4)(x - 1) > 0$

20. $(x + 2)(x - 3)(x + 6) < 0$

21. $(x - 8)(x + 4)(x + 2) \leq 0$

22. $(x + 5)(x + 6)(x + 7) \geq 0$

23. $(x + 2)(x + 3)(x - 1)(x - 2) \geq 0$

24. $(x - 6)(x + 5)(x - 4)(x + 1) > 0$

mini-review

1. The coordinates of three vertices of a rectangle are $(-2, 4)$ $(-2, -7)$ and $(1, -7)$. Find the coordinates of the fourth vertex.

2. Graph $f(x) = |2x| - 1$.

3. Simplify $\sqrt{50} - 7\sqrt{2} + \sqrt{128}$.

4. Solve $x^2 - 4x - 21 = 0$ using the quadratic formula.

5. Solve $x - 12x^{\frac{1}{2}} + 27 = 0$.

Graphing Quadratic Equations

The computer program at the right can help you graph quadratic equations by finding the vertex of the parabola and three points on opposite sides of the axis of symmetry.

```
10  INPUT "ENTER THE COEFFICIENTS OF
    THE EQUATION: "; A, B, C
20  LET V = - B / (2 * A)
30  PRINT "THE VERTEX IS ";
40  PRINT "("V","(A * V * V + B * V +
    C)")"
50  PRINT "HERE IS A LIST OF ORDERED
    PAIRS THAT"
60  PRINT "LIE ON THE PARABOLA:"
70  FOR X = V - 3 TO V + 3
80  LET Y = A * X * X + B * X + C
90  IF X = V THEN 110
100  PRINT "("X","Y")",
110  NEXT X
120  END
```

When you run the program, enter the coefficients of the equation. For $y = x^2 + 4x + 4$, the results are shown at the right.

```
]RUN
ENTER THE COEFFICIENTS OF THE
EQUATION: 1,4,4
THE VERTEX IS (-2,0)
HERE IS A LIST OF ORDERED PAIRS THAT
LIE ON THE PARABOLA:
(-5,9)          (-4,4)          (-3,1)
(-1,1)          (0,4)           (1,9)
```

Exercises

1. Graph $y = -x^2 + 4$ and $y = 3x^2$ on the same set of axes. What is the intersection of the two parabolas?

2. Graph $y = x^2 - 1$ and $y = \frac{1}{4}x^2 + 3$ on the same set of axes. What is the intersection of the two parabolas? Are the points of intersection included when the program is run? If not, why not?

3. If line 20 finds the x-coordinate of the vertex, explain how the y-coordinate is found.

4. How would you change line 70 to help you find eleven ordered pairs?

Vocabulary ▬▬▬▬▬▬▬▬▬▬▬▬▬▬▬▬▬▬▬▬

quadratic function (243)
quadratic term (243)
linear term (243)
constant term (243)
parabola (246)

vertex (246)
axis of symmetry (246)
maximum value (256)
minimum value (256)
boundary (260)

Chapter Summary

1. A quadratic function is a function described by an equation of the form $f(x) = ax^2 + bx + c$ where $a \neq 0$.

   The term ax^2 is called the quadratic term.
   The term bx is called the linear term.
   The term c is called the constant term.   (243)

2. The graph of a quadratic function is called a parabola.   (246)

3. If the sketches of parabolas are folded along their axes of symmetry, the two halves of the parabolas coincide.   (246)

4. In general, as the value of a changes, the graph of $f(x) = a(x - h)^2 + k$ narrows as $|a|$ increases. If $a > 0$, the graph opens upward. If $a < 0$, the graph opens downward.   (250)

5. In general, the graph of $f(x) = a(x - h)^2$ has the same shape and direction of opening as the graph of $f(x) = ax^2$. But its position is translated $|h|$ units to the right or left.   (250)

6. In general, as the value of k changes, the graph of $f(x) = a(x - h)^2 + k$ is translated $|k|$ units up or down.   (253)

7. If a maximum or minimum problem can be described by a quadratic equation, it often can be solved by finding the vertex of the corresponding graph.   (256)

8. The graph of a quadratic inequality will include either the region inside the boundary or outside the boundary. The boundary itself may or may not be included.   (260)

9. Quadratic inequalities can be solved using either graphic or algebraic methods.   (263)

Chapter Review

8–1 **For each equation, identify the quadratic term, the linear term, and the constant term.**

   1. $y = x^2 + 2x + 5$

   3. $y = 16$

   2. $y = x - 7$

   4. $y = -3x^2 + 2$

   Write each equation in quadratic form.

   5. $f(x) = 3(x + 2)^2 - 7$

   7. $f(x) = -2(x - 3)^2 + 9$

   6. $f(x) = -3(x - 7)^2 + 6$

   8. $f(x) = 4(x + 6)^2 - 21$

8–2 **Draw the graph of each equation.**

   9. $y = 2x^2$

   10. $y = -\frac{1}{3}x^2$

   11. $f(x) = -3x^2$

   12. $f(x) = \frac{2}{3}x^2$

   Determine the value of a so that each point is on the graph of $y = ax^2$.

   13. (6, 3)

   14. (2, 2)

   15. (2, 1)

   16. $(-3, -3)$

8–3   **Draw the graph of each equation. Then name the vertex, axis of symmetry, and direction of opening.**

17. $y = (x - 3)^2$ **18.** $y = (x + 2)^2$ **19.** $y = \frac{1}{2}(x - 4)^2$

20. $y = -3(x + 2)^2$ **21.** $f(x) = x^2 + 16x + 64$ **22.** $f(x) = 3x^2 + 30x + 75$

8–4   **Draw the graph of each quadratic equation. Then name the vertex, axis of symmetry, and direction of opening.**

23. $y = (x - 2)^2 - 3$ **24.** $y = -2x^2 - 4$ **25.** $y = -2(x + 1)^2 - 2$

26. $y = \frac{1}{2}(x + 2)^2 - 1$ **27.** $f(x) = 3x^2 - 6x + 10$ **28.** $f(x) = -5x^2 - 20x + 2$

8–5   **29.** Find two numbers whose sum is 64 and whose product is a maximum.   **30.** Find two numbers whose difference is 5 and whose product is a minimum.

8–6   **Draw the graph of each inequality.**

31. $y > x^2 + 3x - 4$ **32.** $y < x^2 + 4x + 3$

8–7   **Solve each inequality.**

33. $(x - 4)(x + 2) < 0$ **34.** $x^2 + 8x - 9 > 0$

Chapter Test

Write each equation in quadratic form.

1. $y = (x + 2)^2 + 8$ **2.** $y = 2(x - 3)^2 + 5$ **3.** $y = \frac{1}{2}(x + 4)^2 - 7$

Draw the graph of each equation. Then name the vertex, axis of symmetry, and direction of opening.

4. $y = -(x + 2)^2$ **5.** $y = (x + 2)^2 + 1$ **6.** $y = (x - 3)^2$

7. $y = \frac{1}{2}(x + 8)^2 - 3$ **8.** $y = -2(x + 4)^2 - 6$ **9.** $y = x^2 + 3x + 6$

10. $y = x^2 - 8x - 9$ **11.** $f(x) = 2x^2 + 8x + 9$ **12.** $f(x) = -x^2 - 10x + 10$

Solve each problem.

13. Find two numbers whose sum is 18 and whose product is a maximum.

14. Find two numbers whose difference is -18 and whose product is a minimum.

15. A rocket is shot upward with an initial velocity of 40 feet per second. Its height above the ground after t seconds is given by $h(t) = 40t - 16t^2$. What is its maximum height? When will it return to earth?

16. Harry plans to build a pen with 90 feet of fence. If a shed is used as one side of the pen, what are the length and width for maximum area?

Graph each inequality.

17. $y \leq x^2 + 6x - 7$ **18.** $y < -x^2 + 4x - 4$

Solve each inequality.

19. $(x + 5)(x + 3) < 0$ **20.** $2x^2 + 3x - 2 > 0$

1. Evaluate $\dfrac{5}{b} + \dfrac{6}{c}$ if $b = \dfrac{1}{4}$ and $c = -\dfrac{1}{6}$.

2. Is i^2 a real number?

3. Graph the set of ordered pairs.
$$\{(5, 12), (-6, -8), (3, 14)\}$$

4. State if the relation is a function.
$$\{(2, 6), (1, 5), (-2, 5), (-1, 5)\}$$

5. Find the slope of the line perpendicular to the graph of $2x + 3y = 1$.

Graph each system and state its solution. Then state whether the system is consistent and independent, consistent and dependent, or inconsistent.

6. $\dfrac{x}{2} = \dfrac{y}{3}$
   $y - x = 1$

7. $3y + 4 = 5x$
   $10x - 3 = 6y$

Solve each system of equations using Cramer's Rule.

8. $2a + 3b = 6$
   $2a - 5b = 22$

9. $3x + 4y = -25$
   $2x - 3y = 6$

10. Write the equation of the plane with x-intercept 4, y-intercept $\dfrac{1}{3}$, and z-intercept $\dfrac{1}{4}$.

11. Solve using augmented matrices.
$$3x - 2y - z = 8$$
$$x + 2y = -1$$
$$x - y + 4z = 25$$

12. Write the following system in matrix equation form. Then solve using inverse matrices.
$$5x + 3y = -7$$
$$3x - 2y = 11$$

Simplify.

13. $(-4ab^2)^5(6a^3)^2$

14. $\dfrac{8m^{-4}}{4m^{-2}}$

15. $\left(\dfrac{3}{a}\right)^{-5}$

16. $-7a^2(a^3 - ab)$

17. $\dfrac{4\sqrt{2} - 8}{\sqrt{2}}$

18. $\dfrac{2 + i\sqrt{3}}{2 - i\sqrt{3}}$

Simplify.

19. $-\sqrt{3} \cdot \sqrt{-18}$

20. $(2 + 5i)(3 - i)$

Given the determinant at the right, find the value of the signed minor for each of the following elements.

$$\begin{vmatrix} 1 & -3 & 2 \\ 5 & -6 & 4 \\ 9 & 3 & 7 \end{vmatrix}$$

21. e_{11}

22. e_{32}

23. e_{21}

Solve each of the following.

24. $m^2 \le 3$

25. $x^4 - 16 = 0$

26. $3x^2 = -4x - 5$

27. State the value of the discriminant for the equation $3y^2 - 2y + 5 = 0$. Then describe the nature of the solutions.

28. Draw the graph of $y = -3(x + 2)^2$. Then name the vertex, axis of symmetry, and direction of opening.

29. Graph $y > x^2 - 3x - 4$.

Problem Solving

30. Elizabeth gets at least a 10% raise in her salary each year. If her salary is $16,000 this year, how much does she expect to be earning in 3 years?

31. A certain positive number decreased by 3 is multiplied by the same number increased by 3. The product is 27. What is the number?

32. Find the two numbers whose sum is 81 and whose product is a maximum.

33. ABC Manufacturing produces bicycles and mopeds. The plant can produce no more than 24 bicycles and 16 mopeds per day. It takes 3 work-hours to make a bicycle and 6 to make a moped. There are 150 work-hours per day. If profits are equal on both items, how many of each should be made to maximize profit?

The test questions on this page deal with expressions and equations. The information at the right may help you with some of the questions.

Directions: Choose the one best answer. Write A, B, C, or D.

1. If $10 - 4y = 18 + 2y$, then what is the value of $3y$?

    (A) -4 (B) -3 (C) $-\frac{4}{3}$ (D) $\frac{4}{3}$

2. If it takes 6 hours for 4 people to paint a room, how many hours will it take 5 people, working at the same rate, to paint a room that is the same size?

    (A) $3\frac{1}{3}$ (B) $4\frac{4}{5}$ (C) $6\frac{1}{2}$ (D) $7\frac{1}{2}$

3. In a college lecture hall, the number of seats in each row is 25 less than the number of rows. If there are 350 seats in all, find the number of rows.

    (A) 10 (B) 14 (C) 25 (D) 35

4. A grocery store sold 500 candy bars for $105.00. A small candy bar sells for 10¢ and a large bar sells for 35¢. How many of the small bars were sold?

    (A) 55 (B) 77 (C) 220 (D) 280

5. If $x > 1$, which of the following increases as x increases?

    I. $x - \dfrac{1}{x}$

    II. $\dfrac{1}{x^2 - x}$

    III. $4x^3 - 2x^2$

    (A) I only   (B) II only
    (C) I and III only (D) I, II and III

6. Evaluate $3x^3 - 2x^2 + x - 1$, if $x = -1$.

    (A) -7 (B) -3 (C) -2 (D) -1

7. A bottle of type B perfume costs two dollars more than 2 bottles of type C perfume. If the total cost for one bottle of each type is $32, how much more does type B cost than type C?

    (A) 10 (B) 12 (C) 22 (D) 32

8. Eight pencils and 5 pens cost $5.41, while 9 pencils and 3 pens cost $3.75. What is the cost of a pencil?

    (A) 12¢ (B) 15¢ (C) 38¢ (D) 89¢

9. John sold 3 less than twice the number of pizzas that Sam sold. If Sam sold x pizzas, how many more did John sell?

    (A) $3x - 3$ (B) $2x - 3$
    (C) $x + 3$ (D) $x - 3$

10. What is the value of $(x - y)^3$ if $y = x + 3$?

    (A) -27 (B) 0 (C) 6 (D) 9

11. What is the value of xy in the equation $21xy + 77 = 32xy$?

    (A) $-\frac{1}{7}$ (B) $\frac{1}{7}$ (C) -7 (D) 7

12. If $a^3 = 7$, then what is the value of $4a^6$?

    (A) 28 (B) 56 (C) 196 (D) 1372

13. Which is the equation of a line that passes through $(2, -5)$ and is parallel to the graph of $y - 3x = 2$?

    (A) $y = -3x - 11$ (B) $y = 3x - 11$
    (C) $y = 3x - 5$ (D) $y = x - 7$

CHAPTER 9

Conics

The Foucault Pendulum shown in this photo demonstrates the rotation of the earth on its axis. Though the pendulum swings back and forth in a single plane, the earth's rotation causes the plane to change position in relation to the earth. The pendulum strikes one of the pegs in the circle with each swing. In 24 hours, all of the pegs in the circle will have been knocked down. The circle is one of four curves formed by the intersection of a plane with the surface of a cone. Parabolas, ellipses, and hyperbolas are also conic sections.

9-1 Distance

The distance between two points on a number line can be found using absolute value.

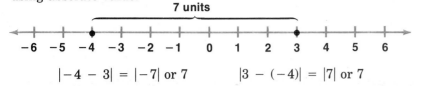

7 units

$|-4 - 3| = |-7|$ or 7 $|3 - (-4)| = |7|$ or 7

On a number line, the distance between two points whose coordinates are a and b is $|a - b|$ or $|b - a|$.	*Distance Between Points on a Number Line*

Consider two points in a plane with coordinates $(-2, -6)$ and $(3, -6)$. These points lie on a horizontal line. You can use absolute value to find the distance between the points.

$|-2 - 3| = |-5|$ or 5   *Find the difference between the x-coordinates.*

The points with coordinates $(-2, 3)$ and $(-2, -6)$ lie on a vertical line. The distance between these two points is 9 units.

$|3 - (-6)| = |9|$ or 9   *Find the difference between the y-coordinates.*

To find the distance between two points in the coordinate plane, use the Pythagorean Theorem.

Example

1 Find the distance between two points with coordinates $(-2, 3)$ and $(2, -4)$.

Form a right triangle by extending vertical and horizontal segments from each point.

The square of the hypotenuse of a right triangle equals the sum of the squares of the other two sides.

$d^2 = |3 - (-4)|^2 + |-2 - 2|^2$
$d^2 = \quad 7^2 \quad + \quad 4^2$
$d^2 = 65$
$d = \sqrt{65}$ *Distance is positive.* $d \approx 8.062$

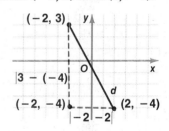

The Pythagorean Theorem can be used to find a formula for the distance between any two points in the plane.

Suppose (x_1, y_1) and (x_2, y_2) name two points in the plane. Form a triangle by drawing a vertical line through (x_1, y_1) and drawing a horizontal line through (x_2, y_2). These lines intersect at the point (x_1, y_2).   *Why?*

$d^2 = |x_2 - x_1|^2 + |y_2 - y_1|^2$
$d^2 = (x_2 - x_1)^2 + (y_2 - y_1)^2$
$d = \sqrt{(x_2 - x_1)^2 + (y_2 - y_1)^2}$

Why can $(x_2 - x_1)^2$ be substituted for $|x_2 - x_1|^2$?

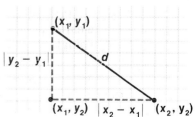

The distance between two points with coordinates (x_1, y_1) and (x_2, y_2) is given by the following formula.
$$d = \sqrt{(x_2 - x_1)^2 + (y_2 - y_1)^2}$$

Distance Formula for Two Points in a Plane

Example

2 Use the distance formula to find the distance between $(-1, 6)$ and $(5, -4)$.

$$
\begin{aligned}
d &= \sqrt{(x_2 - x_1)^2 + (y_2 - y_1)^2} \\
&= \sqrt{(5 - (-1))^2 + (-4 - 6)^2} \\
&= \sqrt{(6)^2 + (-10)^2} \\
&= \sqrt{36 + 100} \\
&= \sqrt{136} \\
&= 2\sqrt{34} \quad \text{The distance is } 2\sqrt{34} \text{ or about 11.66 units.}
\end{aligned}
$$

The distance formula can be used to show that a given point on a line segment is the midpoint of that line segment.

Example

3 The point $(3, 1)$ lies on the line segment having endpoints at $(6, -1)$ and $(0, 3)$. Show that $(3, 1)$ is the midpoint of the line segment.

distance between (3, 1) and (6, -1)

$$
\begin{aligned}
d &= \sqrt{(6 - 3)^2 + (-1 - 1)^2} \\
&= \sqrt{(3)^2 + (-2)^2} \\
&= \sqrt{9 + 4} \\
&= \sqrt{13} \qquad \sqrt{13} \approx 3.6
\end{aligned}
$$

distance between (3, 1) and (0, 3)

$$
\begin{aligned}
d &= \sqrt{(0 - 3)^2 + (3 - 1)^2} \\
&= \sqrt{(-3)^2 + (2)^2} \\
&= \sqrt{9 + 4} \\
&= \sqrt{13}
\end{aligned}
$$

To find the coordinates of the midpoint of a line segment, use the following formula.

If a line segment has endpoints at (x_1, y_1) and (x_2, y_2), then the midpoint of the line segment has coordinates
$$\left(\frac{x_1 + x_2}{2}, \frac{y_1 + y_2}{2}\right).$$

Midpoint Formula

Example

4 Find the coordinates of the midpoint of a line segment having endpoints at $(1, -5)$ and $(-4, -7)$.

The coordinates of the midpoint are $\left(\dfrac{1 + (-4)}{2}, \dfrac{-5 + (-7)}{2}\right)$ or $\left(-\dfrac{3}{2}, -6\right)$.

Exploratory Exercises

In each of the following, the coordinates of two points on the number line are given. Find the distance between these points.

1. 3, 5
2. $-4, -8$
3. $-3, 6$
4. $-6, 9$
5. $-11, 0$
6. $-16, 0$
7. $-32, -16$
8. $-19, 14$
9. $16.2, -14.9$
10. $7.5, -7.5$
11. $14\frac{2}{5}, -8\frac{3}{10}$
12. $3\frac{1}{2}, -6\frac{1}{3}$

Written Exercises

Use the distance formula to find the distance between each pair of points whose coordinates are given below.

1. $(3, 6), (7, -8)$
2. $(4, 2), (-3, -6)$
3. $(-3, 1), (4, -2)$
4. $(-8, -7), (-2, -1)$
5. $(6, 7), (8, 0)$
6. $(9, 3), (-6, -8)$
7. $\left(\frac{1}{3}, \frac{1}{5}\right), (2, -4)$
8. $\left(1, \frac{1}{2}\right), \left(\frac{1}{3}, -2\right)$
9. $(0.2, 0.6), (0.3, 0.4)$
10. $(-0.2, 0.4), (-0.5, -0.6)$
11. $(-2.4, 0.6), (1.7, 0.8)$
12. $(3, 3), (\sqrt{3}, \sqrt{3})$
13. $(3, \sqrt{3}), (4, \sqrt{3})$
14. $(-2\sqrt{7}, 10), (4\sqrt{7}, 8)$
15. $(2\sqrt{3}, 4\sqrt{3}), (2\sqrt{3}, -\sqrt{3})$

Each pair of points represented by the following coordinates is 5 units apart. Find c in each case.

16. $(3,5), (c, 2)$
17. $(-4, c), (-7, 7)$
18. $(c, 1.9), (1.2, 5.9)$
19. $(13, 10.1), (9, c)$

Find the midpoints of line segments having endpoints with the following coordinates.

20. $(6, 7), (8, 0)$
21. $(9, 3), (-6, -8)$
22. $\left(\frac{1}{3}, \frac{1}{5}\right), (2, -4)$
23. $\left(1, \frac{1}{2}\right), \left(\frac{1}{3}, -2\right)$
24. $(-2.4, 0.6), (1.7, 0.8)$
25. $(3, 3), (\sqrt{2}, -\sqrt{2})$

26. Find the perimeter of a quadrilateral with vertices at $(6, 3), (4, 5), (-4, 6)$, and $(-5, -8)$.

27. Find the lengths of the diagonals of a parallelogram with vertices at $(6, 8)$, $(-14, 8), (8, -2)$, and $(-12, -2)$.

28. Parallelogram $ABCD$ has vertices $A(-5, 1), B(0, 2), C(-3, 6)$, and $D(-8, 5)$. Show that the diagonals of $ABCD$ bisect each other.

29. Show that triangle ABC with vertices $A(-3, 0), B(-1, 4)$, and $C(1, -2)$ is an isosceles triangle.

30. Triangle ABC has vertices $A(-2, 8)$, $B(3, 5)$ and $C(7, -4)$. Find the coordinates of the midpoint of each side.

31. Right triangle DEF has vertices $D(0, 1)$, $E(4, 1)$, and $F(0, 7)$. Show that the midpoint of the hypotenuse is the same distance from each vertex.

32. Show that $\left(\frac{x_1 + x_2}{2}, \frac{y_1 + y_2}{2}\right)$ is the midpoint of a line segment having endpoints with coordinates (x_1, y_1) and (x_2, y_2).

33. Show that the points $(-1, 3), (3, 6)$, $(6, 2)$, and $(2, -1)$ are vertices of a square.

Challenge

34. Find the coordinates of a point one-fourth of the distance from $A(3, -2)$ to $B(11, 2)$.

35. Find the coordinates of a point three-fourths of the distance from $X(5, 8)$ to $Y(-7, 16)$.

9-2   Parabolas

The shape of the reflectors in automobile head-
lights is based on the **parabola**. The diagram at
the right shows a cross section of a reflector. The
light source is placed at a special point so the light
is reflected in parallel rays. In this way, a straight
beam of light is formed.

The point where the light source is placed is
called the **focus** of the parabola. Parabolas can be
defined in terms of the focus.

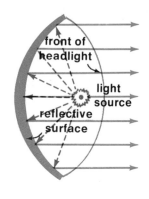

> A parabola is the set of all points in a plane that are the
> same distance from a given point and a given line in the
> plane. The point is called the *focus*. The line is called
> the *directrix*.

Definition of Parabola

The parabola at the right has focus at (3, 4) and directrix
$y = -2$. You can use the distance formula and the definition
of a parabola to find the equation of this parabola. Let (x, y)
be a point on the parabola. This point must be the same distance from the focus, (3, 4), as it is from the directrix,
$y = -2$.

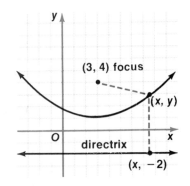

distance between (x, y) and $(3, 4)$ = distance between (x, y) and $(x, -2)$

$$\sqrt{(x - 3)^2 + (y - 4)^2} = \sqrt{(x - x)^2 + (y - (-2))^2}$$
$$(x - 3)^2 + (y - 4)^2 = (x - x)^2 + (y + 2)^2$$
$$(x - 3)^2 + y^2 - 8y + 16 = y^2 + 4y + 4$$
$$(x - 3)^2 = 12y - 12$$
$$\frac{1}{12}(x - 3)^2 + 1 = y$$

The equation of a parabola with focus at (3, 4) and directrix
$y = -2$ is $y = \frac{1}{12}(x - 3)^2 + 1$. The vertex is at (3, 1) and the axis
of symmetry is $x = 3$.

The equation for a parabola can be written in the form
$y = a(x - h)^2 + k$ or in the form $x = a(y - k)^2 + h$. Each form
provides valuable information about the graph.

Information About Parabolas		
form of equation	$y = a(x - h)^2 + k$	$x = a(y - k)^2 + h$
axis of symmetry	$x = h$	$y = k$
vertex	(h, k)	(h, k)
focus	$\left(h, k + \dfrac{1}{4a}\right)$	$\left(h + \dfrac{1}{4a}, k\right)$
directrix	$y = k - \dfrac{1}{4a}$	$x = h - \dfrac{1}{4a}$
direction of opening	upward if $a > 0$, downward if $a < 0$	right if $a > 0$, left if $a < 0$

Example 1

Draw the graph of $y = \frac{1}{4}(x - 2)^2 - 3$. *The graph will be a parabola.*

vertex:	$(2, -3)$
axis of symmetry:	$x = 2$
focus:	$\left(2, -3 + \frac{1}{1}\right)$ or $(2, -2)$
directrix:	$y = -3 - \frac{1}{1}$ or -4
direction of opening:	upward since $a > 0$

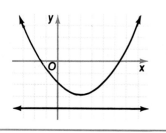

The graph of $y = x^2 - 6x + 11$ is a parabola. This equation can be written in the form $y = a(x - h)^2 + k$ by completing the square.

$$y = x^2 - 6x + 11$$
$$y = x^2 - 6x + \blacksquare - \blacksquare + 11$$
$$y = x^2 - 6x + \left(\frac{-6}{2}\right)^2 - \left(\frac{-6}{2}\right)^2 + 11$$
$$y = (x - 3)^2 + 2$$

Consider the line segment through the focus of a parabola perpendicular to its axis of symmetry with endpoints on the parabola. This segment is called the **latus rectum.** In the figure at the right, the latus rectum is $\overline{AB}$. The length of the latus rectum of the parabola given by the equation $y = a(x - h)^2 + k$ is $\left|\frac{1}{a}\right|$. Points A and B are $\left(\frac{1}{2}\right)\left(\frac{1}{a}\right)$ units each from the focus. This information can also be used in graphing.

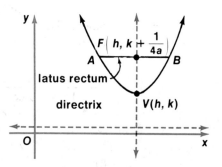

Example 2

Draw the graph of $8x = y^2 + 4y + 28$.

First write the equation in the form $x = a(y - k)^2 + h$.

$$8x = y^2 + 4y + 28$$
$$8x = y^2 + 4y + \left(\frac{4}{2}\right)^2 - \left(\frac{4}{2}\right)^2 + 28 \quad \text{Complete the square.}$$
$$8x = (y + 2)^2 + 24$$
$$x = \frac{1}{8}(y + 2)^2 + 3$$

vertex:	$(3, -2)$
axis of symmetry:	$y = -2$
focus:	$(3 + 2, -2)$ or $(5, -2)$
directrix:	$x = 3 - 2$ or 1
direction of opening:	right since $a > 0$
length of latus rectum:	$\frac{1}{\frac{1}{8}}$ or 8 units; ± 4 units from focus

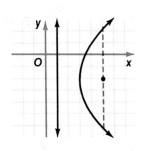

Exploratory Exercises

Complete the square to find the value of c for each expression.

1. $x^2 + 4x + c$
2. $x^2 + 6x + c$
3. $y^2 - 8y + c$
4. $p^2 - 10p + c$
5. $r^2 + 3r + c$
6. $m^2 - 3m + c$
7. $x^2 - 7x + c$
8. $t^2 + 15t + c$

Change each equation to the form $y = a(x - h)^2 + k$.

9. $x^2 = 10y$
10. $x^2 = -2y$
11. $y = x^2 - 6x + 33$
12. $y = x^2 + 4x + 1$
13. $y = 3x^2 - 24x + 50$
14. $y = \frac{1}{2}x^2 - 3x + \frac{19}{2}$

Change each equation to the form $x = a(y - k)^2 + h$.

15. $6x = y^2$
16. $y^2 = -12x$
17. $x = y^2 + 8y + 20$
18. $x = y^2 - 14y + 25$
19. $x = \frac{1}{4}y^2 - \frac{1}{2}y - 3$
20. $x = 5y^2 - 25y + 60$

Written Exercises

Name the vertex, axis of symmetry, focus, directrix, and direction of opening of the parabola whose equation is given. Then, find the length of the latus rectum and draw the graph.

1. $x^2 = 6y$
2. $y^2 = -8x$
3. $(x + 2)^2 = y - 3$
4. $(x - 4)^2 = 4(y + 2)$
5. $(x - 8)^2 = \frac{1}{2}(y + 1)$
6. $(x + 3)^2 = \frac{1}{4}(y - 2)$
7. $x^2 = (y - 1)$
8. $(x + 2)^2 = 6y$
9. $(y + 3)^2 = 4(x - 2)$
10. $(y - 8)^2 = -4(x - 4)$
11. $y = x^2 - 6x + 33$
12. $x = y^2 + 8y + 20$
13. $x = y^2 - 14y + 25$
14. $y = \frac{1}{2}x^2 - 3x + \frac{19}{2}$
15. $x = \frac{1}{4}y^2 - \frac{1}{2}y - 3$
16. $y = x^2 + 4x + 1$
17. $y = 3x^2 - 24x + 50$
18. $x = 5y^2 - 25y + 60$

The focus and directrix of a parabola are given. Write an equation for each parabola. Then, draw the graph of the equation.

19. $(2, 4)$, $y = 6$
20. $(3, 5)$, $y = 1$
21. $(8, 0)$, $y = 4$
22. $(0, 3)$, $y = -1$
23. $(5, 5)$, $y = -3$
24. $(6, 2)$, $x = 4$
25. $(3, -1)$, $x = -2$
26. $(4, -3)$, $y = 6$
27. $(0, 4)$, $x = 1$

Write the equation of each parabola described below. Then draw the graph.

28. Vertex $(0, 0)$, focus $(0, -4)$
29. Vertex $(5, -1)$, focus $(3, -1)$
30. Vertex $(4, 3)$, axis $y = 3$, length of latus rectum 4, $a > 0$
31. Vertex $(-7, 4)$, axis $x = -7$, length of latus rectum 6, $a < 0$

Challenge

32. If the equation of a parabola is $y = a(x - h)^2 + k$, show that the length of the latus rectum is $\frac{1}{a}$.

mini-review

1. Identify the quadratic term, the linear term, and the constant term in $n(x) = -4x^2 - 8x - 9$.
2. Simplify $\sqrt[4]{81m^4p^5}$.
3. Simplify $(4rs^2t)^2\left(-\frac{1}{2}r^2t\right)(3st^3)^4$.
4. Find the standard form of the equation of the line with slope $\frac{4}{3}$ that passes through $(4, 3)$.
5. Solve $3t^2 + 4t - 15 = 0$.

Applications in Communications   Parabolic Reflectors

The parabola is a very practical curve. Recall that if a light source is placed at the focus of a parabolic reflector, the light emitted is reflected off the parabola and straight ahead.

Conversely, with sunlight directed at a reflector, temperatures at the focal point can reach over one thousand degrees Fahrenheit, hot enough to melt steel.

Sound can be reflected in a similar way. If a microphone is placed at the focus of a parabolic reflector, it can pick up very faint noises. You may have seen such a reflector being used at a televised football game. It will pick up the signal calls all the way from the sidelines.

This receiver gathers the sound waves collected by the parabolic reflector. The focus concentrates the waves and produces a stronger signal.

Radar antennas also use parabolic reflectors. Radio signals are focused on a receiver placed at the focus.

The focus for a parabola with equation $y = ax^2 + bx + c$ has the following coordinates.

$$\left(-\frac{b}{2a}, \frac{4ac - b^2 + 1}{4a} \right)$$

Exercises

Find the coordinates of the focus for the parabola with the given equation.

1. $y = x^2 + 6x + 9$

2. $y = 2x^2 + 4x + 7$

3. $y = \frac{1}{2}x^2 - 2x - \frac{5}{2}$

4. $y = \frac{1}{4}x^2 - 2x + 3$

5. $y = x^2 + 2x + 4$

6. $8y = x^2$

9-3　Circles

A **circle** is the set of points in the plane each of which is the same distance from a given point in the plane. The given distance is the *radius* of the circle, and the given point is the *center* of the circle.

The circle at the right has center at $(2, -3)$ and radius of 6 units. You can use the distance formula and the definition of a circle to find the equation of this circle.

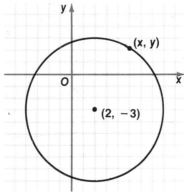

Let (x, y) name a point on the circle. This point must be 6 units from the center of the circle, $(2, -3)$.

$$\text{distance between } (x, y) \text{ and } (2, -3) = 6$$
$$\sqrt{(x - 2)^2 + (y - (-3))^2} = 6$$
$$(x - 2)^2 + (y - (-3))^2 = 6^2$$
$$(x - 2)^2 + (y + 3)^2 = 36$$

The equation of a circle with center at $(2, -3)$ and radius of 6 units is $(x - 2)^2 + (y + 3)^2 = 36$.

The equation of a circle with center at (h, k) and radius of r units is $(x - h)^2 + (y - k)^2 = r^2$.

Equation of Circle with Center (h, k)

Example

1　**Draw the graph of $(x - 8)^2 + (y - 10)^2 = 100$.**

Center:　$(8, 10)$
Radius:　10 units

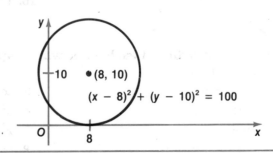

The graph of $x^2 + y^2 - 4x + 10y = 9$ is a circle. To write the equation in the form $(x - h)^2 + (y - k)^2 = r^2$, complete the square for each variable.

$$x^2 + y^2 - 4x + 10y = 9$$
$$x^2 - 4x + \blacksquare + y^2 + 10y + \square = 9 + \blacksquare + \square$$
$$x^2 - 4x + \left(\frac{-4}{2}\right)^2 + y^2 + 10y + \left(\frac{10}{2}\right)^2 = 9 + \left(\frac{-4}{2}\right)^2 + \left(\frac{10}{2}\right)^2$$
$$(x - 2)^2 + (y + 5)^2 = 38$$

The circle has center at $(2, -5)$ and radius of $\sqrt{38}$ units.

Example

2 A circle has equation $x^2 + 3 + y^2 + 9y - 10x = 2$. Find the center and radius of the circle. Then draw the graph.

$$x^2 + 3 + y^2 + 9y - 10x = 2$$
$$x^2 - 10x + \blacksquare + y^2 + 9y + \square = 2 - 3 + \blacksquare + \square$$
$$x^2 - 10x + \left(\frac{-10}{2}\right)^2 + y^2 + 9y + \left(\frac{9}{2}\right)^2 = -1 + \left(\frac{-10}{2}\right)^2 + \left(\frac{9}{2}\right)^2$$
$$(x - 5)^2 + \left(y + \frac{9}{2}\right)^2 = \frac{177}{4}$$

The circle has center at $\left(5, -\frac{9}{2}\right)$ and radius of $\frac{\sqrt{177}}{2}$ or about 6.7 units.

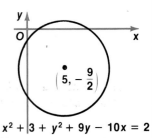

$\left(5, -\frac{9}{2}\right)$

$x^2 + 3 + y^2 + 9y - 10x = 2$

Exploratory Exercises

State whether the graph for each of the following equations is a circle or a parabola.

1. $x^2 + y^2 + 7x - 5 = 0$ **2.** $x^2 + 4x + 4 = 9y + 27$ **3.** $y^2 = 6x - 4$
4. $y = x^2 + 8x + y^2$ **5.** $x^2 + y + y^2 = 12 - 3x$ **6.** $x^2 = 5y$

State the center and radius of each circle whose equation is given.

7. $x^2 + y^2 = 16$ **8.** $x^2 + (y - 2)^2 = 25$
9. $(x - 2)^2 + y^2 = 9$ **10.** $x^2 + y^2 = 40$
11. $(x - 10)^2 + (y + 10)^2 = 100$ **12.** $(x + 2)^2 + (y - 3)^2 = 81$
13. $(x + 4)^2 + \left(y - \frac{1}{2}\right)^2 = 6$ **14.** $(x - 4)^2 + y^2 = \frac{16}{25}$
15. $(x + 5)^2 + (y - 2)^2 = \frac{3}{4}$ **16.** $x^2 + (y + 5)^2 = \frac{81}{64}$

Written Exercises

Find the center and radius of each circle whose equation is given. Then draw the graph.

1. $(x - 2)^2 + y^2 = 9$ **2.** $(x + 4)^2 + y^2 = 49$
3. $x^2 + (y - 8)^2 = 64$ **4.** $x^2 + (y + 2)^2 = 4$
5. $x^2 + y^2 = 64$ **6.** $x^2 + y^2 = 121$
7. $(x - 2)^2 + (y - 5)^2 = 16$ **8.** $(x + 2)^2 + (y - 1)^2 = 81$

9. $(x + 8)^2 + (y - 3)^2 = 25$

10. $(x - 3)^2 + (y + 2)^2 = 169$

11. $(x + 1)^2 + (y + 9)^2 = 36$

12. $(x - 5)^2 + (y - 7)^2 = 49$

13. $x^2 + y^2 - 12x - 16y + 84 = 0$

14. $x^2 + y^2 - 18x - 18y + 53 = 0$

15. $x^2 + y^2 + 8x - 6y = 0$

16. $x^2 + y^2 + 14x + 6y = 23$

17. $x^2 + y^2 - 4x = 9$

18. $x^2 + y^2 - 6y = 16$

19. $3x^2 + 3y^2 + 6y + 9x = 2$

20. $x^2 + y^2 + 9x - 8y = -4$

21. $y^2 + 3 + x^2 + 9x - 10y = 6.75$

22. $4x^2 + 4y^2 + 36y = -5$

23. $x^2 + 2x + y^2 + 4y = 9$

24. $x^2 + y^2 + 4x = 8$

25. $x^2 + 2x + y^2 = 10$

26. $x^2 + y^2 + 14x + 6y = -50$

Write an equation for each circle whose center and radius are given.

27. $(6, 2)$, 5 units

28. $(6, 0)$, 6 in.

29. $(0, 3)$, 2 km

30. $(-3, -5)$, 5 cm

31. $(-6, 2)$, $\frac{1}{4}$ mi

32. $(-1, -3)$, $\frac{2}{3}$ yd

Write the equation of each circle described below.

33. The circle has center at $(1, 5)$ and passes through the origin.

34. The circle has center at $(4, -2)$ and passes through $(9, -3)$.

35. The endpoints of a diameter of the circle are at $(5, 2)$ and $(-1, 2)$.

36. The endpoints of a diameter of the circle are at $(4, -3)$ and $(8, 5)$.

37. Center at $(-3, 8)$ and tangent to x-axis.

38. Center at $(4, -3)$ and tangent to y-axis.

 Using Calculators

Use a calculator to approximate the coordinates of points on a circle. The graph of $(x + 2)^2 + (y - 3)^2 = 81$ is shown at the right. Select a value for x, such as 2. Then calculate the y-coordinates of the points where the line $x = 2$ intersects the circle.

Solve for y in $(x + 2)^2 + (y - 3)^2 = 81$.

$$y = 3 \pm \sqrt{81 - (x + 2)^2}$$

Evaluate $\sqrt{81 - (x + 2)^2}$ for $x = 2$. Store the result.

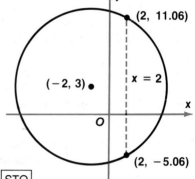

ENTER: 2 $\boxed{+}$ 2 $\boxed{=}$ $\boxed{x^2}$ $\boxed{+/-}$ $\boxed{+}$ 81 $\boxed{=}$ $\boxed{\sqrt{x}}$ $\boxed{STO}$

DISPLAY: 2   2   4   16 −16   81 65 8.06

To obtain one y-coordinate, add the stored value to 3. Subtract to find the other y-coordinate.

ENTER: 3 $\boxed{+}$ $\boxed{RCL}$ $\boxed{=}$ 3 $\boxed{-}$ $\boxed{RCL}$ $\boxed{=}$

DISPLAY: 3   8.06 11.06   3   −8.06 −5.06

Exercises

Given the x-coordinates of two points on the circle above, find the y-coordinates.

1. $x = 3$ **2.** $x = -5$ **3.** $x = -2$ **4.** $x = 4$

9-4 Ellipses

A circle can be considered as a special case of a more general curve called an **ellipse.** A circle is defined in terms of a given point and a given distance. An ellipse is defined in terms of *two* given points and *two* distances. The illustrations below show one way to draw an ellipse.

Use a piece of string about 25 cm long. Tie a knot in the string to make a loop. Put two thumbtacks through a piece of paper from the back, about 10 cm apart. Loop the string around the tacks. Place the pencil in the loop. Keep the string tight and draw around the tacks.

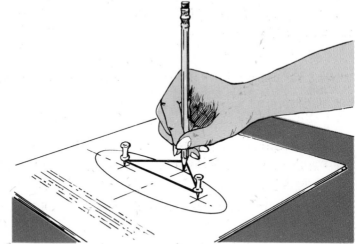

The points where the tacks are placed are called the **foci** (plural of focus) of the ellipse. Ellipses can be defined in terms of their foci.

> **An ellipse is the set of all points in the plane such that the sum of the distances from two given points in the plane, called the foci, is constant.**

Definition of Ellipse

The ellipse at the right has foci at $(-3, 0)$ and $(3, 0)$. The sum of the distance to (x, y) from the two foci is 8 units. You can use the distance formula and the definition of an ellipse to find the equation of this ellipse.

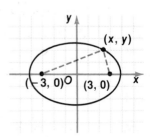

Let (x, y) name a point on the ellipse. The distance between this point and $(-3, 0)$ *plus* the distance between this point and $(3, 0)$ is 8 units.

$$\underset{\substack{\text{distance between} \\ (x, y) \text{ and } (-3, 0)}}{} + \underset{\substack{\text{distance between} \\ (x, y) \text{ and } (3, 0)}}{} = 8$$

$$\sqrt{(x - (-3))^2 + (y - 0)^2} + \sqrt{(x - 3)^2 + (y - 0)^2} = 8$$

$$\sqrt{(x + 3)^2 + y^2} = 8 - \sqrt{(x - 3)^2 + y^2}$$

$$(x + 3)^2 + y^2 = 64 - 16\sqrt{(x - 3)^2 + y^2} + (x - 3)^2 + y^2$$

$$3x - 16 = -4\sqrt{(x - 3)^2 + y^2} \qquad \textit{Simplify.}$$

$$9x^2 - 96x + 256 = 16[(x - 3)^2 + y^2] \qquad \textit{Square both sides.}$$

$$112 = 7x^2 + 16y^2 \qquad \textit{Simplify.}$$

$$1 = \frac{x^2}{16} + \frac{y^2}{7}$$

The equation of an ellipse with foci at $(-3, 0)$ and $(3, 0)$, and with 8 units as the sum of the distances from the two foci is $\frac{x^2}{16} + \frac{y^2}{7} = 1$.

An ellipse has two axes of symmetry. The longer axis of symmetry is called the **major axis.** The shorter axis of symmetry is called the **minor axis.** The intersection of the two axes is the center of the ellipse.

In the figure at the right, the sum of the distances from the foci to any point on the ellipse is $2a$ units. The distance from the center to a focus is c units. Using the Pythagorean Theorem, it can be shown that $b^2 = a^2 - c^2$.

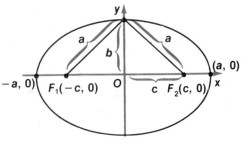

The length of the major axis is 2a. The length of the minor axis is 2b. Notice a > b.

The method used to find the equation of the ellipse on the previous page can be used to find the standard equation of an ellipse.

The standard equation of an ellipse whose foci are at $(-c, 0)$ and $(c, 0)$, and the sum of the distances from the two foci is $2a$ units, is the following.

$$\frac{x^2}{a^2} + \frac{y^2}{b^2} = 1 \text{ where } b^2 = a^2 - c^2$$

Equation of Ellipse with Center at Origin

The standard equation of an ellipse whose foci are at $(0, -c)$ and $(0, c)$ and the sum of the distances from the two foci is $2a$ units, is the following.

$$\frac{y^2}{a^2} + \frac{x^2}{b^2} = 1 \text{ where } b^2 = a^2 - c^2$$

For ellipses, $a^2 > b^2$.

Example

1 **Write the equation of the ellipse shown below.**

To write the equation for this ellipse, you must know the length of the major axis. The distance between $(-5, 0)$ and $(5, 0)$ is 10 units.

$$2a = 10$$
$$a = 5$$

Since the foci are $(-3, 0)$ and $(3, 0)$, $c = 3$.

$$b^2 = a^2 - c^2$$
$$b^2 = 5^2 - 3^2$$
$$b^2 = 16$$
$$b = 4$$

The equation is $\frac{x^2}{5^2} + \frac{y^2}{4^2} = 1$ or $\frac{x^2}{25} + \frac{y^2}{16} = 1$.

The foci will always be on the major axis. In the equation of an ellipse, $a^2 > b^2$. This makes it easy to decide in a given equation whether the foci are on the x-axis or the y-axis. For example, in the ellipse given by the equation $\dfrac{x^2}{16} + \dfrac{y^2}{25} = 1$, $25 > 16$. Therefore, 25 must be a^2 and 16 must be b^2, so the foci are on the y-axis.

Example

2　**An ellipse has equation $9x^2 + y^2 = 36$. Find its foci, the lengths of major axis and minor axis, and draw the graph.**

First, write the equation in the standard form.

$\dfrac{x^2}{4} + \dfrac{y^2}{36} = 1$　　*Divide both sides by 36.*

a^2 must be 36 since $36 > 4$. So, $a = 6$ and $b = 2$.

$b^2 = a^2 - c^2 \blacktriangleright c^2 = a^2 - b^2$
$\qquad\qquad\quad c^2 = 36 - 4$
$\qquad\qquad\quad c = \sqrt{32}$ or $4\sqrt{2}$　$4\sqrt{2} \approx 5.7$

The foci are $(0, 4\sqrt{2})$ and $(0, -4\sqrt{2})$ and are on the vertical axis.
The length of the major axis is $2a$ or 12 units.
The length of the minor axis is $2b$ or 4 units.

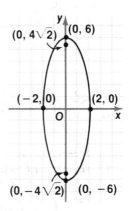

An equation of the form $\dfrac{x^2}{a^2} + \dfrac{y^2}{b^2} = 1$, or $\dfrac{y^2}{a^2} + \dfrac{x^2}{b^2} = 1$, represents an ellipse centered at the origin. Suppose an ellipse has the same shape but its center is at (h, k). The standard equations shown below can be obtained by replacing x with $x - h$ and y with $y - k$.

Length of major axis is 2a.
Length of minor axis is 2b.

> **If the center is at (h, k) and the major axis is horizontal, the equation is $\dfrac{(x - h)^2}{a^2} + \dfrac{(y - k)^2}{b^2} = 1$.**
>
> **If the center is at (h, k) and the major axis is vertical, the equation is $\dfrac{(y - k)^2}{a^2} + \dfrac{(x - h)^2}{b^2} = 1$.**

Standard Equation of Ellipse with Center (h, k)

Example

3　**Draw the graph of $\dfrac{(x + 2)^2}{36} + \dfrac{(y - 3)^2}{9} = 1$.**

The graph has the same shape as the graph of $\dfrac{x^2}{36} + \dfrac{y^2}{9} = 1$, but has center at $(-2, 3)$ rather than at the origin.

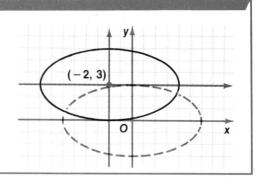

The graph of $x^2 + 2y^2 - 2x + 8y - 11 = 0$ is an ellipse. To write the equation in the form $\dfrac{(x - h)^2}{a^2} + \dfrac{(y - k)^2}{b^2} = 1$, complete the square for each variable.

$$x^2 + 2y^2 - 2x + 8y - 11 = 0$$
$$x^2 - 2x + \blacksquare + 2(y^2 + 4y + \square) = 11 + \blacksquare + 2\square$$
$$x^2 - 2x + \left(\frac{-2}{2}\right)^2 + 2\left[y^2 + 4y + \left(\frac{4}{2}\right)^2\right] = 11 + \left(\frac{-2}{2}\right)^2 + 2\left(\frac{4}{2}\right)^2$$
$$(x - 1)^2 + 2(y + 2)^2 = 20$$
$$\frac{(x - 1)^2}{20} + \frac{(y + 2)^2}{10} = 1$$

The ellipse has center at $(1, -2)$. Since $20 > 10$, $a^2 = 20$. The major axis is horizontal and is $2(\sqrt{20})$ or $4\sqrt{5}$ units long. Since b^2 is 10, the minor axis is $2\sqrt{10}$ units long.

$4\sqrt{5} \approx 8.9$
$2\sqrt{10} \approx 6.3$

Example

4 **An ellipse has equation $4x^2 + y^2 + 24x - 10y + 45 = 0$. Find the coordinates of the center and foci of the ellipse. Then draw the graph.**

$$4x^2 + y^2 + 24x - 10y + 45 = 0$$
$$4x^2 + 24x + y^2 - 10y + 45 = 0$$
$$4(x^2 + 6x + \square) + (y^2 - 10y + \square) = -45 + 4\square + \square$$
$$4\left[x^2 + 6x + \left(\frac{6}{2}\right)^2\right] + \left[y^2 - 10y + \left(\frac{10}{2}\right)^2\right] = -45 + 4\left(\frac{6}{2}\right)^2 + \left(\frac{10}{2}\right)^2$$
$$4(x + 3)^2 + (y - 5)^2 = 16$$
$$\frac{(x + 3)^2}{4} + \frac{(y - 5)^2}{16} = 1$$

The ellipse has center at $(-3, 5)$.

To determine coordinates of the foci, first find c.
$b^2 = a^2 - c^2$
$c^2 = a^2 - b^2$
$c^2 = 16 - 4$ *a is 4 and b is 2.*
$c^2 = 12$
$c = 2\sqrt{3} \approx 3.5$

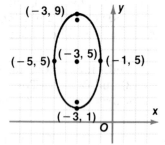

Thus, the foci are $2\sqrt{3}$ units above and below the center, $(-3, 5)$. The coordinates of the foci are $(-3, 5 + 2\sqrt{3})$ and $(-3, 5 - 2\sqrt{3})$ or about $(-3, 8.5)$ and $(-3, 1.5)$.

Exploratory Exercises

Name the center of each ellipse with the given equation and state whether the major axis is horizontal or vertical.

1. $\dfrac{x^2}{9} + \dfrac{y^2}{4} = 1$ **2.** $\dfrac{x^2}{16} + \dfrac{y^2}{1} = 1$ **3.** $\dfrac{x^2}{9} + \dfrac{y^2}{25} = 1$

4. $\dfrac{x^2}{10} + \dfrac{y^2}{36} = 1$ **5.** $\dfrac{x^2}{81} + \dfrac{(y - 5)^2}{49} = 1$ **6.** $\dfrac{(x + 3)^2}{25} + \dfrac{y^2}{9} = 1$

7. $\dfrac{(x - 2)^2}{36} + \dfrac{(y + 5)^2}{16} = 1$ **8.** $\dfrac{(x - 4)^2}{16} + \dfrac{(y - 4)^2}{121} = 1$ **9.** $\dfrac{(x + 2)^2}{81} + \dfrac{(y - 3)^2}{144} = 1$

Name the foci of each ellipse with the given equation.

10. $\dfrac{x^2}{9} + \dfrac{y^2}{4} = 1$

11. $\dfrac{x^2}{16} + \dfrac{y^2}{1} = 1$

12. $\dfrac{x^2}{9} + \dfrac{y^2}{25} = 1$

13. $\dfrac{x^2}{10} + \dfrac{y^2}{36} = 1$

14. $\dfrac{x^2}{81} + \dfrac{(y-5)^2}{49} = 1$

15. $\dfrac{(x+3)^2}{25} + \dfrac{y^2}{9} = 1$

Written Exercises

Find the center, foci, and lengths of the major axis and minor axis of each ellipse whose equation is given. Then draw the graph.

1. $\dfrac{x^2}{4} + \dfrac{y^2}{25} = 1$

2. $\dfrac{x^2}{36} + \dfrac{y^2}{16} = 1$

3. $\dfrac{x^2}{25} + \dfrac{y^2}{9} = 1$

4. $\dfrac{x^2}{10} + \dfrac{y^2}{5} = 1$

5. $9x^2 + 16y^2 = 144$

6. $3x^2 + 9y^2 = 27$

7. $4x^2 + 9y^2 = 36$

8. $4x^2 + y^2 = 4$

9. $36x^2 + 81y^2 = 2916$

10. $x^2 + 16y^2 = 16$

11. $27x^2 + 9y^2 = 81$

12. $\dfrac{(x+3)^2}{36} + \dfrac{(y-4)^2}{9} = 1$

13. $\dfrac{(x+2)^2}{20} + \dfrac{(y+3)^2}{40} = 1$

14. $\dfrac{(x-8)^2}{4} + \dfrac{(y+8)^2}{1} = 1$

15. $\dfrac{(x+2)^2}{5} + \dfrac{(y-3)^2}{2} = 1$

16. $\dfrac{(x-4)^2}{121} + \dfrac{(y+5)^2}{64} = 1$

17. $\dfrac{(x-2)^2}{16} + \dfrac{(y-3)^2}{9} = 1$

18. $9x^2 + 4y^2 - 18x + 16y = 11$

19. $3x^2 + 7y^2 - 12x - 28y = -19$

20. $9x^2 + 16y^2 - 18x + 64y = 71$

21. $16x^2 + 25y^2 + 32x - 150y = 159$

Write the equation of each ellipse described below.

22. The foci are at $(0, 8)$ and $(0, -8)$. The endpoints of the major axis are at $(0, 10)$ and $(0, -10)$.

23. The foci are at $(12, 0)$ and $(-12, 0)$. The endpoints of the minor axis are at $(0, 5)$ and $(0, -5)$.

24. The center has coordinates $(5, 4)$. The major axis is 16 units long and parallel to the x-axis. The minor axis is 9 units long.

25. The center has coordinates $(-2, 3)$. The major axis is 12 units long and parallel to the y-axis. The minor axis is 8 units long.

26. The endpoints of the major axis are at $(2, 12)$ and $(2, -4)$. The endpoints of the minor axis are at $(4, 4)$ and $(0, 4)$.

27. The foci are at $(5, 4)$ and $(-3, 4)$. The major axis is 10 units.

Excursions in Algebra _____ The Capitol

If rays of light or sound are emitted from one focus of an elliptical reflector, these rays are concentrated at the other focus.

The elliptical chamber of the United States Capitol has this property. A person standing at one focus and whispering is easily heard by a person standing at the other focus.

9-5 Hyperbolas

When the light from a table lamp hits the wall, curves called **hyperbolas** are formed.

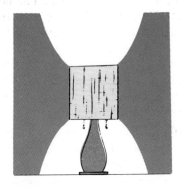

A hyperbola is the set of all points in the plane such that the absolute value of the difference of the distances from two given points in the plane, called the *foci*, is constant.

Definition of Hyperbola

The hyperbola at the right has foci at $(-5, 0)$ and $(5, 0)$. The difference of the distances from the two foci is 8. You can use the distance formula and the definition of a hyperbola to find the equation of this hyperbola.

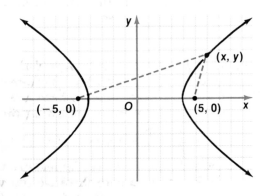

Let (x, y) name a point on the hyperbola. The distance between (x, y) and $(-5, 0)$ *minus* the distance between (x, y) and $(5, 0)$ is ± 8.

$$\begin{array}{cc} \text{\textit{distance between}} & \text{\textit{distance between}} \\ \text{\textit{(x, y) and (}}-5, 0\text{)} & \text{\textit{(x, y) and (5, 0)}} \end{array} = \pm 8$$

$$\sqrt{(x - (-5))^2 + (y - 0)^2} - \sqrt{(x - 5)^2 + (y - 0)^2} = \pm 8$$

$$\sqrt{(x + 5)^2 + y^2} = \pm 8 + \sqrt{(x - 5)^2 + y^2}$$

$$(x + 5)^2 + y^2 = 64 \pm 16\sqrt{(x - 5)^2 + y^2} + (x - 5)^2 + y^2$$

$$5x - 16 = \pm 4\sqrt{(x - 5)^2 + y^2}$$

$$25x^2 - 160x + 256 = 16[(x - 5)^2 + y^2]$$

$$9x^2 - 16y^2 = 144$$

$$\frac{x^2}{16} - \frac{y^2}{9} = 1$$

The equation of a hyperbola with foci at $(-5, 0)$ and $(5, 0)$, and with 8 as the absolute value of the difference between the distances from the two foci is $\dfrac{x^2}{16} - \dfrac{y^2}{9} = 1$.

The **center** of a hyperbola is the midpoint of the segment connecting the foci. The point on each branch of the hyperbola nearest the center is called a **vertex**. The **asymptotes** of a hyperbola are lines that the branches of the curve approach as the curve recedes from the center. Like the ellipse, the distance from the center to a vertex is a units and the distance from the center to a focus is c units.

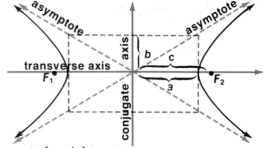

A hyperbola has two axes of symmetry, as shown at the right. The line segment of length $2a$ which has its endpoints at the vertices is called the **transverse axis**. The segment of length $2b$ perpendicular to the transverse axis at its center is called the **conjugate axis**. For a hyperbola, the lengths a, b, and c are related by the formula $a^2 + b^2 = c^2$.

The asymptotes pass through the center of the hyperbola and form the diagonals of the rectangle whose sides are 2a and 2b units.

The relationship between a, b, and c, is different for ellipses and hyperbolas. In an ellipse, $b^2 = a^2 - c^2$. In a hyperbola, $b^2 = c^2 - a^2$.

The method used to find the equation of the hyperbola on the previous page also can be used to find the standard equation of a hyperbola.

> The standard equation of a hyperbola with foci at $(-c, 0)$ and $(c, 0)$, and with the absolute value of the difference between distances from the two foci $2a$ units, can be written in the following form.
>
> $$\frac{x^2}{a^2} - \frac{y^2}{b^2} = 1 \text{ where } c^2 = a^2 + b^2$$
>
> The standard equation of a hyperbola with foci at $(0, -c)$ and $(0, c)$, and with the absolute value of the difference between distances from the two foci $2a$ units, can be written in the following form.
>
> $$\frac{y^2}{a^2} - \frac{x^2}{b^2} = 1 \text{ where } c^2 = a^2 + b^2$$

Equation of Hyperbola with Center at Origin

Example

1 Write the equation of the hyperbola shown below.

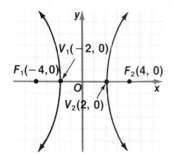

The distance from the center to a vertex is a units.
$$a = 2$$
The distance from the center to a focus is c units.
$$c = 4$$

Now find b.
$$c^2 = a^2 + b^2$$
$$4^2 = 2^2 + b^2$$
$$b = \sqrt{12}$$

The equation is $\dfrac{x^2}{2^2} - \dfrac{y^2}{(\sqrt{12})^2} = 1$ or $\dfrac{x^2}{4} - \dfrac{y^2}{12} = 1.$

Before graphing a hyperbola, it is helpful to sketch the asymptotes. The equations of the asymptotes are given in the chart at the right. The slopes of the asymptotes are shown in color.

Equation of the Hyperbola	Equations of Asymptotes
$\dfrac{x^2}{a^2} - \dfrac{y^2}{b^2} = 1$ *The transverse axis is horizontal.*	$y = \dfrac{b}{a}x$ and $y = -\dfrac{b}{a}x$
$\dfrac{y^2}{a^2} - \dfrac{x^2}{b^2} = 1$ *The transverse axis is vertical.*	$y = \dfrac{a}{b}x$ and $y = -\dfrac{a}{b}x$

Example

2 **Find the slopes of the asymptotes of the graph of $\dfrac{y^2}{16} - \dfrac{x^2}{9} = 1$. Then find the coordinates of the foci and vertices and draw the graph.**

The hyperbola has a vertical transverse axis. Its center has coordinates $(0, 0)$. The slopes are $\dfrac{a}{b}$ and $-\dfrac{a}{b}$ as shown in color above. Since a is 4 and b is 3, the slopes are $\dfrac{4}{3}$ and $-\dfrac{4}{3}$. Sketch a rectangle $2a$ by $2b$ and draw the diagonals as asymptotes with the correct slopes. Since a is 4, the distance from the center to a vertex is 4 units. Thus, the vertices are at $(0, 4)$ and $(0, -4)$.

To locate the foci, find the value of c.

$$c^2 = a^2 + b^2$$
$$c^2 = 4^2 + 3^2$$
$$c = 5$$

So, the foci are at $(0, 5)$ and $(0, -5)$.

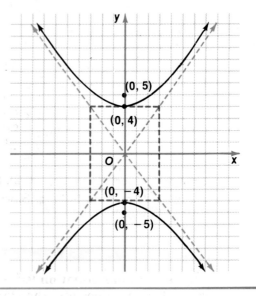

An equation of the form $\dfrac{x^2}{a^2} - \dfrac{y^2}{b^2} = 1$ represents a hyperbola with center $(0, 0)$ and a horizontal transverse axis. Suppose a hyperbola has the same shape with center (h, k). The standard equation below can be obtained by replacing x with $x - h$ and y with $y - k$.

If the center is (h, k) and the transverse axis is horizontal, the equation is $\dfrac{(x-h)^2}{a^2} - \dfrac{(y-k)^2}{b^2} = 1$.

If the center is (h, k) and the transverse axis is vertical, the equation is $\dfrac{(y-k)^2}{a^2} - \dfrac{(x-h)^2}{b^2} = 1$.

Standard Equation of a Hyperbola

For any hyperbola with a vertical transverse axis, the slopes of the asymptotes are $\pm\dfrac{a}{b}$. For any hyperbola with a horizontal transverse axis, the slopes of the asymptotes are $\pm\dfrac{b}{a}$.

Example

3 **Draw the graph of $\dfrac{(y-1)^2}{16} - \dfrac{(x+2)^2}{9} = 1$.**

The graph has the same shape as the graph of $\dfrac{y^2}{16} - \dfrac{x^2}{9} = 1$, but has center at $(-2, 1)$ rather than at the origin.

The slopes of the asymptotes are $\pm\dfrac{4}{3}$.

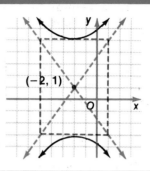

The graph of $x^2 - 4y^2 + 6x + 16y - 11 = 0$ is a hyperbola. To write the equation in the form $\dfrac{(x-h)^2}{a^2} - \dfrac{(y-k)^2}{b^2} = 1$, complete the square for each variable.

$$x^2 - 4y^2 + 6x + 16y - 11 = 0$$
$$x^2 + 6x + \blacksquare - 4(y^2 - 4y + \square) = 11 + \blacksquare - 4\square$$
$$x^2 + 6x + \left(\frac{6}{2}\right)^2 - 4\left[y^2 - 4y + \left(\frac{-4}{2}\right)^2\right] = 11 + \left(\frac{6}{2}\right)^2 + (-4)\left(\frac{-4}{2}\right)^2$$
$$(x+3)^2 - 4(y-2)^2 = 4$$
$$\frac{(x+3)^2}{4} - \frac{(y-2)^2}{1} = 1$$

The center of the hyperbola is at $(-3, 2)$. Since a^2 is 4, the transverse axis is $2(\sqrt{4})$ or 4 units long. Since $b^2 = 1$, the conjugate axis is $2\sqrt{1}$ or 2 units long.

Example

4 **A hyperbola has equation $9x^2 - 4y^2 - 54x - 40y - 55 = 0$. Find the coordinates of the vertices and the slopes of the asymptotes. Then draw the graph.**

$$9x^2 - 4y^2 - 54x - 40y - 55 = 0$$
$$9(x^2 - 6x + \blacksquare) - 4(y^2 + 10y + \square) = 55 + 9\blacksquare - 4\square$$
$$9\left[x^2 - 6x + \left(\frac{-6}{2}\right)^2\right] - 4\left[y^2 + 10y + \left(\frac{10}{2}\right)^2\right] = 55 + 9\left(\frac{-6}{2}\right)^2 + (-4)\left(\frac{10}{2}\right)^2$$
$$9(x-3)^2 - 4(y+5)^2 = 36$$
$$\frac{(x-3)^2}{4} - \frac{(y+5)^2}{9} = 1$$

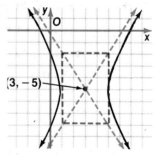

The hyperbola has a horizontal transverse axis. Its center has coordinates $(3, -5)$. The slopes of the asymptotes are $\dfrac{3}{2}$ and $-\dfrac{3}{2}$.

Since a is 2, the distance from the center to a vertex is 2 units. Thus, the coordinates of the vertices are $(5, -5)$ and $(1, -5)$.

Exploratory Exercises

State whether the graph of each of the following equations is an ellipse or a hyperbola.

1. $\dfrac{x^2}{9} + \dfrac{y^2}{4} = 1$

2. $\dfrac{x^2}{16} - \dfrac{y^2}{4} = 1$

3. $\dfrac{y^2}{18} - \dfrac{x^2}{20} = 1$

4. $\dfrac{x^2}{5} + \dfrac{y^2}{5} = 1$

5. $\dfrac{x^2}{36} - \dfrac{y^2}{1} = 1$

6. $\dfrac{x^2}{10} + \dfrac{y^2}{36} = 1$

7. $\dfrac{y^2}{25} + \dfrac{x^2}{9} = 1$

8. $\dfrac{x^2}{81} - \dfrac{y^2}{36} = 1$

Written Exercises

Find the vertices, foci, and slopes of the asymptotes for each hyperbola whose equation is given. Then draw the graph.

1. $\dfrac{x^2}{9} - \dfrac{y^2}{25} = 1$

2. $\dfrac{x^2}{16} - \dfrac{y^2}{4} = 1$

3. $\dfrac{x^2}{36} - \dfrac{y^2}{1} = 1$

4. $\dfrac{y^2}{6} - \dfrac{x^2}{2} = 1$

5. $\dfrac{y^2}{81} - \dfrac{x^2}{25} = 1$

6. $\dfrac{y^2}{18} - \dfrac{x^2}{20} = 1$

7. $\dfrac{x^2}{4} - \dfrac{y^2}{9} = 1$

8. $\dfrac{y^2}{16} - \dfrac{x^2}{25} = 1$

9. $\dfrac{x^2}{81} - \dfrac{y^2}{36} = 1$

10. $\dfrac{y^2}{100} - \dfrac{x^2}{144} = 1$

11. $\dfrac{x^2}{9} - \dfrac{y^2}{16} = 1$

12. $\dfrac{x^2}{9} - \dfrac{y^2}{4} = 1$

13. $25x^2 - 4y^2 = 100$

14. $x^2 - y^2 = 4$

15. $x^2 - 2y^2 = 2$

16. $y^2 - 4x^2 = 4$

17. $y^2 = 36 + 4x^2$

18. $36y^2 - 81x^2 = 2916$

19. $\dfrac{(x + 6)^2}{36} - \dfrac{(y + 3)^2}{9} = 1$

20. $\dfrac{(y - 3)^2}{25} - \dfrac{(x - 2)^2}{16} = 1$

21. $\dfrac{(y - 4)^2}{16} - \dfrac{(x + 2)^2}{9} = 1$

22. $\dfrac{(x + 1)^2}{4} - \dfrac{(y - 4)^2}{9} = 1$

23. $5(x - 4)^2 - 4(y + 2)^2 = 100$

24. $x^2 - 4y^2 + 6x + 16y - 11 = 0$

25. $y^2 - 3x^2 + 6y + 6x = 18$

26. $y^2 - 4x^2 - 2y - 16x = -1$

Write the equation of each hyperbola described below.

27. Center $(0, 0)$, $a = 1$, $b = 4$, horizontal transverse axis

28. Center $(5, 4)$, $a = 2$, $b = 6$, vertical transverse axis

29. Center $(-2, 2)$, $a = 6$, $c = 10$, vertical transverse axis

30. The equations of the asymptotes are $3x - 2y = 0$ and $3x + 2y = 0$. The transverse axis is horizontal. The hyperbola passes through $(2, 0)$.

An equation of the form $xy = k$ when $k \neq 0$ represents a hyperbola having the x-axis and y-axis as asymptotes.

31. Complete the table of values at the right for $xy = 2$.

x	$\cdot 1$	2	4	8	-1	-4	-8
y							

32. Find the domain for $xy = 2$.

33. Find the range for $xy = 2$.

34. Sketch the graph of $xy = 2$.

Challenge

35. Find the equation of a hyperbola whose asymptotes are $5x + 3y = -1$ and $5x - 3y = 11$, and which passes through $(4, -2)$.

36. Using the same asymptotes as in exercise 35, find the equation of a hyperbola that passes through $(1, 3)$.

9-6 Conic Sections

Parabolas, circles, ellipses, and hyperbolas can be formed by slicing a hollow double cone in different directions. The curves, therefore, are called **conic sections.**

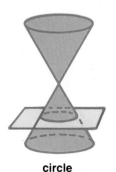

circle

ellipse

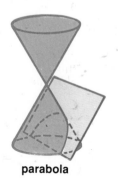

parabola

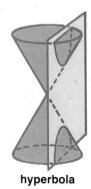

hyperbola

The conic sections are related in another way, too. Each conic section can be described by a quadratic equation in two variables.

> The equation of a conic section can be written in the form $Ax^2 + Bxy + Cy^2 + Dx + Ey + F = 0$ where A, B, and C are not all zero.

Equation for Conic Sections

To identify the conic section a quadratic equation in two variables represents, rewrite the equation in the forms you have learned. The following table summarizes these forms.

Most of the conic sections you have studied have equations with B = 0.

Often this involves completing the square.

Conic Section	Standard Form of Equation
parabola	$y = a(x - h)^2 + k$ or $x = a(y - k)^2 + h$
circle	$(x - h)^2 + (y - k)^2 = r^2$
ellipse	$\dfrac{(x - h)^2}{a^2} + \dfrac{(y - k)^2}{b^2} = 1$ or $\dfrac{(x - h)^2}{b^2} + \dfrac{(y - k)^2}{a^2} = 1$
hyperbola	$\dfrac{(x - h)^2}{a^2} - \dfrac{(y - k)^2}{b^2} = 1$ or $\dfrac{(y - k)^2}{a^2} - \dfrac{(x - h)^2}{b^2} = 1$ or $xy = k$

Examples

1 **Is the graph of $(y - 4)^2 = 9(x - 4)$ a parabola, circle, ellipse, or hyperbola?**

$$(y - 4)^2 = 9(x - 4)$$

$$\frac{1}{9}(y - 4)^2 = x - 4$$

$$\frac{1}{9}(y - 4)^2 + 4 = x \qquad a \text{ is } \frac{1}{9}, k \text{ is } 4, h \text{ is } 4$$

The graph is a parabola.

2 **Is the graph of $x^2 + y^2 = x + 2$ a parabola, circle, ellipse, or hyperbola?**

$$x^2 + y^2 = x + 2$$

$$x^2 - x + \blacksquare + y^2 = 2 + \blacksquare$$

$$x^2 - x + \left(-\frac{1}{2}\right)^2 + y^2 = 2 + \left(-\frac{1}{2}\right)^2 \qquad \textit{Complete the square.}$$

$$x^2 - x + \frac{1}{4} + y^2 = 2 + \frac{1}{4}$$

$$\left(x - \frac{1}{2}\right)^2 + y^2 = \frac{9}{4}$$

$$\left(x - \frac{1}{2}\right)^2 + (y - 0)^2 = \left(\frac{3}{2}\right)^2 \qquad h \text{ is } \frac{1}{2}, k \text{ is } 0, r \text{ is } \frac{3}{2}$$

The graph is a circle. The graph is also an ellipse with a and b both $\frac{3}{2}$.

3 **Is the graph of $x^2 - 4x - 1 = \frac{5}{6}(y - 1)^2$ a parabola, circle, ellipse, or hyperbola?**

$$x^2 - 4x - 1 = \frac{5}{6}(y - 1)^2$$

$$x^2 - 4x + \blacksquare = \frac{5}{6}(y - 1)^2 + 1 + \blacksquare$$

$$x^2 - 4x + \left(\frac{-4}{2}\right)^2 = \frac{5}{6}(y - 1)^2 + 1 + \left(\frac{-4}{2}\right)^2 \qquad \textit{Complete the square.}$$

$$(x - 2)^2 = \frac{5}{6}(y - 1)^2 + 5$$

$$\frac{(x - 2)^2}{5} = \frac{(y - 1)^2}{6} + 1 \qquad \textit{Divide both sides by 5.}$$

$$\frac{(x - 2)^2}{5} - \frac{(y - 1)^2}{6} = 1 \qquad h \text{ is } 2, k \text{ is } 1, a \text{ is } \sqrt{5}, b \text{ is } \sqrt{6}$$

The graph is a hyperbola.

Consider an equation of the form $Ax^2 + Bxy + Cy^2 + Dx + Ey + F = 0$ when $B = 0$. By comparing A and C, you can determine the type of conic section the equation represents.

If $A = C$, the equation represents a circle.
If A and C have the same sign, the equation represents an ellipse.
If A and C have opposite signs, the equation represents a hyperbola.
If either A or C is zero, the equation represents a parabola.

Exploratory Exercises

State whether the graph of each of the following equations is a parabola, a circle, an ellipse, or a hyperbola.

1. $x^2 + y^2 = 9$

2. $\dfrac{y^2}{8} - \dfrac{x^2}{10} = 1$

3. $\dfrac{x^2}{4} + \dfrac{y^2}{6} = 1$

4. $x^2 + y^2 = 4$

5. $y = (x - 3)^2 + 25$

6. $x = \left(y + \dfrac{1}{2}\right)^2$

7. $\dfrac{(x + 3)^2}{1} - \dfrac{(y - 4)^2}{9} = 1$

8. $\dfrac{(y - 7)^2}{3} + \dfrac{(x + 2)^2}{2} = 1$

Written Exercises

Write the standard form of each equation. State whether the graph of each equation is a parabola, a circle, an ellipse, or a hyperbola. Then graph each equation.

1. $x^2 = 8y$

2. $4x^2 + 2y^2 = 8$

3. $3x^2 + 3y^2 = 81$

4. $9x^2 - 4y^2 = 4$

5. $3x^2 + 4y^2 + 8y = 8$

6. $13x^2 - 49 = -13y^2$

7. $y^2 - 2x^2 - 16 = 0$

8. $y = x^2 + 3x + 1$

9. $x^2 - 8y + y^2 = -11$

10. $\dfrac{(y - 5)^2}{4} - (x + 1)^2 = 4$

11. $x^2 + y = x + 2$

12. $(y - 4)^2 = 9(x - 4)$

13. $9x^2 + 25y^2 - 54x - 50y = 119$

14. $x^2 - 4y^2 + 10x - 16y = -5$

15. $3y^2 + 24y - x^2 - 2x = -41$

16. $x^2 + y^2 + 6y - 8x = -24$

Challenge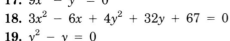

The graph of an equation of the form $Ax^2 + Bxy + Cy^2 + Dx + Ey + F = 0$ is a conic section or a *degenerate case*. The degenerate cases for the conic sections are on the right. Graph each equation and identify the result.

17. $9x^2 - y^2 = 0$

18. $3x^2 - 6x + 4y^2 + 32y + 67 = 0$

19. $y^2 - y = 0$

Conic	Degenerate Case
ellipse or circle	isolated point
hyperbola	two intersecting lines
parabola	two parallel lines or one line

Using Calculators 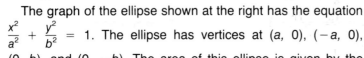 ———— Area of an Ellipse

The graph of the ellipse shown at the right has the equation $\dfrac{x^2}{a^2} + \dfrac{y^2}{b^2} = 1$. The ellipse has vertices at $(a, 0)$, $(-a, 0)$, $(0, b)$, and $(0, -b)$. The area of this ellipse is given by the formula $A = \pi ab$.

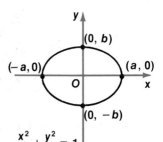

Exercises

Use a calculator to find the area of each ellipse whose equation is given.

1. $\dfrac{x^2}{25} + \dfrac{y^2}{16} = 1$

2. $\dfrac{x^2}{9} + \dfrac{y^2}{49} = 1$

3. $25x^2 + 16y^2 = 400$

4. $32x^2 + 72y^2 = 1152$

5. The ellipse with vertices at $(0, 8)$, $(0, -8)$, $(2, 0)$, and $(-2, 0)$.

6. The ellipse with vertices at $(6, 0)$ and $(-6, 0)$ and foci at $(2\sqrt{5}, 0)$ and $(-2\sqrt{5}, 0)$.

9-7 Graphing Quadratic Systems

Consider the following system of equations.

$$y = x^2 - 4$$
$$y = -2x - 1$$

To solve this system you must find the ordered pairs that satisfy *both* equations. One way is to graph each equation and find the intersection of the two graphs.

The graph of $y = x^2 - 4$ is a parabola. The graph of $y = -2x - 1$ is a line. The parabola and the line intersect at two points, $(-3, 5)$ and $(1, -3)$. The solutions of the system are $(-3, 5)$ and $(1, -3)$.

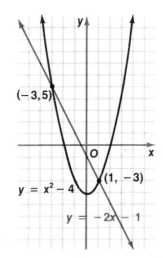

If the graphs of a system of equations are a conic section and a straight line, the system will have zero, one, or two solutions.

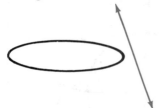

no solutions

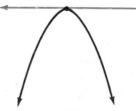

one solution

two solutions

Example

1 Graph the following system. Then state the solutions of the system of equations.

$$x^2 + y^2 = 25$$
$$y - x = 1$$

The graph of $x^2 + y^2 = 25$ is a circle centered at the origin with a radius of 5 units.

The graph of $y - x = 1$ is a line with slope 1 and y-intercept 1.

The solutions of the system are $(3, 4)$ and $(-4, -3)$.

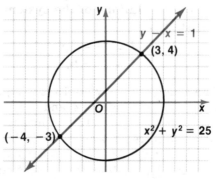

If the graphs of a system of equations are two conic sections, the system will have zero, one, two, three or four solutions.

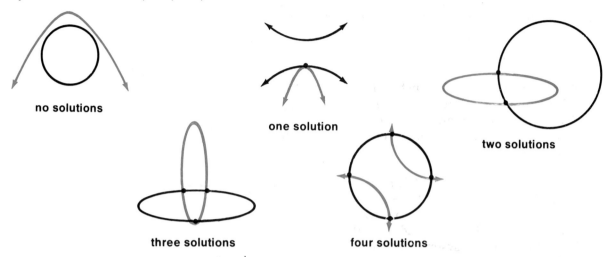

no solutions

one solution

two solutions

three solutions

four solutions

Examples

2 Graph the following system. Then state the solutions of the system of equations.

$$x^2 + y^2 = 25$$
$$4y + x^2 = 25$$

The graph of $x^2 + y^2 = 25$ is a circle centered at the origin with a radius of 5 units. The graph of $4y + x^2 = 25$ is a parabola which opens downward, has vertex $\left(0, 6\frac{1}{4}\right)$, and x-intercepts 5 and -5. The solutions of the system are $(5, 0)$, $(-5, 0)$, $(3, 4)$, and $(-3, 4)$.

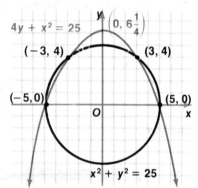

3 Graph the following system. Then state the solutions of the system of equations.

$$y^2 - x^2 = 16$$
$$x^2 - y^2 = 16$$

The graph of $y^2 - x^2 = 16$ is a hyperbola with y-intercepts 4 and -4. The graph of $x^2 - y^2 = 16$ is a hyperbola with x-intercepts 4 and -4. Both hyperbolas have the same asymptotes, $y = \pm x$. The system has no solutions.

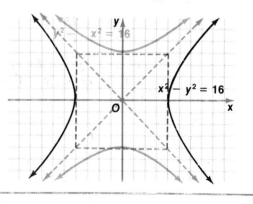

Written Exercises

Graph each system of equations. Then approximate the solutions of each system.

1. $x^2 + y^2 = 16$
   $y = 2$

2. $y = x^2$
   $y - 2 = x$

3. $x^2 - y = 4$
   $y = 3x$

4. $x = y$
   $\dfrac{x^2}{20} + \dfrac{y^2}{5} = 1$

5. $\dfrac{x^2}{9} - \dfrac{y^2}{9} = 1$
   $\dfrac{2}{3}y = \dfrac{1}{3}x - 1$

6. $x^2 + y^2 = 25$
   $x + y = -7$

7. $(y - 1)^2 = x + 4$
   $y + x = -1$

8. $\dfrac{x^2}{16} + \dfrac{y^2}{4} = 1$
   $3y + 5x = 6$

9. $y^2 - x^2 = 9$
   $y = 6$

10. $x^2 + y^2 = 100$
    $x - y = 2$

11. $x^2 + y^2 = 9$
    $x + y = 7$

12. $\dfrac{x^2}{4} + \dfrac{y^2}{1} = 1$
    $x - y = 6$

13. $\dfrac{x^2}{16} - \dfrac{y^2}{4} = 1$
    $y = 3x - 3$

14. $x^2 + 4y^2 = 25$
    $2y = 1 - x$

15. $\dfrac{(x - 2)^2}{16} + \dfrac{y^2}{16} = 1$
    $y - x = 2$

16. $y = -x^2$
    $y = -x - 2$

17. $(x - 1)^2 + 4(y - 1)^2 = 20$
    $x = y$

18. $\dfrac{x^2}{36} - \dfrac{y^2}{4} = 1$
    $y = x$

19. $\dfrac{(x - 3)^2}{25} + \dfrac{(y - 4)^2}{9} = 1$
    $5y + 3x = 44$

20. $(x - 3)^2 + (y + 6)^2 = 36$
    $y + 3 = x$

21. $5x^2 + y^2 = 30$
    $y^2 - 16 = 9x^2$

22. $x^2 + y^2 = 5$
    $2x^2 + y = 0$

23. $2y^2 = 10 - x^2$
    $3x^2 - 9 = y^2$

24. $4x^2 + 9y^2 = 36$
    $4x^2 - 9y^2 = 36$

25. $x^2 + 4y^2 = 4$
    $(x - 2)^2 + (y - 2)^2 = 1$

26. $x^2 + 4y^2 = 36$
    $y = -x^2 + 3$

27. $x^2 - y^2 = 25$
    $x^2 - y^2 = 7$

28. $x^2 + y^2 = 16$
    $x^2 + y^2 = 9$

29. $x^2 + y^2 = 64$
    $x^2 + 64y^2 = 64$

30. $x^2 - y^2 = 16$
    $y^2 - x^2 = 16$

mini-review

1. Find $h\left(\dfrac{1}{2}\right)$ for $h(x) = \dfrac{x^2 + 5x - 6}{x + 3}$.

2. Solve by the elimination method.
   $$2x + y = 0$$
   $$5x + 3y = 1$$

3. Find the value of this determinant.
   $$\begin{vmatrix} 2 & 3 & 4 \\ 3 & 2 & -1 \\ 4 & 3 & 7 \end{vmatrix}$$

4. Divide using synthetic division.
   $$(x^5 - 3x^2 - 20) \div (x - 2)$$

5. Solve $\sqrt{3y - 5} - 3 = 1$.

Problem Solving

The first step in solving some problems is to organize the given information in one of several ways. Sometimes making a list to organize the information is helpful. Another way to classify information is to make a table or chart. Consider the following example.

Example: Rachel is beginning to jog. The first week she jogs 1 block each day. The second week she jogs 3 blocks each day. The third week she jogs 5 blocks each day, and so on. That is, on each successive week she jogs 2 more blocks per day than each day of the previous week. How many blocks will she jog each day of the twelfth week? How many blocks will she have jogged altogether after the twelfth week?

Make a table of the information given. Notice the pattern that develops.

Week	Blocks Jogged Each Day	Total Blocks Jogged
1	1	$7 \times 1 = 7$ or $7 \cdot 1$
2	3	$7 + (7 \times 3) = 28$ or $7 \cdot 4$
3	5	$28 + (7 \times 5) = 63$ or $7 \cdot 9$
4	7	$63 + (7 \times 7) = 112$ or $7 \cdot 16$
.	.	.
.		
n	$2n - 1$	$7n^2$

Thus, the twelfth week she will jog $2(12) - 1$ or 23 blocks each day. After the twelfth week she will have jogged a total of $7 \cdot 12^2$ or 1008 blocks.

Exercises

Solve each problem. Use a table or chart.

1. A large sheet of paper is 0.15 mm thick. Suppose it is torn in half and the two pieces are placed together and torn in half again. Suppose this process continues for a total of 20 tears. How many pieces are in the stack of paper? How high is the stack of paper?

2. Classic Cleaners must clean 105 apartments in 5 days. Each day the owner puts 2 more employees on the job. However, each day after the first, each employee cleans 1 less apartment than each did on the previous day. What is the greatest number of apartments cleaned on any one day?

3. Lou Ann Mathena has a box of oranges to be divided among her seven piano students, who are all of different ages. Lou Ann gives each student the number of oranges by which his age can be divided into the total number of oranges. All the oranges are to be distributed. Tara, who is the middle child in terms of age, receives 18 oranges. How many years older is she than the youngest student?

4. Paul questions Bill about the ages of his three children. Bill replies, "The product of their ages is 36 and the sum of their ages is the same as today's date." But Paul says he still needs more information. Then Bill tells him that the oldest child has blonde hair. Paul says that he now can determine their ages. How old are the three children?

9-8   Solving Quadratic Systems

You can use graphs to help find the solutions of a quadratic system. Often you must use algebra to find the exact solutions.

Examples

1   **Find the solutions of the following system of equations.**

$$x^2 + y^2 = 25$$
$$y - x = 1$$

The graphs of the equations are a circle and a straight line. The graphs show that there are two solutions to the system. Also, the values of x are between -5 and 5. And the values of y are between -5 and 5.

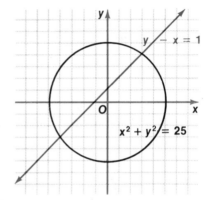

Use the substitution method to find the exact solutions. First rewrite $y - x = 1$ as $y = x + 1$.

$$x^2 + y^2 = 25$$
$$x^2 + (x + 1)^2 = 25 \qquad \text{Substitute } x + 1 \text{ for } y.$$
$$x^2 + x^2 + 2x + 1 = 25$$
$$2x^2 + 2x - 24 = 0$$
$$2(x + 4)(x - 3) = 0$$

$x + 4 = 0$	or	$x - 3 = 0$
$x = -4$		$x = 3$
$y = x + 1$		$y = x + 1$
$= -4 + 1$ or -3		$= 3 + 1$ or 4

The solutions are $(-4, -3)$ and $(3, 4)$.

2   **Find the solutions of the following system of equations.**

$$x^2 + 2y^2 = 10$$
$$3x^2 - y^2 = 9$$

The graphs of the equations are an ellipse and a hyperbola. The graphs show that there are four solutions to the system.

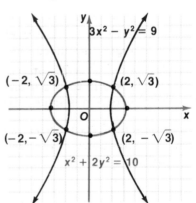

Use the elimination method to find the exact solutions.

$$x^2 + 2y^2 = 10$$
$$3x^2 - y^2 = 9$$

Multiply by 2.

$$x^2 + 2y^2 = 10$$
$$6x^2 - 2y^2 = 18$$

Add the two equations.

$$7x^2 = 28$$
$$x^2 = 4$$
$$x = \pm 2$$

$$x^2 + 2y^2 = 10$$
$$2^2 + 2y^2 = 10$$
$$2y^2 = 6$$
$$y^2 = 3$$
$$y = \pm\sqrt{3}$$

$$x^2 + 2y^2 = 10$$
$$(-2)^2 + 2y^2 = 10$$
$$2y^2 = 6$$
$$y^2 = 3$$
$$y = \pm\sqrt{3}$$

The solutions are $(2, \sqrt{3})$, $(-2, \sqrt{3})$, $(2, -\sqrt{3})$, $(-2, -\sqrt{3})$.

To graph the solutions of a system of inequalities, graph each inequality and find the intersection of the two graphs.

$$x^2 + y^2 \geq 16$$
$$x + y = 2$$

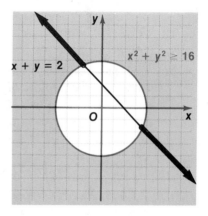

The graph of $x^2 + y^2 \geq 16$ consists of all points on or outside the circle $x^2 + y^2 = 16$. This region is shaded red. The graph of $x + y = 2$ is a straight line with slope -1 and y-intercept 2.

The intersection of the shaded region and the straight line is the graph of the solutions. The graph of the solutions is indicated by the thick rays.

Example

3 Graph the solutions for the following system of inequalities.

$$x^2 + y^2 \leq 25$$
$$4y + x^2 \leq 25$$

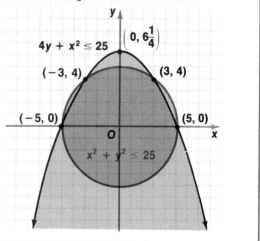

The graph of $x^2 + y^2 \leq 25$ consists of all points on or within the circle $x^2 + y^2 = 25$. This region is shaded red.

The graph of $4y + x^2 \leq 25$ consists of all points on or within the parabola $4y + x^2 = 25$. This region is shaded gray.

The intersection of these two graphs represents the solutions for the system of inequalities.

Written Exercises

Find the solutions of each system of equations.

1. $x^2 + y^2 = 16$
$x = 2$

2. $y = x^2$
$y - 2 = x$

3. $x = y$
$\dfrac{x^2}{20} + \dfrac{y^2}{5} = 1$

4. $x^2 - y = 4$
$y = 3x$

5. $x^2 - y^2 = 9$
$8y = 4x - 12$

6. $x^2 + y^2 = 25$
$x + y = -7$

7. $(y - 1)^2 = x + 4$
$y + x = -1$

8. $\dfrac{x^2}{16} + \dfrac{y^2}{4} = 1$
$2y + 5x = 4$

9. $y^2 - x^2 = 9$
$y = 6$

10. $x^2 + y^2 = 100$
$x - y = 2$

11. $x^2 + y^2 = 9$
$x + y = 7$

12. $x^2 + 4y^2 = 4$
$x - y = 6$

13. $x^2 - 4y^2 = 16$
$y = 3x - 3$

14. $x^2 + 4y^2 = 25$
$2y = 1 - x$

15. $(x - 2)^2 + y^2 = 16$
$y - x = 2$

16. $y = -x^2$
$y = -x - 2$

17. $x^2 - 4y = 0$
$y - 2x = -3$

18. $x^2 - 9y^2 = 36$
$y = x$

19. $\dfrac{(x - 3)^2}{25} + \dfrac{(y - 4)^2}{9} = 1$
$5y + 3x = 44$

20. $(x - 3)^2 + (y + 6)^2 = 36$
$y + 3 = x$

21. $5x^2 + y^2 = 30$
$y^2 - 16 = 9x^2$

22. $x^2 + y^2 = 5$
$2x^2 + y = 0$

23. $2y^2 = 10 - x^2$
$3x^2 - 9 = y^2$

24. $4x^2 + 9y^2 = 36$
$4x^2 - 9y^2 = 36$

25. $x^2 + y^2 = 16$
$x^2 + y^2 = 9$

26. $x^2 + y^2 = 64$
$x^2 + 64y^2 = 64$

27. $x^2 - y^2 = 25$
$x^2 - y^2 = 7$

Graph the solutions for each system of inequalities.

28. $x^2 + y^2 < 9$
$y < -x^2$

29. $\dfrac{x^2}{9} - \dfrac{y^2}{4} < 1$
$x^2 + y^2 < 25$

30. $x^2 + y^2 \geq 4$
$x^2 + y^2 \leq 36$

31. $\dfrac{x^2}{16} - \dfrac{y^2}{1} \geq 1$
$x^2 + y^2 \geq 49$

32. $\dfrac{x^2}{25} - \dfrac{y^2}{16} \geq 1$
$x - y \geq 2$

33. $y \geq x^2 - 4$
$(y - 3)^2 \geq x + 2$

34. $x^2 + y^2 > 16$
$81x^2 + 9y^2 < 729$

35. $x^2 - 4y^2 < 16$
$x > y^2$

36. $x + 3 = y$
$x^2 + y^2 < 25$

37. $9x^2 + 4y^2 \leq 36$
$4x^2 + 9y^2 \geq 36$

38. $x + 2y > 1$
$x^2 + y^2 < 25$

39. $9x^2 - 4y^2 \geq 36$
$x + y = 4$

40. $4x^2 + 9y^2 \leq 36$
$x = 2$

41. $4x^2 + (y - 3)^2 \leq 16$
$2y = x + 1$

42. $y = -x$
$(x + 2)^2 + 16(y + 3)^2 \geq 16$

43. $5x^2 + 5y^2 \geq 25$
$2x - 3y = 5$

44. $x^2 + y^2 \geq 16$
$x = 4$

45. $x^2 + y^2 \leq 36$
$y = 6$

Challenge

Find the solutions of each system of equations or inequalities.

46. $x^2 + 4y^2 = 4$
$(x - 1)^2 + y^2 = 1$

47. $x = -y^2 + 2$
$2y - 2\sqrt{2} = x(\sqrt{2} + 2)$

48. $y \geq x^2 - 4$
$(y - 3)^2 \geq x + 2$

Ellipses

A computer program can be used to find the center, foci, and vertices of the major and minor axes of an ellipse if the equation is in either of the following standard forms.

$$\frac{(x - h)^2}{a^2} + \frac{(y - k)^2}{b^2} = 1 \qquad \text{or} \qquad \frac{(y - k)^2}{a^2} + \frac{(x - h)^2}{b^2} = 1$$

The program below finds the center, foci, and vertices of the major and minor axes for the graph of $\frac{(x - 2)^2}{16} + \frac{(y - 3)^2}{9} = 1$.

```
10  READ H, K, D1, D2
20  PRINT "THE COORDINATES OF THE
    CENTER ARE (";H;",";K;")"
30  IF (D2 > D1) THEN 130
40  LET X = SQR (D1): LET Y = SQR
    (D2)
50  LET M1 = H + X: LET M2 = H - X
60  LET N1 = K + Y: LET N2 = K - Y
70  LET C = SQR (D1 - D2)
80  LET F1 = H + C: LET F2 = H - C
90  PRINT "THE FOCI ARE (";F1;",
    ";K;"), (";F2;",";K;")"
100 PRINT "THE VERTICES OF THE
    MAJOR AXIS ARE (";M1;",  ";K;"),
    (";M2;",""K;")"
110 PRINT "THE VERTICES OF THE
    MINOR AXIS ARE (";H;",  ";N1;"),
    (";H;",";N2;")"
120 GOTO 220
130 LET X = SQR (D2): LET Y = SQR
    (D1)
140 LET M1 = K + X: LET M2 = K - X
150 LET N1 = H + Y: LET N2 = H - Y
160 LET C = SQR (D2 - D1)
170 LET F1 = K + C: LET F2 = K - C
180 PRINT "THE FOCI ARE
    (";H;",";F1;"), (";H;",";F2;")"
190 PRINT "THE VERTICES OF THE
    MAJOR AXIS ARE (";H;",";M1;"),
    (";H;",";M2;")"
200 PRINT "THE VERTICES OF THE
    MINOR AXIS ARE (";N1;",";K;"),
    (";N2;",";K;")"
210 DATA 2,3,16,9
220 END
```

This program includes a data statement (210) that contains H, K, D1, and D2 in that order. D1 refers to the denominator of the $x - h$ term and D2 refers to the denominator of the $y - k$ term. Other equations can be used by changing the DATA statement.

Frequently, computer output must be interpreted because of the rounding errors by the computer. In this case, the coordinates of one vertex of the minor axis are given as $(2, -9.31322575E-10)$. The output $-9.31322575E-10$ is the computer's scientific notation for

$$-9.31322575 \times 10^{-10}$$

or 0.000000000931322575.

Interpret the coordinates as (2, 0).

Enter and run this program. The output should look like the information after the word RUN.

```
]RUN
THE COORDINATES OF
  THE CENTER ARE (2,3)
THE FOCI ARE (4.64575131,3),
  (-.645751311,3)
THE VERTICES OF THE MAJOR
  AXIS ARE (6,3),(-2, 3)
THE VERTICES OF THE MINOR
  AXIS ARE (2,6),
  (2,-9.31322575E-10)
```

Complete the exercises on the next page.

Exercises Write the equation of each ellipse in standard form. Change the DATA statement and use the program to find the center, foci, and vertices of the major and minor axes. Then graph the equation.

1. $\dfrac{(x - 5)^2}{25} + \dfrac{y^2}{4} = 1$

2. $\dfrac{(y + 2)^2}{25} + \dfrac{(x - 1)^2}{4} = 1$

3. $y^2 - 8y + 3x^2 + 30x + 85 = 0$

4. $12x^2 + 36x + 16y^2 + 32y - 5 = 0$

Vocabulary

parabola (274)
focus of parabola (274)
directrix (274)
latus rectum (275)
circle (278)
radius (278)
center of circle (278)

ellipse (281)
foci of ellipse (281)
major axis (282)
minor axis (282)
hyperbola (286)
foci of hyperbola (286)

center of hyperbola (287)
vertex of hyperbola (287)
asymptote (287)
transverse axis (287)
conjugate axis (287)
conic section (291)

Chapter Summary

1. **Distance Between Points on a Number Line:** On a number line, the distance between two points whose coordinates are a and b is $|a - b|$ or $|b - a|$. (271)

2. **Distance Formula for Two Points in the Plane:** The distance between two points with coordinates (x_1, y_1) and (x_2, y_2) is given by the following formula.
$$d = \sqrt{(x_2 - x_1)^2 + (y_2 - y_1)^2} \quad (272)$$

3. **Midpoint Formula:** If a line segment has endpoints with coordinates (x_1, y_1) and (x_2, y_2), then the midpoint of the line segment has coordinates $\left(\dfrac{x_1 + x_2}{2}, \dfrac{y_1 + y_2}{2} \right)$. (272)

4. **Definition of Parabola:** A parabola is the set of all points in a plane that are the same distance from a given point and a given line. The point is called the focus. The line is called the directrix. (274)

5.

Information about Parabolas		
form of equation	$y = a(x - h)^2 + k$	$x = a(y - k)^2 + h$
vertex	(h, k)	(h, k)
axis of symmetry	$x = h$	$y = k$
focus	$\left(h, k + \dfrac{1}{4a} \right)$	$\left(h + \dfrac{1}{4a}, k \right)$
directrix	$y = k - \dfrac{1}{4a}$	$x = h - \dfrac{1}{4a}$
direction of opening	upward if $a > 0$ downward if $a < 0$	right if $a > 0$ left if $a < 0$

(274)

6. **Definition of Circle:** A circle is the set of all points in the plane each of which is the same distance from a given point in the plane. (278)

7. **Equation of Circle:** The equation of a circle with center at (h, k) and radius of r units is $(x - h)^2 + (y - k)^2 = r^2$. (278)

8. **Definition of Ellipse:** An ellipse is the set of all points in the plane such that the sum of the distances from two given points in the plane, called the foci, is constant. (281)

9. **Equation of Ellipse:** The standard equation of an ellipse with center at $(0, 0)$, whose foci are at $(-c, 0)$ and $(c, 0)$, and the sum of the distances from the two foci is $2a$ units, is $\dfrac{x^2}{a^2} + \dfrac{y^2}{b^2} = 1$ where $b^2 = a^2 - c^2$. (282)

10. **Equation of Ellipse:** The standard equation of an ellipse with center at $(0, 0)$, whose foci are at $(0, -c)$ and $(0, c)$, and the sum of the distances from the two foci is $2a$ units, is $\dfrac{y^2}{a^2} + \dfrac{x^2}{b^2} = 1$ where $b^2 = a^2 - c^2$. (282)

11. **Standard Equation of Ellipse with Center (h, k):** If the center is at (h, k) and the major axis is horizontal, the equation is $\dfrac{(x - h)^2}{a^2} + \dfrac{(y - k)^2}{b^2} = 1$. If the center is at (h, k) and the major axis is vertical, the equation is $\dfrac{(y - k)^2}{a^2} + \dfrac{(x - h)^2}{b^2} = 1$. (284)

12. **Definition of Hyperbola:** A hyperbola is the set of all points in the plane such that the absolute value of the difference of the distances from two given points in the plane, called the foci, is constant. (286)

13. **Equation of Hyperbola:** The standard equation of a hyperbola with center at $(0, 0)$ whose foci are at $(-c, 0)$ and $(c, 0)$ and with the absolute value of the difference between distances from the two foci $2a$ units, can be written as $\dfrac{x^2}{a^2} - \dfrac{y^2}{b^2} = 1$ where $c^2 = a^2 + b^2$. (287)

14. **Equation of Hyperbola:** The standard equation of a hyperbola with center at $(0, 0)$, whose foci are at $(0, -c)$ and $(0, c)$, and with the absolute value of the difference between distances from the two foci $2a$ units, can be written as $\dfrac{y^2}{a^2} - \dfrac{x^2}{b^2} = 1$ where $c^2 = a^2 + b^2$. (287)

15. **Standard Equation of Hyperbola with Center at (h, k):** If the center is at (h, k) and the transverse axis is horizontal, the equation is $\dfrac{(x - h)^2}{a^2} - \dfrac{(y - k)^2}{b^2} = 1$. If the center is at (h, k) and the transverse axis is vertical, the equation is $\dfrac{(y - k)^2}{a^2} - \dfrac{(x - h)^2}{b^2} = 1$. (288)

16. **Equation of Conic Sections:** The equation of a conic section can be written in the form $Ax^2 + Bxy + Cy^2 + Dx + Ey + F = 0$ where $A, B,$ and C are not all zero. (291)

17. If the graph of a system of equations is a conic section and a straight line, the system will have zero, one, or two solutions. (294)

18. If the graph of a system of equations is two conic sections, the system will have zero, one, two, three, or four solutions. (295)

Chapter Review

9–1 Use the distance formula to find the distance between each pair of points whose coordinates are given.

1. $(3, 6), (7, -8)$

2. $(-8, -7), (-2, -1)$

3. $(-2.4, 0.6), (1.7, 0.8)$

4. $(2\sqrt{3}, 4\sqrt{3}), (2\sqrt{3}, -\sqrt{3})$

Find the midpoint of each line segment having endpoints with the following coordinates.

5. $(5, 2), (-3, 1)$

6. $(17, -8), (-13, 1)$

7. $(0.2, 0.6), (0.3, 0.4)$

8. $(2, 2), (\sqrt{2}, \sqrt{2})$

9–2 Name the vertex, axis of symmetry, focus, directrix, and direction of opening of the parabola whose equation is given. Then find the length of the latus rectum and draw the graph.

9. $4y = x^2$

10. $y^2 = -8x$

11. $(y - 8)^2 = -4(x - 4)$

9–3 Find the center and radius of each circle whose equation is given. Then draw the graph.

12. $x^2 + y^2 = 25$

13. $(x - 3)^2 + (y + 7)^2 = 81$

14. $x^2 + y^2 - 8x + 10y = 1$

9–4 Find the center, foci, and lengths of the major axis and minor axis for each ellipse whose equation is given. Then draw the graph.

15. $\dfrac{x^2}{8} + \dfrac{y^2}{16} = 1$

16. $\dfrac{(x - 3)^2}{25} + \dfrac{(y + 1)^2}{4} = 1$

17. $9x^2 + 16y^2 = 144$

9–5 Find the vertices, foci, and slopes of the asymptotes for each hyperbola whose equation is given. Then draw the graph.

18. $\dfrac{x^2}{16} - \dfrac{y^2}{81} = 1$

19. $25(y + 6)^2 - 20(x - 1)^2 = 500$

20. $49x^2 - 16y^2 = 784$

9–6 State whether the graph of each of the following equations is a parabola, a circle, an ellipse, or a hyperbola.

21. $(x - 3)^2 = 4y - 4$

22. $3x^2 - 16 = -3y^2$

23. $4x^2 + 5y^2 = 20$

24. $3y^2 - 7x^2 = 21$

9–7 Graph each system of equations. Then state the solutions of each system.

25. $x + y = 1$
$x^2 + y^2 = 9$

26. $x + y = 4$
$y = x^2$

9–8 Find the solutions of each system of equations.

27. $(x - 2)^2 + y^2 = 16$
$y - x = 2$

28. $x^2 - y^2 = 16$
$y^2 - x^2 = 16$

Graph the solutions for each system of inequalities.

29. $x^2 + y^2 < 25$
$x + y > 5$

30. $y \geq x^2 + 4$
$x^2 + y^2 < 49$

Chapter Test

Find the distance between each pair of points whose coordinates are given.

1. $(2, 6), (-7, -2)$

2. $(-3, 5), (-11, -16)$

Find the midpoint of each line segment having endpoints with the following coordinates.

3. $(6, -4), (-8, 3)$

4. $(-5.5, -7.8), (1.3, -9.6)$

State whether the graph of each of the following equations is a parabola, a circle, an ellipse, or a hyperbola. Then draw the graph.

5. $2y = x^2$

6. $x^2 + y^2 + 4x = 6$

7. $9x^2 + 49y^2 = 441$

8. $x^2 - 4y^2 = 4$

9. $(x - 3)^2 = 4(y + 1)$

10. $x^2 + 4x + y^2 - 8y = 2$

11. $6x^2 + 6y^2 = 6$

12. $\dfrac{(x - 3)^2}{81} + \dfrac{(y + 4)^2}{16} = 1$

13. $13y^2 - 2x^2 = 5$

14. $y - x^2 = x + 3$

15. $x^2 + 5y^2 - 16 = 0$

16. $16x^2 - 4y^2 = 64$

Find the solutions of each system of equations.

17. $x^2 + y^2 = 25$
$x + y = -1$

18. $x^2 + y^2 = 16$
$\dfrac{x^2}{16} - \dfrac{y^2}{9} = 1$

Graph the solutions for each system of inequalities.

19. $x^2 + y^2 < 49$
$y < -x^2 + 2$

20. $x + y = 5$
$x^2 + y^2 \geq 49$

Find the equations for each conic section described below.

21. The parabola with vertex $(6, -1)$ and focus $(3, -1)$.

22. The circle that has a diameter with endpoints at $(-2, -3)$ and $(4, 5)$.

23. The ellipse with center $(3, 1)$. The major axis is 12 units long and parallel to the y-axis. The minor axis is $8\sqrt{2}$ units long.

24. The hyperbola with center $(2, -4)$. The horizontal transverse axis is 6 units long. The conjugate axis is 10 units long.

CHAPTER 10

Polynomial Functions

Suppose a certain gift box must have a volume of 4000 cm^3. The width of the box is half the length and the height is 15 cm less than the width. You can write a polynomial equation and apply the theorems in this chapter to find the dimensions of the gift box.

10-1　Polynomial Functions

The following expressions are examples of polynomials in one variable.

$$\frac{1}{3}x + 2$$
$$4a^2 + 8a - 7$$
$$19x^3 + 7x^2 + x - 75$$
$$6y^5 + 62y^3 - 12y + 13$$

> **A polynomial in one variable, x, is an expression of the form**
> $$a_0x^n + a_1x^{n-1} + \cdots + a_{n-2}x^2 + a_{n-1}x + a_n.$$
> **The coefficients $a_0, a_1, a_2, \ldots, a_n$ represent real numbers, and n represents a nonnegative integer.**

Definition of Polynomial in One Variable

Example

1　**Which of the following expressions are polynomials in one variable?**

a.　$7x^4 - 9x^2 + 2x + 1$

This is a polynomial in one variable, x.

b.　$6x^2y^3 - 8xy + 7z + 2$

This is not a polynomial in one variable. There are three variables.

c.　$x + \dfrac{1}{x} - 2$

This is *not* a polynomial in one variable.　$\dfrac{1}{x}$ cannot be written in the form x^n, where n is a nonnegative integer.

d.　$y^2 + 2y + 3$

This is a polynomial on one variable, y.

The degree of a polynomial in one variable is the greatest exponent of its variable.

5	has degree 0.
$3x + 2$	has degree 1.
$4x^2 + 8x + 7$	has degree 2.
$6x^5 + 62x^3 - 12x + 13$	has degree 5.
$a_0x^n + a_1x^{n-1} + \ldots + a_{n-1}x + a_n$	has degree n.

A polynomial of degree 0 is called a **constant.**
A polynomial of degree 1 is called a **linear expression.**
A polynomial of degree 2 is called a **quadratic expression.**
A polynomial of degree 3 is called a **cubic expression.**

Polynomial equations can be used to represent functions. In general, a **polynomial function** is in the form

$$p(x) = a_0 x^n + a_1 x^{n-1} + \cdots + a_{n-1}x + a_n.$$

The coefficients $a_0, a_1, a_2, \ldots, a_{n-1}, a_n$ represent real numbers, and n represents a nonnegative integer.

The equation $p(x) = 3x^2 - 8x + 7$ represents a polynomial function. If 2 is an element of the domain of the function, then $p(2)$ is the corresponding element of the range. To show that the value of $p(2)$ is 3, write $p(2) = 3$.

Examples

2 Find $p(2) + p(-2)$ if $p(x) = 3x^2 - 8x + 7$.

$$
\begin{aligned}
p(2) + p(-2) &= [3(2)^2 - 8(2) + 7] + [3(-2)^2 - 8(-2) + 7] \\
&= \qquad 3 \qquad + \qquad 35 \\
&= \qquad 38
\end{aligned}
$$

3 Find $p(m + 2)$ if $p(x) = 3x - 8x^2 + x^3$.

$$
\begin{aligned}
p(m + 2) &= 3(m + 2) - 8(m + 2)^2 + (m + 2)^3 \\
&= 3m + 6 - 8m^2 - 32m - 32 + m^3 + 6m^2 + 12m + 8 \\
&= m^3 - 2m^2 - 17m - 18
\end{aligned}
$$

4 Find $3\,[p(x)] + 2[\,p(x - 1)]$ if $p(x) = x^3 - 3x^2 + 3x + 1$.

$$
\begin{aligned}
&3[p(x)] + 2[p(x - 1)] \\
&= 3[x^3 - 3x^2 + 3x + 1] + 2[(x - 1)^3 - 3(x - 1)^2 + 3(x - 1) + 1] \\
&= [3x^3 - 9x^2 + 9x + 3] + [2x^3 - 6x^2 + 6x - 2 - 6x^2 + 12x - 6 + 6x - 6 + 2] \\
&= 5x^3 - 21x^2 + 33x - 9
\end{aligned}
$$

Exploratory Exercises

Which of the following expressions are polynomials in one variable?

1. $8x + y + 1$

2. $3x - 2$

3. $xy\sqrt{2} + 3$

4. $x^2 + 8x + 7$

5. $\dfrac{9}{x} + x + 3$

6. $5 + \sqrt{x} + 8y$

7. $x^3 + 5x^2 + x\sqrt{3} + 2$

8. $x^3 + 9x^2 + 8x + 1$

9. $9x^2 + ix^2 + 8x + 3i$

10. $(6 + 2i)x^2 + 3ix + 7i^2$

11. $5x^4 - 2$

12. $9m^2 + \dfrac{3i}{m} + 7$

Written Exercises

Find $p(1)$ for each of the following.

1. $p(x) = 3x + 1$

2. $p(x) = 4x^2 + 3x - 3$

3. $p(x) = -2x^3 + 4x - 1$

4. $p(x) = 5x^4 - 8x^3$

5. $p(x) = 3x - 8x^2 + x^3$

6. $p(x) = 2x^4 - 3x^3 + 8$

7. $p(x) = \dfrac{5}{2}x^3 - 8$

8. $p(x) = 7x^3 + \dfrac{7}{3}x + 1$

9. $p(x) = \dfrac{x^2}{3} + 2x + 4$

Find $f(2)$ for each of the following.

10. $f(x) = 4x - 3$

11. $f(x) = x^2 - 7x + 5$

12. $f(x) = -3x^3 + 2$

13. $f(x) = -\dfrac{x^4}{4} - 2$

14. $f(x) = x^2 - 4x$

15. $f(x) = 5x^2 + 7x - 6$

16. $f(x) = 6x^3 + 11x^2 + 4x$

17. $f(x) = 9x - 6x^2 + x^3$

18. $f(x) = x^5 - x^3$

Find $g(-3)$ for each of the following.

19. $g(x) = 4 - 3x$

20. $g(x) = 2x + x^2$

21. $g(x) = 15x^2 - 4x - 3$

22. $g(x) = (x - 3)^2$

23. $g(x) = -\dfrac{x^3}{3} + 2x^2 - \dfrac{8}{3}x$

24. $g(x) = 25 - \dfrac{x^3}{6}$

25. $g(x) = x^2 + 2x - 15$

26. $2g(x) = 6x^3 - 20x + 18$

27. $3g(x) = 3x^4 + 7x$

Find $f(x + h)$ for each of the following.

28. $f(x) = x$

29. $f(x) = 5x - 10$

30. $f(x) = 6x^2$

31. $f(x) = x^2 - 7x + 4$

32. $f(x) = x^2 - \dfrac{2}{5}x$

33. $f(x) = x^3 + 4x$

34. $f(x) = \dfrac{4}{3}x^3 - 1$

35. $f(x) = x^3 - 4x^2$

36. $f(x) = 2x^3 - x^2 + 4$

Find $3[p(x - 1)]$ for each of the following.

37. $p(x) = 3x + 5$

38. $p(x) = x^2 - 4$

39. $p(x) = x^3$

40. $p(x) = x^2 - 2x + 3$

41. $p(x) = \dfrac{5}{3}x^2 - \dfrac{5}{6}$

42. $p(x) = \dfrac{x^3}{4} + \dfrac{x^2}{2} - x - 2$

Find $2[f(x)] - 3[f(x + 1)]$ for each of the following.

43. $f(x) = 5x - 3$

44. $f(x) = x^2 - 4$

45. $f(x) = x^2 - 7x + 16$

46. $f(x) = \dfrac{5}{2}x^3 + 1$

47. $f(x) = \dfrac{4}{5}x^3 + \dfrac{x^2}{2} - 2$

48. $f(x) = (x - 2)^3$

Challenge

$$f(x) = \dfrac{x^2 - 4}{2x + 4} \qquad g(x) = \dfrac{x^2 + 4x + 4}{3x - 6}$$

$$h(x) = \dfrac{x^3 - 1}{x + 1} \qquad j(x) = \dfrac{x^2 + 2x + 1}{x^2 + x + 1}$$

$$k(x) = \dfrac{x^2 + 2x - 3}{x + 1}$$

Use the functions above to simplify each of the following.

49. $f(x) \cdot g(x)$

50. $\dfrac{f(x)}{g(x)}$

51. $\dfrac{g(x)}{f(x)}$

52. $\dfrac{h(x) \cdot j(x)}{k(x)}$

53. $\dfrac{h(x)}{j(x)} \cdot k(x)$

54. $\dfrac{h(x)}{j(x) \cdot k(x)}$

mini-review

1. Simplify $4i + 3i$.

2. Find the value of c that makes $x^2 - 8x + c$ a perfect square.

3. Graph $f(x) = \dfrac{1}{3}x^2$.

4. Graph $y > x^2 + 5x - 14$.

5. Graph this system of equations.

$$y = -x^2$$
$$y = -x - 2$$

10-2 The Remainder and Factor Theorems

You can divide polynomials by using either long division or synthetic division.

Example 1

Divide $x^3 + 4x^2 + 3x - 2$ by $x - 3$.

Long Division

$$
\begin{array}{r}
x^2 + 7x + 24 \\
x - 3)\overline{x^3 + 4x^2 + 3x - 2} \\
\underline{x^3 - 3x^2} \\
7x^2 + 3x \\
\underline{7x^2 - 21x} \\
24x - 2 \\
\underline{24x - 72} \\
70
\end{array}
$$

Synthetic Division

$$
\begin{array}{r|rrrr}
3 & 1 & 4 & 3 & -2 \\
& & 3 & 21 & 72 \\
\hline
& 1 & 7 & 24 & 70
\end{array}
$$

The numbers 1, 7, and 24 are the coefficients of the quotient $x^2 + 7x + 24$. The remainder is 70.

The quotient is $x^2 + 7x + 24$ with a remainder of 70.

Check: Multiply $x^2 + 7x + 24$ by $x - 3$ and then add 70.

$$
\underset{dividend}{x^3 + 4x^2 + 3x - 2} = \underset{quotient \cdot divisor}{(x^2 + 7x + 24)(x - 3)} + \underset{remainder}{70}
$$

Consider $f(x) = x^3 + 4x^2 + 3x - 2$. The value of $f(3)$ is 70. As shown in the previous example when $f(x)$ is divided by $x - 3$, the remainder is 70. This illustrates the remainder theorem.

> If a polynomial $f(x)$ is divided by $x - a$, the remainder is a constant, $f(a)$, and
>
> $$dividend = quotient \cdot divisor + remainder$$
> $$f(x) = q(x) \cdot (x - a) + f(a)$$
>
> where $q(x)$ is a polynomial with degree one less than the degree of $f(x)$.

The Remainder Theorem

Example 2

Let $f(x) = x^4 + 3x^2 + 4x - 1$. Show that $f(1)$ is the remainder when $f(x)$ is divided by $x - 1$.

$$
\begin{array}{r|rrrrr}
1 & 1 & 0 & 3 & 4 & -1 \\
& & 1 & 1 & 4 & 8 \\
\hline
& 1 & 1 & 4 & 8 & 7
\end{array}
$$

Use synthetic division.

The quotient is $x^3 + x^2 + 4x + 8$ with a remainder of 7.

Now evaluate $f(1)$.

$f(1) = (1)^4 + 3(1)^2 + 4(1) - 1$

$\quad = 7$ The result is the same as the remainder.

The Remainder Theorem and synthetic division can be used to find the value of a function. This process, called *synthetic substitution,* is convenient especially when large powers are involved.

For any polynomial $f(x)$, $f(a)$ is always the same as the remainder when dividing by $(x - a)$.

Example

3 If $f(x) = x^4 - 2x^3 - x^2 - 15x + 2$, find $f(12)$.

The Remainder Theorem says that $f(12)$ is the remainder when $f(x)$ is divided by $x - 12$.

$$
\begin{array}{r|rrrrr}
12 & 1 & -2 & -1 & -15 & 2 \\
   &   & 12 & 120 & 1428 & 16{,}956 \\
\hline
   & 1 & 10 & 119 & 1413 & 16{,}958
\end{array}
$$
$\qquad f(12) = 16{,}958$

Check by using direct substitution.
$$f(12) = 12^4 - 2(12)^3 - 12^2 - 15(12) + 2$$
$$= 20{,}736 - 3456 - 144 - 180 + 2 \text{ or } 16{,}958$$

Consider the polynomial defined by $f(x) = x^3 + 7x^2 + 2x - 40$. If $f(x)$ is divided by $x - 2$, the remainder is zero.

$$
\begin{array}{r|rrrr}
2 & 1 & 7 & 2 & -40 \\
  &   & 2 & 18 & 40 \\
\hline
  & 1 & 9 & 20 & 0
\end{array}
$$
$\qquad f(2) = (2)^3 + 7(2)^2 + 2(2) - 40 \text{ or } 0$

$$
\underset{dividend}{} \quad = \quad \underset{quotient \cdot divisor}{} \quad + \underset{remainder}{}
$$
$$x^3 + 7x^2 + 2x - 40 = (x^2 + 9x + 20)(x - 2) + \quad 0$$
$$= (x^2 + 9x + 20)(x - 2)$$

In other words, $x - 2$ is a factor of $x^3 + 7x^2 + 2x - 40$. This example illustrates the factor theorem, a special case of the remainder theorem.

If the divisor is a factor of a polynomial, then the remainder upon division is zero.

> **The binomial $x - a$ is a factor of the polynomial $f(x)$ if and only if $f(a) = 0$.**

The Factor Theorem

The Factor Theorem can be used to identify the factors of a polynomial.

Example

4 Is $x - 4$ a factor of $x^4 + x^3 - 13x^2 - 25x - 12$?

Let $f(x) = x^4 + x^3 - 13x^2 - 25x - 12$.
If $f(4) = 0$, then $x - 4$ is a factor.
$$f(4) = (4)^4 + (4)^3 - 13(4)^2 - 25(4) - 12 \qquad \text{\textit{a is 4.}}$$
$$= 256 + 64 - 208 - 100 - 12 \text{ or } 0$$

Since $f(4) = 0$, the binomial $x - 4$ is a factor of $f(x)$.

Example

5 **Is $y + 5$ a factor of $3y^5 + y^3 - 2y^2 - 6y + 550$?**

Use synthetic division.

$$
\begin{array}{r|rrrrrr}
-5 & 3 & 0 & 1 & -2 & -6 & 550 \\
   &   & -15 & 75 & -380 & 1910 & -9520 \\
\hline
   & 3 & -15 & 76 & -382 & 1904 & -8970 \\
\end{array}
$$

Since the remainder is not 0, $y + 5$ is *not* a factor.

When a polynomial is divided by one of its factors, the result is called a **depressed polynomial**. The depressed polynomial can sometimes be factored to find the remaining factors. Study how this technique is used in the following example.

Example

6 **Show that $x + 1$ is a factor of $x^3 - x^2 - 10x - 8$. Then find the remaining factors.**

$$
\begin{array}{r|rrrr}
-1 & 1 & -1 & -10 & -8 \\
   &   & -1 & 2 & 8 \\
\hline
   & 1 & -2 & -8 & 0 \\
\end{array}
$$ *The remainder of 0 shows that $x + 1$ is a factor of $x^3 - x^2 - 10x - 8$.*

Thus, $x^3 - x^2 - 10x - 8 = (x^2 - 2x - 8)(x + 1)$.
The quotient, $x^2 - 2x - 8$, is called the depressed polynomial.

$$x^2 - 2x - 8 = (x - 4)(x + 2) \quad \text{Factor } x^2 - 2x - 8.$$

Thus, $x^3 - x^2 - 10x - 8 = (x - 4)(x + 2)(x + 1)$.

Exploratory Exercises

Divide using synthetic division. Write your answer in the form
dividend = quotient · divisor + remainder.

1. $(x^2 - 3x + 1) \div (x - 2)$

2. $(x^3 - 4x^2 + 2x - 6) \div (x - 4)$

3. $(x^3 - 8x^2 + 2x - 1) \div (x + 1)$

4. $(x^2 + 8x - 1) \div (x + 3)$

5. $(x^5 + x^4 + 2x - 1) \div (x - 2)$

6. $(2x^4 - x^2 + 1) \div (x + 1)$

7. $(x^5 + 32) \div (x + 2)$

8. $(x^5 - 3x^2 - 20) \div (x - 2)$

Written Exercises

Divide. Write your answer in the form dividend = quotient · divisor + remainder.

1. $(2x^3 + 8x^2 - 3x - 1) \div (x - 2)$

2. $(x^3 - 64) \div (x - 4)$

3. $(x^4 - 16) \div (x - 2)$

4. $(x^3 + 27) \div (x + 3)$

5. $(4x^4 + 3x^3 - 2x^2 + x + 1) \div (x - 1)$

6. $(6x^3 + 9x^2 - 6x + 2) \div (x + 2)$

7. $(3x^3 + 2x^2 - 4x - 1) \div \left(x + \dfrac{1}{2}\right)$

8. $(x^4 - 2x^3 + 4x^2 + 6x - 8) \div \left(x - \dfrac{1}{2}\right)$

Use synthetic substitution to find $f(3)$ and $f(-2)$ for each of the following.

9. $f(x) = x^3 + 2x^2 - 3x + 1$

10. $f(x) = 2x^2 - 8x + 6$

11. $f(x) = x^3 - 8x^2 - 2x + 5$

12. $f(x) = x^3 + 8x + 1$

13. $f(x) = 3x^4 + 8x^2 - 1$

14. $f(x) = x^4 + x^3 + x^2 + x + 1$

15. $f(x) = x^5 + 8x^3 + 2$

16. $f(x) = 2x^3 + 2x^2 - 2x - 2$

Given a polynomial and one of its factors, find the remaining factors of the polynomial. (Some factors may not be binomials.)

17. $x^3 + x^2 - 4x - 4; x + 1$

18. $x^3 - 6x^2 + 11x - 6; x - 2$

19. $x^3 + 2x^2 - x - 2; x - 1$

20. $2x^3 + 17x^2 + 23x - 42; x + 6$

21. $x^3 - 3x + 2; x - 1$

22. $x^3 - x^2 - 5x - 3; x - 3$

23. $x^4 + 2x^3 - 8x - 16; x + 2$

24. $8x^4 + 32x^3 + x + 4; x + 4$

25. $x^5 + x^4 - x - 1; x + 1$

26. $16x^5 - 32x^4 - 81x + 162; x - 2$

Find values for k so that each remainder is 3.

27. $(x^2 + 8x + k) \div (x - 2)$

28. $(x^2 + kx + 3) \div (x - 1)$

29. $(x^3 + 8x^2 + kx + 4) \div (x + 2)$

30. $(x^3 + 4x^2 + kx + 1) \div (x + 1)$

31. $(x^3 + 3x^2 - 38x - 7) \div (x - k)$

32. $(x^3 + 5x^2 + 6x + 11) \div (x + k)$

⊞ *Using Calculators* _____ Synthetic Substitution

Recall that the calculator may be used to perform synthetic division. The same process is used for synthetic substitution.

Example: Find $p(9)$ if $p(x) = 2x^3 + 3x^2 - x - 79$.

The value of $p(9)$ is the remainder when $2x^3 + 3x^2 - x - 79$ is divided by $x - 9$.

$$
\begin{array}{r|rrrr}
9 & 2 & 3 & -1 & -79 \\
  &   & 18 & 189 & 1692 \\
\hline
  & 2 & 21 & 188 & \boxed{1613}
\end{array}
$$

ENTER: 2 $\times$ 9 $=$ $+$ 3 $=$ $\times$ 9 $=$ $+$ 1 $+/-$ $=$

DISPLAY: 2   9 18   3 21   9 189   1 −1 188

ENTER: $\times$ 9 $=$ $+$ 79 $+/-$ $=$

DISPLAY: 9 1692   79 −79 1613   The value of $p(9)$ is 1613.

Exercises If $g(x) = 3x^3 - 2x^2 + x - 1$, find each of the following using the calculator and synthetic substitution.

1. $g(-2)$

2. $g(5)$

3. $g(4.6)$

4. $g(-11.9)$

5. $g(\sqrt{41})$

Find $h(17) - h(16.5)$ for each of the following using the calculator and synthetic substitution.

6. $h(x) = x^4 - x^3 + x^2 - x + 1$

7. $h(x) = 7x^3 + \frac{7}{3}x + 1$

8. $h(x) = 10x^5 - x^3 - 93x$

Let $f(x) = a_0x^n + a_1 x^{n-1} + \cdots + a_{n-1}x + a_n$ represent a polynomial with integer coefficients and n be a non-negative integer. If $\frac{p}{q}$ is a rational number in simplest form and is a zero of $y = f(x)$, then p is a factor of a_n and q is a factor of a_0.

Rational Zero Theorem

The Rational Zero Theorem can be proven as follows.
Assume $\frac{p}{q}$ is a zero and p and q have no common factors.

$$a_0\frac{p^n}{q^n} + a_1\frac{p^{n-1}}{q^{n-1}} + \cdots + a_{n-1}\frac{p}{q} + a_n = 0 \qquad \textit{Substitute } \frac{p}{q} \textit{ for x.}$$

$$a_0p^n + a_1p^{n-1}q + \cdots + a_{n-1}pq^{n-1} + a_nq^n = 0 \qquad \textit{Multiply both sides by } q^n.$$

$$a_0p^n + a_1p^{n-1}q + \cdots + a_{n-1}pq^{n-1} = -a_nq^n \qquad \textit{Subtract } a_nq^n \textit{ from both sides.}$$

$$p(a_0p^{n-1} + a_1p^{n-2}q + \cdots + a_{n-1}q^{n-1}) = -a_nq^n \qquad \textit{Factor p from the terms on the left side.}$$

Since p is a factor of the left side, it is also a factor of the right side. But p and q have no common factors, so p is a factor of a_n rather than q^n. Using a similar approach but factoring q from the last n terms, you can prove that q is a factor of a_0. Therefore p is a factor of a_n and q is a factor of a_0.

Example

2 **Find all rational zeros of $f(x) = 2x^3 + 3x^2 - 8x + 3$.**

According to the Rational Zero Theorem, if $\frac{p}{q}$ is a zero of the function, then p is a factor of 3 and q is a factor of 2.

$$p \text{ is } \pm 1, \pm 3. \qquad q \text{ is } \pm 1, \pm 2.$$

The possible rational zeros are ± 1, ± 3, $\pm\frac{1}{2}$, and $\pm\frac{3}{2}$. You can test each possible zero using substitution or synthetic division.

$\frac{p}{q}$	2	3	−8	3	
1	2	5	−3	0	*1 is a zero.*
−1	2	1	−9	12	
3	2	9	19	60	
−3	2	−3	1	0	*−3 is a zero.*
$\frac{1}{2}$	2	4	−6	0	*$\frac{1}{2}$ is a zero.*
$-\frac{1}{2}$	2	2	−9	$7\frac{1}{2}$	
$\frac{3}{2}$	2	6	1	$4\frac{1}{2}$	
$-\frac{3}{2}$	2	0	−8	15	

The rational zeros of $f(x) = 2x^3 + 3x^2 - 8x + 3$ are 1, −3, and $\frac{1}{2}$.

It is not always necessary to complete the entire chart. Once a zero is found, the depressed polynomial may be factored.

Examples

3 **Find all zeros of $f(x) = 6x^3 + 4x^2 - 14x + 4$.**

According to the Rational Zero Theorem, if $\frac{p}{q}$ is a zero of the function, then p is a factor of 4 and q is a factor of 6.

p is ± 1, ± 2, or ± 4. q is ± 1, ± 2, ± 3, or ± 6.

$\frac{p}{q}$	6	4	-14	4
1	6	10	-4	0

1 is a zero.

The depressed polynomial is $6x^2 + 10x - 4$.
$$6x^2 + 10x - 4 = 2(3x^2 + 5x - 2)$$
$$= 2(3x - 1)(x + 2)$$

The quotient of the synthetic division provides the coefficients of the depressed polynomial.

Solve $2(3x - 1)(x + 2) = 0$.
$3x - 1 = 0$ or $x + 2 = 0$
$\quad x = \frac{1}{3}$ or $\quad x = -2$

The zeros are 1, $\frac{1}{3}$, and -2.

4 **Find all zeros of $f(x) = x^4 + x^3 - 13x^2 - 25x - 12$.**

p is ± 1, ± 2, ± 3, ± 4, ± 6, ± 12. q is ± 1.

$\frac{p}{q}$	1	1	-13	-25	-12
1	1	2	-11	-36	-48
-1	1	0	-13	-12	0

-1 is a zero.

The depressed polynomial is $x^3 - 13x - 12$.

p is ± 1, ± 2, ± 3, ± 4, ± 6, ± 12. q is ± 1.

$\frac{p}{q}$	1	0	13	-12
1	1	1	-12	-24
-1	1	-1	-12	0

-1 is zero.

The depressed polynomial is $x^2 - x - 12$.
$$x^2 - x - 12 = (x - 4)(x + 3)$$

This depressed polynomial is of degree two. Factor the polynomial, if possible. If not, use the quadratic formula to find the two remaining zeros.

Solve $(x - 4)(x + 3) = 0$.
$x - 4 = 0$ or $x + 3 = 0$
$\quad x = 4$ or $\quad x = -3$

The zeros are -1, -1, 4, and -3.

Exploratory Exercises

State all *possible* rational zeros for each function.

1. $f(x) = x^4 + x^2 - 2$
2. $f(x) = x^3 + 2x^2 - 3x + 5$
3. $f(x) = x^2 - 8x + 6$
4. $f(x) = x^3 + 5x^2 - 3$
5. $f(x) = x^3 - 2x^2 + 3x - 8$
6. $f(x) = x^3 - 4x + 10$
7. $f(x) = x^3 + 8x^2 - 3x + 1$
8. $f(x) = x^3 - 2x^2 - 5x - 9$
9. $f(x) = x^3 - 8x^2 - 11x + 20$
10. $f(x) = x^4 + 2x + 15$
11. $f(x) = 6x^4 + 35x^3 - x^2 - 7x - 1$
12. $f(x) = 6x^3 + 4x^2 - 14x - 2$
13. $f(x) = 3x^4 - 5x^2 + 4$
14. $f(x) = 2x^3 + x^2 + 5x - 3$

Find all rational zeros for each function.

15. $f(x) = (x - 3)(x + 5)(2x + 5)$
16. $f(x) = (x - 8)(7x - 5)(x + 3)$
17. $f(x) = (x - 3)^2(x + 2)(2x - 1)(3x - 2)$
18. $f(x) = (x + 5)^3(4x - 1)^2(5x + 3)$
19. $f(x) = 2(3x - 2)(x - 5)(x + 1)$
20. $f(x) = (x + 1)(2x + 3)(x - 5)$

Written Exercises

Find all rational zeros for each function.

1. $f(x) = x^3 - x^2 - 34x - 56$
2. $f(x) = x^3 + x^2 - 80x - 300$
3. $f(x) = 2x^3 - 11x^2 + 12x + 9$
4. $f(x) = x^3 - 3x - 2$
5. $f(x) = x^3 - 3x^2 + x - 3$
6. $f(x) = x^3 - 3x^2 - 53x - 9$
7. $f(x) = x^4 + 10x^3 + 33x^2 + 38x + 8$
8. $f(x) = x^4 + x^3 - 9x^2 - 17x - 8$
9. $f(x) = x^4 + x^2 - 2$
10. $f(x) = x^4 - 6x^3 - 3x^2 - 24x - 28$
11. $f(x) = 8x^2 - 6x + 1$
12. $f(x) = 2x^2 - 7x + 3$
13. $f(x) = x^3 - 2x^2 - 13x - 10$
14. $f(x) = x^3 + 4x^2 - 3x - 18$
15. $f(x) = x^3 - x^2 - 40x + 12$
16. $f(x) = x^4 - 13x^2 + 36$
17. $f(x) = 12x^4 + 4x^3 - 3x^2 - x$
18. $f(x) = 48x^4 - 52x^3 + 13x - 3$
19. $f(x) = x^4 - 6x^2 + 8$
20. $f(x) = 2x^5 - x^4 - 2x + 1$

Solve each problem.

21. A box is to have a volume of 72 m³. The width is 2 m longer than the height, and the length is 7 m longer than the height. Find the dimensions of the box.

22. A box is to have a volume of 144 cm³. The width is 3 cm longer than the height, and the length is 2 cm longer than the width. Find the dimensions of the box.

mini-review

1. Solve $x^2 - 9x + 21 = 0$ using the quadratic formula.
2. Find the quadratic equation that has roots $\sqrt{3}$ and $2\sqrt{3}$.
3. Write $f(x) = \frac{1}{6}(6x + 12)^2 + 7$ in quadratic form.
4. Draw the graph of $f(x) = 4x^2 + 12x + 9$. Then name the vertex and axis of symmetry.
5. Find the center and radius for the graph of $x^2 + y^2 + 8x - 6y = 0$.

10-4 Nature of Roots

Some polynomial equations, such as $4x^2 - 1 = 0$, have no integral roots. Some, such as $x^2 - 2 = 0$, have no rational roots. Some, such as $x^2 + 1 = 0$, have no real roots. All polynomial equations have *at least one* root in the set of complex numbers. This is stated in the Fundamental Theorem of Algebra.

> **Every polynomial equation with degree greater than zero has at least one root in the set of complex numbers.**

The Fundamental Theorem of Algebra

Another interesting theorem comes from The Fundamental Theorem of Algebra. It states that a polynomial equation has n complex roots if its polynomial has degree n.

For example, $x^3 + 5x^2 + 4x + 20 = 0$ has three roots in the set of complex numbers, $2i$, $-2i$, and -5. The equation $x^3 + 7x^2 + 15x + 9 = 0$ has three roots since -3 is a double root.

Karl Friedrich Gauss (1777–1855) is credited with the first proof of the Fundamental Theorem of Algebra.

$$x^3 + 5x^2 + 4x + 20 = 0 \qquad\qquad x^3 + 7x^2 + 15x + 9 = 0$$
$$(x - 2i)(x + 2i)(x + 5) = 0 \qquad\qquad (x + 1)(x + 3)^2 = 0$$

$x - 2i = 0$ or $x + 2i = 0$ or $x + 5 = 0$ $\qquad$ $x + 1 = 0$ or $(x + 3)^2 = 0$
$\quad x = 2i \qquad\quad x = -2i \qquad\quad x = -5 \qquad\qquad x = -1 \qquad\qquad x = -3$

You may have noticed that imaginary roots of quadratic equations come in pairs. In general, if an imaginary number is a root of a polynomial equation, then its conjugate is also a root.

Remember, the coefficients of a polynomial equation are real numbers.

> **Suppose a and b are real numbers with $b \neq 0$. Then, if $a + bi$ is a root of a polynomial equation, $a - bi$ is also a root of the equation.**

Complex Conjugates Theorem

Example

1 **Find all zeros of $f(x) = x^3 - 7x^2 + 17x - 15$ if $2 - i$ is one root of $f(x) = 0$.**

Since $2 - i$ is a root, $2 + i$ also is a root. Thus, both $x - (2 - i)$ and $x - (2 + i)$ are factors of the polynomial.

$$f(x) = [x - (2 - i)][x - (2 + i)][\ ?\ ]$$
$$= (x^2 - 4x + 5)(\ ?\ )$$

Use division to find the other factor.
$$f(x) = (x^2 - 4x + 5)(x - 3)$$
Since $x - 3$ is a factor, 3 is a root.

The polynomial has degree 3, so it has 3 zeros.

The zeros are $2 - i$, $2 + i$, and 3.

$$
\begin{array}{r}
x - 3 \\
x^2 - 4x + 5\overline{)x^3 - 7x^2 + 17x - 15} \\
\underline{x^3 - 4x^2 + 5x} \\
-3x^2 + 12x - 15 \\
\underline{-3x^2 + 12x - 15} \\
0
\end{array}
$$

More discoveries about the zeros of a polynomial function were made by Rene Descartes (1596–1650), a French mathematician.

> Suppose $p(x)$ is a polynomial whose terms are arranged in descending powers of the variable. The number of positive real zeros of $y = p(x)$ is the same as the number of changes in sign of the coefficients of the terms, or is less than this by an even number. The number of negative real zeros is the same as the number of changes in sign of $p(-x)$, or is less than this by an even number.

Descartes' Rule of Signs

Zero coefficients are ignored.

Example

2 State the number of positive and negative real zeros for $p(x) = 2x^4 - x^3 + 5x^2 + 3x - 9$.

The signs for $p(x)$, in order, are as follows.

$$2x^4 - x^3 + 5x^2 + 3x - 9$$

There are 3 sign changes, so there are 3 or 1 positive real zeros.

Next, evaluate the polynomial for $-x$.

$$p(-x) = 2(-x)^4 - (-x)^3 + 5(-x)^2 + 3(-x) - 9$$
$$= 2x^4 + x^3 + 5x^2 - 3x - 9$$

The signs for $p(-x)$, in order, are as follows.

$$2x^4 + x^3 + 5x^2 - 3x - 9$$

There is 1 sign change, so there is 1 negative real zero.

The polynomial equation in the previous example has degree 4. Thus, it has four zeros. The possibilities for the nature of these solutions can be given in a table.

Number of Positive Real Zeros	Number of Negative Real Zeros	Number of Imaginary Zeros
3	1	0
1	1	2

$3 + 1 + 0 = 4$
$1 + 1 + 2 = 4$

Example

3 Write the simplest polynomial equation with integral coefficients whose roots are 4 and $2 - 3i$.

If $2 - 3i$ is a root, then $2 + 3i$ is also a root.   *Why?*

$$[x - (2 - 3i)][x - (2 + 3i)](x - 4) = [(x - 2) + 3i][(x - 2) - 3i](x - 4)$$
$$= [(x - 2)^2 - 9i^2](x - 4)$$
$$= (x^2 - 4x + 13)(x - 4)$$
$$= x^3 - 8x^2 + 29x - 52$$

Exploratory Exercises

State the number of positive real zeros and negative real zeros for each function.

1. $f(x) = x^4 - 2x^3 + x^2 - 1$
2. $f(x) = 3x^5 + 7x^2 - 8x + 1$
3. $f(x) = 4x^4 - 3x^3 + 2x^2 - x + 1$
4. $f(x) = x^7 - x^3 + 2x - 1$
5. $f(x) = x^4 - x^3 + x^2 + x + 1$
6. $f(x) = -x^4 - x^2 - x - 1$
7. $f(x) = x^6 - 2x^5 + 3x^4 - 8x^3 + 7x^2 - 1$
8. $f(x) = x^3 + x^2 + x + 1$
9. $f(x) = x^4 + x^3 - 7x - 1$
10. $f(x) = x^{10} - 1$

Written Exercises

Copy and complete the chart.

	Function	No. Positive Real Zeros	No. Negative Real Zeros	No. Imaginary Zeros
	$f(x) = -x^3 + x^2 - x + 1$	3 or 1	0	0 or 2
1.	$f(x) = 3x^4 + 2x^3 - 3x^2 - 4x + 1$			
2.	$f(x) = 3x^4 - 8x + 1$			
3.	$f(x) = -7x^3 - 6x + 1$			
4.	$f(x) = x^{10} - x^8 + x^6 - x^4 + x^2 - 1$			
5.	$f(x) = x^5 - x^3 - x + 1$			
6.	$f(x) = 3x^4 - x^2 + x - 1$			
7.	$f(x) = 4x^5 - x^2 + 1$			
8.	$f(x) = x^3 + 1$			
9.	$f(x) = x^{14} + x^{10} - x^9 + x - 1$			
10.	$f(x) = x^4 + x^3 + 2x^2 - 3x - 1$			

11. Let $f(x) = x^3 - 10x^2 + 34x - 40$.
    Find all zeros if $3 + i$ is one solution to $x^3 - 10x^2 + 34x - 40 = 0$.

12. Let $f(x) = x^3 - 3x^2 + 9x + 13$.
    Find all zeros if $2 - 3i$ is one solution to $x^3 - 3x^2 + 9x + 13 = 0$.

13. Let $f(x) = x^3 + 2x^2 - 3x + 20$.
    Find all zeros if $1 + 2i$ is one solution to $x^3 + 2x^2 - 3x + 20 = 0$.

14. Let $f(x) = x^4 - 6x^3 + 12x^2 + 6x - 13$.
    Find all zeros if $3 - 2i$ is one solution to $x^4 - 6x^3 + 12x^2 + 6x - 13 = 0$.

15. Let $f(x) = x^3 + 6x^2 + 21x + 26$.
    Find all zeros if -2 is one solution to $x^3 + 6x^2 + 21x + 26 = 0$.

16. Let $f(x) = 2x^3 - x^2 + 28x + 51$.
    Find all zeros if $-\frac{3}{2}$ is one solution to $2x^3 - x^2 + 28x + 51 = 0$.

Write the simplest polynomial equation that has the given roots. Express the equation using integral coefficients.

17. $2, 1 - i, 1 + i$
18. $-1, 1, 2 + i, 2 - i$
19. $3, 2i$
20. $-2, 2 + 3i$
21. $-2 - i, 1 + 3i$
22. $3, 3, -2i$

23. Explain why $4x^3 + 2x^2 + 1 = 0$ must have two complex roots.

The function $f(x) = x^3 - 7x + 6$ has real zeros 1, 2, and -3. An **upper bound** for the zeros of a function is a number for which no real zero *greater* than that number exists. For example 2, 3, and 10.9 are upper bounds for the zeros of f. A **lower bound** for the zeros of a function is a number for which no real zero *less* than that number exists. Some lower bounds for the zeros of f are -3, -17, and -125.4.

Upper and lower bounds may be found by using synthetic division and applying the theorem below.

> Suppose c is a positive number and $P(x)$ is divided by $x - c$ (using synthetic division). If the resulting quotient and remainder have no change in sign, then $P(x)$ has no real zeros greater than c. Thus, c is an upper bound of the zeros of $P(x)$.

Notice that there can be more than one upper bound. Therefore, it is helpful to find the least integral upper bound of the zeros of a function. The least positive integral upper bound of the zeros of $f(x) = x^3 - 7x + 6$ is 2.

Example: Find the least positive integral upper bound of the zeros of the function $f(x) = x^4 - 3x^3 - 2x^2 + 3x - 5$ using synthetic division.

Divide by increasing values of c until the depressed polynomial and the remainder have no change in sign.

c	1	-3	-2	3	-5
1	1	-2	-4	-1	-6
2	1	-1	-4	-5	-15
3	1	0	-2	-3	-14
4	1	1	2	11	39

This row has no changes in sign.

Thus, 4 is the least positive integral upper bound.
Any value greater than 4 is also an upper bound.

A lower bound of the zeros of $f(x)$ can be found by using synthetic division.

> Suppose c is a nonpositive number and $P(x)$ is divided by $x - c$. If the resulting quotient and remainder have alternating signs, then c is a lower bound of $P(x)$.

Divide by decreasing values of c until the depressed polynomial and the remainder have alternating signs.

Exercises

Find the least positive integral upper bound and the greatest negative integral lower bound of the zeros of each function using synthetic division.

1. $f(x) = x^3 + 3x^2 - 5x - 10$

2. $f(x) = x^4 - 8x + 2$

3. $f(x) = 3x^3 - 2x^2 + 5x - 1$

4. $f(x) = x^5 + 5x^4 - 3x^3 + 20x^2 - 15$

5. $f(x) = x^3 - 4x + 6$

6. $f(x) = 2x^3 - 4x^2 - 3$

10-5 Approximating Zeros

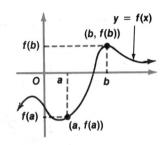

The graph of a continuous curve drawn from a lower point to a higher point must *cross* every horizontal line in between. Thus, if the graph of a polynomial function is in part below the x-axis and in part above the x-axis, it must also *cross* the x-axis. You can use the **location principle** to approximate zeros of a polynomial function.

> Let $y = f(x)$ represent a polynomial function. And suppose a and b are two numbers with $f(a)$ negative and $f(b)$ positive. Then the function has at least one real zero between a and b.

The Location Principle

Example

1 **Approximate to the nearest tenth the real zeros of the function with equation $f(x) = x^4 + x^2 - 6$.**

By Descartes' Rule of Signs, there is one positive real zero and one negative real zero. The other zeros are imaginary. By the Rational Zero Theorem, the possible rational zeros are $-6, -3, -2, -1, 1, 2, 3,$ or 6.

Use synthetic substitution to evaluate $f(x)$ for these values.

x	1	0	1	0	-6	$f(x)$
-6	1	-6	37	-222	1326	1326
-3	1	-3	10	-30	84	84
-2	1	-2	5	-10	14	14
-1	1	-1	2	-2	-4	-4
1	1	1	2	2	-4	-4
2	1	2	5	10	14	14
3	1	3	10	30	84	84
6	1	6	37	222	1326	1326

⟵ By the Location Principle there is at least one zero between -1 and -2, and at least one zero between 1 and 2.

Locate the negative zero.

x	$f(x)$
-1.5	1.3125
-1.4	-0.1984
-1.3	-1.4539
-1.2	-2.4864
-1.1	-3.3259
-1.0	-4

⟵$f(-1.45) \approx 0.5$

The zero is "closer" to -1.4. Why aren't values less than -1.5 tested?

Locate the positive zero.

x	$f(x)$
1.0	-4
1.1	-3.3259
1.2	-2.4864
1.3	-1.4539
1.4	-0.1984
1.5	1.3125

The zero is "closer" to 1.4.

⟵$f(1.45) \approx 0.5$

The real zeros are approximately -1.4 and 1.4.

Example

2 Approximate to the nearest tenth the real zeros of the function with equation $f(x) = x^4 - x^3 - 4x^2 + 8x - 4$.

By Descartes' Rule of Signs, there are three or one positive real zeros and one negative real zero. By the Rational Zero Theorem, the possible rational zeros are -4, -2, -1, 1, 2, or 4.

x	1	-1	-4	8	-4	$f(x)$
-4	1	-5	16	-56	220	220
-2	1	-3	2	4	-12	-12
-1	1	-2	-2	10	-14	-14
1	1	0	-4	4	0	0
2	1	1	-2	4	4	4
4	1	3	8	40	156	156

By the Location Principle there is a zero between -4 and -2.

1 is a zero.

The other two zeros are imaginary.

Locate the zero between -4 and -2.

First, find $f(-3)$.

$$\begin{array}{r|rrrr|r} -3 & 1 & -1 & -4 & 8 & -4 \\ & & 1 & -4 & 8 & -16 & 44 \end{array}$$

By the Location Principle, the zero is between -3 and -2.

x	$f(x)$
-2.5	5.6875
-2.4	0.7616
-2.3	-3.4089

$f(-2.35) \approx -1.414$
The zero is "closer" to -2.4.

The real zeros are 1 and approximately -2.4.

Written Exercises

Approximate to the nearest tenth the real zeros of functions with the following equations. Use a calculator as necessary.

1. $f(x) = x^3 - 2x^2 + 6$

2. $f(x) = x^4 - 4x^2 + 3$

3. $f(x) = 2x^5 + 3x - 2$

4. $f(x) = x^4 - x^2 + 6$

5. $f(x) = x^3 + 2x^2 - 3x - 5$

6. $f(x) = x^3 - 5$

7. $f(x) = x^5 - 6$

8. $f(x) = 3x^3 - 16x^2 + 12x + 6$

9. $f(x) = x^3 - x^2 + 1$

10. $f(x) = x^4 - 4x^2 + 6$

11. $f(x) = 3x^2 - 8x + 1$

12. $f(x) = -7x^3 - 6x + 1$

13. $f(x) = x^5 - x^3 - x + 1$

14. $f(x) = 3x^4 - x^2 + x - 1$

15. $f(x) = x^3 + 1$

16. $f(x) = x^4 - x^2 - 6$

17. $f(x) = x^3 - 4x + 4$

18. $f(x) = x^3 - 3$

Study the mathematical terms used in the statements below.

$x^3 - 7x + 6$ is a **polynomial expression,** or **polynomial.**
Its factors are $(x - 2)$, $(x - 1)$, and $(x + 3)$.

When a polynomial is divided by one of its factors, the remainder is zero.

$x^3 - 7x + 6 = 0$ is an equation.
The **factored form** of the equation is
$$(x - 2)(x - 1)(x + 3) = 0.$$
Its **roots,** or **solutions,** are 2, 1, and -3.

When a root of an equation is substituted for the variable, the two sides are equal.

$f(x) = x^3 - 7x + 6$ is a **function,** or **polynomial function.**
The **zeros** of the function are 2, 1, and -3.

When a zero of a function is substituted for the variable, the result is zero.

The function $f(x) = x^3 - 7x + 6$ may be expressed as $y = x^3 - 7x + 6$. When a value is substituted for x, exactly one value is obtained for y. Each ordered pair (x, y) is a **solution** to the equation $y = x^3 - 7x + 6$. For example, when x is -1, the value of y is 12. So, the ordered pair $(-1, 12)$ is a solution. Some other solutions are $(2, 0)$, $(1, 0)$, and $(-3, 0)$.

We do not use the term root for solutions that are ordered pairs.

Exercises
Choose the correct term in parentheses to complete each statement.

1. $x - 2$ is a (*factor, root*) of the polynomial $x^2 - 4x + 4$.
2. 2 is a (*root, zero*) of the function $f(x) = x^2 - 4x + 4$.
3. $(2, 0)$ is a (*solution, root*) of the equation $y = x^2 - 4x + 4$.
4. 2 is a (*root, zero*) of $x^2 - 4x + 4 = 0$.
5. $y - 6$ is a (*factor, solution*) of $y^2 - 5y - 6$.
6. The zeros of the (*function, expression*) $f(y) = y^2 - 5y - 6$ are 6 and -1.
7. The roots of the (*polynomial, equation*) $y^2 - 5y - 6 = 0$ are 6 and -1.
8. 7 is a (*factor, zero*) of $f(k) = k - 7$.
9. 7 is a (*solution, factor*) of $k - 7 = 0$
10. $(3, -4)$ is a (*solution, root*) of $y = k - 7$.
11. $f(k) = k - 7$ is a (*function, expression*).
12. The factors of the (*equation, expression*) $x^2 - 1$ are $x - 1$ and $x + 1$.
13. The roots of the (*function, equation*) $x^2 - 1 = 0$ are 1 and -1.
14. The equation $y = x^2 - 1$ has two (*roots, solutions*).

10-6 Graphing Polynomials

The simplest polynomial graphs are those with equations of the form $f(x) = x^n$ where n is a positive integer.

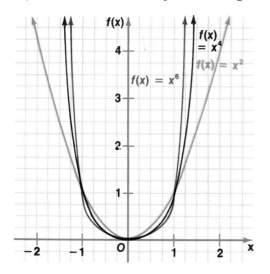

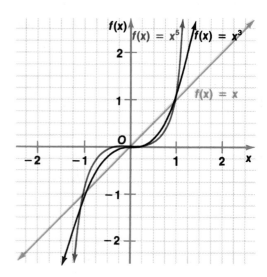

Notice that each graph has only one x-intercept, the origin. The graphs are completed by finding points on the graphs and connecting them with smooth continuous curves.

If a polynomial $f(x)$ can be factored into linear factors, much information about the graph of $y = f(x)$ is available. For example, consider $y = (x - 2)(x - 3)(x + 5)$.

1. The function has three zeros, 2, 3, and -5.
2. The function has negative values when x is less than -5 and when x is between 2 and 3.
3. The function has positive values when x is between -5 and 2 and when x is greater than 3.

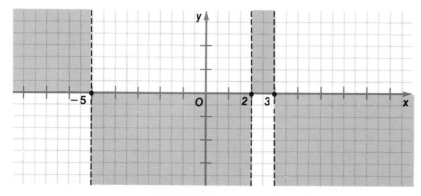

The graph crosses the x-axis at -5, 2, and 3. The shaded regions contain no points of the graph.

To complete the graph, find and plot points on the graph. First, evaluate $f(x)$ for several integer values of x. Connect them with a smooth, continuous curve. Then find and plot extra points that seem important to the graph.

Use a calculator and/or synthetic substitution to find the y-coordinates.

x	y
-6	-72
-5	0
-4	42
-3	60
-2.5	61.875
-2	60
-1	48
0	30
1	12
2	0
2.5	-1.875
3	0
4	18
5	60

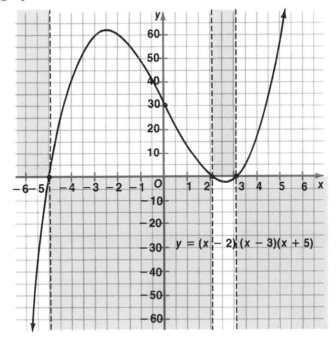

$$y = (x - 2)(x - 3)(x + 5)$$

Notice how the vertical scale has been "condensed" so the graph will fit the space provided.

Example

1 **Graph $f(x) = -x^3 + 2x^2 + 4x - 8$.**

First, factor the polynomial.
$$f(x) = -(x - 2)^2(x + 2)$$

1. The function has two zeros, 2 and -2.
2. The function has positive values when x is less than -2.
3. The function has negative or zero values when x is greater than -2.

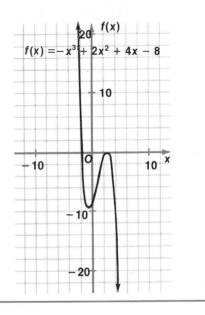

$$f(x) = -x^3 + 2x^2 + 4x - 8$$

x	-4	-3	-2	-1	0	1	2	3	4
$f(x)$	72	25	0	-9	-8	-3	0	-5	-24

In general, the graph of a cubic polynomial function has a *sideways S* shape. Point *A* on each graph is called a **relative maximum** since there are no nearby points that have a *y*-value greater than *A*. Likewise, each point *B* is called a **relative minimum.** You can use this information to help graph functions that have imaginary zeros.

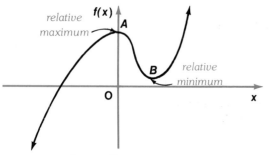

$f(x) = ax^3 + bx^2 + cx + d$, *a* positive

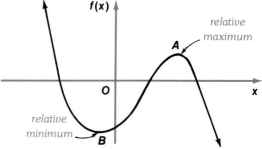

$f(x) = ax^3 + bx^2 + cx + d$, *a* negative

Example

2   **Graph $f(x) = x^3 - 6x - 9$.**

First, factor the polynomial.

$f(x) = (x - 3)(x^2 + 3x + 3)$

The function has one real zero, 3.

The graph of this cubic polynomial function has a *sideways S* shape. Thus, it has one relative maximum and one relative minimum.

The values of $f(-1.5)$ and $f(1.5)$ were computed to approximate the maximum and minimum more closely.

x	f(x)
-3	-18
-2	-5
-1.5	-3.375
-1	-4
0	-9
1	-14
1.5	-14.625
2	-13
3	0
4	31

indicates a relative maximum

indicates a relative minimum

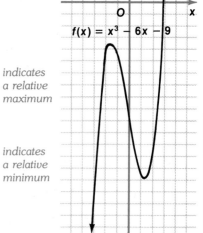

Written Exercises

Graph each of the following. Use a calculator or synthetic substitution to help find points of the graph.

1. $f(x) = x^3$
    2. $f(x) = x^6$
    3. $f(x) = 4x^6$

4. $f(x) = 3x^5$
    5. $f(x) = (x - 1)(x - 2)(x + 2)$ **6.** $f(x) = (x + 4)(x - 1)(x + 1)$

7. $f(x) = (x - 2)^2(x + 3)$
    8. $f(x) = (x - 3)^2(x + 1)$
    9. $f(x) = x^3 - x$

10. $f(x) = -x^3 - x$
    11. $f(x) = x^3 - x^2 - 8x + 12$
    12. $f(x) = x^4 - 81$

13. $f(x) = x^4 - 10x^2 + 9$
    14. $f(x) = x^3 + 5$
    15. $f(x) = 15x^3 - 16x^2 - x + 2$

16. $f(x) = x^3 - 3x - 4$
    17. $f(x) = -x^3 - 13x - 12$
    18. $f(x) = -x^3 - 4x^2 - 8x - 8$

10-7   Composition of Functions

Scientists often use the Kelvin temperature scale. Kelvin temperature readings and Celsius temperature readings are related in the following way.

$$K = C + 273$$

Celsius readings and Fahrenheit readings are related in the following way.

$$C = \frac{5}{9}(F - 32)$$

Using these equations, you can write a new equation that shows how Kelvin readings and Fahrenheit readings are related.

$$
\begin{aligned}
K &= C + 273 \\
&= \frac{5}{9}(F - 32) + 273 \qquad \text{Substitute } \frac{5}{9}(F - 32) \text{ for } C. \\
&= \frac{5}{9}F + \frac{2297}{9}
\end{aligned}
$$

The above example illustrates **composition of functions.**

Given functions f and g, the composite function $f \circ g$ can be described by the following equation. $$[f \circ g](x) = f[g(x)]$$

The range of g is a subset of the domain of f.

Composition of Functions

The symbol $f \circ g$ is read "f composition g", "the composite of f and g", or "f of g".

Examples

1   **If $f(x) = x + 273$ and $g(x) = \frac{5}{9}(x - 32)$, find $[f \circ g](x)$.**

$$
\begin{aligned}
[f \circ g](x) &= f[g(x)] \\
&= f\left[\frac{5}{9}(x - 32)\right] & \text{Substitute } \frac{5}{9}(x - 32) \text{ for } g(x). \\
&= \left[\frac{5}{9}(x - 32)\right] + 273 & \text{Evaluate } f \text{ when } x \text{ is } \frac{5}{9}(x - 32). \\
&= \frac{5}{9}x + \frac{2297}{9} & \text{Simplify.}
\end{aligned}
$$

2   **If $f(x) = x^2 + 3$ and $h(x) = 2x - 1$, find $[f \circ h](2)$.**

$$
\begin{aligned}
[f \circ h](2) &= f[h(2)] \\
&= f[2(2) - 1] & \text{Substitute } 2(2) - 1 \text{ for } h(2). \\
&= f[3] & \text{Substitute 3 for } 2(2) - 1. \\
&= 12 & \text{Evaluate } f \text{ when } x \text{ is 3.}
\end{aligned}
$$

Mappings can be used to show composition of functions. Suppose $f = \{(1, 2), (2, 3), (3, 4)\}$ and $g = \{(2, 3), (3, 1), (4, 2)\}$.

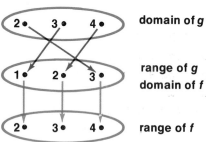

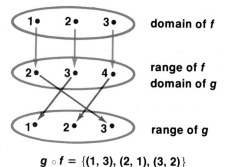

$f \circ g = \{(2, 4), (3, 2), (4, 3)\}$

Notice that in the example above, $f \circ g \neq g \circ f$. In general, composition of functions is not a commutative operation.

$g \circ f = \{(1, 3), (2, 1), (3, 2)\}$

Example

3 If $f(x) = x + 7$ and $g(x) = 3 + 2x$, find $[f \circ g](x)$ and $[g \circ f](x)$.

$$[f \circ g](x) = f[g(x)]$$
$$= f[3 + 2x]$$
$$= (3 + 2x) + 7$$
$$= 2x + 10$$

$$[g \circ f](x) = g[f(x)]$$
$$= g[x + 7]$$
$$= 3 + 2(x + 7)$$
$$= 2x + 17$$

In some cases, given two functions h and k, the composite functions $h \circ k$ or $k \circ h$ may not even exist. For example, let $h = \{(2, 4), (4, 6), (6, 8), (8, 10)\}$ and $k = \{(4, 5), (6, 5), (8, 12), (10, 12)\}$. The range of k is *not* a subset of the domain of h. So, $h \circ k$ *does not exist*. The range of h is a subset of the domain of k. So, $k \circ h$ *does exist*.

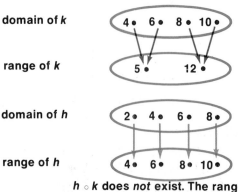

$h \circ k$ does *not* exist. The range of k is not in the domain of h.

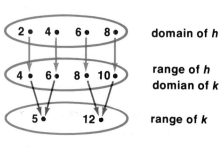

$k \circ h = \{(2, 5), (4, 5), (6, 12), (8, 12)\}$

Exploratory Exercises

In each exercise find $f(2)$, $f(-2)$, and $f(0)$.

1. $f(x) = x - 3$
2. $f(x) = x^2 + 4$
3. $f(x) = x^2 - 2x + 1$
4. $f(x) = |x + 2|$
5. $f(x) = |x| + 2$
6. $f(x) = x^3 - x^2 + x - 1$
7. $f(x) = x^4 - 6$
8. $f(x) = x^2 - 8x + 4$
9. $f(x) = x^5 - x^2 + 2$
10. $f(x) = x^2 - x^3$
11. $f = \{(0, 3), (2, 4), (-2, 9)\}$
12. $f = \{(0, 2), (-2, 2), (5, 2)\}$

Written Exercises

In each exercise, find $[f \circ g](3)$ and $[g \circ f](3.)$.

1. $f(x) = x + 2$
   $g(x) = x - 1$
2. $f(x) = x^2 + 8$
   $g(x) = x - 3$
3. $f(x) = x^3 - 1$
   $g(x) = x + 1$
4. $f(x) = x$
   $g(x) = x$
5. $f(x) = 2x^2 + 1$
   $g(x) = x^2 - 1$
6. $f(x) = x^2$
   $g(x) = x^3$

In each exercise, find $f[g(x)]$ and $g[f(x)]$.

7. $f(x) = 2x + 1$
   $g(x) = x - 3$
8. $f(x) = 3x - 4$
   $g(x) = 2x + 5$
9. $f(x) = x^2 + 3$
   $g(x) = 2x - 1$
10. $f(x) = x + 2$
    $g(x) = 3x^2 - 1$
11. $f(x) = -x^2 - 8$
    $g(x) = x^2 - 1$
12. $f(x) = x + 2$
    $g(x) = x - 2$

In each exercise, find $f[g(-1)]$ and $g[f(-1)]$.

13. $f(x) = x - 1$
    $g(x) = x + 1$
14. $f(x) = x^2 + 2x + 1$
    $g(x) = -2x^2 - 1$
15. $f(x) = 3x^2 + 2$
    $g(x) = x - 3$
16. $f(x) = 2x^2 + 4x^3 + 1$
    $g(x) = x^2 + 1$
17. $f(x) = x - 8$
    $g(x) = |x|$
18. $f(x) = |x + 1|$
    $g(x) = |x + 1|$

If $f(x) = x^2$, $g(x) = 3x$, and $h(x) = x - 1$, find each of the following.

19. $[f \circ g](1)$
20. $[g \circ f](1)$
21. $[h \circ f](3)$
22. $[f \circ h](3)$
23. $g[f(-2)]$
24. $f[h(-3)]$
25. $g[h(-2)]$
26. $h[g(-2)]$
27. $f\left[h\left(-\frac{1}{2}\right)\right]$
28. $g\left[f\left(-\frac{1}{2}\right)\right]$
29. $f[h(\sqrt{2} + 3)]$
30. $f[g(1 + \sqrt{2})]$
31. $f[g(x)]$
32. $g[h(x)]$
33. $[f \circ (g \circ h)](x)$

Express $g \circ f$ and $f \circ g$, if they exist, as sets of ordered pairs.

34. $f = \{(2, 1), (3, 4), (6, -2)\}$
    $g = \{(1, 5), (4, -7), (-2, -3)\}$
35. $f = \{(3, 8), (4, 0), (6, 3), (7, -1)\}$
    $g = \{(8, 6), (0,4), (3, 6), (-1, -8)\}$
36. $f = \{(0, 2), (1, 1), (3, 3), (4, -1)\}$
    $g = \{(0, 0), (1, 1), (2, 4), (3, 9)\}$
37. $f = \{(1, 0), (-1, 7), (5, 0), (9, 1)\}$
    $g = \{(6, 5), (0, -8), (7, -2), (1, -3)\}$

10-8   Inverse Functions

You have learned that two numbers are additive inverses if their sum is 0, the additive identity. Two numbers are multiplicative inverses if their product is 1, the multiplicative identity. The function $I(x) = x$ is called the **identity function,** since for any function f, $[f \circ I](x) = f(x)$ and $[I \circ f](x) = f(x)$. Two functions are **inverse functions** if both their compositions are the identity function.

Suppose $f(x) = 3x - 2$ and $g(x) = \dfrac{x + 2}{3}$. You can determine if they are inverse functions by finding both their compositions.

$$[f \circ g](x) = f[g(x)] \qquad\qquad [g \circ f](x) = g[f(x)]$$

$$= f\left[\dfrac{x + 2}{3}\right] \qquad\qquad\qquad = g[3x - 2]$$

$$= 3\left(\dfrac{x + 2}{3}\right) - 2 \qquad\qquad = \dfrac{(3x - 2) + 2}{3}$$

$$= x \qquad\qquad\qquad\qquad\quad = x$$

Since both their compositions are the identity function, they are inverse functions.

> **Two polynomial functions f and g are inverse functions if and only if both their compositions are the identity function. That is,**
>
> $$[f \circ g](x) = [g \circ f](x) = x.$$

Definition of Inverse Functions

A special notation often is used to show that two functions f and g are inverse functions.

$$g = f^{-1} \text{ and } f = g^{-1}$$

The notation f^{-1} is read "f inverse," or "the inverse of f." The -1 is <u>not</u> an exponent.

The ordered pairs of a function and its inverse are related in a special way. Consider the function $f(x) = 3x - 2$ and its inverse $f^{-1}(x) = \dfrac{x + 2}{3}$.

$$f(5) = 3 \cdot 5 - 2 \qquad\qquad f^{-1}(13) = \dfrac{13 + 2}{3}$$

$$= 13 \qquad\qquad\qquad\qquad\quad = 5$$

The ordered pair $(5, 13)$ belongs to f.

The ordered pair $(13, 5)$ belongs to f^{-1}.

> **Suppose f and f^{-1} are inverse functions. Then $f(a) = b$ if and only if $f^{-1}(b) = a$.**

Property of Inverse Functions

The inverse of a function can be found by reversing the order of each pair in the given function. For example, if $f = \{(1, 2), (2, 7), (3, 12), (4, 17)\}$, then $f^{-1} = \{(2, 1), (7, 2), (12, 3), (17, 4)\}$.

Suppose you wish to find the inverse of function f. By interchanging the variables in the equation for f, the order of each pair in f is interchanged. Thus, you can obtain the ordered pairs in f^{-1} and the equation for f^{-1}.

Example

1 **Suppose $f(x) = 3x - 5$. Find $f^{-1}(x)$. Also, show that f and f^{-1} are inverse functions.**

Rewrite the function $f(x)$ as $y = 3x - 5$.

Next, interchange the variables x and y and solve the equation for y.

$$x = 3y - 5$$
$$3y = x + 5$$
$$y = \frac{x + 5}{3}$$

Thus, $f^{-1}(x) = \dfrac{x + 5}{3}$.

Now show that the compositions of f and f^{-1} are identity functions.

$$
\begin{aligned}
[f \circ f^{-1}](x) &= f[f^{-1}(x)] \\
&= f\left[\frac{x + 5}{3}\right] \\
&= 3\left(\frac{x + 5}{3}\right) - 5 \\
&= x
\end{aligned}
\qquad
\begin{aligned}
[f^{-1} \circ f](x) &= f^{-1}[f(x)] \\
&= f^{-1}[3x - 5] \\
&= \frac{(3x - 5) + 5}{3} \\
&= x
\end{aligned}
$$

So, $[f \circ f^{-1}](x) = [f^{-1} \circ f](x) = x$.

Not all functions have inverses that are functions.

Example

2 **Given $f(x) = x^2 + 3$, find $f^{-1}(x)$.**

Rewrite the function $f(x)$ using y. Interchange the variables and solve for y.

$$y = x^2 + 3$$
$$x = y^2 + 3$$
$$y^2 = x - 3$$
$$y = \pm\sqrt{x - 3} \quad \text{or} \quad f^{-1}(x) = \pm\sqrt{x - 3}$$

This equation does *not* define a function. For a given value of x, there is more than one value of $f^{-1}(x)$. For example, $f^{-1}(7) = 2$ or -2.

The following example shows how the graphs of a function and its inverse are related.

Example

3 If $f(x) = 2x + 1$, find $f^{-1}(x)$. Then graph $f(x)$ and $f^{-1}(x)$ on the same coordinate system.

$$f(x) = 2x + 1 \rightarrow y = 2x + 1$$
$$x = 2y + 1 \qquad \textit{Interchange the variables.}$$
$$y = \frac{x - 1}{2} \qquad \textit{Solve for y.}$$
$$f^{-1}(x) = \frac{x - 1}{2} \qquad \textit{Rewrite using function notation.}$$

Now graph both $f(x)$ and $f^{-1}(x)$. Suppose the plane containing the graphs could be folded along the line $f(x) = x$. Then the graphs would coincide.

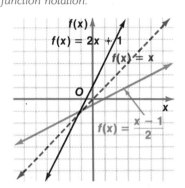

In general, the graphs of a function and its inverse are mirror images of each other with respect to the graph of the identity function, $f(x) = x$.

Exploratory Exercises

Write the inverse of each function and determine if its inverse is a function.

1. $f = \{(3, 1), (2, 4), (1, 5)\}$

2. $f = \{(3, 2), (4, 2)\}$

3. $g = \{(3, 8), (4, -2), (5, -3)\}$

4. $g = \{(-1, -2), (-3, -2), (-1, -4), (0, 6)\}$

5. $h = \{(-3, 1), (2, 4), (7, 8)\}$

6. $h = \{(4, -2), (3, 7), (5, 7), (3, 8)\}$

Written Exercises

Write the equation for the inverse of each function.

1. $y = 2x$

2. $f(x) = x + 2$

3. $f(x) = -6x - 5$

4. $y = 3x - 7$

5. $y = 3$

6. $f(x) = \frac{1}{2}x + 4$

7. $f(x) = 0$

8. $f(x) = -3x - 1$

9. $y = x^2$

10. $y = x^2 - 4$

Graph each function and its inverse.

11. $f = \{(2, 1), (3, -4), (0, 1)\}$

12. $f = \left\{\left(\frac{1}{2}, 3\right), (0, -2), (7, 6)\right\}$

13. $y = x$

14. $y = -2x - 1$

15. $y = 3x$

16. $f(x) = x + 2$

17. $f(x) = \dfrac{3x + 1}{2}$

18. $y = \dfrac{x - 3}{5}$

19. $y = x^2 + 1$

20. $f(x) = (x - 4)^2$

Sketch the graph of the inverse of each of the following. Is the inverse a function?

21.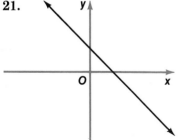

22.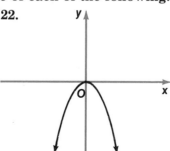

23.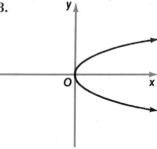

24.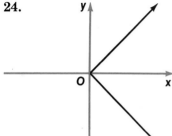

25.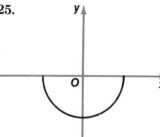

26.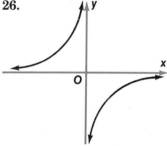

Determine whether the given functions are inverses of one another.

27. $y = 2x + 1$
$y = \dfrac{x - 1}{2}$

28. $y = -2x + 3$
$y = 2x - 3$

29. $y = x + 4$
$y = x - 4$

30. $f(x) = x + 1$
$f(x) = x - 1$

31. $f(x) = 4x - 5$
$f(x) = \dfrac{x + 5}{4}$

32. $f(x) = x - \dfrac{1}{2}$
$f(x) = 2x + 1$

33. $f(x) = x$
$f(x) = -x$

34. $f(x) = -2x + 3$
$f(x) = 2x - 3$

Solve each problem. In each case, assume f is a function.

35. If $f(3) = 4$, find $f^{-1}(4)$.

36. If $f\left(\frac{1}{2}\right) = 6$, find $f^{-1}(6)$.

37. If $f(a) = b$, find $f^{-1}(b)$.

38. If $f(r) = s$, find $f^{-1}(s)$.

39. If $f(a + 1) = 2$, find $f^{-1}(2)$.

40. If $f(m + n) = p$, find $f^{-1}(p)$.

Evaluating a Polynomial Function

Evaluating a polynomial function is done by selecting a value for *x* and substituting that value in the equation. When many values for *p(x)* are needed, the following computer program will be helpful. It evaluates the function for integer values of *x* within a given range.

```
10 PRINT "X ^ 4 - X ^ 3 + X ^ 2 - X + 1"
20 INPUT "ENTER LOWEST VALUE OF X TO BE
   TESTED: ";X1
30 INPUT "ENTER HIGHEST VALUE OF X TO BE
   TESTED: ";X2
40 FOR N = X1 TO X2
50 LET P = N ^ 4 - N ^ 3 + N ^ 2 - N + 1
60 LET P = INT (10 * P + .5) / 10
70 PRINT "P(";N;") = ";P
80 NEXT N
90 END
```

P(-6)	=	1555
P(-5)	=	781
P(-4)	=	341
P(-3)	=	121
P(-2)	=	31
P(-1)	=	5
P(0)	=	1
P(1)	=	1
P(2)	=	11
P(3)	=	61
P(4)	=205	
P(5)	=521	
P(6)	=1111	

This program evaluates $p(x) = x^4 - x^3 + x^2 - x + 1$.
You determine the range of *x* values.

Enter and run this program. Use the range -6 to 6.

Any function can be evaluated using this program by changing statements 10 and 50.

Exercises

Make the necessary changes in the above program to evaluate the following functions in the ranges given.

1. $f(x) = x^3 + 2x^2 - 2$ (-7 to 7)

2. $f(x) = x^2 + 8x - 20$ (-10 to 10)

3. $g(x) = x^2 - 16$ (-8 to 8)

4. $f[g(x)]$ using exercises 2 and 3 (-9 to 9)

5. In exercises 1–4, are any roots indicated? Why or why not?

For the following functions use the computer program, the Rational Zero Theorem, and Descartes' Rule of Signs to find all the roots.

6. $f(x) = x^4 + 2x^3 - 7x^2 - 8x + 12$

7. $g(x) = x^4 + 5x^3 - 37x^2 - 5x + 36$

Vocabulary

polynomial in one variable (307)
constant (307)
linear expression (307)
quadratic expression (307)
polynomial function (308)
synthetic substitution (311)

depressed polynomial (312)
zero (315)
relative maximum (328)
relative minimum (328)
composition of functions (329)
inverse functions (332)

Chapter Summary

1. A polynomial in one variable, x, is an expression of the form $a_0x^n + a_1x^{n-1} + \cdots + a_{n-2}x^2 + a_{n-1}x + a_n$. The coefficients $a_0, a_1, a_2, \ldots, a_n$ represent real numbers, and n represents a nonnegative integer. (307)

2. The Remainder Theorem: If a polynomial $f(x)$ is divided by $x - a$, the remainder is a constant, $f(a)$, and $f(x) = q(x) \cdot (x - a) + f(a)$ where $q(x)$ is a polynomial with degree one less than the degree of $f(x)$. (310)

3. The Factor Theorem: The binomial $x - a$ is a factor of the polynomial $f(x)$ if and only if $f(a) = 0$. (311)

4. The Rational Zero Theorem: Let $f(x) = a_0x^n + a_1x^{n-1} + \cdots + a_{n-1}x + a_n$ represent a polynomial with integral coefficients and n be a nonnegative integer. If $\frac{p}{q}$ is a rational number in simplest form and a zero of $y = f(x)$, then p is a factor of a_n and q is a factor of a_0. (316)

5. The Fundamental Theorem of Algebra: Every polynomial equation with degree greater than zero has at least one root in the set of complex numbers. (319)

6. Complex Conjugates Theorem: Suppose a and b are real numbers with $b \neq 0$. Then, if $a + bi$ is a root of a polynomial equation, $a - bi$ is also a root of the equation. (319)

7. Descartes' Rule of Signs: Suppose $p(x)$ is a polynomial whose terms are arranged in descending powers of the variable. The number of positive real zeros of $y = p(x)$ is the same as the number of changes in sign of the coefficients of the terms, or is less than this by an even number. The number of negative real zeros is the same as the number of changes in sign of $p(-x)$ or is less than this by an even number. (320)

8. The Location Principle: Let $y = f(x)$ represent a polynomial function. And suppose a and b are two numbers with $f(a)$ negative and $f(b)$ positive. Then the function has at least one real zero between a and b. (323)

9. Composition of Functions: Given functions f and g, the composite function $f \circ g$ can be described by the equation $[f \circ g](x) = f[g(x)]$. (329)

10. Definition of Inverse Functions: Two functions f and g are inverse functions if and only if both their compositions are the identity function. That is, $[f \circ g](x) = [g \circ f](x) = x$. (332)

11. Property of Inverse Functions: Suppose f and f^{-1} are inverse functions. Then $f(a) = b$ if and only if $f^{-1}(b) = a$. (332)

Chapter Review

10–1 Find $p(-2)$ for each of the following.

1. $p(x) = 2x^3 + x^2 - 1$

2. $p(x) = 2x^4 - 3x^3 + 8$

Find $f(m + 2)$ for each of the following.

3. $f(x) = x^2 + 3x - 7$

4. $f(x) = -4x^3 - 5$

10–2 Find the remainder for each of the following.

5. $(x^2 + 5x + 6) \div (x + 1)$

6. $(x^3 + 8x + 1) \div (x - 2)$

7. $(x^5 + 8x^3 + 2) \div (x + 2)$

8. $(x^4 + 3x^2 - 1) \div (x - 4)$

Factor each polynomial by using synthetic division.

9. $x^3 + 2x^2 - x - 2$

10. $x^3 + 5x^2 + 8x + 4$

11. $x^3 - 3x + 2$

12. $x^3 - 6x^2 + 11x - 6$

10–3 Find all rational zeros for each function.

13. $f(x) = (x - 1)^2(2x - 3)^2$

14. $f(x) = (x + 2)(x - 2)(x + 5)^3$

15. $f(x) = 6x^3 - 41x^2 + 58x - 15$

16. $f(x) = 2x^3 - 5x^2 - 28x + 15$

10–4 For each function, state the number of positive real zeros, negative real zeros, and imaginary zeros.

17. $f(x) = 2x^4 - x^3 + 5x^2 + 3x - 9$

18. $f(x) = -x^4 - x^2 - x - 1$

19. $f(x) = 7x^3 + 6x - 1$

20. $f(x) = x^4 + x^3 - 7x + 1$

21. Find all zeros of $f(x) = x^3 - 7x^2 + 17x - 15$ if $2 + i$ is one root of $f(x) = 0$.

10–5 Approximate to the nearest tenth the real zeros of functions with the following equations.

22. $f(x) = x^3 - x^2 + 1$

23. $f(x) = 3x^4 - x^2 + x - 1$

24. $f(x) = x^3 - 2x^2 + 6$

25. $f(x) = 4x^3 + x^2 - 20$

10–6 Graph each of the following.

26. $f(x) = (x - 3)^2(x + 2)$

27. $f(x) = x^3 - 3x - 4$

10–7 In each exercise, find $[f \circ g](3)$, $[g \circ f](4)$, and $[f \circ g](x)$.

28. $f(x) = x^2 + 2$
$g(x) = x - 3$

29. $f(x) = x^2 + 2x + 1$
$g(x) = 2x^2 - 1$

30. $f(x) = |x|$
$g(x) = x - 8$

31. $f(x) = |x + 1|$
$g(x) = 2|x - 3|$

10–8 Graph each function and its inverse.

32. $f(x) = 1 - 4x$

33. $f(x) = \dfrac{3x + 2}{2}$

34. $f(x) = (x - 6)^2$

Determine whether the given functions are inverses of each other.

35. $f(x) = 3x - 4$ and $g(x) = \dfrac{x - 4}{3}$

36. $f(x) = \dfrac{x + 5}{4}$ and $g(x) = 4x - 5$

Chapter Test

Find $p(3)$ for each of the following.

1. $p(x) = x^4 - x^3 + x - 1$

2. $p(x) = x^3 - 27$

Find $f(m - 1)$ for each of the following.

3. $f(x) = 3x^2 - 4x + 5$

4. $f(x) = x^3 - x + 7$

Find the remainder for each of the following.

5. $(x^2 + 4x + 4) \div (x + 2)$

6. $(x^3 + 8x + 1) \div (x + 2)$

7. $(x^5 + 8x^3 + 2) \div (x - 2)$

8. $(x^4 + x^3 + x^2 + x + 1) \div (x + 1)$

Factor each polynomial by using synthetic division.

9. $x^4 - 5x^2 + 4$

10. $x^3 - 3x - 2$

11. $x^3 - x^2 - 5x - 3$

12. $x^4 - 3x^3 - 7x^2 - 27x - 24$

Find all rational zeros for each function.

13. $f(x) = x^4 + x^3 - 9x^2 - 17x - 8$

14. $f(x) = x^3 - 3x^2 - 53x - 9$

15. $f(x) = 2x^3 - 5x^2 - 28x + 15$

16. $f(x) = 6x^3 + 4x^2 - 14x + 4$

17. Find all zeros of $f(x) = x^3 - 10x^2 + 34x - 40$ if $3 + i$ is one root of $f(x) = 0$.

18. Approximate to the nearest tenth the real zeros of $f(x) = x^3 - 3x - 4$. Then draw the graph.

If $f(x) = 2x$ and $g(x) = x^2 - 1$, find each of the following.

19. $[f \circ g](-2)$

20. $g[f(3)]$

21. $[g \circ f](x)$

Find the inverse of each function.

22. $f(x) = 3x - 4$

23. $f(x) = x^2 + 2$

24. Show that $f(x) = 2x - 3$ and $g(x) = \dfrac{x + 3}{2}$ are inverses of each other.

25. Graph $f(x) = 3x - 2$ and its inverse.

1. Solve $x = 2 + \dfrac{x^2 - 4}{x}$.

2. Solve $|2x| + 1 = 5$.

3. Graph $y = \dfrac{3}{4}x - 3$.

4. Graph $x - 3y \leq 6$.

5. State whether the graphs of the following equations are parallel, perpendicular, or neither.
$$x + y = -4$$
$$2y = -2x + 5$$

6. Solve the system.
$$2x + 5y = 2$$
$$3x + 6y = 0$$

7. Solve by graphing.
$$x - y \leq 4$$
$$2x + y \leq 3$$

8. Solve the system.
$$4x + 3y + z = -10$$
$$x - 12y + 2z = -5$$
$$x + 18y + z = 4$$

9. Factor $16z^4 - 1$.

10. Factor $9a^2 + 30ab + 25b^2$.

11. Factor $9a^2 + 3a - c - c^2$.

12. Simplify $5\sqrt[3]{16}$.

13. Simplify $(7 + \sqrt{3})(8 - \sqrt{6})$.

14. Simplify $\sqrt{-49}$.

15. Find the value of c that makes $x^2 + 6x + c$ a perfect square.

16. Find the value of the discriminant for $a^2 + a - 5 = 0$. Describe the nature of the roots.

17. Find the quadratic equation having roots -9 and -4.

18. Identify the quadratic term, the linear term, and the constant term of the equation $q = -4x^2 - 2x$.

19. State the vertex, axis of symmetry, and direction of opening of the graph of $y = \dfrac{3}{4}x^2$.

20. Graph $y = 5(x - 2)^2 - 4$. Then state the vertex, axis of symmetry, and direction of opening.

21. Graph $4x^2 - y^2 = 4$.

22. Graph $\dfrac{x^2}{9} + \dfrac{y^2}{25} = 1$.

23. Graph $x^2 + y^2 - 4x + 2y - 4 = 0$.

24. Graph $x = y^2 + 8y + 25$.

25. Given $p(x) = x^2 - 2x + 6$, find the value of $p(1)$ and $p(-2)$.

26. Use synthetic division to find the factors of the polynomial $x^4 + 8x^3 + 23x^2 + 28x + 12$.

27. Find all rational zeros for the function $f(x) = (x + 1)(x - 3)(2x - 5)$.

28. Graph $f(x) = x^3 + 5$.

29. State the possible number of positive real zeros, negative real zeros, and imaginary zeros for $f(x) = x^4 + 1$.

Problem Solving

30. The length of the top of Ron's bookcase is 30 cm more than the width. The area of the top is 1800 cm². What are its dimensions?

31. Find two numbers whose sum is -16 and whose product is a maximum.

32. Bernice has ten more dimes than quarters. All together these coins are worth $4.15. How many of each kind of coin does Bernice have?

33. The sum of two numbers is 3 and the sum of their reciprocals is $\dfrac{12}{5}$. Find the numbers.

The test questions on this page deal with co-ordinates and geometry. The figures shown may not be drawn to scale.

Directions: Choose the one best answer. Write A, B, C, or D.

1. What is the length of a diagonal of a square, if the area is $25x^2$?

   (A) $5x$ (B) $5x\sqrt{2}$ (C) $10x$ (D) $5x^2$

2. What percent of rectangle $ACDF$ is shaded?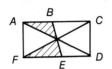

   (A) 25   (B) 30   (C) $33\frac{1}{3}$ (D) 50

3. In $1\frac{1}{2}$ hours, the minute hand of a clock rotates through an angle of how many degrees?

   (A) 60   (B) 180   (C) 540   (D) 720

4. The three straight lines intersect at the same point.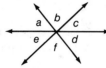

   $a + b =$

   (A) $b + f$ (B) $e + d$
   (C) $f + d$ (D) $c + e$

5. Line p is parallel to line q.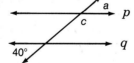

   $c - a =$

   (A) 0   (B) 100   (C) 120   (D) 150

6. $P \vdash \overset{Q}{\underset{}{\rule{0pt}{0pt}\hspace{3cm}}} \dashv R$

   On line segment PR in the figure above, $PQ = 8$ and $QR = 6$. What is the length of the segment joining the midpoints of segments PQ and QR?

   (A) 3   (B) 4   (C) 7   (D) 14

7.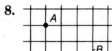

   In the triangle above, $4x =$

   (A) 18   (B) 32   (C) 40   (D) 72

8.

   Above is a section of a graph without the x and y axes. If A has coordinates $(4, 6)$, state the coordinates of B.

   (A) $(4, 7)$ (B) $(4, 1)$
   (C) $(9, 2)$ (D) $(7, 4)$

9.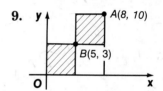

   Point A in the figure above has coordinates $(8, 10)$ and point B has coordinates $(5, 3)$. What is the total area of the shaded rectangles?

   (A) 36   (B) 40   (C) 70   (D) 80

10. If $\ell_1 \perp \ell_2$, what is the value of $a + b$?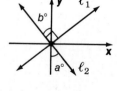

    (A) 45   (B) 90
    (C) 110
    (D) cannot be determined

11.

    $\overline{QR} \perp \overline{RS}$
    $\overline{QR} \perp \overline{PQ}$
    $PQ = 10$
    $QR = 7$
    $RS = 14$

    What is the shortest distance from P to S?

    (A) 24   (B) 25   (C) 28   (D) 31

CHAPTER 11

Rational Polynomial Expressions

John can build a brick wall for an average building in four days. His brother can build the same wall in three days. Suppose they work together. The rational equation $\frac{x}{3} + \frac{x}{4} = 1$ can be used to determine how many days it would take them to complete the job.

11-1 Multiplying Rational Expressions

Rational numbers and **rational algebraic expressions** are similar. A rational number can be expressed as the quotient of two integers.

All polynomials, including constants, are rational expressions. But not all rational expressions are polynomials.

$$\frac{2}{3} \qquad \frac{415}{100} \qquad \frac{-6}{11}$$

A rational algebraic expression can be expressed as the quotient of two polynomials. As with fractions, the denominator cannot be 0.

$$\frac{6}{k} \qquad \frac{2x}{x-5} \qquad \frac{p^2 - 25}{p+6}$$

5 cannot be used as a replacement for x. What number cannot replace p?

To simplify a rational algebraic expression, divide both numerator and denominator by their greatest common factor (GCF).

Examples

1 Simplify $\dfrac{2x(x-5)}{(x-5)(x^2-1)}$.

$$\frac{2x(x-5)}{(x-5)(x^2-1)} = \frac{2x}{x^2-1}$$

The GCF is (x − 5). The expression is undefined when x is 5, 1, or −1. Why?

2 Simplify $\dfrac{x^2y - x^2}{x^3 - x^3y}$.

$$\frac{x^2y - x^2}{x^3 - x^3y} = \frac{x^2(y-1)}{x^3(1-y)}$$

For what values is the expression undefined?

$$= \frac{-1 \cdot x^2(1-y)}{x \cdot x^2(1-y)}$$

$y - 1 = -1(1 - y)$

$$= -\frac{1}{x}$$

The GCF is $x^2(1 - y)$.

Both rational numbers and rational expressions are multiplied the same way. Multiply numerators and multiply denominators.

$$\frac{2}{3} \cdot \frac{4}{5} = \frac{2 \cdot 4}{3 \cdot 5} \text{ or } \frac{8}{15}$$

$$\frac{(x+1)}{(x-4)} \cdot \frac{(2x+3)}{(3x-1)} = \frac{(x+1)(2x+3)}{(x-4)(3x-1)} \text{ or } \frac{2x^2 + 5x + 3}{3x^2 - 13x + 4}$$

This method can be generalized as follows.

> For all rational expressions $\dfrac{a}{b}$ and $\dfrac{c}{d}$, $b \neq 0$ and $d \neq 0$,
> $$\frac{a}{b} \cdot \frac{c}{d} = \frac{ac}{bd}.$$

Multiplying Rational Expressions

Examples

3 Find $\dfrac{4a}{5b} \cdot \dfrac{15b}{16a}$.

$\dfrac{4a}{5b} \cdot \dfrac{15b}{16a} = \dfrac{60ab}{80ab}$ *For what values is the expression undefined?*

$\qquad\qquad = \dfrac{3 \cdot 20ab}{4 \cdot 20ab}$

$\qquad\qquad = \dfrac{3}{4}$ *The GCF is 20ab.*

4 Find $\dfrac{x^2 - 9}{x^2 + x - 12} \cdot \dfrac{x + 2}{x + 3}$.

$\dfrac{x^2 - 9}{x^2 + x - 12} \cdot \dfrac{x + 2}{x + 3} = \dfrac{(x^2 - 9)(x + 2)}{(x^2 + x - 12)(x + 3)}$

$\qquad\qquad = \dfrac{(x - 3)(x + 3)(x + 2)}{(x - 3)(x + 4)(x + 3)}$ *Factor. For what values is the expression undefined? The GCF is $(x - 3)(x + 3)$.*

$\qquad\qquad = \dfrac{x + 2}{x + 4}$

Exploratory Exercises

For each expression, find the greatest common factor (GCF) of the numerator and denominator. Then simplify each expression.

1. $\dfrac{24}{72}$ 2. $\dfrac{99}{132}$ 3. $\dfrac{33}{303}$ 4. $\dfrac{37}{81}$ 5. $\dfrac{13x}{39x^2}$ 6. $\dfrac{42y}{18xy}$

7. $\dfrac{34x^2}{42x^5}$ 8. $\dfrac{42y^3x}{18y^7}$ 9. $\dfrac{38a^2}{42ab}$ 10. $\dfrac{79a^2b}{158a^3bc}$ 11. $\dfrac{-3x^2y^5}{18x^5y^2}$ 12. $\dfrac{14y^2z}{49yz^3}$

13. $\dfrac{(-2x^2y)^3}{4x^5y}$ 14. $\dfrac{a^3b^2}{(-ab)^3}$ 15. $\dfrac{(2xy)^4}{(x^2y)^2}$ 16. $\dfrac{(-3t^2u)^3}{(6tu^2)^2}$ 17. $\dfrac{m + 5}{2m + 10}$ 18. $\dfrac{4x}{x^2 - x}$

Written Exercises

Find each product. Write each answer in simplest form.

1. $\dfrac{3}{8} \cdot \dfrac{16}{7}$ 2. $\dfrac{21}{35} \cdot \dfrac{56}{42}$ 3. $\dfrac{18x}{8y} \cdot \dfrac{3x}{27z}$

4. $\dfrac{3ab}{4ac} \cdot \dfrac{6a^2}{3b^2}$ 5. $\dfrac{7a}{14b} \cdot \dfrac{6b^2}{a}$ 6. $\dfrac{-4ab}{21c} \cdot \dfrac{14c^2}{18a^2}$

7. $\dfrac{7xy}{16z} \cdot \dfrac{-4z^2}{21x^2}$ 8. $\dfrac{x}{3y} \cdot \dfrac{9y^4}{3x^5}$ 9. $\dfrac{3a^2b^3c}{4ab^2} \cdot \dfrac{6c}{1}$

10. $\dfrac{4a^2xy}{12bc} \cdot \dfrac{24bc^2}{6xy}$ 11. $\dfrac{-3abc}{9abd} \cdot \dfrac{7d}{18c^2}$ 12. $\dfrac{11xy}{5xz} \cdot \dfrac{-15z}{-66y^2}$

13. $\dfrac{(cd)^3}{a} \cdot \dfrac{ax^2}{xc^2d}$ 14. $\dfrac{(3a)^3}{18b^3} \cdot \dfrac{12a^4b^5}{(3a)^2}$ 15. $\left(\dfrac{x^2}{y}\right)^2 \cdot \dfrac{5}{3x}$

16. $\left(\dfrac{3a^3}{b^2}\right)^3 \cdot \dfrac{4b^2}{3a^7}$ 17. $\dfrac{y + 2}{x} \cdot \dfrac{x^2}{(y + 2)^2}$ 18. $\dfrac{3(y + 4)^2}{x^2} \cdot \dfrac{2x^3}{9(y + 4)}$

19. $\dfrac{x - 3}{x + 4} \cdot \dfrac{x + 4}{2}$

20. $\dfrac{2n - 4}{5} \cdot \dfrac{10}{n - 2}$

21. $\dfrac{4x + 40}{3x} \cdot \dfrac{9x}{3x + 30}$

22. $\dfrac{4y^2 - 9}{4y^2} \cdot \dfrac{8y}{2y - 3}$

23. $\dfrac{-(2 - b)}{x} \cdot \dfrac{x^2}{b - 2}$

24. $\dfrac{a + b}{14} \cdot \dfrac{7}{b + a}$

For each expression, find the greatest common factor (GCF) of the numerator and denominator. Then simplify each expression.

25. $\dfrac{a + b}{a^2 - b^2}$

26. $\dfrac{1 - x^2}{x + 1}$

27. $\dfrac{8x^2 - x^3}{16 - 2x}$

28. $\dfrac{2y^2 - 18}{2y - 6}$

29. $\dfrac{y^2 - 9}{y^2 + 6y + 9}$

30. $\dfrac{y^2 + 8y - 20}{y^2 - 4}$

31. $\dfrac{2x^2 + 8x}{x^2 + x - 12}$

32. $\dfrac{6y^3 - 9y^2}{2y^2 + 5y - 12}$

33. $\dfrac{x^2 - x - 20}{x^2 + 7x + 12}$

34. $\dfrac{y^2 + 4y + 4}{3y^2 + 5y - 2}$

35. $\dfrac{a^2 + 2a + 1}{2a^2 + 3a + 1}$

36. $\dfrac{2b^2 - 9b + 9}{b^2 - 6b + 9}$

Find each product. Write each answer in simplest form.

37. $\dfrac{x^2 - y^2}{y^2} \cdot \dfrac{y^3}{y - x}$

38. $\dfrac{x^2 - y^2}{x + y} \cdot \dfrac{11}{x - y}$

39. $-\dfrac{x^2 - y^2}{x + y} \cdot \dfrac{1}{x - y}$

40. $\dfrac{(y - 2)^2}{(x - 4)^2} \cdot \dfrac{x - 4}{y - 2}$

41. $\dfrac{a^2 - b^2}{14} \cdot \dfrac{35}{a + b}$

42. $\dfrac{x^2 - y^2}{70} \cdot \dfrac{56}{4x - 4y}$

43. $\dfrac{3x + 15}{2} \cdot \dfrac{8}{x^2 + 4x - 5}$

44. $\dfrac{y^2 + 8y + 15}{y} \cdot \dfrac{y^2}{2y + 10}$

45. $\dfrac{a^3 - b^3}{b^2 - a^2} \cdot \dfrac{a + b}{a^2 + ab + b^2}$

46. $\dfrac{x^2 - 3x - 10}{x + 2} \cdot \dfrac{y^3}{5 - x}$

47. $\dfrac{3m^2 - m}{5m + 10} \cdot \dfrac{4 - m^2}{6m}$

48. $\dfrac{x^2 - 8x - 48}{2(12 - x)} \cdot \dfrac{4x + 4y}{x + y}$

49. $\dfrac{x^2 + 7x + 12}{x^2 - 9} \cdot \dfrac{8x}{16y}$

50. $\dfrac{c^2 - 4cd}{3a} \cdot \dfrac{18a^2b}{c - 4d}$

51. $\dfrac{x^2 + 3x - 10}{x^2 + 8x + 15} \cdot \dfrac{x^2 + 5x + 6}{x^2 + 4x + 4}$

52. $\dfrac{x^3 + y^3}{x^2 - y^2} \cdot \dfrac{3a}{9ab} \cdot \dfrac{6xb}{7x}$

53. $\dfrac{x^3 + 3x^2 + 3x + 1}{x + 5} \cdot \dfrac{x^2 - 25}{x + 1}$

54. $\dfrac{x^4 - 1}{x + 2} \cdot \dfrac{x^2 - 4}{x - 1}$

55. $\dfrac{a^3 - b^3}{a + b} \cdot \dfrac{a^2 - b^2}{a^2 + ab + b^2}$

56. $\dfrac{y^2 - y - 12}{y + 12} \cdot \dfrac{y^2 - 4y - 12}{y - 4}$

57. $\dfrac{w^2 - 11w + 24}{w^2 - 18w + 80} \cdot \dfrac{w^2 - 15w + 50}{w^2 - 9w + 20}$

58. $\dfrac{2x^2 + x - 15}{4x^2 + 2x - 30} \cdot \dfrac{6x^2 - 8x + 2}{3x^2 + 8x - 3}$

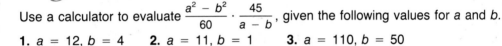

Using Calculators _____ Evaluating Expressions

Use a calculator to evaluate $\dfrac{a^2 - b^2}{60} \cdot \dfrac{45}{a - b}$, given the following values for a and b.

1. $a = 12, b = 4$ **2.** $a = 11, b = 1$ **3.** $a = 110, b = 50$

4. $a = 24, b = 0$ **5.** $a = 25, b = 25$ **6.** $a = 0, b = 60$

7. Simplify the expression above, then repeat exercises 1–6 using the simplified expression. Is the simplified expression equivalent to the original expression for all values of a and b?

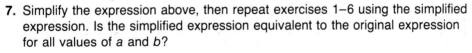

11-2 Dividing Rational Expressions

Recall that dividing by a fraction is the same as multiplying by its multiplicative inverse.

$$\frac{3}{8} \div \frac{3}{4} = \frac{3}{8} \cdot \frac{4}{3}$$
The inverse of $\frac{3}{4}$ is $\frac{4}{3}$.

$$= \frac{12}{24}$$

$$= \frac{1}{2}$$
The GCF is 12.

Similarly, dividing by a rational algebraic expression is the same as multiplying by its multiplicative inverse.

Recall that a fraction names a rational number.

For all rational expressions $\frac{a}{b}$ and $\frac{c}{d}$, b, c, and $d \neq 0$,

$$\frac{a}{b} \div \frac{c}{d} = \frac{a}{b} \cdot \frac{d}{c}.$$

Dividing Rational Expressions

Examples

1 Find $\dfrac{4x^2y}{15a^3b^3} \div \dfrac{2xy^2}{5ab^3}$.

$$\frac{4x^2y}{15a^3b^3} \div \frac{2xy^2}{5ab^3} = \frac{4x^2y}{15a^3b^3} \cdot \frac{5ab^3}{2xy^2}$$
The inverse of $\frac{2xy^2}{5ab^3}$ is $\frac{5ab^3}{2xy^2}$.

$$= \frac{20x^2yab^3}{30xy^2a^3b^3}$$

$$= \frac{2x}{3ya^2}$$
The GCF is $10xyab^3$.

2 Find $\dfrac{x^2}{x^2 - 25y^2} \div \dfrac{x}{x + 5y}$.

$$\frac{x^2}{x^2 - 25y^2} \div \frac{x}{x + 5y} = \frac{x^2}{x^2 - 25y^2} \cdot \frac{x + 5y}{x}$$
The inverse of $\frac{x}{x + 5y}$ is $\frac{x + 5y}{x}$.

$$= \frac{x^2(x + 5y)}{x(x^2 - 25y^2)}$$

$$= \frac{x^2(x + 5y)}{x(x + 5y)(x - 5y)}$$
Factor $x^2 - 25y^2$.

$$= \frac{x}{x - 5y}$$
The GCF is $x(x + 5y)$.

A complex rational expression, also called a **complex fraction,** is an expression whose numerator or denominator, or both, contain rational expressions.

$$\frac{\frac{4 - x^2}{2}}{\frac{2 - x}{5}} \qquad \frac{\frac{1}{x} + 3}{\frac{2}{x} + 5} \qquad \frac{\frac{8}{x}}{3 - y}$$

To simplify a complex fraction, treat it as a division problem.

Example

3 Simplify $\dfrac{\dfrac{4 - x^2}{2}}{\dfrac{2 - x}{5}}$.

$$\frac{\dfrac{4 - x^2}{2}}{\dfrac{2 - x}{5}} = \frac{4 - x^2}{2} \div \frac{2 - x}{5}$$

$$= \frac{4 - x^2}{2} \cdot \frac{5}{2 - x} \qquad \text{The inverse of } \frac{2 - x}{5} \text{ is } \frac{5}{2 - x}.$$

$$= \frac{5(4 - x^2)}{2(2 - x)}$$

$$= \frac{5(2 + x)(2 - x)}{2(2 - x)} \qquad \text{Factor.}$$

$$= \frac{5(2 + x)}{2} \qquad \text{The GCF is } 2 - x.$$

Exploratory Exercises

State the multiplicative inverse of each expression.

1. $\dfrac{3}{8}$

2. $-\dfrac{7}{43}$

3. $\dfrac{7x}{9y}$

4. $\dfrac{18x}{7}$

5. 16

6. $-\dfrac{3}{22}$

7. $\dfrac{x + y}{2}$

8. $\dfrac{x^2 - 8}{x - 1}$

9. $\dfrac{(x + 4)^2}{(x - 3)^2}$

10. $x + a$

11. $\dfrac{1}{x - y}$

12. $-\dfrac{2x}{a^2 - b^2}$

State a multiplication expression for each of the following.

13. $\dfrac{3}{8} \div \dfrac{1}{2}$

14. $-\dfrac{5}{6} \div \dfrac{1}{3}$

15. $\dfrac{a^2}{b^2} \div \dfrac{b^2}{a^2}$

16. $\dfrac{p^3}{2q} \div \dfrac{-p^2}{4q}$

17. $\dfrac{3m}{m + 1} \div (m - 2)$

18. $\dfrac{y^2}{x + 2} \div \dfrac{y}{x + 2}$

Written Exercises

Find the multiplicative inverse of each expression and simplify.

1. $\dfrac{14}{a^2}$

2. $-\dfrac{9}{15ab}$

3. $\dfrac{x + y}{ab}$

4. $\dfrac{3x}{x^2 + 7x}$

5. $\dfrac{a^2 + ab + b^2}{a^2 - b^2}$

6. $\dfrac{y - 4}{y^2 - 4y - 12}$

7. $\dfrac{3x + 3}{x^2 + 2x - 3}$

8. $\dfrac{3x - 21}{x^2 - 49}$

9. $\dfrac{y^2 - yw}{w^2 - y^2}$

Find each quotient. Write each answer in simplest form.

10. $-\dfrac{16.8}{7} \div \dfrac{8.4}{35}$

11. $\dfrac{7}{a} \div \dfrac{14}{a^2}$

12. $-\dfrac{3}{5a} \div -\dfrac{9}{15ab}$

13. $\dfrac{1}{x} \div -\dfrac{3}{x^2}$

14. $-\dfrac{b^3c}{d} \div \dfrac{bc}{d^2}$

15. $\dfrac{a^2b}{2c} \div \dfrac{a^2b^2}{c^2}$

16. $\dfrac{3d^3c}{a^4} \div -\dfrac{6dc}{a^5}$

17. $\dfrac{(ab)^3}{d^3} \div \dfrac{a^2b^4}{(cd)^4}$

18. $\dfrac{13a^2}{14c} \div \dfrac{26a^3}{70c^2}$

19. $\dfrac{(x+y)^2}{a} \div \dfrac{x+y}{ab}$

20. $\dfrac{x+y}{a} \div \dfrac{x+y}{a^2}$

21. $\dfrac{5}{m-3} \div \dfrac{10}{m-3}$

22. $\dfrac{11}{m+6} \div \dfrac{22}{(m+6)^2}$

23. $\dfrac{a^2-b^2}{2a} \div \dfrac{a-b}{6a}$

24. $\dfrac{y-5}{6} \div \dfrac{y-5}{18}$

25. $\dfrac{2x+2}{x^2+5x+6} \div \dfrac{3x+3}{x^2+2x-3}$

26. $\dfrac{3x-21}{x^2-49} \div \dfrac{3x}{x^2+7x}$

27. $\dfrac{a^2+2a-15}{a-3} \div \dfrac{a^2-4}{2}$

28. $\dfrac{y^2-y}{w^2-y^2} \div \dfrac{y^2-2y+1}{1-y}$

Simplify each expression.

29. $\dfrac{\dfrac{x^2-y^2}{2}}{\dfrac{x-y}{4}}$

30. $\dfrac{\dfrac{w^2+2w+1}{w+1}}{3}$

31. $\dfrac{\dfrac{5a^2-20}{2a+2}}{\dfrac{10a-20}{4a}}$

32. $\dfrac{\dfrac{x^2-1}{x^2-3x-10}}{\dfrac{x^2-12x+35}{x^2+3x+2}}$

33. $\dfrac{\dfrac{2y}{y^2-4}}{\dfrac{3}{y^2-4y+4}}$

34. $\dfrac{\dfrac{c^2+2c-3}{3c+3}}{\dfrac{c^2+5c+6}{2c+2}}$

35. $\dfrac{\dfrac{p^2+7p}{3p}}{\dfrac{49-p^2}{3p-21}}$

36. $\dfrac{\dfrac{9-4t^2}{t^2+6t+9}}{\dfrac{8t-12}{2t^2+5t-3}}$

37. $\dfrac{\dfrac{3+10t^2-17t}{5t^2+4t-1}}{\dfrac{4t^2-9}{3+5t+2t^2}}$

38. $\dfrac{\dfrac{m^2+15m+54}{m+6}}{\dfrac{m+9}{3}}$

39. $\dfrac{\dfrac{x}{x^2-9}}{\dfrac{3x-3}{x^2-x-6}}$

40. $\dfrac{\dfrac{3m}{2m^2+7m-15}}{\dfrac{6}{2m^2-3m}}$

Challenge _____

Simplify each expression.

41. $\dfrac{(a^2-5a+6)^{-1}}{(a-2)^{-2}} \div \dfrac{(a-3)^{-1}}{(a-2)^{-2}}$

42. $\dfrac{(x^2+7x+10)^{-1}}{(x+2)(x-5)^{-2}} \div \dfrac{(x+2)^{-2}}{(x-5)^{-2}}$

The position of symbols is very important in algebra. Study the list of expressions below.

$$2x \qquad 2 - x \qquad x - 2 \qquad \frac{x}{2} \qquad \frac{2}{x} \qquad x^2 \qquad \frac{x^2}{x + 2}$$

Each expression contains the symbols 2 and x. However, each expression says something different. The same expressions are listed below. The arrows indicate the order in which the symbols usually are read, and the words on the right are English translations of the expressions.

$2x \rightarrow$ two times x

$2 - x \rightarrow$ two minus x

$x - 2 \rightarrow$ x minus two

$\frac{x}{2}$ x divided by two

$\frac{2}{x}$ two divided by x

x^2 x squared

$\frac{x^2}{x + 2}$ x squared divided by the quantity x plus two.

Exercises

As quickly as possible, look at each list of expressions. Which expressions in the list are the same as the first expression?

1. $\dfrac{x^3}{3}$ **a.** $\dfrac{x}{3}$ **b.** $\dfrac{x^3}{3}$ **c.** $\dfrac{x}{3^3}$ **d.** $\dfrac{3x}{3}$

2. $\dfrac{(cd)^3}{a}$ **a.** $\dfrac{(cd)^3}{a}$ **b.** $\dfrac{cd^3}{a}$ **c.** $\dfrac{3(cd)}{a}$ **d.** $\dfrac{(cd)^3}{a}$

3. $\dfrac{1}{x - y}$ **a.** $\dfrac{1}{y - x}$ **b.** $\dfrac{1}{x + y}$ **c.** $\dfrac{x}{1 - y}$ **d.** $\dfrac{1}{x - y}$

4. $\dfrac{x^2 - 4}{x - 1}$ **a.** $\dfrac{x - 4}{x - 1}$ **b.** $\dfrac{x^2 - 4}{x - 1}$ **c.** $\dfrac{x^2 - 4}{x^2 - 1}$ **d.** $\dfrac{4 - x^2}{x^2 - 1}$

5. $\dfrac{8x^2 - x^3}{16 - 2x}$ **a.** $\dfrac{8x^2 - x^3}{2x - 16}$ **b.** $\dfrac{8x^3 - x^2}{16 - 2x}$ **c.** $\dfrac{8x^2 - x^3}{16 - 2x}$ **d.** $\dfrac{8x^3 - x^2}{2x - 16}$

6–10. In problems 1–5, which expressions are different from the first expression? How are they different?

11. Turn to page 347. Copy each expression in Exploratory Exercises 1–12. Draw an arrow to indicate the order you would read the symbols in each expression.

12. Write an English translation for each expression in problem 11.

11-3 Adding and Subtracting Rational Expressions

You add rational numbers like $\frac{7}{13}$ and $\frac{4}{13}$ in the following way.

$$\frac{7}{13} + \frac{4}{13} = \frac{7+4}{13} \quad \text{or} \quad \frac{11}{13}$$

If two rational expressions have common denominators, add them in a similar fashion.

$$\frac{7x}{13y^2} + \frac{4x}{13y^2} = \frac{7x+4x}{13y^2} \quad \text{or} \quad \frac{11x}{13y^2}$$

The sum of two rational expressions with a common denominator is the sum of the numerators over the common denominator.

To add two rational numbers with different denominators, first find two equivalent rational numbers with common denominators. Then add the equivalent fractions.

$$\frac{3}{8} + \frac{2}{3} = \frac{3 \cdot 3}{8 \cdot 3} + \frac{2 \cdot 8}{3 \cdot 8} \qquad \textit{The least common denominator is 24.}$$

$$= \frac{9}{24} + \frac{16}{24}$$

$$= \frac{9+16}{24}$$

$$= \frac{25}{24}$$

One way to find the least common denominator (LCD) is first to factor each denominator into its prime factors. For example, suppose you wish to add $\frac{5}{36}$ and $\frac{7}{24}$.

The prime factors of 36 and 24 are shown below.

$$36 = 2 \cdot 2 \cdot 3 \cdot 3$$
$$24 = 2 \cdot 2 \cdot 2 \cdot 3$$

The least common denominator of 36 and 24 contains each prime factor the greatest number of times that it appears.

$$\text{LCD} = 2 \cdot 2 \cdot 2 \cdot 3 \cdot 3 \text{ or } 72$$

Now, add the fractions.

$$\frac{5}{36} + \frac{7}{24} = \frac{10}{72} + \frac{21}{72} \qquad \frac{5}{36} = \frac{5 \cdot 2}{36 \cdot 2} = \frac{10}{72} \qquad \frac{7}{24} = \frac{7 \cdot 3}{24 \cdot 3} = \frac{21}{72}$$

$$= \frac{31}{72}$$

To add rational expressions with different denominators, follow the same procedure. First find two equivalent expressions with a common denominator. Then add the equivalent expressions.

350   *Rational Polynomial Expressions*

Examples

1 Find $\dfrac{7x}{15y^2} + \dfrac{y}{18xy}$.

First find the LCD of $15y^2$ and $18xy$.

$$15y^2 = 3 \cdot 5 \cdot y \cdot y \qquad\qquad 18xy = 2 \cdot 3 \cdot 3 \cdot x \cdot y$$

The LCD is $2 \cdot 3 \cdot 3 \cdot 5 \cdot x \cdot y \cdot y$ or $90xy^2$.

Rewrite each term using the LCD and add.

$$\begin{aligned}
\dfrac{7x}{15y^2} + \dfrac{y}{18xy} &= \dfrac{7x \cdot 6x}{15y^2 \cdot 6x} + \dfrac{y \cdot 5y}{18xy \cdot 5y} \\[2mm]
&= \dfrac{42x^2}{90xy^2} + \dfrac{5y^2}{90xy^2} \\[2mm]
&= \dfrac{42x^2 + 5y^2}{90xy^2}
\end{aligned}$$

2 Find $\dfrac{1}{x^2 - 2x - 15} + \dfrac{3x + 1}{2x - 10}$.

$$\begin{aligned}
\dfrac{1}{x^2 - 2x - 15} + \dfrac{3x + 1}{2x - 10} &= \dfrac{1}{(x - 5)(x + 3)} + \dfrac{3x + 1}{2(x - 5)} \\[2mm]
&= \dfrac{2}{2(x - 5)(x + 3)} + \dfrac{(3x + 1)(x + 3)}{2(x - 5)(x + 3)} \quad \text{\textit{The LCD is}} \\
&\hphantom{=} \quad\quad\quad\quad\quad\quad\quad\quad\quad\quad\quad\quad\quad \text{\textit{2(x − 5)(x + 3).}} \\[2mm]
&= \dfrac{2 + (3x + 1)(x + 3)}{2(x - 5)(x + 3)} \\[2mm]
&= \dfrac{2 + 3x^2 + 9x + x + 3}{2(x - 5)(x + 3)} \\[2mm]
&= \dfrac{3x^2 + 10x + 5}{2(x - 5)(x + 3)} \quad \text{\textit{Simplify the numerator.}}
\end{aligned}$$

Use a similar method to subtract rational expressions.

Example

3 Find $\dfrac{x + 4}{2x - 8} - \dfrac{x + 12}{4x - 16}$.

$$\begin{aligned}
\dfrac{x + 4}{2x - 8} - \dfrac{x + 12}{4x - 16} &= \dfrac{x + 4}{2(x - 4)} - \dfrac{x + 12}{4(x - 4)} \quad\quad \text{\textit{Factor each denominator.}} \\[2mm]
&= \dfrac{2(x + 4)}{4(x - 4)} - \dfrac{x + 12}{4(x - 4)} \quad\quad \text{\textit{The LCD is } 4(x − 4).} \\[2mm]
&= \dfrac{(2x + 8) - (x + 12)}{4(x - 4)} \quad\quad \text{\textit{Remember that } −(x + 12) = −x − 12.} \\[2mm]
&= \dfrac{x - 4}{4(x - 4)} \quad \text{or} \quad \dfrac{1}{4} \quad\quad \text{\textit{Simplify.}}
\end{aligned}$$

Complex fractions may involve sums or differences.

Example

4 Simplify $\dfrac{\dfrac{1}{x} - \dfrac{1}{y}}{1 + \dfrac{1}{x}}$.

$$\frac{\dfrac{1}{x} - \dfrac{1}{y}}{1 + \dfrac{1}{x}} = \frac{\dfrac{y}{xy} - \dfrac{x}{xy}}{\dfrac{x}{x} + \dfrac{1}{x}} \qquad \text{\textit{Simplify the numerator and denominator.}}$$

$$= \frac{\dfrac{y - x}{xy}}{\dfrac{x + 1}{x}}$$

$$= \frac{y - x}{xy} \div \frac{x + 1}{x} \qquad \text{\textit{Write the complex fraction as a division problem.}}$$

$$= \frac{y - x}{xy} \cdot \frac{x}{x + 1}$$

$$= \frac{y - x}{y(x + 1)} \quad \text{or} \quad \frac{y - x}{xy + y}$$

Exploratory Exercises

Find the least common denominator (LCD) for each pair of denominators given below.

1. 54, 28

2. 78, 39

3. 80, 125

4. 12, 27

5. $7a^2$, $14ab$

6. $36x^2y$, $20xyz$

7. $x(x - 2)$, $x^2 - 4$

8. $(x + 2)(x + 1)$, $x^2 - 1$

9. $x^2 + 2x + 1$, $x^2 - 9$

10. $3x + 15$, $x^2 + 3x - 15$

11. $x^2 - 8x$, $y^2 - 8y$

12. $96x^2$, $16(x + 9)$

Written Exercises

Find each sum. Write each answer in simplest form.

1. $\dfrac{5}{6a} + \dfrac{7}{4a}$

2. $\dfrac{7}{ab} + \dfrac{9}{b}$

3. $\dfrac{5}{a} + 7$

4. $3t - 7 + \dfrac{3t + 1}{t - 5}$

5. $\dfrac{3x}{x - y} + \dfrac{4x}{y - x}$

6. $\dfrac{3a + 2}{a + b} + \dfrac{4}{2a + 2b}$

7. $-\dfrac{18}{9xy} + \dfrac{7}{2x} - \dfrac{2}{3x^2}$

8. $\dfrac{1}{8b} + \dfrac{5 - 3b}{2b^2} + \dfrac{3b - 2}{16b^3}$

9. $\dfrac{x}{x^2 - 9} + \dfrac{1}{2x + 6}$

10. $y - 1 + \dfrac{1}{y - 1}$

11. $\dfrac{3}{a - 2} + \dfrac{2}{a - 3}$

12. $\dfrac{6}{x^2 + 4x + 4} + \dfrac{5}{x + 2}$

13. $\dfrac{3}{x^2 - 25} + \dfrac{6}{x - 5}$

14. $\dfrac{x - 1}{x^2 - 1} + \dfrac{3}{5x + 5}$

15. $\dfrac{5}{x^2 - 3x - 28} + \dfrac{7}{2x - 14}$

16. $\dfrac{a}{a + 4} + \dfrac{2}{a^2 + 8a + 16}$

17. $\dfrac{2}{y^2 - 4y - 5} + \dfrac{5}{y^2 - 2y - 15}$

18. $\dfrac{2a}{3a - 15} + \dfrac{-16a + 20}{3a^2 - 12a - 15}$

19. $\dfrac{m^2 + n^2}{m^2 - n^2} + \dfrac{m}{n - m} + \dfrac{n}{m + n}$

20. $\dfrac{x}{x - y} + \dfrac{y}{y^2 - x^2} + \dfrac{2x}{x + y}$

21. $\dfrac{x + 1}{x - 1} + \dfrac{x + 2}{x - 2} + \dfrac{x}{x^2 - 3x + 2}$

Find each difference. Write each answer in simplest form.

22. $\dfrac{3}{4a} - \dfrac{2}{5a} - \dfrac{1}{2a}$

23. $\dfrac{11}{9} - \dfrac{7}{2a} - \dfrac{6}{5a}$

24. $\dfrac{9}{y-2} - \dfrac{2}{1-y}$

25. $\dfrac{7}{y-8} - \dfrac{6}{8-y}$

26. $\dfrac{y}{y-9} - \dfrac{-9}{9-y}$

27. $\dfrac{8}{2y-16} - \dfrac{y}{8-y}$

28. $\dfrac{-4y}{y^2-4} - \dfrac{y}{y+2}$

29. $\dfrac{x}{x+3} - \dfrac{6x}{x^2-9}$

30. $3m + 1 - \dfrac{2m}{3m+1}$

31. $\dfrac{y-2}{y-4} - \dfrac{y-8}{y-4}$

32. $\dfrac{6-y}{y-2} - \dfrac{3+y}{2-y}$

33. $\dfrac{x}{x^2+2x+1} - \dfrac{x+2}{x+1} + \dfrac{3x}{x+1}$

34. $\dfrac{x^2-3x+1}{x^2-4} - \dfrac{x^2+2x+4}{2-x} + \dfrac{x-4}{x-2}$

35. $\dfrac{m+3}{m^2-6m+9} - \dfrac{8m-24}{9-m^2}$

36. $\dfrac{3b-1}{b^2-49} - \dfrac{3b+2}{14+5b-b^2}$

Simplify.

37. $\dfrac{\dfrac{x}{2} - \dfrac{x}{5}}{\dfrac{x}{3} - \dfrac{x}{6}}$

38. $\dfrac{\dfrac{2x}{ab} - \dfrac{5x}{4}}{\dfrac{3x}{a} - \dfrac{6x}{5}}$

39. $\dfrac{\dfrac{x+y}{x}}{\dfrac{1}{x} + \dfrac{1}{y}}$

40. $\dfrac{\dfrac{x}{y} - \dfrac{y}{x}}{\dfrac{1}{x} + \dfrac{1}{y}}$

41. $\dfrac{\dfrac{2}{x} + \dfrac{9}{x^2} - \dfrac{5}{x^3}}{2x - \dfrac{1}{2x}}$

42. $\dfrac{\dfrac{1}{a} - \dfrac{1}{a^2} - \dfrac{20}{a^3}}{\dfrac{1}{a} + \dfrac{8}{a^2} - \dfrac{16}{a^3}}$

43. $\dfrac{3 + \dfrac{5}{a+2}}{3 - \dfrac{10}{a+7}}$

44. $\dfrac{\dfrac{2x}{2x+1} - 1}{1 + \dfrac{2x}{1-2x}}$

45. $\dfrac{\dfrac{m+4}{m} - \dfrac{3}{m+5}}{\dfrac{m-1}{m^2+5m} + \dfrac{3}{m+5}}$

46. $\dfrac{\dfrac{5x}{x^2-16}}{\dfrac{10}{x-4} + \dfrac{10}{x+4}}$

47. $\dfrac{\dfrac{x+4}{x-6} + \dfrac{x+1}{x+2}}{\dfrac{4}{x^2-4x-12}}$

48. $\dfrac{\dfrac{5}{y+7} + \dfrac{2}{y}}{\dfrac{2}{y} - \dfrac{10}{y(y+7)}}$

49. $\dfrac{y + 2 + \dfrac{3}{y-5}}{\dfrac{4}{y-5} + 2}$

50. $\dfrac{(x+y)\left(\dfrac{1}{x} - \dfrac{1}{y}\right)}{(x-y)\left(\dfrac{1}{x} + \dfrac{1}{y}\right)}$

51. $\dfrac{n + 1 - \dfrac{2}{n}}{n + 4 + \dfrac{4}{n}}$

52. $\dfrac{m - \dfrac{1}{m}}{1 + \dfrac{4}{m} - \dfrac{5}{m^2}}$

53. $\dfrac{\dfrac{1}{x+5} + \dfrac{1}{x-3}}{\dfrac{2x^2-3x-5}{x^2+2x-15}}$

Challenge

Find each sum. Write each answer in simplest form.

54. $\dfrac{4b-1}{b^2-7b} + \dfrac{2}{b^2-49}$

55. $\dfrac{2x}{x^2-7x+10} + \dfrac{x-1}{x^2-25}$

56. $\dfrac{y}{y^2+4y-21} + \dfrac{4}{y^2+7y} + \dfrac{2y}{y^2-9}$

57. $\dfrac{3x}{4x^2-1} + \dfrac{5}{2x^2-x} + \dfrac{2x+1}{2x^2+5x+2}$

11-4 Solving Rational Equations

An equation that contains one or more rational expressions is called a **rational equation.** One way to solve a rational equation is to multiply both sides of the equation by the least common denominator (LCD).

Examples

1 Solve $\dfrac{x}{9} + \dfrac{x}{7} = 1$.

$$\frac{x}{9} + \frac{x}{7} = 1$$

$$63\left(\frac{x}{9} + \frac{x}{7}\right) = 63(1) \qquad \textit{The LCD is } 3 \cdot 3 \cdot 7 \textit{ or } 63.$$

$$63 \cdot \frac{x}{9} + 63 \cdot \frac{x}{7} = 63 \qquad \textit{Use the distributive property.}$$

$$7x + 9x = 63$$

$$16x = 63$$

$$x = \frac{63}{16}$$

The solution is $\dfrac{63}{16}$.

2 Solve $\dfrac{3}{4} - \dfrac{3}{y+2} = \dfrac{9}{28}$.

$$\frac{3}{4} - \frac{3}{y+2} = \frac{9}{28}$$

$$28(y+2)\left[\frac{3}{4} - \frac{3}{y+2}\right] = 28(y+2)\left[\frac{9}{28}\right] \qquad \textit{The LCD is } 2 \cdot 2 \cdot 7 \cdot (y+2)$$
$$\textit{or } 28(y+2).$$

$$28(y+2)\left(\frac{3}{4}\right) - 28(y+2)\left(\frac{3}{y+2}\right) = 9(y+2)$$

$$21y + 42 - 84 = 9y + 18$$

$$12y = 60$$

$$y = 5$$

Check:
$$\frac{3}{4} - \frac{3}{y+2} = \frac{9}{28}$$

$$\frac{3}{4} - \frac{3}{5+2} \overset{?}{=} \frac{9}{28} \qquad \textit{Substitute 5 for y.}$$

$$\frac{3}{4} - \frac{3}{7} \overset{?}{=} \frac{9}{28}$$

$$\frac{21}{28} - \frac{12}{28} \overset{?}{=} \frac{9}{28}$$

$$\frac{9}{28} = \frac{9}{28}$$

The solution is 5.

A rational expression is not defined when the denominator is zero. Therefore, any values assigned to the variables that result in a denominator of zero must be excluded. After both sides of the equation are multiplied by the LCD, some of these values may appear as solutions of the new equation.

Examples

3 Solve $\dfrac{7}{x-3} = \dfrac{x+4}{x-3}$.

$$\frac{7}{x-3} = \frac{x+4}{x-3}$$

$$(x-3)\left[\frac{7}{x-3}\right] = (x-3)\left[\frac{x+4}{x-3}\right] \qquad \textit{The LCD is x} - 3.$$

$$7 = x+4$$

$$3 = x$$

If x is 3, the denominator, $x - 3$, is 0. But division by zero is not defined. Thus, the original equation is *not* defined for 3 and the equation has *no* solution.

4 Solve $w + \dfrac{w}{w-1} = \dfrac{4w-3}{w-1}$.

$$w + \frac{w}{w-1} = \frac{4w-3}{w-1}$$

$$(w-1)\left[w + \frac{w}{w-1}\right] = (w-1)\left[\frac{4w-3}{w-1}\right] \qquad \textit{The LCD is w} - 1.$$

$$(w-1)w + w = 4w - 3$$

$$w^2 - w + w = 4w - 3$$

$$w^2 - 4w + 3 = 0$$

$$(w-3)(w-1) = 0$$

$$w = 3 \quad \text{or} \quad w = 1$$

The only solution is 3 because the original equation is *not* defined for 1.   *Why?*

Exploratory Exercises

Find the least common denominator (LCD) for the expressions in each equation. State the excluded values.

1. $\dfrac{1}{x} + \dfrac{1}{2} = \dfrac{2}{x}$

2. $\dfrac{3}{x+2} = \dfrac{4}{x-1}$

3. $\dfrac{1}{5} = \dfrac{2}{10y}$

4. $\dfrac{1}{4} = \dfrac{s-3}{8s}$

5. $\dfrac{6}{x} = \dfrac{9}{x^2}$

6. $\dfrac{7}{3a} + \dfrac{6}{5a^2} = 1$

7. $\dfrac{4}{x-3} = \dfrac{7}{x-2}$

8. $\dfrac{9}{x+5} = \dfrac{6}{x-3}$

9. $\dfrac{3}{m-5} = \dfrac{1}{6}$

10. $\dfrac{11}{2y} - \dfrac{2}{3y} = \dfrac{1}{6}$

11. $\dfrac{3m}{2+m} - \dfrac{5}{7} = 4$

12. $\dfrac{1-b}{1+b} + \dfrac{2b}{2b+3} = \dfrac{19}{6}$

Written Exercises

State the excluded values. Then solve and check.

1. $\dfrac{2}{x} + \dfrac{1}{4} = \dfrac{11}{12}$

2. $\dfrac{x^2}{6} - \dfrac{x}{3} = \dfrac{1}{2}$

3. $r^2 + \dfrac{17r}{6} = \dfrac{1}{2}$

4. $\dfrac{2y}{3} - \dfrac{y+3}{6} = 2$

5. $\dfrac{y+1}{3} + \dfrac{y-1}{3} = \dfrac{4}{3}$

6. $\dfrac{2y+1}{5} - \dfrac{2+7y}{15} = \dfrac{2}{3}$

7. $\dfrac{2y-5}{6} - \dfrac{y-5}{4} = \dfrac{3}{4}$

8. $\dfrac{4t-3}{5} - \dfrac{4-2t}{3} = 1$

9. $\dfrac{5+7p}{8} - \dfrac{3(5+p)}{10} = 2$

10. $\dfrac{2q-1}{3} - \dfrac{4q+5}{8} = -\dfrac{19}{24}$

11. $8 - \dfrac{2-5x}{4} = \dfrac{4x+9}{3}$

12. $\dfrac{3x+1}{4} - \dfrac{x+5}{5} = -2$

13. $x + 5 = \dfrac{6}{x}$

14. $a + 1 = \dfrac{6}{a}$

15. $\dfrac{1}{y^2-1} = \dfrac{2}{y^2+y-2}$

16. $\dfrac{x}{x^2-3} = \dfrac{5}{x+4}$

17. $x + \dfrac{12}{x} - 8 = 0$

18. $\dfrac{a}{a-1} + a = \dfrac{4a-3}{a-1}$

19. $x + \dfrac{x}{x-1} = \dfrac{4x-3}{x-1}$

20. $\dfrac{q}{q-5} + \dfrac{q}{q-5} = 3$

21. $1 + \dfrac{3}{y-1} = \dfrac{4}{3}$

22. $\dfrac{5}{6} - \dfrac{2m}{2m+3} = \dfrac{19}{6}$

23. $\dfrac{5}{2x} - \dfrac{3}{10} = \dfrac{1}{x}$

24. $\dfrac{1}{9} + \dfrac{1}{2a} = \dfrac{1}{a^2}$

25. $\dfrac{1}{x-1} + \dfrac{2}{x} = 0$

26. $\dfrac{1}{1-x} = 1 - \dfrac{x}{x-1}$

27. $\dfrac{4t}{3t-2} + \dfrac{2t}{3t+2} = 2$

28. $\dfrac{2p}{2p+3} - \dfrac{2p}{2p-3} = 1$

29. $\dfrac{12}{x^2-16} - \dfrac{24}{x-4} = 3$

30. $\dfrac{4}{x-2} - \dfrac{x+6}{x+1} = 1$

31. $\dfrac{9}{x-3} = \dfrac{x-4}{x-3} + \dfrac{1}{4}$

32. $\dfrac{x-4}{x-2} = \dfrac{x-2}{x+2} + \dfrac{1}{x-2}$

33. $\dfrac{3x-3}{4x} = \dfrac{6x-9}{6x} + \dfrac{1}{3x}$

34. $\dfrac{x-3}{2x} = \dfrac{x-2}{2x+1} - \dfrac{1}{2}$

35. $\dfrac{5}{x+2} = \dfrac{5}{x} + \dfrac{2}{3x}$

36. $\dfrac{6}{a-7} = \dfrac{a-49}{a^2-7a} + \dfrac{1}{a}$

37. $\dfrac{-2}{x-1} = \dfrac{2}{x+2} - \dfrac{4}{x-3}$

38. $\dfrac{2}{y+2} - \dfrac{y}{2-y} = \dfrac{y^2+4}{y^2-4}$

39. $\dfrac{4x^2}{x^2-9} - \dfrac{2x}{x+3} = \dfrac{3}{x-3}$

40. $\dfrac{t+4}{t} + \dfrac{3}{t-4} = \dfrac{-16}{t^2-4t}$

41. $\dfrac{y}{y-5} + \dfrac{17}{25-y^2} = \dfrac{1}{y+5}$

42. $\dfrac{x+3}{x+2} = 2 - \dfrac{3}{x^2+5x+6}$

43. $\dfrac{1}{n-2} = \dfrac{2n+1}{n^2+2n-8} + \dfrac{2}{n+4}$

44. $\dfrac{x}{x^2-1} + \dfrac{2}{x+1} = \dfrac{1}{2x-2}$

Challenge

45. Find the values of A and B, if
$$\dfrac{A}{x+2} + \dfrac{B}{2x-3} = \dfrac{5x-11}{2x^2+x-6}.$$

mini-review

Solve.

1. The Lewis Parcel Service charges $2.50 per pound for the first 3 pounds and $1.00 for each pound thereafter. What is the cost of sending an 8 lb package?

2. The sum of a number and its reciprocal is $\dfrac{10}{3}$. Find the number.

3. Find two numbers whose difference is 48 and whose product is a minimum.

4. Find $f(x+h)$ for $f(x) = x^2 - \dfrac{2}{5}x$.

5. Find the center, foci, and lengths of the major axis and minor axis for the ellipse that has the given equation.
$$4x^2 + y^2 = 4$$

Applications in Photography

Connie Hardesty is a photographer. To take sharp, clear pictures she must focus the camera.

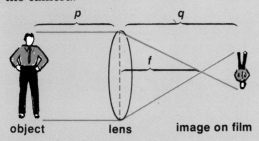

object   lens   image on film

The following formula can be used to determine the distance the lens must be from the film for the camera to be focused.

$$\frac{1}{p} + \frac{1}{q} = \frac{1}{f}$$

p is the distance from the lens to the object.
q is the distance from the lens to the image on the film.
f is the focal length of the lens.

Example: A camera has a lens with a focal length of 10 cm. Connie wants to photograph a flower that is 80 cm away. What must the distance be from the lens to the film for the camera to be in focus?

$$\frac{1}{p} + \frac{1}{q} = \frac{1}{f}$$

$$\frac{1}{80} + \frac{1}{q} = \frac{1}{10} \qquad p = 80, f = 10$$

$$q + 80 = 8q \qquad \text{Multiply both sides by 80q.}$$

$$80 = 7q \quad \text{or} \quad q \approx 11.4$$

The lens must be about 11.4 cm from the film.

Exercises

For the following values of p and f, find q.

1. $p = 45$ cm, $f = 5$ cm

2. $p = 600$ mm, $f = 60$ mm

3. $p = 28$ in., $f = 6$ in.

4. $p = 50$ cm, $f = 0.5$ cm

Solve each problem.

5. A camera has a lens with a focal length of 10 in. When Usha has the lens 12 in. from the film, the camera is focused, to take a picture of her dog. How far from the lens is the dog?

6. Carl wants to take a picture of his house which is 10 m away. When the camera is focused, the lens is 5 cm from the film. What is the focal length of the lens?

11-5 Problem Solving: **Using Rational Equations**

The city swimming pool can be filled from two sources, a well or city water. The pipe for the city water fills the pool in 6 hours. The pipe from the well fills the pool in 10 hours. How long will it take the pool to fill if both sources are piped in at the same time? This question can be answered by solving a rational equation.

Explore   Let h stand for the number of hours it will take to fill the pool.

What fraction of the pool can be filled with city water in 1 hour? $\dfrac{1}{6}$

What fraction of the pool can be filled with well water in 1 hour? $\dfrac{1}{10}$

What fraction of the pool can be filled with city water in h hours? $h \cdot \dfrac{1}{6}$ or $\dfrac{h}{6}$

What fraction of the pool can be filled with well water in h hours? $h \cdot \dfrac{1}{10}$ or $\dfrac{h}{10}$

Plan   Now write an equation.

$$\underset{\substack{\textit{fraction filled with} \\ \textit{city water in h hours}}}{} + \underset{\substack{\textit{fraction filled with} \\ \textit{well water in h hours}}}{} = \underset{\substack{\textit{whole pool filled from} \\ \textit{both sources in h hours}}}{}$$

$$\dfrac{h}{6} \qquad + \qquad \dfrac{h}{10} \qquad = \qquad 1$$

Solve   Solve the equation.

$$\dfrac{h}{6} + \dfrac{h}{10} = 1$$

$$30\left(\dfrac{h}{6} + \dfrac{h}{10}\right) = 30(1) \qquad \textit{The LCD is } 2 \cdot 3 \cdot 5 \textit{ or } 30.$$

$$30 \cdot \dfrac{h}{6} + 30 \cdot \dfrac{h}{10} = 30 \qquad \textit{Use the distributive property.}$$

$$5h + 3h = 30$$

$$8h = 30$$

$$h = \dfrac{30}{8} \text{ or } 3\dfrac{3}{4} \qquad \text{It will take } 3\dfrac{3}{4} \text{ hours.}$$

Examine $\left(3\dfrac{3}{4}\right)\left(\dfrac{1}{6}\right) + \left(3\dfrac{3}{4}\right)\left(\dfrac{1}{10}\right) = \dfrac{5}{8} + \dfrac{3}{8} = 1$ ✔

The following is another example of how rational expressions can be used to solve verbal problems.

Example

1 **A car travels 300 kilometers in the same time that a train travels 200 kilometers. The speed of the car is 20 kilometers per hour more than the speed of the train. Find the speed of the car and the speed of the train.**

Explore Let r stand for the speed of the car.

Plan

$$\text{time car travels} = \text{time train travels}$$

$$\frac{\text{distance car travels}}{\text{rate car travels}} = \frac{\text{distance train travels}}{\text{rate train travels}} \quad \text{Since } d = rt, \text{ we know}$$

$$\frac{300}{r} = \frac{200}{r - 20} \quad \text{that } t = \frac{d}{r}.$$

Solve

$$r(r - 20)\frac{300}{r} = r(r - 20)\frac{200}{r - 20} \quad \text{The LCD is } r(r - 20).$$

$$300(r - 20) = 200(r)$$

$$300r - 6000 = 200r$$

$$-6000 = -100r$$

$$60 = r \quad \text{and } 40 = r - 20$$

The car's speed is 60 kilometers per hour, and the train's speed is 40 kilometers per hour.

Examine The car travels 300 kilometers at 60 kilometers per hour. It travels 5 hours. The train travels 200 kilometers at 40 kilometers per hour. It also travels 5 hours. The speeds are correct.

Written Exercises

Solve each problem.

1. One bricklayer can build a wall of a certain size in 5 hours. Another bricklayer can do the same job in 4 hours. If the bricklayers work together, how long will it take to do the job?

2. One hose can fill the Sunshine's small swimming pool in 6 hours. A second, newer hose can fill the pool in 4 hours. If both hoses are used, how long will it take to fill the pool?

3. Jan Zeiss can tile a floor in 14 hours. Together Jan and her helper Bill can tile the same size floor in 9 hours. How long would it take Bill to do the job alone?

4. Elena Dias can paint a 9 by 12 room in $1\frac{1}{2}$ hours. If Luisa Alicea helps, they can paint the same size room in 1 hour. How long would it take Luisa to paint such a room by herself?

5. A painter works on a job for 10 days and is then joined by her helper. Together they finish the job in 6 more days. Her helper could have done the job alone in 30 days. How long would it have taken the painter to do the job alone?

6. A tank can be filled by a hose in 10 hours. The tank can be emptied by a drain pipe in 20 hours. If the drain pipe is open while the tank is filling, how long will it take to fill?

7. The denominator of a fraction is 1 less than twice the numerator. If 7 is added to both numerator and denominator, the resulting fraction has a value of $\frac{7}{10}$. Find the original fraction.

8. Five times the multiplicative inverse of a number is added to the number and the result is $10\frac{1}{2}$. What is the number?

9. The ratio of 4 less than a number to 26 more than that number is 1 to 3. What is the number?

10. Two numbers are in a ratio of 6 to 7. If the first is increased by 2 and the second is increased by 1, the resulting numbers are in the ratio of 4 to 5. Find the original numbers.

11. A boat travels at a rate of 15 kilometers per hour in still water. It travels 60 kilometers upstream in the same time that it travels 90 kilometers downstream. What is the rate of the current?

12. A plane flies from Chicago to Los Angeles, a distance of 2000 miles, in 4 hours. It flies against a 50 mph wind. It returns in $3\frac{1}{3}$ hours. Find the speed of the plane in still air.

13. Increasing the average speed of the Pickerington Express Bus by 13 km/h resulted in the 260 km trip taking an hour less than before. What was the original average speed of the bus?

14. The speed of the current in the Mississippi River is 5 miles per hour. A boat travels downstream 26 miles and returns in $10\frac{2}{3}$ hours. What is its speed in still water?

15. Conrad can jog to Chris's house in 10 minutes. Chris can ride her bike to Conrad's house in 6 minutes. If they start from their houses at the same time, in how many minutes do they meet?

16. The load capacities of two trucks are in the ratio of 5 to 2. The smaller truck has a capacity 3 tons less than that of the larger truck. What is the capacity of the larger truck?

17. The simple interest for one year on a sum of money is $108. Suppose the interest rate is increased by 2%. Then $450 less than the original sum could be invested and yield the same annual interest. How much is the original sum of money, and what is the original rate of interest?

18. Two candles are the same length. One burns up in 6 hours and the other in 9 hours. If they are both lighted at the same time, how long is it before one is twice as long as the other?

19. Pipe A can fill a tank in 4 hours and pipe B can fill the tank is 3 hours. With the tank empty, pipe A is turned on, and one hour later, pipe B is turned on. How long will pipe B run before the tank is full?

20. A chemist needs to make 1000 milliliters of a 30% alcohol solution by mixing 25% and 55% solutions. How much of each should he use?

21. At what time between 5 o'clock and 6 o'clock do the hands of a clock coincide?

mini-review

Solve.
1. In which quadrant does $(-3, -6)$ lie?
2. Find the transpose and inverse for
$$\begin{bmatrix} -2 & 5 \\ 3 & 1 \end{bmatrix}.$$
3. Find values for x and y for which this sentence is true.
$$(x - y) + (x + y)i = 2 - 4i$$

Simplify.
4. $\dfrac{1 + \sqrt{2}}{3 - \sqrt{2}}$

5. $\dfrac{-39c^3d^4}{13(cd)^2}$

11-6 Graphing Rational Functions

Before graphing a rational function, it is often helpful to find values for which the function is undefined. The graph of the rational function approaches lines that contain these values. However, they do not intersect these lines. These lines are called **asymptotes**.

Examples

1 Graph $y = \dfrac{x}{x-1}$.

The function is undefined when x is 1. The graph of the equation $x = 1$ is a vertical asymptote.

Now solve for x.

$$y = \frac{x}{x-1}$$

$$y(x - 1) = x$$

$$xy - y = x$$

$$xy - x = y$$

$$x(y - 1) = y$$

$$x = \frac{y}{y-1}$$

The function is also undefined when y is 1. The graph of the equation $y = 1$ is a horizontal asymptote.

Then sketch the graph by plotting points. Be sure to test values that are close to and on either side of the asymptotes.

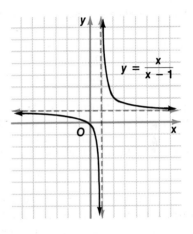

$$y = \frac{x}{x-1}$$

2 Graph $y = \dfrac{2}{(x-2)^2}$.

The graph of the equation $x = 2$ is a vertical asymptote. If y is 0, no value of x exists. Thus, the graph of the equation $y = 0$ is a horizontal asymptote. Also note that the value of y could never be negative.   *Why?*

Sketch the graph by plotting points.

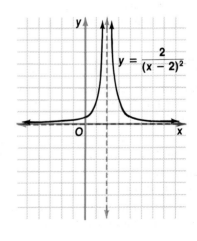

$$y = \frac{2}{(x-2)^2}$$

Example

3 Graph $y = \dfrac{4}{(x + 2)(x - 3)}$.

There are two vertical asymptotes, the graph of the equations $x = -2$ and $x = 3$.

If y is 0, no value of x exists. Thus, the graph of the equation $y = 0$ is a horizontal asymptote.

Plot points on either side of each asymptote and sketch the graph.

A calculator or computer is helpful in determining points on the graph.

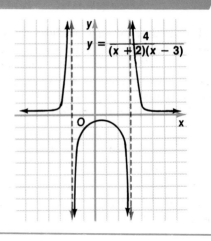

Exploratory Exercises

State the equations of the vertical and horizontal asymptotes for each rational function.

1. $y = \dfrac{3}{x - 1}$

2. $y = \dfrac{1}{x}$

3. $y = \dfrac{1}{x - 3}$

4. $y = \dfrac{4}{x + 2}$

5. $y = \dfrac{6}{(x - 6)^2}$

6. $y = \dfrac{3}{(x + 1)^3}$

7. $y = \dfrac{4}{(x - 1)(x + 5)}$

8. $y = \dfrac{-6}{x - 3}$

9. $y = \dfrac{-2}{(x - 1)(x - 4)}$

Written Exercises

Sketch the graph of each rational function. Be sure to sketch the asymptotes on each graph.

1. $y = \dfrac{x - 1}{x - 4}$

2. $y = \dfrac{3}{x + 2}$

3. $y = \dfrac{x - 5}{x + 1}$

4. $y = \dfrac{1}{x}$

5. $y = \dfrac{x}{x - 2}$

6. $y = \dfrac{-4}{x - 1}$

7. $y = \dfrac{-2}{(x - 3)^2}$

8. $y = \dfrac{2}{(x - 2)(x + 1)}$

9. $y = \dfrac{-1}{x - 6}$

10. $y = \dfrac{-5}{(x - 3)(x + 1)}$

11. $y = \dfrac{4x}{x - 1}$

12. $y = \dfrac{x}{x + 1}$

13. $y = \dfrac{3}{(x - 4)^2}$

14. $y = \dfrac{1}{(x + 2)^2}$

15. $y = \dfrac{8}{(x - 1)(x + 3)}$

Challenge

Sketch the graph of each rational function. Be sure to sketch the asymptotes on each graph.

16. $y = \dfrac{-8}{(x - 1)(x + 3)}$

17. $y = \dfrac{x}{x^2 - 4}$

18. $y = \dfrac{x - 1}{x^2 - 9}$

11-7   Direct and Inverse Variation

Recall that direct variation is a linear function. Direct variation can be described by an equation of the form $y = kx$ where k is a constant *not* equal to zero. For example, gravity on earth is about six times as great as the gravity on the moon. Thus, weight on earth varies directly with weight on the moon. This relationship can be described by the following equation.

$$y = 6x$$

y stands for weight on earth
x stands for weight on moon
6 is the constant of variation

Direct variation can be related to proportion. Suppose that x_1 and y_1 satisfy the equation $y = kx$. And suppose that x_2 and y_2 also satisfy the equation $y = kx$.

$$y_1 = kx_1 \quad \text{and} \quad y_2 = kx_2$$
$$\frac{y_1}{y_2} = \frac{kx_1}{kx_2} \qquad \textit{Division Property of Equality}$$
$$\frac{x_1}{x_2} = \frac{y_1}{y_2} \qquad \textit{Simplify.}$$

Thus, direct variation can be written as a proportion.

What are other forms of this proportion?

Example

1   **If y varies directly as x, and $y = 12$ when $x = 15$, find x when $y = 21$.**

Use the proportion $\dfrac{x_1}{x_2} = \dfrac{y_1}{y_2}$.

$$\frac{15}{x_2} = \frac{12}{21} \qquad \textit{Substitute. } x_1 = 15,\ y_1 = 12,\ y_2 = 21$$
$$x_2 = 26.25 \qquad \textit{Solve for } x_2.$$

Many quantities are said to be **inversely proportional** or to **vary inversely** with each other. For example, the amount of current in a circuit is inversely proportional to the amount of resistance in the circuit. That is, as the amount of resistance decreases, the amount of current increases proportionally. The following chart shows several corresponding values.

Current (amps)	0.5	1.0	1.5	2.0	2.5	3.0	4.0	5.0
Resistance (ohms)	12	6.0	4.0	3.0	2.4	2.0	1.5	1.2

Let c stand for the amount of current.
Let r stand for the amount of resistance.

The relationship between these quantities can be described by the following equation.

$$c = \frac{6}{r}$$

A rational equation in two variables of the form $y = \dfrac{k}{x}$, where k is a constant, is called an **inverse variation**. The constant k is called the **constant of variation**, and y is said to **vary inversely as** x.

Definition of Inverse Variation

Inverse variation can also be related to proportions or products. Suppose x_1 and y_1 satisfy the equation $y = \dfrac{k}{x}$. And suppose that x_2 and y_2 also satisfy the equation $y = \dfrac{k}{x}$.

$$y_1 = \frac{k}{x_1} \quad \text{and} \quad y_2 = \frac{k}{x_2}$$

$$x_1 y_1 = k \qquad\quad x_2 y_2 = k$$

$$x_1 y_1 = x_2 y_2 \qquad \textit{Substitution Property of Equality}$$

$$\frac{x_1}{x_2} = \frac{y_2}{y_1} \qquad \textit{Divide both sides by } y_1\, x_2 \textit{ and simplify.}$$

Note that inverse variation yields a different proportion than direct variation.

Examples

2 **If y varies inversely as x, and $y = 3$ when $x = 4$, find y when $x = 18$.**

Use the proportion $\dfrac{x_1}{x_2} = \dfrac{y_2}{y_1}$.

$$\frac{4}{18} = \frac{y_2}{3} \qquad \textit{Substitute 4 for } x_1,\ 18 \textit{ for } x_2,\ \textit{and 3 for } y_1.$$

$$4 \cdot 3 = 18 \cdot y_2$$

$$\frac{12}{18} = y_2$$

$$y_2 = \frac{2}{3}$$

3 **The volume of any gas varies inversely with its pressure as long as the temperature remains constant. The volume of a particular gas is 1600 milliliters when the pressure is 25 centimeters of mercury. What is the volume of the gas at the same temperature when the pressure is 40 centimeters of mercury?**

Let V_1 stand for the first volume of gas, 1600 ml.
Let P_1 stand for the first gas pressure, 25 cm of mercury.
Let P_2 stand for the second gas pressure, 40 cm of mercury.

Since volume and pressure are inversely proportional, $V_1 P_1 = V_2 P_2$.

$$1600 \cdot 25 = V_2 \cdot 40$$

$$\frac{40{,}000}{40} = V_2$$

$$1000 = V_2 \qquad \text{The volume is 1000 milliliters.}$$

Exploratory Exercises

State whether each equation represents direct variation or inverse variation. Then name the constant of variation.

1. $x = 4y$

2. $xy = -3$

3. $y = -4x$

4. $y = \dfrac{7}{x}$

5. $5 = \dfrac{y}{x}$

6. $\dfrac{x}{y} = -6$

7. $\dfrac{3}{4}y = x$

8. $\dfrac{x}{2} = y$

9. $x = \dfrac{9}{y}$

10. $y = \dfrac{3}{x}$

11. $a = 4b$

12. $\dfrac{3}{5}a = -\dfrac{5}{4}b$

Written Exercises

In each of the following, y varies directly as x.

1. If $y = 8$, then $x = 2$.
Find y when $x = 9$.

2. If $y = 10$, then $x = -3$.
Find x when $y = 4$.

3. If $x = 4$, then $y = 0.5$.
Find y when $x = 9$.

4. If $y = 11$, then $x = \dfrac{1}{5}$.
Find y when $x = \dfrac{2}{5}$.

In each of the following, y varies inversely as x.

5. If $x = 14$, then $y = -6$.
Find x when $y = -11$.

6. If $y = \dfrac{1}{5}$, then $x = 9$.
Find y when $x = -3$.

7. If $y = 11$, then $x = 44$.
Find x when $y = 40$.

8. If $x = 20$, then $y = 10$.
Find x when $y = 14$.

9. If $y = -2$, then $x = -8$.
Find x when $y = \dfrac{2}{3}$.

10. If $y = 7$, then $x = -3$.
Find y when $x = 4$.

Solve each problem.

11. A map is scaled so that 1 cm represents 15 km. How far apart are two towns if they are 7.9 cm apart on the map?

12. A 75-foot tree casts a 40-foot shadow. How tall is a tree that casts a 10-foot shadow at the same time of day?

13. Six feet of steel wire weighs 0.7 kilograms. How much does 100 feet of steel wire weigh?

14. Alan Tokashira invested $5000 at 7% interest. How much must he invest at $6\frac{1}{2}\%$ interest to obtain the same income?

15. The time to drive a certain distance varies inversely according to the rate of speed. Mary Bronson drives 47 mph for 4 hours. How long would it take her to make the same trip at 55 mph?

16. A volume of gas is 120 cubic feet under 6 pounds of pressure. What is the volume at the same temperature when the pressure is 8 pounds?

17. When air is pumped into an automobile tire, the pressure required varies inversely as the volume. If the pressure is 30 pounds when the volume is 140 cubic inches, find the pressure when the volume is 100 cubic inches.

18. In a closed room, the number of hours of safe oxygen level varies inversely as the number of people in the room. If there are 2 hours of safe oxygen level for 100 people, how many hours of safe oxygen level are there for 600 people?

19. A realtor made a commission of $4800 on a sale of a $90,000 house. At that rate how much would she make on a $129,000 house?

20. At Mel's Diner a 10 kg ham serves 44 people. At Joe's Diner a 16 kg ham serves 68 people. Which diner serves larger portions?

21. The time required to travel a given distance is inversely proportional to speed of travel. If it takes 4 hours to make a trip at 60 kmh, how long will it take to make the same trip at 90 kmh?

22. The intensity of illumination on a surface varies inversely as the square of the distance from the light source. A surface is 12 meters from a light source. How far must the surface be from the source to receive twice as much illumination?

23. If y varies directly as x^2, and $y = 7$ when $x = 9$, then find y when $x = 7$.

24. If y^2 varies inversely as x, and $y = 4$ when $x = 2$, find y when $x = 11$.

Using Computers

Euclidean Algorithm

The Greek mathematician Euclid (about 300 B.C.) is credited with developing a method for finding the greatest common factor (GCF) of two integers. This method is called the Euclidean Algorithm.

Example: Find the GCF of 232 and 136.

First, divide the greater by the lesser and express the division in the form

$$dividend = quotient \cdot divisor + remainder$$
$$232 = 1 \cdot 136 + 96$$

Divide the divisor by the remainder until the remainder is 0. The last nonzero remainder is the GCF.

$$136 = 1 \cdot 96 + 40$$
$$96 = 2 \cdot 40 + 16$$
$$40 = 2 \cdot 16 + 8$$
$$16 = 2 \cdot 8 + 0$$

8 is the GCF.

```
10   PRINT "ENTER THE GREATER NUMBER"
20   INPUT X
30   PRINT "ENTER THE LESSER NUMBER"
40   INPUT Y
50   IF INT (X / Y) = X / Y THEN 150
60   PRINT "DIVIDEND = QUOTIENT * DIVISOR +
        REMAINDER"
70   LET Q = INT (X / Y)
80   LET R = X - (Q * Y)
90   PRINT X;" = ";Q;" * ";Y;" + ";R
100  IF R = 0 THEN 150
110  LET X= Y
120  LET Y = R
140  GOTO 70
150  PRINT Y;" IS THE GREATEST COMMON
        FACTOR."
180  END
```

The computer program above performs the Euclidean Algorithm. If the lesser number is the GCF, it will appear without calculations.

Exercises

Use the computer program to find the GCF for each pair of integers.

1. 187, 221
2. 182, 1690
3. 4807, 5083
4. 1078, 1547
5. 41, 3
6. 199, 24
7. 766, 424
8. 197, 37

9. If the GCF of two numbers is 1, the numbers are **relatively prime.** Which of the above pairs are relatively prime? Are both numbers prime in any of the pairs?

Vocabulary

rational algebraic expression (343)
complex fraction (346)
rational equation (354)

asymptote (361)
inverse variation (364)
constant of variation (364)

Chapter Summary

1. To simplify a rational algebraic expression, divide both numerator and denominator by their greatest common factor (GCF). (343)

2. Multiplying Rational Expressions: For all rational expressions $\frac{a}{b}$ and $\frac{c}{d}$, $b \neq 0$ and $d \neq 0$, $\frac{a}{b} \cdot \frac{c}{d} = \frac{ac}{bd}$. (343)

3. Dividing Rational Expressions: For all rational expressions $\frac{a}{b}$ and $\frac{c}{d}$, b, c, and $d \neq 0$, $\frac{a}{b} \div \frac{c}{d} = \frac{a}{b} \cdot \frac{d}{c}$. (346)

4. A complex rational expression, usually called a complex fraction, is an expression whose numerator or denominator, or both, contain rational expressions. (346)

5. The sum of rational expressions with common denominators is the sum of the numerators over the common denominator. (350)

6. To add or subtract two rational expressions with different denominators, first find two equivalent rational expressions with common denominators. Then add or subtract the equivalent fractions. (350)

7. An equation that contains one or more rational expressions is called a rational equation. (354)

8. Before graphing a rational function, it is helpful to graph the asymptotes of the function. (361)

9. Direct variation is a linear function described by $y = kx$ or $f(x) = kx$ where k is a constant *not* equal to zero. (363)

10. Definition of Inverse Variation: A rational equation in two variables of the form $y = \frac{k}{x}$ where k is a constant is called an inverse variation. The constant k is called the constant of variation, and y is said to vary inversely as x. (364)

Chapter Review

11–1 Simplify each expression.

1. $\dfrac{25a^2}{80a}$

2. $\dfrac{(4xy)^3}{xy^4}$

3. $\dfrac{2y^3 + 12y^2}{y^2 + 3y - 18}$

Find each product. Write each answer in simplest form.

4. $\dfrac{-4ab}{21c} \cdot \dfrac{14c^2}{22a^2}$

5. $\dfrac{y - 2}{a - x}(a - 3)$

6. $\dfrac{3a + b}{4c} \cdot \dfrac{16c^2d}{3a^2 + ab}$

11–2 **Find each quotient. Write each answer in simplest form.**

7. $\dfrac{x + y}{a} \div \dfrac{x + y}{a^3}$

8. $\dfrac{a^2 - b^2}{6b} \div \dfrac{a + b}{36b^2}$

9. $\dfrac{y^2 - y - 12}{y + 2} \div \dfrac{y - 4}{y^2 - 4y - 12}$

Simplify each expression.

10. $\dfrac{\dfrac{1}{n^2 - 6n + 9}}{\dfrac{n + 3}{2n^2 - 18}}$

11. $\dfrac{\dfrac{x^2 - y^2}{10x^2}}{\dfrac{x - y}{25xy}}$

12. $\dfrac{\dfrac{x^2 + 7x + 10}{x + 2}}{\dfrac{x^2 + 2x - 15}{x + 2}}$

11–3 **Perform the indicated operation for each of the following. Write each answer in simplest form.**

13. $-\dfrac{9}{4a} + \dfrac{7}{3b}$

14. $\dfrac{x - 1}{x^2 - 1} + \dfrac{2}{5x + 5}$

15. $\dfrac{x + 2}{x - 5} + 6$

16. $\dfrac{7}{y} - \dfrac{2}{3y}$

17. $\dfrac{7}{y - 2} - \dfrac{11}{2 - y}$

18. $\dfrac{14}{x + y} - \dfrac{9}{y^2 - x^2}$

Simplify each expression.

19. $\dfrac{\dfrac{5x}{4} + \dfrac{2x}{ab}}{\dfrac{6x}{5} + \dfrac{3x}{a}}$

20. $\dfrac{x - \dfrac{1}{x}}{\dfrac{1}{x} + 1}$

21. $\dfrac{\dfrac{2a + 4}{a}}{6 + \dfrac{2}{a^2}}$

11–4 **Solve each problem.**

22. $\dfrac{3}{y} + \dfrac{7}{y} = 9$

23. $1 + \dfrac{5}{y - 1} = \dfrac{7}{6}$

24. $\dfrac{3x + 2}{4} = \dfrac{9}{4} - \dfrac{3 - 2x}{6}$

25. $\dfrac{1}{r^2 - 1} = \dfrac{2}{r^2 + r - 2}$

26. $\dfrac{x}{x^2 - 1} + \dfrac{2}{x + 1} = 1 + \dfrac{1}{2x - 2}$

11–5 **Solve each problem.**

27. Bob Lopatka can paint his house in 15 hours. His friend, Jack, can paint the house in 20 hours. If they work together, how long will it take them to paint the house?

28. One integer is 2 less than another integer. Three times the reciprocal of the lesser integer plus five times the reciprocal of the greater integer is $\dfrac{7}{8}$. What are the two integers?

11–6 **Sketch the graph of each rational function.**

29. $y = \dfrac{4}{x - 2}$

30. $y = \dfrac{x}{x - 1}$

31. $y = \dfrac{5}{(x + 1)(x - 3)}$

11–7 **Solve each problem.**

32. Suppose y varies inversely as x, and $y = 9$ when $x = 2\frac{1}{2}$. Find y when x is $-\dfrac{3}{5}$.

33. Suppose y varies directly as x, and $x = 7$ when $y = 21$. Find x when y is -5.

Chapter Test

Perform the indicated operation for each of the following. Write each answer in simplest form.

1. $\dfrac{7ab}{9c} \cdot \dfrac{81c^2}{91a^2b}$

2. $\dfrac{x^2 - y^2}{a^2 - b^2} \cdot \dfrac{a + b}{x - y}$

3. $\dfrac{a^2 - ab}{3a} \div \dfrac{a - b}{15b^2}$

4. $\dfrac{x^2 - 2x + 1}{y - 5} \div \dfrac{x - 1}{y^2 - 25}$

5. $\dfrac{7}{5a} - \dfrac{10}{3ab}$

6. $\dfrac{6}{x - 5} + 7a$

7. $\dfrac{x - y}{a - b} - \dfrac{x + y}{a + b}$

8. $\dfrac{x + 2}{x - 1} + \dfrac{6}{7x - 7}$

Simplify each expression.

9. $\dfrac{\dfrac{2}{x - 4} + \dfrac{5}{x + 1}}{\dfrac{3x}{x^2 - 3x - 4}}$

10. $\dfrac{\dfrac{1}{x} - \dfrac{1}{2x}}{\dfrac{2}{x} + \dfrac{4}{3x}}$

Solve each equation.

11. $\dfrac{3}{x} - \dfrac{7}{x} = 9$

12. $a - \dfrac{5}{a} = 4$

13. $\dfrac{y}{y - 3} + \dfrac{6}{y + 3} = 1$

14. $\dfrac{3}{x} + \dfrac{x}{x + 2} = \dfrac{-2}{x + 2}$

Sketch the graph of each rational function.

15. $y = \dfrac{2}{x - 1}$

16. $y = \dfrac{3x}{x + 2}$

Solve each problem.

17. Joni Mills can type 75 pages of manuscript in 8 hours. Ted Szatro can type the same number of pages in 13 hours. If Joni and Ted work together, how long will it take them to type 75 pages?

18. A fraction has a value of $\dfrac{3}{4}$. If 5 is subtracted from its numerator, its value is $\dfrac{4}{7}$. Find the original fraction.

19. Suppose y varies directly as x. If $y = 10$, then $x = -3$. Find y when x is 20.

20. Suppose y varies inversely as x. If $y = 9$, then $x = -\dfrac{2}{3}$. Find x when y is -7.

21. On a blueprint a square 12 meters on a side was shown as a square 3 cm on a side. A beam is actually 20 meters long. How long does it appear on the blueprint?

22. If two boxes have the same capacity and depth, the length is inversely proportional to the width. One box is 60 cm long and 40 cm wide. A second box is 5 cm long. What is its width if it has the same capacity and depth as the first box?

CHAPTER 12

Exponential and Logarithmic Functions

Jean Garson needs to determine how long it takes two of a certain strain of bacteria to increase to 1000 bacteria. To find an approximate answer she uses the general formula for growth and decay in nature, $y = ne^{kt}$. This formula is an example of an exponential equation.

12-1 Real Exponents

Consider the graph of $y = 2^x$ where x is a rational exponent. The expression $y = 2^x$ represents a function, since for each value of x there is a unique value of y.

x	2^x or y	y (approximate)
-4	$2^{-4} = \dfrac{1}{16}$	0.06
-3	$2^{-3} = \dfrac{1}{8}$	0.12
-2	$2^{-2} = \dfrac{1}{4}$	0.25
-1	$2^{-1} = \dfrac{1}{2}$	0.5
$-\dfrac{1}{2}$	$2^{-\frac{1}{2}} = \dfrac{1}{2}\sqrt{2}$	0.7
0	$2^0 = 1$	1
$\dfrac{1}{2}$	$2^{\frac{1}{2}} = \sqrt{2}$	1.4
1	$2^1 = 2$	2
$\dfrac{3}{2}$	$2^{\frac{3}{2}} = 2\sqrt{2}$	2.8
2	$2^2 = 4$	4
$\dfrac{5}{2}$	$2^{\frac{5}{2}} = 4\sqrt{2}$	5.7
3	$2^3 = 8$	8

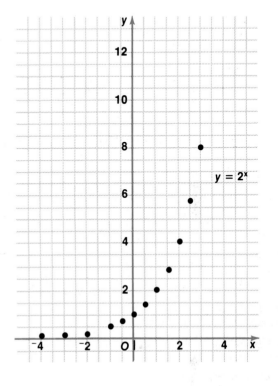

As greater values are selected for x the value of y increases. Thus, the function is increasing.

Since 2^x has not been defined when x is irrational, "holes" still remain in the graph of $y = 2^x$. How could you expand the domain of $y = 2^x$ to include both rational and irrational numbers?

Consider an expression such as $2^{\sqrt{3}}$. Since $1.7 < \sqrt{3} < 1.8$ it follows that $2^{1.7} < 2^{\sqrt{3}} < 2^{1.8}$. By selecting **closer approximations** for $\sqrt{3}$, closer approximations for $2^{\sqrt{3}}$ are possible.

$$2^{1.7} < 2^{\sqrt{3}} < 2^{1.8}$$
$$2^{1.73} < 2^{\sqrt{3}} < 2^{1.74}$$
$$2^{1.732} < 2^{\sqrt{3}} < 2^{1.733}$$
$$2^{1.7320} < 2^{\sqrt{3}} < 2^{1.7321}$$
$$2^{1.73205} < 2^{\sqrt{3}} < 2^{1.73206}$$

Therefore, it is possible to determine an approximate value for 2^x when x represents an irrational number by using rational approximations for x.

Definition of
Irrational Exponents

Since 2^x is defined when x represents an irrational number, the domain of $y = 2^x$ has been expanded to the set of real numbers.

By using a large, accurate graph of $y = 2^x$ you could estimate the value of $2^{\sqrt{3}}$.

Study the following examples.

The "holes" have been filled and the graph is now a smooth curve.

Example

1 **Use the graph of $y = 2^x$ to evaluate y to the nearest tenth.**

a. $y = 2^{\sqrt{3}}$ **b. $y = 2^{2.1}$**

a. $y = 2^{\sqrt{3}}$

The value of x is $\sqrt{3}$ and $1.7 < \sqrt{3} < 1.8$.
From the graph, the value of y is approximately 3.3.

b. $y = 2^{2.1}$

From the graph, the value of y is approximately 4.3.

Verify the values of $2^{\sqrt{3}}$ and $2^{2.1}$ using a calculator.

$2^{\sqrt{3}} = 3.3219971$
$2^{2.1} = 4.2870939$

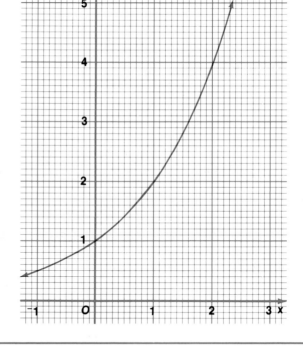

The properties of rational exponents apply to all real exponents.

Example

2 **Simplify $3^{\sqrt{2}} \cdot 3^{\sqrt{5}}$.**

$3^{\sqrt{2}} \cdot 3^{\sqrt{5}} = 3^{\sqrt{2}+\sqrt{5}}$ *Recall that $a^m \cdot a^n = a^{m+n}$.*

3 Simplify $(4^{\sqrt{3}})^{\sqrt{2}}$.

$$(4^{\sqrt{3}})^{\sqrt{2}} = 4^{\sqrt{3}\cdot\sqrt{2}}$$
$$= 4^{\sqrt{6}} \qquad \textit{Recall that } (a^m)^n = a^{m\cdot n}.$$

An equation of the form $y = a^x$ where a is a positive real number other than 1 is called an **exponential function**.

Definition of Exponential Function

The figure at the right shows graphs of several **exponential functions.** Compare the graphs of functions where $a > 1$ and those where $a < 1$. What do you notice? When $a > 1$, is the graph of $y = a^x$ increasing or decreasing? When $a < 1$, is the graph increasing or decreasing?

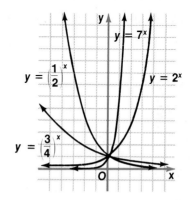

An important property of exponential functions is the property of equality.

Suppose a is a positive number other than 1. Then $a^{x_1} = a^{x_2}$ if and only if $x_1 = x_2$.

Property of Equality for Exponential Functions

What happens when a = 1?

4 Solve $3^5 = 3^{2n-1}$ for n.

$$3^5 = 3^{2n-1}$$
Therefore, $5 = 2n - 1$ *Property of Equality for Exponential Functions*
$$6 = 2n$$
$$n = 3 \qquad \textit{Check this result.}$$

5 Solve $9^{3r} = 27^{r-2}$ for r.

$$9^{3r} = 27^{r-2}$$
$$(3^2)^{3r} = (3^3)^{r-2} \qquad \textit{The bases must be the same. Replace 9 with } 3^2 \textit{ and 27 with } 3^3.$$
$$3^{6r} = 3^{3r-6}$$
Therefore, $6r = 3r - 6$ *Property of Equality for Exponential Functions*
$$3r = -6$$
$$r = -2$$

Exploratory Exercises

Use the graph of $y = 2^x$ on page 372 to evaluate each expression to the nearest tenth.

1. $2^{0.7}$ **2.** $2^{1.1}$ **3.** $2^{-0.3}$ **4.** 2^{-1} **5.** $2^{\sqrt{2}}$ **6.** $2^{\sqrt{5}}$

Use the rules for exponents to simplify each of the following

7. $2^{\sqrt{5}} \cdot 2^{3\sqrt{5}}$ **8.** $7^{\sqrt{3}} \cdot 7^{2\sqrt{3}}$ **9.** $(2^{\sqrt{3}})^{\sqrt{3}}$

10. $(9^{\sqrt{5}})^{\sqrt{5}}$ **11.** $3(2^{\sqrt{2}})(2^{-\sqrt{2}})$ **12.** $\dfrac{8^{2\sqrt{3}}}{8^{\sqrt{12}}}$

Solve each equation.

13. $4^x = 4^{-5}$ **14.** $5^x = 125$ **15.** $7^t = \dfrac{1}{49}$

Written Exercises

Simplify each expression.

1. $(2^{\sqrt{3}})^{\sqrt{12}}$ **2.** $(3^{\sqrt{8}})^{\sqrt{2}}$ **3.** $5^{\sqrt{3}} \cdot 5^{\sqrt{27}}$

4. $11^{\sqrt{5}} \cdot 11^{\sqrt{45}}$ **5.** $16^{\sqrt{7}} \div 2^{\sqrt{7}}$ **6.** $9^{\sqrt{3}} \div 3^{\sqrt{3}}$

7. $8^{\sqrt{3}} \cdot 16^{\sqrt{5}}$ **8.** $64^{\sqrt{2}} \cdot 16^{\sqrt{3}}$ **9.** $y^{\sqrt{5}} \cdot y^{\sqrt{45}}$

10. $(x^{\sqrt{2}})^{\sqrt{8}}$ **11.** $(y^{\sqrt{3}})^{\sqrt{27}}$ **12.** $b^{\sqrt{2}} \cdot b^{\sqrt{32}}$

13. $(m^{\sqrt{2}} \cdot p^{\sqrt{2}})^{\sqrt{2}}$ **14.** $(m^{\sqrt{2}} + n^{\sqrt{2}})^2$

15. $(x^{\sqrt{3}} + y^{\sqrt{2}})^2$ **16.** $(x^{\sqrt{2}} - y^{\sqrt{2}})(x^{\sqrt{2}} + y^{\sqrt{2}})$

Solve each equation.

17. $2^5 = 2^{2x-1}$ **18.** $3^y = 3^{3y+1}$ **19.** $5^{3s+4} = 5^s$

20. $3^x = 9^{x+1}$ **21.** $9^{3y} = 27^{y+2}$ **22.** $8^{r-1} = 16^{3r}$

23. $2^{2m-1} = 8^{m+7}$ **24.** $\left(\dfrac{1}{3}\right)^p = 3^{p-6}$ **25.** $2^{z+3} = \dfrac{1}{16}$

26. $\dfrac{1}{27} = 3^{x-5}$ **27.** $25^{2n} = 125^{n-3}$ **28.** $4^{y-1} = 8^y$

Graph each equation.

29. $y = 3^x$ **30.** $y = \left(\dfrac{1}{3}\right)^x$ **31.** $y = \left(\dfrac{1}{4}\right)^x$ **32.** $y = 4^x$

33. Compare the graphs for exercises 29 and 30. What do you notice?

34. Compare the graphs for exercises 31 and 32. What do you notice?

  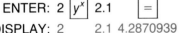

Using Calculators ——————————— Real Exponents

Use the $\boxed{y^x}$ and $\boxed{\sqrt{x}}$ keys on the calculator to evaluate rational and irrational exponents.

Evaluate $2^{2.1}$.

ENTER: 2 $\boxed{y^x}$ 2.1 $\boxed{=}$

DISPLAY: 2   2.1 4.2870939

Evaluate $2^{\sqrt{3}}$.

ENTER: 2 $\boxed{y^x}$ 3 $\boxed{\sqrt{x}}$ $\boxed{=}$

DISPLAY: 2   3 1.7320508 3.3219971

Exercises   Evaluate.

1. $5^{1.2}$ **2.** $3^{3.4}$ **3.** $4^{\sqrt{5}}$ **4.** $3^{\sqrt{2}}$ **5.** $17^{\sqrt{3}}$ **6.** $64^{\sqrt{5}}$

12-2 An Inverse Relation

In the table on the left, x is the exponent. Compute the power of 2 to find y. In the table on the right, the emphasis is shifted. You are given x as the value of the power. Work toward finding the exponent, y.

x	$2^x = y$	y
-1	$2^{-1} = y$	?
2	$2^2 = y$	?
3	$2^3 = y$	?
6	$2^6 = y$	?

Exponent to Power →

y	$2^y = x$	x
?	$2^y = \dfrac{1}{2}$	$\dfrac{1}{2}$
?	$2^y = 4$	4
?	$2^y = 8$	8
?	$2^y = 64$	64

← Exponent from Power

In the relation $2^y = x$, the exponent y is called the **logarithm** of x to base 2. This relation is more conveniently written as $\log_2 x = y$. The equation $\log_2 x = y$ is read *the log of x to the base 2 is equal to y.* The logarithm corresponds to an exponent.

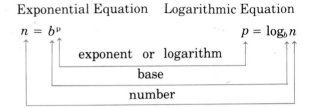

Exponential Equation   Logarithmic Equation

$n = b^v$ $p = \log_b n$

exponent or logarithm
base
number

> **Suppose $b > 0$ and $b \neq 1$. Then for $n > 0$, there is a number p such that $\log_b n = p$ if and only if $b^p = n$.**

Definition of Logarithm

Exponential Equation	Logarithmic Equation
$6^2 = 36$	$\log_6 36 = 2$
$10^4 = 10{,}000$	$\log_{10} 10{,}000 = 4$
$3^0 = 1$	$\log_3 1 = 0$
$2^{-3} = \dfrac{1}{8}$	$\log_2 \dfrac{1}{8} = -3$
$4^{\frac{1}{2}} = 2$	$\log_4 2 = \dfrac{1}{2}$

Example

1 Solve the equation $\log_2 64 = y$.

$\log_2 64 = y$ implies that $2^y = 64$.
Since $2^6 = 64$, $2^y = 2^6$ and $y = 6$.

The solution is 6.

Examples

2 Solve the equation $\log_9 x = \frac{1}{2}$.

$\log_9 x = \frac{1}{2}$ implies that $9^{\frac{1}{2}} = x$.

Since $9^{\frac{1}{2}}$ or $\sqrt{9}$ is 3, $x = 3$.

The solution is 3.

3 Solve the equation $\log_b 16 = 2$.

$\log_b 16 = 2$ implies that $b^2 = 16$.

Since $4^2 = 16$, $b^2 = 4^2$ and $b = 4$.

The solution is 4.

Exploratory Exercises

Change each equation to logarithmic form.

1. $3^3 = 27$
2. $4^2 = 16$
3. $2^{-3} = \frac{1}{8}$
4. $5^{-2} = \frac{1}{25}$
5. $10^3 = 1000$
6. $10^{-2} = 0.01$

Change each equation to exponential form.

7. $\log_4 64 = 3$
8. $\log_3 9 = 2$
9. $\log_9 27 = \frac{3}{2}$
10. $\log_3 \frac{1}{81} = -4$
11. $\log_{10} 0.1 = -1$
12. $\log_{10} 0.0001 = -4$

Evaluate each expression.

13. $\log_{10} 100$
14. $\log_3 81$
15. $\log_7 \frac{1}{343}$
16. $\log_2 \frac{1}{16}$

Written Exercises

Rewrite each equation in logarithmic form.

1. $3^4 = 81$
2. $2^6 = 64$
3. $5^3 = 125$
4. $8^0 = 1$
5. $4^{-2} = \frac{1}{16}$
6. $3^{-1} = \frac{1}{3}$
7. $2^{-4} = \frac{1}{16}$
8. $7^{-2} = \frac{1}{49}$
9. $3^{\frac{1}{2}} = \sqrt{3}$
10. $9^{\frac{3}{2}} = 27$
11. $36^{\frac{3}{2}} = 216$
12. $\left(\frac{1}{9}\right)^{-2} = 81$

Rewrite each equation in exponential form.

13. $\log_2 32 = 5$
14. $\log_8 64 = 2$
15. $\log_{11} 121 = 2$
16. $\log_{13} 13 = 1$
17. $\log_5 1 = 0$
18. $\log_3 243 = 5$
19. $\log_{\frac{1}{2}} 16 = -4$
20. $\log_8 4 = \frac{2}{3}$
21. $\log_{10} \frac{1}{10} = -1$
22. $\log_5 \frac{1}{25} = -2$
23. $\log_{\frac{1}{3}} 81 = -4$
24. $\log_{27} 3 = \frac{1}{3}$

Evaluate each expression.

25. $\log_{10} 1000$
26. $\log_6 36$
27. $\log_{12} 144$
28. $\log_{10} 0.01$
29. $\log_{\frac{1}{4}} 64$
30. $\log_4 2$
31. $\log_9 27$
32. $\log_8 16$

Solve each equation.

33. $\log_{\frac{1}{2}} 8 = x$
34. $\log_{10} 0.001 = x$
35. $\log_b 49 = 2$
36. $\log_b 64 = 3$
37. $\log_6 x = 2$
38. $\log_9 x = -1$
39. $\log_{\frac{1}{2}} 16 = x$
40. $\log_3 27 = x$
41. $\log_b 81 = 4$
42. $\log_b 18 = 1$
43. $\log_5 x = -2$
44. $\log_3 x = -3$
45. $\log_{10} \sqrt{10} = x$
46. $\log_5 \sqrt{5} = x$
47. $\log_a \frac{1}{27} = -3$
48. $\log_b 36 = -2$
49. $\log_{\frac{1}{2}} x = -6$
50. $\log_4 x = -\frac{1}{2}$
51. $\log_2 x = -4$
52. $\log_{\sqrt{3}} x = 6$
53. $\log_{\sqrt{3}} 27 = x$
54. $\log_x \sqrt{5} = \frac{1}{4}$
55. $\log_x \sqrt[3]{7} = \frac{1}{3}$
56. $\log_{10} \sqrt[3]{10} = x$

12-3   Logarithmic Functions

Study the graphs of $y = 2^x$ and $2^y = x$.

$$y = 2^x \qquad \begin{array}{c} 2^y = x \quad \text{or} \\ y = \log_2 x \end{array}$$

x	y
−4	$\dfrac{1}{16}$
−3	$\dfrac{1}{8}$
−2	$\dfrac{1}{4}$
−1	$\dfrac{1}{2}$
0	1
1	2
2	4
3	8

x	y
$\dfrac{1}{16}$	−4
$\dfrac{1}{8}$	−3
$\dfrac{1}{4}$	−2
$\dfrac{1}{2}$	−1
1	0
2	1
4	2
8	3

The x and y values
are reversed.

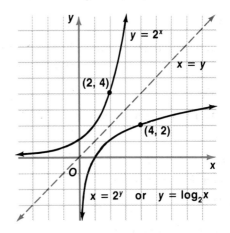

The domain of the
logarithmic function is the
set of all positive numbers.
The range is all real
numbers.

From the graph, $y = \log_2 x$ appears to be a function. A vertical line will not intersect the graph in more than one point. Both graphs are symmetrical with respect to the graph of $y = x$, a diagonal line. For $y = 2^x$, y cannot be negative. For $y = \log_2 x$, x cannot be negative. Both graphs are smooth, unbroken, and continually increasing. By comparing points, such as (2, 4) and (4, 2), you can see that the functions are inverses of each other.

Thus, both $y = b^x$ and its inverse $y = \log_b x$ are functions. Recall that the property of equality holds for exponential functions. That is, $b^{x_1} = b^{x_2}$ if and only if $x_1 = x_2$. A similar property also holds for logarithmic functions.

Suppose $b > 0$ and $b \neq 1$. Then $\log_b x_1 = \log_b x_2$ if and only if $x_1 = x_2$.	**Property of Equality for Logarithmic Functions**

Study the following examples.

Example

1 **Solve the equation $\log_2 (x^2 - 1) = \log_2 8$.**

$$\log_2 (x^2 - 1) = \log_2 8$$
$$x^2 - 1 = 8 \qquad \text{\textit{Property of Equality for Logarithmic Functions}}$$
$$x^2 - 9 = 0$$
$$(x - 3)(x + 3) = 0$$
$$x - 3 = 0 \quad \text{or} \quad x + 3 = 0$$
$$x = 3 \quad \text{or} \qquad x = -3 \qquad \text{The solutions are 3 and } -3.$$

You know that $y = b^x$ and $y = \log_b x$ are inverse functions. Three applications of the property of inverse functions are given below. Find $f(f^{-1}(x))$ and $f^{-1}(f(x))$. Then apply the definition of inverse functions.

$\overset{same}{3^{\log_3 9}} = 3^2 \text{ or } 9$ and $\overset{same}{\log_3 3^2} = \log_3 9 \text{ or } 2$

$4^{\log_4 16} = 4^2 \text{ or } 16$ and $\log_4 4^2 = \log_4 16 \text{ or } 2$

$b^{\log_b x} = x$ and $\log_b b^x = x$

Examples

2 **Evaluate the expression $\log_7 7^4$.**

$$\log_7 7^4 = 4 \qquad \log_b b^x = x$$

The value of the expression is 4.

3 **Solve the equation $3^{\log_3 x} = 3x - 4$.**

$$3^{\log_3 x} = 3x - 4 \qquad b^{\log_b x} = x$$
$$x = 3x - 4$$
$$-2x = -4$$
$$x = 2 \qquad \text{The solution is 2.}$$

Exploratory Exercises

Evaluate each expression.

1. $\log_5 5^2$
2. $\log_9 9^4$
3. $9^{\log_9 2}$
4. $7^{\log_7 3}$
5. $\log_b b^4$
6. $\log_m m^x$
7. $b^{\log_b 5}$
8. $8^{\log_8 x}$

Solve each equation.

9. $\log_2 x = \log_2 4$
10. $\log_4 10 = \log_4 2x$
11. $\log_3 (x + 1) = \log_3 (2x)$
12. $\log_7 (x^2 - 1) = \log_7 3$

Written Exercises

Evaluate each expression.

1. $\log_4 4^3$
2. $\log_r r^4$
3. $6^{\log_6 7}$
4. $9^{\log_9 5}$
5. $\log_n n^5$
6. $3^{\log_3 21}$

Solve each equation.

7. $\log_3 (2x + 1) = \log_3 (3x - 6)$
8. $\log_{10} (4 + y) = \log_{10} (2y)$
9. $\log_{10} (3n) = \log_{10} (n + 2)$
10. $\log_4 (2x - 3) = \log_4 (x + 2)$
11. $\log_3 (3y - 1) = \log_3 (y + 4)$
12. $\log_7 (5x - 1) = \log_7 (3x + 7)$
13. $\log_{10} (x^2 + 36) = \log_{10} 100$
14. $\log_{10} (x - 1)^2 = \log_{10} 0.01$
15. $\log_9 (x^2 + 9x) = \log_9 10$
16. $\log_5 (4x - 4) = \log_5 100$

Graph each pair of equations on the same set of axes.

17. $y = 3^x$ and $y = \log_3 x$
18. $y = \left(\frac{1}{2}\right)^x$ and $y = \log_{\frac{1}{2}} x$
19. $y = 4^x$ and $y = \log_4 x$
20. $y = 10^x$ and $y = \log_{10} x$

Show that each statement is true.

21. $\log_4 4 + \log_4 16 = \log_4 64$
22. $\log_3 27 + \log_3 3 = \log_3 81$
23. $\log_2 32 - \log_2 4 = \log_2 8$
24. $\log_6 36 - \log_6 6 = \log_6 6$
25. $\log_3 27 = 3 \log_3 3$
26. $\log_4 16 = 2 \log_4 4$
27. $\frac{1}{2}\log_3 81 = \log_3 9$
28. $\frac{1}{3}\log_5 25 = 2 \log_5 \sqrt[3]{5}$
29. $\log_2 8 \cdot \log_8 2 = 1$
30. $\log_5 25 \cdot \log_{25} 5 = 1$
31. $\log_{10} [\log_3(\log_4 64)] = 0$
32. $\log_2 64 = 3 \log_8 64$
33. $\log_3 81 = \frac{4}{3} \log_2 8$
34. $\log_4 [\log_2 (\log_3 81)] = \frac{1}{2}$

Challenge

Solve each equation.

35. $6^{\log_6 x^2} = x + 30$
36. $3^{\log_3 x^3} = \frac{1}{27}$
37. $\log_2 [\log_4 (\log_3 x)] = -1$
38. $\log_{10} [\log_2 (\log_7 x)] = 0$

mini-review

1. Simplify $\sqrt[4]{(r + s)^4}$.
2. Find the value of the discriminant for $c^2 - 12c + 42 = 0$.
3. Graph $f(x) = \frac{1}{2}(x + 3)^2 - 5$.
4. Find the distance between $(-8, -7)$ and $(-2, -1)$, using the distance formula.
5. Show that $x + 1$ is a factor of $x^5 + x^4 - x - 1$.

Excursions in Algebra _____ Contest Problem

The following problem appeared in a high school mathematics contest sponsored by the Mathematical Association of America.

A tire on a car has an outside diameter of 25 inches. When the radius has been decreased a quarter of an inch, the number of revolutions per mile will be increased by about what percent?

Applications in Seismology   Earthquakes

Seismology is a science that deals with earthquakes and artificially produced vibrations of the earth. A *logarithmic* scale called the **Richter scale** is used to measure the strength of an earthquake. Each increase of one on the Richter scale corresponds to a ten-times increase in intensity. In other words, an earthquake that registers 8 on the Richter scale is ten times as intense as an earthquake that registers 7. An earthquake that registers 9 is ten times as intense as the one registering 8, and one hundred times as intense as the one registering 7.

The table below gives the effects of earthquakes of various intensities.

Richter Number	Intensity	Effect
1	10^1	only detectable by seismograph
2	10^2	hanging lamps sway
3	10^3	can be felt
4	10^4	glass breaks, buildings shake
5	10^5	furniture collapses
6	10^6	wooden houses damaged
7	10^7	buildings collapse
8	10^8	catastrophic damage

The photo below shows the earth's shift along the San Andreas fault. Scientists claim that shifts in the earth's surface along this fault could cause major earthquakes in the near future. Small earthquakes are a common occurrence in California.

On April 18, 1906, one of the worst California earthquakes in recent history hit San Francisco. It caused a fire that burned more than 4 square miles. Hundreds of people died. There was from 250 to 300 million dollars worth of property damage. It is believed that this earthquake would have measured 8.3 on the Richter scale.

Exercises
Solve each problem.

1. An earthquake with a rating of 7 is how much stronger than one with a rating of 6?

2. An earthquake with a rating of 7 is how much stronger than one with a rating of 4?

3. Which was stronger, the San Francisco earthquake or the Alaska earthquake that rated 8.4?

4. Which was stronger, the Ecuador earthquake that rated 8.9 or the Alaska earthquake?

5. Compare earthquakes rated 6.5 and 7.1. How many times stronger is the latter?
Hint: Divide $10^{7.1}$ by $10^{6.5}$.

12-4 Properties of Logarithms

Logarithms are exponents. Thus, the properties of logarithms can be derived from the properties of exponents.

For example, to find the product of powers, add exponents. To find the logarithm of a product, add logarithms.

$$\log_2 (8 \cdot 32)$$
$$= \log_2 (2^3 \cdot 2^5)$$
$$= \log_2 (2^{3+5})$$
$$= 3 + 5$$

← *Notice that these two expressions are equivalent.* →

$$\log_2 8 + \log_2 32$$
$$= \log_2 2^3 + \log_2 2^5$$
$$= 3 + 5$$

This example illustrates the product property of logarithms.

> **For all positive numbers m, n, and b, where $b \neq 1$,**
>
> $$\log_b mn = \log_b m + \log_b n.$$

Product Property of Logarithms

To prove the product property, let $b^x = m$ and $b^y = n$.
Then $\log_b m = x$ and $\log_b n = y$.

$b^x b^y = mn$	
$b^{x+y} = mn$	*Property of Exponents*
$\log_b b^{x+y} = \log_b mn$	*Property of Equality for Logarithmic Functions*
$x + y = \log_b mn$	*Definition of Inverse Functions*
$\log_b m + \log_b n = \log_b mn$	*Substitution*

Example

1 **Given $\log_3 5 = 1.465$, find $\log_3 45$ and $\log_3 25$.**

$$\log_3 45 = \log_3 (3^2 \cdot 5)$$
$$= \log_3 3^2 + \log_3 5$$
$$= 2 + 1.465 \quad \text{or} \quad 3.465$$

$$\log_3 25 = \log_3 (5 \cdot 5)$$
$$= \log_3 5 + \log_3 5$$
$$= 1.465 + 1.465 \text{ or } 2.930$$

To find the quotient of powers, subtract exponents. Similarly, to find the logarithm of a quotient, subtract logarithms.

$$\log_2 (32 \div 8)$$
$$= \log_2 (2^5 \div 2^3)$$
$$= \log_2 (2^{5-3})$$
$$= 5 - 3$$

← *Notice that these two expressions are equivalent.* →

$$\log_2 32 - \log_2 8$$
$$= \log_2 2^5 - \log_2 2^3$$
$$= 5 - 3$$

This example illustrates the Quotient Property of Logarithms.

For all positive numbers m, n, and b, where $b \neq 1$,
$$\log_b \frac{m}{n} = \log_b m - \log_b n.$$

To prove, let $b^x = m$ and $b^y = n$. Then $\log_b m = x$ and $\log_b n = y$.

$$\frac{b^x}{b^y} = \frac{m}{n}$$

$$b^{x-y} = \frac{m}{n} \qquad \textit{Property of Exponents}$$

$$\log_b b^{x-y} = \log_b \frac{m}{n} \qquad \textit{Property of Equality for Logarithmic Functions}$$

$$x - y = \log_b \frac{m}{n} \qquad \textit{Definition of Inverse Functions}$$

$$\log_b m - \log_b n = \log_b \frac{m}{n} \qquad \textit{Substitution}$$

Example

2 **Solve the equation $\log_{12} 72 - \log_{12} 9 = \log_{12} 4m$.**

$$\log_{12} 72 - \log_{12} 9 = \log_{12} 4m$$

$$\log_{12} \frac{72}{9} = \log_{12} 4m \qquad \textit{Quotient Property of Logarithms}$$

$$8 = 4m \qquad \textit{Property of Equality for Logarithmic Functions}$$

$$2 = m$$

Check: $\log_{12} 72 - \log_{12} 9 = \log_{12} 4m$

$\log_{12} 72 - \log_{12} 9 \stackrel{?}{=} \log_{12} (4 \cdot 2)$

$\log_{12} 8 = \log_{12} 8$

The solution is 2.

To determine the logarithm of a power, multiply the logarithm by the exponent.

$\log_2 8^4 \qquad \leftarrow$ *These two* $\rightarrow 4 \log_2 8$

$= \log_2 (2^3)^4 \qquad$ *expressions* $\qquad = (\log_2 8) \cdot 4$

$= \log_2 2^{3 \cdot 4} \qquad$ *are equiva-* $\qquad = (\log_2 2^3) \cdot 4$

$= 3 \cdot 4 \qquad$ *lent.* $\qquad = 3 \cdot 4$

This example illustrates the power property of logarithms.

For any real number p and positive numbers m and b, $b \neq 1$,
$$\log_b m^p = p \cdot \log_b m.$$

Power Property of Logarithms

To prove, let $b^x = m$. Then $\log_b m = x$.

$$(b^x)^p = m^p$$
$$b^{xp} = m^p \qquad \textit{Power property of Exponents}$$
$$\log_b b^{xp} = \log_b m^p \qquad \textit{Property of Equality for Logarithmic functions}$$
$$xp = \log_b m^p \qquad \textit{Definition of Inverse Functions}$$
$$p \log_b m = \log_b m^p \qquad \textit{Substitution}$$

Examples

3 **Solve the equation $4 \log_5 x - \log_5 4 = \log_5 4$.**

$$4 \log_5 x - \log_5 4 = \log_5 4$$
$$4 \log_5 x = 2 \log_5 4$$
$$2 \log_5 x = \log_5 4$$
$$\log_5 x^2 = \log_5 4 \qquad \textit{Power Property of Logarithms}$$
$$x^2 = 4$$
$$x = 2 \qquad \textit{-2 is not a solution because $\log_b x$ is not defined for negative numbers.}$$

4 **Solve the equation $\log_3 (y + 4) + \log_3 (y - 4) = 2$.**

$$\log_3 (y + 4) + \log_3 (y - 4) = 2$$
$$\log_3 (y + 4)(y - 4) = 2 \qquad \textit{Product Property of Logarithms}$$
$$(y + 4)(y - 4) = 3^2 \qquad \textit{Definition of Logarithm}$$
$$y^2 - 16 = 9$$
$$y^2 - 25 = 0$$
$$(y - 5)(y + 5) = 0$$
$$y - 5 = 0 \quad \text{or} \quad y + 5 = 0$$
$$y = 5 \quad \text{or} \quad y = -5$$

Check:

$$\log_3 (y + 4) + \log_3 (y - 4) = 2$$
$$\log_3 (5 + 4) + \log_3 (5 - 4) \stackrel{?}{=} 2$$
$$\log_3 9 + \log_3 1 \stackrel{?}{=} 2$$
$$2 + 0 = 2$$

$$\log_3 (y + 4) + \log_3 (y - 4) = 2$$
$$\log_3 (-5 + 4) + \log_3 (-5 - 4) \stackrel{?}{=} 2$$
$$\log_3 (-1) + \log_3 (-9) \stackrel{?}{=} 2$$

Since log is not defined for negative numbers, -5 is not an acceptable solution.

The only solution is 5.

Exploratory Exercises

Solve each equation.

1. $\log_2 3 + \log_2 7 = \log_2 x$

2. $\log_5 4 + \log_5 x = \log_5 36$

3. $\log_4 18 - \log_4 x = \log_4 6$

4. $\log_3 56 - \log_3 8 = \log_3 x$

5. $2 \log_7 3 + 3 \log_7 2 = \log_7 x$

6. $2 \log_6 4 - \frac{1}{3} \log_6 8 = \log_6 x$

Express each logarithm as the sum or difference of simpler logarithmic expressions.

7. $\log_3 (xy)$

8. $\log_4 (rst)$

9. $\log_2 (m^4 y)$

10. $\log_2 \left(\frac{y}{r}\right)$

11. $\log_b \left(\frac{\sqrt{x}}{p}\right)$

12. $\log_4 \left(\frac{xy}{z}\right)$

13. $\log_3 (5\sqrt[3]{a})$

14. $\log_{10} (ac)^2$

15. $\log_2 (ax^{\frac{1}{2}})$

Evaluate each expression.

16. $5^{\log_5 3 + \log_5 2}$

17. $7^{\log_7 8 - \log_7 4}$

18. $6^{3\log_6 2}$

Written Exercises

Use $\log_{10} 3 = 0.4771$ and $\log_{10} 7 = 0.8451$ to evaluate each expression.

1. $\log_{10} 21$

2. $\log_{10} \left(\frac{7}{3}\right)$

3. $\log_{10} 27$

4. $\log_{10} 63$

5. $\log_{10} 30$

6. $\log_{10} 0.03$

7. $\log_{10} (70 \cdot 3)$

8. $\log_{10} 4.9$

9. $\log_{10} 700$

10. $\log_{10} 90$

11. $\log_{10} \left(3\frac{1}{3}\right)$

12. $\log_{10} \left(\frac{1}{9}\right)$

Solve each equation.

13. $\log_3 7 + \log_3 x = \log_3 14$

14. $\log_2 10 - \log_2 t = \log_2 2$

15. $\log_3 y - \log_3 2 = \log_3 12$

16. $\log_3 14 + \log_3 m = \log_3 42$

17. $\log_5 x = 3 \log_5 7$

18. $\log_2 p = \frac{1}{2}\log_2 81$

19. $\log_9 x = \frac{1}{2}\log_9 144 - \frac{1}{3}\log_9 8$

20. $\log_7 m = \frac{1}{3}\log_7 64 + \frac{1}{2}\log_7 121$

21. $\log_{10} 7 + \log_{10} (n - 2) = \log_{10} 6n$

22. $\log_{10} (m + 3) - \log_{10} m = \log_{10} 4$

23. $\log_{10} x + \log_{10} x + \log_{10} x = \log_{10} 27$

24. $4 \log_5 x - \log_5 4 = \log_5 4$

25. $\log_2 15 + \log_2 14 - \log_2 105 = \log_2 x$

26. $2 \log_3 x + \log_3 \frac{1}{10} = \log_3 5 + \log_3 2$

27. $\log_4 (x + 2) + \log_4 (x - 4) = 2$

28. $\log_4 (y - 1) + \log_4 (y - 1) = 2$

29. $\log_{10} (y - 1) + \log_{10} (y + 2) = \log_7 7$

30. $\log_{10} y + \log_{10} (y + 21) = 2$

31. $\log_4 (x + 3) + \log_4 (x - 3) = 2$

32. $\log_2 (9x + 5) - \log_2 (x^2 - 1) = 2$

33. $\log_8 (m + 1) - \log_8 m = \log_8 4$

34. $\log_2 (y + 2) - 1 = \log_2 (y - 2)$

Challenge

Solve for a.

35. $\log_m 3 + \log_m a = \log_m (y + 3)$

36. $\log_r a = 5 \log_r x + \log_r a^2$

37. $\log_b 2a - \log_b x = \log_b x^3$

38. $2 \log_x a = 2 \log_x (k + 1) - \log_x 4$

12-5 Common Logarithms

Logarithms were invented to make computation easier. Using logarithms, multiplication changes to addition and division changes to subtraction. Logarithms to base 10 are most useful because our number system has base 10. These logarithms are called **common logarithms.** $\text{Log}_{10} x$ is written as $\log x$.

A table of common logarithms for numbers between 1 and 10 may be found on pages 613 and 614. To find log 1.23, read across the row labeled 12 and down the column labeled 3.

Common Logarithms of Numbers

n	0	1	2	3	4
10	0000	0043	0086	0128	0170
11	0414	0453	0492	0531	0569
12	0792	0828	0864	0899	0934
13	1139	1173		1239	

The values in the table are rounded to the nearest ten-thousandth.

$$\log 1.23 = 0.0899$$

For numbers greater than 10 or less than 1, scientific notation and the properties of logarithms are used to find the logarithm.

Example

1   **Find log 745,000 to the nearest ten-thousandth.**

$745,000 = 7.45 \times 10^5$ *Scientific notation*

$\log 745,000 = \log(7.45 \times 10^5)$ *Property of Equality for Logarithmic Functions*

$\qquad\quad = \log 7.45 + \log 10^5$ *Product Property of Logarithms*

$\qquad\quad = \log 7.45 + 5$

$\qquad\quad = 0.8722 + 5 \text{ or } 5.8722$ *From the table, log 7.45 = 0.8722.*

The log of 745,000 is 5.8722.

Every logarithm has two parts, the **characteristic** and the **mantissa.** The mantissa is the logarithm of a number between 1 and 10. When the number is expressed in scientific notation, the characteristic is the power of 10.

Mantissas range from 0 to 1.

$$\log 745,000 = \underset{\substack{\uparrow \qquad \uparrow \\ characteristic \quad mantissa}}{5.8722}$$

Since 745,000 = 7.45 × 10^5, the characteristic is 5.

The table of logarithms is really a table of mantissas. You must supply the characteristic.

2 **Find log 0.000524.**

$$\log 0.000524 = \log (5.24 \times 10^{-4}) \qquad \textit{Substitution}$$
$$= \log 5.24 + \log 10^{-4} \qquad \textit{Product Property}$$
$$= 0.7193 + (-4)$$
$$= 0.7193 - 4 \qquad \text{The logarithm is approximately } 0.7193 - 4.$$

Logarithm tables are tables of positive mantissas. To avoid a negative mantissa, do *not* add the -4 and 0.7193. The negative characteristic may be written in many ways.

$$\log 0.000524 = 0.7193 - 4$$
$$\log 0.000524 = 6.7193 - 10 \qquad \textit{Note } 6 - 10 = -4.$$

We usually use $6 - 10$ for -4. But, in some cases it may be more convenient to use another difference such as $26 - 30$.

Sometimes a logarithm is given and you must find the number. To find the number, use the table of mantissas in reverse. The number is called the **antilogarithm.** *If log x = a, then x = antilog a.*

Example

3 **If log x = 3.5821, find x.**

$$\log x = 3.5821 \qquad \textit{3 is the characteristic and 0.5821 is the mantissa.}$$
$$x = \text{antilog } 3.5821$$
$$= (\text{antilog } 0.5821) \times 10^3$$

Find antilog 0.5821 in the table of mantissas. It is in the row labeled 38 and the column labeled 2.

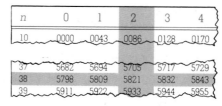

$$x = (\text{antilog } 0.5821) \times 10^3$$
$$= 3.82 \times 10^3$$
$$= 3820 \qquad \text{The solution is 3820.}$$

Exploratory Exercises

If log 483 = 2.6839, find each number.

1. characteristic of log 483
2. mantissa of log 483
3. log 48.3
4. log 4830
5. log 0.004830
6. antilog 0.6839
7. antilog 5.6839
8. antilog (0.6839 − 4)

State the characteristic of the logarithm of each number. Then use the table on pages 613 and 614 to find the logarithm.

9. 47.5   **10.** 370   **11.** 4.61   **12.** 0.076
13. 0.209   **14.** 6870   **15.** 55   **16.** 0.00213

State the characteristic of each logarithm and use the table to find the antilogarithm.

17. 1.5527   **18.** 3.8096   **19.** $0.8376 - 2$ **20.** $7.6263 - 10$
21. 4.5955   **22.** $5.9513 - 10$ **23.** $0.7910 - 1$ **24.** 2.1106

Written Exercises

Use the table of mantissas to find the logarithm of each number.

1. 58.2   **2.** 715   **3.** 9.58   **4.** 0.000741
5. 7420   **6.** 0.3   **7.** 0.00211   **8.** 841,000
9. 0.0385   **10.** 0.671   **11.** 62,700   **12.** 0.113

Find the antilogarithm of each logarithm.

13. 1.0899   **14.** $0.8727 - 2$ **15.** 3.9581   **16.** $0.7846 - 1$
17. $0.9542 - 2$ **18.** 5.7451   **19.** $9.2014 - 10$ **20.** $8.1673 - 10$
21. 5.7168   **22.** 1.3075   **23.** $7.6656 - 10$ **24.** 0.6304

Using Calculators _____ **Logarithms**

Many calculators have keys for logarithmic and exponential functions. For example, you can use the $\boxed{\text{LOG}}$ key to find logarithms.

Example 1: Find the logarithm of 76,500.

ENTER: 76500 $\boxed{\text{LOG}}$
DISPLAY: 76500   4.8836614

The logarithm of 76500 is approximately 4.8837.
Notice that the mantissa is .8837 and the characteristic is 4.

A check of the correspondence between logarithms and exponents is easily shown by storing the logarithm and then raising 10 to the power of the stored number.

ENTER: 10 $\boxed{y^x}$ $\boxed{\text{RCL}}$ $\boxed{=}$
DISPLAY: 10   4.8836614   76499.994   *This is approximately 76,500.*

Antilogarithms can also be found on the calculator by using the $\boxed{\text{INV}}$ and $\boxed{\text{LOG}}$ keys.

Example 2: Find the antilogarithm of 4.8836614.

ENTER: 4.8836614 $\boxed{\text{INV}}$ $\boxed{\text{LOG}}$ *If you chose to use the rounded*
DISPLAY: 4.8836614   76499.994   *logarithm 4.8837, the antilog*
                                               would be 76,506.

Antilog 4.8836614 is approximately 76,500.

The logarithms for numbers less than one are negative. The mantissa and characteristic are *not* obvious for negative logarithms, as shown in the following example.

Example 3: Find the logarithm of 0.00169. Then name the mantissa and characteristic.

ENTER: 0.00169 $\boxed{\text{LOG}}$

DISPLAY: 0.00169 -2.7721133

The logarithm of 0.00169 is -2.7721133, or about -2.7721. Recall that the mantissa is a number between 0 and 1. The characteristic is the greatest integer less than the logarithm. The characteristic of -2.7721 is -3. To find the mantissa, add 3 to -2.7721.

ENTER: 2.7721 $\boxed{+/-}$ $\boxed{+}$ 3 $\boxed{=}$

DISPLAY: 2.7721 -2.7721 3 .2279

The sum of the mantissa and the characteristic is the logarithm.

The mantissa is 0.2279. So, -2.7721 may be expressed as $0.2279 - 3$.

Check:
$$0.00169 = 1.69 \times 10^{-3}$$
$$\log 0.00169 = \log 1.69 + \log 10^{-3}$$
$$= 0.2279 - 3 \quad \textit{mantissa and characteristic}$$
$$= -2.7721$$

A negative logarithm is sometimes written in the mantissa and characteristic form. Two methods can be used to compute the antilog.

Example 4: Find antilog $(0.3711 - 2)$.

Method 1
$$\text{antilog } (0.3711 - 2) = \text{antilog } (-1.6289)$$

ENTER: 1.6289 $\boxed{+/-}$ $\boxed{\text{INV}}$ $\boxed{\text{LOG}}$

DISPLAY: 1.6289 -1.6289 0.02350174

Method 2
$$\text{antilog}(0.3711 - 2) = \text{antilog}(0.3711) \times [\text{antilog}(-2)]$$
$$= \text{antilog}(0.3711) \times 10^{-2}$$

ENTER: 0.3711 $\boxed{\text{INV}}$ $\boxed{\text{LOG}}$ $\boxed{\times}$ 0.01 $\boxed{=}$

DISPLAY: 0.3711 2.3501739 0.01 0.02350174

Exercises

Use a calculator to find each of the following logarithms. Identify the mantissa and characteristic. Use the y^x key to check each result.

1. 89.3	**2.** 398.4	**3.** 413,000	**4.** 213.47
5. 0.00165	**6.** 0.03748	**7.** 0.0000052	**8.** 0.00000291

Use a calculator to find the following antilogarithms.

9. 2.4270	**10.** 0.8914	**11.** 2.9921	**12.** 5.9847
13. -1.8684	**14.** -2.0159	**15.** -2.1931	**16.** -4.4855
17. antilog $(0.6735 - 1)$		**18.** antilog $(0.3569 - 2)$	
19. antilog $(0.7186 - 3)$		**20.** antilog $(0.2475 - 4)$	
21. antilog $(9.1826 - 10)$		**22.** antilog $(8.7654 - 10)$	

12-6 Interpolation

The table of logarithms in this text includes mantissas of numbers with three significant digits. You can approximate logarithms of numbers with four significant digits by a method known as interpolation. When using a calculator instead of tables, it is not necessary to interpolate.

Example

1 **Approximate the value of log 1.327.**

n	0	1	2	3	4
10	0000	0043	0086	0128	0170
11	0414	0453	0492	0531	0569
12	0792	0828	0864	0899	0934
13	1139	1173	1206	1239	1271

The logarithm of 1.327 must be between log 1.32 and log 1.33.

Form a proportion of differences.

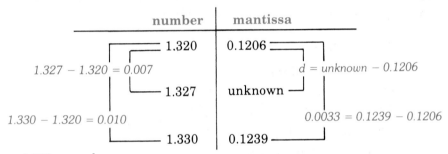

$$\frac{0.007}{0.010} = \frac{d}{0.0033}$$
$$0.00231 = d$$
$$0.0023 \approx d$$

Since the values in the table are increasing, add 0.0023 to the mantissa of 1.320.

$$\log 1.327 = \log 1.320 + d$$
$$= 0.1206 + 0.0023$$
$$= 0.1229$$

The logarithm of 1.327 is approximately 0.1229.

Interpolation can also be used to find an antilogarithm that cannot be obtained directly from the table.

Example

2 **Find antilog 2.4356.**

antilog $2.4356 = ($antilog $0.4356) \times 10^2$

In the table of mantissas 4356 lies between 4346 and 4362.

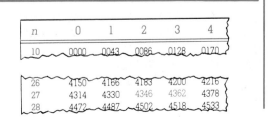

n	0	1	2	3	4
10	0000	0043	0086	0128	0170
26	4150	4166	4183	4200	4216
27	4314	4330	4346	4362	4378
28	4472	4487	4502	4518	4533

Again, form a proportion of differences.

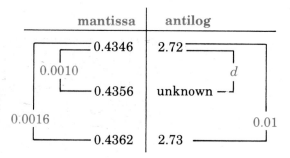

	mantissa	antilog
	0.4346	2.72
	0.4356	unknown
	0.4362	2.73

$$\frac{0.0010}{0.0016} = \frac{d}{0.01}$$

$$0.00625 = d$$

$$0.006 = d$$

Since the values in the table are increasing, add 0.006 to 2.72.

antilog 2.4356 = (antilog 0.4356) × 10^2
      = (2.72 + 0.006) × 10^2
      = 2.726 × 10^2
      = 272.6

The antilog of 2.4356 is about 272.6.

Exploratory Exercises

State the two numbers whose logarithms you would use to find the logarithm of each number below.

1. 7.413   **2.** 32,520   **3.** 0.0007463   **4.** 0.01234

State two numbers between which the antilog of each logarithm lies.

5. 0.6209   **6.** 2.7295   **7.** 3.9788   **8.** 0.7885 − 2

Written Exercises

Interpolate to find the logarithm of each number.

1. 5.273   **2.** 7.184   **3.** 27.53
4. 604.7   **5.** 0.1952   **6.** 0.07635
7. 0.003148   **8.** 7.003   **9.** 4167
10. 60.06   **11.** 329.4   **12.** 19.79
13. 0.04729   **14.** 8.871   **15.** 5.008
16. 0.005364   **17.** 80.08   **18.** 0.7214
19. 2148 × 10^3 **20.** 305.4 × 10^{-4} **21.** 16.57 × 10^{-2}

Interpolate to find the antilog of each logarithm.

22. 0.4861   **23.** 0.5506   **24.** 3.5748
25. 2.7792   **26.** 0.3353 − 2   **27.** 7.6173 − 10
28. 8.6409 − 10   **29.** 0.4399 − 3   **30.** 3.4193
31. 4.2173   **32.** 0.5915 − 2   **33.** 0.6778 − 3
34. 0.1177 − 3   **35.** 8.8787 − 10   **36.** 2.5082
37. 5.5958   **38.** 4.6279   **39.** 3.4170
40. 0.9172 − 3   **41.** 6.5688 − 10   **42.** 0.8713 − 2

Interpolation can be used to solve problems. Suppose the deer population of a certain area is known for 1980 and 1985. Estimate the deer population in 1982.

$$5\begin{bmatrix} 2\begin{bmatrix} \begin{array}{ll} \textbf{Year} & \textbf{Number of Deer} \\ 1980 & 4320 \\ 1982 & \text{unknown} \\ 1985 & 6780 \end{array} \end{bmatrix}^x \end{bmatrix}2460$$

The increase in the number of deer in 2 years is unknown but the increase in 5 years is 2460, or about 2500. Use the following proportion to estimate the increase for 2 years.

$$\frac{2}{5} = \frac{x}{2500}$$
$$x = 1000$$

Increase the original number, 4320, by about 1000. The 1982 deer population was approximately 5300.

Exercises
Estimate using interpolation.

1. The following are two monthly phone bills. Each bill lists the number of calls and the amount that is charged. Estimate the charge for 76 calls.

Number of Calls	Charges
25	$17.50
100	$25.00

2. A salesman earned $1700 in the month that he sold 35 computers. Another month he received $1300 when he sold 15 computers. Estimate how much he would earn if he sold 21 computers in a month.

3. Ann rented a car for seven days for $210. Another time she paid $75 to rent a car for two days from the same agency. Estimate the cost of renting a car for four days from this agency.

4. In 1970 the population of a city was 540,025. In 1980 it was 564,871. Estimate the population for 1975.

12-7 Exponential Equations

Equations in which the variables appear as exponents are called
exponential equations. Such equations can be solved by using
the property of equality for logarithmic functions.

Examples

1 Solve the equation $2^x = 27$.

$$2^x = 27$$
$$\log 2^x = \log 27$$
$$x \log 2 = \log 27 \qquad \textit{Power Property}$$
$$x = \frac{\log 27}{\log 2}$$
$$= \frac{1.4314}{0.3010} \text{ or } 4.7555$$

Check: 4.7555 is between 4 and 5. So, $2^{4.7555}$ is between 2^4 and 2^5. Since $2^4 = 16$ and $2^5 = 32$, the solution is reasonable. The solution is approximately 4.7555.

2 Express $\log_3 35$ in terms of common logarithms. Then find its value.

$$\text{Let } x = \log_3 35$$
$$\text{Then, } 3^x = 35$$
$$\log 3^x = \log 35$$
$$x \log 3 = \log 35 \qquad \textit{Power Property}$$
$$x = \frac{\log 35}{\log 3}$$

The logarithm may be expressed as $\dfrac{\log 35}{\log 3}$.

$$\log_3 35 = \frac{\log 35}{\log 3}$$
$$= \frac{1.5441}{0.4771} \text{ or } 3.2364$$

Check: 3.2364 is between 3 and 4. So, $3^{3.2364}$ is between 3^3 and 3^4. Since $3^3 = 27$ and $3^4 = 81$, the solution is reasonable. The value of $\log_3 35$ is approximately 3.2364.

In Example 2 notice that $\log_3 35 = \dfrac{\log_{10} 35}{\log_{10} 3}$.

This and other similar examples suggest the following rule.

Suppose a, b, and n are positive numbers, and neither a nor b is 1. Then the following equation is true.

Change of Bases

$$\log_a n = \frac{\log_b n}{\log_b a}$$

Examples

3 **Find the value of $\log_4 8$ using the formula above.**

$\log_4 8 = \dfrac{\log_2 8}{\log_2 4}$ *$\log_2$ was chosen because 8 and 4 are powers of 2.*

$ = \dfrac{3}{2}$

Check: $\log_4 8 \overset{?}{=} \dfrac{3}{2}$

$ 4^{\frac{3}{2}} \overset{?}{=} 8$

$ \sqrt{4^3} \overset{?}{=} 8$

$ \sqrt{64} \overset{?}{=} 8$

$ 8 = 8$

The value of $\log_4 8$ is $\dfrac{3}{2}$.

4 **Solve the equation $2^{3y} = 3^{y+1}$.**

$$2^{3y} = 3^{y+1}$$
$$\log 2^{3y} = \log 3^{y+1}$$
$$3y \log 2 = (y + 1) \log 3 \qquad \textit{Power Property}$$
$$3y \log 2 = y \log 3 + \log 3 \qquad \textit{Distributive Property}$$
$$3y \log 2 - y \log 3 = \log 3$$
$$y(3 \log 2 - \log 3) = \log 3 \qquad \textit{Distributive Property}$$
$$y = \frac{\log 3}{3 \log 2 - \log 3}$$
$$ = \frac{0.4771}{3(0.3010) - 0.4771}$$
$$ = 1.1202$$

Check: Substitute 1.12 for y in the equation. Do the two sides have about the same value?

$$2^{3(1.12)} \approx 2^{3.36} \approx 10.27$$
$$3^{1.12+1} \approx 3^{2.12} \approx 10.27 \quad \boldsymbol{\checkmark}$$

The solution is approximately 1.1202.

Example

5 **Solve the equation $m^{\frac{3}{2}} = 17$.**

$$m^{\frac{3}{2}} = 17$$
$$(m^{\frac{3}{2}})^{\frac{2}{3}} = 17^{\frac{2}{3}} \quad \textit{Raise both sides of the equation to the } \frac{2}{3} \textit{ power.}$$
$$m = 17^{\frac{2}{3}}$$
$$\log m = \log 17^{\frac{2}{3}}$$
$$= \frac{2}{3} \log 17$$
$$= \frac{2}{3}(1.2305)$$
$$= 0.8203$$
$$m = \text{antilog } 0.8203$$
$$= 6.6115$$

The solution is about 6.61.

Exponential equations occur in compound interest problems. In the compound interest formula below, P is the investment, r is the interest rate per year, n is the number of times the interest is compounded yearly, t is the number of years of the investment, and A is the amount of money accumulated.

$$A = P\left(1 + \frac{r}{n}\right)^{nt}$$

Compound Interest Formula

Example

6 **How long would it take to double an investment of $1000 at 9% interest compounded quarterly?**

$$A = P\left(1 + \frac{r}{n}\right)^{nt} \qquad \begin{array}{l} \textit{P is \$1000, r is 0.09,} \\ \textit{and n is 4.} \end{array}$$
$$2000 = 1000\,(1 + 0.0225)^{4t}$$
$$2 = (1.0225)^{4t} \qquad \textit{Simplify.}$$
$$\log 2 = 4t \log (1.0225) \qquad \textit{Power Property}$$
$$\frac{\log 2}{4 \log(1.0225)} = t \qquad \textit{Solve for t.}$$
$$t = 7.7879 \qquad \begin{array}{l} \textit{Use tables or a calculator} \\ \textit{to evaluate.} \end{array}$$

It would take about 7.8 years for the money to double.

Exploratory Exercises

State x in terms of common logarithms.

1. $3^x = 55$
2. $5^x = 61$
3. $7^{2x} = 74$
4. $10^{3x} = 191$
5. $x = \log_6 144$
6. $x = \log_5 81$
7. $x = \log_3 12$
8. $x = \log_5 30$
9. $2^{-x} = 10$
10. $3^{-x} = 15$
11. $3^x = \sqrt{13}$
12. $2^x = 3\sqrt{2}$

Written Exercises

1–12. Solve each equation in Exploratory Exercises 1–12.

Approximate each logarithm to three decimal places.

13. $\log_3 7$
14. $\log_7 12$
15. $\log_4 22$
16. $\log_{3.21} 10$
17. $\log_6 11$
18. $\log_4 24$
19. $\log_6 72$
20. $\log_5 104$

Solve each equation using logarithms.

21. $2.7^x = 52.3$
22. $4.3^x = 78.5$
23. $7.6^{n-2} = 41.7$
24. $2.1^{x-5} = 9.32$
25. $9^{x-4} = 6.28$
26. $5^{y+2} = 15.3$
27. $x = \log_4 51.6$
28. $x = \log_3 19.8$
29. $x^{\frac{3}{2}} = 240$
30. $x^{\frac{3}{4}} = 93.7$
31. $5^{x-1} = 3^x$
32. $7^{x-2} = 5^x$
33. $5^{2x} = 9^{x-1}$
34. $12^{x-4} = 4^{2-x}$
35. $7^{x-2} = 5^{3-x}$
36. $3^{3x} = 2^{2x+3}$
37. $32^{2y} = 5^{4y+1}$
38. $2^{5x-1} = 3^{2x+1}$
39. $4^{5y-6} = 3^{2y+5}$
40. $15x^{\frac{5}{3}} = 62$
41. $6x^{\frac{3}{7}} = 105$

42. Let x be any real number and n, a, and b be positive real numbers where a and b do not equal 1. Show that if $x = \log_a n$, then $x = \dfrac{\log_b n}{\log_b a}$.

43. Suppose $2500 is invested at 6% interest compounded quarterly. How long will it take for the amount to triple?

44. Sara deposited $650 in an account that earned 12% interest compounded monthly. The account contained $2500 when she withdrew her money. How long was the money in the account?

45. If Joe invests $2000 at 12% interest compounded monthly, will he have at least $3000 in two years?

Challenge

46. Jan invested some money at 12% interest compounded monthly. At the same time, Joe invested some money at $12\frac{1}{2}$%, compounded yearly. Whose money will double more quickly?

mini-review

1. Write the slope-intercept form of the equation of the line that has a slope of $-\dfrac{8}{3}$ and passes through $(0, 6)$.

2. Solve this system of equations.
$$6x + y = 9$$
$$3x + 2y = 0$$

3. Factor $(x - y)^2 - z^2$.

4. Use a calculator to approximate to the nearest tenth the real zeros of the function
$$f(x) = 3x^3 - 16x^2 + 12x + 6.$$

5. State the multiplicative inverse of $x + 2y$. Assume $x + 2y \neq 0$.

Before the invention of handheld calculators, logarithms were often used to do computation.

Example 1: Evaluate $\dfrac{(673)(549)(13.82)}{147,900}$.

Let $A = \dfrac{(673)(549)(13.82)}{147,900}$.

$$\begin{aligned} \text{Then, } \log A &= \log \left[\frac{(673)(549)(13.82)}{147,900} \right] \\ &= \log 673 + \log 549 + \log 13.82 - \log 147,900 \\ &= 2.8280 + 2.7396 + 1.1405 - 5.1700 \\ &= 1.5381 \end{aligned}$$

$$\begin{aligned} \text{And, } A &= \text{antilog } (1.5381) \\ &= 34.52 \end{aligned}$$

The value is about 34.52.

Example 2: Use logarithms to estimate the value of $(47.9)^5$.

$$\text{Let } A = (47.9)^5$$

$$\begin{aligned} \text{Then, } \log A &= \log (47.9)^5 \\ &= 5 \log (47.9) \\ &= 5(1.6803) \\ &= 8.4015 \end{aligned}$$

$$\begin{aligned} \text{And, } A &= \text{antilog } 8.4015 \\ &= \text{antilog} (0.4015 + 8) \\ &= [\text{antilog} (0.4015)] \times 10^8 \\ &= 2.520 \times 10^8 \\ &= 252,000,000 \end{aligned}$$

The value of $(47.9)^5$ is about 252,000,000.

To evaluate roots, such as $\sqrt[4]{0.0815}$, first rewrite the expression with exponents as shown below.

$$\sqrt[4]{0.0815} = (0.0815)^{\frac{1}{4}}$$

Then use the procedure shown in Example 2.

Exercises **Use logarithms to evaluate each expression.**

1. $\dfrac{(812)(41.5)}{431}$

2. $\dfrac{(71.63)(313.4)}{(489.2)}$

3. $\dfrac{(665)(899)(0.000172)}{(0.00035)(491)}$

4. $(1790)^5$

5. $(384)^3$

6. $(905)^4$

7. $\sqrt[4]{0.0815}$

8. $\sqrt[4]{594}$

9. $\sqrt[3]{0.0017}$

12-8   Problem Solving: **Logarithms**

The irrational number e is an important number to mathematicians and scientists. It is used in growth and decay problems, and in many other types of problems. The value of e is approximately 2.718 and log e is approximately 0.4343.

e and π are both irrational numbers.

The general formula for growth and decay is

$$y = ne^{kt}.$$

In the formula, y represents the final amount, n the initial amount, k a constant, and t time. The constant k is greater than zero for growth and less than zero for decay.

Examples

1   **For a certain strain of bacteria, k represents 0.775 when t is measured in hours. How long will it take 2 bacteria to increase to 1000 bacteria?**

Explore   The final amount is 1000 bacteria. The initial amount is 2.

Plan   Use the growth formula $y = ne^{kt}$. Replace y with 1000, k with 0.775, and n with 2. Then solve for t to find the time in hours.

Solve

$$y = ne^{kt}$$
$$1000 = 2e^{0.775t}$$
$$500 = e^{0.775t}$$

$$\log 500 = \log e^{0.775t}$$
$$\log 500 = 0.775t \log e$$
$$\frac{\log 500}{0.775 \log e} = t$$
$$\frac{2.6990}{(0.775)(0.4343)} = t$$

The solution is approximately 8.019 hours.

Examine   Substitute 8.019 for t in the equation $1000 = 2e^{0.775t}$. The value of $2e^{(0.755 \times 8.019)}$ is approximately 1000.

2   **Radioactive substances decay with time. In 10 years, the mass of a 200-gram sample of an element is reduced to 100 grams. This period is called the half-life. Find the constant k for this element.**

$$y = ne^{kt}$$ *Since this problem involves decay, k will be negative.*
$$100 = 200e^{k \cdot 10}$$ *Substitute 100 for y, 200 for n, and 10 for t.*
$$0.5 = e^{k \cdot 10}$$
$$\log 0.5 = \log e^{k \cdot 10}$$
$$\frac{\log 0.5}{10 \log e} = k$$ *Solve using logarithms and a calculator.*
$$\frac{-0.3010}{10(0.4343)} = k$$
$$-0.06931 = k$$ The solution is approximately -0.06931.

When interest is compounded *continuously,* the formula

$A = P\left(1 + \dfrac{r}{n}\right)^{nt}$ becomes:

$$A = Pe^{rt}.$$

In the formula, A represents the final amount, P represents the beginning investment, r represents the annual interest rate, and t represents the time in years.

Example

3   **Assume $100 is deposited in a savings account. The interest rate is 6% compounded continuously. When will the money be double the original amount?**

If the money is to be doubled, the final amount will be $200.

$$A = Pe^{rt}$$
$$200 = 100e^{0.06t} \qquad \text{Substitute 200 for A, 100 for P, and 0.06 for r.}$$
$$2 = e^{0.06t}$$
$$\log 2 = \log e^{0.06t}$$
$$\log 2 = 0.06t \log e$$
$$\frac{\log 2}{0.06 \log e} = t$$
$$\frac{0.3010}{(0.06)(0.4343)} = t$$
$$11.55 = t \qquad \text{The solution is approximately 11.55 years.}$$

In business, the formula $V_n = P(1 + r)^n$ can be used to find the value of equipment or assets. In the formula, r represents the fixed rate of appreciation or depreciation, P the initial value, and V_n the new value at the end of n years.

Appreciation is an increase in value. Depreciation is a decrease in value.

Example

4   **A piece of machinery valued at $25,000 depreciates at a steady rate of 10% yearly. When will the value be $5000?**

$$V_n = P(1 + r)^n$$
$$5000 = 25{,}000(1 - 0.10)^n \qquad \text{Substitute 5000 for } V_n,$$
$$5000 = 25{,}000(0.9)^n \qquad \text{25,000 for P, and } -0.10$$
$$0.2 = 0.9^n \qquad \text{for r. The value of r is}$$
$$\log 0.2 = \log 0.9^n \qquad \text{negative since it represents depreciation.}$$
$$\log 0.2 = n \log 0.9$$
$$\frac{\log 0.2}{\log 0.9} = n$$
$$\frac{-0.6990}{-0.0458} = n$$
$$15.26 = n \qquad \text{The solution is approximately 15.26 years.}$$

Exploratory Exercises

Solve each problem.

1. A certain culture of bacteria will grow from 500 to 4000 bacteria in 1.5 hours. Find the constant k for the growth formula.

2. For a radioactive substance, the constant k is -0.08042 when t is in years. How long will it take 250 grams of the substance to reduce to 50 grams?

3. If $500 is invested at 8% annual interest compounded continuously, when will the investment be tripled?

4. In $2\frac{1}{2}$ years a deposit of $1000 grew to $1276. What was the rate of interest, assuming continuous compounding?

Written Exercises

Solve each problem.

1. After 9 years, half of a 20 milligram sample of a radioactive element is left. Find k for this element.

2. Bacteria of a certain type can grow from 80 to 164 bacteria in 3 hours. Find k for the growth formula.

3. For a certain strain of bacteria, k is 0.783 when t is measured in hours. How long will it take 10 bacteria to increase to 100 bacteria?

4. For a certain strain of bacteria, k is 0.782 when t is measured in hours. How long will it take 10 bacteria to increase to 500 bacteria?

5. Rachel has saved $2000 to buy a piano that will cost about $2500. If the money is in a savings account paying 7.25% interest compounded continuously, when will she be able to buy the piano?

6. Mr. Winters has $2500 to invest. If he hopes to have $5000 after 8 years, what interest rate is needed, assuming continuous compounding?

7. Suppose $10 is invested at 8% interest compounded continuously. When will the investment be worth $100? Worth $1000?

8. A piece of machinery valued at $50,000 depreciates 10% per year by the fixed rate method. After how many years will the value have depreciated to $25,000?

9. Citizen's Bank promises to double your money in $8\frac{1}{2}$ years. Assuming continuous compounding of interest, what rate of interest must the bank pay?

10. Electronic equipment valued at $150,000 depreciates 20% per year by the fixed rate method. After how many years will the value have depreciated to $15,000?

11. A radioactive substance decays according to the equation $A = A_0 \times 10^{-0.024t}$, where t is in hours. Find the half life of the substance, when $A = 0.5A_0$.

12. Radium-226 decomposes radioactively. Its half-life (the time half the sample takes to decompose) is 1800 years. Find the constant k for the decay formula. Use 100 grams as the original amount.

13. The output in watts of a satellite's power supply is given by $w = 50e^{-0.004t}$ where t is the time in days. In how many days will the power output be reduced to 20 watts?

14. Mike has $500 in his savings account. He is spending 10% of the balance each week. After how many weeks of this spending will the balance be under $1? Use $V_n = P(1 + r)^n$, where n is the number of weeks.

15. Jim and Agnes bought a new house 10 years ago for $49,000. The house is now worth $120,000. Assuming a steady growth rate, what was the yearly rate of appreciation?

16. A new car purchased 10 years ago for $6,000 is worth $600 today. Assuming a steady depreciation, what was the yearly rate of depreciation?

Using Calculators_____ Natural Logarithms

Logarithms to the base e are called natural logarithms. The natural logarithm of x is denoted ln x. Equations of the form $y = ne^{kt}$ or $A = Pe^{rt}$ are easier to solve on a calculator with a natural log key, labeled $\boxed{\ln x}$ or $\boxed{\ln}$.

Example 1: Solve $800 = 400e^{0.0875t}$.

$$800 = 400\ e^{0.0875t}$$
$$2 = e^{0.0875t}$$
$$\ln(2) = 0.0875t \times \ln(e) \qquad \textit{The power property of logarithms}$$
$$\ln(2) = 0.0875t \qquad\qquad \textit{Note that } \ln(e) = 1, \textit{ just as log } 10 = 1.$$
$$\frac{\ln(2)}{0.0875} = t$$

ENTER: 2 $\boxed{\ln}$ $\boxed{\div}$ 0.0875 $\boxed{=}$

DISPLAY: 2   0.6931472   0.0875   7.9216821

The value of t is about 7.922.

On many calculators the power function e^x is the inverse of $\ln(x)$. For e^x use $\boxed{\text{INV}}$ and $\boxed{\ln}$.

Example 2: Evaluate $1850e^{(0.0975 \times 15)}$.

ENTER: 1850 $\boxed{\times}$ $\boxed{(}$ 0.0975 $\boxed{\times}$ 15 $\boxed{)}$ $\boxed{\text{INV}}$ $\boxed{\ln}$ $\boxed{=}$

DISPLAY: 1850   0.0975   15   1.4625   4.3167379   7985.96

The value is about 7986.

Exercises

1. Susan deposited $500 in the bank. If the interest rate is 10.9% compounded continuously, how long will it take Susan to double her money?

2. If $2500 is invested in a bank paying 8.5% interest compounded continuously, how much will be in the account in 5 years?

3. Which method would yield $1000 in the shortest amount of time, investing $800 at 8% or investing $500 at 20%? Assume continuous compounding.

4. Which yields more, $275 invested at 10% for 15 years, or $275 invested at 12% for 13 years? Both are compounded continuously.

Accumulated Savings

The computer program below finds the value of the accumulated savings in an account based on the following formula.

$$S = R\left(\frac{(1 + I)^N - 1}{I}\right)$$

S is the amount in the account immediately after the final payment. No interest is added after the final payment.

In this formula S is the accumulated sum; R is the amount of each payment; I is the interest rate per payment period given as a decimal fraction; and N is the number of payments.

```
10  PRINT "INTEREST","PAYMENT","NUMBER OF","ACCUMULATED"
20  PRINT "RATE","PER PERIOD","PAYMENTS","SAVINGS"
30  READ I,R,N
40  IF I = 0 THEN 90
50  S = ((1 + I) ^ N - 1) / I * R
60  PRINT I,R,N,S
70  GOTO 30
80  DATA .09,50,24,.0975,50,24,.079,75,24,.1138,100,24,0,0,0
90  END
```

Notice that the data statement ends in three zeros. These zeros are used with line 40 to flag the end of data. Because, I, R, and N are read in the READ statement, three zeros are needed.

The output for the program is the chart shown below. Notice the use of commas in lines 10, 20, and 60. Commas provide spacing for the columns. This chart shows the accumulated savings if payments are made *once a year* for 24 years, for various interest rates and payment amounts.

INTEREST RATE	PAYMENT PER PERIOD	NUMBER OF PAYMENTS	ACCUMULATED SAVINGS
.09	50	24	3839.49066
.0975	50	24	4269.88989
.079	75	24	4938.37593
.1138	100	24	10795.5659

Exercises

Enter and run the above program. Then change the DATA statements and use the program to solve the following problems.

1. Find the accumulated savings if a $50 payment is made monthly for 10 years at annual interest rates of **(a)** 9%, **(b)** 12%, and **(c)** 15% compounded monthly. Hint: Divide by 12 to find the monthly interest rate.

2. The annual interest rate is 9% compounded monthly, and there are 120 payments. Find the accumulated savings for monthly payments of **(a)** $50, **(b)** $75, **(c)** $100, **(d)** $125, and **(e)** $150.

3. The monthly payments are $40 and the annual interest rate is 12%, compounded monthly. Find the accumulated savings after 1 year, 2 years, 3 years, 4 years, 5 years, 6 years, 7 years, and 8 years.

Vocabulary

Chapter Summary

1. **Definition of Irrational Exponents:** If x is an irrational number and $a > 0$, then a^x is the real number between a^{x_2} and a^{x_2}, for all possible choices of rational numbers x_1 and x_2 such that $x_1 < x < x_2$. (372)

2. **Property of Equality for Exponential Functions:** Suppose a is a positive number other than 1. Then $a^{x_1} = a^{x_2}$ if and only if $x_1 = x_2$. (373)

3. A logarithm corresponds to an exponent. (375)

4. **Definition of Logarithm:** Suppose $b > 0$ and $b \neq 1$. Then for $n > 0$ there is a number p such that $\log_b n = p$ if and only if $b^p = n$. (375)

5. Both $y = b^x$ and its inverse $y = \log_b x$ are functions. (377)

6. **Property of Equality for Logarithmic Functions:** Suppose $b > 0$ and $b \neq 1$. Then $\log_b x_1 = \log_b x_2$ if and only if $x_1 = x_2$. (377)

7. Because the logarithmic and exponential functions are inverses, $b^{\log_b x} = x$ and $\log_b b^x = x$. (378)

8. **Properties of Logarithms:** Suppose m and n are positive numbers, b is a positive number other than 1, and p is any number. Then the following properties hold.

   Product Property: $\log_b mn = \log_b m + \log_b n$ (381)

   Quotient Property: $\log_b \dfrac{m}{n} = \log_b m - \log_b n$ (382)

   Power Property: $\log_b m^p = p \log_b m$ (383)

9. Common logarithms are logarithms to base 10. (385)

10. To find the common logarithm of any number, first write the number in scientific notation. If r is the positive number, $r = a \times 10^n$, where $1 \leq a < 10$ and n is an integer. Then, $\log r = \log a + \log 10^n$ and $\log r = \log a + n$. Log a is found in the table of logarithms. It is called the mantissa of $\log r$. The integer n is the characteristic of $\log r$. (385)

11. To find an antilogarithm, use the table to find the antilog of the mantissa. Multiply by the power of ten corresponding to the characteristic. (386)

12. Interpolation is a procedure whereby logarithms and antilogarithms *not* directly found in the table may be calculated. (389)

13. Exponential equations have variables as exponents. They can be solved by using logarithms. (392)

14. Change of Bases: Suppose a, b, and n are positive numbers, and neither a nor b is 1. Then $\log_a n = \dfrac{\log_b n}{\log_b a}$. (393)

15. The general formula for growth and decay in nature, $y = ne^{kt}$, has many applications. In the formula, y represents the final amount, n represents the initial amount, k represents a constant, and t represents time. (397)

Chapter Review

12–1 **Solve each equation.**

  1. $2^{6x} = 4^{5x+2}$ **2.** $(\sqrt{3})^{n+1} = 9^{n-1}$ **3.** $49^{3p+1} = 7^{2p-5}$

  Simplify.

  4. $3^{\sqrt{2}} \cdot 3^{\sqrt{2}}$ **5.** $(9^{\sqrt{2}})^{\sqrt{2}}$ **6.** $\dfrac{49^{\sqrt{2}}}{7^{\sqrt{12}}}$

12–2 **Change each equation to logarithmic form.**

  7. $7^3 = 343$ **8.** $5^{-2} = \dfrac{1}{25}$

  9. $4^0 = 1$ **10.** $4^{\frac{3}{2}} = 8$

  Change each equation to exponential form.

  11. $\log_4 64 = 3$ **12.** $\log_8 2 = \dfrac{1}{3}$

  13. $\log_6 \dfrac{1}{36} = -2$ **14.** $\log_6 1 = 0$

  Solve each equation.

  15. $\log_b 9 = 2$ **16.** $\log_b 9 = \dfrac{1}{2}$

  17. $\log_{16} 2 = x$ **18.** $\log_4 x = -\dfrac{1}{2}$

12–3 **Evaluate each expression.**

  19. $\log_5 5^7$ **20.** $6^{\log_6 7}$

  21. $\log_n n^3$ **22.** $n^{\log_n 3}$

  Solve each equation.

  23. $\log_6 12 = \log_6 (5x - 3)$ **24.** $\log_3 3y = \log_3 (2y + 5)$
  25. $\log_5 y = \log_5 (14 - y)$ **26.** $\log_3 3x = \log_3 (x + 7)$
  27. $\log_2 (3x - 2) = \log_2 (2x + 6)$ **28.** $\log_4 (1 - 2x) = \log_4 (x + 10)$
  29. $\log_7 (x^2 + x) = \log_7 12$ **30.** $\log_2 (x - 1)^2 = \log_2 7$

12–4 Use $\log_{10} 7 = 0.8451$ and $\log_{10} 4 = 0.6021$ to evaluate each expression.

31. $\log_{10} \dfrac{7}{4}$

32. $\log_{10} 700$

33. $\log_{10} 0.004$

34. $\log_{10} \dfrac{49}{4}$

Solve each equation.

35. $\log_3 x - \log_3 4 = \log_3 12$

36. $\log_5 x + \log_5 3 = \log_5 15$

37. $\log_2 x = \dfrac{1}{3} \log_2 27$

38. $\log_4 y = 4 \log_4 3$

39. $\log_5 7 + \dfrac{1}{2} \log_5 4 = \log_5 x$

40. $\log_7 (m + 1) + \log_7 (m - 5) = 1$

41. $\log_6 (r - 3) + \log_6 (r + 2) = 1$

42. $\dfrac{1}{2}(2 \log_{10} 4 + 2 \log_{10} 2) = \log_{10} x$

12–5 Find the logarithm of each number.

43. 2.65

44. 632

45. 0.0777

46. 51.2

Find the antilog of each logarithm.

47. 0.7364

48. 3.8299

49. $0.4409 - 2$

50. 1.5587

12–6 Interpolate to find the logarithm of each number.

51. 3.415

52. 463.2

53. 0.04111

54. 2004

Interpolate to find the antilog of each logarithm.

55. 0.3355

56. $0.7963 - 2$

57. 1.0725

58. $0.8736 - 3$

12–7 Solve each equation using logarithms.

59. $2^x = 53$

60. $4.5^x = 36.2$

61. $\log_4 11.2 = x$

62. $\log_3 45.2 = x$

63. $3.4^{x-2} = 15.6$

64. $2.3^{x+1} = 66.6$

65. $x^{\frac{3}{4}} = 24$

66. $8^{x-2} = 5^x$

12–8 Solve each problem.

67. Assume $200 is deposited in a savings account at 6% annual interest rate compounded continuously. When will the value of the account be $300? Use $A = Pe^{rt}$.

68. A bacterial culture will grow from 400 to 5000 bacteria in $1\dfrac{1}{4}$ hours. Find the constant k for the growth formula $y = ne^{kt}$ where t is in hours.

Solve problems 1–16 without using a table of logarithms or a calculator.

Change to logarithmic form.

1. $6^4 = 1296$

2. $3^7 = 2187$

Change to exponential form.

3. $\log_5 625 = 4$

4. $\log_8 16 = \dfrac{4}{3}$

Evaluate each expression.

5. $\log_{12} 12^2$

6. $4^{\log_4 3}$

7. $\log_b b^{1.6}$

Solve each equation.

8. $\log_m 144 = 2$

9. $\log_7 x = 2$

10. $\log_2 64 = y$

11. $\log_5 (8r - 7) = \log_5 (r^2 + 5)$

12. $\log_9 (x + 4) + \log_9 (x - 4) = 1$

Use $\log_b 5 = 0.8271$ and $\log_b 3 = 0.5645$ to evaluate each expression.

13. $\log_b 15$

14. $\log_b 9$

15. $\log_b 45$

16. $\log_b \dfrac{5}{3}$

Find the logarithm of each number.

17. 769,000

18. 0.01473

Find the antilog of each logarithm.

19. 3.2754

20. $(0.8351 - 4)$

Solve.

21. $4^{3x} = 16^{x - \frac{1}{2}}$

22. $9^x = 3^{3x - 2}$

23. $27^{2p + 1} = 3^{4p - 1}$

24. $3^x = 35$

25. $\log_4 37 = x$

26. $3^x = 5^{x - 1}$

27. $7.6^{x - 1} = 439$

28. A Pilgrim ancestor of Carrie Seltzer left \$10 in a savings account in the Provident Savings Bank. Interest was compounded continuously at 4%. The account is now worth \$75,000. How long ago was the account started? ($A = Pe^{rt}$, $e = 2.718$, and $\log e = 0.4343$)

CHAPTER 13

Sequences and Series

The following sequence of numbers has been discovered in the pattern of beehive construction, in pine cones, and seeds in flowers.

1, 1, 2, 3, 5, 8, 13, 21, 34, . . .

Can you tell what the next number will be? What is the pattern?
In this chapter you will learn more about sequences and series.

13-1 Arithmetic Sequences

John Dalton is a race car driver. He enters the straightaway at 91 miles per hour. While on the straightaway he increases his speed by 29.7 mph. After nine seconds, his speed is 120.7 mph.

The speed at each second is shown below.

number of seconds	0	1	2	3	4	5	6	7	8	9
speed in mph	91	94.3	97.6	100.9	104.2	107.5	110.8	114.1	117.4	120.7

These numbers, which represent speeds, are an example of a **sequence.** A set of numbers in a specific order is called a sequence. Each number in a sequence is called a **term.** The first term is denoted a_1, the second term a_2, and so on to a_n, the nth term.

symbol	a_1	a_2	a_3	a_4	a_5	a_6	a_7	a_8	a_9	a_{10}
term	91	94.3	97.6	100.9	104.2	107.5	110.8	114.1	117.4	120.7

Definition of an Arithmetic Sequence

An arithmetic sequence is a sequence in which the difference between any two consecutive terms is the same.

The common difference is found by subtracting any term from its succeeding term. What is the common difference, d, for the arithmetic sequence of speeds listed above?

Find d for each of the following arithmetic sequences.

$$3, 7, 11, 15, \ldots \qquad d = 4$$

The three dots mean that the sequence continues indefinitely in the same pattern.

$$2, \frac{3}{2}, 1, \frac{1}{2}, 0, -\frac{1}{2}, -1, \ldots \qquad d = -\frac{1}{2}$$

Example

1 **Find the next three terms of the sequence 21, 27, 33, ...**

Find the common difference.

$33 - 27 = 6$ $27 - 21 = 6$ $d = 6$

Add 6 to the third term to get the fourth, and so on.

$33 + 6 = 39$ $39 + 6 = 45$ $45 + 6 = 51$

The next three terms are 39, 45, 51.

There is a pattern in the way terms of an arithmetic sequence are formed. Consider the terms of the sequence in Example 1.

a_1	a_2	a_3	a_4	a_5
21	27	33	39	45
$21 + 0 \cdot 6$	$21 + 1 \cdot 6$	$21 + 2 \cdot 6$	$21 + 3 \cdot 6$	$21 + 4 \cdot 6$
$a_1 + 0 \cdot d$	$a_1 + 1 \cdot d$	$a_1 + 2 \cdot d$	$a_1 + 3 \cdot d$	$a_1 + 4 \cdot d$

How would you write an addition expression for the term a_n?

The nth term, a_n, of an arithmetic sequence with first term a_1 and common difference d is given by the following equation.

$$a_n = a_1 + (n - 1)d$$

Definition of the nth Term of an Arithmetic Sequence

Example

2 **Suppose the race car driver continues to increase his speed at the same rate. What will be his speed after 15 seconds?**

$a_1 = 91$ $d = 3.3$

Find a_{16} using $a_n = a_1 + (n - 1)d$.   *a_{16} is the speed after 15 seconds. Why?*

$$\begin{aligned} a_{16} &= 91 + (16 - 1)3.3 \\ &= 91 + 15(3.3) \\ &= 91 + 49.5 \\ &= 140.5 \end{aligned}$$

His speed will be 140.5 mph.

The terms between any two nonconsecutive terms of an arithmetic sequence are called **arithmetic means**.

$$12, 21, 30, 39, 48, 57, 66, 75, \ldots$$

Thus 30, 39, and 48 are the three arithmetic means between 21 and 57.

Examples

3 **Find the four arithmetic means between 12 and 47. Use $a_n = a_1 + (n - 1)d$.**

$a_1 = 12$ $12, \underline{\hspace{0.5cm}}, \underline{\hspace{0.5cm}}, \underline{\hspace{0.5cm}}, \underline{\hspace{0.5cm}}, 47$ $a_6 = 47$

$a_6 = a_1 + (5)d$

$47 = 12 + 5d$

$35 = 5d$

$7 = d$ *The common difference is 7.*

$12 + 7 = 19$ $19 + 7 = 26$ $26 + 7 = 33$ $33 + 7 = 40$

The arithmetic means are 19, 26, 33, and 40.

4 **Find the number of multiples of 13 between 29 and 258.**

The least and greatest multiples of 13 between 29 and 258 are 39 and 247. A sequence where $a_1 = 39$, $d = 13$, and $a_n = 247$ will have the required number of terms.

Use $a_n = a_1 + (n - 1)d$.

$247 = 39 + (n - 1)13$ *Here $a_n = 247$, $a_1 = 39$, $d = 13$.*

$208 = (n - 1)13$

$17 = n$

There are 17 multiples of 13 between 29 and 258.

Exploratory Exercises

Name the first five terms of each arithmetic sequence described below.

1. $a_1 = 4, d = 3$

2. $a_1 = 7, d = 5$

3. $a_1 = 16, d = -2$

4. $a_1 = 38, d = -4$

5. $a_1 = \frac{3}{4}, d = -\frac{1}{4}$

6. $a_1 = \frac{3}{8}, d = \frac{5}{8}$

7. $a_1 = 2.3, d = 1.6$

8. $a_1 = 0.88, d = 0$

9. $a_1 = -\frac{1}{3}, d = -\frac{2}{3}$

10. $a_1 = -\frac{4}{5}, d = 1$

11. $a_1 = -4.2, d = -1.3$

12. $a_1 = 2, d = -2.5$

Name the next four terms of each of the following arithmetic sequences.

13. $5, 9, 13, \ldots$

14. $11, 14, 17, \ldots$

15. $2, -3, -8, \ldots$

16. $21, 15, 9, \ldots$

17. $\frac{1}{2}, \frac{3}{2}, \frac{5}{2}, \ldots$

18. $-5.4, -1.4, 2.6, \ldots$

19. $-\frac{5}{4}, -\frac{7}{4}, -\frac{9}{4}, \ldots$

20. $9.9, 13.7, 17.5, \ldots$

21. $-0.06, 2.24, 4.54, \ldots$

Written Exercises

Use $a_n = a_1 + (n - 1)d$ to find the nth term of each arithmetic sequence described below.

1. $a_1 = 7, d = 3, n = 14$

2. $a_1 = -3, d = -9, n = 11$

3. $a_1 = -1, d = -10, n = 25$

4. $a_1 = -7, d = 3, n = 17$

5. $a_1 = 2, d = \frac{1}{2}, n = 8$

6. $a_1 = \frac{3}{4}, d = -\frac{5}{4}, n = 13$

7. $a_1 = 20, d = 4, n = 100$

8. $a_1 = 13, d = 3, n = 101$

9. $a_1 = 27, d = 16, n = 23$

10. $a_1 = 15, d = 80, n = 10$

11. $a_1 = \sqrt{3}, d = -\sqrt{2}, n = 11$

12. $a_1 = 2i, d = -5i, n = 12$

Find the indicated term in each arithmetic sequence.

13. a_{12} for $-17, -13, -9, \ldots$

14. a_{21} for $10, 7, 4, \ldots$

15. a_{32} for $4, 7, 10, 13, \ldots$

16. a_{10} for $8, 3, -2, \ldots$

17. a_{12} for $\frac{3}{4}, \frac{3}{2}, \frac{9}{4}, \ldots$

18. a_{10} for $\frac{5}{6}, \frac{7}{6}, \frac{3}{2}, \ldots$

Answer each question by finding n, the number of the term.

19. Which term of $-2, 5, 12, \ldots$ is 124?

20. Which term of $-3, 2, 7, \ldots$ is 142?

21. Which term of $7, 2, -3, \ldots$ is -28?

22. Which term of $2\frac{1}{4}, 2, 1\frac{3}{4}, \ldots$ is $-\frac{17}{4}$?

Find the missing terms of the following arithmetic sequences.

23. $55, \underline{\quad}, \underline{\quad}, \underline{\quad}, 115$

24. $-8, \underline{\quad}, \underline{\quad}, 3$

25. $-10, \underline{\quad}, \underline{\quad}, \underline{\quad}, \underline{\quad}, 2$

26. $2, \underline{\quad}, \underline{\quad}, \underline{\quad}, \underline{\quad}, \underline{\quad}, 20$

27. $\underline{\quad}, -6, \underline{\quad}, \underline{\quad}, 15, \underline{\quad}$

28. $\underline{\quad}, 49, \underline{\quad}, \underline{\quad}, 28$

Solve each problem.

29. The last term of an arithmetic sequence is 207, the common difference is 3, and the number of terms is 14. What is the first term of the sequence?

30. If a car depreciates in value $1200 each year, what will it be worth at the end of its sixth year? The original cost of the car was $13,600.

31. How many multiples of 7 are there between 11 and 391?

32. How many multiples of 12 are there between 16 and 415?

33. During a free-fall, a skydiver falls 16 feet in the first second, 48 feet in the second second, and 80 feet in the third second. If she continues to fall at this rate, how many feet will she fall in the 10th second?

34. A salesman receives $25 for every vacuum cleaner he sells. If he sells more than 10 vacuum cleaners he will receive an additional $1.75 for each successive sale until he is paid a maximum of $46 per vacuum cleaner. How many must he sell to reach this maximum?

35. Mr. Mark's salary is $12,500. His raises will be $700 per year. What will be his salary after 8 years?

36. The third term of an arithmetic sequence is 14 and the ninth term is -1. Find the first four terms.

Challenge

37. The 5th term of an arithmetic sequence is 19 and the 11th term is 43. Find the first term and the 87th term.

38. Find three numbers that have a sum of 27 and a product of 288, and form an arithmetic sequence.

13-2 Arithmetic Series

Dana Thompson is starting a savings program. She plans to save five cents the first day, ten cents the second day, fifteen cents the third day, and so on. How much will she save in the first week using this plan?

If the amount Dana saves each day is listed, the list is a sequence.

$$5, 10, 15, 20, 25, 30, 35$$

Ths sum of this sequence is indicated as follows.

$$5 + 10 + 15 + 20 + 25 + 30 + 35$$

The sum is 140.
Dana has saved $1.40.

The indicated sum of the terms of a sequence is called a series.

Definition of Series

The chart below contains examples of arithmetic sequences and their corresponding series.

Arithmetic Sequence	Arithmetic Series
3, 6, 9, 12, 15	$3 + 6 + 9 + 12 + 15$
$-4, -1, 2$	$-4 + (-1) + 2$
$\dfrac{5}{3}, \dfrac{8}{3}, \dfrac{11}{3}, \dfrac{14}{3}$	$\dfrac{5}{3} + \dfrac{8}{3} + \dfrac{11}{3} + \dfrac{14}{3}$
$a_1, a_2, a_3, a_4, \ldots a_n$	$a_1 + a_2 + a_3 + a_4 + \ldots + a_n$

The symbol S_n is used to represent the *sum of the first n terms of a series*. For example, S_3 represents the sum of the first three terms of the series $3 + 6 + 9 + 12 + 15$, which is $3 + 6 + 9$ or 18.

If a series has a large number of terms, it is not convenient to find the sum by adding its terms. To write a general formula for the sum of a series of n terms, consider S_7 for the series

$$3 + 7 + 11 + 15 + 19 + 23 + 27.$$

Express the terms of S_7 in ascending order, then descending order, as shown below. Then add each column.

$$
\begin{array}{rcl}
S_7 &=& 3 + 7 + 11 + 15 + 19 + 23 + 27 \\
+ \; S_7 &=& 27 + 23 + 19 + 15 + 11 + 7 + 3 \\
\hline
2 \cdot S_7 &=& 30 + 30 + 30 + 30 + 30 + 30 + 30
\end{array}
$$

Notice that the sum of each column is 30.

$$\underbrace{\qquad\qquad\qquad\qquad\qquad\qquad\qquad}_{7 \text{ sums}}$$

$$2 \cdot S_7 = 7 \cdot 30$$

Since $30 = 3 + 27$, each column sum of 30 could be written as the sum of the first and last terms of S_7.

$$
\begin{aligned}
2 \cdot S_7 &= 7(a_1 + a_7) \\
S_7 &= \frac{7}{2}(a_1 + a_7) \qquad \textit{Divide both sides by 2.}
\end{aligned}
$$

The same method can be used to write a formula for an arithmetic series with n terms. Let $S_n = a_1 + a_2 + a_3 + a_4 + \ldots + a_n$. To write an expression for $2 \cdot S_n$, write each column sum as the sum of the first and last terms of S_n.

$$2 \cdot S_n = \underbrace{(a_1 + a_n) + (a_1 + a_n) + (a_1 + a_n) + \ldots + (a_1 + a_n)}_{n \text{ sums}}$$

$$
\begin{aligned}
2 \cdot S_n &= n(a_1 + a_n) \\
S_n &= \frac{n}{2}(a_1 + a_n) \qquad \textit{Divide both sides by 2.}
\end{aligned}
$$

> **The sum, S_n, of the first n terms of an arithmetic series is given by the following formula.**
>
> $$S_n = \frac{n}{2}(a_1 + a_n)$$

Sum of an Arithmetic Series

Example

1 **Find the sum of the first 50 positive integers.**

$a_1 = 1, a_n = 50, n = 50$

$$S_n = \frac{n}{2}(a_1 + a_n)$$

$$S_{50} = \frac{50}{2}(1 + 50) \qquad \textit{Substitute 1 for } a_1, \text{ 50 for } a_n, \text{ and 50 for } n.$$

$$= 25(51)$$

$$= 1275$$

The sum of the first 50 positive integers is 1275.

You know that $a_n = a_1 + (n - 1)d$. Using substitution gives another formula for S_n.

$$S_n = \frac{n}{2}(a_1 + a_n)$$
$$= \frac{n}{2}\{a_1 + [a_1 + (n - 1)d]\} \qquad \textit{Use } a_n = a_1 + (n - 1)d.$$
$$= \frac{n}{2}[2a_1 + (n - 1)d]$$

Examples

2 **Find the sum of the first 60 terms of an arithmetic series where $a_1 = 15$, $n = 60$, and $d = 80$.**

$$S_n = \frac{n}{2}[2a_1 + (n - 1)d]$$
$$S_{60} = \frac{60}{2}[2 \cdot 15 + (59)80]$$
$$= 30(30 + 59 \cdot 80)$$
$$= 142{,}500$$

3 **A supermarket display consists of cans stacked as shown at the right. The bottom row has 27 cans. Each row above has one less can than the row below it. The display has 15 rows. How many cans are in the display?**

Find the sum of an arithmetic series where $a_1 = 27$, $d = -1$, and $n = 15$.

$$S_n = \frac{n}{2}[2a_1 + (n - 1)d]$$
$$S_n = \frac{15}{2}[2 \cdot 27 + (15 - 1)(-1)]$$
$$= \frac{15}{2}(54 - 14)$$
$$= 300 \qquad \text{There are 300 cans in the display.}$$

4 **Find the first three terms of an arithmetic series where $a_1 = 17$, $a_n = 101$, and $S_n = 472$.**

$$S_n = \frac{n}{2}(a_1 + a_n) \qquad\qquad\quad a_n = a_1 + (n - 1)d$$
$$472 = \frac{n}{2}(17 + 101) \qquad\qquad 101 = 17 + (8 - 1)d)$$
$$472 = 59n \qquad\qquad\qquad\qquad\quad 84 = 7d$$
$$n = 8 \qquad\qquad\qquad\qquad\qquad\quad 12 = d$$

$a_2 = 17 + 12$ or 29 $\qquad$ $a_3 = 29 + 12$ or 41

The first three terms are 17, 29, and 41.

Exploratory Exercises

Evaluate each of the following series.

1. $4 + 7 + 10 + 13 + 16 + 19 + 22 + 25$

2. $1 + 5 + 9 + 13 + 17 + 21 + 25 + 29$

Find S_n for each series.

3. $a_1 = 2, a_n = 200, n = 100$

4. $a_1 = 5, a_n = 100, n = 200$

5. $a_1 = 4, n = 15, d = 3$

6. $a_1 = 50, n = 20, d = -4$

7. $9 + 11 + 13 + 15 + \ldots$ for $n = 12$

8. $-3 + (-7) + (-11) + \ldots$ for $n = 10$

9. Find the sum of the first 100 positive integers.

10. An arithmetic series has a sum of 77. The first term is 2 and the last term is 12. How many terms are there?

Written Exercises

Find S_n for each series described below.

1. $a_1 = 11, a_n = 44, n = 23$

2. $a_1 = 3, a_n = -38, n = 8$

3. $a_1 = 5, n = 18, a_n = 73$

4. $a_1 = 85, n = 21, a_n = 25$

5. $a_1 = 3, n = 9, a_n = 27$

6. $a_1 = 34, n = 9, a_n = 2$

7. $a_1 = 9, n = 22, a_n = 101$

8. $a_1 = 76, n = 16, a_n = 31$

9. $a_1 = 5, d = 12, n = 7$

10. $a_1 = 4, d = -1, n = 7$

11. $a_1 = 9, d = -6, n = 14$

12. $a_1 = 5, d = \frac{1}{2}, n = 13$

Find the sum of each series.

13. $7 + 14 + 21 + 28 + \ldots + 98$

14. $6 + 12 + 18 + \ldots + 96$

15. $10 + 4 + (-2) + (-8) + \ldots + (-50)$

16. $34 + 30 + 26 + \ldots + 2$

Find S_n for each series described below.

17. $d = -4, n = 9, a_n = 27$

18. $a_1 = 91, d = -4, a_n = 15$

19. $a_1 = -2, d = \frac{1}{2}, a_n = 5$

20. $d = 5, n = 16, a_n = 72$

Find the first three terms for each series described below.

21. $a_1 = 6, a_n = 306, S_n = 1716$

22. $a_1 = 7, a_n = 139, S_n = 876$

23. $n = 14, a_n = 53, S_n = 378$

24. $n = 21, a_n = 78, S_n = 1008$

Solve each problem.

25. Find the sum of the odd integers from 1 to 100.

26. Find the sum of the positive integers less than 100 and divisible by 6.

27. A pile of fireplace logs has 1 log in the top layer, 2 logs in the next layer, and so on. How many logs are in the pile if it contains 21 layers?

28. The cost of repairs for a certain automobile increases $60 each year. If the cost of repairs for the first year is $125, what is the total amount spent on repairs for the automobile after 7 years?

29. An auditorium has 21 seats in the first row. Each of the other rows has one more seat than the row in front of it. If there are 30 rows of seats, what is the seating capacity of the auditorium?

30. The prize for the correct solution to a certain crossword puzzle is $100. If the prize is uncollected, it is increased by $5 each week. At the end of 20 weeks, how large is the prize?

Suppose you borrow some money from the local bank. As a general rule, the amount of interest is not the same for each month. You owe more interest the first month than you do the last month. Do you see why? For a one-year loan, the following series may be used in figuring the amount of interest for each month.

$$12 + 11 + 10 + 9 + 8 + 7 + 6 + 5 + 4 + 3 + 2 + 1 \text{ or } 78$$

How many months are there in a year? How many addends are there in the series shown above?

The example below shows how this series is used to figure amounts of interest.

Example: What part of the interest is paid during the first month of a one-year loan? What part of the interest is paid during the first three months of a one-year loan? What part of the interest is paid during the first six months of a one-year loan?

$\frac{12}{78}$ of the total interest is paid in the first month.

$\frac{12 + 11 + 10}{78}$ or $\frac{33}{78}$ is paid in the first three months.

$\frac{12 + 11 + 10 + 9 + 8 + 7}{78}$ or $\frac{57}{78}$ is paid in the first six months.

The above method is called the **rule of 78.** Do you see why?

For a two-year loan, find the number of months in 2 years. The interest series has how many addends? What are the addends?

Exercises

Find the part of the interest owed for each of the following using the rule of 78.

1. first two months of a one-year loan
2. first four months of a one-year loan
3. last month of a one-year loan
4. first month of a two-year loan
5. first three months of a two-year loan
6. first six months of a two-year loan
7. first month of a three-year loan
8. last month of a three-year loan

Example 1

Find the sum of the first six terms of a geometric series for which $a_1 = 3$ and $r = -2$. Use the formula $S_n = \dfrac{a_1 - a_1 r^n}{1 - r}$.

$$S_n = \frac{a_1 - a_1 r^n}{1 - r}$$

$$S_6 = \frac{3 - 3(-2)^6}{1 - (-2)} \qquad \textit{Substitute 3 for } a_1,\ -2 \textit{ for r, and 6 for n.}$$

$$= -63$$

The sum of the first six terms is -63.

You know that $a_n = a_1 r^{n-1}$. Then $a_n \cdot r = a_1 r^{n-1} \cdot r$ or $a_1 r^n$. Replacing $a_1 r^n$ by $a_n r$ gives another formula for finding the value of S_n.

$$S_n = \frac{a_1 - a_1 r^n}{1 - r}$$

$$= \frac{a_1 - a_n r}{1 - r} \qquad \textit{Substitute } a_n r \textit{ for } a_1 r^n.$$

Example 2

Find the sum of a geometric series for which $a_1 = 48$, $a_n = 3$, and $r = -\dfrac{1}{2}$. Use the formula $S_n = \dfrac{a_1 - a_n r}{1 - r}$.

$$S_n = \frac{a_1 - a_n r}{1 - r}$$

$$= \frac{48 - 3\left(-\dfrac{1}{2}\right)}{1 - \left(-\dfrac{1}{2}\right)} \qquad \textit{Substitute 48 for } a_1,\ 3 \textit{ for } a_n, \textit{ and } -\dfrac{1}{2} \textit{ for r.}$$

$$= \frac{\dfrac{99}{2}}{\dfrac{3}{2}}$$

$$= 33$$

The sum S_n is 33.

When $r = 1$, S_n is found by the formula $S_n = n \cdot a_1$. For example, the sum of the series $3 + 3 + 3 + 3 + 3 + 3$ is given by $S_n = 6 \cdot 3$ or 18.

Exploratory Exercises

For each geometric series described below, state the first term, the common ratio, the last term, and the number of terms.

1. $9 - 18 + 36 - 72 + 144$

2. $3 + 1.5 + 0.75 + 0.375 + 0.1875$

3. $a_1 - 5 + \dfrac{5}{4} - \dfrac{5}{16} + a_5$

4. $a_1 + 6 - 3 + \dfrac{3}{2} + a_5$

5. $a_1 = 2, a_4 = 128, n = 5$

6. $a_2 = 6, a_4 = 24, n = 5$

7. $a_2 = -12, a_4 = -108, n = 6$

8. $a_5 = \dfrac{1}{64}, n = 5, a_3 = \dfrac{1}{8}$

Find the sum of each geometric series described below.

9. $2 + (-6) + 18 + \ldots$ to 6 terms.

10. $3 + 6 + 12 + \ldots$ to 6 terms.

11. $8 + 4 + 2 + \ldots$ to 6 terms.

12. $\dfrac{1}{9} - \dfrac{1}{3} + 1 - \ldots$ to 5 terms.

13. $1296 - 216 + 36 - \ldots$ to 5 terms.

14. $7 + 7 + 7 + \ldots$ to 9 terms.

Written Exercises

Find the sum of each geometric series. Use calculators if necessary.

1. $75 + 15 + 3 + \ldots$ to 10 terms.

2. $16 + 16 + 16 + \ldots$ to 11 terms.

3. $a_1 = 7, r = 2, n = 14$

4. $a_1 = 5, r = 3, n = 12$

5. $a_1 = 12, a_5 = 972, r = -3$

6. $a_1 = 256, r = \dfrac{3}{4}, n = 9$

7. $a_1 = 243, r = -\dfrac{2}{3}, n = 5$

8. $a_1 = 16, r = -\dfrac{1}{2}, n = 10$

9. $a_1 = 625, a_5 = 81, r = \dfrac{3}{5}$

10. $a_1 = 625, r = \dfrac{2}{5}, n = 8$

11. $a_1 = 4, a_6 = \dfrac{1}{8}, r = \dfrac{1}{2}$

12. $a_1 = 1, a_5 = \dfrac{1}{16}, r = -\dfrac{1}{2}$

13. $a_1 = 125, a_5 = \dfrac{1}{5}, r = \dfrac{1}{5}$

14. $a_1 = 343, a_4 = -1, r = -\dfrac{1}{7}$

15. $a_3 = \dfrac{3}{4}, a_6 = \dfrac{3}{32}, n = 6$

16. $a_3 = \dfrac{5}{4}, a_4 = -\dfrac{5}{16}, n = 6$

17. $a_2 = 1.5, a_5 = 0.1875, n = 9$

18. $a_2 = -12, a_5 = -324, n = 10$

Find a_1 for each geometric series described below.

19. $S_n = 32, r = 2, n = 6$

20. $S_n = 244, r = -3, n = 5$

21. $a_n = 324, r = 3, S_n = 484$

22. $S_n = 635, a_n = 320, r = 2$

23. $S_n = 1022, r = 2, n = 9$

24. $S_n = 15\dfrac{3}{4}, r = \dfrac{1}{2}, a_n = \dfrac{1}{4}$

Solve each problem.

25. Find the sum of the first nine terms of the geometric series whose 4th term is 20 and whose 8th term is 1620.

26. One minute after it is released, a hot air balloon rises 80 feet. In each succeeding minute the balloon rises only 60% as far as it rose in the previous minute. How far will the balloon rise in 6 minutes?

27. The teaching staff of Fairmeadow High School informs its members of school cancellation by telephone. The principal calls 2 teachers, each of whom in turn calls 2 other members, and so on. This process must be repeated 6 times counting the principal's calls as the first time. How many teachers, including the principal, work at Fairmeadow High?

13-5　Infinite Geometric Series

The first swing of a pendulum measures 25 centimeters. The lengths of the successive swings form the geometric sequence 25, 20, 16, 12.8, ...

Suppose this pendulum continues to swing back and forth infinitely. Then the sequence shown above is called an *infinite geometric sequence*.

The distances traveled by the pendulum can be added.

The sum of these distances is an infinite geometric series with $a_1 = 25$ and $r = \dfrac{20}{25}$ or 0.8.

$$25 + 20 + 16 + 12.8 + \cdots$$

The series can be written as follows.

$$25 + 25(0.8)^1 + 25(0.8)^2 + 25(0.8)^3 + 25(0.8)^4 + 25(0.8)^5 + 25(0.8)^6 + \cdots$$

Notice what happens as 0.8 is raised to various powers.

$$(0.8)^1 = 0.8 \qquad (0.8)^{10} \approx 0.1074 \qquad (0.8)^{50} \approx 0.00001$$

As the values of n become greater, what happens to $(0.8)^n$?

What happens to the terms of the series as the exponents increase?

$$a_1 = 25 \qquad a_{10} \approx 3.3554 \qquad a_{50} \approx 0.0004$$

What happens to the sums S_n as n becomes greater?

$$S_1 = 25 \qquad S_{10} \approx \frac{25 - 25(0.1074)}{0.2} \qquad S_{50} \approx \frac{25 - 25(0.00001)}{0.2}$$

$$\approx \frac{25 - 2.685}{0.2} \qquad \approx \frac{25 - 0.00025}{0.2}$$

$$\approx 111.575 \qquad \approx 124.9988$$

Find S_{100}. Do you think that S_{500} is greater than 125?

In any geometric series, the sum of the first n terms can be found by using either of the following formulas.

$$S_n = \frac{a_1 - a_1 r^n}{1 - r} \quad \text{or} \quad S_n = \frac{a_1(1 - r^n)}{1 - r}, \, r \neq 1$$

Suppose the value of r^n is very close to zero. Then the value of S_n is very close to the following expression, called the *sum of an infinite series*.

$$\frac{a_1(1 - 0)}{1 - r} \quad \text{or} \quad \frac{a_1}{1 - r}$$

> **The sum, S, of an infinite geometric series where $-1 < r < 1$ is given by the following formula.**
>
> $$S = \frac{a_1}{1 - r}$$

Sum of an Infinite Geometric Series

An infinite geometric series where r is not between -1 and 1 does not have a sum.

Examples

1 **Find the sum of the series 25 + 20 + 16 + 12.8 + ...**

$S = \dfrac{a_1}{1 - r}$ $r = \dfrac{20}{25}$ *Since* $-1 < 0.8 < 1$, *you can use the formula.*

$S = \dfrac{25}{1 - 0.8}$ *Substitute 25 for* a_1 *and 0.8 for r.*

$\quad = 125$

The sum of the series is 125.

2 **Find the sum of the infinite geometric series** $\dfrac{4}{3} - \dfrac{2}{3} + \dfrac{1}{3} - \dfrac{1}{6} + \cdots$.

First find r. $a_2 = a_1 r$

$\qquad -\dfrac{2}{3} = \left(\dfrac{4}{3}\right) r$ *Substitute* $-\dfrac{2}{3}$ *for* a_2 *and* $\dfrac{4}{3}$ *for* a_1.

$\qquad -\dfrac{1}{2} = r$

Next, find the sum using $S = \dfrac{a_1}{1 - r}$. $S = \dfrac{\dfrac{4}{3}}{1 - \left(-\dfrac{1}{2}\right)} = \dfrac{\dfrac{4}{3}}{\dfrac{3}{2}} = \dfrac{8}{9}$ The sum is $\dfrac{8}{9}$.

3 **Express the repeating decimal 0.11111 . . . or $0.\overline{1}$ as a fraction.**

Write $0.\overline{1}$ as an infinite geometric series.

$0.\overline{1} = 0.1 + 0.01 + 0.001 + \ldots$

Then $a_1 = 0.1$ and $r = 0.1$ since $0.01 = 0.1(r)$.

$S = \dfrac{a_1}{1 - r}$

$S = \dfrac{0.1}{1 - 0.1}$ *Substitute 0.1 for* a_1 *and 0.1 for r.*

$\quad = \dfrac{0.1}{0.9}$

$\quad = \dfrac{1}{9}$ The repeating decimal $0.\overline{1}$ is equal to the common fraction $\dfrac{1}{9}$.

4 **A rubber ball dropped 30 feet bounces $\dfrac{2}{5}$ of the height from which it fell on each bounce. How far will it travel before coming to rest?**

downward distance   *upward distance*

$S = \dfrac{30}{1 - 0.4}$ *Note that* a_1 *is 30 and r is 0.4* $S = \dfrac{12}{1 - 0.4}$ *Note that* a_1 *is* $\dfrac{2}{5}$ *of 30, or 12, and r is 0.4.*

$\quad = \dfrac{30}{0.6}$ $\quad = \dfrac{12}{0.6}$

$\quad = 50$ $\quad = 20$

The total distance is 50 + 20 or 70 feet.

Exploratory Exercises

Find a_1 and r for each series. Then find the sum, if it exists.

1. $\frac{1}{2} + \frac{1}{3} + \frac{2}{9} + \frac{4}{27} + \cdots$

2. $12 + 3 + \frac{3}{4} + \frac{3}{16} + \cdots$

3. $1 - \frac{1}{3} + \frac{1}{9} - \frac{1}{27} + \cdots$

4. $1 - 3 + 9 - 27 + \cdots$

5. $1 + \frac{3}{2} + \frac{9}{4} + \frac{27}{8} + \cdots$

6. $48 + 16 + \frac{16}{3} + \frac{16}{9} + \cdots$

Express each repeating decimal as an infinite geometric series. State the ratio for each.

7. $0.\overline{7}$ 8. $0.\overline{3}$ 9. $0.7\overline{3}$ 10. $0.\overline{8}$ 11. $0.\overline{152}$ 12. $0.\overline{746}$ 13. $0.9\overline{3}$ 14. $0.\overline{75}$

Written Exercises

Find the sum of each infinite geometric series described below.

1. $a_1 = 6, r = \frac{11}{12}$

2. $a_1 = 18, r = -\frac{2}{7}$

3. $a_1 = 7, r = -\frac{3}{4}$

4. $a_1 = 27, r = -\frac{4}{5}$

5. $9 + 6 + 4 + \cdots$

6. $\frac{1}{3} + \frac{1}{9} + \frac{1}{27} + \cdots$

7. $3 - 2 + \frac{4}{3} - \cdots$

8. $\frac{3}{4} + \frac{1}{2} + \frac{1}{3} + \cdots$

9. $12 - 4 + \frac{4}{3} - \frac{4}{9} + \cdots$

10. $1 - \frac{1}{4} + \frac{1}{16} - \cdots$

11. $10 - \frac{5}{2} + \frac{5}{8} - \cdots$

12. $2 + 6 + 18 + 54 + \cdots$

13. $3 - 9 + 27 - \cdots$

14. $12 + 6 + 3 + \cdots$

15. $10 - 1 + 0.1 - \cdots$

Find a common fraction equivalent to each repeating decimal below.

16. $0.\overline{3}$ 17. $0.\overline{9}$ 18. $0.\overline{15}$ 19. $0.\overline{31}$ 20. $0.\overline{075}$ 21. $0.4\overline{10}$ 22. $0.3\overline{7}$ 23. $0.4\overline{5}$

Find the first three terms of each infinite geometric series described below.

24. $S = 9, r = \frac{1}{3}$

25. $S = 16, r = \frac{3}{4}$

26. $S = 28, r = -\frac{2}{7}$

27. $S = \frac{27}{4}, r = -\frac{1}{3}$

Solve each problem.

28. The end of a swinging pendulum 90 cm long moves through 50 cm on its first swing. Each succeeding swing is $\frac{9}{10}$ of the preceding one. How far will the pendulum travel before coming to rest?

29. The end of a swinging pendulum 30 cm long moves through 20 cm on its first swing. Each succeeding swing is $\frac{10}{11}$ of the preceding one. How far will it travel before coming to rest?

30. A silicon ball dropped 12 feet rebounds $\frac{7}{10}$ of the height from which it fell on each bounce. How far will it travel before coming to rest?

31. A hot-air balloon rises 80 feet in the first minute of flight. If in each succeeding minute the balloon rises only 90 percent as far as in the previous minute, what will be its maximum altitude?

Challenge

32. A side of an equilateral triangle is 20 inches. The midpoints of its sides are joined to form an inscribed equilateral triangle. If this process is continued without end, find the sum of the perimeters of the triangles.

33. Find the sum of the areas of the series of triangles in the previous exercise.

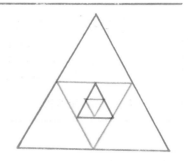

13-6 Sigma Notation

Consider the sum of the first ten positive even integers.

$$2 + 4 + 6 + 8 + \ldots + 20$$

This series can be written in a more concise way. First, notice the following pattern.

$$2(1) + 2(2) + 2(3) + 2(4) + \ldots + 2(10)$$

The Greek letter sigma, Σ, can be used to indicate this sum.

stop at 10 $\longrightarrow$ $\displaystyle\sum_{n=1}^{10} 2n$ This is read *the summation from 1 to 10 of 2n.*

start n at 1 $\longrightarrow$

Using this technique to indicate the sum of a series is called sigma or summation notation. When using this notation, the variable defined at the bottom of the sigma is called the *index of summation*. The terms of the series above are generated by successively replacing the index of summation with 1, 2, 3, . . . 10.

Any letter can be used for the index of summation.

Examples

1 Write $\displaystyle\sum_{k=1}^{5} 4k$ in expanded form.

Replace k with 1, 2, 3, 4, 5 successively.

$$\sum_{k=1}^{5} 4k = \overset{k=1}{4 \cdot 1} + \overset{k=2}{4 \cdot 2} + \overset{k=3}{4 \cdot 3} + \overset{k=4}{4 \cdot 4} + \overset{k=5}{4 \cdot 5}$$
$$= 4 \ + \ 8 \ + \ 12 \ + \ 16 \ + \ 20$$

2 Write $\displaystyle\sum_{n=3}^{7} (3n - 2)$ in expanded form and find the sum.

$$\sum_{n=3}^{7} (3n - 2) = \overset{n=3}{(3 \cdot 3 - 2)} + \overset{n=4}{(3 \cdot 4 - 2)} + \overset{n=5}{(3 \cdot 5 - 2)} + \overset{n=6}{(3 \cdot 6 - 2)} + \overset{n=7}{(3 \cdot 7 - 2)}$$
$$= (9 - 2) \ + \ (12 - 2) \ + \ (15 - 2) \ + \ (18 - 2) \ + \ (21 - 2)$$
$$= (7 + 10 + 13 + 16 + 19) \text{ or } 65$$

The sum is 65.

3 Write $\displaystyle\sum_{j=1}^{5} 2(4)^{j-1}$ in expanded form and find the sum.

$$\sum_{j=1}^{5} 2(4)^{j-1} = \overset{j=1}{2 \cdot 4^{1-1}} + \overset{j=2}{2 \cdot 4^{2-1}} + \overset{j=3}{2 \cdot 4^{3-1}} + \overset{j=4}{2 \cdot 4^{4-1}} + \overset{j=5}{2 \cdot 4^{5-1}}$$
$$= 2 \cdot 4^0 \quad \cdot \quad 2 \cdot 4^1 \ + \ 2 \cdot 4^2 \ + \ 2 \cdot 4^3 \ + \ 2 \cdot 4^4$$
$$= 2 \cdot 1 \ + \ 2 \cdot 4 \ + \ 2 \cdot 16 + 2 \cdot 64 \ + \ 2 \cdot 256$$
$$= (2 + 8 + 32 + 128 + 512) \ \text{ or } \ 682$$

The sum is 682.

Examples

4 Find the sum of $\sum_{x=1}^{9} [3 + (x - 1)5]$.

$$\sum_{x=1}^{9} [3 + (x - 1)5] = (3 + 0 \cdot 5) + (3 + 1 \cdot 5) + (3 + 2 \cdot 5) + \ldots + (3 + 8 \cdot 5)$$
$$= \quad 3 \quad + \quad 8 \quad + \quad 13 \quad + \ldots + \quad 43$$

Since this is an arithmetic series, use $S_n = \dfrac{n}{2}(a_1 + a_n)$.

$S_n = \dfrac{9}{2}(3 + 43)$ $a_1 = 3, a_n = 43, n = 9$.

$ = \dfrac{9}{2}(46)$

$ = 207$

The sum is 207.

5 Use sigma notation to express $5 + 9 + 13 + 17 + 21$.

First, search for a pattern.

$$5 \quad + \quad 9 \quad + \quad 13 \quad + \quad 17 \quad + \quad 21$$
$$= (5 + 0 \cdot 4) + (5 + 1 \cdot 4) + (5 + 2 \cdot 4) + (5 + 3 \cdot 4) + (5 + 4 \cdot 4)$$

The pattern is $5 + (n - 1)4$, if n is replaced successively with 1, 2, 3, 4, 5. Therefore, the series can be expressed as:

$\sum_{n=1}^{5} [5 + (n - 1)4]$ or $\sum_{n=1}^{5} (4n + 1)$ *Why are parentheses necessary around $4n + 1$?*

6 Use sigma notation to express $1 - 3 + 9 - 27 + 81 - 243$.

Since $1 - 3 + 9 - 27 + 81 - 243$ is a geometric series, use $a_n = a_1 r^{n-1}$.

$a_n = 1 \cdot (-3)^{n-1}$ $a_1 = 1$ and $r = -3$

Therefore the series can be expressed as:

$$\sum_{n=1}^{6} (-3)^{n-1}$$

Exploratory Exercises

For each of the following state the index and the number of terms in the series. Then, state each series in expanded form.

1. $\sum_{j=1}^{4} (j + 2)$ 2. $\sum_{k=3}^{5} 4k$ 3. $\sum_{r=1}^{3} (r - 1)$ 4. $\sum_{k=2}^{6} (3 - k)$

5. $\sum_{i=0}^{4} 2i$ 6. $\sum_{m=6}^{8} (-m)$ 7. $\sum_{p=4}^{7} (p + 2)$ 8. $\sum_{i=2}^{5} (i + 9)$

Written Exercises

Write each expression in expanded form and find the sum.

1. $\displaystyle\sum_{t=0}^{4} (13 + 7t)$

2. $\displaystyle\sum_{i=1}^{5} (1 + 7i)$

3. $\displaystyle\sum_{p=3}^{7} (2p - 1)$

4. $\displaystyle\sum_{j=0}^{6} (24 - 9j)$

5. $\displaystyle\sum_{b=2}^{6} (2b + 1)$

6. $\displaystyle\sum_{y=5}^{11} (3y - 5)$

7. $\displaystyle\sum_{i=1}^{7} 2i$

8. $\displaystyle\sum_{r=3}^{6} (r + 2)$

9. $\displaystyle\sum_{z=1}^{9} (10 - z)$

10. $\displaystyle\sum_{s=3}^{8} (2s - 1)$

11. $\displaystyle\sum_{x=6}^{10} (x + 4)$

12. $\displaystyle\sum_{j=-3}^{3} (2j + 2)$

13. $\displaystyle\sum_{n=4}^{8} 4^n$

14. $\displaystyle\sum_{k=1}^{7} 2^{k-2}$

15. $\displaystyle\sum_{s=1}^{4} 24\left(-\frac{1}{2}\right)^s$

16. $\displaystyle\sum_{b=1}^{4} 2\left(\frac{3}{8}\right)^b$

Find the sum of each series.

17. $\displaystyle\sum_{n=1}^{25} 2n$

18. $\displaystyle\sum_{n=1}^{30} (2n - 1)$

19. $\displaystyle\sum_{n=1}^{40} (3n + 2)$

20. $\displaystyle\sum_{n=10}^{50} (3n - 1)$

21. $\displaystyle\sum_{n=21}^{75} (2n + 5)$

22. $\displaystyle\sum_{j=1}^{6} (-2)^j$

23. $\displaystyle\sum_{k=1}^{8} 2^{k-4}$

24. $\displaystyle\sum_{s=1}^{5} \left(\frac{3}{10}\right)^s$

Use sigma notation to express each of the following.

25. $7 + 10 + 13 + 16 + 19$

26. $3 + 10 + 17 + 24 + 31$

27. $15 + 11 + 7 + 3 + (-1)$

28. $7 + 6\frac{1}{2} + 6 + 5\frac{1}{2} + 5$

29. $1 + 3 + 5 + 7 \ldots + 25$

30. $5 + 10 + 15 + 20 + \ldots + 50$

31. $8 + 4 + 2 + 1 + \frac{1}{2} + \frac{1}{4}$

32. $2 - 6 + 18 - 54 + 162 - 486$

33. $243 - 162 + 108 - 72 + 48 - 32$

34. $625 + 375 + 225 + 135 + 81$

35. $1^2 + 2^2 + 3^2 + 4^2 + 5^2$

36. $\frac{1}{2} + \frac{1}{3} + \frac{1}{4} + \frac{1}{5} + \frac{1}{6}$

mini-review

1. Find the value of the discriminant for $x^2 - x + 1 = 0$.

2. Solve $z - 16\sqrt{z} + 64 = 0$.

3. Draw the graph for $f(x) = 2x^2 + 8x + 10$.

4. Triangle ABC has vertices $A(-2, 8)$, $B(3, 5)$, and $C(7, -4)$. Find the coordinates of the midpoint of each side.

5. Write the equation of the parabola which has vertex $(5, -1)$ and focus $(3, -1)$.

Challenge

State whether the sums are equivalent.

37. $\displaystyle\sum_{a=1}^{4} a^2 \overset{?}{=} \sum_{a=3}^{6} (a - 2)^2$

38. $\displaystyle 2\sum_{k=3}^{7} k^2 \overset{?}{=} \sum_{k=3}^{7} 2k^2$

13-7   The General Term

Sequences and series often are described by giving a formula for their general term. This formula may show how to find the nth term.

Sequence type	Formula for the nth term
Arithmetic	$a_n = 7 + (n - 1) \cdot 3$
Geometric	$a_n = 5 \cdot 4^{n-1}$

Sometimes a sequence or series may be described recursively. A **recursive formula** depends on knowing one or more previous terms.

Sequence type	Recursive formula
Arithmetic	$a_{n+1} = a_n + 3,\ a_1 = 7$
Geometric	$a_{n+1} = a_n \cdot 4,\ a_1 = 5$

When a sequence or series is described by a formula for its nth term, any term can be computed directly.

Example

1   **Find the 99th term of the sequence in which $a_n = 7 + (n - 1)3$.**

$a_n = 7 + (n - 1)3$

$a_{99} = 7 + (99 - 1)3$ *Substitute 99 for n.*

$\quad = 7 + 98 \cdot 3$

$\quad = 7 + 294$

$\quad = 301$

When a sequence or series is described by a recursive formula, you may need to compute several terms to find the terms desired.

Example

2   **Find the first six terms of the sequence in which $a_1 = 1$, $a_2 = 1$ and $a_{n+2} = a_n + 2 \cdot a_{n+1}$.**

$a_3 = a_{1+2}$

$\quad = a_1 + 2 \cdot a_2$

$\quad = 1 + 2(1)$ or 3

$a_4 = a_{2+2}$

$\quad = a_2 + 2 \cdot a_3$

$\quad = 1 + 2(3)$ or 7

$a_5 = a_{3+2}$

$\quad = a_3 + 2 \cdot a_4$

$\quad = 3 + 2(7)$ or 17

$a_6 = a_{4+2}$

$\quad = a_4 + 2 \cdot a_5$

$\quad = 7 + 2(17)$ or 41

The first six terms are 1, 1, 3, 7, 17, and 41.

Examples

3 **Find the 51st through the 54th terms of the sequence for which $a_n = 2n + 1$.**

These can be written in a chart as follows.

n	$a_n = 2n + 1$
51	$a_{51} = 2(51) + 1$ or 103
52	$a_{52} = 2(52) + 1$ or 105
53	$a_{53} = 2(53) + 1$ or 107
54	$a_{54} = 2(54) + 1$ or 109

4 **Find both a recursive formula and a formula for the nth term of the sequence $3, -6, 12, -24, 48, \ldots$.**

$$3 \qquad -6 \qquad 12 \qquad -24 \qquad 48$$
$$3 \cdot (-2) \quad -6 \cdot (-2) \quad 12 \cdot (-2) \quad -24 \cdot (-2)$$

Consider the ratio of two consecutive terms.

A recursive formula is $a_{n+1} = a_n(-2)$ and $a_1 = 3$.
A formula for the nth term is $a_n = 3(-2)^{n-1}$.   *Recall $a_n = a_1 r^{n-l}$.*

5 **Find a formula for the nth term of the following series and express the series using sigma notation.**

$$7 + 9 + 11 + 13 + 15 + 17$$
$$\quad 2 \quad 2 \quad\ 2 \quad\ 2 \quad\ 2$$

What is the difference between any two terms?

$$a_n = a_1 + (n - 1)d$$
$$a_n = 7 + (n - 1)2 \qquad \text{Substitute 7 for } a_1 \text{ and 2 for } d.$$
$$a_n = 5 + 2n$$

$$7 + 9 + 11 + 13 + 15 + 17 = \sum_{n=1}^{6} (5 + 2n)$$

Exploratory Exercises

Find the ninth and tenth terms of each sequence.

1. $a_n = n(n + 2)$

2. $a_n = 3n - 4$

3. $a_n = n^2 - 1$

4. $a_n = (-1)^n$

Find the first four terms of each sequence.

5. $a_1 = 8, a_{n+1} = a_n - 1$

6. $a_1 = 13, a_{n+1} = a_n + 2$

7. $a_1 = -2, a_{n+1} = 3a_n$

8. $a_1 = 7, a_{n+1} = 2a_n$

9. $a_1 = -4, a_{n+1} = (-1)^{n+1}a_n$

10. $a_1 = 3, a_{n+1} = (-1)^n a_n$

11. $a_1 = 3, a_2 = 1, a_{n+2} = a_n + a_{n+1}$

12. $a_1 = 0, a_2 = 1, a_{n+2} = a_n + a_{n+1}$

Find a formula for the nth term of each sequence.

13. 2, 4, 6, 8, 10, 12, 14, . . .

14. 3, 5, 7, 9, 11, 13, . . .

15. $\dfrac{2}{1}, \dfrac{3}{2}, \dfrac{4}{3}, \dfrac{5}{4}, \dfrac{6}{5}, \ldots$

16. $\dfrac{1}{3}, \dfrac{1}{5}, \dfrac{1}{7}, \dfrac{1}{9}, \dfrac{1}{11}, \dfrac{1}{13}, \ldots$

Find a recursive formula for each sequence.

17. $1, \dfrac{1}{3}, \dfrac{1}{9}, \dfrac{1}{27}, \ldots$

18. $1, -1, 1, -1, \ldots$

19. $1, -\dfrac{1}{2}, \dfrac{1}{4}, -\dfrac{1}{8}, \ldots$

Written Exercises

Find the eighth, ninth, and tenth terms of each sequence.

1. $a_n = 4n - 3$

2. $a_n = \dfrac{n}{n + 1}$

3. $a_n = \dfrac{2n + 1}{n + 2}$

4. $a_n = \dfrac{n(n - 1)}{3}$

5. $a_n = \dfrac{2}{n}$

6. $a_n = 4n^2$

7. $a_n = (-1)^{n+1}2n$

8. $a_n = \dfrac{1}{2}(n^2 + n + 4)$

9. $a_n = n^2 + 2n + 1$

Find the first six terms of each sequence.

10. $a_1 = 2, a_{n+1} = 3a_n$

11. $a_1 = 7, a_{n+1} = a_n + 5$

12. $a_1 = 3, a_2 = 5, a_{n+2} = a_n + a_{n+1}$

13. $a_1 = 1, a_2 = 2, a_{n+2} = a_n + a_{n+1}$

14. $a_1 = 2, a_2 = 3, a_{n+2} = 2a_n + a_{n+1}$

15. $a_1 = 5, a_2 = 11, a_{n+2} = a_{n+1} - a_n$

Find both a recursive formula and a formula for the nth term of each of the following sequences.

16. 3, 7, 11, 15, 19, . . .

17. 4, 9, 14, 19, 24, . . .

18. 3, 15, 75, 375, 1875, . . .

19. $\dfrac{3}{2}, \dfrac{3}{4}, \dfrac{3}{8}, \dfrac{3}{16}, \dfrac{3}{32}, \ldots$

20. 5, 10, 15, 20, 25, . . .

21. $\dfrac{7}{2}, \dfrac{7}{10}, \dfrac{7}{50}, \dfrac{7}{250}, \ldots$

Express each series using sigma notation.

22. $3 + 10 + 17 + 24 + 31$

23. $\dfrac{3}{3} + \dfrac{6}{4} + \dfrac{9}{5} + 2 + \dfrac{15}{7}$

24. $\dfrac{3}{4} + \dfrac{3}{2} + \dfrac{9}{4} + 3 + \dfrac{15}{4} + \dfrac{9}{2}$

25. $2 \cdot 5 + 4 \cdot 7 + 6 \cdot 9 + 8 \cdot 11 + 10 \cdot 13$

26. $\dfrac{4}{5} + \dfrac{7}{5} + 2 + \dfrac{13}{5} + \dfrac{16}{5}$

27. $6 - 2 + \dfrac{2}{3} - \dfrac{2}{9} + \dfrac{2}{27}$

28. $2 + 2\dfrac{1}{2} + 3\dfrac{1}{3} + 4\dfrac{1}{4} + 5\dfrac{1}{5} + 6\dfrac{1}{6}$

29. $1 + \left(-\dfrac{1}{3}\right) + \dfrac{1}{5} + \left(-\dfrac{1}{7}\right) + \dfrac{1}{9} + \left(-\dfrac{1}{11}\right)$

mini-review

1. Solve $|7 + 3a| = 11 - a$.

2. Find the slope-intercept form of the equation of the line that passes through $(6, 1)$ and has a slope of $-\dfrac{3}{2}$.

3. Solve the system using Cramer's Rule:
$$3x + y = -8$$
$$4x - 2y = -14$$

4. Factor $r^4 - s^4$.

5. Simplify $(1 - \sqrt{5})^2$.

13-8　Special Sequences and Series

The base of this pine cone shows an example of a pattern that is often found in nature.

Count the number of strips that spiral to the left.

Count the number of strips that spiral to the right.

These two numbers shown in color below belong to a very special sequence.

This sequence is named after its discoverer, Leonardo Fibonacci.

$$1, 1, 2, 3, 5, 8, 13, 21, 34, 55, 89, 144, \ldots$$

Can you see what the next term will be? What do you think is the pattern used in the *Fibonacci sequence*?

Let F_n be a term of the sequence.

$F_1 = 1$ $\quad$ $F_2 = 1$ $\quad$ $F_3 = 2$ or $1 + 1$
$F_4 = 3$ or $2 + 1$ $\quad$ $F_5 = 5$ or $3 + 2$

How do you find the next term from the two previous terms?

Then $F_5 = 3 + 2$. Thus, $F_5 = F_4 + F_3$.

In general, if F_n is the nth term of the Fibonacci sequence, then

$$F_n = F_{n-1} + F_{n-2}.$$

The Fibonacci sequence is the basis of other sequences as well. One of these is the sequence of ratios found by dividing each term of the Fibonacci sequence by the preceding term.

$$\frac{1}{1}, \frac{2}{1}, \frac{3}{2}, \frac{5}{3}, \frac{8}{5}, \frac{13}{8}, \frac{21}{13}, \frac{34}{21}, \frac{55}{34}, \frac{89}{55}, \frac{144}{89}$$

Notice that the spirals of the pine cone have the ratio $\frac{13}{8}$. Some other pine cones have the ratio $\frac{8}{5}$. Some daisies have the ratio $\frac{34}{21}$.

Sunflower heads have spirals of seeds which may have ratios of $\frac{21}{13}, \frac{34}{21}$, or $\frac{55}{34}$.

The following examples illustrate methods for finding patterns.

Examples

1 **Find the missing terms of the following sequence.**
6, 10, 15, 21, 28, ____ , ____ , ____ , . . .

6,   10,   15,   21,   28,   ____ ,   ____ ,   ____

+4   +5   +6   +7   +8   +9   +10

Find the difference of consecutive terms.

The difference increases by one for each term

The missing terms are 36, 45, and 55.

2 **Find the missing terms of the sequence 1, 2, 6, 24, 120, ____ , ____ , ...**

1,   2,   6,   24,   120,   ____ ,   ____

$\times 2$ $\times 3$ $\times 4$ $\times 5$ $\times ?$ $120 \times 6 = 720$ $720 \times 7 = 5040$

Note that each term is multiplied by an integer.

The integers increase by one each time.

The next two terms are 720 and 5040.

3 **Complete the sequence 4, 9, 16, 25, ____ , ____ , ____ , ...**

4,   9,   16,   25,   ____ ,   ____ ,   ____
↓   ↓   ↓   ↓
2^2 3^2 4^2 5^2

Notice that each term is a perfect square.

The next terms are $6^2 = 36$, $7^2 = 49$, and $8^2 = 64$.

4 **Complete the sequence 1, 1, 4, 10, 28, 76, ____ , ____ , ...**

1,   1,   4,   10,   28,   76,   ____ ,   ____

$2(1 + 1), 2(4 + 1), 2(10 + 4), 2(28 + 10)$

Notice that each term seems to be double the sum of the two previous terms.

The next two terms are 208 and 568.

Some special series often are used in more advanced mathematics. One of these is the Leibniz series for calculating π.

$$\frac{\pi}{4} = 1 + \left(-\frac{1}{3}\right) + \frac{1}{5} + \left(-\frac{1}{7}\right) + \frac{1}{9} + \cdots + \frac{(-1)^{n-1}}{2n-1} + \cdots$$

An approximation for π can be found by taking a finite number of terms in the sum.

Another special series can be used to find natural logarithms (to the base e).

$$\log_e x = \left(\frac{x-1}{x}\right) + \frac{1}{2}\left(\frac{x-1}{x}\right)^2 + \frac{1}{3}\left(\frac{x-1}{x}\right)^3 + \cdots \text{ for } x > \frac{1}{2}$$

What happens to the series if x equals $\frac{1}{2}$? If x is less than $\frac{1}{2}$? Why must x be greater than $\frac{1}{2}$?

Written Exercises

Find the missing terms of each sequence.

1. 52, 156, 468, ——, ——
2. 1, 2, 4, 7, 11, ——, ——
3. 2, 2.5, 2.75, ——, 2.9375
4. 2, 6, 30, 210, ——
5. 1, 3, 7, 13, 21, ——, ——
6. 64, 32, 8, 1, ——, ——
7. 1, 5, 14, 30, 55, ——, ——
8. 1, 8, 27, 64, 125, ——
9. 1, 3, 4, 7, 11, ——, ——, ——
10. 1, 1, 3, 7, 17, 41, ——, ——

Solve each problem.

11. Find the first twenty terms of the Fibonacci sequence.

12. Find the first 15 terms of the ratios of the Fibonacci sequence $\frac{1}{1}, \frac{2}{1}, \frac{3}{2}, \frac{5}{3}, \ldots$ Express each as a decimal rounded to the nearest hundredth.

13. Find the sum of the first 8 terms of the series $\log_e 2$.

14. Find the sum of the first 8 terms of the series $\log_e 10$.

15. The Lucas sequence is 1, 3, 4, 7, 11, 18, 29, 47. Let L_n be a term of the Lucas sequence. Describe L_n in terms of the Fibonacci sequence.

16. Compute e to 4 decimal places by using this series:
$$2 + \frac{1}{2 \cdot 1} + \frac{1}{3 \cdot 2 \cdot 1} + \frac{1}{4 \cdot 3 \cdot 2 \cdot 1} + \frac{1}{5 \cdot 4 \cdot 3 \cdot 2 \cdot 1} + \frac{1}{6 \cdot 5 \cdot 4 \cdot 3 \cdot 2 \cdot 1}.$$

Using Calculators ———— Limits of Sequences and Series

Certain types of sequences approach a specific number as more and more terms are found. This number is called a **limit**. You can use your calculator to find the limit of the geometric sequence $1, \frac{1}{2}, \frac{1}{4}, \frac{1}{8}, \frac{1}{16}, \frac{1}{32}, \ldots \left(\frac{1}{2}\right)^n$. Try several values for n to determine what happens as n increases. Use $a_n = a_1 r^{n-1}$ where $a_1 = 1$ and $r = \frac{1}{2}$.

$$a_5 = 1 \cdot \left(\frac{1}{2}\right)^{5-1} = (0.5)^4 \qquad a_{10} = 1 \cdot \left(\frac{1}{2}\right)^{10-1} = (0.5)^9 \qquad a_{20} = 1 \cdot \left(\frac{1}{2}\right)^{20-1} = (0.5)^{19}$$

ENTER: .5 $\boxed{y^x}$ 4 $\boxed{=}$ .5 $\boxed{y^x}$ 9 $\boxed{=}$ .5 $\boxed{y^x}$ 19 $\boxed{=}$

DISPLAY: .5   4   0.0625   .5   9   0.00195   .5   19   0.00000191

Notice that as n increases, the sequence approaches 0.   *The limit is 0.*

Consider the geometric series $1 + \frac{1}{2} + \frac{1}{4} + \frac{1}{8} + \frac{1}{16} + \ldots$ Use your calculator and $S_n = \frac{a_1 - a_1 r^n}{1 - r}$ to find S_5, S_{10}, and S_{20} for this series. Compare these results to the sum of the series found by using $S = \frac{a_1}{1 - r}$. What can you conclude?

Exercises   Use your calculator to find the limit of each sequence or series.

1. $\frac{1}{2}, \frac{2}{3}, \frac{3}{4}, \frac{4}{5}, \frac{5}{6}, \ldots \frac{n}{n + 1}$
2. $\frac{2}{3}, \frac{4}{9}, \frac{8}{27}, \frac{16}{81}, \ldots \left(\frac{2}{3}\right)^n$
3. $\frac{1}{5}, \frac{2}{7}, \frac{3}{9}, \ldots \frac{n}{2n + 3}$
4. $2 + \frac{2}{3} + \frac{2}{9} + \frac{2}{27} + \frac{2}{81} + \ldots$
5. $\frac{1}{3} + \frac{1}{6} + \frac{1}{12} + \frac{1}{24} + \frac{1}{48} + \ldots$
6. $3 + 1 + \frac{1}{3} + \frac{1}{9} + \frac{1}{27} + \ldots$

What is the sum of the series formed by the first n positive odd integers?

$$1 + 3 + 5 + 7 + \ldots + (2n - 1)$$

One approach is to make a table.

n	1	2	3	4	5 . . .
Positive Odd Integers	1	3	5	7	9 . . .
Cumulative Sums	1	4	9	16	25 . . .

Notice that each cumulative sum is the square of the number of terms, n.

$n = 1$	$n = 2$	$n = 3$	$n = 4$
$1^2 = 1$	$2^2 = 4$	$3^2 = 9$	$4^2 = 16$

This pattern suggests that $1 + 3 + 5 + 7 + \ldots + (2n - 1) = n^2$. However, this is only a hypothesis based on observation. A hypothesis such as this becomes a theorem only when it is proved.

A common method of proof is called **induction**. A proof by mathematical induction is much like climbing a ladder. You must get on the first step. Then you must show that you can always advance to the next step and so on up the ladder for all steps.

The sum of the series formed by the first n positive odd integers can be proved by mathematical induction.

$$1 + 3 + 5 + \ldots + (2n - 1) = n^2$$

Step 1 **First verify that the formula is valid for the first possible case, usually $n = 1$.**

For $n = 1$, it is true that $2 \cdot 1 - 1 = 1^2$, therefore $S_n = n^2$ is valid for the first case.

Step 2 **Assume that the formula is valid for $n = k$. Using this information, prove that it is also valid for $n = k + 1$.**

Assume that $1 + 3 + 5 + 7 + \ldots (2k - 1) = k^2$ is true. Then if the $(k + 1)st$ integer is added to both sides the result is an equivalent equation.

$$\underbrace{1 + 3 + 5 + 7 + \ldots + 2k - 1}_{\substack{k \text{ integers} \\ \text{by assumption}}} + \underbrace{[2(k + 1) - 1]}_{\substack{(k + 1)st \\ \text{integer}}} = k^2 + \underbrace{[2(k + 1) - 1]}_{\substack{\text{Add } [2(k + 1) - 1] \\ \text{to both sides.}}}$$

$$= k^2 + 2k + 1$$
$$= (k + 1)^2$$

The formula is valid for the $(k + 1)st$ integer, since the sum of $(k + 1)$ odd integers is $(k + 1)^2$.

Conclusion The formula is valid for $n = 1$. Step 2 illustrates that the formula is valid for the next positive integer $n + 1$ or 2. Since the formula is valid when $n = 2$, it is also valid for $n + 1$ or 3, and so on, indefinitely.

What is the sum of the first n positive integers?

n	1	2	3	4	5 . . .
Positive Integers	1	2	3	4	5 . . .
Cumulative sum	1	3	6	10	15 . . .

This pattern suggests $1 + 2 + 3 + \ldots + n = \dfrac{n(n + 1)}{2}$. Prove this by mathematical induction.

Step 1 $\dfrac{1 \cdot (1 + 1)}{2} = 1$ So the formula is valid for $n = 1$.

Step 2 Assume that the formula is then valid for $n = k$.

$$1 + 2 + 3 + \ldots + k = \frac{k(k + 1)}{2}$$

Prove that it is also valid for $n = k + 1$.

$$1 + 2 + 3 + \ldots + k = \frac{k(k + 1)}{2}$$

$$1 + 2 + 3 + \ldots + k + (k + 1) = \frac{k(k + 1)}{2} + (k + 1) \qquad \text{\textit{Add k + 1 to both sides.}}$$

$$= \frac{k(k + 1) + 2(k + 1)}{2}$$

$$= \frac{(k + 1)(k + 2)}{2}$$

If $k + 1$ is substituted for n in the original formula, the same result is obtained.

$$1 + 2 + \ldots + (k + 1) = \frac{(k + 1)[(k + 1) + 1]}{2}$$

$$= \frac{(k + 1)(k + 2)}{2}$$

Thus, the formula is valid for $n = k + 1$.

So $1 + 2 + 3 + \ldots + n = \dfrac{n(n + 1)}{2}$.

Exercises

Prove that each statement is true for all positive integers n.

1. $2 + 4 + 6 + \ldots + 2n = n(n + 1)$

2. $1 + 2 + 3 + \ldots + n = \dfrac{n(n + 1)}{2}$

3. $-\dfrac{1}{2} - \dfrac{1}{4} - \dfrac{1}{8} - \ldots - \dfrac{1}{2^n} = \dfrac{1}{2^n} - 1$

4. $3 + 6 + 9 + \ldots + 3n = \dfrac{3n(n + 1)}{2}$

5. $1^3 + 2^3 + 3^3 + \ldots + n^3 = \dfrac{n^2(n + 1)^2}{4}$

6. $\dfrac{1}{2} + \dfrac{1}{2^2} + \dfrac{1}{2^3} + \ldots + \dfrac{1}{2^n} = 1 - \dfrac{1}{2^n}$

7. $2 + 2^2 + 2^3 + \ldots + 2^n = 2^{n+1} - 2$

8. $1 + 2 + 4 + 8 + \ldots + 2^{n-1} = 2^n - 1$

9. $1^2 + 2^2 + 3^2 + \ldots + n^2 = \dfrac{n(n + 1)(2n + 1)}{6}$

10. $1^2 + 3^2 + 5^2 + \ldots + (2n - 1)^2 = \dfrac{n(2n - 1)(2n + 1)}{3}$

13-9   The Binomial Theorem

The binomial expression $(a + b)$ can be raised to various powers. There are patterns to be found in the powers of $(a + b)$ listed below.

$$(a + b)^0 = 1$$
$$(a + b)^1 = 1a + 1b$$
$$(a + b)^2 = 1a^2b^0 + 2ab + 1a^0b^2$$
$$(a + b)^3 = 1a^3b^0 + 3a^2b^1 + 3a^1b^2 + 1a^0b^3$$
$$(a + b)^4 = 1a^4b^0 + 4a^3b^1 + 6a^2b^2 + 4a^1b^3 + 1a^0b^4$$

Note that the coefficients are one.
Why can b^0 and a^0 be written here?
What happened to the powers of a?
What about powers of b?

Note the sum of the exponents in any term of $(a + b)^4$.
How many terms are in the expansion of $(a + b)^4$?

The following patterns are seen in the expansion of $(a + b)^n$.

1. The exponent of $(a + b)^n$ is the exponent of a in the first term and the exponent of b in the last term.
2. In successive terms, the exponent of a decreases by one. It is n in the first term and zero in the last term.
3. In successive terms, the exponent of b increases by one. It is zero in the first term and n in the last term.
4. The sum of the exponents of each term is n.
5. The coefficients are symmetric. They increase at the beginning and decrease at the end of the expansion.

If the coefficients are displayed alone, a definite pattern appears.

This is known as Pascal's Triangle. Each new row is formed by adding elements of the previous row in pairs as marked. Each row begins and ends with 1. The triangle can go on indefinitely.

Notice that the expansion of $(a + b)^n$ has $n + 1$ terms.

Example

1   **Use the pattern to write $(a + b)^7$ in expanded form. $(a + b)^7$ will have 8 terms.**

The next line of Pascal's Triangle is

$$1 \quad 7 \quad 21 \quad 35 \quad 35 \quad 21 \quad 7 \quad 1.$$

$$(a + b)^7 = 1a^7b^0 + 7a^6b^1 + 21a^5b^2 + 35a^4b^3 + 35a^3b^4 + 21a^2b^5 + 7a^1b^6 + a^0b^7$$
$$(a + b)^7 = a^7 + 7a^6b + 21a^5b^2 + 35a^4b^3 + 35a^3b^4 + 21a^2b^5 + 7ab^6 + b^7$$

Here is another way to show the coefficients.

$(a + b)^0$ 1

$(a + b)^2$ 1 $\dfrac{1}{1}$

$(a + b)^2$ 1 $\dfrac{2}{1}$ $\dfrac{2 \cdot 1}{1 \cdot 2}$

$(a + b)^3$ 1 $\dfrac{3}{1}$ $\dfrac{3 \cdot 2}{1 \cdot 2}$ $\dfrac{3 \cdot 2 \cdot 1}{1 \cdot 2 \cdot 3}$

$(a + b)^4$ 1 $\dfrac{4}{1}$ $\dfrac{4 \cdot 3}{1 \cdot 2}$ $\dfrac{4 \cdot 3 \cdot 2}{1 \cdot 2 \cdot 3}$ $\dfrac{4 \cdot 3 \cdot 2 \cdot 1}{1 \cdot 2 \cdot 3 \cdot 4}$

Eliminate common factors that are shown in color. The coefficients are symmetrical.

This pattern can provide the coefficients of a binomial expansion without writing the previous rows of coefficients. The Binomial Theorem summarizes these patterns.

If n is a positive integer, then the following is true.

$$(a + b)^n = 1a^n b^0 + \frac{n}{1}a^{n-1}b^1 + \frac{n(n-1)}{1 \cdot 2}a^{n-2}b^2 + \ldots + 1a^0 b^n$$

The Binomial Theorem

Example

2   **Use the Binomial Theorem to find the terms in the expansion of $(x + y)^8$.**

Find the first 5 terms. Then, use symmetry to find the remaining terms.

$$(x + y)^8 = 1 \cdot x^8 y^0 + \frac{8}{1}x^7 y^1 + \frac{8 \cdot 7}{1 \cdot 2}x^6 y^2 + \frac{8 \cdot 7 \cdot 6}{1 \cdot 2 \cdot 3}x^5 y^3 + \frac{8 \cdot 7 \cdot 6 \cdot 5}{1 \cdot 2 \cdot 3 \cdot 4}x^4 y^4 + \ldots$$

$$= x^8 + 8x^7 y + 28x^6 y^2 + 56x^5 y^3 + 70x^4 y^4 + \ldots$$

$$= x^8 + 8x^7 y + 28x^6 y^2 + 56x^5 y^3 + 70x^4 y^4 + 56x^3 y^5 + 28x^2 y^6 + 8xy^7 + y^8$$

Note that in terms having the same coefficients the exponents are reversed, as in $28x^6 y^2$ and $28x^2 y^6$.

In Example 2, some of the denominators are written as shown below.

$1 \cdot 2 \cdot 3 \cdot 4 = 4 \cdot 3 \cdot 2 \cdot 1$

$1 \cdot 2 \cdot 3 = 3 \cdot 2 \cdot 1$

The product $4 \cdot 3 \cdot 2 \cdot 1$ is called 4 factorial and is expressed as 4!.

If n is a positive integer, the expression $n!$ (n factorial) is defined as follows.

$$n! = n(n - 1)(n - 2) \ldots (1)$$

Definition of n Factorial

By definition, $0! = 1$.

Example

3   **Evaluate $\dfrac{8!}{2!6!}$.**

$$\frac{8!}{2!6!} = \frac{8 \cdot 7 \cdot 6 \cdot 5 \cdot 4 \cdot 3 \cdot 2 \cdot 1}{2 \cdot 1 \cdot 6 \cdot 5 \cdot 4 \cdot 3 \cdot 2 \cdot 1} = 28$$

Notice that the coefficients in Example 2 are equivalent to the factorial expressions below.

$$\frac{8}{1} = \frac{8!}{1!7!} \qquad \frac{8 \cdot 7}{1 \cdot 2} = \frac{8!}{2!6!} \qquad \frac{8 \cdot 7 \cdot 6}{1 \cdot 2 \cdot 3} = \frac{8!}{3!5!}$$

Thus, another way to write the expansion is:

$$(x + y)^8 = \frac{8!}{0!8!}x^8 + \frac{8!}{1!7!}x^7y^1 + \frac{8!}{2!6!}x^6y^2 + \frac{8!}{3!5!}x^5y^3 + \frac{8!}{4!4!}x^4y^4 + \frac{8!}{5!3!}x^3y^5 +$$

$$\frac{8!}{6!2!}x^2y^6 + \frac{8!}{7!1!}x^1y^7 + \frac{8!}{8!0!}y^8$$

An equivalent form of the Binomial Theorem uses both sigma and factorial notation.

$$(a + b)^n = \frac{n!}{0!(n - 0)!}a^n + \frac{n!}{1!(n - 1)!}a^{n-1}b^1 + \frac{n!}{2!(n - 2)!}a^{n-2}b^2 + \cdots$$

$$= \sum_{k=0}^{n} \frac{n!}{k!(n - k)!}a^{n-k}b^k \qquad \text{\textit{Here n is a positive integer,}}$$
$$\text{\textit{k is a positive integer or zero.}}$$

Using sigma notation, $(x + y)^8$ can be expressed as follows.

$$(x + y)^8 = \sum_{k=0}^{8} \frac{8!}{k!(8 - k)!}a^{8-k}b^k$$

Example

4   **Express $(s + t)^4$ using sigma notation. Then find the terms in the expansion.**

$$(s + t)^4 = \sum_{k=0}^{4} \frac{4!}{k!(4 - k)!}s^{4-k}t^k \qquad \text{\textit{Now construct each term.}}$$

$$= \frac{4!}{0!(4 - 0)!}s^{4-0}t^0 + \frac{4!}{1!(4 - 1)!}s^{4-1}t^1 + \frac{4!}{2!(4 - 2)!}s^{4-2}t^2 + \frac{4!}{3!(4 - 3)!}s^{4-3}t^3 + \frac{4!}{4!(4 - 4)!}s^{4-4}t^4$$

$$= \frac{4 \cdot 3 \cdot 2 \cdot 1}{1 \cdot 4 \cdot 3 \cdot 2 \cdot 1}s^4 + \frac{4 \cdot 3 \cdot 2 \cdot 1}{1 \cdot 3 \cdot 2 \cdot 1}s^3t + \frac{4 \cdot 3 \cdot 2 \cdot 1}{2 \cdot 1 \cdot 2 \cdot 1}s^2t^2 + \frac{4 \cdot 3 \cdot 2 \cdot 1}{3 \cdot 2 \cdot 1 \cdot 1}st^3 + \frac{4 \cdot 3 \cdot 2 \cdot 1}{4 \cdot 3 \cdot 2 \cdot 1 \cdot 1}t^4$$

$$= s^4 + 4s^3t + 6s^2t^2 + 4st^3 + t^4$$

Sometimes a particular term in the binomial expansion is needed. In the example above, k is 0 for the first term, 1 for the second term, and so on. In general, the value of k is one less than the number of the term.

Example

5 Find the fifth term of $(p + q)^9$.

$$(p + q)^9 = \sum_{k=0}^{9} \frac{9!}{k!(9 - k)!} p^{9-k} q^k$$ *In the fifth term, k will be 4 since k starts at zero.*

The fifth term, $\dfrac{9!}{4!(9 - 4)!} p^{9-4} q^4$, is $\dfrac{9 \cdot 8 \cdot 7 \cdot 6}{1 \cdot 2 \cdot 3 \cdot 4} p^5 q^4$ or $126 p^5 q^4$.

Exploratory Exercises

Evaluate each of the following.

1. $7!$
2. $9!$
3. $10!$
4. $12!$
5. $\dfrac{10!}{8!}$
6. $\dfrac{31!}{28!}$
7. $\dfrac{6!}{3!}$
8. $\dfrac{10!}{4!6!}$

State the number of terms for the expanded form of each expression. Then, find the fourth term for each.

9. $(r + s)^4$
10. $(a + b)^5$
11. $(k - m)^7$
12. $(a - 3)^4$
13. $(x - 2)^5$
14. $(b - z)^5$

Written Exercises

Expand each binomial.

1. $(x + m)^4$
2. $(r + s)^6$
3. $(y + p)^7$
4. $(x - y)^3$
5. $(b - z)^5$
6. $(r - m)^6$
7. $(2m + y)^5$
8. $(3r + y)^4$
9. $(2b + x)^6$
10. $(2x + 3y)^4$
11. $(3x - 2y)^5$
12. $(2m - 3)^6$
13. $(2y + 1)^5$
14. $\left(2 + \dfrac{x}{2}\right)^6$
15. $\left(\dfrac{y}{3} + 3\right)^6$

Find the requested term of each of the following.

16. Fifth term of $(x + y)^7$
17. Fourth term of $(2x + 3y)^9$
18. Seventh term of $(x - y)^{15}$
19. Fifth term of $(x - 2)^{10}$
20. Sixth term of $(2m + 3n)^{12}$
21. Eighth term of $(3a + 5b)^{11}$

Solve each problem.

22. Jorma Johnson invested $5000 at 8% annual interest for 3 years. The interest is compounded semiannually. Find the value of Jorma's investment after 3 years. Use $A = 5000(1 + 0.04)^6$.

23. Joanne Mauch owns a tree plantation. The value of her trees increases about 10% each year. The trees are now worth $10,000. What will be their value 6 years from now? Use $V = 10,000(1 + 0.10)^6$.

Challenge

Simplify each of the following.

24. $\dfrac{k!}{(k - 1)!}$
25. $\dfrac{(k + 3)!}{(k + 2)!}$
26. $(k + 1)!(k + 2)$
27. $\dfrac{3!4(k - 3)!}{(k - 2)!}$

Pascal's Triangle

Blaise Pascal (1623–1662) was a French mathematician. At age nineteen he invented a computing machine, a forerunner of today's computers and calculators. He also devised a quick method for finding the coefficients of the expansion for $(a + b)^n$.

You can make the following observations in the triangle of coefficients.
  1. *Each row begins and ends with 1.*
  2. *Each coefficient is the sum of the two coefficients to the left and right in the row directly above.*

Power	Coefficients of the Expansion
$(a + b)^0$	1
$(a + b)^1$	1 1
$(a + b)^2$	1 2 1 $1 + 1 = 2$
$(a + b)^3$	1 3 3 1
$(a + b)^4$	1 4 6 4 1
$(a + b)^5$	1 5 10 10 5 1 $6 + 4 = 10$

The program at the right uses Pascal's triangle. It provides the coefficients for the expansion of $(a + b)^n$ when $n = 0$ to 10.

Enter and run this program. Your output will be in slightly different form. The first six lines are shown below.

```
]RUN
1
1   1
1   2   1
1   3   3   1
1   4   6   4   1
1   5   10   10   5   1
```

```
10  FOR N = 0 TO 10
20  FOR R = 0 TO N
30  LET C = 1
40  IF N < N - R + 1 THEN 80
50  FOR X = N TO N - R + 1 STEP - 1
60  LET C = C * X / (N - X + 1)
70  NEXT X
80  PRINT C;"    ";
90  NEXT R
100  PRINT
110  NEXT N
120  END
```

Example: Expand $(x + y)^5$.
$$(x + y)^5 = 1 \cdot x^5 y^0 + 5x^4 y^1 + 10x^3 y^2 + 10x^2 y^3 + 5x^1 y^4 + 1x^0 y^5$$
$$= x^5 + 5x^4 y + 10x^3 y^2 + 10x^2 y^3 + 5xy^4 + y^5$$

Notice the patterns of coefficients and exponents.

Exercises

Use the computer program for Pascal's triangle to find the coefficients for the expansion of the following expressions.

1. $(a + b)^4$ **2.** $(a + b)^6$ **3.** $(a + b)^7$

4. $(a + b)^8$ **5.** $(a + b)^9$ **6.** $(x - y)^6$

Make the necessary changes in the computer program to find the coefficients for the expansion of the following expressions.

7. $(a + b)^{12}$ **8.** $(x - y)^{12}$

Vocabulary

arithmetic sequence (40)
nth term, a_n (408)
common difference, d (408)
arithmetic means (409)
series (411)
arithmetic series (411)
sum of an arithmetic series, S_n (411)
geometric sequence (416)
common ratio, r (416)

geometric means (417)
sum of a geometric series (421)
infinite geometric series (424)
sigma notation (427)
index of summation (427)
recursive formula (430)
Fibonacci sequence (435)
Binomial Theorem (438)
n factorial (439)

Chapter Summary

1. **Definition of an Arithmetic Sequence:** An arithmetic sequence is a sequence in which the difference between any two consecutive terms is the same. (407)

2. **Definition of the nth term of an Arithmetic Sequence:** The nth term, a_n, of an arithmetic sequence with first term, a_1, and common difference, d, is given by $a_n = a_1 + (n - 1)d$. (408)

3. **Definition of Series:** The indicated sum of the terms of a sequence is called a series. (411)

4. **The Sum of an Arithmetic Series:** The sum, S_n, of the first n terms of an arithmetic series is given by $S_n = \dfrac{n}{2}(a_1 + a_n)$. (412)

5. **Definition of Geometric Sequence:** In a geometric sequence, each term after the first is found by multiplying the previous term by a constant. (416)

6. **Definition of the nth term of a Geometric Sequence:** The nth term, a_n, of a geometric sequence with first term, a_1, and common ratio, r, is given by either $a_n = a_1 r^{n-1}$ or $a_n = a_{n-1}r$. (416)

7. **Sum of a Geometric Series:** The sum, S_n, of the first n terms of a geometric series is given by $S_n = \dfrac{a_1 - a_1 r^n}{1 - r}$ where $r \neq 1$. (421)

8. **Sum of an Infinite Geometric Series:** The sum, S, of an infinite geometric series where $-1 < r < 1$ is given by $S = \dfrac{a_1}{1 - r}$. (424)

9. **The Binomial Theorem:** If n is a positive integer, then $(a + b)^n = 1a^n b^0 + \dfrac{n}{1}a^{n-1}b^1 + \dfrac{n(n - 1)}{1 \cdot 2}a^{n-2}b^2 + \ldots + 1a^0 b^n$. (439)

10. **Definition of n Factorial:** $n! = n(n - 1)(n - 2) \ldots (1)$. (439)

11. The following equivalent form of the Binomial Theorem uses both sigma and factorial notation.

$$(a + b)^n = \sum_{k=0}^{n} \frac{n!}{k!(n - k)!} a^{n-k}b^k \quad (440)$$

Chapter Review

13–1
1. Find the first 5 terms of the arithmetic sequence when $a_1 = 6$, $d = 8$.
2. Find the next 4 terms of the arithmetic sequence 9, 12, 15, ...

Find the nth term of each arithmetic sequence described below.
3. $a_1 = 3$, $d = 7$, $n = 34$ 4. $a_1 = -9$, $d = -2$, $n = 21$
5. Which term of $-5, 2, 9, . . .$ is 142?
6. Find the missing terms for the arithmetic sequence -7, ____, ____, ____, 9.
7. A stack of boxes in a warehouse is arranged so that there are 5 boxes in the top row, 7 boxes in the second row, 9 boxes in the third row, and so on. How many boxes are in the twentieth row?

13–2 **Find S_n for each arithmetic series described below.**
8. $a_1 = 12$, $a_n = 117$, $n = 36$ 9. $a_1 = 4$, $d = 6$, $n = 18$
10. Find the sum of the series $7 + 10 + 13 + . . . + 97$.

13–3
11. Find the common ratio of the sequence $\dfrac{2}{3}, \dfrac{4}{3}, \dfrac{8}{3}, \dfrac{16}{3}, ...$

12. Find the next 2 terms for the geometric sequence $\dfrac{15}{2}$, 15, 30, ____, ____.

13. Find the 5th term of the geometric sequence in which $a_1 = 7$ and $r = 3$.

14. Find the geometric means of 4, ____, ____, ____, 324.

13–4 **Find the sum of each geometric series described below.**
15. $a_1 = 6$, $r = 3$, $n = 5$ 16. $a_1 = 625$, $a_n = 16$, $r = \dfrac{2}{5}$

17. A ball dropped from a height of 21 feet rebounds $\dfrac{2}{3}$ of the distance from which it was dropped on each bounce. How far has the ball traveled after 6 bounces (rebounds)?

18. For a geometric series, find a_1 given that $S_n = 1441$, $r = \dfrac{3}{5}$, and $n = 5$.

13–5
19. Find the sum of the series $\dfrac{1}{2} + \dfrac{1}{3} + \dfrac{2}{9} + \dfrac{4}{27} + ...$

Find a common fraction equivalent to the repeating decimals.
20. $0.\overline{4}$ 21. $0.1\overline{7}$

13–6
22. Write the sum $\displaystyle\sum_{k=8}^{11} (3k - 4)$ in expanded form.

23. Evaluate $\displaystyle\sum_{r=0}^{10} (5 + 8r)$.

13–7
24. Find the first 5 terms of this sequence: $a_1 = 1$, $a_2 = 3$, $a_{n+2} = a_{n+1} + 2 \cdot a_n$.

25. Express the following series using sigma notation: $2 + 6 + 12 + 20 + 30 + 42$.

13–8
26. Find a pattern and complete the sequence for 3, 7, 12, 18, 25, ____, ____, ____, ____.

13–9
27. Find the fourth term of $(x + 2y)^6$.   28. Expand $(3a + b)^5$.

Chapter Test

Find S_n for each arithmetic series.

1. $a_1 = 7$, $n = 31$, $a_n = 127$

2. $a_1 = 13$, $d = -2$, $n = 17$

Find the sum of each geometric series.

3. $a_1 = 125$, $r = \frac{2}{5}$, $n = 4$

4. $a_1 = 16$, $a_n = -\frac{1}{2}$, $r = -\frac{1}{2}$

Solve each problem.

5. Find the next 4 terms of the arithmetic sequence 42, 37, 32, ...

6. Find the 27th term of an arithmetic sequence when $a_1 = 2$, $d = 6$.

7. Which term of the arithmetic sequence 7, 13, 19, . . . is 193?

8. How many integers between 26 and 415 are multiples of 9?

9. Find the first 3 terms of this arithmetic series: $a_1 = 7$, $n = 13$, $S_n = 1027$.

10. Find the sum of the series $91 + 85 + 79 + \ldots + (-29)$.

11. Find the next 2 terms of the geometric sequence $\frac{1}{81}$, $\frac{1}{27}$, $\frac{1}{9}$, ——, ——.

12. Find the sixth term of a geometric sequence if $a_1 = 5$ and $r = -2$.

13. Find the geometric means of 7, ——, ——, 189.

14. A vacuum pump removes $\frac{1}{7}$ of the air from a jar on each stroke of its piston. What percent of the air remains after 4 strokes of the piston?

15. Find the sum of the series $12 - 6 + 3 - \frac{3}{2} + \ldots$.

16. Find common fractions equivalent to the repeating decimals $0.\overline{7}$ and $0.3\overline{2}$.

17. Describe the sequence 2, 6, 18, 54, 162, . . . in terms of n.

18. Write $\sum_{k=2}^{6} (3k^2 - 1)$ in expanded form.

19. Find the sum of $\sum_{k=3}^{15} (14 - 2k)$.

20. Describe this sequence recursively: 2, 6, 18, 54, 162, ...

21. Find the first 5 terms of this sequence: $a_1 = 3$, $a_2 = 1$, $a_{n+2} = a_{n+1} + 2 \cdot a_n$.

22. Find a pattern and complete the sequence 3, 3, 6, 18, 72, ——, ——, ——.

23. Find the third term of $(x + y)^8$.

24. Expand $(2s + 3t)^5$.

25. A grocery stock boy makes a display of cans of corn for a sale. He puts 20 cans in the bottom row and each row above it contains 3 fewer cans than the previous row. He continues until there are only 2 cans in the top row. How many rows are there and what is the total number of cans in the display?

26. A tank contains 9000 gallons of water and each day $\frac{2}{3}$ of the water is removed. How much water has been removed by the end of the fifth day?

1. Solve $\frac{b}{2} - 1 > 3 - b$. Graph the solutions on the number line.

2. Solve $|2n - 5| < 7$. Graph the solutions on a number line.

3. Find the intercepts of the graph of $2x - 3y = 12$.

4. Find the standard form of the equation of the line having slope $-\frac{2}{3}$ and that passes through $(5, 1)$.

5. Find an equation of the line that passes through $(6, 2)$ and is perpendicular to the graph of $y = 2x + 1$.

6. Find the value of $\begin{vmatrix} 2 & 0 \\ -3 & 4 \end{vmatrix}$.

7. Evaluate $(2.1 \times 10^{12})(5.64 \times 10^{6})$. Express the result in scientific notation.

8. Divide $x^3 - 3x + 10$ by $x - 1$.

9. Simplify $-\sqrt{121}$.

10. Simplify $\sqrt{100a^4}$.

11. Simplify $(2\sqrt{6})(5\sqrt{3})$.

12. Simplify $3\sqrt{54} + 4\sqrt{6} + 8\sqrt{18}$.

13. Solve $3x^2 - 2x - 2 = 0$ using the quadratic formula.

14. Solve $x^4 - 16 = 0$ over the set of complex numbers.

15. Draw the graph of $y > x^2 + 5x - 10$.

16. Solve $b^2 \geq 3b + 28$.

17. Find the midpoint of the line segment that has endpoints $(9, 3)$ and $(-6, -8)$.

18. Graph the solutions for the system $x^2 + y^2 \geq 16$ and $y \leq 3$.

19. Graph the following system of equations and approximate the solutions.
$$4x^2 + 9y^2 = 36$$
$$4x^2 - 9y^2 = 36$$

20. State the possible number of positive real zeros, negative real zeros, and imaginary zeros for
$f(x) = x^3 - 7x^2 + 17x - 15$.

If $f(x) = 2x + 3$, $g(x) = x - 1$, and $h(x) = x^2 + 4$, find each of the following.

21. $[g \circ h](2)$

22. $[f \circ g](3)$

23. $h[f(x)]$

24. $g[f(-1)]$

25. Find the sum of $\frac{6}{x^2 + 4x + 4}$ and $\frac{5}{x + 2}$. Simplify the result.

26. Solve $\frac{4}{x - 2} + \frac{x + 6}{x + 1} = 1$.

27. Solve $\log_5 (4x - 4) = \log_5 100$.

28. Graph the equation $y = \frac{-2}{(x - 3)^2}$. Show the asymptotes.

29. Rewrite $7^{-2} = \frac{1}{49}$ in logarithmic form.

30. Find the twelfth term in the arithmetic sequence $-17, -13, -9, \ldots$.

31. Find S_n for $d = 5$, $n = 16$, and $a_n = 72$.

32. Find the geometric means for the sequence $3, \underline{\hspace{1cm}}, \underline{\hspace{1cm}}, \underline{\hspace{1cm}}, 48$.

Problem Solving

33. The sum of the digits of a three-digit number is 14. The tens digit is twice the units digit. The units digit is twice the hundreds digit. Find the number.

34. The number of a certain type of bacteria can increase from 80 to 164 in 3 hours. Find the value of k in the growth formula.

35. A tank can be filled by a hose in 12 hours. The tank can be emptied by a drain pipe in 24 hours. If the drain pipe is left open while the tank is filling, how long will it take to fill the tank?

The test questions on this page deal with rational expressions and radicals. Keep in mind that many questions can be solved by writing the expression in a different form.

> Most standardized text have a time limit, so you must budget your time carefully. Some questions will be much easier than others. If you cannot answer a question within a few minutes, go on to the next one. If there is still time left when you get to the end of the test, go back to the ones that you skipped.

Directions: Choose the one best answer. Write A, B, C, or D.

1. If $\dfrac{x}{y} = z$ and $y = z$, find y in terms of x.

   (A) y (B) $\pm\sqrt{y}$
   (C) $\pm\sqrt{x}$ (D) $\pm\sqrt{xz}$

2. If the average of x and y equals the average of x, y, and z, then express z in terms of x and y.

   (A) $x + y$ (B) $2(x + y)$
   (C) $\dfrac{x + y}{2}$ (D) $\dfrac{x + y}{3}$

3. If the product of a number and $2b$ is increased by y, the result is p. Find the number in terms of b, y, and p.

   (A) $2by - p$ (B) $\dfrac{2b}{y - p}$
   (C) $\dfrac{p - y}{2b}$ (D) $\dfrac{y - b}{2b}$

4. If $\dfrac{1}{p} = \sqrt{0.25}$, then $p^2 =$

   (A) 0.25 (B) 4 (C) 25 (D) 400

5. Of the following numbers, which is the greatest?

   (A) $\dfrac{1}{3\sqrt{3}}$ (B) $\dfrac{1}{3}$ (C) $\dfrac{\sqrt{3}}{3}$ (D) $\sqrt{3}$

6. If $\dfrac{a + b}{a} = \dfrac{5}{4}$, then $\dfrac{b}{a} =$

   (A) $\dfrac{1}{4}$ (B) $\dfrac{5}{4}$ (C) $\dfrac{7}{4}$ (D) $\dfrac{9}{4}$

7. Of the following, which is closest to the value of $\dfrac{65.9 \times 0.49}{3.3}$?

   (A) 10 (B) 80 (C) 100 (D) 450

8. The reciprocal of $\dfrac{5}{b - 1} + \dfrac{3}{b}$ is

   (A) $\dfrac{b^2 - b}{15}$ (B) $\dfrac{b - 1}{2}$
   (C) $\dfrac{b^2 - b}{8b - 3}$ (D) $\dfrac{2b - 1}{8}$

9. Simplify $\dfrac{1 \div \dfrac{1}{b}}{\dfrac{1}{b}}$.

   (A) 1 (B) $\dfrac{1}{b^2}$ (C) b (D) b^2

10. If $4b - 3a = 0$, then what is the value of $\dfrac{16b^2}{a^2}$?

    (A) $\dfrac{1}{9}$ (B) 9 (C) 16 (D) $\dfrac{256}{9}$

11. If $xyz = 8$ and $y = z$, then $x =$

    (A) y^2 (B) $\dfrac{8}{y^2}$ (C) $8y^2$ (D) $\dfrac{1}{y^2}$

12. If $\dfrac{2b}{5a} = 12$, then $\dfrac{2b - 10a}{5a} =$

    (A) 5 (B) 10 (C) 14 (D) 24

13. If $\dfrac{x}{6} + 4 = 1$, the value of $\dfrac{x}{3}$ is

    (A) -36 (B) -18 (C) -6 (D) 6

14. If $3 + \dfrac{d}{4} = 8\dfrac{1}{2}$, then $d =$

    (A) -2 (B) 5 (C) 16 (D) 22

CHAPTER 14

Probability

The plants produced by these dandelion seeds will not all be exactly alike. In studying generations of plants, botanists often gather extensive data. Sometimes they can discover genetic patterns and use probability to predict characteristics of future generations.

14-1 Counting

Jana Lee is ordering a new automobile. She still has three choices to make.

    1. 4-cylinder or 6-cylinder engine?
    2. Standard or automatic transmission?
    3. Maroon, white, or tan?

These three choices are called **independent events.** That is, the choice of one of them does *not* affect the others. Jana's possible choices can be shown in a diagram.

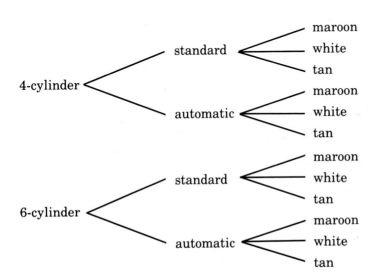

This diagram is called a tree diagram.

Notice there are 12 different choices.

You can find the total number of choices that Jana has without drawing a diagram.

	Choices:	4-cyl. or 6-cyl.	standard or automatic	blue or white or orange
Number of choices:		2	2	3

Multiplication can be used to find the total number of choices that Jana has.

$$2 \cdot 2 \cdot 3 = 12$$

> **Suppose an event can occur in *p* different ways. Another event can occur in *q* different ways. There are *p · q* ways both events can occur.**

Basic Counting Principle

This principle can be extended to any number of events. Some events are dependent. In dependent events the number of choices is altered by the choice in the previous event.

Examples

1 **How many different three-letter patterns can be formed using the letters *a*, *b*, and *c*, if a letter can be used more than once?**

Letters:	1st	2nd	3rd
Ways to choose:	3	3	3

A pattern is a selection of three letters. Each one must be an a, b, or c.

There are $\underline{3} \cdot \underline{3} \cdot \underline{3}$ or 27 possible patterns.

2 **How many different three-letter patterns can be formed using the letters *a*, *b*, and *c* if each letter is used exactly once?**

Letters:	1st	2nd	3rd
Ways to choose:	3	2	1

Note that after the first letter is chosen, it may not be chosen again. These events are called <u>dependent events</u>.

There are $\underline{3} \cdot \underline{2} \cdot \underline{1} = 3!$ or 6 patterns.

3 **How many seven-digit phone numbers can begin with the prefix 457?**

Digit in phone number:	4th	5th	6th	7th
Ways to choose:	10	10	10	10

There are $\underline{10} \cdot \underline{10} \cdot \underline{10} \cdot \underline{10} = 10^4$ or 10,000 numbers.

Exploratory Exercises

Tell whether each choice is independent or dependent.

1. Choose color and size to order an item of clothing.

2. Choose a president, secretary, and treasurer for a club.

3. Choose five numbers in a bingo game.

4. Choose the winner and loser of a chess game.

5. Each of five people guess the total number of runs in a baseball game. They write down the guess, without telling what it is.

6. The numerals 0 through 9 are written on pieces of paper and placed in a jar. Three of them are selected one after the other, without replacement.

Written Exercises

Solve each problem.

1. The letters *g, h, j, k,* and *l* are to be used to form five-letter patterns. How many patterns can be formed if repetitions are allowed?

2. A license plate must have two letters (not I or O) followed by three digits. The last digit cannot be zero. How many possible plates are there?

3. There are five roads from Albany to Briscoe, six from Briscoe to Chadwick, three from Chadwick to Dover. How many different routes are there from Albany to Dover?

4. A store has 15 sofas, 12 lamps, and 10 tables at half price. How many different combinations of a sofa, a lamp, and a table can be bought at the sale?

5. A restaurant serves 5 main dishes, 3 salads, and 4 desserts. How many different meals could be ordered if each has a main dish, a salad, and a dessert?

6. A car dealer offers a choice of 6 vinyl top colors, 18 body colors, and 7 upholstery colors. How many color combinations are there?

7. Four ferry boats make the crossing between Harrod and Lafayette. How many different ways can a traveler make a round trip?

8. Using the ferry boats in problem 7, how many different ways can a traveler make a round trip, but return on a different ferry boat from the one she went on?

9. How many ways can six different books be placed on a shelf?

10. How many ways can six books be placed on a shelf if the only dictionary must be on an end?

11. How many different 4-letter patterns can be formed from the letters, *a, e, i, o, r, s,* and *t* if no letter occurs more than once?

12. How many of the patterns in exercise 11 begin with a vowel and end with a consonant?

13. How many 4-digit patterns are there in which all the digits are different?

14. In how many ways can 3 dice of different colors be thrown at the same time?

15. Using the letters from the word *equation,* how many 5-letter patterns can be formed in which *q* is followed immediately by *u*?

16. How many five-digit numbers between and including 65,000 and 69,999 can be made if no digit is repeated?

17. Draw a tree diagram to show the possibilities for boys and girls in a family with 2 children.

18. Draw a tree diagram to show the possibilities for boys and girls in a family with 3 children.

Exploratory Exercises

Tell whether each statement below is true or false.

1. $5! - 3! = 2!$
2. $6 \cdot 5! = 6!$
3. $\dfrac{6!}{3!} = 2!$
4. $(6 - 3)! = 6! - 3!$
5. $\dfrac{6!}{30} = 4!$
6. $\dfrac{6!}{8!} \cdot \dfrac{8!}{6!} = 1$
7. $3! + 4! = 5 \cdot 3!$
8. $1!2!3!2! = 4!$
9. $\dfrac{P(9, 9)}{9!} = 1$
10. $\dfrac{3!}{3} = \dfrac{2!}{2}$

Written Exercises

How many different ways can the letters of the following words be arranged?

1. FLOWER
2. STUDY
3. POP
4. SEE
5. PEGGY
6. LEVEL
7. MISSISSIPPI
8. ALASKA
9. ALGEBRA
10. PARALLEL
11. ESSENTIAL
12. PERPENDICULAR

Find the value of each of the following.

13. $\dfrac{P(6, 4)}{P(5, 3)}$
14. $\dfrac{P(10, 3)}{P(5, 3)}$
15. $\dfrac{P(6, 3) \cdot P(4, 2)}{P(5, 2)}$
16. $\dfrac{P(5, 3)}{P(8, 5)P(5, 5)}$

Solve each problem.

17. Don has 5 pennies, 3 nickels, and 4 dimes. The coins of each denomination are indistinguishable. How many ways can he arrange the coins in a row?

18. Estelle has 8 quarters, 5 dimes, 3 nickels, and a penny. The coins of each denomination are indistinguishable. How many ways can she place the coins in a straight line?

19. Ten scores received on a test were 82, 91, 75, 83, 91, 64, 83, 77, 91, and 75. In how many different orders might they be recorded?

20. How many 6-digit numbers can be made using the digits from 833,284?

21. There are 3 identical red flags and 5 identical white flags that are used to send signals. All 8 flags must be used. How many signals can be given?

22. Five algebra and four geometry books are to be placed on a shelf. How many ways can they be arranged if all the algebra books are together?

23. How many ways can 4 nickels and 5 dimes be distributed among 9 children if each is to receive one coin?

24. There are 4 green, 1 red, and 1 blue books on a shelf. How many ways can they be arranged if the red book and the blue book are separated?

Challenge

Find n in each of the following equations.

25. $n[P(5, 3)] = P(7, 5)$
26. $P(n, 4) = 3[P(n, 3)]$
27. $P(n, 4) = 40[P(n - 1, 2)]$
28. $7[P(n, 5)] = P(n, 3) \cdot P(9, 3)$
29. $9 P(n, 5) = P(n, 3) \cdot P(9, 3)$
30. $208 P(n, 2) = P(16, 4)$

14-3　Circular Permutations

A food vending machine has 6 items on each of the revolving trays. One such tray has an orange, an apple, a can of juice, a salad, a cup of yogurt, and a boiled egg. How many ways can these items be arranged on the tray?

Think of each tray as a circle. Let the letters *o, a, j, s, y,* and *e* stand for the various items on the tray. Three possible arrangements are shown below.

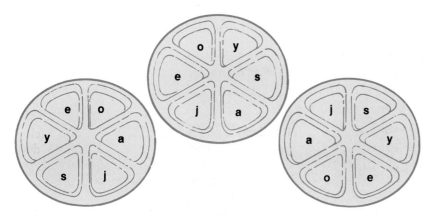

How does the first arrangement change as the tray is turned? Which arrangement is *really* different from the other two?

When 6 objects are placed in a line, there are 6! or 720 arrangements of the 6 objects taken 6 at a time. However, when they are arranged in a circle, some of the arrangements are alike. These arrangements fall into groups of six, each of which can be found from one another by turning the circle. Thus, the number of really different arrangements around a circle is $\frac{1}{6}$ of the total number of arrangements in a line.

$$\frac{1}{6} \cdot 6! = \frac{6 \cdot 5 \cdot 4 \cdot 3 \cdot 2 \cdot 1}{6}$$
$$= 5 \cdot 4 \cdot 3 \cdot 2 \cdot 1$$
$$= 5! \text{ or } (6-1)!$$

There are $(6-1)!$ arrangements of 6 objects in a circle.

> If n objects are arranged in a circle, then there are $\dfrac{n!}{n}$ or $(n - 1)!$ permutations of the n objects around the circle.

Circular Permutations

Example

1 **Five people are to be seated at a round table. How many seating arrangements are possible?**

$(5 - 1)! = 4!$
$\qquad = 4 \cdot 3 \cdot 2 \cdot 1$ or 24

Suppose the people are seated around the table. Everyone moves one chair to the left. Each person is still sitting next to the same two people as before.

If n objects on a circle are arranged in relation to a fixed point, then there are $n!$ permutations. Even though the objects are on a circle, the permutations are linear since a reference point has been established.

Suppose now that five people are to be seated at a round table. One of them is seated close to the door as shown. How many arrangements are possible?

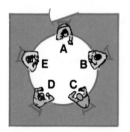 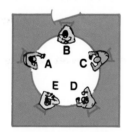 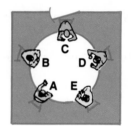

 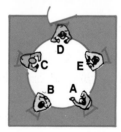

These arrangements are different. In each one, a different person sits closest to the door. Thus, there are $P(5, 5)$ or $5!$ arrangements relative to a fixed point which is the door.

$$5! = 5 \cdot 4 \cdot 3 \cdot 2 \cdot 1 \text{ or } 120$$

Suppose three keys are placed on a key ring. Then it appears that there are at most $(3 - 1)!$ or 2 different arrangements of keys on the ring.

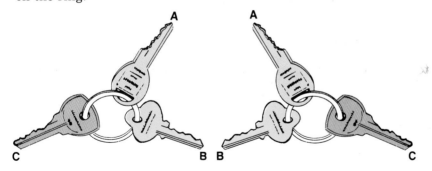

But what happens if the key ring with the first arrangement is turned over? The second arrangement appears. Then there is really only one arrangement of the three keys. These two arrangements are **reflections** of one another. There are only half as many arrangements when reflections are possible.

$$\frac{(3 - 1)!}{2} = \frac{2}{2} \text{ or } 1$$

Examples

2 **How many different ways can 5 charms be placed on a bracelet that has no clasp?**

This is a circular permutation. Because the bracelet can be turned over, it is also reflective.

$$\frac{(5 - 1)!}{2} = \frac{4!}{2}$$

$$= \frac{4 \cdot 3 \cdot 2 \cdot 1}{2} \text{ or } 12$$

There are 12 different ways to arrange the charms.

3 **How many different ways can 5 charms be placed on a bracelet that has a clasp?**

This is no longer a circular permutation since objects are arranged with respect to a fixed point, the clasp. However, it is still reflective.

$$\frac{5!}{2} = \frac{5 \cdot 4 \cdot 3 \cdot 2 \cdot 1}{2}$$

$$= \frac{5 \cdot 4 \cdot 3 \cdot 2 \cdot 1}{2} \text{ or } 60$$

There are 60 different ways to arrange the charms.

Exploratory Exercises

State whether arrangements of the following objects are reflective or not reflective. Then, state whether their permutations are linear or circular.

1. charms on a charm bracelet, having no clasp
2. a football huddle of 11 players
3. chairs arranged in a circle
4. beads on a necklace with no clasp
5. chairs in a row
6. a pearl necklace that is open
7. four people seated around a square table relative to each other
8. people seated around a square table relative to one chair
9. a baseball team's batting order
10. a list of students in a given class
11. placing 6 coins in a circular pattern on a table

Written Exercises

Evaluate each of the following.

1. $8! - 6!$
2. $5!3!$
3. $6! + 5!$
4. $3 \cdot 5!$
5. $\dfrac{6!}{4!}$
6. $\dfrac{8! + 6!}{8! - 6!}$
7. $P(8, 5)$
8. $P(10, 4)$
9. $3! P(6, 5) \cdot P(9, 2)$
10. $4!3! P(7, 3)$
11. $\dfrac{P(6, 4) \cdot P(5, 2)}{5!}$
12. $\dfrac{P(8, 3) \cdot P(5, 4)}{P(6, 6)}$
13. $\dfrac{P(12, 6)}{P(12, 3) \cdot P(8, 2)}$
14. $\dfrac{P(10, 8)}{5! P(8, 5)}$
15. $\dfrac{P(7, 6)}{7! P(9, 3)}$

Solve each of the following.

16. How many ways can 6 keys be arranged on a key ring?
17. How many ways can 6 people be seated around a campfire?
18. How many ways can 8 charms be arranged on a bracelet that has no clasp?
19. How many ways can 4 men and 4 women be seated alternately at a round table?
20. How many ways can 5 people be seated at a round table relative to each other?
21. How many ways can 6 people be seated at a round table relative to the door in the room?
22. How many ways can 5 people be seated around a circular table if 2 of the people must be seated next to each other?
23. Twenty beads are strung in a circle. Fourteen are brown and 6 are red. How many ways can the beads be strung in the circle if a clasp is used?
24. There are 8 chairs around a table. One chair is reserved for the President. How many seating arrangements are possible for the President and his 7 advisors?
25. A charm bracelet has 20 links and no clasp. How many ways can 6 charms be arranged on the bracelet if each charm requires one link?

mini-review

1. Find all the rational zeros for $f(x) = x^3 + 4x^2 - 3x - 18$.
2. Solve $\dfrac{t + 4}{t} + \dfrac{3}{t - 4} = \dfrac{-16}{t^2 - 4t}$.
3. Use the tables or a calculator to find the logarithm of 329.4.
4. Find S_n for the arithmetic series if $a_1 = 50$, $n = 20$, and $d = -4$.
5. Find the sum of the geometric series if $a_1 = 16$, $r = -\dfrac{1}{2}$, and $n = 6$.

14-4 Combinations

Suppose that from a group of nine girls, five are chosen to start the basketball game. In this case, the order in which the girls are chosen is not important. Such a selection is called a **combination.**

The combination of nine things taken five at a time is written $C(9, 5)$.

You know that five things can be arranged in 5! ways. These arrangements are eliminated when finding the number of combinations.

$$C(9, 5) = \frac{P(9, 5)}{5!}$$

$$= \frac{9!}{(9 - 5)! \cdot 5!} \quad P(9, 5) = \frac{9!}{(9 - 5)!}$$

$$= \frac{9!}{4! \cdot 5!} \text{ or } 126$$

The number of combinations of n objects, taken r at a time, is written $C(n, r)$.

$$C(n, r) = \frac{n!}{(n - r)!r!}$$

Definition of $C(n, r)$

The main difference between a permutation and a combination is whether order is considered (permutation) or not (combination).

Example

1 From a group of 6 men and 4 women, how many committees of 2 men and 3 women can be formed?

Order is not considered. The questions are: How many ways can 2 men be chosen from 6? How many ways can 3 women be chosen from 4?

$$C(6, 2) \cdot C(4, 3) = \frac{6!}{(6 - 2)!2!} \cdot \frac{4!}{(4 - 3)!3!}$$

$$= \frac{6!}{4!2!} \cdot \frac{4!}{1!3!}$$

$$= \frac{6 \cdot 5}{2 \cdot 1} \cdot \frac{4}{1}$$

Write out the factorials to see how to get the next line.

$$= 15 \cdot 4 \text{ or } 60$$

There are 60 possible committees.

Examples

2 **In an urn, there are 17 numbered discs. Eight are red, 5 are white, and 4 are blue. How many ways can 2 red, 1 white, and 2 blue discs be chosen?**

$C(8, 2)$ Select 2 of the 8 red discs.

$C(5, 1)$ Select 1 of the 5 white discs.

$C(4, 2)$ Select 2 of the 4 blue discs.

$$C(8, 2) \cdot C(5, 1) \cdot C(4, 2) = \frac{8 \cdot 7}{2 \cdot 1} \cdot 5 \cdot \frac{4 \cdot 3}{2 \cdot 1}$$

$$= 28 \cdot 5 \cdot 6$$

$$= 840$$

Note $\dfrac{8!}{6!2!} \cdot \dfrac{5!}{4!1!} \cdot \dfrac{4!}{2!2!} =$

$\dfrac{8 \cdot 7 \cdot 6!}{6!2!} \cdot \dfrac{5 \cdot 4!}{4!1!} \cdot \dfrac{4 \cdot 3 \cdot 2!}{2!2!}$

There are 840 ways to choose the discs.

3 **Find the total number of diagonals that can be drawn in a decagon.**

Each diagonal has two endpoints. Suppose one has endpoints A and B. Then segment AB and segment BA are the same. Thus, order is not considered, and the combination of 10 points, taken two at a time, is desired. This gives the total number of line segments. But 10 of them are sides, so the number of diagonals is as follows.

$$C(10, 2) - 10 = \frac{10!}{(10 - 2)!2!} - 10$$

$$= \frac{10!}{8!2!} - 10$$

$$= \frac{10 \cdot 9 \cdot 8!}{8!2!} - 10$$

$$= \frac{10 \cdot 9}{2 \cdot 1} - 10$$

$$= 35$$

Note $10! = 10 \cdot 9 \cdot 8 \cdot 7 \cdot 6 \cdot 5 \cdot 4 \cdot 3 \cdot 2 \cdot 1$
$= 10 \cdot 9 \cdot 8!$

There are 35 diagonals.

4 **From a deck of 52 cards, how many ways can 5 cards be drawn so that 3 are of 1 suit and 2 are of another?**

$P(4, 2)$ First, select 2 suits from the 4 suits.

$C(13, 3)$ Then, select 3 cards from 1 suit of 13 cards.

$C(13, 2)$ Next, select 2 cards from the other suit.

This is a permutation since the 3 cards come from either of the two suits selected.

Thus, the number of ways is as follows.

$$P(4, 2) \cdot C(13, 3) \cdot C(13, 2) = \frac{4!}{2!} \cdot \frac{13!}{10!3!} \cdot \frac{13!}{11!2!}$$

$$= \frac{4 \cdot 3}{1} \cdot \frac{13 \cdot 12 \cdot 11}{3 \cdot 2 \cdot 1} \cdot \frac{13 \cdot 12}{2 \cdot 1}$$

$$= 12 \cdot 286 \cdot 78$$

$$= 267{,}696$$

There are 267,696 ways to draw the cards.

Exploratory Exercises

State whether arrangements of the following represent a combination or a permutation.

1. a team of 5 people, chosen from a group of 12 people
2. three-letter patterns, chosen from the letters of the word *algebra*
3. a hand of 5 cards
4. a batting order in baseball
5. seating students in a row
6. the answers on a true-false test
7. a committee of 4 men and 5 women, chosen from 8 men and 7 women
8. people seated around a table

Written Exercises

Evaluate.

1. $C(8, 3)$
2. $C(8, 5) \cdot C(7, 3)$
3. $C(7, 2)$
4. $C(24, 21)$

Find the value of *n* in each of the following.

5. $C(n, 3) = C(n, 8)$
6. $C(n, 5) = C(n, 7)$
7. $C(n, 12) = C(30, 18)$
8. $C(14, 3) = C(n, 11)$

Solve each of the following.

9. From a list of 12 books, how many groups of 5 books can be selected?
10. How many baseball teams of 9 members can be formed from 14 players?
11. Suppose there are 9 points on a circle. How many different 4-sided polygons can be formed by joining any 4 of these points?
12. There are 85 telephones at Kennedy High School. How many 2-way connections can be made among the school telephones?
13. How many different groups of 25 people can be formed from 27 people?
14. Suppose there are 8 points in a plane, no 3 of which are collinear. How many distinct triangles could be formed with these points as vertices?
15. From a deck of 52 playing cards, how many different 5-card hands can have 5 cards of the same suit?
16. From a deck of 52 playing cards, how many different 4-card hands can have each card from a different suit?

A bag contains 4 red, 6 white, and 9 blue marbles. How many ways can 5 marbles be selected to meet the following conditions?

17. All the marbles are white.
18. All the marbles are blue.
19. All the marbles are red.
20. Two are red, 2 are white, and 1 is blue.
21. Two must be blue.
22. Two are 1 color and 3 are another color.

From a group of 8 men and 10 women, a committee of 5 is to be formed. How many committees can be formed if the committee is to be comprised as follows?

23. All are men.
24. There are 3 men and 2 women.
25. There is 1 man and 4 women.
26. All are women.

14-5 Probability

When a coin is tossed, only two outcomes are possible. Either the coin will show a *head* or a *tail*. The desired outcome is called a **success.** Any other outcome is called a **failure.**

An event is a set of outcomes.

> **If an event can succeed in s ways and fail in f ways, then the probabilities of success $P(s)$ and of failure $P(f)$ are as follows.**
>
> $$P(s) = \frac{s}{s + f} \qquad P(f) = \frac{f}{s + f}$$

Probability of Success and of Failure

If the event cannot succeed, $P(s) = 0$. If the event cannot fail, $P(s) = 1$.

$$P(s) + P(f) = \frac{s}{s + f} + \frac{f}{s + f}$$

This is an important property of probabilities.

$$= \frac{s + f}{s + f} \text{ or } 1$$

Because their sum is one, $P(s)$ and $P(f)$ are called *complements.*

For example, if $P(s)$ is $\frac{1}{3}$, Then $P(f)$ is $1 - \frac{1}{3}$ or $\frac{2}{3}$.

Examples

1 A bag contains 5 blue marbles and 4 white marbles. If one marble is chosen at random, what is the probability that it is blue?

$$P(blue\ marble) = \frac{s}{s + f}$$

P(blue marble) is read the probability of selecting a blue marble.
A blue marble is a success.
A white marble is a failure.

$$= \frac{5}{5 + 4} \text{ or } \frac{5}{9}$$

The probability of selecting a blue marble is $\frac{5}{9}$.

2 A committee of 2 is to be selected from a group of 6 men and 3 women. What is the probability that the 2 selected are women?

$$P(two\ women) = \frac{C(3, 2)}{C(9, 2)}$$

There are C(3, 2) ways to select 2 of 3 women.
There are C(9, 2) ways to select 2 of 9 people.

$$= \frac{\dfrac{3!}{1!2!}}{\dfrac{9!}{7!2!}}$$

$$= \frac{3}{36} \text{ or } \frac{1}{12}$$

The probability that the 2 selected are women is $\frac{1}{12}$.

The odds of the successful outcome of an event is expressed as the ratio of the number of ways it can succeed to the number of ways it can fail.

Definition of Odds

$$\text{Odds} = \text{the ratio of } s \text{ to } f \text{ or } \frac{s}{f}$$

Examples

3 **What are the odds of tossing a die and getting a 3?**

The number 3 is on only one face of the die. The other five faces have a number other than 3.

$\text{Odds} = \frac{1}{5}$ *A 3 can appear only 1 way.*
            Other numbers can appear 5 ways.

The odds of getting a 3 are 1 to 5.

4 **Suppose Michael draws 5 cards from a deck of 52 cards. What are the odds that 4 of the cards will be of one suit and the fifth of another suit?**

$P(4, 2)$ Select 2 suits among 4.

$C(13, 4)$ Select 4 cards from a suit containing 13 cards.

$C(13, 1)$ Select 1 card from the other suit.

Since a different number of cards are to be selected from each suit, order is important.

The number of ways to select 4 cards from one suit and 1 card from another is found as follows.

$$P(4, 2) \cdot C(13, 4) \cdot C(13, 1) = \frac{4!}{2!} \cdot \frac{13!}{4!9!} \cdot \frac{13!}{1!12!}$$

$$= \frac{4 \cdot 3}{1} \cdot \frac{13 \cdot 12 \cdot 11 \cdot 10}{4 \cdot 3 \cdot 2 \cdot 1} \cdot \frac{13}{1}$$

$$= 12 \cdot 715 \cdot 13$$

$$= 111{,}540$$

Thus the number of outcomes that can be considered successful is 111,540. The total number of outcomes is the combination of 52 cards taken 5 at a time.

$$C(52, 5) = \frac{52!}{47!5!}$$

$$= \frac{52 \cdot 51 \cdot 50 \cdot 49 \cdot 48}{5 \cdot 4 \cdot 3 \cdot 2 \cdot 1}$$

$$= \frac{311{,}875{,}200}{120}$$

$$= 2{,}598{,}960$$

The total number of outcomes, including successful outcomes and failures, is 2,598,960. Thus, the number of failures is 2,598,960 − 111,540 or 2,487,420. The odds of selecting 4 cards from one suit and 1 card from another suit are $\frac{111{,}540}{2{,}487{,}420}$ or $\frac{143}{3189}$. This is approximately 1 to 22.

Exploratory Exercises

State the odds of an event occurring given the probability that it occurs as follows.

1. $\frac{1}{2}$ 　2. $\frac{3}{4}$ 　3. $\frac{1}{7}$ 　4. $\frac{5}{8}$ 　5. $\frac{7}{15}$ 　6. $\frac{8}{9}$

State the probability of an event occurring given the following odds.

7. $\frac{3}{4}$ 　8. $\frac{5}{1}$ 　9. $\frac{6}{5}$ 　10. $\frac{3}{7}$ 　11. $\frac{5}{11}$ 　12. $\frac{1}{1}$

Solve each of the following.

13. The odds are 6-to-1 *against* an event occurring. What is the probability that it will occur?

14. The probability of an event occurring is $\frac{3}{4}$. What are the odds that it will not occur?

Written Exercises

In a bag are 7 pennies, 4 nickels, and 5 dimes. Three coins are selected at random. Find the probability of each of the following selections.

1. all 3 pennies　　　　　2. all 3 nickels　　　　　3. all 3 dimes
4. 2 pennies, 1 dime　　　5. 1 penny, 1 dime, 1 nickel　　6. 1 dime, 2 nickels

In a bag are 5 red, 9 blue, and 6 white marbles. Two are selected at random. Find the probability of each of the following selections.

7. 2 red　　　　　8. 2 blue　　　　　9. 1 red and 1 blue　　　10. 1 red and 1 white

There are 5 fudgesicles and 8 popsicles in the freezer. If 2 are selected at random, find the probability of each of the following.

11. 2 fudgesicles　　　　　　　　　　12. 2 popsicles

Suppose you select 2 letters from the word *algebra*. What is the probability of selecting 2 letters and having the following occur?

13. 1 vowel and 1 consonant　　14. 2 vowels　　　　　15. 2 consonants

Sharon has 8 mystery books and 9 science fiction books. Four are selected. Find the probability of each of the following.

16. 4 mystery books　　　　　　　　17. 4 science fiction books
18. 2 mysteries and 2 science fiction　　19. 3 mysteries and 1 science fiction

From a deck of 52 cards, 5 cards are dealt. What are the odds of the following?

20. 5 aces　　　　　21. 5 face cards　　　　　22. 5 from one suit

Using Calculators ——————————— Probability

To "round" a value for probability, express it as a unit fraction. A unit fraction has a numerator of 1. Round $\frac{63}{486}$ as follows.

$\frac{63}{486} = \frac{1}{x}$　　Find x.　　ENTER: 486 $\boxed{\div}$ 63 $\boxed{=}$ 7.714　　Since x is about 8, the probability is about $\frac{1}{8}$.

Exercises

Round each value to the nearest unit fraction.

1. $\frac{13}{198}$　　2. $\frac{9}{84}$　　3. $\frac{66}{5136}$　　4. $\frac{37}{6218}$　　5. $\frac{324}{90,125}$　　6. $\frac{50}{652}$

Companies often use games of chance to increase sales. By law, the company must explain how many game tickets will be distributed, and how many prizes will be awarded. From this information, you can compute the odds of winning a certain prize.

Here is an easy way to compute the odds of winning:

1. Find the probability and express it as a unit fraction.
2. Subtract 1 from the denominator to obtain the odds.

This method works because of the relationship between probability $\dfrac{s}{s + f}$ *and odds* $\dfrac{s}{f}$. *When s is 1, the denominator for probability is one greater than the denominator for odds.*

Example: **Suppose a company distributes 2400 game tickets, including 50 for wristwatches and 30 for radios.**

    a. What are the odds of winning a wristwatch?

$$\text{Probability} = \frac{50}{2400} = \frac{1}{48} \qquad \text{Odds} = \frac{1}{48-1} = \frac{1}{47}$$

The odds are $\dfrac{1}{47}$ or 1 to 47.

    b. What are the odds of winning a wristwatch or a radio?

$$\text{Probability} = \frac{50 + 30}{2400} = \frac{1}{30} \qquad \text{Odds} = \frac{1}{30-1} = \frac{1}{29}$$

The odds are $\dfrac{1}{29}$ or 1 to 29.

Exercises

A company plans to give out 24,864,840 game tickets. Winning tickets can be exchanged for cash prizes of $25, $10, or $5. The following chart shows the number of winning tickets that will be distributed. Complete the chart by finding the values of the winning tickets, the probability of winning, and the odds.

Prize Category	Quantity of Winning Tickets	Value of Winning Tickets	Probability of Winning	Odds of Winning
$25	1656	$25 × 1656 = $41,400	1 to 15,015	1 to 15,014
$10	4620	**1.**	**2.**	**3.**
$ 5	6210	**4.**	**5.**	**6.**

7. If all prize tickets are exchanged for cash, how much money will the company pay in prizes?

8. What are the odds of winning anything?

9. If the company's sales increase by $500,000 and 30% of this amount is profit, how much money will the company earn as a result of the game? Assume that all prizes will be awarded.

14-6 Multiplying Probabilities

The Basic Counting Principle can be used to help find probabilities. Suppose you toss a white die and then toss a green die. The probability that the white die shows a 2 is $\frac{1}{6}$. The probability that the green die shows a 2 is $\frac{1}{6}$. The probability that both dice show a 2 is $\frac{1}{6} \cdot \frac{1}{6}$ or $\frac{1}{36}$. Since the outcome of tossing the white die does *not* affect the outcome of tossing the green die, the events are independent.

> **If two events, *A* and *B*, are independent, then the probability of both events occurring is found as follows.**
>
> $$P(A \text{ and } B) = P(A) \cdot P(B)$$

Probability of Two Independent Events

Example

1 **A bag contains 5 red marbles and 4 white marbles. A marble is to be selected, and replaced in the bag. A second selection is then made. What is the probability of selecting 2 red marbles?**

These events are independent because the first marble selected is replaced. The outcome of the second selection is not affected by the results of the first selection.

$$P(both\ red) = P(red) \cdot P(red)$$

$$= \frac{5}{9} \cdot \frac{5}{9} \text{ or } \frac{25}{81}$$

The probability is a little less than $\frac{1}{3}$.

What is the probability of selecting 2 red marbles from 5 red ones and 4 white ones if the first selection is *not* replaced? These events are *dependent* because the outcome of the first selection affects the outcome of the second selection. Suppose the first selection is red.

first selection   second selection

$$P(red) = \frac{5}{9} \qquad\qquad P(red) = \frac{4}{8}$$

$$P(both\ red) = P(red) \cdot P(red\ following\ red)$$

$$= \frac{5}{9} \cdot \frac{4}{8} \text{ or } \frac{5}{18}$$

> **Suppose two events, *A* and *B*, are dependent. Then the probability of both occurring is found as follows.**
>
> $$P(A \text{ and } B) = P(A) \cdot P(B \text{ following } A)$$

Probability of Two Dependent Events

2 There are 5 nickels, 7 dimes, and 9 pennies in a coin purse. Suppose two coins are to be selected, without replacing the first one. What is the probability of selecting a penny and then a dime?

$$P(penny \text{ and } dime) = P(penny) \cdot P(dime \text{ following penny})$$
$$= \frac{9}{21} \cdot \frac{7}{20} \quad P(A \text{ and } B) = P(A) \cdot P(B \text{ following } A)$$
$$= \frac{3}{20}$$

The probability is $\frac{3}{20}$.

3 What is the probability of selecting an eight followed by a nine from a deck of 52 cards if the first card is replaced before the second card is drawn? What is the probability if the first card is not replaced?

If the first card is replaced before the second card is drawn, then the events are independent.

$$P(eight \text{ and } nine) = P(eight) \cdot P(nine) \qquad P(eight) = \frac{4}{52} \text{ or } \frac{1}{13}$$
$$= \frac{1}{13} \cdot \frac{1}{13} \qquad\qquad P(nine) = \frac{4}{52} \text{ or } \frac{1}{13}$$
$$= \frac{1}{169}$$

If the first card is not replaced before the second card is drawn, then the events are dependent.

$$P(eight \text{ and } nine) = P(eight) \cdot P(nine \text{ after eight is drawn})$$
$$= \frac{1}{13} \cdot \frac{4}{51}$$
$$= \frac{4}{663}$$

The probability is $\frac{4}{663}$, or about $\frac{1}{166}$.

Exploratory Exercises

Identify the events in each of the following problems as *independent* or *dependent*.

1. In a bag are 5 red, 3 green, and 8 blue marbles. Three are selected in sequence without replacement. What is the probability of selecting a red, green, and blue, in that order?

2. There are 4 glasses of root beer and 3 glasses of ice tea on the counter. Bill drinks two of them. What is the probability that he drank 2 root beers?

3. In a bag are 5 apricots and 4 plums. Marie selects one, replaces it, and selects another. What is the probability that both selections were apricots?

4. When James plays Ted in cribbage, the odds are 3 to 2 that he will win. What is the probability that he will win the next 4 games?

Written Exercises

1–4. Solve each problem in Exploratory Exercises 1–4.

A bag contains 5 red, 3 white, and 7 blue marbles. If 3 marbles are selected in succession, what is the probability that they are red, white, and blue, in that order?

5. Suppose no marbles are replaced.

6. Suppose each marble is replaced.

In a bag are 5 red, 3 blue, and 7 black marbles. Three marbles are chosen, one after the other. What is the probability that there is one of each color under the following conditions?

7. No replacement occurs

8. Replacement occurs each time

One hundred tickets, numbered consecutively 1 to 100, are placed in a box. What is the probability that in 5 separate drawings, the following selections occur?

9. 5 odd numbers, if replacement occurs

10. 5 odd numbers, if no replacement occurs

11. 5 consecutive numbers if no replacement occurs

The letters *A, B, E, I, J, K,* and *M* are written on cards that are placed in a box. Two letters are selected. What is the probability that the following occurs?

12. two vowels, if no replacement occurs

13. two vowels, if replacement occurs

14. two the same letter, if no replacement occurs

There are 6 plates, 5 saucers, and 5 cups on the counter. Charlie accidentally knocks off two and breaks them. What is the probability that he broke the following?

15. 2 plates

16. 2 cups

17. a cup and a saucer, in that order

18. a cup and a saucer, in any order

A red and a green die are tossed. What is the probability that the following occurs?

19. both show 3

20. neither show 3

21. the red shows a 3 and the green shows a 4

22. the red shows a 3 and the green shows any other number

23. both show the same number

24. both show different numbers

Excursions in Algebra —————————————— History

Maria Agnesi (ähn yā' zē) was an Italian mathematician who lived from 1718 to 1799. At one time, she was a professor of mathematics at Bologna, Italy. In 1748, she wrote about a special set of curves that she called *versiera*. The general equation for those curves is $yx^2 = a^2(a - y)$.

The popular name for this type of curve is the *Witch of Agnesi*, because the curve resembles the outline of a witch's hat.

Exercises

Graph each of the following *versiera*. State the value of *a*.

1. $yx^2 = 4(2 - y)$

2. $yx^2 = -64 - 16y$

14-7 Adding Probabilities

Suppose a card is to be drawn from a standard deck of 52 cards. What is the probability of drawing an ace or a king? Since no card is both an ace and a king, the events are said to be **mutually exclusive.** That is, the two events cannot occur simultaneously.

ways to draw an ace

There are 4 aces in a deck. $\frac{4}{52}$ or $\frac{1}{13}$

ways to draw a king

$\frac{4}{52}$ or $\frac{1}{13}$ *There are 4 kings in a deck.*

ways to draw an ace or a king

$$\underset{ace}{\frac{1}{13}} + \underset{king}{\frac{1}{13}} = \underset{ace\ or\ king}{\frac{2}{13}}$$

The probability of one of two mutually exclusive events occurring is the sum of their probabilities. $$P(A\ or\ B) = P(A) + P(B)$$

Probability of Mutually Exclusive Events

This rule can be extended to any number of mutually exclusive events. **Inclusive events** are *not* mutually exclusive.

What is the probability of drawing an ace or a red card? Since there are two red aces, the events are inclusive.

ways to select an ace

There is an ace in each suit, hearts, diamonds, spades, and clubs. $\frac{4}{52}$

ways to select a red card

$\frac{26}{52}$ *Hearts and diamonds are red.*

ways to select a red ace

$\frac{2}{52}$ *There are two red aces.*

Now the ways to select a red ace are counted twice, once in the ways to select an ace and once in the ways to select a red card.

ways to select an ace or a red card

$$\underset{ace}{\frac{4}{52}} + \underset{red}{\frac{26}{52}} - \underset{red\ ace}{\frac{2}{52}} = \underset{ace\ or\ red}{\frac{28}{52}}$$
$$= \frac{7}{13}$$

> The probability of one of two inclusive events, *A* and *B*, occurring is the sum of the individual probabilities decreased by the probability of both occurring.
>
> $$P(A \text{ or } B) = P(A) + P(B) - P(A \text{ and } B)$$

Probability of Inclusive Events

Examples

1 Vivian has 6 nickels, 4 pennies, and 3 dimes in her purse. She selects one. What is the probability it is a penny or a nickel?

$$P(penny \text{ or } nickel) = P(penny) + P(nickel)$$

There is no coin that is both a penny and a nickel. These events are mutually exclusive.

$$= \frac{4}{13} + \frac{6}{13}$$

$$= \frac{10}{13}$$

The probability of selecting a penny or a nickel is $\frac{10}{13}$.

2 A card is to be selected from a deck of 52 cards. What is the probability that it is a red card or a face card?

$$P(red \text{ or } face \ card) = P(red) + P(face \ card) - P(red \ face \ card)$$

$$= \frac{26}{52} + \frac{12}{52} - \frac{6}{52}$$

There are 6 face cards that are red. Thus, the events are inclusive.

$$= \frac{32}{52}$$

$$= \frac{8}{13}$$

The probability of selecting a red card or a face card is $\frac{8}{13}$.

3 A committee of 5 people is to be formed from a group of 7 men and 6 women. What is the probability that the committee will have at least 3 women?

At least 3 women means that the committee may have 3, or 4, or 5 women. It is not possible to select a group of 3, a group of 4, and a group of 5 women all to be on the same 5-member committee. The events are mutually exclusive.

$$P(at \ least \ 3 \ women) = P(3 \ women) + P(4 \ women) + P(5 \ women)$$

$$= \frac{C(6, 3) \cdot C(7, 2)}{C(13,5)} + \frac{C(6, 4) \cdot C(7, 1)}{C(13,5)} + \frac{C(6, 5) \cdot C(7, 0)}{C(13, 5)}$$

$$= \frac{140}{429} + \frac{35}{429} + \frac{2}{429}$$

$$= \frac{177}{429} \text{ or } \frac{59}{143}$$

The probability of at least 3 women on the committee is $\frac{59}{143}$.   *This is a little less than $\frac{1}{2}$.*

Exploratory Exercises

Identify each of the following events as inclusive or exclusive.

1. In a box are slips of paper numbered from 1 to 10. A slip of paper is drawn and a die is tossed. What is the probability of getting a 2 on one of them?

2. Two cards are drawn from a standard deck of playing cards. What is the probability that the 2 cards are both kings or both queens?

3. In her pocket, Linda has 5 nickels, 3 dimes, and 7 pennies. She selects 3 coins. What is the probability that she has selected 3 nickels or 3 pennies?

4. The Dodger pitching staff has 4 left-handers and 7 right-handers. If 2 are selected, what is the probability that at least one of them is a left-hander?

5. From a standard deck of playing cards, 2 cards are drawn. What is the probability of having drawn a black card or an ace?

6. Five coins are dropped. What is the probability of having at least 3 heads?

7. In one class, 3 of the 12 girls are redheads and 2 of the 15 boys are redheads. What is the probability of selecting a boy or a redhead?

8. There are 8 red, 3 blue, and 12 black marbles in a bag. If 3 are selected, what is the probability that all are red or all are blue?

Written Exercises

1–8. Solve each problem in Exploratory Exercises 1–8.

In a bag are 6 red and 5 white marbles. Three are selected. What is the probability that the following occurs?

9. all 3 red or all 3 white

10. at least 2 red

11. at least 2 white

12. exactly 2 white

Two cards are drawn from a standard deck of cards. What is the probability that the following occurs?

13. both aces or both face cards

14. both black or both face cards

15. both aces or both red

16. both either red or an ace

Seven coins are tossed. What is the probability that the following occurs?

17. 3 heads or 2 tails

18. at least 5 heads

19. 3 heads or 3 tails

20. all tails or all heads

From a group of 6 men and 8 women, a committee of 6 is to be selected. What is the probability of the following?

21. all men or all women

22. 5 men or 5 women

23. 3 men and 3 women

24. 4 men or 4 women

The numerals 1 through 25 are written on slips of paper and placed in a bag. The numerals 20 through 40 are written on slips of paper and placed in a different bag. One slip of paper is selected at random from each bag. What is the probability that the following occurs?

25. Both numerals are 20.

26. Neither numeral is 20.

27. Both numerals are greater than 10.

28. At least one of the numerals is 22.

Recall that the binomial expansion of $(a + b)^n$ can be written using sigma and factorial notation.

$$(a + b)^n = \frac{n!}{0!(n - 0)!}a^n + \frac{n!}{1!(n - 1)!}a^{n-1}b^1 + \frac{n!}{2!(n - 2)!}a^{n-2}b^2 + \cdots$$

$$= \sum_{k=0}^{n} \frac{n!}{k!(n - k)!}a^{n-k}b^k \qquad \text{Here } n \text{ is a positive integer,}$$
$$k \text{ is a positive integer or zero.}$$

Study the expansion of $(x + y)^5$.

$$(x + y)^5 = \sum_{k=0}^{5} \frac{5!}{k!(5 - k)!} x^{5-k}y^k$$

$$= \frac{5!}{0!5!}x^5 + \frac{5!}{1!4!}x^4y + \frac{5!}{2!3!}x^3y^2 + \frac{5!}{3!2!}x^2y^3 + \frac{5!}{4!1!}xy^4 + \frac{5!}{5!0!}y^5$$

$$= x^5 + 5x^4y + 10x^3y^2 + 10x^2y^3 + 5xy^4 + y^5$$

The coefficient of each term may be expressed using combination notation. Recall that $C(n, r)$ means $\frac{n!}{(n-r)!r!}$.

$$(x + y)^5 = \underbrace{C(5, 5)x^2}_{1} + \underbrace{C(5, 4)x^4y}_{5} + \underbrace{C(5, 3)x^3y^2}_{10} + \underbrace{C(5, 2)x^2y^3}_{10} + \underbrace{C(5, 1)xy^4}_{5} + \underbrace{C(5, 0)y^5}_{1}$$

The coefficients of a binomial expansion are symmetric. Study the values of the coefficients of $(x + y)^5$.

$$C(5, 0) = C(5, 5) \qquad C(5, 1) = C(5, 4) \qquad C(5, 2) = C(5, 3)$$

In general, $C(n, k)$ is equivalent to $C(n, n - k)$. Thus, the following two formulas for binomial expansions are equivalent. Both formulas use sigma notation and combination notation.

$$(a + b)^n = \sum_{k=0}^{n} C(n, n - k)a^{n-k}b^k \qquad \text{or} \qquad (a + b)^n = \sum_{k=0}^{n} C(n, k)a^{n-k}b^k$$

Exercises

Write each expansion using combination notation for the coefficients. Then simplify by evaluating each coefficient.

1. $(r + s)^3$
2. $(m + n)^6$
3. $(v + w)^4$
4. $(c + d)^7$
5. $(f + g)^9$
6. $(p + q)^8$

Are the two expressions equivalent? Write *yes* or *no*.

7. $C(6, 4)$ and $C(6, 2)$
8. $C(4, 3)$ and $C(3, 1)$
9. $C(5, 5)$ and $C(6, 6)$
10. $C(7, 1)$ and $C(7, 7)$
11. $C(n, 0)$ and $C(n, n)$
12. $C(a, b)$ and $C(a, a - b)$

14-8 Binomial Trials

Arthur normally wins 1 out of every 3 backgammon games he plays. In other words, the probability that Arthur wins when he plays backgammon is $\frac{1}{3}$.

Suppose Arthur plays 4 games. What is the probability that he will win 3 and lose only one?

The possible ways of winning 3 games and losing one are shown at the right. The illustration shows the combinations of four things, namely games, taken three at a time, namely wins. That is, $C(4, 3)$.

W	W	W	L		W	W	L	W	
W	L	W	W		L	W	W	W	

The terms of the binomial expansion of $(W + L)^4$ are used to find the probability.

$$(W + L)^4 = W^4 + 4W^3L + 6W^2L^2 + 4WL^3 + L^4$$

coefficient	term	meaning
$C(4, 4)$	W^4	1 way to win all 4 games
$C(4, 3)$	$4W^3L$	4 ways to win 3 games and lose 1 game
$C(4, 2)$	$6W^2L^2$	6 ways to win 2 games and lose 2 games
$C(4, 1)$	$4WL^3$	4 ways to win 1 game and lose 3 games
$C(4, 0)$	L^4	1 way to lose all 4 games

The probability that Arthur wins when he plays is $\frac{1}{3}$. And, thus, the probability that he loses is $\frac{2}{3}$. Substitute $\frac{1}{3}$ for W and $\frac{2}{3}$ for L in the term $4W^3L$. For example, the probability of winning 3 out of 4 games is $4\left(\frac{1}{3}\right)^3\left(\frac{2}{3}\right)$ or $\frac{8}{81}$.

What is the probability of winning 2 games and losing 2 games?

Problems that can be solved using a binomial expansion are called **binomial trials.**

> **A binomial trial exists if and only if the following conditions occur.**
>
> 1. **There are only two possible outcomes.**
> 2. **The events are independent.**

Conditions of Binomial Trials

Examples

1 **What is the probability that 3 coins show heads and 2 show tails when 5 coins are tossed?**

There are only 2 possible outcomes: heads (H) or tails (T). The tosses of 5 coins are independent events. When $(H + T)^5$ is expanded, the term containing H^3T^2 is used to get the desired probability.

$$C(5, 3)H^3T^2 = \frac{5 \cdot 4}{2 \cdot 1}\left(\frac{1}{2}\right)^3\left(\frac{1}{2}\right)^2 \text{ or } \frac{5}{16}$$

Replace H by P(H) which is $\frac{1}{2}$ and T by P(T) or $\frac{1}{2}$.

The probability of 3 heads and 2 tails is $\frac{5}{16}$.

2 **Suppose Amy and Marla play 7 games. The probability that Amy wins a game is $\frac{1}{5}$, and that Marla wins is $\frac{4}{5}$. What is the probability that Amy will win at least 3 of the games?**

There are only two outcomes of each game: Amy wins (A) or Marla wins (M). The binomial expansion of $(A + M)^7$ follows.

$$(A + M)^7 = A^7 + 7A^6M + 21A^5M^2 + 35A^4M^3 + 35A^3M^4 + 21A^2M^5 + 7AM^6 + M^7$$

Amy must win 7, 6, 5, 4, or 3 games, so use these terms from the expansion.

$A^7 + 7A^6M + 21A^5M^2 + 35A^4M^3 + 35A^3M^4$

$$= \left(\frac{1}{5}\right)^7 + 7 \cdot \left(\frac{1}{5}\right)^6\left(\frac{4}{5}\right) + 21\left(\frac{1}{5}\right)^5\left(\frac{4}{5}\right)^2 + 35\left(\frac{1}{5}\right)^4\left(\frac{4}{5}\right)^3 + 35\left(\frac{1}{5}\right)^3\left(\frac{4}{5}\right)^4$$

Substitute $\frac{1}{5}$ for A and $\frac{4}{5}$ for M.

$$= \frac{1}{78125} + 7\left(\frac{1}{15625}\right)\left(\frac{4}{5}\right) + 21\left(\frac{1}{3125}\right)\left(\frac{16}{25}\right) + 35\left(\frac{1}{625}\right)\left(\frac{64}{125}\right) + 35\left(\frac{1}{125}\right)\left(\frac{256}{625}\right)$$

$$= \frac{1 + 28 + 336 + 2240 + 8960}{78,125}$$

$$= \frac{11,565}{78,125} \text{ or } \frac{2313}{15,625}$$

The probability that Amy will win at least 3 games is $\frac{2313}{15,625}$.

This is a little greater than $\frac{1}{7}$.

Exploratory Exercises

Tell whether each of the following in exercises 1–9 represents a binomial trial or not. State how to solve those that represent a binomial trial.

1. Ann tosses a coin 3 times. What is the probability of 2 heads and 1 tail?

Jess draws 4 cards from a deck of 52 playing cards. What is the probability of drawing 4 aces if the following occurs?

2. He replaces the card.

3. He does not replace the card.

There are 8 algebra books, 4 geometry books, and 6 trigonometry books on a shelf. If 2 are selected, with replacement after the first selection, what is the probability of the following?

4. both algebra

5. both geometry

6. both trigonometry

7. one algebra, one geometry

8. one algebra, one trigonometry

9. one geometry, one trigonometry

Written Exercises

A coin is tossed 4 times. What is the probability of the following?

1. no heads

2. 2 heads and 2 tails

3. 3 or more tails

A die is tossed 5 times. What is the probability of the following?

4. only one 4

5. at least three 4's

6. no more than two 4's

Cathy Black has a bent coin. The probability of heads is $\frac{2}{3}$ with this coin. She flips the coin 4 times. What is the probability of the following?

7. no heads

8. at least 3 heads

9. no more than 2 heads

Joey Diller guesses on all 10 questions on a true-false test. What is the probability of the following?

10. 7 correct

11. at least 6 correct

12. all incorrect

A batter is now batting 0.200 (meaning 200 hits in 1000 times at bat). In the next 5 at-bats, what is the probability of having the following?

13. exactly 3 hits

14. at least 4 hits

15. at least 2 hits

Three coins are tossed. What is the probability of the following?

16. 3 heads

17. 3 tails

18. at least 2 heads

19. exactly 2 tails

If a tack is dropped, the probability that it will land point up is $\frac{2}{5}$. Ten tacks are dropped. What is the probability of the following?

20. all point up

21. exactly 3 point up

22. exactly 5 point up

23. at least 6 point up

Harold is a skeet shooter. He will hit the clay pigeon 9 of 10 times. If he shoots 12 times, what is the probability of the following?

24. all misses

25. exactly 7 hits

26. all hits

27. at least 10 hits

mini-review

Write *true* or *false*.

1. $-5.4, -1.4, 2.6 \ldots$ is a geometric sequence.

2. $9, 6, 4, \frac{2}{3} \ldots$ is a geometric sequence.

3. Zero is the additive identity for complex numbers.

4. $x^2 + y^2 = (x + y)(x - y)$ for all real numbers x and y.

5. The equation of a circle with center (h, k) and radius r units is
$$(x + k)^2 + (y + h)^2 = r^2.$$

Coin Tossing

Probability is used to predict the outcome in games of chance involving tossing coins, rolling dice, selecting cards, or winning sweepstakes. A computer program can be used to do the actual counting in simulated situations where large samples are needed.

```
10 LET T2 = 0: LET T3 = 0
20 LET H2 = 0: LET H3 = 0
30 FOR I = 1 TO 100
40 LET T = 0: LET H = 0
50 FOR N = 1 TO 3
60 LET R = RND (1)
70 IF R < 0.5 THEN 110
80 PRINT "TAIL";" ";
90 LET T = T + 1
100 GOTO 130
110 PRINT "HEAD";" ";
120 LET H = H + 1
130 NEXT N
134 PRINT
140 IF H = 3 THEN 180
150 IF T = 3 THEN 200
160 IF H = 2 AND T = 1 THEN 220
170 IF H = 1 AND T = 2 THEN 240
180 LET H3 = H3 + 1
190 GOTO 250
200 LET T3 = T3 + 1
210 GOTO 250
220 LET H2 = H2 + 1
230 GOTO 250
240 LET T2 = T2 + 1
250 NEXT I
254 PRINT
260 PRINT "HHH: ";H3
270 PRINT "TTT: ";T3
280 PRINT "HHT: ";H2
290 PRINT "HTT: ";T2
300 END
```

The program at the left simulates tossing three coins, prints the outcomes, and keeps totals of the possible outcomes of the 100 samples. Each time the program is run, the totals may be different due to the random selection of values in line 60.

The random numbers selected by the computer lie between 0 and 1. The program defines heads as numbers less than 0.5. Tails are defined as numbers greater than or equal to 0.5.

The output shows each toss of the coin and lists the totals for the four possible combinations; 3 heads; 3 tails; 2 heads and 1 tail; or 1 head and 2 tails.

Enter and run the program several times. Notice the change in the totals.

In the exercises below it will take the computer several minutes to complete the large samples. Be prepared to wait for the totals.

A possible outcome is given below.

```
HHH:   11
TTT:   19
HHT:   38
HTT:   32
```

Exercises

1. Run the above program once. Write the actual percentage of HHH, TTT, HHT, and HTT.

2. Calculate the expected probabilities of HHH, TTT, HHT, and HTT by the methods in this chapter.

3. Change the program to increase the sample size to 1000. Delete lines 80 and 110. Then run the program and find the percentage of each outcome.

Vocabulary

Chapter Summary

1. Two events are independent if the result of the first event has no effect on the second. (449)

2. **Basic Counting Principle:** Suppose an event can be chosen in p different ways. Another independent event can be chosen in q different ways. Then the two events can be chosen successively in $p \cdot q$ ways. (450)

3. **Definition of $P(n, r)$:** The number of permutations of n objects, taken r at a time, is defined as follows.

$$P(n, r) = \frac{n!}{(n - r)!} \quad (452)$$

4. **Permutations with Repetition:** The number of permutations of n objects of which p are alike and q are alike is found by evaluating the following expression.

$$\frac{n!}{p!q!} \quad (453)$$

5. **Circular Permutations:** If n objects are arranged in a circle, then there are $\frac{n!}{n}$ or $(n - 1)!$ arrangements. (456)

6. **Definition of $C(n, r)$:** The number of combinations of n objects, taken r at a time, is written $C(n, r)$.

$$C(n, r) = \frac{n!}{(n - r)!r!} \quad (459)$$

7. **Probability of Success and of Failure:** If an event can succeed in s ways and fail in f ways, then the probabilities of success $P(s)$ and of failure $P(f)$ are as follows.

$$P(s) = \frac{s}{s + f} \qquad P(f) = \frac{f}{s + f} \quad (462)$$

8. **Definition of Odds:** The odds of the successful outcome of an event is expressed as the ratio of the number of ways it can succeed to the number of ways it can fail.

$$\text{Odds} = \text{the ratio of } s \text{ to } f \text{ or } \frac{s}{f} \quad (463)$$

9. **Probability of Two Independent Events:** If two events, A and B, are independent, then the probability of both events occurring is found as follows.

$$P(A \text{ and } B) = P(A) \cdot P(B). \quad (466)$$

10. **Probability of Two Dependent Events:** Suppose two events, A and B, are dependent. Then the probability of both occurring is found as follows.

$$P(A \text{ and } B) = P(A) \cdot P(B \text{ following } A) \quad (466)$$

11. **Probability of Mutually Exclusive Events:** The probability of one of two mutually exclusive events occurring is the sum of their probabilities.

$$P(A \text{ or } B) = P(A) + P(B) \quad (469)$$

12. **Probability of Inclusive Events:** The probability of one of two inclusive events, A and B, is the sum of the individual probabilities decreased by the probability of both occurring.

$$P(A \text{ or } B) = P(A) + P(B) - P(A \text{ and } B) \quad (470)$$

13. **Conditions of Binomial Trials:** A binomial trial problem exists if the following conditions hold.
    1. There are only two possible outcomes.
    2. The events are independent. (473)

Chapter Review

14–1 **Using only the digits 0, 1, 2, 3, and 4, how many 3-digit patterns can be formed under the following conditions?**

   1. Repetitions are allowed.

   2. No repetitions are allowed.

14–2 **On a shelf are 8 mystery and 7 romance novels. How many ways can they be arranged as follows?**

   3. all mysteries together

   4. all mysteries together, romances together.

   5. Evaluate $\dfrac{P(8, 5)}{P(5, 3)}$

   6. Evaluate $\dfrac{P(7, 3)}{P(5, 2)}$

14–3 **Solve each problem.**

   7. How many ways can 8 people be seated at a round table?

   8. How many ways can 10 charms be placed on a bracelet that has a clasp?

14–4 **9.** How many baseball teams can be formed from 15 players if only 3 pitch while the others play the remaining 8 positions?

   10. From a deck of 52 cards, how many different 4-card hands exist?

14–5 **11.** A card is selected from a deck of 52 cards. What is the probability that it is a queen?

12. In a bag are 6 red and 2 white marbles. If two marbles are selected, what is the probability that one is red and the other is white?

14–6 **13.** In his pocket, Jose has 5 dimes, 7 nickels, and 4 pennies. He selects 4 coins. What is the probability that he has 2 dimes and 2 pennies?

14. Ben has 6 navy blue socks and 4 black socks in a drawer. One dark morning he pulls out 2 socks. What is the probability that he has 2 black socks?

14–7 **15.** From a deck of 52 cards, one card is selected. What is the probability that it is an ace or a face card?

16. If a letter is selected at random from the alphabet, what is the probability that it is a letter from the words CAT or SKATE?

14–8 **17.** Four coins are tossed. What is the probability that they show 3 heads and 1 tail?

18. A die is tossed 5 times. What is the probability of at least two 3's?

Chapter Test

Solve each of the following.

1. From 8 shirts, 6 pair of slacks, and 4 jackets, how many different outfits can be made?

2. In a row are 8 chairs. How many ways can 5 people be seated?

3. How many ways can 11 books be arranged on a shelf?

4. How many ways can the letters from the word *television* be arranged?

5. How many ways can 6 keys be placed on a key ring?

6. How many different basketball teams could be formed from a group of 12 girls?

7. Nine points are placed on a circle. How many triangles can be formed using these points, three at a time, as vertices?

8. From a group of 4 men and 5 women, a committee of 3 is to be formed. What is the probability that it will have 2 men and 1 woman?

9. A red die and a green die are tossed. What is the probability that the red will show even and the green will show a number greater than four?

10. From a deck of cards, what is the probability of selecting a 4 followed by a 7 if no replacement occurs?

11. While shooting arrows, William Tell can hit an apple 9 out of 10 times. What is the probability that he will hit it exactly 4 out of the next 7 times?

12. Five bent coins are tossed. The probability of heads is $\frac{2}{3}$ for each of them. What is the probability that no more than 2 will show heads?

Find the value of each of the following.

13. $P(8, 3)$ **14.** $P(6, 4)$ **15.** $C(8, 3)$ **16.** $C(6, 4)$

CHAPTER 15

Statistics

Insurance companies use statistics extensively in calculating rates. For example, an automobile insurance company compiles data such as a number of accidents, amount of damages, road conditions, age of drivers, and so on.

15-1   Organizing Data

Statistics provide techniques for collecting, organizing, analyzing, and interpreting numerical information called **data.** Organized data is easier to read and interpret. One way to organize data is by using tables. The following table shows the normal monthly precipitation for selected cities in the United States.

Normal Monthly Precipitation in Inches

City	Jan.	Feb.	Mar.	Apr.	May	Jun.	July	Aug.	Sep.	Oct.	Nov.	Dec.	Total
Albuquerque, NM	0.30	0.39	0.47	0.48	0.53	0.50	1.39	1.34	0.77	0.79	0.29	0.52	7.77
Boston, MA	3.69	3.54	4.01	3.49	3.47	3.19	2.74	3.46	3.16	3.02	4.51	4.24	42.52
Chicago, IL	1.85	1.59	2.73	3.75	3.41	3.95	4.09	3.14	3.00	2.62	2.20	2.11	34.44
Houston, TX	3.57	3.54	2.68	3.54	5.10	4.52	4.12	4.35	4.65	4.05	4.03	4.04	48.19
Mobile, AL	4.71	4.76	7.07	5.59	4.52	6.09	8.86	6.93	6.59	2.55	3.39	5.92	66.98
San Francisco, CA	4.37	3.04	2.54	1.59	0.41	0.13	0.01	0.03	0.16	0.98	2.29	3.98	19.53

The table organizes the data so that you can quickly answer questions like the following.

What city has the most precipitation in January?

What is the driest month in Houston?

The totals provided help you answer questions like the following.

Which city has the most precipitation in one year?

How many of the cities have more than 30 inches of precipitation in one year?

Some tables group data together. For example, you could make a table which provides the normal precipitation in selected cities by seasons.

Example

1   **Make a table which provides the normal precipitation in selected cities, by seasons. Use the data from the table shown above.**

City	Winter Jan.–Mar.	Spring Apr.–Jun.	Summer Jul.–Sep.	Fall Oct.–Dec.
Albuquerque	1.16	1.51	3.50	1.60
Boston	11.24	10.15	9.36	11.77
Chicago	6.17	11.11	10.23	6.93
Houston	9.79	13.16	13.12	12.12
Mobile	16.54	16.20	22.38	11.86
San Francisco	9.95	2.13	0.20	7.25

Notice that once data has been grouped, individual measurements lose their identities.

Example

2 **Use the table shown below to answer the following questions.**

1. How many master's degrees were earned in 1960?

2. How many degrees were earned in 1970?

3. Did the total number of degrees earned increase from 1940 to 1980?

Earned Degrees (in thousands)

Year	Bachelor's	Master's	Doctorate	Total
1940	187	27	3.4	217.4
1950	434	58	1.6	498.6
1960	395	75	9.8	479.8
1970	833	209	29.9	1071.9
1980	1017	315	33.0	1365.0

1. There were 75 thousand or 75,000 master's degrees earned in 1960.

2. There were a total of 1071.9 thousand or 1,071,900 degrees earned in 1970.

3. There were a total of 1365.0 thousand degrees earned in 1980 and 217.4 thousand degrees earned in 1940. The total number of degrees earned did increase from 1940 to 1980.

Exploratory Exercises

Use the table below to solve each of the following problems.

**U.S. Imports and Exports
in Millions of Dollars, 1982**
Source: Statistical Abstracts
of the United States, 1984

Region	Imports	Exports
Africa	17,770	10,271
Asia	85,170	64,822
Oceania	3,131	5,700
Europe	53,413	63,664
North America	70,094	52,057
South America	14,373	15,257

1. In 1982, how much were U.S. exports to North America?

2. In 1982, how much were U.S. imports from South America?

3. In 1982, how much were U.S. imports from Oceania?

4. In 1982, how much were U.S. exports to Africa?

5. In 1982, how much were U.S. exports to Europe?

6. In 1982, how much were U.S. imports from Asia?

7. Find each entry for a new column on the table with the heading, **Difference.**

8. Find each entry for a new column on the table with the heading, **Imports as a Percent of Exports.**

Written Exercises

Two dice were tossed 64 times. The total number of dots for each toss was recorded.

5	8	11	10	8	8	7	10	3	9	10	8	2	9	12	3
11	5	2	3	5	7	11	7	11	10	11	10	6	7	8	7
9	5	6	4	4	5	10	8	6	7	4	8	5	10	5	5
8	5	11	9	12	4	7	2	7	4	3	9	2	11	7	6

1. Organize the data into a table with the headings **Number of Dots,** and **Frequency of Occurrences.**
2. Which number or numbers of dots occurred most frequently?
3. Which number or numbers of dots occurred least frequently?

Cars in use, by Age, 1982
Source: Statistical Abstracts
of the United States, 1984

Age of Autos	Number (millions)	Percent
Under 3 years	21.5	20.1
3–5 years	29.9	28.0
6–8 years	22.2	20.7
9–11 years	17.9	16.7
12 years and over	15.4	14.4
Average Age	7.2 Years	

4. What percent of automobiles in use were between 9 and 11 years old in 1982?
5. How many automobiles were over 8 years old in 1982?
6. How many automobiles were between 3 and 11 years old in 1982?
7. What percent of automobiles were 12 years old or older in 1982?

Passenger Car Production by Makes (in thousands)
Source: *Automotive News*, Jan. 12, 1981

Company	1965	1970	1975	1980
American Motors Corporation	346.4	276.1	323.7	167.8
Chrysler Corporation	1,467.6	1,273.5	902.9	639.0
Ford Motor Company	2,565.8	2,017.2	1,808.0	1,306.9
General Motors Corporation	4,949.4	2,979.2	3,679.1	4,063.6
Other	6.1	4.1	3.2	200.3

8. What company produced the most cars in 1980?
9. What company produced the most cars in 1970?
10. In what year did Ford Motor Company produce the most cars?
11. In what year did General Motors Corporation produce the least cars?
12. How many cars were produced in 1965?
13. How many cars were produced in 1980?

Each number below represents the total precipitation in inches for a certain city in 1980.

31	26	35	20	38	30	41	21	23	25	24	27	30	19	27
38	30	31	33	20	22	30	33	27	25	33	25	27	31	27
17	38	46	33	22	27	22	19	25	33	36	30	45	31	45
35	23	25	40	36	20	30	22	26	41	35	25	30	30	27
33	25	28	27	24	45	26	21	41	26	22	31	37	38	26
20	22	26	25	20	27	25	23	27	31	35	27	25	40	24
41	30	17	22	26	19	33	36	30	28					

14. Organize the data into a table with the headings **Precipitation** and **Number of Cities**. Under **Precipitation** include each number from 17 through 46.

15. Which number of inches occurred most frequently?

16. How many cities had 38 inches of precipitation?

17. What is the greatest number of inches of precipitation for any of the cities?

18. What is the least number of inches of precipitation for any of the cities?

19. Organize the data into a table with the headings **Precipitation** and **Number of Cities**. Under **Precipitation** group the data by threes. For example, the first entry under **Precipitation** is 17–19.

20. How many cities had from 32–34 inches of precipitation?

21. How many cities had from 23–25 inches of precipitation?

Excursions in Algebra ——————————————— History

Edmund Halley

Jacob Bernoulli

Statistical methods have been developed in the last 350 years. This has happened as researchers in other fields needed better methods for analyzing data.

In 1661, **John Graunt** collected and studied records of births and deaths in London. Graunt, a merchant, was one of the first to study population in this way. A pamphlet he wrote told about the life expectancy of differerent people at different ages.

Edmund Halley, an astronomer, made a similar study in 1693 in Breslau, Germany. He had promised to provide some "filler" for a scientific publication. This study led to improvements in public record keeping. He also showed how to make calculations for life insurance purposes. He used his tables of life expectancy in this study.

A book by **Jacob Bernoulli,** who is considered the founder of probability theory, was published in 1713. This book showed how probability theory can be applied to a great number of collected statistical data.

15-2 Graphs

Graphs often are used to present data and show relationships. There are several ways of presenting the data in the following table.

Average Motor Fuel Consumption in U.S.
gallons per automobile

Year	1950	1955	1960	1965	1970	1975	1980
Consumption	603	644	661	656	722	685	600

This graph is called a **bar graph.** It shows how specific quantities compare.

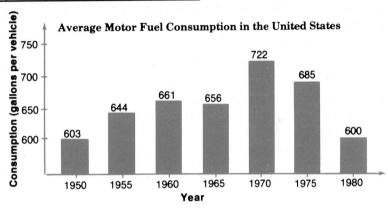

This graph is called a **pictograph.** Like a bar graph, it shows how specific quantities compare.

Which is easier to draw, a bar graph or a pictograph?

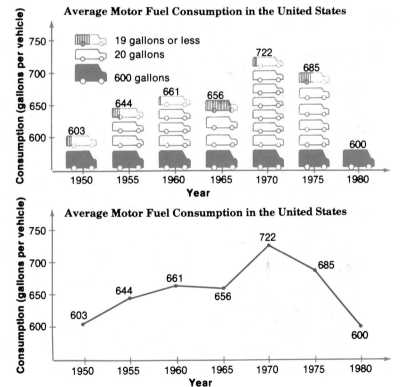

This graph is called a **line graph.** It is helpful for showing trends or changes.

1   **Draw a bar graph and a line graph to present the following data.**

Percent of 18 Year Olds with High School Diplomas

Year	1950	1955	1960	1965	1970	1975	1980
Percent	60.0	62.5	70.0	73.9	75.6	74.3	74.5

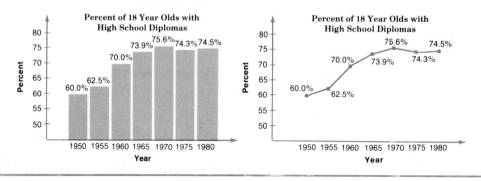

Circle graphs show how parts are related to the whole. For example, the following graph shows how the cost of a $4 paperback book is broken down.

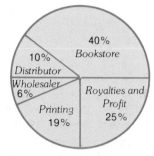

The circle is separated into proportional parts. For example, 25% of the book's cost goes to royalties and profit. Thus, 25% of the circle, 90°, is used to show this part of the book's cost.

2   **Draw a circle graph to show how the cost of a $5.98 record is broken down. The manufacturer's cost is $1.83. The manufacturer's income is $0.68. The distributor's income is $0.41. The retailer's income is $3.06.**

First, find the percent of a circle represented by each cost. Then, figure the number of degrees represented by each cost and draw the graph.

Cost	Percent of Circle	Approximate Degrees
Manufacturer's cost	$\frac{1.83}{5.98}$ or 31%	360 × 31% or 111.6
Manufacturer's income	$\frac{0.68}{5.98}$ or 11%	360 × 11% or 39.6
Distributor's income	$\frac{0.41}{5.98}$ or 7%	360 × 7% or 25.2
Retailer's income	$\frac{3.06}{5.98}$ or 51%	360 × 51% or 183.6

Exploratory Exercises

Use the bar graph below to solve each of the following.

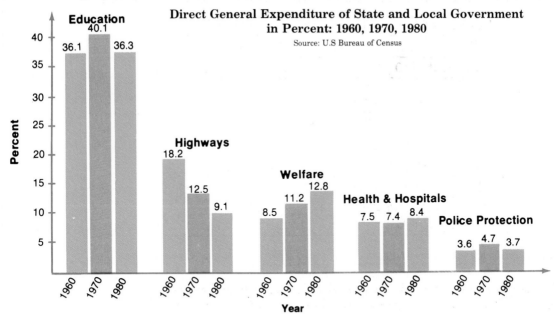

1. In 1960, what percent of expenditures was for highways?
2. In 1960, what percent of expenditures was for police protection?
3. In 1970, what percent of expenditures was for health and hospitals?
4. In 1980, what percent of expenditures was for education?
5. In which year, 1960, 1970, or 1980, was the percent of expenditures for education greatest?
6. In which year, 1960, 1970, or 1980, was the percent of expenditures for welfare least?
7. In 1970 was a greater percent spent on health and hospitals or on police protection?
8. In 1960 was a greater percent spent on highways or on welfare?

Written Exercises

Draw bar graphs for the data in each of the following tables.

1. **Record Album Shipments (in millions)**

Year	1976	1978	1980	1982
Units	273	341	323	242

2. **Home Runs Hit by NL Home Run Champions**

Year	1960	1965	1970	1975	1980
Home Runs	41	52	45	38	48

3. **Indianapolis 500-Winner's Speed**

Year	1960	1965	1970	1975	1980
Speed/mph	138.7	150.6	155.7	149.2	142.8

4. **Postal Rates for First Class mail**

Years	1966	1969	1972	1975	1978	1981	1984	1987 (est.)
Cost/ounce	5¢	6¢	8¢	13¢	15¢	20¢	20¢	25¢

5. Consumer Spending on Food (in billions)

Year	1930	1940	1950	1960	1970	1980
Dollars	18.0	16.6	46.0	73.7	116.9	302.9

6. World Population by Regions (in millions), 1983

Continent	Africa	N. America	Latin America	Asia	Europe	Oceania
Population	516	259	390	2,771	761	24

7. School Days Missed Due to Illness or Injury, Ages 6–16

Year	1970	1972	1974	1976	1978
Days in Millions	222	236	242	193	201

8. World and U.S. Populations (in millions)

Year	1900	1925	1950	1975	2000 (estimated)
World	1,600	1,900	2,510	4,100	6,353
U.S.	76	116	152	214	260

9. U.S. Energy Consumption

Year	Coal	Refined Petroleum	Natural Gas	Other
1965	22%	44%	30%	4%
1970	19%	44%	33%	4%
1975	18%	46%	28%	8%
1980	20%	45%	27%	8%

10–18. Draw line graphs for the data in problems 1–9.

The following table gives the population distribution by age in the U.S. for 1880 and 1980.

Year	Under 5	5–19	20–44	45–64	65 and over
1880	13.8%	34.3%	35.9%	12.6%	3.4%
1980	7.2%	24.8%	37.1%	19.6%	11.3%

19. Draw a circle graph to show the population distribution by age in 1880.

20. Draw a circle graph to show the population distribution by age in 1980.

The data in the following table gives a breakdown of the civilian labor force in the United States for various years, in millions of persons.

Employment Status	1970	1975	1980
Employed in nonagricultural industries	75.2	82.4	95.9
Employed in agriculture	3.5	3.4	3.4
Unemployed	4.1	7.9	7.6
Total civilian labor force	82.8	93.7	106.9

21–23. For each year, draw a circle graph to show the breakdown of the civilian labor force.

Reading Algebra

Sometimes graphs contain information on two or more related topics and are given to show the comparisons between them. These **comparative graphs** can be quite helpful for showing trends in certain areas. Analysis of these comparative data requires that you read the graphs carefully.

Exercises

Use the graphs below to answer exercises 1–3.

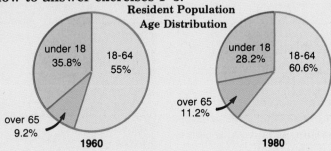

Resident Population
Age Distribution

1960 — under 18 35.8%, 18-64 55%, over 65 9.2%

1980 — under 18 28.2%, 18-64 60.6%, over 65 11.2%

1. Did the percentage of people under 18 increase or decrease from 1960 to 1980?
2. Which age group had the least number of people in both years?
3. If the population in 1960 was 200 million and in 1980 it was 230 million, how many more people were in the 18–64 age group in 1980 than in 1960?

Use the graphs below to answer exercises 4–11.

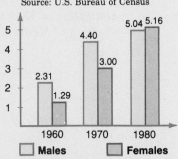

College Enrollment (in millions)
Source: U.S. Bureau of Census

1960: Males 2.31, Females 1.29
1970: Males 4.40, Females 3.00
1980: Males 5.04, Females 5.16

□ Males   ■ Females

U.S. Pistachio Production
(millions of pounds)
Source: *USA Today*

U.S. Production
Imports

1978 1979 1980 1981 1982 1983 1984

4. How many more men were enrolled in college than women in 1960?

5. Find the percent of increase of women's enrollments from 1970 to 1980.

6. Find the percent of increase of men's enrollments from 1970 to 1980.

7. How many more women were enrolled in college than men in 1980?

8. How many pounds of pistachios were produced by the U.S. in 1981? How many were imported?

9. Was U.S. production of pistachios increasing or decreasing in 1979?

10. Was the number of pounds of imported pistachios ever greater than those produced by the U.S.? When?

11. In general, has U.S. production increased or decreased over the seven years shown?

15-3 Central Tendency

During a cold spell lasting 43 days, the following high temperatures (in degrees Fahrenheit) were recorded in Chicago. What temperature is most representative of the high temperatures for that period?

26	17	12	5	4	25	17	23
6	25	19	27	22	26	20	31
12	27	16	27	16	30	7	31
5	29	18	16	22	29	8	31
13	24	5	−7	20	29	18	12
13	16	24					

The most representative temperature, the average temperature, is neither the greatest nor the least temperature. It is a value somewhere in the middle of the group.

The most commonly used averages are the **median, mode,** and **mean.** They are defined in the following way.

> **The median of a set of data is the middle value. If there are two middle values, it is the value halfway between.**
>
> **The mode of a set of data is the most frequent value. Some sets of data have multiple modes.**
>
> **The mean of a set of data is the sum of all the values divided by the number of values.**

Definition of Median, Mode, and Mean

To find the median of the Chicago temperatures, arrange the values in descending order, as shown in the margin. Then, find the middle value. In this case, the median temperature is 19.

To find the mode, determine how many times each particular high temperature occurred. Then find the most frequently occurring value. In this case, the mode is 16.

To find the mean, add all the values. Then divide by 43, the number of values. In this case, the mean temperature to the nearest tenth is 18.5.

This example shows that median, mode, and mean are not always the same value.

temperatures

31	24	16
31	24	16
31	23	13
30	22	13
29	22	12
29	20	12
29	20	12
27	19	8
27	18	7
27	18	6
26	17	5
26	17	5
25	16	5
25	16	4
		−7

The value of every item in a set of data affects the value of the mean. Thus, when extreme values are included, the mean may become less representative of the set. The values of the median and the mode are *not* affected by extreme values.

Examples

1 **Find the mean of {1, 2, 4, 93} and {24, 25, 25, 26}.**

{1, 2, 4, 93}

$$\text{mean} = \frac{1 + 2 + 4 + 93}{4}$$

$$= \frac{100}{4} \text{ or } 25$$

The mean is not close to any one of the four values in this set. In this case, it *is not* a particularly representative value.

The mean for both sets is 25.

{24, 25, 25, 26}

$$\text{mean} = \frac{24 + 25 + 25 + 26}{4}$$

$$= \frac{100}{4} \text{ or } 25$$

There are *no* extreme values in this set. In this case, the mean is a representative value.

2 **Find the median, mode, and mean of the hourly wages of 80 workers. Five workers make $4.60 per hour, fifteen make $4.40 per hour, thirty make $5.70 per hour, ten make $6.60 per hour, and twenty make $4.50 per hour.**

Arrange the wages in descending order. Then find the middle value.

$6.60	10 workers
5.70	30 workers
4.60	5 workers
4.50	20 workers
4.40	15 workers

There are two middle values, the 40th value $5.70, and the 41st value $4.60. The median is the value halfway between, $\frac{5.70 + 4.60}{2}$ or $5.15.

More workers make $5.70 per hour than any other wage. So it is the most frequently occurring value. The mode is $5.70.

Add all 80 values. There are 10 values of $6.60, 30 values of $5.70, 5 values of $4.60, and so on. You can use multiplication to shorten the additions.

$$\text{mean} = \frac{10(6.60) + 30(5.70) + 5(4.60) + 20(4.50) + 15(4.40)}{80}$$

$$= \frac{66.00 + 171.00 + 23.00 + 90.00 + 66.00}{80}$$

$$= \frac{416}{80} \text{ or } 5.20$$

The median is $5.15, the mode is $5.70, and the mean is $5.20.

Exploratory Exercises

Find the median for each set of data.

1. {1, 2, 3, 4, 5}

2. {2, 4, 6, 8, 10}

3. {1, 1, 2, 4, 1}

4. {7, 7, 7, 7, 7, 7, 7}

5. {8, 43, 2, 56, 44}

6. {7.1, 5.0, 2.7, 9.1, 8.1, 6.3, 8.5}

7. {2.1, 4.8, 2.1, 5.7, 2.1, 4.8, 2.1}

8. {1, 7, 7, 0, 2, 0, 4, 1, 3, 7, 7, 5, 4, 1, 8}

9. {11, 10, 13, 12, 12, 13, 15}

10. {50, 75, 65, 70, 55, 65, 50, 80}

11–20. Find the mode for each set of data in Exercises 1–10.

21–30. Find the mean for each set of data in Exercises 1–10.

Written Exercises

1. A die was tossed 25 times with the following results. Find the median, mode, and mean for the tosses.

5	3	1	6	5	2	1	5	4	1	6	6	4
6	5	6	3	6	4	4	4	1	1	2	2	

2. Two dice were tossed 64 times. Find the median, mode and mean for the following results.

8	11	10	8	8	7	10	3	9	10	8	2	9
5	2	3	5	7	11	7	11	10	11	10	6	7
5	6	4	4	5	10	8	6	7	4	8	5	10
5	11	9	12	4	7	2	7	4	3	9	2	11
5	11	9	8	12	3	7	8	5	5	7	6	

3. The heights in feet of the 20 highest mountains in the world are given below. Find the median, mode, and mean for the heights.

29,002	14,255	18,700	28,146	22,835
13,653	14,431	28,250	13,202	14,408
25,263	19,344	19,565	19,887	14,701
15,781	18,481	14,495	14,110	20,270

4. Find the median, mode, and mean of the hourly wages of 200 workers. One hundred workers make $4.00 per hour, ten make $5.50 per hour, ten make $6.75 per hour, twenty make $3.80 per hour, and sixty make $5.25 per hour.

5. Find the median, mode, and mean of the hourly wages of 500 workers. Two hundred workers make $3.75 per hour, two hundred make $4.25 per hour, sixty make $6.75 per hour, and forty make $10.50 per hour.

mini-review

1. Is the graph of the following equation a parabola, circle, ellipse, or hyperbola? $y^2 + 2y = -x^2 + 4x$

2. Graph $y = \dfrac{1}{x - 1}$.

3. Find the third, fourth, and fifth terms of this sequence: $a_n = 7n^{-1} + 1$.

4. How many six-letter patterns can be formed from the letters in *hoopla*?

5. State the number of positive real, negative real and imaginary zeros for $f(x) = -x^5 + 9x^3 - 4x^2 - x + 1$.

15-4   Dispersion

If 10,000 family incomes in a city were all the same, you would know all there is to know about the incomes. However, values in a set of data usually vary. The variation is called **dispersion.**

There are several kinds of measures of dispersion. The simplest measure is called the **range.**

Example

1   **The heights of a group of young pine trees in a reforestation plot are 58 cm, 56 cm, 51 cm, 54 cm, 49 cm, 61 cm, 54 cm, and 49 cm. Find the range.**

The greatest value is 61 centimeters.
The least value is 49 centimeters.

range = 61 − 49   *The range is the difference between the greatest and least values.*
    = 12

Because the range is the difference between the greatest and least values in a set of data, it is affected by unusually extreme values. In such cases, it is not a good measure of dispersion.

The most commonly used measure of dispersion is called the **standard deviation.** The standard deviation for a set of data is an average measure of how much each value differs from the mean.

From a set of data, the standard deviation is calculated by following these steps.

1. Find the mean.
2. Find the difference between each measurement and the mean.
3. Square each difference.
4. Find the mean of the squares.
5. Take the positive square root of this mean.

From a set of data with n values, if x_i represents a value such that $1 \leq i \leq n$, and $\bar{x}$ represents the mean, then the standard deviation can be found as follows.

Definition of Standard Deviation

$$\text{standard deviation} = \sqrt{\frac{\sum\limits_{i=1}^{n} (x_i - \bar{x})^2}{n}}$$

Example

2 The heights of a group of young pine trees in a reforestation plot are 58 cm, 56 cm, 51 cm, 54 cm, 49 cm, 61 cm, 54 cm, and 49 cm. Find the standard deviation.

$$\text{mean height} = \frac{58 + 56 + 51 + 54 + 49 + 61 + 54 + 49}{8} \text{ or } 54 \qquad \bar{x} = 54$$

$$\text{standard deviation} = \sqrt{\frac{\sum\limits_{i=1}^{n} (x_i - \bar{x})^2}{n}} \qquad \begin{array}{l} n \text{ is } 8 \\ x_1 - \bar{x} \text{ is } 58 - 54 \text{ or } 4 \\ x_2 - \bar{x} \text{ is } 56 - 54 \text{ or } 2 \text{ and so on.} \end{array}$$

$$= \sqrt{\frac{(4)^2 + (2)^2 + (-3)^2 + (0)^2 + (-5)^2 + (7)^2 + (0)^2 + (-5)^2}{8}}$$

$$= \sqrt{\frac{16 + 4 + 9 + 0 + 25 + 49 + 0 + 25}{8}}$$

$$= \sqrt{\frac{128}{8}}$$

$$= \sqrt{16} \text{ or } 4$$

The standard deviation is 4.

When studying standard deviation of a set of data, it is important to keep the mean in mind. For example, suppose a firm manufactures televisions and the standard deviation of the average monthly prices for televisions sold in the last two years is $50.

If the mean price over the last two years was $200, the standard deviation indicates a great deal of variation. If the mean price over the last two years was $600, the standard deviation indicates very little variation.

Exploratory Exercises

Find the range for each set of data.

1. {1, 4, 11, 7, 2}

2. {2, 2, 8, 14, 6, 4}

3. {39, 47, 51, 38, 45, 29, 37, 40, 36, 48}

4. {70, 86, 81, 86, 81, 84, 89, 77, 80, 87, 83, 87, 90, 92, 87}

5. {50, 92, 79, 61, 76, 83, 65, 98, 82, 64, 76, 63, 57, 96, 75, 53, 66, 88, 59, 85, 95, 65, 81, 71}

6. {14.1, 15.8, 15.2, 14.0, 14.8, 14.1, 12.9, 14.4, 16.8, 16.2, 13.2, 15.9, 13.9, 15.4, 13.6, 15.1, 14.7, 13.2}

7. {250, 275, 325, 300, 200, 225, 175}

8. {132, 150, 138, 160, 133, 143, 148, 148, 151, 148, 141}

9. {81, 80, 87, 97, 82, 86, 85, 82, 72, 80, 85, 84, 84, 63, 90, 82, 85, 79, 95, 81}

10. {1050, 1175, 1075, 1025, 1100, 1125, 975, 1125, 1075, 1055}

Written Exercises

1–10. Find the standard deviation for each set of data in Exploratory Exercises 1–10.

The weights in pounds of 11 of the players on each of two college football teams is as follows.

How College: 160, 180, 190, 200, 210, 170, 250, 220, 180, 200, 240

Now College: 160, 190, 210, 230, 240, 220, 150, 190, 210, 160, 240

11. Find the range in weights for the How College team.

12. Find the range in weights for the Now College team.

13. Find the mean weight for the How College team.

14. Find the mean weight for the Now College team.

15. Find the standard deviation in weights for the How College team.

16. Find the standard deviation in weights for the Now College team.

The mileage in miles per gallon obtained by the Electric Company and Gas Company cars is as follows.

Electric Company: 25, 13, 24, 18, 29, 12, 30, 16, 25, 21, 28, 25, 33, 11, 22, 12, 30, 16, 28, 23

Gas Company: 32, 16, 22, 24, 23, 13, 23, 31, 15, 21, 24, 27, 30, 21, 12, 24

17. Find the range in mileage for the Electric Company cars.

18. Find the range in mileage for the Gas Company cars.

19. Find the mean mileage in miles per gallon for the Electric Company cars.

20. Find the mean mileage in miles per gallon for the Gas Company cars.

21. Find the standard deviation in mileage for the Electric Company cars.

22. Find the standard deviation in mileage for the Gas Company cars.

The following tables give two frequency distributions for items. Bar graphs for these distributions are shown.

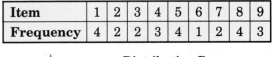

Item	1	2	3	4	5	6	7	8	9
Frequency	1	0	1	7	9	4	1	1	1

Item	1	2	3	4	5	6	7	8	9
Frequency	4	2	2	3	4	1	2	4	3

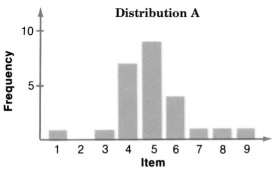

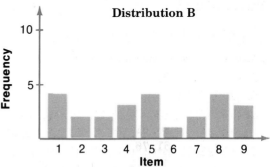

23. Find the range for distribution A.

24. Find the range for distribution B.

25. Find the mean for distribution A.

26. Find the mean for distribution B.

27. Find the standard deviation for distribution A.

28. Find the standard deviation for distribution B.

29. Look at the two graphs. Which distribution has its values clustered more around its mean?

30. Make a frequency distribution for the following set of data: {10, 12, 20, 20, 19, 13, 14, 10, 11, 18, 14, 15, 0, 5, 17, 2, 3, 27, 1, 30, 13, 9, 12, 11, 4, 10, 8, 21, 23, 7}. Find the mean, median, mode, range, and standard deviation.

mini-review

1. Evaluate $\dfrac{P(6, 2) \cdot P(9, 7)}{3! \, P(5, 2)}$.

2. Two cards are drawn from a standard deck of cards. What is the probability that they are both spades or both queens?

3. Use the Binomial Theorem to expand $(2a + b)^7$.

4. Graph $f(x) = x^4 - 1$.

5. If $f(x) = x^2 - 2x$ and $g(x) = x^3$, find $[f \circ g](x)$ and $[g \circ f](x)$.

Using Calculators ————————— Standard Deviation

You can find the standard deviation of a set of data on your calculator using the x^2 and $\sqrt{x}$ keys. Find the standard deviation of the set of data below.

$$\{3, 5, 19, 2, 1, 11, 8\}$$

First, find the mean and store it in memory.

ENTER: $(\;\;3\;\;+\;\;5\;\;+\;\;19\;\;+\;\;2\;\;+\;\;1\;\;+\;\;11\;\;+\;\;8\;\;)\;\;\div\;\;7\;\;=\;\;$ STO

DISPLAY: 3   5 8 19 27 2 29 1 30 11 41 8 49   7 7

Then find the sum of the *squared deviations*. Use this sequence for each element of the set.

ENTER: $(\;\;3\;\;-\;$ RCL $\;)\;\;x^2\;\;+\;\;\dots$

DISPLAY: 3   7 -4 16

Remember, $s = \sqrt{\dfrac{\Sigma(x - \bar{x})^2}{n}}$

After finding the sum of the squared deviations, divide by the number of elements, and take the square root of the quotient.

ENTER: $=\;\;\div\;\;7\;\;=\;\;\sqrt{x}$

DISPLAY: 231   7 33 5.745   The standard deviation is 5.745.

If your calculator has a statistical mode, consult your manual to help you use it. This will make computation easier.

Exercises

Find the standard deviation for each set of data to two decimal places.

1. {7, -2, 4, 3, 5, -14}   **2.** {1.5, 7.3, 5.9, 2.1, 4.7, 9.2, -1.1}

3. {2, 0, 4, 9}   **4.** {-8, 4.1, 3.9, -2.2, 7, 10}

15-5   The Normal Distribution

One way of analyzing data is to consider the frequency with which each value occurs. The table on the right gives the frequencies of certain scores on a mechanical aptitude test taken by 175 people.

The following bar graph shows the frequencies of the scores in the table.

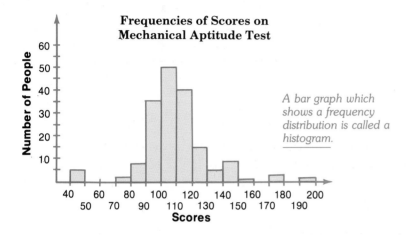

A bar graph which shows a frequency distribution is called a histogram.

Score	Number of People
40–49	5
50–59	0
60–69	0
70–79	2
80–89	8
90–99	35
100–109	50
110–119	40
120–129	15
130–139	5
140–149	9
150–159	1
160–169	0
170–179	3
180–189	0
190–199	2

The bar graph shows the **frequency distribution** of the scores. In other words, it shows how the scores are spread out.

Frequency distributions are often shown by curves rather than histograms, especially when the distribution contains a great number of values. These curves may be of many different shapes. Many distributions have graphs like the following. Distributions with such a graph are called **normal distributions.**

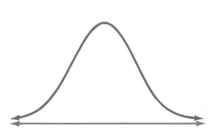

The curve is bell-shaped and symmetric. The shape of the curve indicates that frequencies in a normal distribution are concentrated in the center portion of the distribution. What does this tell you about the mean?

Normal distributions occur very frequently. For example, the diameter of a hole made by a drill press, the number of errors made by a typist, the tosses in a dart game if the player aims at the bull's-eye, the scores on tests, the grain yield on a farm, and the length of a newborn child can all be approximated by a normal distribution provided the number of data is sufficiently great.

Suppose a set of data consists of weights for 600 young people. Also, suppose the mean weight is 100 pounds and the standard deviation is 20 pounds. If the frequency distribution of these weights is a normal distribution, then the graph approximates the curve on the right.

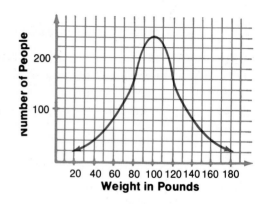

Normal distributions have these properties.

1. The graph is maximized at the mean.
2. About 68% of the items are within one standard deviation from the mean.

Of the 68%, by symmetry, 34% are greater than the mean, and 34% are less.

3. About 95% of the items are within two standard deviations from the mean.

Of the 95%, by symmetry, 47.5% are greater than the mean, and 47.5% are less.

4. About 99% of the items are within three standard deviations from the mean.

Of the 99%, by symmetry, 49.5% are greater than the mean, and 49.5% are less.

As the graph of the distribution above shows, the mean, 100 pounds, is the most frequent weight. Out of 600 young people, about 408 have weights between 80 pounds and 120 pounds. About 570 have weights between 60 pounds and 140 pounds. And about 594 have weights between 40 pounds and 160 pounds.

Example

1   **The approximate number of hours worked per week for 100 people is normally distributed. The mean is 40 hours per week and the standard deviation is 2 hours per week. About how many people work more than 42 hours per week?**

This frequency distribution is shown by the following curve. The percentages represent the percentage of 100 people working the number of hours within the given interval.

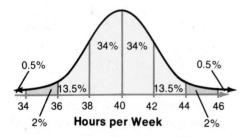

The percentage of people working more than 42 hours per week is 13.5% + 2% + 0.5% or 16%.

$$100 \times 16\% = 16$$

Thus, 16 people work more than 42 hours per week.

Exploratory Exercises

Suppose 500 items are normally distributed. Solve each problem.

1. How many items are within one standard deviation from the mean?

2. How many items are within two standard deviations from the mean?

3. How many items are within three standard deviations from the mean?

4. How many items are within one standard deviation less than the mean?

5. How many items are within one standard deviation greater than the mean?

6. How many items are within two standard deviations greater than the mean?

7–12. Answer Exercises 1–6 for a normal distribution of 2000 items.

13–18. Answer Exercises 1–6 for a normal distribution of 16,000 items.

Written Exercises

The lifetimes of 10,000 light bulbs are normally distributed. The mean lifetime is 300 days, and the standard deviation is 40 days.

1. How many light bulbs will last between 260 and 340 days?

2. How many light bulbs will last between 220 and 380 days?

3. How many light bulbs will last less than 300 days?

4. How many light bulbs will last more than 300 days?

5. How many light bulbs will last more than 380 days?

6. How many light bulbs will last less than 180 days?

The diameters of metal fittings produced by a machine is normally distributed. The mean diameter is 7.5 centimeters and the standard deviation is 0.5 centimeters.

7. What percentage of the fittings have diameters between 7.0 centimeters and 8.0 centimeters?

8. What percentage of the fittings have diameters between 7.5 centimeters and 8.0 centimeters?

9. What percentage of the fittings have diameters between 6.5 centimeters and 7.5 centimeters?

10. What percentage of the fittings have diameters between 6.5 centimeters and 8.0 centimeters?

If you toss a fair coin 100 times, the least number of heads possible is 0, and the most is 100. If this experiment is repeated many times, the number of heads obtained for every 100 tosses is distributed almost normally. There would be a mean of 50 and a standard deviation of 5.

11. What percentage of the experiments will show less than 50 heads?

12. What percentage of the experiments will show more than 50 heads?

13. What percentage of the experiments will show more than 65 heads?

14. What percentage of the experiments will show between 40 and 60 heads?

The number of hours of TV watched weekly by families in Westerville is normally distributed. The mean number of hours is 22 and the standard deviation is 7.5 hours.

15. What percentage of the families watch TV at least 22 hours per week?

16. What percentage of the families watch TV more than 14.5 hours per week?

17. What percentage of the families watch TV more than 37 hours per week?

18. What percentage of the families watch TV between 7 and 29.5 hours per week?

Gloria Lay is a demographer. Her job is to use mathematical methods to study the size, distribution and composition of populations. Every ten years, the government agency for which she works, the Bureau of the Census, takes a census, or counting, of American citizens. The results are a study of American lifestyles which are useful to educators, advertisers, politicians, and other professionals.

A census is taken by asking a specific set of questions to a group of people and then using statistical methods to classify them. The questions asked often inquire about age, gender, race, marital status, size of household, length of employment and level of education reached. Also asked are questions concerning the number of televisions owned, the type(s) of car(s) owned, and the ages of children still living at home.

Exercises

Take a poll of at least 20 people, asking at least five different questions (two must be concerning age and gender), and answer the following questions.

1. What is the size of your sample?

2. Find the mean, median and mode age of the respondents to your poll.

3. Make a table for the responses to one of your questions, with the males' responses in one column, and the females' in the other.

4. Make a frequency table and bar graph for another question. Be sure to label the axes.

5. Find the standard deviation of the ages in your poll. How many fall within one standard deviation of the mean? Within two standard deviations? Within three?

15-6 Predictions

The first step in determining how quantities are related often is making a **scatter diagram.** Such a diagram shows visually the nature of a relationship, both its shape and dispersion.

Suppose, for example, you wish to predict the quantity of a food product sold based on its weekly selling price. The following table shows the quantity sold for each of the last ten weeks, and its selling price.

Quantity Sold (dozens)	30	47	38	28	49	23	47	46	39	42
Price (cents per dozen)	28	22	29	32	20	35	21	20	24	29

The graph on the left is a scatter diagram for the data. The scatter of dots suggests a straight line that slopes downward from the upper left corner to the lower right corner.

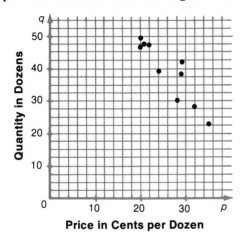

Price in Cents per Dozen

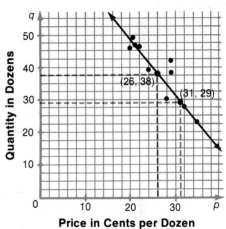

Price in Cents per Dozen

You can draw the line that is suggested by the dots. It represents the relationship between quantity and price. By choosing several points on the line, you can find the equation of the line. This equation is called the **prediction equation** for the relationship.

$$\text{slope} = \frac{38 - 29}{26 - 31} \text{ or } -1.8$$

$q = -1.8p + b$ *q stands for quantity and p stands for price*

$38 = -1.8(26) + b$

$84.8 = b$ The equation is $q = -1.8p + 84.8$.

Now, suppose that next week, the price of the food product will be 30 cents. Using the *prediction equation,* you can estimate that 30.8 dozen items will be sold.

$$q = -1.8p + 84.8$$
$$= -1.8(30) + 84.8 \text{ or } 30.8$$

1 **Draw a scatter diagram and find a prediction equation to show how typing speed and experience are related. Use the data in the following table.**

Typing speed (wpm)	33	45	46	20	40	30	38	22	52	44	42	55
Experience (weeks)	4	7	8	1	6	3	5	2	9	6	7	10

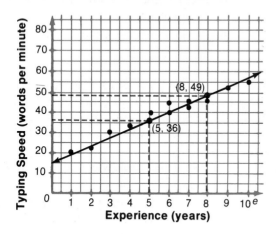

The black line is suggested by the pattern of dots. Two points with coordinates (5, 36) and (8, 49) lie on the line.

$$\text{slope} = \frac{49 - 36}{8 - 5}$$

$$= \frac{13}{3} \text{ or about } 4.3$$

Let e stand for experience.
Let t stand for typing speed.

$$t = 4.3e + b \qquad y = mx + b$$
$$36 = 4.3(5) + b$$
$$36 = 21.5 + b$$
$$14.5 = b$$

The prediction equation is $t = 4.3e + 14.5$.

The procedure for determining a prediction equation is dependent on your judgment. Such an equation is satisfactory only when rough prediction is desired. Statisticians normally use other, more precise procedures to determine prediction equations.

Exploratory Exercises

The prediction equation in a study of the relationship between plant height in centimeters, h, and number of times watered per month, t, is $h = 0.5t + 0.5$. Predict the plant height for each of the following numbers of waterings.

1. 1 **2.** 3 **3.** 5 **4.** 8

5. 9 **6.** 10 **7.** 12 **8.** 15

A study of the relationship between cost for a unit of living space, c, and the number of square feet per unit, a, of living space resulted in the prediction equation $c = -0.2a + 200$. Predict the cost of units of living space for each of the following areas.

9. 200 **10.** 300 **11.** 350 **12.** 400

13. 450 **14.** 550 **15.** 600 **16.** 800

Written Exercises

According to a certain prediction equation, if Acme Soap spends $20,000 on advertising, sales will be $10,000,000. If Acme Soap spends $50,000 on advertising, sales will be $22,000,000. Let x stand for advertising expenditure and y stand for sales revenue.

1. Find the slope of the prediction equation.

2. Find the y-intercept of the prediction equation.

3. Find the prediction equation.

4. Predict sales revenue if $10,000 is spent on advertising.

5. Predict sales revenue if $15,000 is spent on advertising.

6. Predict sales revenue if $35,000 is spent on advertising.

A certain study claims that the number of yearly visits to a public health clinic is related to a family's weekly income. According to the study's prediction equation, a family that earns $170 a week will visit the clinic 11 times a year. A family that earns $220 a week will visit the clinic 6 times a year. Let x stand for family income and y stand for number of visits.

7. Find the slope of the prediction equation.

8. Find the y-intercept of the prediction equation.

9. Find the prediction equation.

10. Predict the number of yearly visits if a family earns $140 a week.

11. Predict the number of yearly visits if a family earns $250 a week.

12. Predict the number of yearly visits if a family earns $200 a week.

The following table shows the amount of sales for each of eight sales representatives during a given period, and the years of sales experience for each representative.

Amount of Sales	$9,000	$6,000	$4,000	$3,000	$3,000	$5,000	$8,000	$2,000
Years of Experience	6	5	3	1	4	3	6	2

13. Draw a scatter diagram to show how amount of sales and years of experience are related.

14. Find a prediction equation to show how amount of sales and years of experience are related.

15. Predict the amount of sales for a representative with 8 years of experience.

16. Predict the amount of sales for a representative with no experience.

The following table shows the statistics grades and the economics grades for a group of college students at the end of a given semester.

Statistics Grades	95	51	49	27	42	52	67	48	46
Economics Grades	88	70	65	50	60	80	68	49	40

17. Draw a scatter diagram to show how statistics grades and economics grades are related.

18. Find a prediction equation to show how statistics grades and economics grades are related.

19. Predict the economics grade of a student who receives a 75 in statistics.

20. Predict the statistics grade of a student who receives an 85 in economics.

Bar Graphs

The program below uses the data at the right to make a bar graph. Understanding the use of variables can help you see how the program works.

```
10    FOR N = 1 TO 5
20    READ A(N),B(N)
30    NEXT N
40    DATA 1950,9,1960,86.7,1970,
      92.3,1980,94.5,1982,97.6
50    FOR N = 1 TO 5
60    FOR BL = 1 TO 2
70    PRINT
80    NEXT BL
90    FOR W = 1 TO 3
100   IF W < > 2 THEN 130
110   PRINT A(N); TAB (10);
120   GOTO 140
130   PRINT TAB( 10)
140   FOR L = 1 TO INT ((B(N)
      / 4) + 0.5)
150   PRINT "*";
160   NEXT L
170   IF W < > 2 THEN 200
180   PRINT " ";B(N)
190   GOTO 210
200   PRINT
210   NEXT W
220   NEXT N
230   END
```

Percent of Households
with TV Sets

1950	1960	1970	1980	1982
9	86.7	92.3	94.5	97.6

```
RUN
        **
1950 **  9
        **

     * * * * * * * * * * * * * * * * * * * * *
1960 * * * * * * * * * * * * * * * * * * * * *   86.7
     * * * * * * * * * * * * * * * * * * * * *

     * * * * * * * * * * * * * * * * * * * * * *
1970 * * * * * * * * * * * * * * * * * * * * * *   92.3
     * * * * * * * * * * * * * * * * * * * * * *

     * * * * * * * * * * * * * * * * * * * * * *
1980 * * * * * * * * * * * * * * * * * * * * * * *   94.5
     * * * * * * * * * * * * * * * * * * * * * * *

     * * * * * * * * * * * * * * * * * * * * * * *
1982 * * * * * * * * * * * * * * * * * * * * * * *   97.6
     * * * * * * * * * * * * * * * * * * * * * * *
```

N = Number of bars
BL = Number of lines
      between bars
W = Width of bars
L = Length of bars

There are only 30 spaces available for the longest bar and the number beside it. On line 140, a number must be chosen by which to divide B(N) so that the result is always less than 30.

Exercises
Change lines 40 and 140 to make bar graphs for each of the following tables.

1. *Life Expectancies (Years)*

1940	1950	1960	1970	1980
62.9	68.2	69.7	70.9	73.7

2. *Percent of Households with Video Games*

1978	1979	1980	1981	1982
1.8	2.9	4.5	9.2	17.0

3. *Percent of Families with Children Under 18, 1982*

0	1	2	3	4 or more
49.2	20.9	19.0	7.4	3.5

4. *Purchases of Footwear (Millions of pairs)*

1960	1965	1970	1975	1980
623.4	711.3	801.7	727.9	734.5

5. What do you think the TAB(10) in lines 110 and 130 does?

6. How would you change the program so that there would be six bars on your graph, instead of five?

Vocabulary

data (481)
bar graph (485)
pictograph (485)
line graph (485)
circle graph (486)
median (490)
mode (490)
mean (490)

dispersion (493)
range (493)
standard deviation (493)
histogram (497)
frequency distribution (497)
normal distribution (497)
scatter diagram (501)
prediction equation (501)

Chapter Summary

1. Graphs are used to show relationships among data. Bar graphs and pictographs compare specific quantities. Line graphs show trends. Circle graphs compare parts to the whole. (485)

2. The median of a set of data is the middle value. If there are two middle values, it is the value halfway between. (490)

3. The mode of a set of data is the most frequent value. (490)

4. The mean of a set of data is the sum of all the values divided by the number of values. (490)

5. Definition of Range: The range of a set of data is the difference between the greatest and least values in the set. (493)

6. Definition of Standard Deviation: From a set of data with n values, x_i represents a value such that $1 \leq i \leq n$, and $\bar{x}$ represents the mean, then the standard deviation is

$$\sqrt{\frac{\sum_{i=1}^{n}(x_i - \bar{x})^2}{n}}.\quad (493)$$

7. Frequency distributions show how data are spread out. A histogram is a bar graph that shows a frequency distribution. The normal distribution commonly occurs. (497)

8. Normal distributions have the following properties.
   The graph is maximized at the mean.
   About 68% of the items are within one standard deviation from the mean.
   About 95% of the items are within two standard deviations from the mean.
   About 99% of the items are within three standard deviations from the mean.   (497)

9. Scatter diagrams picture how quantities are related. Prediction equations give an approximate description of the relationship.   (501)

Chapter Review

15–1 **The following table gives the median family income for the years 1976 to 1982.**

Year	1976	1977	1978	1979	1980	1981	1982
Median Income	$14,958	$16,009	$17,640	$19,587	$21,023	$22,388	$23,433

1. What was the median family income in 1976?

2. Did the median family income increase or decrease from 1976 to 1977?

3–8. Find all the entries for a new row to the table with the heading, *Amount of Gain or Loss*.

15–2 **The following table gives the frequency of the number of diseased plants in garden plots from a certain nursery.**

Number of Diseased Plants per Plot	8	9	10	11	12	13	14	15	16	17	18	19	20	21	22	23	24	25
Number of Plots	1	0	3	5	0	8	0	7	13	16	15	10	9	12	10	18	17	19

9. Draw a line graph to present the data in the table above.

15–3 **10.** Find the median for the distribution in the table above.
   11. Find the mode for the distribution in the table above.
   12. Find the mean for the distribution in the table above.

15–4 **13.** Find the range for the distribution in the table above.
   14. Find the standard deviation for the distribution in the table above.

15–5 **The monthly incomes of 10,000 workers in King City are distributed normally. Suppose the mean monthly income is $1250 and the standard deviation is $250.**

15. How many workers earn more than $1500 a month?

16. How many workers earn less than $750 a month?

15–6 According to a certain prediction equation, if a person is 180 centimeters tall, that person weighs about 76 kilograms. A person 160 centimeters tall weighs about 57 kilograms. Let *x* stand for height in centimeters, and *y* stand for weight in kilograms.

17. Find the slope of the prediction equation.

18. Find the *y*-intercept of the prediction equation.

19. Find the prediction equation.

20. Predict the weight of a person who is 174 centimeters tall.

Chapter Test

The following high temperatures in degrees Fahrenheit were recorded during a cold spell in Cleveland lasting 40 days.

26	17	12	5	4	25	17	23
6	25	20	27	22	26	30	31
12	27	16	27	16	30	6	16
5	29	18	16	22	29	8	23
13	24	5	−7	20	29	18	2

1. Use the data to make a table with headings *Temperature in Degrees Fahrenheit,* and *Frequency.*
2. How many days was the high temperature 13 degrees?
3. How many days was the high temperature less than 20 degrees?
4. Draw a line graph to show the frequency distribution of the temperature.
5. Find the median of the distribution.
6. Find the mode of the distribution.
7. Find the mean of the distribution.
8. Find the range of the distribution.
9. Find the standard deviation of the distribution.

The frequencies of the scores on a college entrance examination are normally distributed. Suppose the mean score is 510 and the standard deviation is 80. And suppose 50,000 people took the examination.

10. What percentage of the scores is above 750?

11. How many people scored between 430 and 590?

According to a certain prediction equation, if a person is 50 years old, that person's systolic blood pressure is 135 millimeters. The blood pressure of a person 35 years old is 127.5 millimeters. Let *x* stand for age in years, and *y* stand for blood pressure in millimeters.

12. Find the slope of the prediction equation.

13. Find the *y*-intercept of the prediction equation.

14. Find the prediction equation.

15. Predict the systolic blood pressure of a person who is 45 years old.

1. Given $f(x) = 3x^2 - 2x$, find the value of $f(-2)$.

2. Graph the system and state the solution. Then state whether the system is consistent and dependent, consistent and independent, or inconsistent.
$$-2x + 5y = -14$$
$$x - y = 1$$

3. Graph the system. Name the vertices of the region formed.
$$y \leq 0, \quad x \geq 0, \quad y \geq 2x - 4$$

4. Write the equation of a plane with x-intercept 5, y-intercept 8, and z-intercept 4.

5. Simplify $\left(\dfrac{4}{3x^{-2}}\right)^2$.

6. Multiply $4y^2 - 7y + 3$ by $y - 2$.

7. Solve $\sqrt{2y + 12} = 10$.

8. Simplify $\dfrac{\sqrt{2} + i\sqrt{3}}{\sqrt{2} - i\sqrt{3}}$.

9. Solve $a^3 = 81a$.

10. Solve $x^2 + 8x - 9 > 0$.

11. Write $f(x) = 2(4x + 1)^2$ in quadratic form.

12. Graph $f(x) = -\dfrac{1}{4}x^2$ and $f(x) = -\dfrac{1}{4}(x + 2)^2$ on the same set of of axes.

13. Graph $y^2 + 2 + x^2 + 6x - 12y = 4$. Identify the conic section.

14. Graph $\dfrac{(y + 2)^2}{9} - \dfrac{(x - 1)^2}{16} = 1$. Identify the conic section.

15. Approximate to the nearest tenth the real zeros of the function $f(x) = x^3 - 4x + 4$.

16. Graph $f(x) = x^3 - x$. Use a calculator to help find points on the graph.

17. Simplify $\dfrac{8x - 8y}{16x - 16y} \cdot \dfrac{(x - y)^2}{2}$.

18. Simplify $\dfrac{x + 2xy}{3x^2} \div \dfrac{2y + 1}{6x}$.

19. Suppose y varies directly as x. If $y = 9$, then $x = -5$. Find y when x is 42.

20. Simplify $\dfrac{1}{x^{\frac{2}{3}}}$.

21. Simplify $\dfrac{x + y}{x^{\frac{1}{2}} - y^{\frac{1}{2}}}$.

22. Solve $\log_{\sqrt{2}} 16 = x$.

23. Solve $\log_4 (3x + 2) = \log_4 (6x - 1)$.

24. Find the sum of the first five terms of a geometric series if $a_1 = 125$ and $r = \dfrac{1}{5}$.

25. Find the sum of the infinite geometric series if the first term is 27 and the common ratio is $-\dfrac{4}{5}$.

26. State the number of terms in the expansion of $(r + s)^4$.

Seven coins are tossed. What is the probability that the following occurs?

27. 2 tails or 3 heads

28. at least 5 tails

29. 3 or more tails

30. no heads

Problem Solving

31. The sum of Alice's age and Zoe's age now is 41 years. In five years Zoe will be half as old as Alice. How old is Alice now?

32. A car dealer offers a choice of 8 vinyl top colors, 16 body colors, and 10 upholstery colors. How many color combinations are there?

33. The number of hours of TV watched weekly by families in Toledo is normally distributed. The mean number of hours is 34 and the standard deviation is 7.5 hours. What percentage of the families watch TV more than 19 hours a week?

The questions on this page involve comparing two quantities, one in Column A and one in Column B. In certain questions, information related to one or both quantities is centered above them. All variables used stand for real numbers.

Directions:
Write A if the quantity in Column A is greater.
Write B if the quantity in Column B is greater.
Write C if the quantities are equal.
Write D if there is not enough information to determine the relationship.

	Column A	Column B
1.	0.4	$\sqrt{0.4}$
2.	$0 < x < 7$ $0 < y < 9$	
	y	x
3.	$n < 0$ $b < 0$	
	$n + b$	$n - b$
4.	One tenth of the product of the first ten integers.	The product of the first nine integers.
5.	$a > b > c > d > 0$	
	$a - d$	$b - c$
6.	$\dfrac{4}{k} < 0$	
	$-\dfrac{1}{k}$	$4k$
7.	$y \neq 0$	
	$\dfrac{y}{3}$	$\dfrac{3}{y}$
8.	$\dfrac{\frac{2}{3}}{\frac{5}{7}}$	$\dfrac{6}{17}$

Examples

	Column A	Column B
I.	$\dfrac{1}{k} < 0$	
	$-\dfrac{1}{k}$	k

The answer is A because $-\dfrac{1}{k}$ is positive, while k is negative.

	Column A	Column B
II.	$\dfrac{3^4 + 3^5}{3^4}$	$\dfrac{3^2 + 3^3}{3^2}$

The answer is C because the simplest form of each quantity is $1 + 3$ or 4.

$Hint:\ \dfrac{3^4 + 3^5}{3^4} = \dfrac{3^4}{3^4} + \dfrac{3^5}{3^4}$

	Column A	Column B
9.	Let $\star y$ denote the least integer equal to or greater than y.	
	$\star 0.4$	$\star 1.0$
10.	$b = d + 1$	
	The average of a, b, and c.	The average of a, c, and d.
11.	c and d are integers greater than 1.	
	$[1 + (-c)]^d$	$(-c)^d$
12.	$b < 0$	
	$\dfrac{b^9}{b^4}$	$\dfrac{b^{10}}{b^5}$
13.	$\dfrac{5}{b} = 2;\ 5 = \dfrac{2}{c}$	
	$c + \dfrac{1}{3}$	$b - \dfrac{11}{6}$
14.	12% of 1600	16.5% of 1200

CHAPTER 16

Trigonometric Functions and Identities

It has been found that musical sounds are made of precise patterns of waves. These vibrational waves can be described by trigonometric functions.

16-1 Angles and the Unit Circle

Consider a circle, centered at the origin, with two rays extending from the center as shown. One ray is fixed along the positive x-axis. The other ray can rotate about the center.

These rays form an angle. The fixed ray is called the initial side of the angle. The other is called the terminal side of the angle.

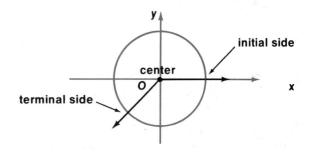

An angle with its vertex at the origin and its initial side along the positive x-axis is said to be in <u>standard position</u>.

Start with both sides along the positive x-axis. As the terminal side is rotated counterclockwise, the measure of the angle formed increases.

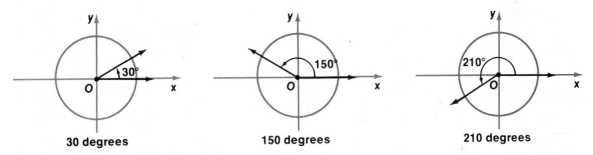

| 30 degrees | 150 degrees | 210 degrees |

The rotation of the terminal side of the angle may include one or more complete revolutions about the center. The measurement of an angle representing one complete revolution of the circle is 360 degrees, usually written 360°.

The most widely used unit of angle measure is the degree.

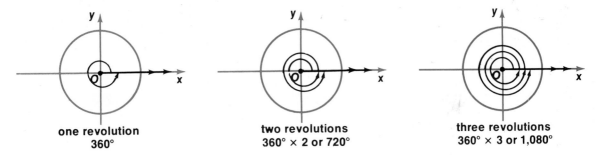

| one revolution 360° | two revolutions 360° × 2 or 720° | three revolutions 360° × 3 or 1,080° |

Angles that differ by one or more complete rotations of the circle are called **coterminal angles.** For example, 74°, 434°, and 794° are coterminal angles.

The terminal side of an angle can also rotate in a clockwise direction. A negative number is used to denote the measure of an angle formed in such a way.

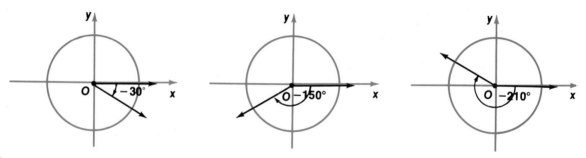

A unit other than the degree may be used in angle measurements.

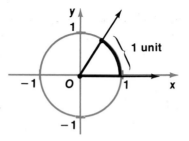

Suppose a circle with a radius of 1 unit is centered at the origin. This circle is called a **unit circle.** Form an angle in standard position so that it intercepts an arc whose length is 1 unit. This angle is given the measurement 1 **radian.**

The circumference of a circle with a radius of 1 unit is $2\pi(1)$ or 2π units. Thus, an angle representing one complete revolution of the circle is 2π radians or 360 degrees. To change radian measure to degree measure, or vice versa, use the following equations.

1 radian is $\dfrac{360}{2\pi}$ or $\dfrac{180}{\pi}$ degrees

1 degree is $\dfrac{2\pi}{360}$ or $\dfrac{\pi}{180}$ radians

When no unit of measure is written, it is assumed the unit is the radian. For example, 2π means 2π radians.

To change radian measure to degree measure, multiply the number of radians by $\dfrac{180}{\pi}$.

To change degree measure to radian measure, multiply the number of degrees by $\dfrac{\pi}{180}$.

Example

1 **Change 45°, 240°, and −150° to radians.**

$$45 \cdot \frac{\pi}{180} = \frac{45\pi}{180} \text{ or } \frac{\pi}{4}$$

$$240 \cdot \frac{\pi}{180} = \frac{240\pi}{180} \text{ or } \frac{4\pi}{3}$$

$$-150 \cdot \frac{\pi}{180} = -\frac{150\pi}{180} \text{ or } -\frac{5\pi}{6}$$

2 Change $\frac{5\pi}{3}$, $-\frac{4\pi}{3}$, and $\frac{3}{4}$ to degrees.

$$\frac{5\pi}{3} \cdot \frac{180}{\pi} = \left(\frac{900\pi}{3\pi}\right)^\circ \text{ or } 300°$$

$$-\frac{4\pi}{3} \cdot \frac{180}{\pi} = \left(-\frac{720\pi}{3\pi}\right)^\circ \text{ or } -240°$$

$$\frac{3}{4} \cdot \frac{180}{\pi} = \left(\frac{540}{4\pi}\right)^\circ \text{ or } \frac{135°}{\pi}$$

Exploratory Exercises

Suppose angles with the following measurements are in standard position. For each angle, name the quadrant which contains the terminal side.

1. 245°	**2.** 397°	**3.** 800°	**4.** 275°
5. $\frac{\pi}{3}$	**6.** $\frac{3}{5}\pi$	**7.** $\frac{11}{3}\pi$	**8.** $2\frac{1}{3}\pi$
9. $-240°$	**10.** $-32°$	**11.** 440°	**12.** 300°
13. $\frac{5}{3}\pi$	**14.** $-\frac{12}{5}\pi$	**15.** $-\frac{4}{7}\pi$	**16.** $\frac{5}{9}\pi$
17. 945°	**18.** $-210°$	**19.** 198°	**20.** $-94°$
21. $-\frac{9}{4}\pi$	**22.** 4	**23.** $\frac{2}{3}\pi$	**24.** 7

Written Exercises

Change each of the following degree measures to radians.

1. 90°	**2.** 120°	**3.** $-45°$	**4.** 60°
5. 450°	**6.** $-300°$	**7.** 150°	**8.** $-600°$
9. 45°	**10.** $-120°$	**11.** 330°	**12.** $-240°$
13. 270°	**14.** $-135°$	**15.** 180°	**16.** $-210°$
17. 405°	**18.** 810°	**19.** $-315°$	**20.** $-270°$

Change each of the following radian measures to degrees.

21. π	**22.** $-\frac{\pi}{2}$	**23.** $\frac{\pi}{4}$	**24.** $-\frac{\pi}{6}$
25. 3π	**26.** $-\frac{5}{4}\pi$	**27.** $-\frac{8}{3}\pi$	**28.** $-\frac{7}{4}\pi$
29. $\frac{\pi}{6}$	**30.** $\frac{5}{6}\pi$	**31.** $-\frac{\pi}{4}$	**32.** $\frac{3}{4}\pi$
33. $\frac{11\pi}{6}$	**34.** $\frac{7\pi}{4}$	**35.** 5	**36.** 2
37. $5\frac{1}{2}\pi$	**38.** $4\frac{1}{3}\pi$	**39.** $6\frac{1}{2}$	**40.** $3\frac{1}{3}$

16-2   Sine and Cosine

The display below is called an oscillogram. It represents a single pure musical tone.

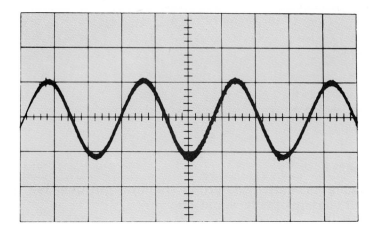

Both the **sine** function and the **cosine** function are used to describe phenomena like musical tones. These functions can be defined in terms of the unit circle.

Consider an angle in standard position. Let the Greek letter θ (theta) stand for the measurement of the angle. The terminal side of this angle intersects the unit circle at a particular point. The x-coordinate of the point is called cosine θ. The y-coordinate of the point is called sine θ.

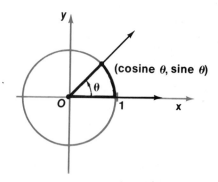

Let θ stand for the measurement of an angle in standard position. Let (x, y) represent the coordinates of the point where the terminal side intersects the unit circle. Then the following equations hold.

cosine θ = x and sine θ = y

Definition of Sine and Cosine

Sine is abbreviated *sin*. Cosine is abbreviated *cos*.

You can use geometry to find values of the sine and cosine functions for certain angles.

Examples

1 Find sin 45°.

Consider the right triangle formed by two sides and a diagonal of a square. One side and the hypotenuse of this right triangle are part of the initial and terminal sides of a 45° angle.

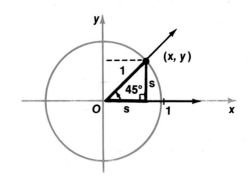

$$s^2 + s^2 = 1^2 \qquad \text{Use the Pythagorean}$$
$$2s^2 = 1 \qquad \text{Theorem to find } s.$$
$$s^2 = \frac{1}{2}$$
$$s = \sqrt{\frac{1}{2}} \text{ or } \frac{\sqrt{2}}{2}$$

The length of each side is $\frac{\sqrt{2}}{2}$ units. Thus, the coordinates of the point labeled (x, y) are $\left(\frac{\sqrt{2}}{2}, \frac{\sqrt{2}}{2}\right)$. Therefore, $\sin 45° = \frac{\sqrt{2}}{2}$.

2 Find cos 60°.

Look at the graph on the right. The dashed line segment cuts the x-axis and the terminal side of the angle to form a 30°–60° right triangle. The lengths of the sides of the triangle are 1 unit, $\frac{1}{2}$ unit, and $\frac{\sqrt{3}}{2}$ units. Thus, the x-coordinate of the point labeled (x, y) is $\frac{1}{2}$. Therefore, $\cos 60° = \frac{1}{2}$.

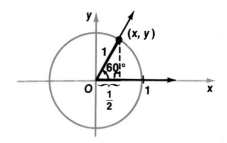

3 Find sin 210°.

Notice that the dashed line segment cuts the x-axis and the terminal side of the angle to form a 30°–60° right triangle.

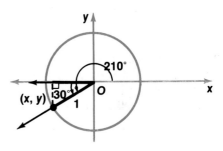

$$x^2 + y^2 = 1 \qquad \text{Use the Pythagorean}$$
$$\left(\frac{\sqrt{3}}{2}\right)^2 + y^2 = 1 \qquad \text{Theorem to find } y.$$
$$y^2 = 1 - \left(\frac{\sqrt{3}}{2}\right)^2$$
$$y = \pm\sqrt{1 - \left(\frac{3}{4}\right)} \text{ or } \pm\frac{1}{2}$$
$$\sin 210° = -\frac{1}{2} \qquad \text{Since the terminal side of the}$$
$$\text{angle lies in the third quadrant,}$$
$$\text{the sine is negative.}$$

The table at the right lists the sign of the sine and cosine functions in each of the four quadrants.

Quadrant II		Quadrant I	
$\cos\theta$	$-$	$\cos\theta$	$+$
$\sin\theta$	$+$	$\sin\theta$	$+$
Quadrant III		Quadrant IV	
$\cos\theta$	$-$	$\cos\theta$	$+$
$\sin\theta$	$-$	$\sin\theta$	$-$

Using the technique shown in the examples, you should be able to complete a chart like the following.

degrees	0	30	45	60	90	120	135	150	180	210	225	240	270	300	315	330	360
radians	0	$\frac{\pi}{6}$	$\frac{\pi}{4}$	$\frac{\pi}{3}$	$\frac{\pi}{2}$	$\frac{2\pi}{3}$	$\frac{3\pi}{4}$	$\frac{5\pi}{6}$	π	$\frac{7\pi}{6}$	$\frac{5\pi}{4}$	$\frac{4\pi}{3}$	$\frac{3\pi}{2}$	$\frac{5\pi}{3}$	$\frac{7\pi}{4}$	$\frac{11\pi}{6}$	2π
$\sin\theta$	0	$\frac{1}{2}$	$\frac{\sqrt{2}}{2}$	$\frac{\sqrt{3}}{2}$	1	$\frac{\sqrt{3}}{2}$	$\frac{\sqrt{2}}{2}$	$\frac{1}{2}$	0	$-\frac{1}{2}$	$-\frac{\sqrt{2}}{2}$	$-\frac{\sqrt{3}}{2}$	-1	$-\frac{\sqrt{3}}{2}$	$-\frac{\sqrt{2}}{2}$	$-\frac{1}{2}$	0
$\cos\theta$	1	$\frac{\sqrt{3}}{2}$	$\frac{\sqrt{2}}{2}$	$\frac{1}{2}$	0	$-\frac{1}{2}$	$-\frac{\sqrt{2}}{2}$	$-\frac{\sqrt{3}}{2}$	-1	$-\frac{\sqrt{3}}{2}$	$-\frac{\sqrt{2}}{2}$	$-\frac{1}{2}$	0	$\frac{1}{2}$	$\frac{\sqrt{2}}{2}$	$\frac{\sqrt{3}}{2}$	1

The chart below lists the same information for angles from 360° to 720°. Are the values for $\sin\theta$ and $\cos\theta$ identical to those in the first chart?

degrees	360	390	405	420	450	480	495	510	540	570	585	600	630	660	675	690	720
radians	2π	$\frac{13\pi}{6}$	$\frac{9\pi}{4}$	$\frac{7\pi}{3}$	$\frac{5\pi}{2}$	$\frac{8\pi}{3}$	$\frac{11\pi}{4}$	$\frac{17\pi}{6}$	3π	$\frac{19\pi}{6}$	$\frac{13\pi}{4}$	$\frac{10\pi}{3}$	$\frac{7\pi}{2}$	$\frac{11\pi}{3}$	$\frac{15\pi}{4}$	$\frac{23\pi}{6}$	4π
$\sin\theta$	0	$\frac{1}{2}$	$\frac{\sqrt{2}}{2}$	$\frac{\sqrt{3}}{2}$	1	$\frac{\sqrt{3}}{2}$	$\frac{\sqrt{2}}{2}$	$\frac{1}{2}$	0	$-\frac{1}{2}$	$-\frac{\sqrt{2}}{2}$	$-\frac{\sqrt{3}}{2}$	-1	$-\frac{\sqrt{3}}{2}$	$-\frac{\sqrt{2}}{2}$	$-\frac{1}{2}$	0
$\cos\theta$	1	$\frac{\sqrt{3}}{2}$	$\frac{\sqrt{2}}{2}$	$\frac{1}{2}$	0	$-\frac{1}{2}$	$-\frac{\sqrt{2}}{2}$	$-\frac{\sqrt{3}}{2}$	-1	$-\frac{\sqrt{3}}{2}$	$-\frac{\sqrt{2}}{2}$	$-\frac{1}{2}$	0	$\frac{1}{2}$	$\frac{\sqrt{2}}{2}$	$\frac{\sqrt{3}}{2}$	1

Every 360°, or 2π radians, represents one complete revolution of a circle. Every 360°, or 2π radians, the sine and cosine functions repeat their values. Because of this, we say that the sine and cosine functions are periodic. Each has a **period** of 360°, or 2π radians.

A function f is called periodic if there is a number a such that $f(x) = f(x + a)$ for all x in the domain of the function. The least positive value of a for which $f(x) = f(x + a)$ is the period of the function.

Definition of Periodic Function

Example

4 Find sin 930°.

$$\sin 930° = \sin (570 + 360)° \qquad 930° = 570° + 360°$$
$$= \sin 570° \qquad \textit{The sine function has a period of } 360°$$
$$= \sin (210 + 360)° \qquad 570° = 210° + 360°$$
$$= \sin 210°$$
$$= -\frac{1}{2}$$

Exploratory Exercises

State whether the value of each is positive or negative.

1. $\sin 300°$ 2. $\sin 240°$ 3. $\cos (-210°)$ 4. $\cos (-45°)$

5. $\sin 225°$ 6. $\cos (-135°)$ 7. $\sin (-270°)$ 8. $\sin 315°$

9. $\sin \dfrac{\pi}{3}$ 10. $\cos \dfrac{7\pi}{3}$ 11. $\cos \dfrac{5}{3}\pi$ 12. $\sin \left(-\dfrac{3}{4}\pi\right)$

Written Exercises

For each of the following, find the least positive angle that is coterminal.

1. $420°$ 2. $-40°$ 3. $1020°$ 4. $-450°$

5. 3π 6. $-120°$ 7. $\dfrac{9}{2}\pi$ 8. $\dfrac{11}{5}\pi$

9. $-\dfrac{\pi}{4}$ 10. $600°$ 11. $1200°$ 12. $1400°$

13. $\dfrac{13}{3}\pi$ 14. $\dfrac{27}{4}\pi$ 15. $\dfrac{11}{4}\pi$ 16. $680°$

17. $-600°$ 18. $1240°$ 19. $-\dfrac{8}{9}\pi$ 20. $-240°$

21. $-\dfrac{7}{4}\pi$ 22. $\dfrac{31}{6}\pi$ 23. $-\dfrac{2}{3}\pi$ 24. $\dfrac{21}{4}\pi$

25. $960°$ 26. $-300°$ 27. $-760°$ 28. $240°$

Find each of the following.

29. $\cos 150°$ 30. $\cos -150°$ 31. $\cos \dfrac{11}{3}\pi$ 32. $\sin \dfrac{17}{4}\pi$

33. $\cos \left(-\dfrac{3}{4}\pi\right)$ 34. $\sin \left(-\dfrac{5}{3}\pi\right)$ 35. $\sin \dfrac{3\pi}{2}$ 36. $\cos \dfrac{7}{4}\pi$

37. $\cos 390°$ 38. $\sin -240°$ 39. $\cos \left(-\dfrac{7}{4}\pi\right)$ 40. $\sin 660°$

41. $\sin 300°$ 42. $\cos 900°$ 43. $\cos 330°$ 44. $\sin -180°$

45. $\cos -60°$ 46. $\sin \left(-\dfrac{\pi}{6}\right)$ 47. $\sin \dfrac{4}{3}\pi$ 48. $\cos 1560°$

Evaluate each expression.

49. $\dfrac{\sin 30° + \cos 60°}{2}$ 50. $\dfrac{4 \sin 300° + 2 \cos 30°}{3}$ 51. $4(\sin 30°)(\cos 60°)$

52. $\sin 30° + \sin 60°$ 53. $(\sin 60°)^2 + (\cos 60°)^2$ 54. $8(\sin 120°)(\cos 120°)$

16-3 Graphing the Sine and Cosine Functions

To graph the sine function, use the horizontal axis for the values of θ in either degrees or radians. Use the vertical axis for values of $\sin \theta$.

degrees	0	30	45	60	90	120	135	150	180	210	225	240	270	300	315	330	360
$\sin\theta$	0	$\frac{1}{2}$	$\frac{\sqrt{2}}{2}$	$\frac{\sqrt{3}}{2}$	1	$\frac{\sqrt{3}}{2}$	$\frac{\sqrt{2}}{2}$	$\frac{1}{2}$	0	$-\frac{1}{2}$	$-\frac{\sqrt{2}}{2}$	$-\frac{\sqrt{3}}{2}$	-1	$-\frac{\sqrt{3}}{2}$	$-\frac{\sqrt{2}}{2}$	$-\frac{1}{2}$	0
nearest tenth	0	0.5	0.7	0.9	1	0.9	0.7	0.5	0	-0.5	-0.7	-0.9	-1	-0.9	-0.7	-0.5	0

After plotting several points, complete the graph by connecting the points with a smooth, continuous curve.

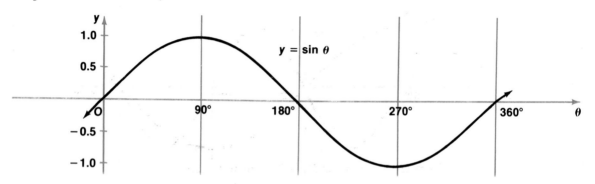

The graph of the cosine function is done in a similar manner.

degrees	0	30	45	60	90	120	135	150	180	210	225	240	270	300	315	330	360
$\cos\theta$	1	$\frac{\sqrt{3}}{2}$	$\frac{\sqrt{2}}{2}$	$\frac{1}{2}$	0	$-\frac{1}{2}$	$-\frac{\sqrt{2}}{2}$	$-\frac{\sqrt{3}}{2}$	-1	$-\frac{\sqrt{3}}{2}$	$-\frac{\sqrt{2}}{2}$	$-\frac{1}{2}$	0	$\frac{1}{2}$	$\frac{\sqrt{2}}{2}$	$\frac{\sqrt{3}}{2}$	1
nearest tenth	1	0.9	0.7	0.5	0	-0.5	-0.7	-0.9	-1	-0.9	-0.7	-0.5	0	0.5	0.7	0.9	1

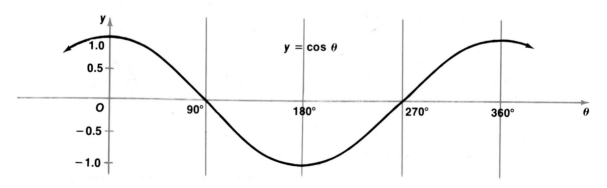

Recall that both the sine and cosine functions have a period of 360° or 2π radians. The graph of either function repeats itself every 360°. The following examples are variations of the sine function that have periods other than 360°.

Examples

1 Graph $y = \sin 2\theta$. State the period.

First, complete a table of values.

θ	0°	15°	30°	45°	60°	75°	90°	105°	120°	135°	150°	165°	180°
2θ	0°	30°	60°	90°	120°	150°	180°	210°	240°	270°	300°	330°	360°
$\sin 2\theta$	0	$\frac{1}{2}$	$\frac{\sqrt{3}}{2}$	1	$\frac{\sqrt{3}}{2}$	$\frac{1}{2}$	0	$-\frac{1}{2}$	$-\frac{\sqrt{3}}{2}$	-1	$-\frac{\sqrt{3}}{2}$	$-\frac{1}{2}$	0

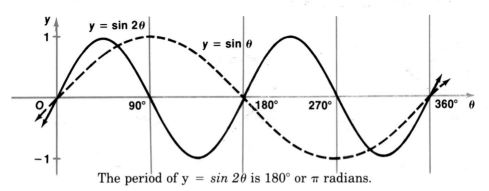

The period of $y = \sin 2\theta$ is 180° or π radians.

2 Graph $y = \sin \frac{1}{2}\theta$. State the period.

θ	0°	60°	90°	120°	180°	240°	270°	300°	360°
$\frac{1}{2}\theta$	0°	30°	45°	60°	90°	120°	135°	150°	180°
$\sin\frac{1}{2}\theta$	0	$\frac{1}{2}$	$\frac{\sqrt{2}}{2}$	$\frac{\sqrt{3}}{2}$	1	$\frac{\sqrt{3}}{2}$	$\frac{\sqrt{2}}{2}$	$\frac{1}{2}$	0

For the graph below, note that the θ-axis is drawn to a different scale than the above graph.

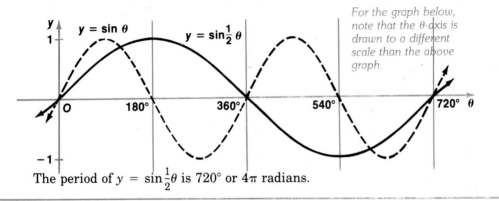

The period of $y = \sin\frac{1}{2}\theta$ is 720° or 4π radians.

All the trigonometric functions you have graphed so far have a maximum value of 1 and a minimum value of -1. The amplitude of these graphs is 1. The graphs in the following examples have amplitudes other than 1.

Examples

3 **Graph $y = 2 \cos \theta$. State the amplitude.**

θ	0°	30°	60°	90°	120°	150°	180°	210°	240°	270°	300°	330°	360°
$\cos\theta$	1	$\frac{\sqrt{3}}{2}$	$\frac{1}{2}$	0	$-\frac{1}{2}$	$-\frac{\sqrt{3}}{2}$	-1	$-\frac{\sqrt{3}}{2}$	$-\frac{1}{2}$	0	$\frac{1}{2}$	$\frac{\sqrt{3}}{2}$	1
$2\cos\theta$	2	$\sqrt{3}$	1	0	-1	$-\sqrt{3}$	-2	$-\sqrt{3}$	-1	0	1	$\sqrt{3}$	2

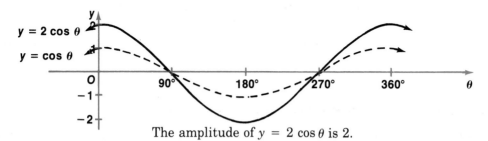

The amplitude of $y = 2 \cos \theta$ is 2.

4 **Graph $y = \frac{1}{2} \cos \theta$. State the amplitude.**

θ	0°	30°	60°	90°	120°	150°	180°	210°	240°	270°	300°	330°	360°
$\cos\theta$	1	$\frac{\sqrt{3}}{2}$	$\frac{1}{2}$	0	$-\frac{1}{2}$	$-\frac{\sqrt{3}}{2}$	-1	$-\frac{\sqrt{3}}{2}$	$-\frac{1}{2}$	0	$\frac{1}{2}$	$\frac{\sqrt{3}}{2}$	1
$\frac{1}{2}\cos\theta$	$\frac{1}{2}$	$\frac{\sqrt{3}}{4}$	$\frac{1}{4}$	0	$-\frac{1}{4}$	$-\frac{\sqrt{3}}{4}$	$-\frac{1}{2}$	$-\frac{\sqrt{3}}{4}$	$-\frac{1}{4}$	0	$\frac{1}{4}$	$\frac{\sqrt{3}}{4}$	$\frac{1}{2}$

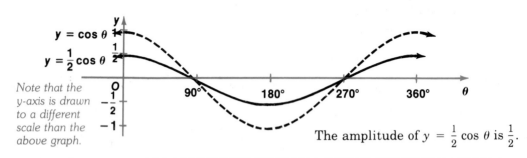

Note that the y-axis is drawn to a different scale than the above graph.

The amplitude of $y = \frac{1}{2} \cos \theta$ is $\frac{1}{2}$.

From these examples the following generalizations can be made.

For functions of the form $y = a \sin b\theta$ and $y = a \cos b\theta$ the amplitude is $|a|$ and the period is $\dfrac{2\pi}{|b|}$.

Amplitudes and Periods

Example

5 Graph $y = \frac{3}{2} \cos\frac{1}{2}\theta$.

The amplitude is $\left|\frac{3}{2}\right|$ or $\frac{3}{2}$. The period is $\frac{2\pi}{\left|\frac{1}{2}\right|}$ or 4π.

The graph has a shape like $y = \cos\theta$.

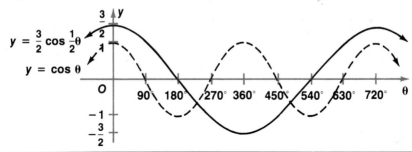

Exploratory Exercises

State the amplitude and period for each of the following.

1. $y = \sin\theta$
2. $y = \frac{1}{2}\cos\theta$
3. $y = \frac{2}{3}\cos\theta$
4. $y = 3\sin\theta$
5. $y = 6\sin\frac{2}{3}\theta$
6. $y = 3\cos\frac{1}{2}\theta$
7. $y = 4\cos\frac{3}{4}\theta$
8. $y = 2\sin\frac{1}{5}\theta$
9. $y = 5\sin\theta$
10. $y = \sin 4\theta$
11. $y = \cos 3\theta$
12. $y = \cos 2\theta$
13. $y = 4\sin\frac{1}{2}\theta$
14. $y = -2\sin\theta$
15. $y = -3\sin\frac{2}{3}\theta$
16. $y = -6\sin 2\theta$
17. $y = -\frac{1}{2}\cos\frac{3}{4}\theta$
18. $3y = 2\sin\frac{1}{2}\theta$
19. $\frac{1}{2}y = 3\sin 2\theta$
20. $\frac{3}{4}y = \frac{2}{3}\sin\frac{3}{5}\theta$

Written Exercises

Graph each of the following.

1. $y = \sin\theta$
2. $y = \frac{1}{2}\cos\theta$
3. $y = \frac{2}{3}\cos\theta$
4. $y = 3\sin\theta$
5. $y = 6\sin\frac{2}{3}\theta$
6. $y = 3\cos\frac{1}{2}\theta$
7. $y = 4\cos\frac{3}{4}\theta$
8. $y = 2\sin\frac{1}{5}\theta$
9. $y = 5\sin\theta$
10. $y = \sin 4\theta$
11. $y = \cos 3\theta$
12. $y = \cos 2\theta$
13. $y = 4\sin\frac{1}{2}\theta$
14. $y = -2\sin\theta$
15. $y = -3\sin\frac{2}{3}\theta$
16. $y = -6\sin 2\theta$
17. $y = -\frac{1}{2}\cos\frac{3}{4}\theta$
18. $3y = 2\sin\frac{1}{2}\theta$
19. $\frac{1}{2}y = 3\sin 2\theta$
20. $\frac{3}{4}y = \frac{2}{3}\sin\frac{3}{5}\theta$

mini-review

1. Express 0.00008790 in scientific notation.

2. Solve $\log_x \sqrt{6} = \frac{1}{2}$.

3. Solve $2.43^x = 7.91$ using logarithms.

4. Complete the sequence: 3, 3, 6, 9, 15, 24, ___, ___, ___.

5. Find the mean, median, and mode for {3, 5, 19, 0, 27, 6, −2, 0, −4}.

16-4 Other Trigonometric Functions

Other trigonometric functions are defined using sine and cosine.

Let θ stand for the measurement of an angle in standard position on the unit circle. Then the following equations hold.

$$\tan \theta = \frac{\sin \theta}{\cos \theta} \left.\right\} \text{ if } \cos \theta \neq 0$$

$$\sec \theta = \frac{1}{\cos \theta}$$

$$\cot \theta = \frac{\cos \theta}{\sin \theta} \left.\right\} \text{ if } \sin \theta \neq 0$$

$$\csc \theta = \frac{1}{\sin \theta}$$

Definition of Tangent (tan), Cotangent (cot), Secant (sec), and Cosecant (csc)

Examples

1 Find tan 150°.

$$\tan 150° = \frac{\sin 150°}{\cos 150°}$$

$$= \frac{\frac{1}{2}}{-\frac{\sqrt{3}}{2}}$$

$$= -\frac{1}{\sqrt{3}} \text{ or } -\frac{\sqrt{3}}{3}$$

2 Find sec 45°.

$$\sec 45° = \frac{1}{\cos 45°}$$

$$= \frac{1}{\frac{\sqrt{2}}{2}}$$

$$= \frac{2}{\sqrt{2}} \text{ or } \sqrt{2}$$

After completing a table of values, you can graph $y = \tan \theta$.

θ	0°	30°	45°	60°	90°	120°	135°	150°	180°	210°	225°	240°	270°	300°	315°	330°	360°
$\tan \theta$	0	$\frac{\sqrt{3}}{3}$	1	$\sqrt{3}$	not defined	$-\sqrt{3}$	-1	$-\frac{\sqrt{3}}{3}$	0	$\frac{\sqrt{3}}{3}$	1	$\sqrt{3}$	not defined	$-\sqrt{3}$	-1	$\frac{\sqrt{3}}{3}$	0

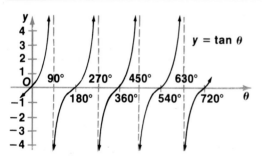

The tangent function is not defined for 90°, 270°, etc. (We say that it is not defined for 90° + k · 180°, where k is an integer.) The graph is separated by vertical asymptotes, indicated by dashed lines

The period of the tangent function is 180° or π radians. What is the amplitude?

The following are graphs of the secant, cotangent, and cosecant functions. Compare them to the graphs of the cosine, tangent, and sine functions, shown as dashed curves.

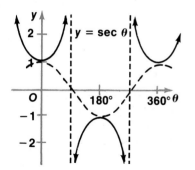

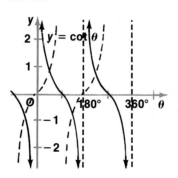

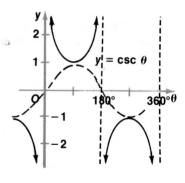

Note that the period of the secant and cosecant functions is 360° or 2π radians. The period of the cotangent function is 180° or π radians.

Example

3   **Draw the graph of $y = -\dfrac{1}{2}\csc 2\theta$.**

θ	0°	15°	30°	45°	60°	75°	90°	105°	120°	135°	150°	165°	180°
2θ	0°	30°	60°	90°	120°	150°	180°	210°	240°	270°	300°	330°	360°
$-\dfrac{1}{2}\csc 2\theta$	not defined	-1	$-\dfrac{\sqrt{3}}{3}$	$-\dfrac{1}{2}$	$-\dfrac{\sqrt{3}}{3}$	-1	not defined	1	$\dfrac{\sqrt{3}}{3}$	$\dfrac{1}{2}$	$\dfrac{\sqrt{3}}{3}$	1	not defined

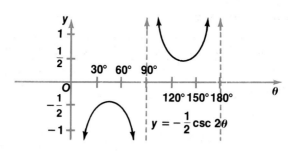

Exploratory Exercises

State the period of each function.

1. $y = \tan\dfrac{1}{2}\theta$ 2. $y = \sec 3\theta$ 3. $y = \csc 2\theta$ 4. $y = \cot 5\theta$

5. $y = \tan 3\theta$ 6. $y = 4\sec\theta$ 7. $y = \csc\dfrac{3}{4}\theta$ 8. $y = \cot\dfrac{1}{3}\theta$

9. $y = 3\tan\theta$ 10. $y = \dfrac{1}{2}\sec\dfrac{1}{2}\theta$ 11. $y = \dfrac{3}{4}\csc\dfrac{2}{3}\theta$ 12. $y = 6\cot 2\theta$

Written Exercises

State whether values of the following functions are increasing or decreasing in each of the four quadrants. Also state the values between 0° and 360° for which y is not defined.

1. $y = \sin\theta$ 2. $y = \cos\theta$ 3. $y = \tan\theta$

4. $y = \cot\theta$ 5. $y = \sec\theta$ 6. $y = \csc\theta$

Find each of the following.

7. $\sec 60°$ 8. $\tan 120°$ 9. $\cot 135°$ 10. $\csc 45°$

11. $\tan\left(-\dfrac{\pi}{3}\right)$ 12. $\csc(-210°)$ 13. $\sec 300°$ 14. $\cot(-60°)$

15. $\sec(-120°)$ 16. $\cot\left(-\dfrac{\pi}{6}\right)$ 17. $\csc\left(-\dfrac{\pi}{6}\right)$ 18. $\tan\dfrac{7}{6}\pi$

19. $\cot\dfrac{7}{4}\pi$ 20. $\tan(-300°)$ 21. $\sec 240°$ 22. $\cot 210°$

23. $\cot 540°$ 24. $\csc 180°$ 25. $\tan\dfrac{9}{4}\pi$ 26. $\csc\dfrac{\pi}{2}$

27. $\tan\left(-\dfrac{5}{6}\pi\right)$ 28. $\csc\dfrac{4}{3}\pi$ 29. $\cot 270°$ 30. $\sec 390°$

31. $\cot(-600°)$ 32. $\sec(-30°)$ 33. $\tan 405°$ 34. $\csc\left(-\dfrac{7}{6}\pi\right)$

Graph each of the following.

35. $y = 3\sec\theta$ 36. $y = \csc\dfrac{1}{3}\theta$ 37. $y = \dfrac{1}{3}\sec\theta$ 38. $y = \cot\theta$

39. $y = \sec 3\theta$ 40. $y = \csc 2\theta$ 41. $y = 2\sec\theta$ 42. $y = 2\tan\theta$

43. $y = \dfrac{1}{2}\tan\theta$ 44. $y = -\dfrac{1}{2}\cot 2\theta$ 45. $y = 3\csc\dfrac{1}{2}\theta$ 46. $y = -\cot\theta$

 Using Calculators ——— **The Trigonometric Function Keys**

Your calculator can help you find the sine, cosine, or tangent of any angle. To evaluate, enter the angle measure and then press the correct trigonometric function key.

Example 1: Find $\cos 54°$.

ENTER: 54 $\boxed{\text{COS}}$ *Be sure your calculator*
DISPLAY: 54   0.5878   *is in degree mode.*

To find the trigonometric value of an angle given in radians, first press the $\boxed{\text{RAD}}$ or $\boxed{\text{DRG}}$ key. Use the $\boxed{\pi}$ key or 3.1415927.

Example 2: Find $\tan\dfrac{\pi}{4}$.

ENTER : $\boxed{\pi}$ $\boxed{\div}$ 4 $\boxed{=}$ $\boxed{\text{TAN}}$ *Be sure your*
DISPLAY: 3.1415927   4   0.7853981   1   *calculator is in*
                                   radian mode.

Exercises   Find each value to four decimal places.

1. $\cos 85°$ 2. $\sin\dfrac{7\pi}{3}$ 3. $\sin 530°$ 4. $\cos 5\pi$ 5. $\tan\dfrac{-11\pi}{8}$

6. $\tan -90°$ 7. $(\sin 95°)(\tan 37°)$

8. $\left(\sin\dfrac{\pi}{3}\right)\left(\cos\dfrac{\pi}{8}\right)$ 9. $\dfrac{3(\sin 50°) + 9(\cos 10°)}{\tan 290°}$

Applications in Music

Simple Tone

We have defined periodic functions as those functions whose graphs are **periodic,** or repetitive. For example, the period of $y = \sin \theta$ and of $y = \cos \theta$ is 360°. Music is also periodic in nature. In fact, musical tones measured on an oscilloscope closely resemble the sine curve. Hence, the sine curve is called pure or simple tone by musicians.

Graphs of the form $y = \sin b\theta$ all have similar shapes, however they differ in period and frequency (the number of repetitions during a given interval). In music, frequency is measured in Hertz (cycles/second). A higher frequency produces a higher pitch. The lowest frequency is called the fundamental, and any multiple of it is called a harmonic.

The illustration at the right shows how the vibration of a string produces a musical tone. Doubling the frequency raises the pitch one octave. Therefore, the second harmonic is an octave above the fundamental, and the fourth harmonic is an octave above the second. For example, when the fundamental is 440 Hertz, the second harmonic is 880 Hertz, and so on.

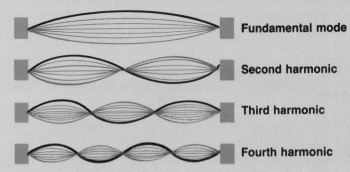

Fundamental mode

Second harmonic

Third harmonic

Fourth harmonic

Exercises

Write an equation for each of the oscillograms below of the form $y = \sin b\theta$. State the period.

1.
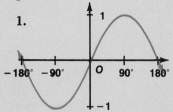

2.
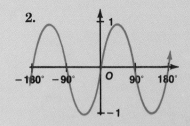

3.
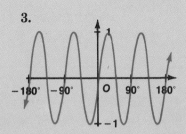

Given the notes below and their frequencies, state the frequencies of the same notes x octaves higher. (Frequencies given in Hertz.)

4. A, 440; $x = 4$

5. C, 66; $x = 3$

6. G, 196; $x = -2$

7. E, 1319; $x = 1$

Chapter 16 **525**

16-5 Trigonometric Identities

Let θ be the measurement of an angle in standard position. Let (x, y) be the coordinates of the point of intersection of the terminal side and the circle. Then the following equations hold.

$$\cos \theta = x \text{ and } \sin \theta = y$$

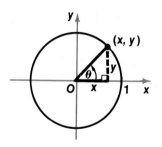

The equation for the unit circle is $x^2 + y^2 = 1$. By substituting $\cos \theta$ for x and $\sin \theta$ for y, you obtain the following equation.

$$(\cos \theta)^2 + (\sin \theta)^2 = 1$$

Normally, this equation is written in the following way.

$$\sin^2 \theta + \cos^2 \theta = 1$$

An equation like $\sin^2 \theta + \cos^2 \theta = 1$ is called an **identity** because it is true for all values of θ. Some trigonometric identities are given below.

Equations which are true for all values of the variables for which they are defined are called identities.

> The following trigonometric identities hold for all values of θ except those for which either side of the equation is undefined.
>
> $$\sin^2 \theta + \cos^2 \theta = 1$$
> $$1 + \tan^2 \theta = \sec^2 \theta$$
> $$1 + \cot^2 \theta = \csc^2 \theta$$

Basic Trigonometric Identities

Examples

1 Show that $\cot \theta = \dfrac{1}{\tan \theta}$.

$\cot \theta = \dfrac{\cos \theta}{\sin \theta}$ *Definition of $\cot \theta$*

$= \dfrac{1}{\dfrac{\sin \theta}{\cos \theta}}$ $\dfrac{\cos \theta}{\sin \theta} \cdot \dfrac{\dfrac{\cos \theta}{1}}{\dfrac{1}{\cos \theta}} = \dfrac{1}{\dfrac{\sin \theta}{\cos \theta}}$

$= \dfrac{1}{\tan \theta}$ *Definition of $\tan \theta$*

2 Show that $\sec^2 \theta + \csc^2 \theta = \dfrac{1}{\sin^2 \theta \cos^2 \theta}$.

$\sec^2 \theta + \csc^2 \theta = \dfrac{1}{\cos^2 \theta} + \dfrac{1}{\sin^2 \theta}$ *Definition of $\sec \theta$ and $\csc \theta$*

$= \dfrac{\sin^2 \theta + \cos^2 \theta}{\sin^2 \theta \cos^2 \theta}$ $\dfrac{\sin^2 \theta}{\sin^2 \theta} \cdot \dfrac{1}{\cos^2 \theta} + \dfrac{\cos^2 \theta}{\cos^2 \theta} \cdot \dfrac{1}{\sin^2 \theta}$

$= \dfrac{1}{\sin^2 \theta \cos^2 \theta}$ $\sin^2 \theta + \cos^2 \theta = 1$

Examples

3 **Show that $1 + \tan^2\theta = \sec^2\theta$.**

$$1 + \tan^2\theta = 1 + \left(\frac{\sin\theta}{\cos\theta}\right)^2 \qquad \textit{Definition of } \tan\theta.$$

$$= 1 + \frac{\sin^2\theta}{\cos^2\theta}$$

$$= \frac{\cos^2\theta}{\cos^2\theta} + \frac{\sin^2\theta}{\cos^2\theta} \qquad 1 = \frac{\cos^2\theta}{\cos^2\theta}$$

$$= \frac{\cos^2\theta + \sin^2\theta}{\cos^2\theta}$$

$$= \frac{1}{\cos^2\theta} \qquad \sin^2\theta + \cos^2\theta = 1$$

$$= \sec^2\theta$$

4 **Suppose $\cot\theta = \frac{3}{5}$. Find $\csc\theta$.**

$$\csc^2\theta = 1 + \cot^2\theta$$

$$= 1 + \left(\frac{3}{5}\right)^2$$

$$= \frac{34}{25}$$

$$\csc\theta = \pm\sqrt{\frac{34}{25}} \text{ or } \pm\frac{\sqrt{34}}{5}$$

The trigonometric identities can be used to evaluate or simplify expressions containing trigonometric functions.

Example

5 **Simplify $\dfrac{1}{1 + \sin x} + \dfrac{1}{1 - \sin x}$.**

$$\frac{1}{1 + \sin x} + \frac{1}{1 - \sin x} = \frac{(1 - \sin x) + (1 + \sin x)}{(1 + \sin x)(1 - \sin x)}$$

$$= \frac{2}{1 - \sin^2 x}$$

$$= \frac{2}{\cos^2 x} \qquad \sin^2 x + \cos^2 x = 1$$

$$= 2\sec^2 x \qquad \sec x = \frac{1}{\cos x}$$

Exploratory Exercises

Which of the following are identities?

1. $\sin(-\theta) = -\sin\theta$

2. $\cos\theta\sec\theta = 1$

3. $\csc^2\theta = \cot^2\theta + 1$

4. $\sin^2\theta - \cos^2\theta = 1$

5. $\cot\theta\sin\theta = \cos\theta$

6. $\cos(-\theta) = \cos\theta$

Written Exercises

Solve each of the following for values of θ between 0° and 90°.

1. If $\sin\theta = \frac{1}{2}$, find $\cos\theta$.

2. If $\cos\theta = \frac{2}{3}$, find $\sin\theta$.

3. If $\sin\theta = \frac{4}{5}$, find $\cos\theta$.

4. If $\sin\theta = \frac{3}{4}$, find $\sec\theta$.

5. If $\cos\theta = \frac{2}{3}$, find $\csc\theta$.

6. If $\cos\theta = \frac{4}{5}$, find $\tan\theta$.

7. If $\tan\theta = 4$, find $\sin\theta$.

8. If $\cot\theta = 2$, find $\tan\theta$.

Solve each of the following for values of θ between 90° and 180°.

9. If $\sin\theta = \frac{3}{5}$, find $\cos\theta$.

10. If $\sin\theta = \frac{1}{2}$, find $\tan\theta$.

11. If $\cos\theta = -\frac{3}{5}$, find $\csc\theta$.

12. If $\tan\theta = -2$, find $\sec\theta$.

Solve each of the following for values of θ between 180° and 270°.

13. If $\cot\theta = \frac{1}{4}$, find $\csc\theta$.

14. If $\sec\theta = -3$, find $\tan\theta$.

15. If $\sin\theta = -\frac{1}{2}$, find $\cos\theta$.

16. If $\cos\theta = -\frac{3}{5}$, find $\csc\theta$.

Solve each of the following for values of θ between 270° and 360°.

17. If $\cos\theta = \frac{5}{13}$, find $\sin\theta$.

18. If $\tan\theta = -1$, find $\sec\theta$.

19. If $\sec\theta = \frac{5}{3}$, find $\cos\theta$.

20. If $\csc\theta = -\frac{5}{3}$, find $\cos\theta$.

Simplify each of the following.

21. $\tan\theta\cot\theta$

22. $\sec^2\theta - 1$

23. $\sin x + \cos x \tan x$

24. $\csc\theta\cos\theta\tan\theta$

25. $2(\csc^2\theta - \cot^2\theta)$

26. $\dfrac{\tan^2\theta - \sin^2\theta}{\tan^2\theta\sin^2\theta}$

Show that each of the following is an identity.

27. $1 + \cot^2\theta = \csc^2\theta$

28. $\dfrac{\sec\theta}{\csc\theta} = \tan\theta$

29. $\sin x \sec x = \tan x$

30. $\sec a - \cos a = \sin a \tan a$

Challenge

31. If $\cos\theta = \frac{1}{4}$, find $\sin\theta$.

32. If $\sin\theta = \frac{1}{3}$, find $\tan\theta$.

33. If $\sin\theta = \frac{1}{3}$, find $\dfrac{\cos\theta\tan\theta}{\csc\theta}$

34. If $\tan\theta = \frac{3}{4}$, find $\dfrac{\sin\theta\sec\theta}{\cot\theta}$.

mini-review

1. If y varies inversely as x and $y = 15$ when $x = 7$, find y when $x = 3$.

2. Solve $x^4 - 10x^2 + 24 = 0$.

3. Solve $\log_5(3x - 10) = \log_5 125$.

4. How many Social Security numbers (nine digits) can begin with 127?

5. Find the range and standard deviation for {85, 60, 93, 57, 82, 97, 100}.

16-6   Verifying Trigonometric Identities

You can use the basic trigonometric identities, along with the definitions of the trigonometric functions, to verify other identities. For example, suppose you wish to know if $\sin \theta \sec \theta \cot \theta = 1$ is an identity. To find out, simplify the expression on the left side of the equation by using the identities and definitions.

$$\sin \theta \sec \theta \cot \theta \overset{?}{=} 1$$

$$\sin \theta \cdot \frac{1}{\cos \theta} \cdot \frac{1}{\tan \theta} \overset{?}{=} 1 \qquad sec\,\theta = \frac{1}{\cos\theta} \text{ and } cot\,\theta = \frac{1}{\tan\theta}$$

$$\frac{\sin \theta}{\cos \theta} \cdot \frac{1}{\tan \theta} \overset{?}{=} 1 \qquad Multiply\ \sin\theta\ and\ \frac{1}{\cos\theta}.$$

$$\tan \theta \cdot \frac{1}{\tan \theta} \overset{?}{=} 1 \qquad tan\,\theta = \frac{\sin\theta}{\cos\theta}$$

$$1 = 1$$

Thus, $\sin \theta \sec \theta \cot \theta = 1$ is an identity.

In a way, verifying an identity is like checking the solution to an equation. You do not know if the expressions on each side are equal. That is what you are trying to verify. So, you must simplify one or both sides of the sentence *separately* until they are the same.

Often it is easiest to work with only one side of the sentence. You may choose either side.

Examples

1 **Verify $\tan^2 x - \sin^2 x = \tan^2 x \sin^2 x$.**

$$\tan^2 x - \sin^2 x \overset{?}{=} \tan^2 x \sin^2 x$$

$$\left(\frac{\sin x}{\cos x}\right)^2 - \sin^2 x \overset{?}{=} \tan^2 x \sin^2 x$$

$$\sin^2 x \left(\frac{1}{\cos^2 x} - 1\right) \overset{?}{=} \tan^2 x \sin^2 x$$

$$\sin^2 x (\sec^2 x - 1) \overset{?}{=} \tan^2 x \sin^2 x$$

$$\sin^2 x \tan^2 x \overset{?}{=} \tan^2 x \sin^2 x$$

$$\tan^2 x \sin^2 x = \tan^2 x \sin^2 x$$

Thus, the identity has been verified.

2 **Verify $\cot^2 x \sec^2 x = 1 + \cot^2 x$.**

$$\cot^2 x \sec^2 x \overset{?}{=} 1 + \cot^2 x$$

$$cot\ x = \frac{\cos x}{\sin x} \qquad \left(\frac{\cos x}{\sin x}\right)^2 \left(\frac{1}{\cos x}\right)^2 \overset{?}{=} \csc^2 x \qquad 1 + cot^2 x = \csc^2 x$$

$$sec\ x = \frac{1}{\cos x} \qquad \frac{\cos^2 x}{\sin^2 x} \cdot \frac{1}{\cos^2 x} \overset{?}{=} \left(\frac{1}{\sin x}\right)^2 \qquad csc\ x = \frac{1}{\sin x}$$

$$\frac{1}{\sin^2 x} = \frac{1}{\sin^2 x}$$

Thus, the identity has been verified.

The following suggestions are helpful in verifying trigonometric identities. Study the examples to see how these suggestions can be used to verify an identity.

1. **Start with the more complicated side of the equation. Transform the expression into the form of the simpler side.**

2. **Substitute one or more basic trigonometric identities to simplify the expression.**

3. **Try factoring or multiplying to simplify the expression.**

4. **Multiply both numerator and denominator by the same trigonometric expression.**

There is often more than one way to verify an identity. Remember that verifying an identity is not the same as solving an equation.

Examples

3 Verify that $1 - \cot^4 x = 2 \csc^2 x - \csc^4 x$.

$$1 - \cot^4 x \overset{?}{=} 2 \csc^2 x - \csc^4 x$$

$$(1 - \cot^2 x)(1 + \cot^2 x) \overset{?}{=} 2 \csc^2 x - \csc^4 x \qquad \textit{Factor.}$$

$$[1 - (\csc^2 x - 1)][\csc^2 x] \overset{?}{=} 2 \csc^2 x - \csc^4 x \qquad \textit{1 + cot}^2 \textit{ x = csc}^2 \textit{ x}$$

$$[2 - \csc^2 x][\csc^2 x] \overset{?}{=} 2 \csc^2 x - \csc^4 x \qquad \textit{Simplify.}$$

$$2 \csc^2 x - \csc^4 x = 2 \csc^2 x - \csc^4 x$$

4 Verify that $\dfrac{1 - \cos x}{\sin x} = \dfrac{\sin x}{1 + \cos x}$.

$$\frac{1 - \cos x}{\sin x} \overset{?}{=} \frac{\sin x}{1 + \cos x}$$

$$\frac{1 - \cos x}{\sin x} \overset{?}{=} \frac{\sin x(1 - \cos x)}{(1 + \cos x)(1 - \cos x)} \qquad \textit{Multiply numerator and denominator by 1 − cos x.}$$

$$\frac{1 - \cos x}{\sin x} \overset{?}{=} \frac{\sin x(1 - \cos x)}{1 - \cos^2 x} \qquad \textit{Simplify the denominator.}$$

$$\frac{1 - \cos x}{\sin x} \overset{?}{=} \frac{\sin x(1 - \cos x)}{\sin^2 x} \qquad \textit{Substitute sin}^2 \textit{x for 1 − cos}^2 \textit{x.}$$

$$\frac{1 - \cos x}{\sin x} = \frac{1 - \cos x}{\sin x} \qquad \textit{Simplify.}$$

Exploratory Exercises

Simplify each of the following.

1. $\csc^2\theta - \cot^2\theta$

2. $\tan\theta\cos^2\theta$

3. $\dfrac{\sin^2\theta + \cos^2\theta}{\sin^2\theta}$

4. $\dfrac{\tan x}{\sin x}$

5. $\csc^2\gamma - \cot^2\gamma$

6. $\cos\alpha\csc\alpha$

7. $\sin\theta\cot\theta$

8. $\tan x\csc x$

9. $\dfrac{\cos x\csc x}{\tan x}$

Written Exercises

Verify each identity.

1. $\tan\beta(\cot\beta + \tan\beta) = \sec^2\beta$

2. $\cos^2\theta + \tan^2\theta\cos^2\theta = 1$

3. $\csc x\sec x = \cot x + \tan x$

4. $\sec^2 x - \tan^2 x = \tan x\cot x$

5. $\dfrac{\sec\theta}{\sin\theta} - \dfrac{\sin\theta}{\cos\theta} = \cot\theta$

6. $\dfrac{1}{\sec^2\theta} + \dfrac{1}{\csc^2\theta} = 1$

7. $\dfrac{\sin\alpha}{1 - \cos\alpha} + \dfrac{1 - \cos\alpha}{\sin\alpha} = 2\csc\alpha$

8. $\dfrac{\sec\alpha + \csc\alpha}{1 + \tan\alpha} = \csc\alpha$

9. $\dfrac{\cos^2 x}{1 - \sin x} = 1 + \sin x$

10. $\dfrac{1 - \cos\theta}{1 + \cos\theta} = (\csc\theta - \cot\theta)^2$

11. $\dfrac{\sin\theta}{\sec\theta} = \dfrac{1}{\tan\theta + \cot\theta}$

12. $\dfrac{\sec\theta + 1}{\tan\theta} = \dfrac{\tan\theta}{\sec\theta - 1}$

13. $\dfrac{\cot x + \csc x}{\sin x + \tan x} = \cot x\csc x$

14. $\dfrac{1 - 2\cos^2\theta}{\sin\theta\cos\theta} = \tan\theta - \cot\theta$

15. $\cos^2 x + \tan^2 x\cos^2 x = 1$

16. $\dfrac{\cos x}{1 + \sin x} + \dfrac{\cos x}{1 - \sin x} = 2\sec x$

17. $\dfrac{1 + \tan^2\theta}{\csc^2\theta} = \tan^2\theta$

18. $\tan x(\cot x + \tan x) = \sec^2 x$

19. $\dfrac{\sec x}{\sin x} - \dfrac{\sin x}{\cos x} = \cot x$

20. $\dfrac{1 + \tan\gamma}{1 + \cot\gamma} = \dfrac{\sin\gamma}{\cos\gamma}$

21. $\cos^4 x - \sin^4 x = \cos^2 x - \sin^2 x$

22. $1 + \sec^2 x\sin^2 x = \sec^2 x$

23. $\dfrac{\tan^2 x}{\sec x - 1} = 1 + \dfrac{1}{\cos x}$

24. $\sin\theta + \cos\theta = \dfrac{1 + \tan\theta}{\sec\theta}$

25. $\dfrac{1 + \sin x}{\sin x} = \dfrac{\cot^2 x}{\csc x - 1}$

26. $\dfrac{\sin x}{\sin x + \cos x} = \dfrac{\tan x}{1 + \tan x}$

 # Using Calculators _____ **The Reciprocal Key**

To evaluate the secant, cosecant, or cotangent of an angle, use the $\boxed{1/x}$ key with the cosine, sine, or tangent keys.

Example: Evaluate $\cot\dfrac{7\pi}{6}$.   *Make sure the calculator is in radian mode.*

ENTER: 7 $\boxed{\times}$ $\boxed{\pi}$ $\boxed{\div}$ 6 $\boxed{=}$ $\boxed{\text{TAN}}$ $\boxed{1/x}$

DISPLAY: 7   3.1415927 21.991149 6 3.6651914 0.064057 15.611082

Exercises   Find each value to four decimal places.

1. $\sec 87°$

2. $\cot\dfrac{9\pi}{11}$

3. $\csc 12°$

4. $\sec\dfrac{3\pi}{5}$

5. $\csc 90°$

6. $\cot\dfrac{8\pi}{3}$

7. What happens when you try to evaluate $\sec 90°$, $\csc 0$, or $\cot\pi$?   Why?

16-7   Differences and Sums

It is often helpful to use formulas for the trigonometric values of the difference or sum of two angles. For example, you could find sin 15° by evaluating sin (45 − 30)°.

The following diagram shows two different angles in standard position on the unit circle.

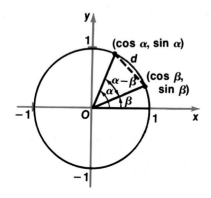

Use the distance formula to find d.

$$d = \sqrt{(\cos\alpha - \cos\beta)^2 + (\sin\alpha - \sin\beta)^2}$$

$$
\begin{aligned}
d^2 &= (\cos\alpha - \cos\beta)^2 + (\sin\alpha - \sin\beta)^2 \\
&= (\cos^2\alpha - 2\cos\alpha\cos\beta + \cos^2\beta) \\
&\quad + (\sin^2\alpha - 2\sin\alpha\sin\beta + \sin^2\beta) \\
&= \cos^2\alpha + \sin^2\alpha + \cos^2\beta + \sin^2\beta \\
&\quad - 2\cos\alpha\cos\beta - 2\sin\alpha\sin\beta \\
&= 1 + 1 - 2\cos\alpha\cos\beta - 2\sin\alpha\sin\beta \\
&= 2 - 2\cos\alpha\cos\beta - 2\sin\alpha\sin\beta
\end{aligned}
$$

The diagram below shows the angle having measure $\alpha - \beta$ in standard position on the unit circle.

$$d = \sqrt{[\cos(\alpha - \beta) - 1]^2 + [\sin(\alpha - \beta) - 0]^2}$$

$$
\begin{aligned}
d^2 &= [\cos(\alpha - \beta) - 1]^2 + [\sin(\alpha - \beta) - 0]^2 \\
&= [\cos^2(\alpha - \beta) - 2\cos(\alpha - \beta) + 1] + [\sin^2(\alpha - \beta)] \\
&= \cos^2(\alpha - \beta) + \sin^2(\alpha - \beta) - 2\cos(\alpha - \beta) + 1 \\
&= \qquad\qquad 1 \qquad\qquad - 2\cos(\alpha - \beta) + 1 \\
&= 2 - 2\cos(\alpha - \beta)
\end{aligned}
$$

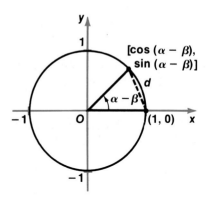

By equating the two expressions obtained for d^2, it is possible to find a formula for $\cos(\alpha - \beta)$.

$$2 - 2\cos(\alpha - \beta) = 2 - 2\cos\alpha\cos\beta - 2\sin\alpha\sin\beta$$

$$-1 + \cos(\alpha - \beta) = -1 + \cos\alpha\cos\beta + \sin\alpha\sin\beta \qquad \textit{Divide both sides by } -2.$$

$$\cos(\alpha - \beta) = \cos\alpha\cos\beta + \sin\alpha\sin\beta \qquad \textit{Add 1 to both sides.}$$

Using the formula for $\cos(\alpha - \beta)$, you can find a formula for the expression $\cos(\alpha + \beta)$.

$$
\begin{aligned}
\cos(\alpha + \beta) &= \cos[\alpha - (-\beta)] \\
&= \cos\alpha\cos(-\beta) + \sin\alpha\sin(-\beta) \\
&= \cos\alpha\cos\beta - \sin\alpha\sin\beta
\end{aligned}
$$

Examples

1 Use the formula for cos (α − β) to find cos (90° − θ).

$$\cos (90° - \theta) = \cos 90° \cos \theta + \sin 90° \sin \theta$$
$$= 0 \cdot \cos \theta + 1 \cdot \sin \theta$$
$$= \sin \theta$$

2 Use the formula cos (90° − θ) = sin θ to find sin (90° − γ).

$$\sin (90° - \gamma) = \cos [90° - (90° - \gamma)]$$
$$= \cos (90° - 90° + \gamma)$$
$$= \cos \gamma$$

3 Find sin (α − β).

$$\sin (\alpha - \beta) = \cos [90° - (\alpha - \beta)]$$
$$= \cos [(90° - \alpha) + \beta]$$
$$= \cos (90° - \alpha) \cos \beta - \sin (90° - \alpha) \sin \beta$$
$$= \sin \alpha \cos \beta - \cos \alpha \sin \beta$$

In a similar manner, you can derive two formulas for sin (α + β).

The following identities hold for all values of α and β.

$$\cos (\alpha \pm \beta) = \cos\alpha \cos\beta \mp \sin\alpha \sin\beta$$
$$\sin (\alpha \pm \beta) = \sin\alpha \cos\beta \pm \cos\alpha \sin\beta$$

Difference and Sum Formulas

The examples below show how to evaluate expressions using the sum and difference formulas.

Examples

4 Find sin 15°.

$$\sin 15° = \sin (45° - 30°)$$
$$= \sin 45° \cos 30° - \cos 45° \sin 30°$$
$$= \frac{\sqrt{2}}{2} \cdot \frac{\sqrt{3}}{2} - \frac{\sqrt{2}}{2} \cdot \frac{1}{2}$$
$$= \frac{\sqrt{6} - \sqrt{2}}{4}$$

5 Find cos 75°.

$$\cos 75° = \cos (45° + 30°)$$
$$= \cos 45° \cos 30° - \sin 45° \sin 30°$$
$$= \frac{\sqrt{2}}{2} \cdot \frac{\sqrt{3}}{2} - \frac{\sqrt{2}}{2} \cdot \frac{1}{2}$$
$$= \frac{\sqrt{6} - \sqrt{2}}{4}$$

Exploratory Exercises

Write each angle measure in terms of sums or differences of 30°, 45°, 60°, and 90° or their multiples.

1. 105°
2. −15°
3. −165°
4. 165°
5. 75°
6. −75°
7. 285°
8. 255°

Written Exercises

Evaluate each expression.

1. sin 75°
2. sin 165°
3. sin 285°
4. cos 105°
5. cos 195°
6. cos 255°
7. cos 15°
8. sin 105°
9. cos 165°
10. cos 345°

Verify each of the following.

11. $\sin(270° − \theta) = −\cos\theta$
12. $\cos(270° − \theta) = −\sin\theta$
13. $\sin(180° + \theta) = −\sin\theta$
14. $\cos(180° + \theta) = −\cos\theta$
15. $\sin(90° + \theta) = \cos\theta$
16. $\cos(90° + \theta) = −\sin\theta$

Evaluate each expression.

17. $\cos 25° \cos 5° − \sin 25° \sin 5°$
18. $\sin 40° \cos 20° + \cos 40° \sin 20°$
19. $\cos 80° \cos 20° + \sin 80° \sin 20°$
20. $\sin 65° \cos 35° − \cos 65° \sin 35°$

Verify each of the following identities.

21. $\sin(x + y)\sin(x − y) = \sin^2 x − \sin^2 y$
22. $\sin\left(\theta + \dfrac{\pi}{3}\right) − \cos\left(\theta + \dfrac{\pi}{6}\right) = \sin\theta$
23. $\sin(60° + \theta) + \sin(60° − \theta) = \sqrt{3}\cos\theta$
24. $\cos(x + y) + \cos(x − y) = 2\cos x \cos y$
25. $\cos(x + y)\cos(x − y) = \cos^2 y − \sin^2 x$
26. $\sin(x + 30°) + \cos(x + 60°) = \cos x$
27. $\cos(30° + x) − \cos(30° − x) = −\sin x$
28. $\sin\left(x + \dfrac{\pi}{4}\right) + \cos\left(x + \dfrac{\pi}{4}\right) = \sqrt{2}\cos x$

Use the identity $\tan(\alpha − \beta) = \dfrac{\tan\alpha − \tan\beta}{1 + \tan\alpha\,\tan\beta}$ to find the following.

29. $\tan(225° − 120°)$
30. $\tan(315° − 120°)$
31. $\tan(225° − 240°)$
32. $\tan(315° + 60°)$
33. $\tan(30° + 30°)$
34. $\tan(210° + 120°)$
35. $\tan 285°$
36. $\tan 195°$
37. $\tan 165°$
38. $\tan 75°$
39. $\tan(180° − \theta)$
40. $\tan(45° + \beta)$

Challenge

41. Use the formulas for $\sin(\alpha − \beta)$ and $\cos(\alpha − \beta)$ to derive the formula for $\tan(\alpha − \beta)$.

    (*Hint:* Divide all terms of the expression by $\cos\alpha \cos\beta$.)

42. Use the sum and difference formulas for sin and cos to verify the following identities.

    $\cos(−\alpha) = \cos\alpha$
    $\sin(−\alpha) = −\sin\alpha$

Problem Solving

In most problems, a set of conditions or facts is given and you must arrive at a solution. However, in some cases, you are given the final solution or goal and then asked for an intermediate condition. In other cases, it may be faster to determine how the problem ends and then work backwards rather than to start from the beginning. Consider the following example.

Example: If the sum of two numbers is 2 and the product of these same two numbers is 3, find the sum of the reciprocals of these two numbers.

A first reaction might be to set up the following system of equations.

$$x + y = 2$$
$$xy = 3$$

But solving this system is very complicated, involving complex numbers. Rather than using this approach, work backwards. The desired outcome is $\frac{1}{x} + \frac{1}{y}$.

$$\frac{1}{x} + \frac{1}{y} = \frac{y}{xy} + \frac{x}{xy} \qquad \textit{The LCD is xy.}$$
$$= \frac{x + y}{xy}$$

The two original equations immediately reveal the numerator and denominator of this fraction.

$$\frac{x + y}{xy} = \frac{2}{3} \qquad \textit{Substitute.}$$

The sum of the reciprocals is $\frac{2}{3}$.

Exercises
Solve each problem.

1. A pirate found a treasure chest containing silver coins. He buried half of them and gave half of the remaining coins to his mother. If he was left with 4550 coins, how many were in the treasure chest that he found?

2. Tim collects model cars. He decides to give them away. First he gives half of them plus half a car more to Amy. Then he gives half of what is left plus half a car more to Tina. Then he has one car left which he gives to Aaron. How many cars did Tim start with? (Assume that no car is cut in half.)

3. Paul, Eric, and Garnet are playing a card game. They have a rule that when a player loses a hand, he must subtract enough points from his score to double each of the other players' scores. First Paul loses a hand, then Eric, and then Garnet. Each player now has 8 points. Who lost the most points?

4. If the sum of two numbers is 2 and the product of the same two numbers is 3, find the sum of the squares of the reciprocals of these numbers.

16-8 Double Angles and Half Angles

You can use the formula for $\sin(\alpha + \beta)$ to find $\sin 2\theta$.

$$\begin{aligned}
\sin 2\theta &= \sin(\theta + \theta) \\
&= \sin\theta\cos\theta + \cos\theta\sin\theta \\
&= 2\sin\theta\cos\theta
\end{aligned}$$

Similarly, a formula for $\cos 2\theta$ can be found.

$$\begin{aligned}
\cos 2\theta &= \cos(\theta + \theta) \\
&= \cos\theta\cos\theta - \sin\theta\sin\theta \\
&= \cos^2\theta - \sin^2\theta
\end{aligned}$$

Alternate forms can also be found by making substitutions.

$\cos^2\theta - \sin^2\theta = (1 - \sin^2\theta) - \sin^2\theta$ or $1 - 2\sin^2\theta$ *Substitute $1 - \sin^2\theta$ for $\cos^2\theta$.*

$\cos^2\theta - \sin^2\theta = \cos^2\theta - (1 - \cos^2\theta)$ or $2\cos^2\theta - 1$ *Substitute $1 - \cos^2\theta$ for $\sin^2\theta$.*

These formulas are known as the **double-angle formulas.**

The following identities hold for all values of θ.

$$\sin 2\theta = 2\sin\theta\cos\theta \qquad \begin{aligned} \cos 2\theta &= \cos^2\theta - \sin^2\theta \\ &= 1 - 2\sin^2\theta \\ &= 2\cos^2\theta - 1 \end{aligned}$$

Double-Angle Formulas

Example

1 **Suppose x is between $90°$ and $180°$ and $\sin x = \dfrac{3}{5}$. Find $\sin 2x$.**

Since $\sin 2x = 2\sin x\cos x$, find $\cos x$ first. Use $\cos^2 x + \sin^2 x = 1$.

$$\cos^2 x + \sin^2 x = 1$$

$$\cos^2 x + \left(\frac{3}{5}\right)^2 = 1 \qquad \textit{Substitute } \frac{3}{5} \textit{ for sin x.}$$

$$\cos^2 x = 1 - \left(\frac{3}{5}\right)^2$$

$$= \frac{16}{25}$$

$$\cos x = \pm\sqrt{\frac{16}{25}} \text{ or } \pm\frac{4}{5}$$

But x is between $90°$ and $180°$, so $\cos x$ must be negative.

$$\begin{aligned}
\sin 2x &= 2\sin x\cos x \\
&= 2\left(\frac{3}{5}\right)\left(-\frac{4}{5}\right) \\
&= -\frac{24}{25}
\end{aligned}$$

There are also formulas for $\cos\frac{\alpha}{2}$ and $\sin\frac{\alpha}{2}$.

$$2\cos^2\theta - 1 = \cos 2\theta$$

Use double-angle formulas.
Substitute α for 2θ
and $\frac{\alpha}{2}$ for θ.

$$1 - 2\sin^2\theta = \cos 2\theta$$

$$2\cos^2\frac{\alpha}{2} - 1 = \cos\alpha$$

$$1 - 2\sin^2\frac{\alpha}{2} = \cos\alpha$$

$$\cos^2\frac{\alpha}{2} = \frac{1+\cos\alpha}{2}$$

Solve for the squared term.

$$\sin^2\frac{\alpha}{2} = \frac{1-\cos\alpha}{2}$$

$$\cos\frac{\alpha}{2} = \pm\sqrt{\frac{1+\cos\alpha}{2}}$$

Take the square root of both sides.

$$\sin\frac{\alpha}{2} = \pm\sqrt{\frac{1-\cos\alpha}{2}}$$

These formulas are known as the half-angle formulas.

The following identities hold for all values of α.

$$\cos\frac{\alpha}{2} = \pm\sqrt{\frac{1+\cos\alpha}{2}} \text{ and } \sin\frac{\alpha}{2} = \pm\sqrt{\frac{1-\cos\alpha}{2}}$$

Half-Angle Formulas

Examples

2 **Find $\cos 105°$.**

$$\cos 105° = \cos\frac{210°}{2}$$

$$= \pm\sqrt{\frac{1+\cos 210°}{2}} \qquad \cos 210° = -\frac{\sqrt{3}}{2}$$

$$= \pm\sqrt{\frac{1+\left(-\frac{\sqrt{3}}{2}\right)}{2}} \text{ or } \pm\frac{\sqrt{2-\sqrt{3}}}{2}$$

Since $105°$ is between $90°$ and $180°$, the value of $\cos 105°$ is negative.

The solution is $-\frac{\sqrt{2-\sqrt{3}}}{2}$.

3 **Find $\sin 67\frac{1}{2}°$.**

$$\sin 67\frac{1}{2}° = \sin\frac{135°}{2}$$

$$= \pm\sqrt{\frac{1-\cos 135°}{2}} \qquad \cos 135° = -\frac{\sqrt{2}}{2}$$

$$= \pm\sqrt{\frac{1+\frac{\sqrt{2}}{2}}{2}} \text{ or } \pm\frac{\sqrt{2+\sqrt{2}}}{2}$$

Since $67\frac{1}{2}°$ is between $0°$ and $90°$ the value of $\sin 67\frac{1}{2}°$ is positive.

The solution is $\frac{\sqrt{2+\sqrt{2}}}{2}$.

Exploratory Exercises

Answer each of the following.

1. x is a first quadrant angle. In which quadrant does the terminal side for $2x$ lie?

2. x is a second quadrant angle. In which quadrant does the terminal side for $2x$ lie?

3. x is a third quadrant angle. In which quadrant does the terminal side for $2x$ lie?

4. x is a fourth quadrant angle. In which quadrant does the terminal side for $2x$ lie?

5. $2x$ is a first quadrant angle. In which quadrant does the terminal side for x lie?

6. $2x$ is a second quadrant angle. In which quadrant does the terminal side for x lie?

7. $2x$ is a third quadrant angle. In which quadrant does the terminal side for x lie?

8. $2x$ is a fourth quadrant angle. In which quadrant does the terminal side for x lie?

9. $\frac{x}{2}$ is a first quadrant angle. In which quadrant does the terminal side for x lie?

10. $\frac{x}{2}$ is a second quadrant angle. In which quadrant does the terminal side for x lie?

11. $\frac{x}{2}$ is a third quadrant angle. In which quadrant does the terminal side for x lie?

12. $\frac{x}{2}$ is a fourth quadrant angle. In which quadrant does the terminal side for x lie?

13. x is a first quadrant angle. In which quadrant does the terminal side for $\frac{x}{2}$ lie?

14. x is a second quadrant angle. In which quadrant does the terminal side for $\frac{x}{2}$ lie?

15. x is a third quadrant angle. In which quadrant does the terminal side for $\frac{x}{2}$ lie?

16. x is a fourth quadrant angle. In which quadrant does the terminal side for $\frac{x}{2}$ lie?

Written Exercises

Find $\sin 2x$, $\cos 2x$, $\sin \frac{x}{2}$, and $\cos \frac{x}{2}$ for each of the following.

1. $\sin x = \frac{1}{2}$, x is in the first quadrant

2. $\cos x = \frac{3}{5}$, x is in the first quadrant

3. $\cos x = -\frac{2}{3}$, x is in the third quadrant

4. $\sin x = \frac{4}{5}$, x is in the second quadrant

5. $\sin x = \frac{5}{13}$, x is in the second quadrant

6. $\cos x = \frac{1}{5}$, x is in the fourth quadrant

7. $\sin x = -\frac{3}{4}$, x is in the fourth quadrant

8. $\cos x = -\frac{1}{3}$, x is in the third quadrant

9. $\cos x = -\frac{1}{4}$, x is in the second quadrant

10. $\sin x = -\frac{3}{5}$, x is in the third quadrant

11. $\sin x = -\frac{3}{8}$, x is in the fourth quadrant

12. $\cos x = \frac{1}{6}$, x is in the first quadrant

13. $\sin x = -\frac{1}{4}$, x is in the third quadrant

14. $\cos x = -\frac{1}{3}$, x is in the second quadrant

Verify each identity.

15. $\cos^2 2x + 4 \sin^2 x \cos^2 x = 1$

16. $(\sin x + \cos x)^2 = 1 + \sin 2x$

17. $\sin^4 x - \cos^4 x = 2 \sin^2 x - 1$

18. $\sin 2x = 2 \cot x \sin^2 x$

19. $\sin^2 \theta = \frac{1}{2}(1 - \cos 2\theta)$

20. $\frac{1}{\sin x \cos x} - \frac{\cos x}{\sin x} = \tan x$

21. $\tan^2 \frac{x}{2} = \frac{1 - \cos x}{1 + \cos x}$

22. $2 \cos^2 \frac{x}{2} = 1 + \cos x$

16-9   Solving Trigonometric Equations

Trigonometric identities are true for *all* values of the variable involved. Most trigonometric equations are true for *some* but *not all* values of the variable.

Example

1   **Solve $\sin 2\theta + \sin \theta = 0$ if $0° \leq \theta < 360°$.**

$$\sin 2\theta + \sin \theta = 0$$

$$2 \sin \theta \cos \theta + \sin \theta = 0 \qquad \text{\small $\sin 2\theta = 2 \sin \theta \cos \theta$}$$

$$\sin \theta (2 \cos \theta + 1) = 0 \qquad \text{\small Factor.}$$

$$\sin \theta = 0 \quad \text{or} \quad 2 \cos \theta + 1 = 0$$

$$\theta = 0°, 180° \qquad\qquad \cos \theta = -\frac{1}{2}$$

$$\theta = 120°, 240° \qquad \text{\small The graphs often help you find the values of θ.}$$

The solutions are 0°, 120°, 180°, and 240°.

Usually trigonometric equations are solved for values of the variable between 0° and 360° or 0 radians and 2π radians. There are solutions outside that interval. These other solutions differ by integral multiples of the period of the function.

Example

2   **Solve $\cos \theta + 1 = 0$ for all values of θ if θ is measured in radians.**

The equation can be written in the form $\cos \theta = -1$. By looking at the graph, the solutions are π, 3π, 5π, and so on and $-\pi$, -3π, -5π, and so on.

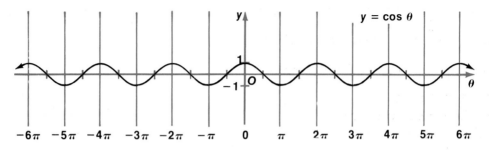

The only solution in the interval 0 radians to 2π radians is π. The period of cosine is 2π radians. So the solutions can be written as $\pi + 2n\pi$ where n is an integer.

If an equation cannot be easily solved by factoring, try writing the expression in terms of only one trigonometric function.

Example

3 **Solve $4 \sin x \cos x = -\sqrt{3}$.**

$$4 \sin x \cos x = -\sqrt{3}$$

$$2(2 \sin x \cos x) = -\sqrt{3}$$

$$2 \sin x \cos x = -\frac{\sqrt{3}}{2}$$

$$\sin 2x = -\frac{\sqrt{3}}{2} \qquad 2 \sin x \cos x = \sin 2x$$

$$2x = \frac{4\pi}{3} + 2n\pi, \frac{5\pi}{3} + 2n\pi \text{ for } n \text{ an integer}$$

$$x = \frac{2}{3}\pi + n\pi, \frac{5}{6}\pi + n\pi$$

The solutions are $\frac{2}{3}\pi + n\pi$ and $\frac{5}{6}\pi + n\pi$, where n is an integer.

Some trigonometric equations have *no solutions*. In other words, there is no replacement for the variable that will make the sentence true. For example, the equation $\cos x = 2$ has no solution. The solution set is $\emptyset$.

In the following examples, the solutions are found for values of the variable between 0 radians or 0° and 2π radians or 360°. The other solutions differ by integral multiples of the period of the function.

Example

4 **Solve $2 \cos^2 \theta - 3 \cos \theta - 2 = 0$ if $0 \le \theta < 2\pi$.**

$$2 \cos^2 \theta - 3 \cos \theta - 2 = 0$$

$$(\cos \theta - 2)(2 \cos \theta + 1) = 0$$

$$\cos \theta - 2 = 0 \qquad \text{or} \qquad 2 \cos \theta + 1 = 0$$

$$\cos \theta = 2 \qquad\qquad\qquad 2 \cos \theta = -1$$

There is no solution to $\cos \theta = 2$ because all values of $\cos \theta$ are between -1 and 1 inclusive.

$$\cos \theta = -\frac{1}{2}$$

$$\theta = \frac{2\pi}{3} \text{ or } \frac{4\pi}{3}$$

The solutions are $\frac{2\pi}{3}$ and $\frac{4\pi}{3}$.

It is important to check your solutions. Some algebraic operations may introduce answers that are *not* solutions to the original equation.

Example

5 **Solve $\sin x = 1 - \cos x$ if $0° \le x < 360°$.**

$$\sin x = 1 - \cos x$$
$$\sin^2 x = 1 - 2\cos x + \cos^2 x \qquad \text{Square both sides.}$$
$$1 - \cos^2 x = 1 - 2\cos x + \cos^2 x \qquad \sin^2 x = 1 - \cos^2 x$$
$$0 = 2\cos^2 x - 2\cos x$$
$$0 = 2\cos x(\cos x - 1)$$

$$2\cos x = 0 \qquad \text{or} \qquad \cos x - 1 = 0$$
$$\cos x = 0 \qquad\qquad\qquad \cos x = 1$$
$$x = 90°, 270° \qquad\qquad\qquad x = 0°$$

The solutions appear to be 90°, 270°, 0°. But, 270° does *not* satisfy the original equation. Thus, the solutions are 0° and 90°.

Exploratory Exercises

How many solutions does each equation have if $0° \le \theta < 360°$?

1. $\sin \theta = 1$

2. $\sin \theta = \frac{1}{2}$

3. $\cos \theta = -\frac{\sqrt{3}}{2}$

4. $\tan \theta = 1$

5. $\tan \theta = -3$

6. $\tan^2 \theta = 1$

7. $\sin 2\theta = \frac{1}{2}$

8. $\cos 2\theta = \frac{3}{2}$

9. $\sin 2\theta = -\frac{\sqrt{3}}{2}$

10. $\cos^2 \theta = 1$

11. $\sin 3\theta = -2$

12. $\cos 8\theta = 1$

Written Exercises

Find all solutions if $0° \le x < 360°$.

1. $2\sin^2 x - 1 = 0$

2. $4\cos^2 x = 1$

3. $2\sin^2 x + \sin x = 0$

4. $2\cos^2 x = \sin x + 1$

5. $\sin 2x = \cos x$

6. $\cos x = 3\cos x - 2$

7. $\sin^2 x + \cos 2x - \cos x = 0$

8. $\sin 2x = 2\cos x$

9. $4\sin^2 x - 4\sin x + 1 = 0$

10. $\sin^2 x = \cos^2 x - 1$

Solve each equation for all values of x.

11. $\cos 2x = \cos x$

12. $\sin^2 x - 2\sin x - 3 = 0$

13. $\sin x = \cos x$

14. $\tan x = \sin x$

15. $3\cos 2x - 5\cos x = 1$

16. $\tan^2 x - \sqrt{3}\tan x = 0$

17. $\sin x = 1 + \cos x$

18. $\cos 2x + \cos x + 1 = 0$

19. $\sin \frac{x}{2} + \cos x = 1$

20. $\sin \frac{x}{2} + \cos \frac{x}{2} = \sqrt{2}$

mini-review

1. Solve $\sqrt{5x - 1} = x - 3$.

2. Express $\log_x \left(\frac{ab}{c} \right)$ as the sum or difference of simpler logarithmic expressions.

3. Find the sum of this series:
$$1 + \frac{1}{2} + \frac{1}{4} + \frac{1}{8} + \ldots.$$

4. What are the odds of tossing a die and getting a 3 or a 5?

5. The number of baskets made by the five-man basketball team is normally distributed. The mean is 9 baskets and the standard deviation is 2 baskets. What percentage of the players made between 5 and 13 baskets?

16-10   Inverse Trigonometric Functions

The inverse of a function can be found by reversing the order of the components of each ordered pair in the given function.

> Since $(0, 1)$ is on the graph of the cosine function, $(1, 0)$ is on the graph of its inverse.
> Since $(2\pi, 1)$ is on the graph of the cosine function, $(1, 2\pi)$ is on the graph of its inverse.

The inverse of the cosine function is *not* a function. Why?
   Consider only a part of the domain of the cosine function, namely any x so that $0 \le x \le \pi$. It is possible to define a new function, called Cosine, whose inverse is a function.

$$y = \text{Cos}\,x \text{ if and only if } y = \cos x \text{ and } 0 \le x \le \pi$$

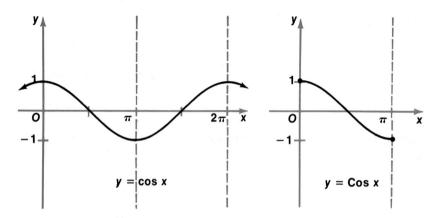

$y = \cos x$	$y = \text{Cos } x$

The domain is
   $\{x \,|\, x \text{ is a real number}\}$.
The range is $\{y \,|\, -1 \le y \le 1\}$.
The inverse is *not* a function.

The domain is $\{x \,|\, 0 \le x \le \pi\}$.
The range is $\{y \,|\, -1 \le y \le 1\}$.
The inverse is a function.

   The values in the domain of Cosine are called **principal values.** Other new functions that have inverses can be defined in a similar way.

$$y = \text{Sin}\,x \text{ if and only if } y = \sin x \text{ and } -\frac{\pi}{2} \le x \le \frac{\pi}{2}.$$

$$y = \text{Tan}\,x \text{ if and only if } y = \tan x \text{ and } -\frac{\pi}{2} < x < \frac{\pi}{2}.$$

The principal values of x in $y = \text{Sin}\,x$ are $\left\{x \,\middle|\, -\frac{\pi}{2} \le x \le \frac{\pi}{2}\right\}$.

The principal values of x in $y = \text{Tan}\,x$ are $\left\{x \,\middle|\, -\frac{\pi}{2} < x < \frac{\pi}{2}\right\}$.

The inverse cosine function is also called the Arccosine function and is symbolized by **Cos**$^{-1}$ or **Arccos.**

> **Given $y = \text{Cos}\,x$, the inverse cosine function is defined by the following equation.**
>
> $$y = \text{Cos}^{-1}x$$

Definition of Inverse Cosine

The Arccosine function has the following characteristics.

1. Its domain is the set of real numbers from -1 to 1.
2. Its range is the set of angle measurements from 0 to π.
3. $\text{Cos}\,x = y$ if and only if $\text{Cos}^{-1}y = x$.
4. $(\text{Cos}^{-1} \circ \text{Cos})(x) = (\text{Cos} \circ \text{Cos}^{-1})(x) = x$
5. Its graph is shown at the right.

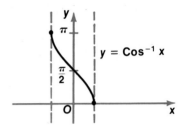

The Arcsine and Arctangent functions are defined similarly.

> **Given $y = \text{Sin}\,x$, the inverse sine function is defined by the following equation.**
>
> $$y = \text{Sin}^{-1}x$$

Definition of Inverse Sine

> **Given $y = \text{Tan}\,x$, the inverse tangent function is defined by the following equation.**
>
> $$y = \text{Tan}^{-1}x$$

Definition of Inverse Tangent

The graphs of the inverse sine and inverse tangent functions are shown at the right.

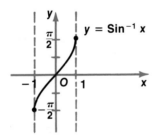
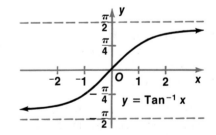

Examples

1 Find $\text{Cos}^{-1}\left(-\dfrac{\sqrt{3}}{2}\right)$.

$$\theta = \text{Cos}^{-1}\left(-\frac{\sqrt{3}}{2}\right)$$

$$\text{Cos}\,\theta = -\frac{\sqrt{3}}{2}$$

$$\theta = 150° \quad \textit{Why is } \theta \textit{ not } 210°?$$

2 Find $\cos\left(\text{Sin}^{-1}\dfrac{1}{2}\right)$.

$$\text{Let } \theta = \text{Sin}^{-1}\frac{1}{2}$$

$$\text{then Sin}\,\theta = \frac{1}{2} \text{ so } \theta = 30°$$

$$\text{Cos}\left(\text{Sin}^{-1}\frac{1}{2}\right) = \text{Cos}\,30°$$

$$= \frac{\sqrt{3}}{2}$$

In the examples thus far, the principal value of each inverse trigonometric function was known to be the value of a trigonometric function for some angle. Sometimes it is *not* known which angle the principal value corresponds to. In such a case, a diagram may be helpful.

Examples

3 Find $\sin\left(\text{Cos}^{-1}\frac{2}{3}\right)$.

Let $\theta = \text{Cos}^{-1}\frac{2}{3}$.

From the diagram, we see

that $\left(\frac{2}{3}\right)^2 + \sin^2\theta = 1$.

$\sin^2\theta = 1 - \frac{4}{9}$ *Solve for $\sin\theta$.*

$\sin^2\theta = \frac{5}{9}$

$\sin\theta = \frac{\sqrt{5}}{3}$

Therefore, $\sin\left(\text{Cos}^{-1}\frac{2}{3}\right) = \frac{\sqrt{5}}{3}$.

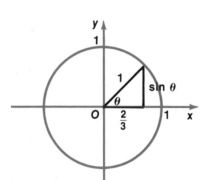

4 Find $\sin\left[\text{Cos}^{-1}\left(-\frac{1}{2}\right) + \text{Tan}^{-1}1\right]$.

Let $\alpha = \text{Cos}^{-1}\left(-\frac{1}{2}\right)$ and let $\beta = \text{Tan}^{-1}1$.

$\text{Cos}\,\alpha = -\frac{1}{2}$ $\text{Tan}\,\beta = 1$

$\alpha = 120°$ $\beta = 45°$

$\sin\left[\text{Cos}^{-1}\left(-\frac{1}{2}\right) + \text{Tan}^{-1}1\right] = \sin(\alpha + \beta)$

$= \sin(120° + 45°)$

$= \sin 120° \cos 45° + \cos 120° \sin 45°$

$= \frac{\sqrt{3}}{2} \cdot \frac{\sqrt{2}}{2} + \left(-\frac{1}{2}\right) \cdot \frac{\sqrt{2}}{2}$ or $\frac{\sqrt{6} - \sqrt{2}}{4}$

Exploratory Exercises

Find each of the following.

1. $\text{Sin}\,\frac{\pi}{6}$

2. $\text{Cos}^{-1}\frac{1}{2}$

3. $\text{Sin}^{-1}\left(-\frac{\sqrt{3}}{2}\right)$

4. $\text{Cos}\,300°$

5. $\text{Tan}\,\pi$

6. $\text{Arctan}\,1$

7. $\text{Tan}\,\frac{\pi}{4}$

8. $\text{Sin}^{-1}\left(-\frac{1}{2}\right)$

9. $\text{Cos}^{-1}\left(-\frac{\sqrt{3}}{2}\right)$

10. $\text{Sin}\,270°$

11. $\text{Tan}^{-1}(1)$

12. $\text{Sin}^{-1}\,0$

13. $\text{Cos}\left(-\frac{3}{4}\pi\right)$

14. $\text{Arcsin}\,\frac{\sqrt{3}}{2}$

15. $\text{Sin}^{-1}\,\frac{\sqrt{3}}{2}$

16. $\text{Tan}^{-1}\left(\frac{\sqrt{3}}{3}\right)$

17. $\text{Cos}\,45°$

18. $\text{Sin}^{-1}\,1$

19. $\text{Sin}^{-1}(-1)$

20. $\text{Sin}\,\frac{5}{6}\pi$

21. $\text{Cos}^{-1}\,0$

22. $\text{Sin}^{-1}\frac{1}{2}$

23. $\text{Sin}\,0°$

24. $\text{Tan}\left(-\frac{\pi}{4}\right)$

Written Exercises

Find each of the following.

1. $\text{Sin } \frac{\pi}{6}$

2. $\text{Tan}^{-1}(-1)$

3. $\text{Sin}^{-1} 1$

4. $\text{Cos}^{-1}\left(-\frac{1}{2}\right)$

5. $\sin\left(\text{Sin}^{-1}\frac{1}{2}\right)$

6. $\text{Sin}^{-1}\left(\cos\frac{\pi}{2}\right)$

7. $\cos\left(\text{Cos}^{-1}\frac{1}{2}\right)$

8. $\cos\left(\text{Cos}^{-1}\frac{4}{5}\right)$

9. $\tan\left(\text{Sin}^{-1}\frac{5}{13}\right)$

10. $\text{Arccos }\frac{\sqrt{3}}{2}$

11. $\sin\left(2 \text{ Cos}^{-1}\frac{3}{5}\right)$

12. $\text{Arctan }\sqrt{3}$

13. $\sin\left(2 \text{ Sin}^{-1}\frac{1}{2}\right)$

14. $\text{Sin}^{-1}\left(\tan\frac{\pi}{4}\right)$

15. $\cos\left[\text{Cos}^{-1}\left(-\frac{\sqrt{2}}{2}\right) - \frac{\pi}{2}\right]$

16. $\sin\left(\text{Sin}^{-1}\frac{\sqrt{3}}{2}\right)$

17. $\tan\left[\text{Cos}^{-1}\left(-\frac{3}{5}\right)\right]$

18. $\sin\left[\text{Arctan}(-\sqrt{3})\right]$

19. $\cos(\text{Tan}^{-1}\sqrt{3})$

20. $\cos\left[\text{Arcsin}\left(-\frac{1}{2}\right)\right]$

21. $\cos(\text{Tan}^{-1} 1)$

22. $\sin\left[\frac{\pi}{2} - \text{Tan}^{-1}(1)\right]$

23. $\cos\left[\frac{4}{3}\pi - \text{Cos}^{-1}\left(-\frac{1}{2}\right)\right]$

24. $\sin\left(\frac{\pi}{2} - \text{Cos}^{-1}\frac{1}{2}\right)$

25. $\sin\left(\text{Sin}^{-1} 1 - \text{Cos}^{-1}\frac{1}{2}\right)$

26. $\cos\left(\text{Cos}^{-1} 0 + \text{Sin}^{-1}\frac{1}{2}\right)$

27. $\cos\left(\text{Tan}^{-1}\sqrt{3} - \text{Sin}^{-1}\frac{1}{2}\right)$

28. $\sin\left(2 \text{ Sin}^{-1}\frac{\sqrt{3}}{2}\right)$

29. $\sin(\text{Tan}^{-1} 1 + \text{Sin}^{-1} 1)$

30. $\cos\left[\text{Cos}^{-1}\left(-\frac{1}{2}\right) - \text{Sin}^{-1} 1\right]$

❐⁄❍✱❐⁄❍✱ *Using Computers* ❐⁄❍✱❐⁄❍✱

Coterminal Angles

We have defined coterminal angles as those angles whose measures differ by a multiple of 360°. If the measure of an angle is entered into the program at the right, the coterminal angle between 0° and 360° will be printed.

The program uses loops to cause it to keep adding or subtracting 360 until the angle measure is between 0° and 360°.

```
10 PRINT "ENTER AN ANGLE MEASURE:"
20 INPUT A
30 IF A < 360 THEN 60
40 LET A = A - 360
50 GOTO 30
60 IF A > = 0 THEN 90
70 LET A = A + 360
80 GOTO 60
90 PRINT "ITS COTERMINAL ANGLE
       MEASURES ";A;" DEGREES."
100 END
```

When the program is run, the results should resemble those shown below.

```
]RUN
ENTER AN ANGLE MEASURE:
?-1276
ITS COTERMINAL ANGLE MEASURES 164 DEGREES.
```

Exercises

Find the coterminal angle between 0° and 360°.

1. 720°   **2.** 1373.56°   **3.** −981°   **4.** −13,472°

State whether the two angles are coterminal.

5. −59°, 661°   **6.** 29°, 9361°   **7.** 49°, 1129°   **8.** 75°, −275°

9. How would you change lines 30, 40, and 70 if the angle measure given was in radians?

Vocabulary

coterminal angles (511)   tangent (522)
unit circle (512)   cotangent (522)
radian (512)   secant (522)
sine (514)   cosecant (522)
cosine (514)   principal values (542)
period (516)   Arccosine (543)
periodic (516)   Arcsine (543)
amplitude (520)   Arctangent (543)

Chapter Summary

1. Definition of Sine and Cosine: Let θ stand for the measurement of an angle in standard position. Let (x, y) represent the coordinates of the point where the terminal side of the angle intersects the unit circle. Then sine $\theta = y$ and cosine $\theta = x$. (514)

2. Definition of Periodic Function: A function f is called periodic if there is a number a such that $f(x) = f(x + a)$. The least positive value of a for which $f(x) = f(x + a)$ is the period of the function. (516)

3. Amplitudes and Periods: For functions of the form $y = a \sin b\theta$ and $y = a \cos b\theta$, the amplitude is $|a|$ and the period is $\frac{2\pi}{|b|}$. (520)

4. Definition of Tangent, Cotangent, Secant, and Cosecant: Let θ stand for the measurement of an angle in standard position. Then the following equations hold wherever they are defined. (522)

$$\tan \theta = \frac{\sin \theta}{\cos \theta} \qquad \cot \theta = \frac{\cos \theta}{\sin \theta} \qquad \sec \theta = \frac{1}{\cos \theta} \qquad \csc \theta = \frac{1}{\sin \theta}$$

5. Basic Trigonometric Identities: The following trigonometric identities hold for all values of θ except those for which either side of the equation is undefined. (526)

$$\sin^2\theta + \cos^2\theta = 1$$
$$1 + \tan^2\theta = \sec^2\theta$$
$$1 + \cot^2\theta = \csc^2\theta$$

6. Difference and Sum Formulas: The following identities hold for all values of α and β. (533)

$$\cos(\alpha \pm \beta) = \cos\alpha\cos\beta \mp \sin\alpha\sin\beta$$
$$\sin(\alpha \pm \beta) = \sin\alpha\cos\beta \pm \cos\alpha\sin\beta$$

7. Double-Angle Formulas: The following identities hold for all values of θ. (526)

$$\sin 2\theta = 2\sin\theta\cos\theta \qquad \cos 2\theta = \cos^2\theta - \sin^2\theta$$
$$= 1 - 2\sin^2\theta$$
$$= 2\cos^2\theta - 1$$

8. Half-Angle Formulas: The following identities hold for all values of α. (537)

$$\cos\frac{\alpha}{2} = \pm\sqrt{\frac{1 + \cos\alpha}{2}} \text{ and } \sin\frac{\alpha}{2} = \pm\sqrt{\frac{1 - \cos\alpha}{2}}$$

9. Definition of Inverse Cosine: Given $y = \text{Cos } x$, the inverse cosine function is defined by the following equation.
$$y = \text{Cos}^{-1}x. \quad (543)$$

10. Definition of Inverse Sine: Given $y = \text{Sin } x$, the inverse sine function is defined by the following equation.
$$y = \text{Sin}^{-1}x. \quad (543)$$

11. Definition of Inverse Tangent: Given $y = \text{Tan } x$, the inverse tangent function is defined by the following equation.
$$y = \text{Tan}^{-1} x. \quad (543)$$

Chapter Review

16–1 Change each of the following degree measures to radians.

    1. $120°$ **2.** $-315°$ **3.** $270°$ **4.** $225°$

Change each of the following radian measures to degrees.

    5. $\dfrac{\pi}{3}$ **6.** $-\dfrac{5}{12}\pi$ **7.** $\dfrac{4}{3}$ **8.** $\dfrac{7}{4}\pi$

16–2 For each of the following, find the least positive angle that is coterminal.

    9. $-155°$ **10.** $830°$ **11.** $540°$ **12.** $945°$

    13. $\dfrac{20}{3}\pi$ **14.** $-\dfrac{4}{3}\pi$ **15.** $-\dfrac{2}{9}\pi$ **16.** $-\dfrac{11}{6}\pi$

Find each of the following.

    17. $\sin 120°$ **18.** $\cos 210°$ **19.** $\cos 3\pi$ **20.** $\sin(-150°)$

    21. $\sin(-30°)$ **22.** $\sin\dfrac{5}{4}\pi$ **23.** $\cos(-135°)$

    24. $\cos(300°)$ **25.** $(\sin 30°)^2 + (\cos 30°)^2$ **26.** $(\sin 45°)(\sin 225°)$

16–3 **Graph each of the following. State the amplitude and period for each graph.**

27. $y = \sin x$ **28.** $y = -\dfrac{1}{2} \cos \theta$ **29.** $y = 4 \sin 2\theta$

16–4 **Find each of the following.**

30. $\csc \pi$ **31.** $\sec(-30°)$ **32.** $\csc 135°$ **33.** $\cos 600°$

34. $\sin \dfrac{4}{3}\pi$ **35.** $\cot \dfrac{7}{6}\pi$ **36.** $\tan 120°$ **37.** $\sec(-60°)$

16–5 **Solve each of the following for values of θ between 90° and 180°.**

38. If $\sin \theta = \dfrac{1}{2}$, find $\cos \theta$.   **39.** If $\csc \theta = \dfrac{5}{3}$, find $\cos \theta$.

40. If $\sec \theta = -3$, find $\tan \theta$.   **41.** If $\cot \theta = -\dfrac{1}{4}$, find $\csc \theta$.

Solve each of the following for values of θ between 270° and 360°.

42. If $\sin \theta = -\dfrac{4}{5}$, find $\cos \theta$.   **43.** If $\sec \theta = 1$, find $\tan \theta$.

44. If $\csc \theta = -\dfrac{5}{3}$, find $\cot \theta$.   **45.** If $\sin \theta = -\dfrac{1}{2}$, find $\sec \theta$.

16–6 **Verify each identity.**

46. $\sin^4 x - \cos^4 x = \sin^2 x - \cos^2 x$ **47.** $\dfrac{\sin \theta}{\tan \theta} + \dfrac{\cos \theta}{\cot \theta} = \cos \theta + \sin \theta$

48. $\dfrac{\sin \theta}{1 - \cos \theta} = \csc \theta + \cot \theta$ **49.** $\tan x + \cot x = \sec x \csc x$

16–7 **Find each of the following.**

50. $\sin 105°$ **51.** $\cos 240°$ **52.** $\cos 15°$ **53.** $\sin(-255°)$

Verify each of the following identities.

54. $\cos(90° - \theta) = \sin \theta$ **55.** $\cos(60° + \theta) + \cos(60° - \theta) = \cos \theta$

16–8 **56.** If $\sin x = -\dfrac{3}{5}$ and x is in the third quadrant, find $\sin 2x$.

57. If $\sin x = \dfrac{1}{4}$ and x is in the first quadrant, find $\cos 2x$.

58. If $\cos 2x = -\dfrac{17}{25}$ and $\cos x = \dfrac{2}{5}$, find $\sin x$.

16–9 **Find all solutions if $0° \le x < 360°$.**

59. $2 \cos^2 x + \sin^2 x = 2 \cos x$ **60.** $\cos 2x = \cos x$ **61.** $\cos 2x \sin x = 1$

62. $\cos x = 1 - \sin x$ **63.** $2 \sin 2x = 1$ **64.** $\tan^2 x + \tan x = 0$

16–10 **Find each of the following.**

65. $\text{Cos}^{-1}\left(\dfrac{\sqrt{3}}{2}\right)$ **66.** $\text{Sin}^{-1}(-1)$ **67.** $\text{Tan}^{-1}\sqrt{3}$

68. $\text{Sin}^{-1}\left(\tan \dfrac{\pi}{4}\right)$ **69.** $\cos(\text{Sin}^{-1} 1)$ **70.** $\sin\left(2 \text{Sin}^{-1}\dfrac{1}{2}\right)$

Chapter Test

Change each of the following degree measures to radians.

1. 135° **2.** 275° **3.** −150° **4.** −4°

Change each of the following radian measures to degrees.

5. $\frac{4}{5}\pi$ **6.** $\frac{12}{5}\pi$ **7.** $-\frac{7}{4}\pi$ **8.** 7

For each of the following, find the least positive angle that is coterminal.

9. 620° **10.** −260° **11.** 595° **12.** −1270°

Find each value.

13. sin 225° **14.** cos (−120°) **15.** $\cos\frac{3}{4}\pi$ **16.** $\sin\frac{7}{4}\pi$

Graph each of the following. Then state the amplitude and period.

17. $y = 2 \sin 2x$ **18.** $y = \frac{3}{4}\cos\frac{2}{3}x$

Find each of the following.

19. tan 225° **20.** csc −120° **21.** $\cos\frac{2}{3}\pi$ **22.** sec 150°

Solve each of the following for values of θ between 180° and 270°.

23. If $\sin\theta = -\frac{1}{2}$, find $\tan\theta$. **24.** If $\cot\theta = \frac{3}{4}$, find $\sec\theta$.

Verify each identity.

25. $\dfrac{\cos x}{1 - \sin^2 x} = \sec x$ **26.** $\dfrac{\sec x}{\sin x} - \dfrac{\sin x}{\cos x} = \cot x$ **27.** $\dfrac{1 + \tan^2\theta}{\cos^2\theta} = \sec^4\theta$

Evaluate each of the following.

28. sin 255° **29.** cos 165°

30. If x is in the first quadrant and $\cos x = \frac{3}{4}$, find $\sin\frac{1}{2}x$.

31. If $\cos 2x = \frac{2}{9}$ and $\sin x = \frac{1}{3}$, find $\cos x$.

Find all solutions of $0° \le x < 360°$.

32. $2 \sin x \cos x - \sin x = 0$ **33.** $\cos 2x + \sin x = 1$

34. $\sec x = 1 + \tan x$ **35.** $2 \cos^2 2x + \cos 2x - 1 = 0$

Find each of the following.

36. $\mathrm{Tan}^{-1}\dfrac{\sqrt{3}}{3}$ **37.** $\mathrm{Sin}^{-1}\left(-\dfrac{1}{2}\right)$ **38.** $\mathrm{Cos}^{-1}(\sin 30°)$ **39.** $\sin 2\left(\mathrm{Cos}^{-1}\dfrac{1}{2}\right)$

CHAPTER 17

Triangle Trigonometry

For maximum strength, structures must be constructed as designed. Civil engineers often use surveying equipment and trigonometry to check building construction.

17-1   Right Triangles

Trigonometry can be used to find the missing measures of triangles. Consider the right triangle below.

The **hypotenuse** of the triangle is side AB. Its length is c units.

The side opposite angle A is side BC. Its length is a units.

The side adjacent to angle A is side AC. Its length is b units.

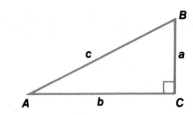

For convenience of notation, we refer to the angle with vertex at A as angle A and use A to stand for its measurement. Similarly, we refer to angle B and its measurement, B. And we refer to angle C and its measurement, C.

Suppose a unit circle is drawn with its center at vertex A as shown below.

The triangle in the interior of the unit circle is similar to triangle ABC. Hence, the measures of the corresponding sides of the triangles are proportional.

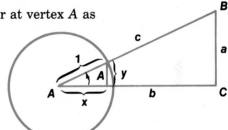

In this figure, $\sin A = y$. Since the two triangles are similar, $\dfrac{y}{a} = \dfrac{1}{c}$. Hence, $y = \dfrac{a}{c}$ and $\sin A = \dfrac{a}{c}$. Using the figure, trigonometric values can be defined in the following way.

$$\sin A = \frac{a}{c} \qquad \cos A = \frac{b}{c} \qquad \tan A = \frac{a}{b}$$

$$\csc A = \frac{c}{a} \qquad \sec A = \frac{c}{b} \qquad \cot A = \frac{b}{a}$$

SOH-CAH-TOA is a helpful mnemonic device for remembering the first 3 equations.

$$\sin = \frac{opposite}{hypotenuse}$$
$$\cos = \frac{adjacent}{hypotenuse}$$
$$\tan = \frac{opposite}{adjacent}$$

Example

1 **Find the sine, cosine, tangent, cosecant, secant, and cotangent of angle A rounded to four decimal places.**

$\sin A = \dfrac{6}{10}$ or 0.6000

$\cos A = \dfrac{8}{10}$ or 0.8000

$\tan A = \dfrac{6}{8}$ or 0.75000

$\csc A = \dfrac{10}{6}$ or 1.6667

$\sec A = \dfrac{10}{8}$ or 1.2500

$\cot A = \dfrac{8}{6}$ or 1.3333

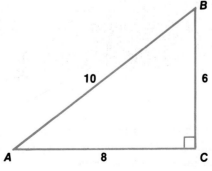

Example

Example

2 **Find sin A rounded to four decimal places.**

First, use the Pythagorean Theorem to find the value of a.

$$a^2 + 7^2 = 11^2$$
$$a^2 = 72$$
$$a = \sqrt{72}$$

Then, find the value of $\frac{a}{c}$.

$$\sin A = \frac{\sqrt{72}}{11}$$

$$\sin A = 0.7714 \qquad \text{The sine of angle } A \text{ is about } 0.7714.$$

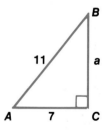

Consider two special right triangles. Triangle ABC is an isosceles right triangle. Assume the congruent sides are each 1 unit long. Use the Pythagorean Theorem to find the length of the hypotenuse.

$$1^2 + 1^2 = x^2$$
$$2 = x^2$$
$$\sqrt{2} = x \qquad \text{The hypotenuse is } \sqrt{2} \text{ units long.}$$

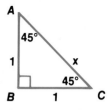

Now, write the values of the trigonometric functions.

$$\sin 45° = \frac{1}{\sqrt{2}} \text{ or } \frac{\sqrt{2}}{2} \qquad \cos 45° = \frac{1}{\sqrt{2}} \text{ or } \frac{\sqrt{2}}{2} \qquad \tan 45° = \frac{1}{1} \text{ or } 1$$

$$\csc 45° = \frac{\sqrt{2}}{1} \text{ or } \sqrt{2} \qquad \sec 45° = \frac{\sqrt{2}}{1} \text{ or } \sqrt{2} \qquad \cot 45° = \frac{1}{1} \text{ or } 1$$

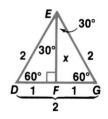

Triangle DEG is an equilateral triangle. Assume each side is 2 units long. The altitude EF forms a triangle whose angle measurements are 30°, 60°, and 90°. Since altitude EF is the perpendicular bisector of side DG, the length of side DF is 1. Find the length of side EF.

$$x^2 + 1^2 = 2^2$$
$$x^2 = 3$$
$$x = \sqrt{3} \qquad \text{Side } EF \text{ is } \sqrt{3} \text{ units long.}$$

Now, write the trigonometric values.

$$\sin 30° = \frac{1}{2} \qquad\qquad \cos 30° = \frac{\sqrt{3}}{2} \qquad\qquad \tan 30° = \frac{1}{\sqrt{3}} \text{ or } \frac{\sqrt{3}}{3}$$

$$\csc 30° = \frac{2}{1} \text{ or } 2 \qquad\quad \sec 30° = \frac{2}{\sqrt{3}} \text{ or } \frac{2\sqrt{3}}{3} \qquad \cot 30° = \frac{\sqrt{3}}{1} \text{ or } \sqrt{3}$$

$$\sin 60° = \frac{\sqrt{3}}{2} \qquad\qquad \cos 60° = \frac{1}{2} \qquad\qquad \tan 60° = \frac{\sqrt{3}}{1} \text{ or } \sqrt{3}$$

$$\csc 60° = \frac{2}{\sqrt{3}} \text{ or } \frac{2\sqrt{3}}{3} \qquad \sec 60° = \frac{2}{1} \text{ or } 2 \qquad\quad \cot 60° = \frac{1}{\sqrt{3}} \text{ or } \frac{\sqrt{3}}{3}$$

Exploratory Exercises

For each triangle, give the sine of each acute angle. State each answer in fraction form.

1.

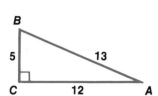

2.

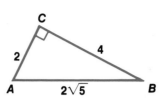

3.

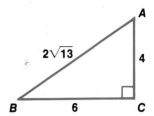

4–6. Give the cosine of each acute angle in problems **1–3.**

7–9. Give the tangent of each acute angle in problems **1–3.**

Written Exercises

Find each value rounded to four decimal places.

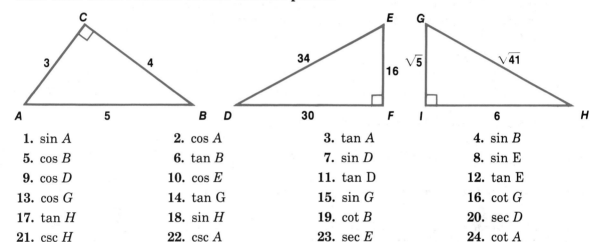

1. sin A	**2.** cos A	**3.** tan A	**4.** sin B
5. cos B	**6.** tan B	**7.** sin D	**8.** sin E
9. cos D	**10.** cos E	**11.** tan D	**12.** tan E
13. cos G	**14.** tan G	**15.** sin G	**16.** cot G
17. tan H	**18.** sin H	**19.** cot B	**20.** sec D
21. csc H	**22.** csc A	**23.** sec E	**24.** cot A

For each triangle, find sin A, cos A, and tan A rounded to four decimal places.

25.

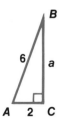

26.

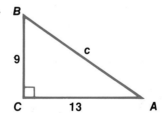

27.

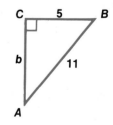

Find the value of each expression. Write each answer in fraction form.

28. $2 \cos 30°$

29. $-\sin 60°$

30. $\sin^2 45° + \cos^2 45°$

31. $2 \sin 60° \cos 60°$

32. $\cos^2 30° - \sin^2 30°$

33. $\sin 30° \cos 60° - \sin 60° \cos 30°$

34. $\csc 45° - \sec 30°$

35. $\sec 60° + \cot 30°$

17-2 Trigonometric Tables

Decimal approximations for values of trigonometric functions are given in the back of this book. Angles with measurements from 0° to 90° at intervals of ten minutes are provided. Part of the table of values is shown below.

Values of Trigonometric Functions

Angle	Sin	Cos	Tan	Cot	Sec	Csc	
27°00′	0.4540	0.8910	0.5095	1.963	1.122	2.203	63°00′
10′	0.4566	0.8897	0.5132	1.949	1.124	2.190	50′
20′	0.4592	0.8884	0.5169	1.935	1.126	2.178	40′
30′	0.4617	0.8870	0.5206	1.921	1.127	2.166	30′
40′	0.4643	0.8857	0.5243	1.907	1.129	2.154	20′
50′	0.4669	0.8843	0.5280	1.894	1.131	2.142	10′
28°00′	0.4695	0.8829					
35°00′	0.5736	0.8192	0.7002	1.428	1.221	1.743	55°00′
10′	0.5760	0.8175	0.7046	1.419	1.223	1.736	50′
20′	0.5783	0.8158	0.7089	1.411	1.226	1.729	40′
30′	0.5807	0.8141	0.7133	1.402	1.228	1.722	30′
40′	0.5831	0.8124	0.7177	1.393	1.231	1.715	20′
50′	0.5854	0.8107	0.7221	1.385	1.233	1.708	10′
36°00′	0.5878	0.8090	0.7265	1.376	1.236	1.701	54°00′
	Cos	Sin	Cot	Tan	Csc	Sec	Angle

Degrees are separated into minutes. Sixty minutes are equivalent to one degree.

For example, $1\frac{1}{2}$ degrees can be expressed as 1 degree 30 minutes, and is abbreviated 1°30′.

Angle measurements from 0°00′ to 45°00′ are listed on the left-hand side of the table. Use the column headings at the top along with angle measurements by reading *down* the left-hand side. For example, cos 27°10′ = 0.8897.

Angle measurements from 45°00′ to 90°00′ are listed on the right-hand side of the table. Use the column headings at the bottom along with angle measurements by reading *up* the right-hand side. For example, tan 54°30′ = 1.402.

Examples

1 **Find tan 31°40′.**

Since 31°40′ is found on the left side of the table, use tan on the top of the table. Look below tan and to the right of 31°40′.

tan 31°40′ = 0.6168   Therefore, tan 31°40′ is about 0.6168.

2 **Round 55°12′ to the nearest 10 minutes. Then find an approximate value for sin 55°12′.**

12 rounded to the nearest tens place is 10. Thus, 55°12′ rounded to the nearest 10 minutes is 55°10′. Since 55°10′ is on the right side of the table, use sin on the bottom of the table. Look above sin and to the left of 55°10′.

sin 55°10′ = 0.8208   Therefore, sin 55°12′ is about 0.8208.

A more accurate approximation of trigonometric values can be found by using **interpolation.** For example, suppose you wish to find sin 28°23'. Use the table to find sin 28°20' and sin 28°30'.

10' $\Big[$ 3' $\Big[$ sin 28°20' = 0.4746 $\Big]$ d $\Big]$ 0.0026
sin 28°23' = unknown
sin 28°30' = 0.4772

d stands for the difference between 0.4746 and the unknown value.

Then set up a proportion and solve for d.

$$\frac{3}{10} = \frac{d}{0.0026}$$
$$10d = 3(0.0026)$$
$$10d = 0.0078$$
$$d = 0.00078$$
$$\text{or } 0.0008$$

The table gives the values rounded to four decimal places. Therefore, round the value for d to four decimal places.

Add 0.0008 to the value of sin 28°20'.

sin 28°23' = 0.4746 + 0.0008 or 0.4754

The value of sin 28°23' is about 0.4754.

Example

3 **Find cot 31°47'.**

10' $\Big[$ 7' $\Big[$ cot 31°40' = 1.621 $\Big]$ d $\Big]$ −0.010
cot 31°47' = unknown
cot 31°50' = 1.611

$$\frac{7}{10} = \frac{d}{-0.010}$$

$$10d = 7(-0.010)$$
$$10d = -0.070$$
$$d = -0.007$$

cot 31°47' = 1.621 − 0.007
= 1.614

The value of cot 31°47' is about 1.614.

Example 4

Suppose sin x = 0.7820. Find the measure of x to the nearest minute.

$$\left.\begin{array}{l} 10' \left[\begin{array}{l} d \left[\begin{array}{l} \text{sin } 51°20' = 0.7808 \\ \text{sin } x \quad= 0.7820 \end{array}\right] 0.0012 \\ \text{sin } 51°30' = 0.7826 \end{array}\right] 0.0018$$

Use the table to find those values which the given value is between.

$$\frac{d}{10} = \frac{0.0012}{0.0018}$$
$$0.0018d = 0.0120$$
$$d = 6.66$$
$$\approx 7 \quad \textit{Round to the nearest whole number.}$$
$$x \approx 51°20' + 7' \text{ or } 51°27'$$

The value of x is about 51°27'.

The sum and difference formulas for sine and cosine can be used to find the trigonometric values of angles whose measures are not listed in the table.

$$\cos (a \pm b) = \cos a \cos b \mp \sin a \sin b$$
$$\sin (a \pm b) = \sin a \cos b \pm \cos a \sin b$$

Example 5

Find sin 153°.

$$\begin{aligned} \sin 153° &= \sin (180° - 27°) \\ &= \sin 180° \cos 27° - \cos 180° \sin 27° \\ &= 0 \cdot \cos 27° - (-1) \sin 27° \\ &= \sin 27° \\ &= 0.4540 \end{aligned}$$

153° is not listed in the table.
sin (a − b) = sin a cos b − cos a sin b

The value of sin 153° is about 0.4540.

Exploratory Exercises

Use the table to find each trigonometric value.

1. sin 42°   2. cos 81°   3. sin 68°   4. tan 5°
5. tan 89°50'   6. cos 42°20'   7. tan 49°30'   8. sin 3°10'

Round each angle measurement to the nearest 10 minutes. Then approximate each value.

9. cos 63°18'   10. tan 77°14'   11. sin 73°46'   12. cos 73°58'
13. cos 18°2'   14. tan 43°51'   15. sin 27°18'   16. sin 53°43'

Written Exercises

Approximate each trigonometric value. Use interpolation when necessary.

1. cos 38°
2. tan 12°
3. sin 68°
4. tan 88°
5. sin 16°20′
6. tan 85°16′
7. tan 77°30′
8. sin 38°15′
9. cos 59°10′
10. sin 127°40′
11. tan 88°52′
12. sec 47°10′
13. csc 33°33′
14. cot 44°44′
15. tan 110°55′
16. sec 11°11′
17. sin 194°35′
18. cot 47°18′
19. tan 42°42′
20. csc 273°18′

Find the measure of x to the nearest minute.

21. cos x = 0.5132
22. tan x = 1.705
23. sin x = 0.3291
24. tan x = 0.3147
25. cos x = 0.7193
26. sin x = 0.1111
27. tan x = 0.2222
28. cos x = 0.3333
29. sin x = 0.8081
30. tan x = 42.71
31. csc x = 1.412
32. cot x = 0.1234
33. sec x = 1.319
34. csc x = 1.319
35. cot x = 1.384
36. sec x = 2.8672

Using Calculators ——————— Degrees and Minutes

In order to use your calculator to find trigonometric values, minutes must be changed to decimal form. This is done by dividing the minutes portion by 60.

Example 1: Find tan 58°21′.

ENTER: 58 [+] 21 [÷] 60 [=] [tan]
DISPLAY: 58   58   21   21   60   58.35   1.6223029

Therefore, tan 58°21′ is approximately 1.6223.

You can find angle measures using the [INV] key. To convert degrees in decimal form to minutes, multiply by 60.

Example 2: Find x if cos x = 0.5030 to the nearest minute.

ENTER: 0.503 [INV]   [cos]   So x = 59.80°.
DISPLAY: 0.503   0.503   59.801322

Remember, only the decimal portion should be converted to minutes.

ENTER: [−]   59   [=]   [×]   60   [=]
DISPLAY: 59.801322   59   0.801322   60   48.079337

Therefore, x = 59°48′.

Exercises

Use your calculator to find each trigonometric value.

1. sin 136.25°
2. tan 65°14′
3. csc 98°36′
4. cot 10°56′

Find x to the nearest minute.

5. cos x = 0.2489
6. sin x = 0.4683
7. sec x = 1.1573
8. tan x = 9.876

17-3 Solving Right Triangles

Trigonometric functions can be used to solve problems involving right triangles. To solve a right triangle means to find all the measures of the sides and angles.

Consider triangle ABC shown at the right. Notice that C is a right angle, and A and B are acute angles. Lower case letters a, b, and c are used to denote the measures of the sides opposite these angles. The measure of the hypotenuse is c.

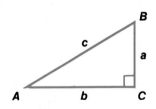

Examples

1 **Solve the right triangle.**

$$\frac{a}{14} = \sin 42°$$

$$\frac{a}{14} = 0.6691$$

$$a = 9.4 \qquad \textit{Round to the nearest tenth.}$$

$$\frac{b}{14} = \cos 42°$$

$$\frac{b}{14} = 0.7431$$

$$b = 10.4 \qquad \textit{Round to the nearest tenth.}$$

$$42° + B = 90° \qquad \textit{Angles A and B are complementary.}$$
$$B = 48°$$

Therefore, $a = 9.4$, $b = 10.4$, and $B = 48°$.

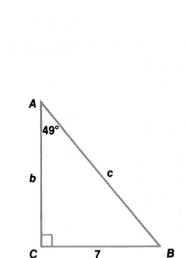

2 **Solve the right triangle.**

$$49° + B = 90°$$
$$B = 41°$$

$$\frac{7}{c} = \sin 49°$$

$$\frac{7}{c} = 0.7547$$

$$7 = 0.7547c$$

$$c = 9.3 \qquad \textit{Round to the nearest tenth.}$$

$$\frac{7}{b} = \tan 49°$$

$$7 = 1.150b$$

$$b = 6.1 \qquad \textit{Round to the nearest tenth.}$$

Therefore $B = 41°$, $c = 9.3$, and $b = 6.1$.

3 **Solve the right triangle.**

$$7^2 + b^2 = 16^2 \qquad \textit{Use the Pythagorean Theorem.}$$
$$49 + b^2 = 256$$

$$b^2 = 207$$
$$b \approx 14.4$$
$$\sin A = \frac{7}{16}$$
$$\sin A = 0.4375$$
$$A = 25°57'$$
$$25°57' + B = 90°$$
$$B = 64°3'$$

Therefore, $b = 14.4$, $A = 25°57'$, and $B = 64°3'$.

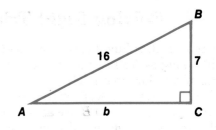

Exploratory Exercises

State equations that would enable you to solve each problem. Use the triangle below.

1. If $A = 15°$ and $c = 37$, find a.
2. If $A = 76°$ and $a = 13$, find b.
3. If $A = 49°13'$ and $a = 10$, find c.
4. If $a = 21.2$ and $A = 71°13'$, find b.
5. If $a = 13$ and $B = 16°$, find c.
6. If $A = 19°07'$ and $b = 11$, find c.

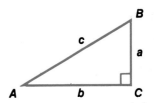

7. If $c = 16$ and $a = 7$, find b.
8. If $b = 10$ and $c = 20$, find a.
9. If $a = 7$ and $b = 12$, find A.
10. If $a = b$ and $c = 12$, find B.

Written Exercises

Solve each triangle described. Round to two decimal places or the nearest minute.

1. $a = 2$, $b = 7$
2. $c = 10$, $a = 8$
3. $c = 13$, $a = 12$
4. $a = 11$, $b = 21$
5. $b = 6$, $c = 13$
6. $c = 21$, $b = 18$
7. $A = 16°$, $c = 14$
8. $A = 63°$, $a = 9.7$
9. $A = 37°15'$, $b = 11$
10. $B = 64°$, $c = 19.2$
11. $B = 42°10'$, $a = 9$
12. $B = 83°$, $b = \sqrt{31}$
13. $c = 6$, $B = 13°$
14. $a = 9$, $B = 49°$
15. $b = 42$, $A = 77°$
16. $b = 22$, $A = 22°22'$
17. $a = 33$, $B = 33°$
18. $a = 44$, $B = 44°44'$
19. $A = 55°55'$, $c = 16$
20. $B = 18°$, $a = \sqrt{15}$
21. $A = 45°$, $c = 7\sqrt{2}$
22. $B = 30°$, $b = 11$
23. $c = 25$, $A = 15°$
24. $a = 7$, $A = 27°$

mini-review

1. Solve this system: $x^2 - 2y^2 = -14$
   $2x^2 + 5y = -7$

2. Show that $x - 4$ is a factor of $x^4 - 4x^3 - 7x^2 + 22x + 24$. Then find the remaining factors.

3. Write the equation for the inverse of $f(x) = \dfrac{x^2 - 9}{5}$.

4. Simplify $\dfrac{\dfrac{x^2 - 7x - 8}{y}}{\dfrac{x + 1}{y^2}}$.

5. Express $\sqrt[5]{64xy^3z^7}$ using exponents.

One of the keys to solving problems using trigonometry is drawing a figure, or **model,** of the problem. Read the problem given below.

> Sandra is watching Johnny from a window 100 feet above the ground while Johnny plays 20 feet from the base of the building. What is the measurement of the angle Sandra's line of sight forms with the ground where Johnny is playing?

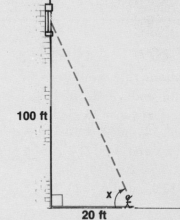

You can draw a figure to represent the problem above. The problem states that the window is 100 feet above the ground, so label that distance on your figure. The problem also states that Johnny is playing 20 feet from the base of the building, so label that distance. Finally, find the measurement of the angle Sandra's line of sight forms with the ground where Johnny is playing.

Write an equation for the problem. Since you are given the opposite and adjacent sides to the angle, use the tangent function to find x.

$$\tan x = \frac{100}{20}$$
$$\tan x = 5$$
$$x = 78°41'$$

Her line of sight forms an angle measuring 78°41' with the ground.

Exercises

Draw a figure and solve each problem.

1. The tortoise and the hare are 60 meters apart. A boy sitting in a tree at the finish line can see the hare as the tortoise crosses the line, winning the race. The measurement of the angle his line of sight forms with the tree is 75°29'. How far above the ground is the boy?

2. Patty, a basketball player, knows that the rim of the basket is 10 feet from the floor. From where she is standing, the angle of elevation to the rim is 33°33'. Find the distance from Patty's feet to the rim.

3. Two cars leave the same point at the same time. Car A goes east at 50 miles per hour, and car B goes south at 30 miles per hour. After one hour, what is the measurement of the angle the path of car A forms with the line between cars A and B?

4. A tent has a center pole that is 6 feet high, and a floor 8 feet wide. Find the measurement of the angle the tent side forms with the ground.

17-4   Problem Solving: Using Right Triangles

Right triangles and the trigonometric functions can be used to solve a number of problems.

Example

1   A ladder 14 meters long rests against the wall of a house. The foot of the ladder rests on level ground 2 meters from the wall. What angle does the ladder form with the ground?

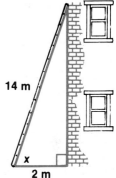

Explore	Draw a diagram. Let x = angle measure.
Plan	$\text{Cos } x = \dfrac{2}{14}$
Solve	$\text{Cos } x = 0.1429$ $x = 81°47'$
Examine	According to the drawing, the measure of angle x is less than 90°. The answer $81°47'$ seems reasonable.

14 m

x

2 m

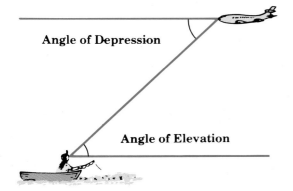

Angle of Depression

Angle of Elevation

A person fishing on a lake sees an airplane flying overhead. The angle formed by her line of sight to the plane and a horizontal is called the **angle of elevation.** The angle formed by the line of sight from the pilot to the boat and a horizontal is called the **angle of depression.** The angles of elevation and depression are alternate interior angles and have equal measures.

Example

2   Two hikers are 300 meters from the base of a radio tower. The measurement of the angle of elevation to the top of the tower is 40°. How high is the tower?

$$\frac{x}{300} = \tan 40°$$

$$\frac{x}{300} = 0.8391$$

$$x = 0.8391(300) \text{ or } 251.73$$

The height of the tower is about 252 meters.

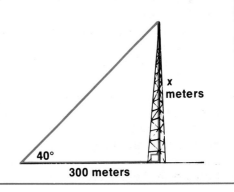

x meters

40°

300 meters

Examples

3 Robert is standing on top of a cliff 200 feet above a lake. The measurement of the angle of depression to a boat on the lake is 21°. How far is the boat from the base of the cliff?

$$\frac{200}{x} = \tan 21°$$

$$\frac{200}{x} = 0.3839$$

$$0.3839x = 200$$

$$x = 521$$

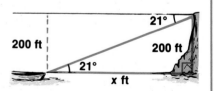

The boat is about 521 feet from the base of the cliff.

4 The base of a television antenna and two points on the ground are in a straight line. The two points are 100 feet apart. From the two points, the measurements of the angles of elevation to the top of the antenna are 30° and 20°. Find the height of the antenna.

$$\tan 30° = \frac{y}{x}$$

$$x \tan 30° = y$$

$$\tan 20° = \frac{y}{x + 100}$$

$$x \tan 30° = (x + 100) \tan 20°$$

$$y = (x + 100)\tan 20°$$

$$x \tan 30° = x \tan 20° + 100 \tan 20°$$

$$x \tan 30° - x \tan 20° = 100 \tan 20°$$

$$x (\tan 30° - \tan 20°) = 100 \tan 20°$$

$$x = \frac{100 \tan 20°}{\tan 30° - \tan 20°}$$

$$= \frac{100(0.3640)}{0.5774 - 0.3640}$$

$$= 170.6$$

$$y = 170.6 \tan 30°$$

$$= 170.6(0.5774)$$

$$= 98.5$$

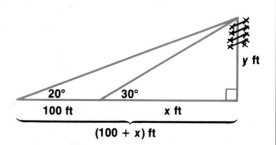

The height is 99 feet to the nearest foot.

Written Exercises

Solve each problem. Round all answers to two decimal places.

1. At a point on the ground that is 30 meters from the base of a tree, the measurement of the angle of elevation to the top of the tree is 65°. How tall is the tree?

2. A flagpole casts a shadow 40 feet long when the measurement of the angle of elevation to the sun is 31°20′. How tall is the flagpole?

3. The measurement of the angle of depression of an aircraft carrier from a plane 1000 feet above the water is 63°18′. How far is the plane from the carrier?

4. At the point from which it is being flown, the measurement of the angle of elevation of a kite is 70°. It is held by a string 65 meters long. How far is the kite above the ground?

5. A 24-foot ladder leans against a building. It forms an angle with the building measuring 18°. How far is the foot of the ladder from the base of the building?

6. The top of a lighthouse is 120 meters above sea level. From the top of the lighthouse, the measurement of the angle of depression of a boat at sea is 43°. Find the distance of the boat from the foot of the lighthouse.

7. A tree is broken by the wind. The top touches the ground 13 meters from the base. It makes an angle with the ground measuring 29°. How tall was the tree before it was broken?

8. The pilot of a plane flying 5000 feet above sea level observes two ships in line due east. The measurements of the angles of depression are 30° and 39°. How far apart are the ships?

9. In a parking garage, each floor is 20 feet apart. The ramp to each floor is 120 feet long. What is the measurement of the angle of elevation of the ramp?

10. A railroad track rises 10 feet for every 400 feet along the track. What is the measurement of the angle the track forms with the horizontal?

11. The Washington Monument is 555 feet high. What is the measurement of the angle of elevation of the top when observed from a point $\frac{1}{4}$ mile from the base? (1 mile = 5280 feet)

12. A train travels 5000 meters along a track whose angle of elevation has a measurement of 3°. How much did it rise during this distance?

13. The diagram shows square $ABCD$. The midpoint of side AD is E. Find the values of x, y, and z to the nearest minute.

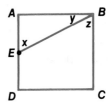

14. The measurement of the angle of elevation to the top of a building from a point on the ground is 38°20′. From a point 50 feet closer to the building, the measurement of the angle of elevation is 45°. What is the height of the building?

15. Two observers 200 feet apart are in line with the base of a flagpole. The measurement of the angle of elevation of the top from one observer is 30° and from the other 60°. How far is the flagpole from each observer?

16. To find the height of a mountain peak two points, A and B, were located on a plain in line with the peak. The angles of elevation were measured from each point. The angle at A was 36°40′ and the angle at B was 21°10′. The distance from A to B was 720 feet. How high is the peak above the level of the plain?

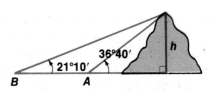

17. Two buildings are separated by an alley. Joe is looking out of a window 60 feet above the ground in one building. He observes the measurement of the angle of depression of the base of the second building to be 50°, and the angle of elevation of the top to be 40°. How high is the second building?

18. A television antenna sits atop a building. From a point 200 feet from the base of the building, the measurement of the angle of elevation of the top of the antenna is 80°. The angle of elevation of the bottom of the antenna from the same point is 75°. How tall is the antenna?

19. The isosceles triangle RST below has base TS measuring 10 centimeters and base angles each measuring 39°. Find the length of the altitude QR.

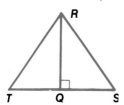

20. A pendulum 50 centimeters long is moved 40° from the vertical. How far did the tip of the pendulum rise?

21. A ship sails due north from port for 90 kilometers, then 40 kilometers east, and then 70 kilometers north. How far is the ship from port?

mini-review

1. Simplify $\dfrac{x}{x^2 - 4} + \dfrac{3}{x^2 + 2x - 8}$.

2. Find the sum of the series
$$\sum_{i=-1}^{7} (2i - 3).$$

3. Draw a bar graph for the following.

Avg. Grades for Mr. Johnson's Classes				
Year	1981	1982	1983	1984	1985
Grade	78	83	69	61	77

4. Convert $7\frac{1}{2}\pi$ to degrees.

5. Find $\text{Tan}^{-1}\, 0$.

Excursions in Algebra _____ History

Eratosthenes, an astronomer who lived in Greece in the 3rd century B.C., is credited with providing the first accurate measure of the earth's circumference. To do this, Eratosthenes reasoned as follows.

At noon on the day of the summer solstice, the sun is directly over the city of Syene. At the same time, in Alexandria, which is north of Syene, the sun is 7°12′ south of being directly overhead. Since the distance between the two cities is 5,000 stadia, the following proportion can be written.

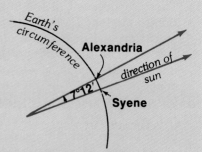

$$\frac{360°}{7°12′} = \frac{c}{5,000}$$

Solving the proportion gives the value of c, the earth's circumference, as 250,000 stadia, or 24,661 miles. This is only 158 miles less than the currently accepted value. *The stadium (singular form of stadia) is an ancient unit of measurement.*

17-5 Law of Sines

The trigonometric functions also can be used to solve problems involving triangles that are *not* right triangles.

Consider $\triangle ABC$ with height h units and sides with lengths a units, b units, and c units. The area of this triangle is given by area $= \frac{1}{2}bh$. Also, $\sin A = \frac{h}{c}$. By combining these equations, you can find a new formula for the area of the triangle.

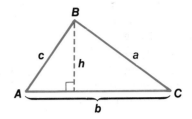

$$\text{area} = \frac{1}{2}bh$$

$$= \frac{1}{2}b(c \sin A) \qquad \sin A = \frac{h}{c}, \text{ so } h = c \sin A$$

In a similar way, you can find two other formulas for the area of a triangle.

$$\text{area} = \frac{1}{2}ac \sin B \qquad\qquad \text{area} = \frac{1}{2}ab \sin C$$

All of these formulas represent the area of the same triangle. Thus, the following must be true.

$$\frac{1}{2}bc \sin A = \frac{1}{2}ac \sin B = \frac{1}{2}ab \sin C$$

The **Law of Sines** is obtained by dividing each of the above expressions by $\frac{1}{2}abc$.

$$\frac{\sin A}{a} = \frac{\sin B}{b} = \frac{\sin C}{c}$$

Let $\triangle ABC$ be any triangle with a, b, and c representing the measures of sides opposite angles with measurements A, B, and C respectively. Then,

$$\frac{\sin A}{a} = \frac{\sin B}{b} = \frac{\sin C}{c}.$$

Law of Sines

Example

1 Find the area of $\triangle ABC$ if $a = 6$, $b = 10$, and $C = 40°$.

$$\text{area} = \frac{1}{2}(6)(10) \sin 40°.$$

$$= \frac{1}{2}(6)(10)(0.6428)$$

$$= 19.284 \qquad \text{To the nearest whole unit, the area is 19 square units.}$$

Examples

2 **Solve the triangle.**

$$\frac{\sin B}{14} = \frac{\sin 105°}{18}$$

$$\sin B = \frac{14 \sin 105°}{18}$$

$$= \frac{14(0.9659)}{18}$$

$$= 0.7513$$

$$B = 48°42'$$

$$48°42' + 105° + C = 180°$$

$$C = 26°18'$$

$$\frac{\sin 26°18'}{c} = \frac{\sin 105°}{18}$$

$$c = \frac{18 \sin 26°18'}{\sin 105°}$$

$$= \frac{18(0.4431)}{0.9659}$$

$$= 8.26$$

Therefore, $B = 48°42'$, $C = 26°18'$, and $c = 8.26$.

3 **A surveyor measures a fence 440 meters long. She takes bearings of a land-mark C from A and B and finds that $A = 48°$ and $B = 75°$. Find the distance from A to C.**

$$48° + 75° + C = 180°$$

$$C = 57°$$

$$\frac{\sin 75°}{b} = \frac{\sin 57°}{440}$$

$$b = \frac{440 \sin 75°}{\sin 57°}$$

$$= 506.7$$

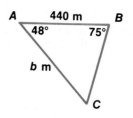

To the nearest meter, the distance is 507 meters.

Exploratory Exercises

State an equation that would enable you to find the area of each triangle.

1. $a = 10$, $b = 17$, $C = 46°$

2. $b = 15$, $c = 20$, $A = 63°$

3. $a = 15$, $b = 30$, $C = 90°$

4. $a = 6$, $c = 4$, $B = 52°$

State an equation that would enable you to solve each triangle described below.

5. If $b = 10$, $a = 14$, and $A = 50°$, find B.

6. If $A = 40°$, $B = 60°$, and $a = 20$, find b.

7. If $b = 2.8$, $A = 53°$, and $B = 61°$, find a.

8. If $b = 16$, $c = 12$, and $B = 42°$, find C.

Written Exercises

Find the area of each triangle described below.

1. $a = 12$, $b = 12$, $C = 50°$

2. $a = 15$, $b = 22$, $C = 90°$

3. $b = 11.5$, $c = 14$, $A = 20°$

4. $a = 11$, $c = 5$, $B = 50°6'$

5. $a = 11$, $b = 13$, $C = 31°10'$

6. $b = 4$, $c = 19$, $A = 73°24'$

7. $a = 9.4$, $c = 13.5$, $B = 95°$

8. $b = 17.3$, $c = 12.4$, $A = 110°$

Solve each triangle described below.

9. $a = 8$, $A = 49°$, $B = 57°$

10. $A = 45°$, $a = 83$, $b = 79$

11. $A = 83°10'$, $a = 80$, $b = 70$

12. $A = 40°$, $B = 60°$, $c = 20$

13. $B = 70°$, $C = 58°$, $a = 84$

14. $A = 30°$, $C = 70°$, $c = 8$

15. $b = 15$, $c = 17$, $C = 64°40'$

16. $a = 23$, $A = 73°25'$, $C = 24°30'$

17. $B = 36°36'$, $C = 119°$, $b = 8$

18. $a = 14$, $b = 7.5$, $A = 103°$

Solve each problem. Round all answers to two decimal places.

19. An isosceles triangle has a base of 22 centimeters and a vertex angle measuring 36°. Find its perimeter.

20. The longest side of a triangle is 34 yards. Two angles of the triangle are 40° and 65°. Find the length of the other two sides.

21. A triangular lot faces two streets that meet at an angle measuring 85°. The sides of the lot facing the streets are each 160 feet in length. Find the perimeter of the lot.

22. A ship is sighted at sea from two observation points A and B. Points A and B are 30 miles apart. The angle at A between line AB and the ship is 34°. The angle at point B is 45°34'. How far is the ship from point B, to the nearest tenth of a mile?

23. Two planes leave an airport at the same time. Each flies at a speed of 110 miles per hour. One flies in the direction 60° east of north. The other flies in the direction 40° east of south. How far apart are the planes after 3 hours?

24. Points X and Y are on opposite sides of a valley. Point C is 60 kilometers from point X. Angle YXC is 108°, and angle YCX is 35°. Find the width of the valley.

25. A building 60 feet tall is on top of a hill. A surveyor is at a point on the hill and observes that the angle of elevation to the top of the building has measurement 42° and to the bottom of the building has measurement 18°. How far is the surveyor from the building?

26. A flower bed is in the shape of an obtuse triangle. One angle is 45° and the opposite side is 28 feet long. The longest side is 36 feet long. Find the measures of the remaining angles and side.

17-6   Law of Cosines

If two sides and the included angle, or three sides of a triangle, are given, the Law of Sines cannot be used to solve the triangle. Another formula is needed.

Consider triangle ABC with height measuring h units and sides with lengths a units, b units, and c units. Suppose segment AD is x units long. Then segment DC is $(b - x)$ units long.

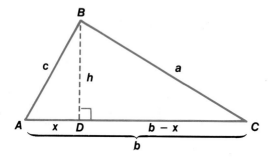

Use the Pythagorean Theorem and the definition of the cosine function to find how A, a, b, and c are related.

$$\begin{aligned}
a^2 &= (b - x)^2 + h^2 && \text{\textit{Use the Pythagorean Theorem.}} \\
&= b^2 - 2bx + x^2 + h^2 && \text{\textit{Expand }} (b - x)^2. \\
&= b^2 - 2bx + c^2 && c^2 = x^2 + h^2. \\
&= b^2 - 2b(c \cos A) + c^2 && \cos A = \frac{x}{c} \text{ \textit{so} } x = c \cos A. \\
&= b^2 + c^2 - 2bc \cos A
\end{aligned}$$

In a similar way, two other formulas can be found relating the lengths of sides to the cosine of B and C. All three formulas, the **Law of Cosines,** can be summarized as follows.

Law of Cosines

Let triangle ABC be any triangle with a, b, and c representing the measures of sides opposite angles with measurements A, B, and C respectively. Then, the following equations are true.

$$a^2 = b^2 + c^2 - 2bc \cos A$$
$$b^2 = a^2 + c^2 - 2ac \cos B$$
$$c^2 = a^2 + b^2 - 2ab \cos C$$

Use the Law of Cosines to solve a triangle in the following cases.
1. To find the length of the third side of any triangle if the lengths of two sides and the measurement of the included angle are given.
2. To find the measurement of an angle of a triangle if the lengths of three sides are given.

Examples

1 **Solve the triangle where $A = 35°$, $b = 16$, and $c = 19$.**

$$a^2 = 16^2 + 19^2 - 2(16)(19) \cos 35° \quad \textit{Use the Law of Cosines.}$$
$$= 16^2 + 19^2 - 2(16)(19)(0.8192)$$
$$= 118.93$$
$$a = 10.9$$
$$\frac{\sin 35°}{10.9} = \frac{\sin B}{16} \quad \textit{Use the law of Sines.}$$
$$\sin B = \frac{16 \sin 35°}{10.9}$$
$$= \frac{16(0.5736)}{10.9}$$
$$= 0.8420$$
$$B = 57°21'$$

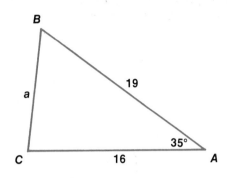

$$35° + 57°21' + C = 180°$$
$$C = 180° - 35° - 57°21'$$
$$= 87°39'$$

Therefore, $a = 10.9$, $B = 57°21'$, and $C = 87°39'$.

2 **Solve the triangle where $a = 11$, $b = 13$, and $c = 15$.**

$$11^2 = 13^2 + 15^2 - 2(13)(15) \cos A \quad \textit{Use the Law of Cosines.}$$
$$2(13)(15) \cos A = 13^2 + 15^2 - 11^2$$
$$\cos A = \frac{13^2 + 15^2 - 11^2}{2(13)(15)}$$
$$= 0.7000$$
$$A = 45°34'$$

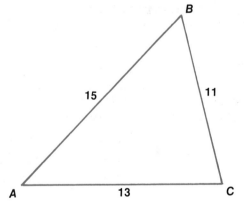

$$\frac{\sin 45°34'}{11} = \frac{\sin B}{13} \quad \textit{Use the Law of Sines.}$$
$$\sin B = \frac{13 \sin 45°34'}{11}$$
$$= \frac{13(0.7141)}{11}$$
$$= 0.8439$$
$$B = 57°33'$$

$$45°34' + 57°33' + C = 180°$$
$$C = 180° - 45°34' - 57°33'$$
$$= 76°53'$$

Therefore, $A = 45°34'$, $B = 57°33'$, and $C = 76°53'$.

Exploratory Exercises

Determine whether the Law of Sines or the Law of Cosines should be used first to solve each triangle described below.

1. $A = 40°$, $b = 6$, $c = 7$

2. $a = 10$, $A = 40°$, $c = 8$

3. $a = 14$, $b = 15$, $c = 16$

4. $A = 40°$, $C = 70°$, $c = 14$

5. $C = 35°$, $a = 11$, $b = 10.5$

6. $c = 21$, $a = 14$, $B = 60°$

7. $c = 10.3$, $a = 21\frac{1}{2}$, $b = 16.71$

8. $b = 17$, $B = 42°58'$, $a = 11$

9. $c = 14.1$, $A = 29°$, $b = 7.6$

10. $A = 28°50'$, $b = 5$, $c = 4.9$

Written Exercises

Solve each triangle described below.

1. $a = 140$, $b = 185$, $c = 166$

2. $A = 51°$, $b = 40$, $c = 45$

3. $a = 5$, $b = 6$, $c = 7$

4. $a = 5$, $b = 12$, $c = 13$

5. $a = 20$, $c = 24$, $B = 47°$

6. $b = 13$, $a = 21.5$, $C = 39°20'$

7. $A = 40°$, $B = 59°$, $c = 14$

8. $B = 19°$, $a = 51$, $c = 61$

9. $a = 345$, $b = 648$, $c = 442$

10. $A = 25°26'$, $a = 13.7$, $B = 78°$

Solve each problem.

11. A triangular plot of land has two sides which have length 400 feet and 600 feet. The measurement of the angle between those sides is 46°20'. Find its perimeter and area.

12. The sides of a triangular city lot have length 50 meters, 70 meters, and 85 meters. Find the measurement of the angle opposite the short side.

13. A pilot is flying from Chicago to Columbus, a distance of 300 miles. He starts his flight 15° off course and flies on this course for 75 miles. How far is he from Columbus and by how much must he correct his error?

14. Two ships leave San Francisco at the same time. One travels 40° west of north at a speed of 20 knots. The other travels 10° west of south at a speed of 15 knots. How far apart are they after 11 hours? (1 knot = 1 nautical mile per hour)

15. A ship at sea is 70 miles from one radio transmitter and 130 miles from another. The measurement of the angle between the signals is 130°. How far apart are the transmitters?

16. A 40-foot television antenna stands on top of a building. From a point on the ground, the angles of elevation of the top and bottom of the antenna, respectively, have measurements of 56° and 42°. How tall is the building?

17. The sides of a triangle are 6.8 cm, 8.4 cm, and 4.9 cm. Find the measure of the smallest angle.

18. The sides of a parallelogram are 55 cm and 71 cm. Find the length of each diagonal if the larger angle is 106°.

19. A plane flew 1200 kilometers north. It then changed direction by turning 15 degrees clockwise and flew for another 850 kilometers. How far was the plane from its starting point?

20. Circle Q has a radius of 15 cm. Two radii, $\overline{QA}$ and $\overline{QB}$, form an angle of 123°. Find the length of chord AB.

Applications in Engineering Tension and Compression

Jon Thomas is a civil engineer. Part of his job is to determine if machinery is being overloaded. Overloading can ruin equipment or make it wear out sooner. Sometimes, it is a potential danger to human safety.

The boom hoist shown below carries a load of 900 pounds. Jon needs to find the tension, t, in the cable and the compression, c, in the boom. To do this, he uses the following method.

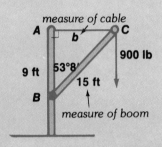

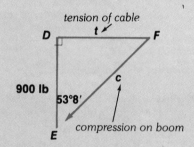

First, assume triangle ABC is a right triangle, and find b.
Use the Pythagorean Theorem.

$$b^2 = 15^2 - 9^2$$
$$= 225 - 81$$
$$= 144$$
$$b = 12 \quad \text{the measure of the cable}$$

Since triangle ABC is similar to triangle DEF, the following proportions can be used.

$$\frac{t}{900} = \frac{12}{9} \quad since \ \frac{DF}{DE} = \frac{AC}{AB} \qquad \frac{c}{900} = \frac{15}{9} \quad since \ \frac{EF}{DE} = \frac{BC}{AB}$$
$$9t = 10{,}800 \qquad\qquad\qquad\qquad 9c = 13{,}500$$
$$t = 1200 \qquad\qquad\qquad\qquad\quad c = 1500$$

The tension is 1200 pounds. The compression is 1500 pounds.

Exercises

Find the tension and compression for each load on the hoist described above.

1. 500 pounds
2. 1000 pounds
3. 1200 pounds
4. 1500 pounds

17-7 Examining Solutions

When the lengths of two sides of a triangle and the measurement of the angle opposite one of them are given, one solution does not always exist. In such a case, one of the following will be true.

1. No triangle exists.
2. Exactly one triangle exists.
3. Two triangles exist.

In other words, the triangle may have no solution, one solution, or two solutions.

Suppose you are given a, b, and A. First, consider the case where $A < 90°$.

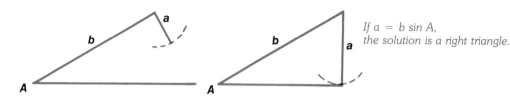

If $a < b \sin A$, no solution exists.   *If $a = b \sin A$, one solution exists.*

If $a = b \sin A$,
the solution is a right triangle.

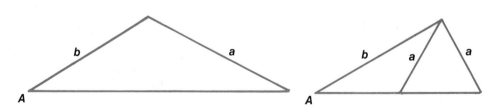

If $a > b > b \sin A$, one solution exists.   *If $b \sin A < a < b$, two solutions exist.*

Consider the case where $A \geq 90°$.

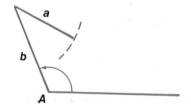
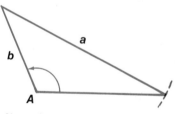

If $a \leq b$, no solution exists.   *If $a > b$, one solution exists.*

Examples

1 Solve the triangle where $A = 50°$, $b = 10$, and $a = 2$.

$b \sin A = 10 \sin 50°$
$\quad = 10(0.7660)$
$\quad = 7.66$

Since $50° < 90°$ and $2 < 7.66$, no solution exists.

2 Solve the triangle where $A = 40°$, $b = 10$, and $a = 8$.

$b \sin A = 10 \sin 40°$
$\quad = 10(0.6428)$
$\quad = 6.428$

Since $40° < 90°$ and $6.428 < 8 < 10$, two solutions exist.

$$\frac{\sin 40°}{8} = \frac{\sin B}{10}$$

$$\sin B = \frac{10 \sin 40°}{8}$$

$$= \frac{10(0.6428)}{8}$$

$$= 0.8035$$

$B = 53°28'$ or $126°32'$ *Since two solutions exist, there must be two values for B. The equation sin (180° − a) = sin a is used to find the second value.*

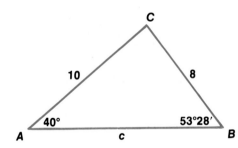
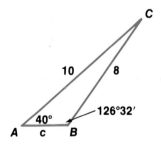

One solution	Another solution
$40° + 53°28' + C = 180°$	$40° + 126°32' + C = 180°$
$\quad C = 180° - 40° - 53°28'$	$\quad C = 180° - 40 - 126°32'$
$\quad C = 86°32'$	$\quad C = 13°28'$

$$c = \frac{8 \sin 86°32'}{\sin 40°}$$

$$= \frac{8(0.9981)}{(0.6428)} \text{ or } 12.4$$

$$c = \frac{8 \sin 13°28'}{\sin 40°}$$

$$= \frac{8(0.2328)}{(0.6428)} \text{ or } 2.9$$

One solution is $B = 53°28'$,
$C = 86°32'$, and $c = 12.4$.

Another solution is $B = 126°32'$,
$C = 13°28'$, and $c = 2.9$.

3 **Solve the triangle where $A = 40°$, $b = 10$, and $a = 14$.**

Since $40° < 90°$ and $14 > 10$, one solution exists.

$$\frac{\sin 40°}{14} = \frac{\sin B}{10}$$

$$\sin B = \frac{10 \sin 40°}{14}$$

$$= \frac{10(0.6428)}{14}$$

$$= 0.4591$$

$$B = 27°20'$$

$$40° + 27°20' + C = 180°$$
$$C = 180° - 40° - 27°20'$$
$$C = 112°40'$$

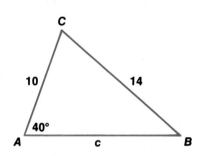

$$\frac{\sin 40°}{14} = \frac{\sin 112°40'}{c}$$

$$c = \frac{14 \sin 112°40'}{\sin 40°}$$

$$= \frac{14(0.9228)}{0.6428}$$

$$= 20.1$$

Therefore, $B = 27°20'$, $C = 112°40'$, and $c = 20.1$.

Exploratory Exercises

State if the given information determines one triangle, two triangles, or no triangle.

1. $A = 140°$, $b = 10$, $a = 3$

2. $A = 118°$, $b = 11$, $a = 17$

3. $A = 30°$, $a = 4$, $b = 8$

4. $A = 43°$, $b = 20$, $a = 11$

5. $A = 58°$, $a = 17$, $b = 13$

6. $A = 38°$, $b = 10$, $a = 8$

Written Exercises

Determine the number of possible solutions. If a solution exists, solve the triangle.

1. $a = 6$, $b = 10$, $A = 36°52'$

2. $a = 6$, $b = 8$, $A = 150°$

3. $a = 12$, $b = 19$, $A = 57°$

4. $a = 7$, $b = 6$, $A = 30°$

5. $a = 64$, $c = 90$, $C = 98°$

6. $a = 26$, $b = 29$, $A = 58°$

7. $b = 40$, $a = 32$, $A = 125°20'$

8. $a = 9$, $b = 20$, $A = 31°$

9. $a = 12$, $b = 14$, $A = 90°$

10. $A = 25°$, $a = 125$, $b = 150$

11. $A = 40°$, $b = 16$, $a = 10$

12. $A = 76°$, $a = 5$, $b = 20$

13. $B = 34°20'$, $b = 5$, $a = 11$

14. $A = 120°$, $b = 20$, $a = 18$

15. $a = 3$, $b = 4$, $c = 8$

16. $a = 16$, $b = 17$, $c = 24$

Examining Solutions

The computer program below can help you find whether certain triangles have one solution, two solutions, or no solution at all.

```
10  INPUT A,A1,B1
20  LET B = B1 * SIN (A * 3.1415927 / 180)
30  PRINT "B SIN A= ";B
40  IF A > = 90 THEN 110
50  IF A1 < B THEN 120
60  IF A1 = B THEN 130
70  IF A1 < B1 THEN 90
80  IF A1 > B THEN 130
90  IF B < A1 THEN
100 PRINT "TWO SOLUTIONS EXIST." : GOTO 140
110 IF A1 > B1 THEN 130
120 PRINT "NO SOLUTION EXISTS.": GOTO 140
130 PRINT "ONE SOLUTION EXISTS."
140 END
```

Lesson 17-7 was used as the basis for the program. If you study the lesson carefully, you can understand how the program works.

Be sure to enter the degree measure of angle A and the lengths of sides a and b (called A1 and B1 in the program) in the order given.

```
]RUN
?26,3,7
B SIN A=3.06859807
NO SOLUTION EXISTS.
```

Exercises

Determine the number of possible solutions. State the value of $b \sin A$ to four decimal places.

1. $A = 103°, a = 5, b = 2$

2. $A = 175°, a = 19, b = 2$

3. $A = 77°, a = 1, b = 5$

4. $A = 130°, a = 8, b = 10$

5. $A = 38.62°, a = 15, b = 16$

6. $A = 10.524°, a = 1, b = 2$

7. $A = 53°20', a = 9, b = 6$

8. $A = 9°55', a = 3, b = 6$

9. Why is A multiplied by 3.1415927/180 in line 20?

10. What happens when the values for A, A1, and B1 are entered out of order? Why?

Vocabulary

hypotenuse (551)
opposite side (551)
adjacent side (551)
sine (551)
cosine (551)
tangent (551)
cosecant (551)

secant (551)
cotangent (551)
interpolation (555)
angle of elevation (561)
angle of depression (561)
Law of Sines (565)
Law of Cosines (568)

Chapter Summary

1. The trigonometric functions relate the sides and acute angles of a right
triangle as follows. (551)

$$\sin A = \frac{a}{c}$$

$$\cos A = \frac{b}{c}$$

$$\tan A = \frac{a}{b}$$

$$\csc A = \frac{c}{a}$$

$$\sec A = \frac{c}{b}$$

$$\cot A = \frac{b}{a}$$

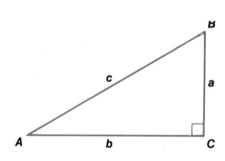

2. The special triangle with angle measurements of 45°, 45°, and 90° has
sides whose lengths are in the ratio of 1 to 1 to $\sqrt{2}$. (552)

3. The special triangle with angle measurements of 30°, 60°, and 90° has
sides whose lengths are in the ratio of 1 to $\sqrt{3}$ to 2. (552)

4. The values of trigonometric functions may be found in a table. Sometimes
interpolation is needed to find a value which is between consecutive entries in the table. (554)

5. Trigonometric functions can be used to solve right triangles. (558)

6. Trigonometric functions may be used to solve many problems including
those involving angles of elevation and depression. (561)

7. Law of Sines: Let triangle ABC be any triangle with a, b, and c representing the measures of sides opposite angles with measurements A, B,
and C respectively. Then the following equations are true.

$$\frac{\sin A}{a} = \frac{\sin B}{b} = \frac{\sin C}{c} \quad (565)$$

8. Law of Cosines: Let Triangle ABC be any triangle with a, b, and c representing the measures of sides opposite angles with measurements A, B, and C respectively. Then, the following equations are true.

$$a^2 = b^2 + c^2 - 2bc \cos A$$
$$b^2 = a^2 + c^2 - 2ac \cos B$$
$$c^2 = a^2 + b^2 - 2ab \cos C \quad (568)$$

9. When the lengths of two sides of a triangle and the measurement of the angle opposite one of them are given, one solution does not always exist. No triangle may exist, one triangle may exist, or two triangles may exist.   (572)

Chapter Review

17–1   **Find each value to the nearest four decimal places.**

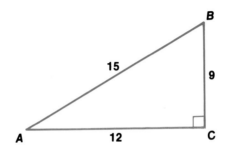

1. $\sin A$

2. $\sin B$

3. $\cos A$

4. $\cos B$

5. $\tan A$

6. $\tan B$

7. $\csc A$

8. $\sec A$

9. $\cot B$

Find the value of each expression. Write each answer in fraction form.

10. $\cos 30°$

11. $\tan 60°$

12. $\sin 45°$

17–2   **Use a table to approximate each trigonometric value. Use interpolation when necessary.**

13. $\sin 70°$

14. $\sin 18°20'$

15. $\cos 35°$

16. $\cos 81°40'$

17. $\tan 47°$

18. $\tan 16°35'$

Find the measure of x to the nearest minute.

19. $\sin x = 0.9272$

20. $\sin x = 0.2164$

21. $\cos x = 0.9171$

22. $\cos x = 0.5150$

23. $\tan x = 0.3476$

24. $\tan x = 1.664$

17–3 **Solve each right triangle.**

25. $A = 25°, c = 6$

26. $A = 50°, a = 11$

27. $B = 85°, a = 6.21$

28. $B = 31°, c = 12$

29. $a = 1, b = 3$

30. $a = 15, c = 20$

31. $b = 7, c = 10$

32. $a = 10, b = 24$

17–4 **Solve each problem. Round all answers to two decimal places.**

33. From a point on the ground 50 meters from the base of a flagpole, the measurement of the angle of elevation of the top is 48°. How tall is the flagpole?

34. A pilot 3000 feet above the ocean notes the measurement of the angle of depression of a ship is 42°. How far is the plane from the ship?

35. A building is 80 feet tall. Find the measurement of the angle of elevation to the top of the building from a point on the ground 100 feet from the base of the building.

36. The base of a monument and two points on the ground are in a straight line. The two points are 50 meters apart. The measurements of the angles of elevation to the top of the monument are 45° and 25°. Find the height of the monument.

17–5 **Use the Law of Sines to solve each triangle.**

37. $A = 50°, b = 12, a = 10$

38. $A = 83°10', a = 80, b = 70$

39. $B = 46°, C = 83°, b = 65$

40. $A = 45°, B = 30°, b = 20$

17–6 **Use the Law of Cosines to solve each triangle.**

41. $A = 60°, b = 2, c = 5$

42. $C = 65°, a = 4, b = 7$

43. $C = 40°, a = 6, b = 7$

44. $B = 24°, a = 42, c = 6.5$

17–7 **Determine the number of possible solutions. If a solution exists, solve the triangle.**

45. $A = 36°, a = 2, b = 14$

46. $A = 40°, a = 8, b = 10$

47. $A = 46°, a = 10, b = 8$

48. $A = 130°, a = 25, b = 16$

Find each value to the nearest four decimal places.

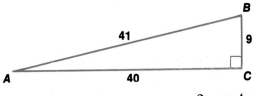

1. sin A

2. cos A

3. tan A

4. cos B

Find the value of each expression. Write each answer in fraction form.

5. cos 60°

6. tan 45°

Use a table to approximate each trigonometric value. Use interpolation when necessary.

7. sin 67°

8. cos 38°10′

9. tan 59°38′

10. sin 13°3′

Find the measure of x to the nearest minute.

11. cos x = 0.4384

12. tan x = 0.4734

13. sin x = 0.4423

14. tan x = 1.635

Solve each right triangle.

15. $A = 36°, b = 14$

16. $B = 75°, b = 6$

17. $A = 22°, c = 8$

18. $a = 7, c = 12$

Solve each problem.

19. A 32-foot ladder leans against a building. The top touches the building 26 feet above the ground. What is the measurement of the angle formed by the ladder with the ground?

20. From the top of a cliff, a camper sees a deer. The measurement of the angle of depression to the deer is 70°. The cliff is 50 meters high. How far is the deer from the base of the cliff?

21. A plane flew 1000 kilometers north. It then changed direction by turning 20 degrees clockwise and flew for another 700 kilometers. How far was the plane from its starting point?

22. The longest side of a triangle is 23 yards. Two of the angles are 23° and 49°. Find the measures of the other two sides and the other angle.

Determine the number of possible solutions. If a solution exists, solve each triangle.

23. $a = 13, b = 11, c = 17$

24. $A = 46°, B = 77°, a = 6$

25. $A = 75°, b = 21, a = 30$

26. $A = 65°, b = 21, a = 6$

27. $A = 70°, B = 31°, c = 17$

28. $A = 44°, a = 12, b = 14$

29. $A = 140°, b = 10, a = 7$

30. $C = 48°, a = 7, b = 9$

1. Is π a rational number?

2. Graph the function $g(x) = -[x]$.

3. Find an equation of the line that passes through $(6, 4)$ and is parallel to the graph of $y = 2x - 1$.

4. Solve the system. Use augmented matrices.
$$5x - 2y + 3z = -7$$
$$-2x + 4y + z = 4$$
$$3x - 3y + 4z = 2$$

5. Divide using synthetic division.
$(x^3 + 2x^2 - 5x - 6) \div (x - 2)$

6. Simplify $\dfrac{1}{z^{\frac{3}{5}}}$.

7. Simplify $\sqrt{\dfrac{3}{8}} + \sqrt{72} - \sqrt{\dfrac{8}{3}}$.

8. Simplify $\sqrt{\dfrac{4}{7}}$.

9. Solve $6x^2 - x - 1 = 0$.

10. Find the value of the discriminant for $6a^2 - a + 2 = 0$. Describe the nature of the roots.

11. Graph $f(x) = -3x^2$.

12. Graph $x^2 - 2x + 4y + 5 = 0$. Then state the axis of symmetry, vertex, and direction of opening.

13. Use the distance formula to find the distance between $(2\sqrt{3}, 4\sqrt{3})$ and $(2\sqrt{3}, -\sqrt{3})$.

14. Graph the following system of inequalities. $(y - 3)^2 \le x + 2$
$y \ge x^2 - 4$

15. Use synthetic division to find the factors of $x^4 - x^3 - 17x^2 + 21x + 36$.

16. Find the rational zeros of $f(x) = 2x^3 + 7x^2 - 42x - 72$.

17. Graph the equation $y = \dfrac{x}{x - 2}$. Show the asymptotes.

Find the logarithm of each number.

18. 25,300

19. 0.0001582

Find the antilogarithm of each logarithm.

20. 4.4232

21. $(0.4600 - 3)$

Write in expanded form and find the sum.

22. $\displaystyle\sum_{k=1}^{3} (2k - 1)^k$

How many different ways can the letters in the following words be arranged?

23. LETTER

24. GEOMETRY

Evaluate.

25. $\dfrac{P(8, 3) \cdot P(5, 4)}{P(6, 6)}$

26. $\dfrac{7!}{4!}$

Use the frequency distribution for exercises 27–30.

Item	1	2	3	4	5	6	7	8	9
Frequency	4	2	2	3	4	1	2	4	3

27. Draw a bar graph to show the data.

28. Find the range.

29. Find the mean.

30. Find the standard deviation.

Verify.

31. $\dfrac{1}{\sec^2 \theta} + \dfrac{1}{\csc^2 \theta} = 1$

32. $\sin (x + 30°) + \cos (x + 60°) = \cos x$.

Problem Solving

33. A 24-foot ladder leans against a building. It forms an angle of 42° with the building. How far is the foot of the ladder from the base of the building?

34. Eric can rake the leaves in his yard in 10 hours. Eric and Mark together can rake the leaves in 4 hours. How long will it take Mark to rake the leaves alone?

The test questions on this page deal with expressions and equations. The information at the right may help you with some of the questions.

1. Many problems can be solved without much calculating if the basic mathematical concepts are understood. Always look carefully at what is asked, and think of possible shortcuts for solving the problem.

2. Check your solutions by substituting values for the variables.

Directions: Choose the one best answer. Write A, B, C, or D.

1. If $\frac{x}{6} > x$, which could be a value for x?

   (A) -6 (B) 0   (C) 5   (D) 6

2. If $n^2 - 4 = -3n$, what is the value of $\left(n + \frac{3}{2}\right)^2$?

   (A) 5   (B) $6\frac{1}{4}$ (C) 11

   (D) cannot be determined

3. If b is an odd integer greater than one, which of the following must be an odd integer?

   (A) $b^3 - 1$ (B) $b^3 - b^2$

   (C) $1 + b^3$ (D) $\frac{3b - 3}{b - 1}$

4. If $0 < n < 1$, which of the following increases as n increases?

   I. $1 - n^2$

   II. $n - 1$

   III. $\frac{1}{n^2}$

   (A) II only   (B) III only

   (C) I and III only   (D) II and III only

5. If $-a < 0 < -b$, which of the following is true?

   (A) $0 < b < 0$ (B) $a < 0 < b$

   (C) $b < 0 < a$ (D) $0 < b < a$

6. If $x^2 = 25$, then 2^{x-1} could equal

   (A) 2   (B) 4   (C) 8   (D) 16

7. If k is any odd integer and $x = 6k$, then $\frac{x}{2}$ will always be

   (A) odd   (B) even

   (C) positive   (D) negative

8. If $a + b = 8$ and $3b - 4 = -13a$, then what is the value of a?

   (A) $-\frac{13}{3}$ (B) -3 (C) -2 (D) 10

9. $q \diamond t$ is defined as $q^2 + t^2 + qt$. What is the value of $4 \diamond -2$?

   (A) 4   (B) 12   (C) 26   (D) 28

10. If $x > y$ and $z < 0$, which of the following are true?

    I. $xz < yz$

    II. $x + z > y + z$

    III. $x - z < y - z$

    (A) I only   (B) II only

    (C) I and II only   (D) I, II and III

11. If $5y + 1$ is an odd integer, what is the next consecutive odd integer?

    (A) $3y + 1$ (B) $5y + 3$

    (C) $7y + 1$ (D) $7y + 3$

12. A man owns $\frac{1}{4}$ of a business. He sells half of his share for $12,000. What is the total value of the business?

    (A) $1500   (B) $48,000

    (C) $96,000   (D) $108,000

Appendix: BASIC

The Language of BASIC

BASIC is a computer language. It has many similarities to algebra. Some of the characters that differ are shown below.

Algebra	BASIC		Algebra	BASIC	
$\leq$	< =		3^2	3 ↑ 2	*In BASIC, raising to a*
$>$	>		a	A	*power is indicated by ↑*
$\geq$	> =		$\times$	*	*or $\wedge$.*
$\neq$	<>		$\div$	/	

A variable is represented by a letter or by a letter and a numeral.

> **A, B, M, Z1, R3, A6**   *Notice that a letter precedes a numeral.*

In BASIC, an operation symbol can never be left out. To write A times B, write A*B, not ab as in algebra.

A computer program is a series of statements that give directions to the computer. A program is used to put information into the computer *(input)*, have the calculations done, and get the results out of the computer *(output)*. A sample program follows.

line numbers →   5   PRINT 6.731 + 8.213 + 3.726 ←   *Some computer terminals*
                     10   END ←   *statements*   *type only capital letters.*

In a BASIC program each statement has a line number. Usually, integers from 1 to 9999 can be used as line numbers. The computer performs the instructions in numerical order by line number. The last statement in any BASIC program must be an **END** statement.

Most programs use only a few statements. In the sample program above each statement begins with a word. One begins with PRINT, the other with END. Other words that are often used are READ and DATA. Each **READ statement** must be accompanied by a **DATA statement**.

Example

1 **Write a program to compute the sum and product of three numbers.**

```
10   READ A, B, C
20   PRINT A + B + C
30   PRINT A*B*C
40   DATA 71, 16, 84
50   END
```

The computer assigns the numbers from the DATA statement to the variables A, B, and C in order.
A = 71   B = 16   C = 84

The sum and product of any three numbers can be found simply by changing the numbers in the DATA statement in line 40.

Before the computer will do a program it must be given the RUN command. Commands do *not* have line numbers.

10 READ A, B, C	*The computer assigns 16 to A, 13 to B, and*
20 PRINT A + B + C	*7 to C from the data in line 40.*
30 PRINT A*B*C	
40 DATA 16, 13, 7	
50 END	

RUN	*The RUN command tells the computer to execute the program.*
36	*A + B + C = 16 + 13 + 7 or 36*
1456	*A*B*C = 16*13*7 or 1456*

There is a specific order of operations used by the computer.

1. **Do all operations in parentheses, from the innermost parentheses outward.**
2. **Evaluate all powers from left to right.**
3. **Do all multiplications and/or divisions from left to right.**
4. **Do all additions and/or subtractions from left to right.**

Order of Operations in BASIC

The order of operations is illustrated in the next example.

Example

2 **Evaluate 12/2 − (5 + 3) ∗ 4 ↑ 2 + 3.**

$12/2 - (5 + 3) * 4 \uparrow 2 + 3$	$= 12/2 - 8{*}4 \uparrow 2 + 3$	*Do operations in parentheses.*
	$= 12/2 - 8{*}16 + 3$	*Evaluate powers.*
	$= 6 - 128 + 3$	*Do the division and multiplication.*
	$= -119$	*Do the addition and subtraction.*

The value of the expression is −119.

When the results of computations exceed six significant digits the computer will use **E notation.** This is the computer equivalent of scientific notation. The E means *times 10 to the given power.*

Result of Computation	E Notation	Meaning
37867275	3.78673E + 07	3.78673×10^7
0.003629	3.629E − 03	3.629×10^{-3}

Written Exercises

Write an expression in BASIC for each of the following.

1. $3x + 5y - 7$

2. $a \cdot b \cdot c - 3$

3. $5m - 3b + 8$

4. $17 \div a$

5. 8^2

6. $-4(a + b)^2$

Evaluate each of the following.

7. $6 + 8 * 2$

8. $(3 + 2) \uparrow 2$

9. $(2 * (5 + 8))/13$

10. $((14 + 10)/4)/2$

11. $3 * (5 \uparrow 2)$

12. $(6 + 8)/2 + 5$

Evaluate each of the following. Let A = 5, B = 6, C = 15.

13. $A * B + 3$

14. $A + 3 * B$

15. $C - B + 5$

16. C/A

17. $A * (B + 3)$

18. $(A + 3) * B$

Write an expression in BASIC for each of the following.

19. $3x^2 + 2x + 5$

20. a^{x+2}

21. $\dfrac{x + 5}{2y}$

22. $\dfrac{5x + 3}{2x + 4}$

23. $\dfrac{a}{b} + n$

24. $\dfrac{(x^3 + 7x^2 + 5)^3}{x + 1}$

Write each of the following in scientific notation.

25. $6.17324E + 04$

26. $7.9E + 08$

27. $2.176E + 17$

28. $1.325E - 06$

29. $4.0005E + 03$

30. $7.304E - 11$

Write each of the following in E notation.

31. $16{,}500{,}000$

32. 0.0000127

33. 9.0087×10^5

Write the printout for each statement. Let A = 3, B = 4, and R6 = 8.

34. 130   PRINT 7*B

35. 710   PRINT 121 + 19

36. 75   PRINT A*R6 + 7

37. 30   PRINT A + B + R6

38. 40   PRINT 4*B + R6*2

39. 90   PRINT (2*R6)/4

Write a BASIC program to compute and print each of the following. Use only PRINT and END statements.

40. The sum and product of 31, 14, 62, and 29.

41. The difference of 673 and 49 and the quotient of 673 ÷ 49.

42. The perimeter and area of a rectangle with length 4.7 cm and width 2.8 cm.

43. The circumference and area of a circle with radius 6.37 cm. Use 3.1416 for π.

Write a BASIC program to compute and print each of the following. Use READ and DATA statements.

44. The sum and product of 31, 14, 62, and 29.

45. The difference of 673 and 49 and the quotient of 673 ÷ 49.

46. The perimeter and area of a rectangle with length 4.7 cm and width 2.8 cm.

47. The circumference and area of a circle with radius 6.37 cm. Use 3.1416 for π.

Assignment of Variables

In BASIC the equals sign, $=$, has a slightly different use than in algebra. Unlike algebra, the left side of an equation in BASIC can have exactly one variable and nothing else. Compare the equations below.

<table>
<tr><td style="text-align:center">Algebra</td><td style="text-align:center">BASIC</td></tr>
<tr><td style="text-align:center">$2x + 15y = 27 + 36y$</td><td style="text-align:center">$X = 16*Y + 37*Z - 5$</td></tr>
</table>

In this equation both right and left members have two terms. This algebraic sentence is *not* acceptable in BASIC.

In this statement the value of the expression on the right is computed and *assigned* to the variable on the left.

In BASIC the equals sign tells the computer to assign the value of the expression on the right to the variable on the left. Assignment statements are called **LET statements.**

The word LET may be omitted on many computers.

```
10   READ Y,Z
20   LET X = 16*Y + 37*Z - 5
30   PRINT X
40   DATA 47, 38
50   END
```

In this program, the data are assigned to the variables as follows: Y = 47, Z = 38. The computation is 16 · 47 + 37 · 38 − 5 which is 752 + 1406 − 5 or 2153. This value is assigned to X, and then printed.

```
RUN
2153
```

Consider the program at the right. It counts how many numbers are printed. What does the value of K in line 80 tell you? It tells you that three "compute and print" operations were performed.

```
10   LET K = 0
20   PRINT 2 ↑ 3
30   LET K = K + 1
40   PRINT 2 ↑ 4
50   LET K = K + 1
60   PRINT 2 ↑ 5
70   LET K = K + 1
80   PRINT K
90   END
```

In algebra, line 30 is nonsense. But in BASIC it means that 1 is added to the old value of K to obtain a new value for K.

The two programs below accomplish the same task. Which do you prefer? Why?

```
10   LET A = 3
11   LET B = 4
12   LET C = 5
13   LET D = 6
14   LET X = 2
20   LET Y = A*X ↑ 3 + B*X − (C*D)
30   PRINT Y
40   END
```

```
10   READ A,B,C,D,X
15   DATA 3, 4, 5, 6, 2
20   LET Y = A*X ↑ 3 + B*X − (C*D)
30   PRINT Y
40   END
```

Another kind of variable used in BASIC is called a string variable. String variable names consist of a letter followed by "$". For example, A$, B$, C$, etc., are all string variable names. These allow the computer to work with characters other than numbers. The characters must be placed within quotation marks.

20 LET A$ = "HELLO"   *The computer places the characters H, E, L, L, O in the string.*
30 PRINT A$
40 END

RUN
HELLO   *The computer prints HELLO when it executes line 30.*

Special commands are available which will allow you to print only certain characters from the string. Check the manual for the particular computer that you are using to find out how this is done.

Written Exercises

Let A = 3, B = 4, and M1 = 16. Find the value of X.

1. 190 LET X = 6*A   2. 30 LET X = M1/B   3. 25 LET X = A*B + 5
4. 170 LET X = A ↑ 4   5. 20 LET X = B + M1*3   6. 40 LET X = M1 − B + 3*A

Each mathematical expression below is followed by an incorrect BASIC expression. Correct the BASIC expression.

7. $\dfrac{m + 2}{r + 4}$ M + 2/R + 4

8. $\dfrac{ab}{y + 3}$ AB/(Y + 3)

9. $\dfrac{(x + a)^2}{2z}$ (X + A) ↑ 2/2*Z

10. $\left(\dfrac{x}{y}\right)^{n-3}$ (X/Y) ↑ N − 3

Correct the error in each expression or statement below.

11. 7X + 34   12. (7 + 8/2   13. 3*X ↑ 2 + 4X
14. 20 LET Y = 3A   15. 20 LET 2*X = 5 + 13   16. 30 LET X$ = PENELOPE

Identify what each program does. Then determine the output for each program.

17. 5 DATA 6, 8   18. 5 DATA 7, 12   19. 5 DATA "GOOD   ",
    10 READ L,W   10 READ B,H   "AFTERNOON"
    15 LET P = 2*L + 2*W   15 LET A = (1/2)*B*H   10 READ A$, B$
    20 PRINT P   20 PRINT A   20 PRINT A$; B$
    25 END   25 END   30 END

For each of the following, write a program that will compute and print the value of X.

20. A = 3, B = 7, C = 9, X = A + B(C − 1)

21. A = 6, B = 18, C = 30, X = $\dfrac{3}{2}\left(\dfrac{B}{A} + C\right)$

22. M = 1, R = 2, Q = 6, X = $\dfrac{Q^R − M}{Q + M}$

23. P1 = 3.1416, R = 5, X = P1(R²)

24. A = 6, B = 7, C = 8, D = 9, E = 10, X = $\dfrac{A + B + C + D + E}{5}$

IF-THEN Statements and Loops

Operations in a program may be repeated by using a **GO TO statement** as in the following program.

10 READ S	*The computer returns to line 10*
20 DATA 3, 7, 15	*each time it executes line 50 and*
30 A = S ↑ 2	*uses the next number on the data*
40 PRINT A,	*list. The comma in line 40 causes the*
50 GO TO 10	*output to be printed in one line.*
60 END	

The printout is as follows.

9	49	225	*When all the data have been used, the computer*
OUT OF DATA IN LINE 10			*prints OUT OF DATA and ends the program.*

The GO TO statement has the following form.

line number GO TO line number

Suppose you wish to find the area of each of ten different circles with radii of 1 unit, 2 units, 3 units, and so on to 10 units. Consider the following program.

10 LET R = 1	
20 A = (3.1416)∗R ↑ 2	*The approximation 3.1416 is used for π.*
30 PRINT A	
40 LET R = R + 1	
50 GO TO 20	*The computer goes back to 20.*
60 END	*Can line 60 ever be reached?*

In its present form this program will never stop. An IF-THEN statement can be used as a test line so that the program will stop when R > 10. Study the sequence of the revised program as shown below.

10 LET R = 1	*Begin.*
20 A = (3.1416)∗R ↑ 2 ←	*Compute and print in the <u>operations</u> area.*
30 PRINT A	
40 LET R = R + 1	*<u>Change</u> to the next greater radius.*
50 IF R< = 10 THEN 20	*<u>Test</u> by asking, "Is the radius less*
↓no yes	*than or equal to 10?" If yes, the*
	program is looped back to line 20.
60 END	*If no, the program ends.*

The IF-THEN statement compares two numbers and tells the computer what to do based on the results of the comparison. The general form of the IF-THEN statement is as follows.

line number IF *algebraic sentence* THEN *line number*

If the algebraic sentence is true, then the computer proceeds to the line whose number follows THEN. If the algebraic sentence is false, the computer simply goes to the next line of the program.

The algebraic sentence uses one of the following symbols.

BASIC SYMBOL	EXAMPLE	
=	A = B	
<	A<B	
< =	A< = B	*"A is less than or equal to B"*
>	A>B	
> =	A> = B	*"A is greater than or equal to B"*
<>	A<>B	*"A is not equal to B"*

Consider the revised program on the preceding page again. Since lines 20 through 50 are repeated in the program, they form a **loop.** All loops must have a beginning (line 10), a set of operations to be performed (lines 20 and 30), a change in the input variable (line 40), and a test line to continue or break the loop (line 50).

In line 40 the value of R is increased by 1 each time through the loop. Suppose that the areas of circles are wanted whose radii are even integers from 2 to 10. How would lines 10 and 40 be changed?

Sometimes a programmer needs to count how many times an operation is performed. In the following program, line 15 keeps the count. Each time through the loop the count is increased by one.

Example

1 **Write a program to count the multiples of 3 between 10 and 100.**

5	LET K = 0	*Assign a zero starting value for K, the "counter."*
10	LET X = 12	*Assign the first multiple of 3 greater than 10 to X.*
15	LET K = K + 1	*Increase the counter by 1.*
20	LET X = X + 3	*The next multiple of 3 is found.*
25	IF X< = 100 THEN 15	*Test line. The computer loops back to line 15 until X>100.*
30	PRINT K	*Output*
35	END	

An IF-THEN statement may be used with READ and DATA statements to end a program. Consider the following example.

Example

2 **Write a program that finds the area of each of three squares with sides of 3 cm, 7 cm, and 15 cm. Use an IF-THEN statement to end the program.**

```
10   READ S
20   DATA 3, 7, 15, -1
30   IF S = -1 THEN 70
40   A = S ↑ 2
50   PRINT "THE AREA IS   " A "   SQ CM."
60   GO TO 10
70   END
```

The final number is <u>not</u> one of the side measures.
What does line 30 do?

```
RUN
THE AREA IS 9 SQ CM.
THE AREA IS 49 SQ CM.
THE AREA IS 225 SQ CM.
```

Output

No OUT OF DATA statement is printed.

In a PRINT statement words and punctuation marks enclosed in quotation marks are printed exactly as they are typed. Line 50 in the program above is an example. This and other uses of the PRINT statement are listed below.

10 PRINT A	*There is a single output.*
20 PRINT X, Y, Z	*There are three outputs on the same line.*
30 PRINT X; Y; Z	*There are three outputs close together.*
40 PRINT A + B	*There is one computation, one output.*
50 PRINT 7 + A, B - 9	*There are two computations; two outputs.*
60 PRINT "EXAMPLE"	*Prints text.*
70 PRINT "SOLUTION IS " X	*Prints text and numerical output close together.*
80 PRINT	*The line is left blank.*

Example

3 **Write two print statements. In the first, set up headings for computing the area of triangles. In the second, print the data and the results. Include a READ line for variables B and A.**

```
10   READ B, A
20   PRINT "BASE", "ALTITUDE", "AREA OF TRIANGLE"
30   PRINT B, A, (B*A)/2
```

Written Exercises

Let A = 5, B = 8, and X = 10. Tell the number of the statement that the computer will do next.

1. 10   IF A<20 THEN 75
    15   PRINT B

2. 15   IF A>=4 THEN 90
    20   PRINT 2*A

3. 10   IF A<>B THEN 50
    20   PRINT X

4. 10   IF (A+B)<X THEN 60
    20   PRINT 2*X

5. 50   IF (A−B)>X THEN 75
    60   PRINT B−A

6. 45   IF (B*X)<A ↑ 3 THEN 10
    50   PRINT B*X

Use the program below to answer exercises 7–10. Tell whether A, B, or both A and B will be printed, and give the values of any variables printed.

```
10   IF A>B THEN 40
20   LET A=A+10
25   LET B=B+2
30   IF A>=B THEN 50
40   PRINT A
50   PRINT B
60   END
```

7. Let A = 12, B = 12

8. Let A = 14, B = 19

9. Let A = 9, B = 21

10. Let A = 21, B = 5

Describe what each program will do.

11.
```
10   LET M=0
20   PRINT M, M↑2
30   LET M=M+3
40   IF M<=30 THEN 20
50   END
```

12.
```
10   LET X=1
20   PRINT 4*X
30   LET X=X+1
40   IF X<21 THEN 20
50   END
```

Write a BASIC program to do each of the following. Use an IF-THEN statement.

13. Print the squares of the integers from 21 to 35 inclusive.

14. Print the cubes of the even integers from 10 to 36 inclusive.

15. Print the multiples of 5 from 10 to 100.

16. Count the multiples of 4 from 4 through 125 inclusive, and print the count.

17. Count the multiples of 7 from 20 through 1000 inclusive, and print the count.

18. Print the integers from 10 to 1 in descending order.

19. Given two unequal numbers a and b, print them in ascending order.

20. Print a table showing the radii and volumes of spheres with radii of 7 cm, 3.2 cm, and 6.8 cm. Volume of sphere: $V = \frac{4}{3}\pi r^2$.

21. Compute and print the product $9 \cdot 8 \cdot 7 \cdot 6 \cdot 5 \cdot 4 \cdot 3 \cdot 2 \cdot 1$ (*Hint:* Let P represent the product and begin the program with P = 1. Use a loop.)

FOR-NEXT Loops

FOR-NEXT statements can increase the efficiency of a program. Compare the programs below.

Begin	10 LET R=1	10 FOR R=1 TO 10 STEP 1	
	20 A=(3.1416)*R↑2	20 A=(3.1416)*R↑2	*The lines in color create the*
	30 PRINT A	30 PRINT A	*loops in each program.*
Increment	40 LET R=R+1	40 NEXT R	
Test	50 IF R<=10 THEN 20	50 END	
	60 END		

In a single line at the right, line 10, the value of R is started at 1 and is increased by 1 until it reaches 10.

10 FOR R=1	TO 10	STEP 1
begin	*test*	*increment*
LET R=1	Is R≤10?	LET R=R+1

The general form of a FOR statement is as follows.

line number FOR *variable* = _____   TO _____   STEP _____

The blanks may include numbers, variables, or expressions.

A FOR statement must always be paired with a NEXT statement. The steps may be positive, negative, or fractions as shown below.

240   FOR X=8 TO 3 STEP−1
270   NEXT X

110   FOR J=−3 TO 12 STEP 1/2
200   NEXT J

120   FOR R5=(17+A↑2)/3 TO 3*B↑2 STEP .1
140   NEXT R5

330   FOR X=2 TO 10   *No step size means increments of 1.*
380   NEXT X   *Any other step size must be indicated.*

Example

1 **Write a program that prints the odd integers from 1 to 25, their squares, and their cubes.**

10   PRINT "N", "N↑2", "N↑3"   *This line places headings on the table.*
20   FOR N=1 TO 25 STEP 2
30   PRINT N, N↑2, N↑3
40   NEXT N
50   END

Example 2

Write a program that adds the even integers from 2 to 100 inclusive.

10 LET S = 0	The variable S represents the sum, set at zero.
20 FOR X = 2 TO 100 STEP 2	
30 LET S = S + X	In line 30, the sum of the even integers is accumulated. When $X = 2$, $S = 0$ and $S + X = 2$.
40 NEXT X	When $X = 4$, $S = 2$ and $S + X = 6$, and so on.
50 PRINT "SUM OF EVEN INTEGERS IS " S	
60 END	

It is often useful to have loops within loops. These are called nested loops. There are only two ways these loops can appear in a program as shown.

Nested Loops	Independent Loops	Not Acceptable
FOR X	FOR X	FOR X
FOR Y	NEXT X	FOR Y
NEXT Y	FOR Y	NEXT X
NEXT X	NEXT Y	NEXT Y

The loops do not cross. The loops do not cross. They are not nested. These loops cross.

Written Exercises

Use a FOR-NEXT loop to rewrite each program.

1.
```
10   LET M = 1
20   PRINT M, M ↑ 2, M ↑ 3
30   LET M = M + 1
40   IF M < = 5 THEN 20
50   END
```

2.
```
10   LET K = 0
15   LET S = 0
20   LET K = K + 1
30   IF K > 5 THEN 60
40   LET S = S + K
50   GO TO 20
60   PRINT "SUM IS   " S
70   END
```

Correct the errors in the following programs. Then run your corrected program if possible.

3.
```
10   FOR X = 1 TO 5
20   FOR Y = 2 TO 4 STEP 2
30   PRINT X*Y
40   NEXT X
50   NEXT Y
60   END
```

4.
```
10   FOR X = 7 TO 15 STEP 3
20   PRINT X, X ↑ 3
30   FOR Y = 2 TO 5
40   PRINT Y, Y + 2 ↑ Y
50   NEXT X
60   NEXT Y
70   END
```

Write a program to do each of the following. Use a FOR-NEXT statement.

5. For the integers from 10 to 20, print each integer, its third power, and its fifth power.

6. Use the expression $X \uparrow (1/2)$ to indicate square root and $X \uparrow (1/3)$ to indicate cube root. For the integers from 1 to 15, print the integer, its square root, and its cube root. Check these results with the table on pages 611 and 612.

7. The formula for changing Fahrenheit temperature to Celsius is $C = \frac{5}{9} \cdot (F - 32)$. Print the Fahrenheit temperature and Celsius temperatures for $F = 0$ to 100 in steps of 5.

8. The lengths and widths of 3 rectangles are as follows: 8, 5; 9, 6; 13, 17. Print a table that includes the lengths, widths, perimeters, and areas of the rectangles. (*Hint:* Use a FOR-NEXT loop that loops 3 times.)

9. The bases and heights of 4 triangles are as follows: 6, 8; 8, 12; 9, 10; 200, 300. Compute and print the areas of the triangles.

10. Compute and print the sum of the integers from 1 to 100 inclusive.

11. Compute and print the sum of the multiples of 3 from 3 to 99 inclusive.

12. Compute and print the sum of the squares of the integers from 1 to 20 inclusive. Have your program check its answers with the formula $S = \frac{n(n+1)(2n+1)}{6}$ where $n = 20$.

13. Compute and print the sum of the cubes of the integers from 1 to 10 inclusive. Have your program check its answer with the formula $S = \left(\frac{n(n+1)}{2}\right)^2$ where $n = 10$.

Write a program to solve each of the following problems. Use the formula $A = A(1 + r)$, starting with the original deposit as the value of A. Then repeat the formula as necessary.

14. One hundred dollars is deposited in a bank that pays 9% annual interest compounded monthly. Compute and print the value of the account after 10 years. (*Hint:* The monthly interest is 0.75%. The formula is repeated 120 times.)

15. Five hundred dollars is deposited in a bank that pays 11.5% annual interest compounded semiannually. Compute and print the value of the account after $7\frac{1}{2}$ years.

16. Ten thousand dollars is deposited in a money market account that pays 8.875% annual interest compounded daily. Compute and print its value after 1 year.

Flow Charts

Programmers often use diagrams called **flow charts** to organize their programs. Some shapes have special meanings in flow charts.

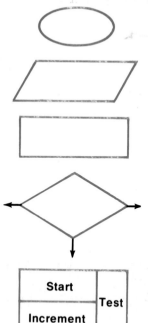

An oval is used to begin or end a program.

A parallelogram is used to show input or output. Use it with READ or PRINT statements.

A rectangle shows processing operations. Use it with a LET statement.

A diamond shows a decision. Arrows show how the flow continues. Use it with IF-THEN statements.

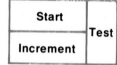

An iteration box shows all parts of a loop. *Iterate* means to do over and over. Use it with FOR-NEXT statements.

Below is a program and a flow chart to print the integers and their squares from 1 to 100.

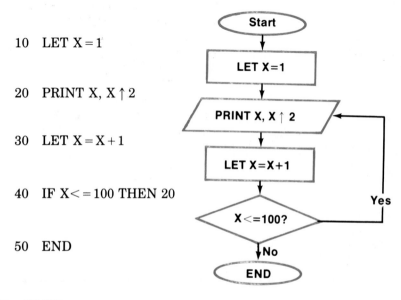

```
10   LET X = 1

20   PRINT X, X ↑ 2

30   LET X = X + 1

40   IF X < = 100 THEN 20

50   END
```

The following example uses an iteration box for a loop.

Examples

1 **Make a flow chart and write a program to sum the even integers from 2 to 100.**

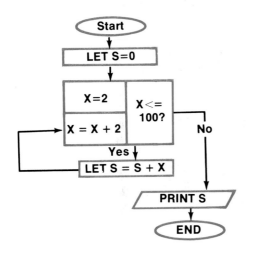

```
10   LET S = 0
20   FOR X = 2 TO 100 STEP 2
30   LET S = S + X
40   NEXT X
50   PRINT S
60   END
```

2 **Suppose you are given a set of 5 test scores for each of 25 students. Write a flow chart and a program to print the average for each student. Print "FAIL" if the average is less than 60. Print "PASS" if the average is 60 or more. The processing ends after the twenty-fifth average is printed.**

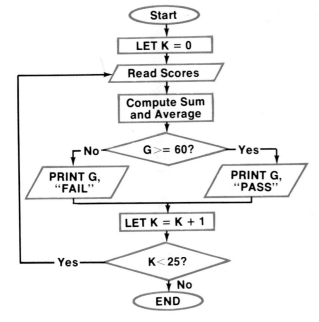

```
10    LET K = 0
20    READ A,B,C,D,E
30    LET G = (A + B + C + D + E)/5
40    IF G > = 60 THEN 70
50    PRINT G, "FAIL"
60    GO TO 80
70    PRINT G, "PASS"
80    LET K = K + 1
90    IF K < 25 THEN 20
95    DATA. . .        To use the program,
100   END              the twenty-five sets
                       of scores listed are
                       in the data line.
```

Written Exercises

Make a flow chart for each of the following.

1.
```
10  LET Y=1
20  PRINT Y, Y↑3
30  LET Y=Y+1
40  IF Y↑3<=1000 THEN 20
50  END
```

2.
```
10  LET S= 0
20  FOR M=1 TO 20
30  LET S=S+M
40  NEXT M
50  LET A=S↑(1/2)
60  PRINT A
70  END
```

Write a program from each flow chart below.

3.

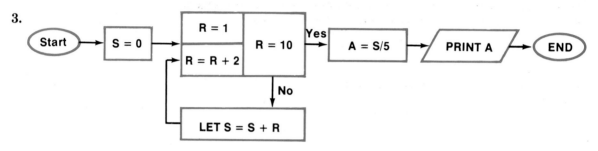

4.

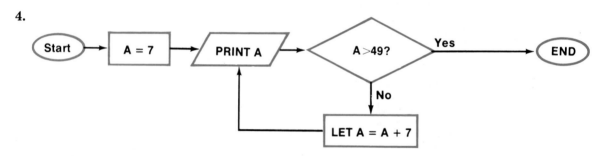

Write a flow chart and a program for each of the following.

5. Find the sum of the first n positive integers, where $n = 50$.

6. You are given three numbers the values of which are unknown to you beforehand. Print the three numbers in increasing order from least to greatest. Make comparisons by pairs and exhaust all possibilities.

7. You are given the coordinates of a point in the xy-plane. Decide in which quadrant the point lies. If the point lies on an axis, decide on which axis the point lies. Include the origin as a possibility.

Subscripted Variables

Sometimes it is difficult to provide enough labels for variables in a large amount of data. When this happens, **subscripted variables** may be used in BASIC.

Algebra	**BASIC**
$x_1, x_2, x_3, \ldots, x_n$	$X(1), X(2), X(3), \ldots, X(N)$

In BASIC, subscripted variables consist of a single letter and a pair of parentheses. Either a positive integer or an ordered pair of positive integers may appear within the parentheses. These integers may be represented by variables or BASIC expressions.

A(10)
Z(6)
B(3,4)   ← *This variable refers to an item in the 3rd row, 4th column of an array of data.*

B(A)   *The computer finds the*
Q(M)   *values of A and M and R*
N(4 + R)   *from the program.*

Z1(Q)   *This is not allowed. Z1 is a variable that may <u>not</u> be subscripted. Z1(Q) is not a single letter followed by parentheses.*

Consider the following program.

```
10   DATA 2,3,5,2.2,7,6,9,18,24,11
20   FOR R=1 TO 10
30   READ A(R)
40   PRINT A(R)*3.1416
50   NEXT R
60   END
```

*Data are diameters of circles. This loop yields A(1), A(2), A(3), . . . , A(10). What is the value of A(7)? Of A(7)*3.1416? What does this program do?*

If the value of any of the subscripts is greater than 10, the size of the list must be given. A dimension statement, DIM, can do this.

10 DIM R(17)

The statement above tells the computer to reserve 17 memory spaces for subscripted variables.

The program on the next page shows the use of the DIM statement.

1 **Write a program to print the square root of the following numbers: 3, 9.2, 7, 11.6, 0, 254, 113, 73.9, 46, 19, 79, 101.**

```
10   DIM R(12)              Reserve 12 memory spaces.
20   FOR M = 1 TO 12        Set up FOR-NEXT loop.
30   READ R(M)
40   PRINT R(M) ↑ (1/2)     Compute and print square root.

50   NEXT M
60   DATA 3,9.2,7,11.6,0,254,113,73.9,46,19,79,101
```

The program below enters into the computer the hourly earnings of fifteen workers. It computes and prints the average wage.

```
10    DIM G(15)             Reserve 15 memory spaces.
20    LET S = 0             S is the sum of wages. It begins at zero.
30    FOR I = 1 TO 15
40    READ G(I)             Which entry in the data list is G(7)?
50    LET S = S + G(I)      Add the next wage to the
60    NEXT I                sum of the previous wages.
70    LET A = S/15          Why divide by 15?
80    PRINT "AVERAGE WAGE IS", A
90    PRINT "HOURLY WAGES"
100   FOR X = 1 TO 15
105   PRINT G(X);
110   NEXT X
120   DATA 4.20,3.15,3.60,4.35,5.10,3.20,3.15,4.05
130   DATA 4.65,3.40,5.50,6.05,4.75,3.80,4.90
140   END
```

Suppose the following array is to be read into the computer. The program on the right will do this.

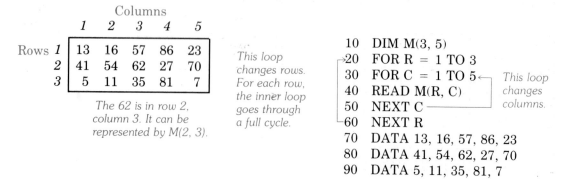

Columns

	1	2	3	4	5
Rows 1	13	16	57	86	23
2	41	54	62	27	70
3	5	11	35	81	7

The 62 is in row 2, column 3. It can be represented by M(2, 3).

This loop changes rows. For each row, the inner loop goes through a full cycle.

```
10  DIM M(3, 5)
20  FOR R = 1 TO 3
30  FOR C = 1 TO 5          This loop
40  READ M(R, C)           changes
50  NEXT C                  columns.
60  NEXT R
70  DATA 13, 16, 57, 86, 23
80  DATA 41, 54, 62, 27, 70
90  DATA 5, 11, 35, 81, 7
```

Written Exercises

Refer to the array on page 598. Use the letter M and a set of parentheses to write a correct subscripted variable to refer to each of these entries in the array.

1. 13   **2.** 5   **3.** 86   **4.** 7

5. 35   **6.** 16   **7.** 41   **8.** 70

Write a BASIC subscripted variable for each of the following.

9. m_3 **10.** t_4 **11.** r_y **12.** z_{x+1}

13. q_{24} **14.** k_{m+n} **15.** $x_{(1,3)}$ **16.** $y_{(a,r)}$

The first four lines of a program are shown below. Use them to evaluate the following.

```
10   DATA 8, −4, 16, −12,2,17
20   FOR R = 1 TO 6
30   READ A(R)
40   NEXT R
```

17. A(2)   **18.** A(5−1)

19. A(3)−1   **20.** 2∗A(4)

21. A(1)/2   **22.** A(A(5))

23. 6+A(3)   **24.** A(6)−A(4)

Let K = 3 and J = 2. Evaluate the following. Use the same program lines as in exercises 17–24.

25. A(J)∗A(K)   **26.** A(J∗K)   **27.** 2∗A(J)   **28.** A(2∗J)

Write the necessary DIM statement.

29. $[a_1, a_2, \ldots, a_{40}]$ **30.** $[m_{41}, m_{42}, \ldots m_{79}]$

Write BASIC programs that will do the following.

31. Kristy has grades of 67, 72, 74, 63, and 81 in Algebra One. Anne Marie has grades of 91, 87, 81, 83, and 89. Find and print the average of each girl's grades.

32. Print each of the following numbers and its absolute value. Use 5, 3, 7, 0, −1, 15, −11, −12, −6, −22 in the DATA statement.

33. The table below shows the scores for one game in a bowling league. The program computes the average for each team. Copy and complete the program. Use S(M,T) as the variable for entries in the table. Print both the team number and its average.

```
 5   FOR M = 1 TO 5
10   FOR T = _____
15   READ S(M,T)
20   NEXT _____
25   NEXT _____
30   FOR T = 1 TO 6
35   LET S = _____
40   FOR M = 1 TO 5
45   LET S = S + _____
50   NEXT _____
55   PRINT T, _____
60   NEXT _____
65   DATA . . .
70   END
```

Teams		1	2	3	4	5	6
Members	1	165	151	130	147	137	132
	2	135	122	146	123	153	114
	3	149	155	101	181	166	127
	4	118	140	135	110	111	175
	5	102	119	179	129	146	159

Matrices

Subscripted variables can be used to identify terms of a matrix. Two subscripts separated by a comma are written inside the parentheses following the variable. The first subscript indicates the row and the second subscript indicates the column.

Consider the matrix, $A = \begin{bmatrix} 9 & -1 & 6 \\ 4 & 7 & -8 \end{bmatrix}$. In BASIC, the values of $A(1,2)$ and $A(2,1)$ would be -1 and 4, respectively. The DIM statement for this matrix would be 10 DIM A(2,3). The DIM statement is necessary only if either of the subscripts is greater than ten.

Suppose the above matrix is to be read and stored in the computer. This can be accomplished by using nested loops.

	10 DIM A(2,3)	*This line is optional.*
	20 FOR R = 1 TO 2	
This loop changes rows. In	30 FOR C = 1 TO 3	
each row, the inner loop	40 READ A(R,C)	*This loop changes columns.*
goes through a full cycle.	50 NEXT C	
	60 NEXT R	
	70 DATA 9, $-$ 1,6,4,7, $-$ 8	*Note that the terms*
	80 END	*are listed by rows.*

A BASIC program may be used to find the value of the determinant of a matrix.

Examples

1 **Write a program to find the value of the determinant of the matrix,**
$Z = \begin{bmatrix} 2 & -8 \\ 9 & 3 \end{bmatrix}$.

```
10   FOR R = 1 TO 2
20   FOR C = 1 TO 2
30   READ Z(R,C)
40   NEXT C
50   NEXT R
60   PRINT "DETERMINANT IS    " Z(1,1)*Z(2,2) − Z(1,2)*Z(2,1)
65   DATA 2, − 8,9,3
70   END
```

A BASIC program may be used to add matrices or multiply a matrix by a constant. Consider the following examples.

Examples

2 Write a program to add A and B if $A = \begin{bmatrix} 7 & -2 & 1 & -3 \\ 9 & 1 & 4 & -5 \\ 0 & -8 & -1 & 9 \end{bmatrix}$

and $B = \begin{bmatrix} 1 & -8 & 3 & 5 \\ -2 & 1 & -4 & 6 \\ 1 & 0 & -9 & 7 \end{bmatrix}$. **Then show the output of the program.**

10	DIM A(3,4),B(3,4)	*This statement may be omitted in this case.*
20	FOR R = 1 TO 3	
30	FOR C = 1 TO 4	*These loops read and store the elements*
40	READ A(R,C)	*of matrix A.*
50	NEXT C	
60	NEXT R	
70	FOR R = 1 TO 3	
80	FOR C = 1 TO 4	
90	READ B(R,C)	*These loops read and store the elements*
100	PRINT A(R,C) + B(R,C);	*of matrix B. Then the sum of corresponding*
110	NEXT C	*elements is computed and printed.*
120	PRINT	*Line 120 causes the matrix to be printed row by row.*
130	NEXT R	
140	DATA 7, − 2,1, − 3,9,1,4, − 5,0, − 8, − 1,9,1, − 8,3,5, − 2,1, − 4,6,1,0, − 9,7	
150	END	

```
RUN
8   − 10   4      2
7   2       0      1
1   − 8    − 10  16
```

3 Write a program to multiply a 6 × 8 matrix, X, by a constant, S.

10	DIM X(6,8)	
20	READ S	
30	FOR R = 1 TO 6	
40	FOR C = 1 TO 8	
50	READ X(R,C)	
60	PRINT X(R,C)*S;	
70	NEXT C	
80	PRINT	
90	NEXT R	
100	DATA . . .	*The first number in the DATA statement must be the value of S.*
110	END	*Then the terms of the matrix are listed row by row.*

Written Exercises

Write a BASIC subscripted variable to name each of the following terms in matrix A shown at the right.

1. 1
2. -1
3. 4
4. 8
5. -2
6. -6
7. 3
8. -7
9. 2

$$A = \begin{bmatrix} 1 & 2 & 8 \\ -2 & -1 & 3 \\ 4 & -7 & -6 \end{bmatrix}$$

Write the output when the following statements are added to the program shown at the right.

10. 40 PRINT X(R,C);

11. 40 PRINT X(R,C);
    55 PRINT

12. 40 PRINT X(R,C)

```
10   FOR R=1 TO 2
20   FOR C=1 TO 4
30   READ X(R,C)
50   NEXT C
60   NEXT R
70   DATA 1,9,5,1,-7,6,8,-3
```

Let $A = \begin{bmatrix} -3 & 6 & -9 \\ 4 & -3 & 0 \\ 8 & -2 & 7 \end{bmatrix}$, $B = \begin{bmatrix} 1 & 5 & 7 \\ -11 & 13 & -8 \\ 0 & -2 & 4 \end{bmatrix}$, and $C = \begin{bmatrix} 4 & 6 & 4 \\ 11 & -4 & 6 \\ -2 & 2 & 8 \end{bmatrix}$. Write a program in BASIC to find each of the following.

13. $A + C$
14. $B + C$
15. $A + (-B)$
16. $C - A$
17. $3C$
18. $4B + A$

Let $D = \begin{bmatrix} 1 & 3 \\ 2 & 2 \end{bmatrix}$ and $E = \begin{bmatrix} 4 & 7 & 0 \\ 6 & -1 & 9 \end{bmatrix}$. Write a program in BASIC to find each of the following.

19. determinant of D
20. $D \times E$
21. D^2

Write a program in BASIC to solve each of the following.

22. Find the sum of the numbers in each column of a 4×4 matrix. Have the sums printed in a 1×4 matrix.

23. Find the greatest term in a given matrix. Print the term and its row and column.

24. Given two matrices, find their sum if possible. If not possible, print "CANNOT BE ADDED."

25. Find the mean of the numbers in each row of 4×4 matrix. Have the means printed in a 4×1 matrix.

Internal Functions

In BASIC there are several subprograms that are used with problems that occur frequently. Such programs are called **internal functions**. Each one has an abbreviation and an argument. The argument is the symbol in parentheses. Some common functions follow.

Abbreviation (argument)

ABS(X)	*This function finds the absolute value of X.*
SQR(X)	*This function finds the square root of X.*
INT(X)	*This function finds the greatest integer less than or equal to X.*
RND(X)	*This function generates a random number between 0 and 1.*

Functions used in trigonometry are also available.

SIN(X)	*This function finds the sine of X.*
COS(X)	*This function finds the cosine of X.*
TAN(X)	*This function finds the tangent of X.*

The INT function is called the greatest integer function. Here are some examples. If necessary, refer to page 61.

$$INT(2) = 2 \quad INT(3.5) = 3 \quad INT(-2) = -2 \quad INT(-2.5) = -3$$

Do you see why the result in the last example is -3?

The INT function is useful in finding factors of a number.

Examples

1 **Write a test to tell whether 2 is a factor of 5.**

Is it true that INT(5/2) = 5/2?
INT(5/2) = INT(2.5)
        = 2

What is the greatest integer less than or equal to 2.5?
Thus 2 is not a factor of 5 since 5/2 = 2.5 and INT(5/2) = 2.

2 **Write a program to find all the factors of a given positive integer.**

```
10   READ N
20   FOR X = 1 TO SQR(N)        Why SQR(N)?
30   IF INT(N/X)<>N/X THEN 50
40   PRINT X, N/X
50   NEXT X
60   GO TO 10
70   DATA 48,102,235
80   END
```

RND(1) is a BASIC function that generates random numbers. The 1 in RND(1) is a placeholder. Each random number generated is a six-digit decimal between 0 and 1. Two such numbers generated by RND(1) are shown below.

0.627590   and   0.218802

If integers greater than one are desired, the two functions INT(X) and RND(1) are used together as follows.

PRINT INT(10*RND(1))

The computer would do the following calculations for the two numbers generated above.

$$\text{INT}(10*\text{RND}(1)) = \text{INT}(10*0.627590)$$
$$= \text{INT}(6.27590)$$
$$= 6$$

$$\text{INT}(10*\text{RND}(1)) = \text{INT}(10*0.218802)$$
$$= \text{INT}(2.18802)$$
$$= 2$$

Example

3 Write a statement that will give random integers with values from 1 to 9.

There are 9 integers that can be used. Multiplying a decimal between 0 and 1 by nine gives a number between 0.0 and 8.9999. If 1 is added, the number is between 1.0 and 9.9999. Taking the greatest integer gives a number between 1 and 9. PRINT INT(9*RND(1) + 1) is the desired statement. It yields numbers such as 7, 2, 1, 3, 9, 6, 3, and 4.

Some computers always print the same series of random numbers unless the statement RANDOMIZE is included in the program. The range of the random numbers can be varied.

Example

4 Write a statement that will generate random integers with values from 10 to 20 inclusive.

There are 11 integers that could be used. Multiplying by 11 yields results from 0.0 to 10.9999. Since the series is to start with 10, the number 10 is added to each number generated. Then the greatest integer function is used. PRINT INT(11*RND(1) + 10) is the desired statement. It yields numbers such as 20, 17, 18, 12, 13, 19, and 15.

In general, when random integers are to be chosen from a set containing A integers, with B the least one, the following can be used.

PRINT INT(A*RND(1) + B)

Suppose the results of ten throws of a single die are desired. The throw of a single die may result in 1, 2, 3, 4, 5, or 6. The functions INT(X) and RND(1) can be used to simulate the six results.

Example

5 Write a program to simulate the results of ten throws of a single die.

```
10 FOR T=1 TO 10
20 PRINT INT(6*RND(1) + 1)
30 NEXT T
40 END
```

Suppose you throw a red die and a green die. Each combination of the dice is equally likely. The combinations occur at random. But each *sum* of two dice is *not* equally likely. The necessary BASIC line to simulate the sum when throwing two dice is as follows.

PRINT INT(6*RND(1) + 1) + INT(6*RND(1) + 1)

Written Exercises

Describe the result of each of the following PRINT statements.

1. PRINT INT(3.6)

2. PRINT INT(3.4 − 3.7)

3. PRINT ABS(−5)

4. PRINT SQR(36)

5. PRINT INT(10*RND(1) + 2)

6. PRINT (12*RND(1) + 29)

Write a PRINT statement to yield each of the following.

7. The decimal numbers from 0 through 9.9999.

8. The integers from 23 through 38.

Write programs using internal functions to do the following.

9. Select five random integers from 1 to 10,000 as winning numbers for a local lottery.

10. Write a program to find the real roots of any quadratic equations of the form $ax^2 + bx + c = 0$.

11. A state lottery commission uses lottery tickets that are printed in random sequence. Write a program to print 5-digit integers (0 through 99,999). Print a sample of ten such numbers.

12. Simulate the throw of a pair of dice using the random number function. Print the integer appearing on each die for each throw. Keep a count of the number of throws. Print the count the first time two sixes appear.

Computer Programming Exercises

The following section provides a variety of problems that are to be solved using computer programs. The BASIC programming techniques in the previous lessons are to be used when writing the computer programs. The problems are listed by chapter for easy reference.

Most of the problems do not have specific data. In these problems, insert a blank DATA statement into the program. Before running the program, insert data into the DATA statement(s). If specific data is given, solve the problem using this data only. Also, be sure to label all of the output with appropriate headings.

Chapter 1   Equations and Inequalities

1. Find the interest on a sum of money given the principal, p, rate of interest, r, and time, t. Use the information given in Written Exercises 35–40 on page 5 as the data.

2. Write a program to evaluate $3n^2 + 5$ for $n = -1$, 2.57, 14, 0, and -9.1. Then write a program to evaluate an algebraic expression of your choice for five different values.

3. Write a program to determine the absolute value of a number. Use 6, -3, 21, 9.7, -8.2, and 0 as data.

4. Find the area of a trapezoid, given the height, h, and both bases, b and B. Use the information given in Written Exercises 41–48 on page 6 as the data.

Chapter 2   Linear Relations and Functions

1. Given the coordinates of two points on a line, find an equation of the line.

2. Generate a set of ordered pairs that satisfy the equation $y = x + |x|$. Then use these ordered pairs to graph the function.

3. Generate a set of ordered pairs that satisfy the equation $y = [x] + x$. Then use these ordered pairs to graph the function $y = [x]$.

4. Choose a linear function and write a program that will generate ordered pairs for the function which could be used as an aid in drawing the graph.

5. Given the coordinates of two points in the coordinate plane, find the slope of the line between the two points, if defined, or state that the slope is undefined.

Chapter 3   Systems of Equations and Inequalities

1. Write a program to find the equation of a line passing through (p, q) and parallel to a line whose equation is $ax + by = c$.

2. Write a program to find the equation of a line passing through (p, q) and perpendicular to a line whose equation is $ax + by = c$.

3. Write a program to solve the system $ax + by = c$ and $dx + ey = f$. Input the values of a, b, c, d, e, and f. Print the system and its solution, if it exists.

4. Use Cramer's Rule to solve the following system of equations:
$$0.61x + 0.63y = 61$$
$$0.63x - 0.77y = 0.6$$

Chapter 4   More Systems of Equations

1. Write a program that will evaluate the determinant of a third order matrix.

2. Given an equation of the form $ax + by + cz = d$, write a program that finds the x-, y-, and z- intercepts and the xy-, xz, and yz-traces.

Chapter 5   Polynomials

1. Find the factors of any positive integer greater than 1, using the INT function. (*Hint:* 4 is a factor of 52 only if INT(52/4) $= 52/4$).

2. Express an integer in terms of its prime factors. For example, $24 = 2 \times 2 \times 2 \times 3$. If the integer itself is prime, then the output of the program should print that fact.

3. Write a program to generate all prime numbers between 1 and 100. (*Hint:* a prime number is divisible only by itself and one.)

4. Write a program that will multiply two binomials. Use an INPUT statement to enter the coefficients. The results should be in the form $AX \uparrow 2 + BX + C$.

Challenge

5. Write a program that will factor trinomials of the form $AX^2 + BX + C$, where $A \neq 0$. The factors should be in the form $(AX + B)(CX + D)$, where A, B, C, and D are all integers. Otherwise, the program should print that the program cannot be factored using integers.

Chapter 6   Roots

1. Use the divide-and-average method to find the square root of a number. You must input the radicand and an estimate for the square root. Have the program stop when two successive estimates are identical to at least four decimal places.

2. Iteration formulas can be used to approximate numbers. To find cube roots, the formula is $X(N + 1) = \frac{1}{3}(2 \cdot X(N) + A/X(N)^2$. You must input the radicand, A, and an estimate, $X(0)$. The program should start with $N = 0$, $N = 1$, $N = 2, \ldots$, and repeat the formula until two successive $X(N)$'s are identical to at least four decimal places.

3. Write a program which prints the square roots of negative numbers as imaginary numbers. Example: $SQR(-36) = 6I$.

4. Print a table of integers, their cubes and cube roots for the integers from 1 to 20. Use the exponent $\frac{1}{3}$ to find the roots. Compare your table with the one on page 612.

Chapter 7 Quadratic Equations

1. Write a program to find the value of the discriminant for any given quadratic equation. The program should print the value of the discriminant and describe the nature of the solutions for each equation.

2. Write a program that will solve any quadratic equation using the quadratic formula. Be sure to print out complex solutions if they exist.

3. Write a program to find only the real roots of quadratic equations.

4. Write a program to find the sum and product of the roots of a quadratic equation.

Chapter 8 Quadratic Relations and Functions

1. Given any quadratic equation $f(x) = ax^2 + bx + c$, find the equation of the axis of symmetry, the coordinates of the vertex, and direction of opening of the graph. (*Hint:* rewrite the equation in the form $f(x) = a(x - h)^2 + k$. State the expression for h and k in terms of a, b, and c.)

2. If you hit a baseball up in the air with a velocity of v meters per second, its height after t seconds is given by the formula $h = vt - 4.9t^2$. Find and print the height of the baseball for any given input of velocity (meters) and time (seconds).

Chapter 9 Conics

1. Find the radius and coordinates of the center of a circle given by the equation $Ax^2 + Cy^2 + Dx + Ey + F = 0$.

2. Write a program to find the distance between any two points given the coordinates of the points.

Chapter 10 Polynomial Functions

1. Write a program using the Factor Theorem to find the factors of the polynomial $P(x) = ax^3 + bx^2 + cx + d$.

2. Write a program using the Rational Zero Theorem to find all possible rational roots of the equation $ax^3 + bx^2 + cx + d = 0$ given that a, b, c, and d are integers.

3. Write a program that will find $f[g(x)]$ for the values of x from -6 to 6 for the functions $f(x) = x^2 + 8x - 1$ and $g(x) = x^2 + 2$.

Chapter 11 Rational Polynomial Expressions

1. Write a program to find the multiplicative inverse of any nonzero rational number. Print out the results in fractional form and decimal form.

2. Evaluate $f(x) = \dfrac{-5x(x + 2)}{(x - 3)(x + 1)}$ for integer values of x between -10 and 10 inclusive. Use these ordered pairs to graph $f(x)$.

Chapter 12 Exponential and Logarithmic Functions

1. Print a table of logarithms base 2 for the integers from 1 through 16.

2. Native Americans were paid $24 for Manhattan Island in 1626. Suppose this money was put in a savings account at 4% interest compounded quarterly. Then in 1913 the total savings account was invested in IBM stock. Find the value of the investment in 1980. (Assume a $10 share purchased in 1913 is worth $260,000 in 1980.)

Chapter 13   Sequences and Series

1. Find the sum of an arithmetic series given the first term, a_1, the number of terms, n, and the common difference, d.

2. Find the sum of a geometric series given the first term, a_1, the common ratio, r, and the number of terms, n.

3. Write a program to evaluate the series $\sum_{k=1}^{20} k^3$. Have the program also complete and print $\dfrac{(20)^2(21)^2}{4}$.

4. Write a program to generate the first 30 terms of the Fibonacci sequence. Then modify the program so that each term is divided by the next term in the sequence. Notice the pattern in the result.

5. Find the value of e to four decimal places using the following formula.

$$e = 2 + \frac{1}{2!} + \frac{1}{3!} + \frac{1}{4!} + \frac{1}{5!} + \frac{1}{6!} + \frac{1}{7!}$$

Chapter 14   Probability

1. Evaluate the expression $P(n, r)$ for any values of n and r.

2. Evaluate the expression $C(n, r)$ for any values of n and r.

3. Write a program to simulate the tossing of a coin. Use the random number generator and count the number of heads and tails. Have the computer simulate at least 1000 tosses.

4. Modify the program in Exercise 3 to simulate the tossing of two coins. Print out the number of times two heads are tossed, one head and one tail are tossed, and two tails are tossed. Have the computer simulate at least 1000 tosses.

Chapter 15   Statistics

Write a program to solve each problem using any thirty elements of data.

1. Find the mean of the data.

2. Arrange the data in order from least to greatest.

3. Find the median of the data.

4. Find the mode of the data.

5. Find the standard deviation of the data.

Chapter 16   Trigonometric Functions and Identities

1. Make a table of the degree measures of angles given their radian measures in increments of 0.01 from 0 to 2.

2. Write a program to convert degree measure to radian measure.

3. Given the value of a sine function for an angle between $0°$ and $90°$, find the angle. (Note: Most computers have the Arctan function only, given as ATN(X).)

Chapter 17   Triangle Trigonometry

1. Given the lengths of three sides of a right triangle, find the measures of the two acute angles of the triangle.

2. Find the length of one side of any triangle, given the lengths of the other two sides and the measure of the angle included between them.

3. Write a program that uses the Law of Sines to find angles and sides of a triangle when two angles and the side opposite one of these angles is given. All angle measures should be given in degrees and fractions of degrees. No minutes should be used.

Symbols

a^n	the nth power of a
$\lvert a \rvert$	the absolute value of a
^-a	additive inverse of a or the opposite of a
Cos^{-1}	Arccosine
$C(n, r)$	combinations of n elements taken r at a time
$a + bi$	complex number
$^\circ$	degrees
det	determinant
e	base of natural logarithms
$\in$	is an element of
$\emptyset$	empty set
$=$	equals or is equal to
$\neq$	does not equal
$\approx$	approximately equal to
$f(x)$	f of x or the value of f at x
f^{-1}	inverse function of f

$!$	factorial
$f \circ g$	composition function f of g
$>$	is greater than
$<$	is less than
$\geq$	is greater than or equal to
$\leq$	is less than or equal to
$\log_b x$	the logarithm to the base b of x
$P(n, r)$	permutations of n things taken r at a time
$\pm$	positive or negative
$\{\ \}$	set
$\sqrt{}$	the principal square root of
$\sqrt[n]{}$	the nth root of
Σ	(sigma) summation symbol

Squares and Square Roots

n	n^2	$\sqrt{n}$	$\sqrt{10n}$	n	n^2	$\sqrt{n}$	$\sqrt{10n}$
1.0	1.00	1.000	3.162	5.5	30.25	2.345	7.416
1.1	1.21	1.049	3.317	5.6	31.36	2.366	7.483
1.2	1.44	1.095	3.464	5.7	32.49	2.387	7.550
1.3	1.69	1.140	3.606	5.8	33.64	2.408	7.616
1.4	1.96	1.183	3.742	5.9	34.81	2.429	7.681
1.5	2.25	1.225	3.873	6.0	36.00	2.449	7.746
1.6	2.56	1.265	4.000	6.1	37.21	2.470	7.810
1.7	2.89	1.304	4.123	6.2	38.44	2.490	7.874
1.8	3.24	1.342	4.243	6.3	39.69	2.510	7.937
1.9	3.61	1.378	4.359	6.4	40.96	2.530	8.000
2.0	4.00	1.414	4.472	6.5	42.25	2.550	8.062
2.1	4.41	1.449	4.583	6.6	43.56	2.569	8.124
2.2	4.84	1.483	4.690	6.7	44.89	2.588	8.185
2.3	5.29	1.517	4.796	6.8	46.24	2.608	8.246
2.4	5.76	1.549	4.899	6.9	47.61	2.627	8.307
2.5	6.25	1.581	5.000	7.0	49.00	2.646	8.367
2.6	6.76	1.612	5.099	7.1	50.41	2.665	8.426
2.7	7.29	1.643	5.196	7.2	51.84	2.683	8.485
2.8	7.84	1.673	5.292	7.3	53.29	2.702	8.544
2.9	8.41	1.703	5.385	7.4	54.76	2.720	8.602
3.0	9.00	1.732	5.477	7.5	56.25	2.739	8.660
3.1	9.61	1.761	5.568	7.6	57.76	2.757	8.718
3.2	10.24	1.789	5.657	7.7	59.29	2.775	8.775
3.3	10.89	1.817	5.745	7.8	60.84	2.793	8.832
3.4	11.56	1.844	5.831	7.9	62.41	2.811	8.888
3.5	12.25	1.871	5.916	8.0	64.00	2.828	8.944
3.6	12.96	1.897	6.000	8.1	65.61	2.846	9.000
3.7	13.69	1.924	6.083	8.2	67.24	2.864	9.055
3.8	14.44	1.949	6.164	8.3	68.89	2.881	9.110
3.9	15.21	1.975	6.245	8.4	70.56	2.898	9.165
4.0	16.00	2.000	6.325	8.5	72.25	2.915	9.220
4.1	16.81	2.025	6.403	8.6	73.96	2.933	9.274
4.2	17.64	2.049	6.481	8.7	75.69	2.950	9.327
4.3	18.49	2.074	6.557	8.8	77.44	2.966	9.381
4.4	19.36	2.098	6.633	8.9	79.21	2.983	9.434
4.5	20.25	2.121	6.708	9.0	81.00	3.000	9.487
4.6	21.16	2.145	6.782	9.1	82.81	3.017	9.539
4.7	22.09	2.168	6.856	9.2	84.64	3.033	9.592
4.8	23.04	2.191	6.928	9.3	86.49	3.050	9.644
4.9	24.01	2.214	7.000	9.4	88.36	3.066	9.695
5.0	25.00	2.236	7.071	9.5	90.25	3.082	9.747
5.1	26.01	2.258	7.141	9.6	92.16	3.098	9.798
5.2	27.04	2.280	7.211	9.7	94.09	3.114	9.849
5.3	28.09	2.302	7.280	9.8	96.04	3.130	9.899
5.4	29.16	2.324	7.348	9.9	98.01	3.146	9.950

Cubes and Cube Roots

n	n^3	$\sqrt[3]{n}$	$\sqrt[3]{10n}$	$\sqrt[3]{100n}$	n	n^3	$\sqrt[3]{n}$	$\sqrt[3]{10n}$	$\sqrt[3]{100n}$
1.0	1.000	1.000	2.154	4.642	5.5	166.375	1.765	3.803	8.193
1.1	1.331	1.032	2.224	4.791	5.6	175.616	1.776	3.826	8.243
1.2	1.728	1.063	2.289	4.932	5.7	185.193	1.786	3.849	8.291
1.3	2.197	1.091	2.351	5.066	5.8	195.112	1.797	3.871	8.340
1.4	2.744	1.119	2.410	5.192	5.9	205.379	1.807	3.893	8.387
1.5	3.375	1.145	2.466	5.313	6.0	216.000	1.817	3.915	8.434
1.6	4.096	1.170	2.520	5.429	6.1	226.981	1.827	3.936	8.481
1.7	4.913	1.193	2.571	5.540	6.2	238.328	1.837	3.958	8.527
1.8	5.832	1.216	2.621	5.646	6.3	250.047	1.847	3.979	8.573
1.9	6.859	1.239	2.668	5.749	6.4	262.144	1.857	4.000	8.618
2.0	8.000	1.260	2.714	5.848	6.5	274.625	1.866	4.021	8.662
2.1	9.261	1.281	2.759	5.944	6.6	287.496	1.876	4.041	8.707
2.2	10.648	1.301	2.802	6.037	6.7	300.763	1.885	4.062	8.750
2.3	12.167	1.320	2.844	6.127	6.8	314.432	1.895	4.082	8.794
2.4	13.824	1.339	2.884	6.214	6.9	328.509	1.904	4.102	8.837
2.5	15.625	1.357	2.924	6.300	7.0	343.000	1.913	4.121	8.879
2.6	17.576	1.375	2.962	6.383	7.1	357.911	1.922	4.141	8.921
2.7	19.683	1.392	3.000	6.463	7.2	373.248	1.931	4.160	8.963
2.8	21.952	1.409	3.037	6.542	7.3	389.017	1.940	4.179	9.004
2.9	24.389	1.426	3.072	6.619	7.4	405.224	1.949	4.198	9.045
3.0	27.000	1.442	3.107	6.694	7.5	421.875	1.957	4.217	9.086
3.1	29.791	1.458	3.141	6.768	7.6	438.976	1.966	4.236	9.126
3.2	32.768	1.474	3.175	6.840	7.7	456.533	1.975	4.254	9.166
3.3	35.937	1.489	3.208	6.910	7.8	474.552	1.983	4.273	9.205
3.4	39.304	1.504	3.240	6.980	7.9	493.039	1.992	4.291	9.244
3.5	42.875	1.518	3.271	7.047	8.0	512.000	2.000	4.309	9.283
3.6	46.656	1.533	3.302	7.114	8.1	531.441	2.008	4.327	9.322
3.7	50.653	1.547	3.332	7.179	8.2	551.368	2.017	4.344	9.360
3.8	54.872	1.560	3.362	7.243	8.3	571.787	2.025	4.362	9.398
3.9	59.319	1.574	3.391	7.306	8.4	592.704	2.033	4.380	9.435
4.0	64.000	1.587	3.420	7.368	8.5	614.125	2.041	4.397	9.473
4.1	68.921	1.601	3.448	7.429	8.6	636.056	2.049	4.414	9.510
4.2	74.088	1.613	3.476	7.489	8.7	658.503	2.057	4.431	9.546
4.3	79.507	1.626	3.503	7.548	8.8	681.472	2.065	4.448	9.583
4.4	85.184	1.639	3.530	7.606	8.9	704.969	2.072	4.465	9.619
4.5	91.125	1.651	3.557	7.663	9.0	729.000	2.080	4.481	9.655
4.6	97.336	1.663	3.583	7.719	9.1	753.571	2.088	4.498	9.691
4.7	103.823	1.675	3.609	7.775	9.2	778.688	2.095	4.514	9.726
4.8	110.592	1.687	3.634	7.830	9.3	804.357	2.103	4.531	9.761
4.9	117.649	1.698	3.659	7.884	9.4	830.584	2.110	4.547	9.796
5.0	125.000	1.710	3.684	7.937	9.5	857.375	2.118	4.563	9.830
5.1	132.651	1.721	3.708	7.990	9.6	884.736	2.125	4.579	9.865
5.2	140.608	1.732	3.733	8.041	9.7	912.673	2.133	4.595	9.899
5.3	148.877	1.744	3.756	8.093	9.8	941.192	2.140	4.610	9.933
5.4	157.464	1.754	3.780	8.143	9.9	970.299	2.147	4.626	9.967

Common Logarithms of Numbers

n	0	1	2	3	4	5	6	7	8	9
10	0000	0043	0086	0128	0170	0212	0253	0294	0334	0374
11	0414	0453	0492	0531	0569	0607	0645	0682	0719	0755
12	0792	0828	0864	0899	0934	0969	1004	1038	1072	1106
13	1139	1173	1206	1239	1271	1303	1335	1367	1399	1430
14	1461	1492	1523	1553	1584	1614	1644	1673	1703	1732
15	1761	1790	1818	1847	1875	1903	1931	1959	1987	2014
16	2041	2068	2095	2122	2148	2175	2201	2227	2253	2279
17	2304	2330	2355	2380	2405	2430	2455	2480	2504	2529
18	2553	2577	2601	2625	2648	2672	2695	2718	2742	2765
19	2788	2810	2833	2856	2878	2900	2923	2945	2967	2989
20	3010	3032	3054	3075	3096	3118	3139	3160	3181	3201
21	3222	3243	3263	3284	3304	3324	3345	3365	3385	3404
22	3424	3444	3464	3483	3502	3522	3541	3560	3579	3598
23	3617	3636	3655	3674	3692	3711	3729	3747	3766	3784
24	3802	3820	3838	3856	3874	3892	3909	3927	3945	3962
25	3979	3997	4014	4031	4048	4065	4082	4099	4116	4133
26	4150	4166	4183	4200	4216	4232	4249	4265	4281	4298
27	4314	4330	4346	4362	4378	4393	4409	4425	4440	4456
28	4472	4487	4502	4518	4533	4548	4564	4579	4594	4609
29	4624	4639	4654	4669	4683	4698	4713	4728	4742	4757
30	4771	4786	4800	4814	4829	4843	4857	4871	4886	4900
31	4914	4928	4942	4955	4969	4983	4997	5011	5024	5038
32	5051	5065	5079	5092	5105	5119	5132	5145	5159	5172
33	5185	5198	5211	5224	5237	5250	5263	5276	5289	5302
34	5315	5328	5340	5353	5366	5378	5391	5403	5416	5428
35	5441	5453	5465	5478	5490	5502	5514	5527	5539	5551
36	5563	5575	5587	5599	5611	5623	5635	5647	5658	5670
37	5682	5694	5705	5717	5729	5740	5752	5763	5775	5786
38	5798	5809	5821	5832	5843	5855	5866	5877	5888	5899
39	5911	5922	5933	5944	5955	5966	5977	5988	5999	6010
40	6021	6031	6042	6053	6064	6075	6085	6096	6107	6117
41	6128	6138	6149	6160	6170	6180	6191	6201	6212	6222
42	6232	6243	6253	6263	6274	6284	6294	6304	6314	6325
43	6335	6345	6355	6365	6375	6385	6395	6405	6415	6425
44	6435	6444	6454	6464	6474	6484	6493	6503	6513	6522
45	6532	6542	6551	6561	6571	6580	6590	6599	6609	6618
46	6628	6637	6646	6656	6665	6675	6684	6693	6702	6712
47	6721	6730	6739	6749	6758	6767	6776	6785	6794	6803
48	6812	6821	6830	6839	6848	6857	6866	6875	6884	6893
49	6902	6911	6920	6928	6937	6946	6955	6964	6972	6981
50	6990	6998	7007	7016	7024	7033	7042	7050	7059	7067
51	7076	7084	7093	7101	7110	7118	7126	7135	7143	7152
52	7160	7168	7177	7185	7193	7202	7210	7218	7226	7235
53	7243	7251	7259	7267	7275	7284	7292	7300	7308	7316
54	7324	7332	7340	7348	7356	7364	7372	7380	7388	7396

The values given are mantissas correct to four decimal
places. For example, log 5.42 = 0.7340.

Common Logarithms of Numbers

n	0	1	2	3	4	5	6	7	8	9
55	7404	7412	7419	7427	7435	7443	7451	7459	7466	7474
56	7482	7490	7497	7505	7513	7520	7528	7536	7543	7551
57	7559	7566	7574	7582	7589	7597	7604	7612	7619	7627
58	7634	7642	7649	7657	7664	7672	7679	7686	7694	7701
59	7709	7716	7723	7731	7738	7745	7752	7760	7767	7774
60	7782	7789	7796	7803	7810	7818	7825	7832	7839	7846
61	7853	7860	7868	7875	7882	7889	7896	7903	7910	7917
62	7924	7931	7938	7945	7952	7959	7966	7973	7980	7987
63	7993	8000	8007	8014	8021	8028	8035	8041	8048	8055
64	8062	8069	8075	8082	8089	8096	8102	8109	8116	8122
65	8129	8136	8142	8149	8156	8162	8169	8176	8182	8189
66	8195	8202	8209	8215	8222	8228	8235	8241	8248	8254
67	8261	8267	8274	8280	8287	8293	8299	8306	8312	8319
68	8325	8331	8338	8344	8351	8357	8363	8370	8376	8382
69	8388	8395	8401	8407	8414	8420	8426	8432	8439	8445
70	8451	8457	8463	8470	8476	8482	8488	8494	8500	8506
71	8513	8519	8525	8531	8537	8543	8549	8555	8561	8567
72	8573	8579	8585	8591	8597	8603	8609	8615	8621	8627
73	8633	8639	8645	8651	8657	8663	8669	8675	8681	8686
74	8692	8698	8704	8710	8716	8722	8727	8733	8739	8745
75	8751	8756	8762	8768	8774	8779	8785	8791	8797	8802
76	8808	8814	8820	8825	8831	8837	8842	8848	8854	8859
77	8865	8871	8876	8882	8887	8893	8899	8904	8910	8915
78	8921	8927	8932	8938	8943	8949	8954	8960	8965	8971
79	8976	8982	8987	8993	8998	9004	9009	9015	9020	9025
80	9031	9036	9042	9047	9053	9058	9063	9069	9074	9079
81	9085	9090	9096	9101	9106	9112	9117	9122	9128	9133
82	9138	9143	9149	9154	9159	9165	9170	9175	9180	9186
83	9191	9196	9201	9206	9212	9217	9222	9227	9232	9238
84	9243	9248	9253	9258	9263	9269	9274	9279	9284	9289
85	9294	9299	9304	9309	9315	9320	9325	9330	9335	9340
86	9345	9350	9355	9360	9365	9370	9375	9380	9385	9390
87	9395	9400	9405	9410	9415	9420	9425	9430	9435	9440
88	9445	9450	9455	9460	9465	9469	9474	9479	9484	9489
89	9494	9499	9504	9509	9513	9518	9523	9528	9533	9538
90	9542	9547	9552	9557	9562	9566	9571	9576	9581	9586
91	9590	9595	9600	9605	9609	9614	9619	9624	9628	9633
92	9638	9643	9647	9652	9657	9661	9666	9671	9675	9680
93	9685	9689	9694	9699	9703	9708	9713	9717	9722	9727
94	9731	9736	9741	9745	9750	9754	9759	9763	9768	9773
95	9777	9782	9786	9791	9795	9800	9805	9809	9814	9818
96	9823	9827	9832	9836	9841	9845	9850	9854	9859	9863
97	9868	9872	9877	9881	9886	9890	9894	9899	9903	9908
98	9912	9917	9921	9926	9930	9934	9939	9943	9948	9952
99	9956	9961	9965	9969	9974	9978	9983	9987	9991	9996

Values of Trigonometric Functions

Angle	Sin	Cos	Tan	Cot	Sec	Csc	
0°00'	0.0000	1.0000	0.0000	—	1.000	—	90°00'
10'	0.0029	1.0000	0.0029	343.8	1.000	343.8	50'
20'	0.0058	1.0000	0.0058	171.9	1.000	171.9	40'
30'	0.0087	1.0000	0.0087	114.6	1.000	114.6	30'
40'	0.0116	0.9999	0.0116	85.94	1.000	85.95	20'
50'	0.0145	0.9999	0.0145	68.75	1.000	68.76	10'
1°00'	0.0175	0.9998	0.0175	57.29	1.000	57.30	89°00'
10'	0.0204	0.9998	0.0204	49.10	1.000	49.11	50'
20'	0.0233	0.9997	0.0233	42.96	1.000	42.98	40'
30'	0.0262	0.9997	0.0262	38.19	1.000	38.20	30'
40'	0.0291	0.9996	0.0291	34.37	1.000	34.38	20'
50'	0.0320	0.9995	0.0320	31.24	1.001	31.26	10'
2°00'	0.0349	0.9994	0.0349	28.64	1.001	28.65	88°00'
10'	0.0378	0.9993	0.0378	26.43	1.001	26.45	50'
20'	0.0407	0.9992	0.0407	24.54	1.001	24.56	40'
30'	0.0436	0.9990	0.0437	22.90	1.001	22.93	30'
40'	0.0465	0.9989	0.0466	21.47	1.001	21.49	20'
50'	0.0494	0.9988	0.0495	20.21	1.001	20.23	10'
3°00'	0.0523	0.9986	0.0524	19.08	1.001	19.11	87°00'
10'	0.0552	0.9985	0.0553	18.07	1.002	18.10	50'
20'	0.0581	0.9983	0.0582	17.17	1.002	17.20	40'
30'	0.0610	0.9981	0.0612	16.35	1.002	16.38	30'
40'	0.0640	0.9980	0.0641	15.60	1.002	15.64	20'
50'	0.0669	0.9978	0.0670	14.92	1.002	14.96	10'
4°00'	0.0698	0.9976	0.0699	14.30	1.002	14.34	86°00'
10'	0.0727	0.9974	0.0729	13.73	1.003	13.76	50'
20'	0.0756	0.9971	0.0758	13.20	1.003	13.23	40'
30'	0.0785	0.9969	0.0787	12.71	1.003	12.75	30'
40'	0.0814	0.9967	0.0816	12.25	1.003	12.29	20'
50'	0.0843	0.9964	0.0846	11.83	1.004	11.87	10'
5°00'	0.0872	0.9962	0.0875	11.43	1.004	11.47	85°00'
10'	0.0901	0.9959	0.0904	11.06	1.004	11.10	50'
20'	0.0929	0.9957	0.0934	10.71	1.004	10.76	40'
30'	0.0958	0.9954	0.0963	10.39	1.005	10.43	30'
40'	0.0987	0.9951	0.0992	10.08	1.005	10.13	20'
50'	0.1016	0.9948	0.1022	9.788	1.005	9.839	10'
6°00'	0.1045	0.9945	0.1051	9.514	1.006	9.567	84°00'
10'	0.1074	0.9942	0.1080	9.255	1.006	9.309	50'
20'	0.1103	0.9939	0.1110	9.010	1.006	9.065	40'
30'	0.1132	0.9936	0.1139	8.777	1.006	8.834	30'
40'	0.1161	0.9932	0.1169	8.556	1.007	8.614	20'
50'	0.1190	0.9929	0.1198	8.345	1.007	8.405	10'
7°00'	0.1219	0.9925	0.1228	8.144	1.008	8.206	83°00'
10'	0.1248	0.9922	0.1257	7.953	1.008	8.016	50'
20'	0.1276	0.9918	0.1287	7.770	1.008	7.834	40'
30'	0.1305	0.9914	0.1317	7.596	1.009	7.661	30'
40'	0.1334	0.9911	0.1346	7.429	1.009	7.496	20'
50'	0.1363	0.9907	0.1376	7.269	1.009	7.337	10'
8°00'	0.1392	0.9903	0.1405	7.115	1.010	7.185	82°00'
10'	0.1421	0.9899	0.1435	6.968	1.010	7.040	50'
20'	0.1449	0.9894	0.1465	6.827	1.011	6.900	40'
30'	0.1478	0.9890	0.1495	6.691	1.011	6.765	30'
40'	0.1507	0.9886	0.1524	6.561	1.012	6.636	20'
50'	0.1536	0.9881	0.1554	6.435	1.012	6.512	10'
9°00'	0.1564	0.9877	0.1584	6.314	1.012	6.392	81°00'
	Cos	Sin	Cot	Tan	Csc	Sec	Angle

For the values of cos, sin, tan, and so on for angles greater than 45°, use the angle measures listed on the right and the functions on the bottom. For example, cos 81° = 0.1564.

Values of Trigonometric Functions

Angle	Sin	Cos	Tan	Cot	Sec	Csc	
9°00′	0.1564	0.9877	0.1584	6.314	1.012	6.392	81°00′
10′	0.1593	0.9872	0.1614	6.197	1.013	6.277	50′
20′	0.1622	0.9868	0.1644	6.084	1.013	6.166	40′
30′	0.1650	0.9863	0.1673	5.976	1.014	6.059	30′
40′	0.1679	0.9858	0.1703	5.871	1.014	5.955	20′
50′	0.1708	0.9853	0.1733	5.769	1.015	5.855	10′
10°00′	0.1736	0.9848	0.1763	5.671	1.015	5.759	80°00′
10′	0.1765	0.9843	0.1793	5.576	1.016	5.665	50′
20′	0.1794	0.9838	0.1823	5.485	1.016	5.575	40′
30′	0.1822	0.9833	0.1853	5.396	1.017	5.487	30′
40′	0.1851	0.9827	0.1883	5.309	1.018	5.403	20′
50′	0.1880	0.9822	0.1914	5.226	1.018	5.320	10′
11°00′	0.1908	0.9816	0.1944	5.145	1.019	5.241	79°00′
10′	0.1937	0.9811	0.1974	5.066	1.019	5.164	50′
20′	0.1965	0.9805	0.2004	4.989	1.020	5.089	40′
30′	0.1994	0.9799	0.2035	4.915	1.020	5.016	30′
40′	0.2022	0.9793	0.2065	4.843	1.021	4.945	20′
50′	0.2051	0.9787	0.2095	4.773	1.022	4.876	10′
12°00′	0.2079	0.9781	0.2126	4.705	1.022	4.810	78°00′
10′	0.2108	0.9775	0.2156	4.638	1.023	4.745	50′
20′	0.2136	0.9769	0.2186	4.574	1.024	4.682	40′
30′	0.2164	0.9763	0.2217	4.511	1.024	4.620	30′
40′	0.2193	0.9757	0.2247	4.449	1.025	4.560	20′
50′	0.2221	0.9750	0.2278	4.390	1.026	4.502	10′
13°00′	0.2250	0.9744	0.2309	4.331	1.026	4.445	77°00′
10′	0.2278	0.9737	0.2339	4.275	1.027	4.390	50′
20′	0.2306	0.9730	0.2370	4.219	1.028	4.336	40′
30′	0.2334	0.9724	0.2401	4.165	1.028	4.284	30′
40′	0.2363	0.9717	0.2432	4.113	1.029	4.232	20′
50′	0.2391	0.9710	0.2462	4.061	1.030	4.182	10′
14°00′	0.2419	0.9703	0.2493	4.011	1.031	4.134	76°00′
10′	0.2447	0.9696	0.2524	3.962	1.031	4.086	50′
20′	0.2476	0.9689	0.2555	3.914	1.032	4.039	40′
30′	0.2504	0.9681	0.2586	3.867	1.033	3.994	30′
40′	0.2532	0.9674	0.2617	3.821	1.034	3.950	20′
50′	0.2560	0.9667	0.2648	3.776	1.034	3.906	10′
15°00′	0.2588	0.9659	0.2679	3.732	1.035	3.864	75°00′
10′	0.2616	0.9652	0.2711	3.689	1.036	3.822	50′
20′	0.2644	0.9644	0.2742	3.647	1.037	3.782	40′
30′	0.2672	0.9636	0.2773	3.606	1.038	3.742	30′
40′	0.2700	0.9628	0.2805	3.566	1.039	3.703	20′
50′	0.2728	0.9621	0.2836	3.526	1.039	3.665	10′
16°00′	0.2756	0.9613	0.2867	3.487	1.040	3.628	74°00′
10′	0.2784	0.9605	0.2899	3.450	1.041	3.592	50′
20′	0.2812	0.9596	0.2931	3.412	1.042	3.556	40′
30′	0.2840	0.9588	0.2962	3.376	1.043	3.521	30′
40′	0.2868	0.9580	0.2994	3.340	1.044	3.487	20′
50′	0.2896	0.9572	0.3026	3.305	1.045	3.453	10′
17°00′	0.2924	0.9563	0.3057	3.271	1.046	3.420	73°00′
10′	0.2952	0.9555	0.3089	3.237	1.047	3.388	50′
20′	0.2979	0.9546	0.3121	3.204	1.048	3.356	40′
30′	0.3007	0.9537	0.3153	3.172	1.049	3.326	30′
40′	0.3035	0.9528	0.3185	3.140	1.049	3.295	20′
50′	0.3062	0.9520	0.3217	3.108	1.050	3.265	10′
18°00′	0.3090	0.9511	0.3249	3.078	1.051	3.236	72°00′
	Cos	Sin	Cot	Tan	Csc	Sec	Angle

Values of Trigonometric Functions

Angle	Sin	Cos	Tan	Cot	Sec	Csc	
18°00′	0.3090	0.9511	0.3249	3.078	1.051	3.236	72°00′
10′	0.3118	0.9502	0.3281	3.047	1.052	3.207	50′
20′	0.3145	0.9492	0.3314	3.018	1.053	3.179	40′
30′	0.3173	0.9483	0.3346	2.989	1.054	3.152	30′
40′	0.3201	0.9474	0.3378	2.960	1.056	3.124	20′
50′	0.3228	0.9465	0.3411	2.932	1.057	3.098	10′
19°00′	0.3256	0.9455	0.3443	2.904	1.058	3.072	71°00′
10′	0.3283	0.9446	0.3476	2.877	1.059	3.046	50′
20′	0.3311	0.9436	0.3508	2.850	1.060	3.021	40′
30′	0.3338	0.9426	0.3541	2.824	1.061	2.996	30′
40′	0.3365	0.9417	0.3574	2.798	1.062	2.971	20′
50′	0.3393	0.9407	0.3607	2.773	1.063	2.947	10′
20°00′	0.3420	0.9397	0.3640	2.747	1.064	2.924	70°00′
10′	0.3448	0.9387	0.3673	2.723	1.065	2.901	50′
20′	0.3475	0.9377	0.3706	2.699	1.066	2.878	40′
30′	0.3502	0.9367	0.3739	2.675	1.068	2.855	30′
40′	0.3529	0.9356	0.3772	2.651	1.069	2.833	20′
50′	0.3557	0.9346	0.3805	2.628	1.070	2.812	10′
21°00′	0.3584	0.9336	0.3839	2.605	1.071	2.790	69°00′
10′	0.3611	0.9325	0.3872	2.583	1.072	2.769	50′
20′	0.3638	0.9315	0.3906	2.560	1.074	2.749	40′
30′	0.3665	0.9304	0.3939	2.539	1.075	2.729	30′
40′	0.3692	0.9293	0.3973	2.517	1.076	2.709	20′
50′	0.3719	0.9283	0.4006	2.496	1.077	2.689	10′
22°00′	0.3746	0.9272	0.4040	2.475	1.079	2.669	68°00′
10′	0.3773	0.9261	0.4074	2.455	1.080	2.650	50′
20′	0.3800	0.9250	0.4108	2.434	1.081	2.632	40′
30′	0.3827	0.9239	0.4142	2.414	1.082	2.613	30′
40′	0.3854	0.9228	0.4176	2.394	1.084	2.595	20′
50′	0.3881	0.9216	0.4210	2.375	1.085	2.577	10′
23°00′	0.3907	0.9205	0.4245	2.356	1.086	2.559	67°00′
10′	0.3934	0.9194	0.4279	2.337	1.088	2.542	50′
20′	0.3961	0.9182	0.4314	2.318	1.089	2.525	40′
30′	0.3987	0.9171	0.4348	2.300	1.090	2.508	30′
40′	0.4014	0.9159	0.4383	2.282	1.092	2.491	20′
50′	0.4041	0.9147	0.4417	2.264	1.093	2.475	10′
24°00′	0.4067	0.9135	0.4452	2.246	1.095	2.459	66°00′
10′	0.4094	0.9124	0.4487	2.229	1.096	2.443	50′
20′	0.4120	0.9112	0.4522	2.211	1.097	2.427	40′
30′	0.4147	0.9100	0.4557	2.194	1.099	2.411	30′
40′	0.4173	0.9088	0.4592	2.177	1.100	2.396	20′
50′	0.4200	0.9075	0.4628	2.161	1.102	2.381	10′
25°00′	0.4226	0.9063	0.4663	2.145	1.103	2.366	65°00′
10′	0.4253	0.9051	0.4699	2.128	1.105	2.352	50′
20′	0.4279	0.9038	0.4734	2.112	1.106	2.337	40′
30′	0.4305	0.9026	0.4770	2.097	1.108	2.323	30′
40′	0.4331	0.9013	0.4806	2.081	1.109	2.309	20′
50′	0.4358	0.9001	0.4841	2.066	1.111	2.295	10′
26°00′	0.4384	0.8988	0.4877	2.050	1.113	2.281	64°00′
10′	0.4410	0.8975	0.4913	2.035	1.114	2.268	50′
20′	0.4436	0.8962	0.4950	2.020	1.116	2.254	40′
30′	0.4462	0.8949	0.4986	2.006	1.117	2.241	30′
40′	0.4488	0.8936	0.5022	1.991	1.119	2.228	20′
50′	0.4514	0.8923	0.5059	1.977	1.121	2.215	10′
27°00′	0.4540	0.8910	0.5095	1.963	1.122	2.203	63°00′
	Cos	Sin	Cot	Tan	Csc	Sec	Angle

Values of Trigonometric Functions

Angle	Sin	Cos	Tan	Cot	Sec	Csc	
27°00′	0.4540	0.8910	0.5095	1.963	1.122	2.203	63°00′
10′	0.4566	0.8897	0.5132	1.949	1.124	2.190	50′
20′	0.4592	0.8884	0.5169	1.935	1.126	2.178	40′
30′	0.4617	0.8870	0.5206	1.921	1.127	2.166	30′
40′	0.4643	0.8857	0.5243	1.907	1.129	2.154	20′
50′	0.4669	0.8843	0.5280	1.894	1.131	2.142	10′
28°00′	0.4695	0.8829	0.5317	1.881	1.133	2.130	62°00′
10′	0.4720	0.8816	0.5354	1.868	1.134	2.118	50′
20′	0.4746	0.8802	0.5392	1.855	1.136	2.107	40′
30′	0.4772	0.8788	0.5430	1.842	1.138	2.096	30′
40′	0.4797	0.8774	0.5467	1.829	1.140	2.085	20′
50′	0.4823	0.8760	0.5505	1.816	1.142	2.074	10′
29°00′	0.4848	0.8746	0.5543	1.804	1.143	2.063	61°00′
10′	0.4874	0.8732	0.5581	1.792	1.145	2.052	50′
20′	0.4899	0.8718	0.5619	1.780	1.147	2.041	40′
30′	0.4924	0.8704	0.5658	1.767	1.149	2.031	30′
40′	0.4950	0.8689	0.5696	1.756	1.151	2.020	20′
50′	0.4975	0.8675	0.5735	1.744	1.153	2.010	10′
30°00′	0.5000	0.8660	0.5774	1.732	1.155	2.000	60°00′
10′	0.5025	0.8646	0.5812	1.720	1.157	1.990	50′
20′	0.5050	0.8631	0.5851	1.709	1.159	1.980	40′
30′	0.5075	0.8616	0.5890	1.698	1.161	1.970	30′
40′	0.5100	0.8601	0.5930	1.686	1.163	1.961	20′
50′	0.5125	0.8587	0.5969	1.675	1.165	1.951	10′
31°00′	0.5150	0.8572	0.6009	1.664	1.167	1.942	59°00′
10′	0.5175	0.8557	0.6048	1.653	1.169	1.932	50′
20′	0.5200	0.8542	0.6088	1.643	1.171	1.923	40′
30′	0.5225	0.8526	0.6128	1.632	1.173	1.914	30′
40′	0.5250	0.8511	0.6168	1.621	1.175	1.905	20′
50′	0.5275	0.8496	0.6208	1.611	1.177	1.896	10′
32°00′	0.5299	0.8480	0.6249	1.600	1.179	1.887	58°00′
10′	0.5324	0.8465	0.6289	1.590	1.181	1.878	50′
20′	0.5348	0.8450	0.6330	1.580	1.184	1.870	40′
30′	0.5373	0.8434	0.6371	1.570	1.186	1.861	30′
40′	0.5398	0.8418	0.6412	1.560	1.188	1.853	20′
50′	0.5422	0.8403	0.6453	1.550	1.190	1.844	10′
33°00′	0.5446	0.8387	0.6494	1.540	1.192	1.836	57°00′
10′	0.5471	0.8371	0.6536	1.530	1.195	1.828	50′
20′	0.5495	0.8355	0.6577	1.520	1.197	1.820	40′
30′	0.5519	0.8339	0.6619	1.511	1.199	1.812	30′
40′	0.5544	0.8323	0.6661	1.501	1.202	1.804	20′
50′	0.5568	0.8307	0.6703	1.492	1.204	1.796	10′
34°00′	0.5592	0.8290	0.6745	1.483	1.206	1.788	56°00′
10′	0.5616	0.8274	0.6787	1.473	1.209	1.781	50′
20′	0.5640	0.8258	0.6830	1.464	1.211	1.773	40′
30′	0.5664	0.8241	0.6873	1.455	1.213	1.766	30′
40′	0.5688	0.8225	0.6916	1.446	1.216	1.758	20′
50′	0.5712	0.8208	0.6959	1.437	1.218	1.751	10′
35°00′	0.5736	0.8192	0.7002	1.428	1.221	1.743	55°00′
10′	0.5760	0.8175	0.7046	1.419	1.223	1.736	50′
20′	0.5783	0.8158	0.7089	1.411	1.226	1.729	40′
30′	0.5807	0.8141	0.7133	1.402	1.228	1.722	30′
40′	0.5831	0.8124	0.7177	1.393	1.231	1.715	20′
50′	0.5854	0.8107	0.7221	1.385	1.233	1.708	10′
36°00′	0.5878	0.8090	0.7265	1.376	1.236	1.701	54°00′
	Cos	Sin	Cot	Tan	Csc	Sec	Angle

Values of Trigonometric Functions

Angle	Sin	Cos	Tan	Cot	Sec	Csc	
36°00′	0.5878	0.8090	0.7265	1.376	1.236	1.701	54°00′
10′	0.5901	0.8073	0.7310	1.368	1.239	1.695	50′
20′	0.5925	0.8056	0.7355	1.360	1.241	1.688	40′
30′	0.5948	0.8039	0.7400	1.351	1.244	1.681	30′
40′	0.5972	0.8021	0.7445	1.343	1.247	1.675	20′
50′	0.5995	0.8004	0.7490	1.335	1.249	1.668	10′
37°00′	0.6018	0.7986	0.7536	1.327	1.252	1.662	53°00′
10′	0.6041	0.7969	0.7581	1.319	1.255	1.655	50′
20′	0.6065	0.7951	0.7627	1.311	1.258	1.649	40′
30′	0.6088	0.7934	0.7673	1.303	1.260	1.643	30′
40′	0.6111	0.7916	0.7720	1.295	1.263	1.636	20′
50′	0.6134	0.7898	0.7766	1.288	1.266	1.630	10′
38°00′	0.6157	0.7880	0.7813	1.280	1.269	1.624	52°00′
10′	0.6180	0.7862	0.7860	1.272	1.272	1.618	50′
20′	0.6202	0.7844	0.7907	1.265	1.275	1.612	40′
30′	0.6225	0.7826	0.7954	1.257	1.278	1.606	30′
40′	0.6248	0.7808	0.8002	1.250	1.281	1.601	20′
50′	0.6271	0.7790	0.8050	1.242	1.284	1.595	10′
39°00′	0.6293	0.7771	0.8098	1.235	1.287	1.589	51°00′
10′	0.6316	0.7753	0.8146	1.228	1.290	1.583	50′
20′	0.6338	0.7735	0.8195	1.220	1.293	1.578	40′
30′	0.6361	0.7716	0.8243	1.213	1.296	1.572	30′
40′	0.6383	0.7698	0.8292	1.206	1.299	1.567	20′
50′	0.6406	0.7679	0.8342	1.199	1.302	1.561	10′
40°00′	0.6428	0.7660	0.8391	1.192	1.305	1.556	50°00′
10′	0.6450	0.7642	0.8441	1.185	1.309	1.550	50′
20′	0.6472	0.7623	0.8491	1.178	1.312	1.545	40′
30′	0.6494	0.7604	0.8541	1.171	1.315	1.540	30′
40′	0.6517	0.7585	0.8591	1.164	1.318	1.535	20′
50′	0.6539	0.7566	0.8642	1.157	1.322	1.529	10′
41°00′	0.6561	0.7547	0.8693	1.150	1.325	1.524	49°00′
10′	0.6583	0.7528	0.8744	1.144	1.328	1.519	50′
20′	0.6604	0.7509	0.8796	1.137	1.332	1.514	40′
30′	0.6626	0.7490	0.8847	1.130	1.335	1.509	30′
40′	0.6648	0.7470	0.8899	1.124	1.339	1.504	20′
50′	0.6670	0.7451	0.8952	1.117	1.342	1.499	10′
42°00′	0.6691	0.7431	0.9004	1.111	1.346	1.494	48°00′
10′	0.6713	0.7412	0.9057	1.104	1.349	1.490	50′
20′	0.6734	0.7392	0.9110	1.098	1.353	1.485	40′
30′	0.6756	0.7373	0.9163	1.091	1.356	1.480	30′
40′	0.6777	0.7353	0.9217	1.085	1.360	1.476	20′
50′	0.6799	0.7333	0.9271	1.079	1.364	1.471	10′
43°00′	0.6820	0.7314	0.9325	1.072	1.367	1.466	47°00′
10′	0.6841	0.7294	0.9380	1.066	1.371	1.462	50′
20′	0.6862	0.7274	0.9435	1.060	1.375	1.457	40′
30′	0.6884	0.7254	0.9490	1.054	1.379	1.453	30′
40′	0.6905	0.7234	0.9545	1.048	1.382	1.448	20′
50′	0.6926	0.7214	0.9601	1.042	1.386	1.444	10′
44°00′	0.6947	0.7193	0.9657	1.036	1.390	1.440	46°00′
10′	0.6967	0.7173	0.9713	1.030	1.394	1.435	50′
20′	0.6988	0.7153	0.9770	1.024	1.398	1.431	40′
30′	0.7009	0.7133	0.9827	1.018	1.402	1.427	30′
40′	0.7030	0.7112	0.9884	1.012	1.406	1.423	20′
50′	0.7050	0.7092	0.9942	1.006	1.410	1.418	10′
45°00′	0.7071	0.7071	1.000	1.000	1.414	1.414	45°00′
	Cos	Sin	Cot	Tan	Csc	Sec	Angle

Glossary

absolute value The absolute value of a number is the number of units that it is from zero on the number line. For any number a:
$$\text{If } a \geq 0, \text{ then } |a| = a.$$
$$\text{If } a < 0, \text{ then } |a| = -a. \quad (21)$$

additive identity Zero is the additive identity. The sum of any number and zero is identical to the original number. (10)

additive inverse If the sum of two numbers is 0, they are called additive inverses of each other. (10)

algebraic expressions Algebraic expressions are mathematical expressions having at least one variable. (4)

amplitude For functions of the form $y = a \sin b\theta$ and $y = a \cos b\theta$, the amplitude is $|a|$. (520)

angle of depression An angle of depression is the angle formed by a horizontal line and the line of sight to an object at a lower level. (561)

angle of elevation The angle of elevation is the angle formed by a horizontal line, and the line of sight to an object at a higher level. (561)

antilogarithm If $\log x = a$, then $x = $ antilog, a. (386)

Arccosine Given $y = \text{Cos } x$, the inverse cosine function is defined by $y = \text{Cos}^{-1} x$. (543)

Arcsine Given $y = \text{Sin } x$, the inverse sine function is defined by $y = \text{Sin}^{-1} x$. (543)

Arctangent Given $y = \text{Tan } x$, the inverse tangent function is defined by $y = \text{Tan}^{-1} x$. (543)

arithmetic means The terms between any two nonconsecutive terms of an arithmetic sequence are called arithmetic means. (409)

arithmetic sequence An arithmetic sequence is a sequence in which the difference between any two consecutive terms is the same. (407)

arithmetic series The indicated sum of the terms of an arithmetic sequence is called an arithmetic series. (411)

associativity The way you group, or associate, three or more numbers does not change their sum or their product. That is, for all numbers a, b, and c, $(a + b) + c = a + (b + c)$ and $(a \cdot b) \cdot c = a \cdot (b \cdot c)$. (10)

asymptote Asymptotes are lines that a curve approaches. (287)

augmented matrix An augmented matrix is a matrix representation of a system of equations. Each row of the matrix corresponds to an equation in the system. Each column corresponds to the coefficients of a given variable or the constant term. (117)

axis of symmetry An axis of symmetry is the line about which a figure is symmetric. (246)

bar graph A bar graph shows how specific quantities compare to one another. (485)

BASIC The word BASIC is the name of a computer language. The letters in BASIC stand for **B**eginner's **A**ll-Purpose **S**ymbolic **I**nstruction **C**ode. (582)

binomial A polynomial with two unlike terms is a binomial. (154)

Binomial Theorem If n is a positive integer, then the following is true.

$$(a + b)^n = 1a^n b^0 + \frac{n}{1} a^{n-1} b^1$$
$$+ \frac{n(n - 1)}{1 \cdot 2} a^{n-2} b^2 + \dots$$
$$+ \frac{n}{1} a^1 b^{n-1} + 1a^0 b^n \quad (439)$$

binomial trial A binomial trial exists if and only if the following conditions occur. 1. There are only two possible outcomes. 2. The events are independent. (473)

center of circle *See* circle.

center of hyperbola The center of hyperbola is the midpoint of the segment connecting the foci of a hyperbola. (287)

characteristic The characteristic is the power of 10 by which that number is multiplied when the number is expressed in scientific notation. (385)

circle The definition of circle is a set of points in a plane each of which is the same distance from a given point. The given distance is the radius of the circle and the given point is the center of the circle. (278)

circle graph A circle graph shows how parts are related to the whole. (486)

circular permutations If n objects are arranged in a circle, then there are $\frac{n!}{n}$ or $(n - 1)!$ permutations of the n objects around the circle. (456)

coefficient The numerical factor of a monomial is the coefficient. (145)

coefficient matrix A coefficient matrix is a matrix representation of the coefficients of the variables in a system of equations. Each row of the matrix corresponds to an equation in the system. Each column corresponds to the coefficients of a given variable. (130)

column matrix A column matrix is a matrix containing only one column. (120)

combination The number of combinations of n objects, taken r at a time, is written $C(n, r)$.

$$C(n, r) = \frac{n!}{(n - r)! r!} \quad (459)$$

common difference The common difference of an arithmetic sequence is the constant that is the difference between successive terms. (407)

common logarithms Common logarithms are logarithms to base 10. (385)

common ratio The common ratio of a geometric sequence is the constant that is the ratio of successive terms. (416)

commutativity The order in which two numbers are added or multiplied does not change their sum or product. That is, for all numbers a and b, $a + b = b + a$ and $a \cdot b = b \cdot a$. (10)

complex conjugates Complex conjugates are complex numbers of the form $a + bi$ and $a - bi$. (207)

complex fraction A complex rational expression, also called a complex fraction, is an expression whose numerator or denominator, or both, contain rational expressions. (346)

complex number A complex number is any number that can be written in the form $a + bi$ where a and b are real numbers and i is the imaginary unit. (204)

composition of functions Given functions f and g, the composite function $f \circ g$ can be described by the following equation.
$$[f \circ g](x) = f[g(x)] \quad (329)$$

compound interest The compound interest formula is $A = P\left(1 + \frac{r}{n}\right)^{nt}$ where P is the investment, r is the interest rate, n is the number of times the interest is compounded yearly, t is the number of years of the investment, and A is the amount of money accumulated. (394)

computer program A computer program is a series of statements that give directions to the computer. (582)

conic section A conic section is a curve formed by slicing a hollow double cone with a plane. The equation of a conic section can be written in the form $Ax^2 + Bxy + Cy^2 + Dx + Ey + F = 0$ where $A, B,$ and C are not all zero. (291)

conjugate axis The conjugate axis of a hyperbola is the segment perpendicular to the transverse axis at its center. (287)

conjugates Binomials that are of the form $a + b\sqrt{c}$ and $a - b\sqrt{c}$ are conjugates of each other. (188)

consistent and dependent system A system of equations where the graphs of the equations are the same line is called a consistent and dependent system. There is an infinite number of solutions to this system of equations. (81)

consistent and independent system A system of equations that has one ordered pair as its solution is a consistent and independent system. (81)

constant A monomial that contains no variable is a constant. (145)

constant function A constant function is a function of the form $f(x) = b$ where the slope is zero. (601)

constant of variation The constant k in either of the equations $y = kx$ or $y = \frac{k}{x}$ is called the constant of variation. (364)

coordinate plane The plane determined by the perpendicular axes is called the coordinate plane. (41)

coordinates Each point in the coordinate plane corresponds to an ordered pair of numbers called its coordinates. (41)

cosecant Let θ stand for the measurement of an angle in standard position on the unit circle. Then the following equation holds whenever it is defined.

$$\csc \theta = \frac{1}{\sin \theta} \quad (522)$$

cosine Let θ stand for the measurement of an angle in standard position on the unit circle. Let (x, y) represent the point where the terminal side intersects the unit circle. Then the following equation holds.

$$\cos \theta = x \quad (514)$$

cotangent Let θ stand for the measurement of an angle in standard position on the unit circle. Then the following equation holds whenever it is defined.

$$\cot \theta = \frac{\cos \theta}{\sin \theta} \quad (522)$$

coterminal angles Coterminal angles differ by a complete rotation of the circle. (511)

Cramer's Rule The solution to the system of equations

$$\begin{matrix} ax + by = c \\ dx + ey = f \end{matrix} \text{ is } (x, y) \text{ where}$$

$$x = \frac{\begin{vmatrix} c & b \\ f & e \end{vmatrix}}{\begin{vmatrix} a & b \\ d & e \end{vmatrix}} \text{ and } y = \frac{\begin{vmatrix} a & c \\ d & f \end{vmatrix}}{\begin{vmatrix} a & b \\ d & e \end{vmatrix}} \text{ and } \begin{vmatrix} a & b \\ d & e \end{vmatrix} \neq 0.$$

(88)

data Numerical observations are called data. (481)

DATA statement A DATA statement is a BASIC statement that lists information to be used in a computer program. (582)

degree of monomial The degree of a monomial is the sum of the exponents of its variables. (145)

degree of polynomial The degree of a polynomial is the degree of the monomial of greatest degree. (307)

dependent events Two events are dependent when the outcome of the first event affects the outcome of the second event. If two events, A and B, are dependent, then the probability of both occurring is found as follows.

$P(A \text{ and } B) = P(A) \cdot P(B \text{ following } A)$ (466)

depressed polynomial A polynomial whose degree is less than the original polynomial is called a depressed polynomial. It is the result of factoring out a factor of the original polynomial. (312)

determinant A determinant is a square array of numbers having a numerical value. (87)

dimension In a matrix consisting of n rows and m columns, the matrix is said to have dimension $n \times m$ (read "n by m"). (120)

direct variation A direct variation is a linear function described by $y = mx$ or $f(x) = mx$ where $m \neq 0$. (60)

discriminant In the quadratic formula, the expression under the radical sign, $b^2 - 4ac$, is called the discriminant. (226)

dispersion Dispersion is the variation of values in a set of data. (493)

distance The distance between two points with coordinates (x_1, y_1) and (x_2, y_2) is given by the following formula.

$$d = \sqrt{(x_2 - x_1)^2 + (y_2 - y_2)^2}$$ (272)

distributive property For all numbers a, b, and c, $a(b + c) = ab + ac$ and $(b + c)a = ba + ca$. (11)

domain The domain is the set of all first coordinates of the ordered pairs of a relation. (43)

e e is the base of the natural system of logarithms. Its numerical value is 2.7182818284 . . . , which is an irrational number. (397)

ellipse An ellipse is the set of all points in the plane such that the sum of the distances from two given points, called the foci, is constant. The standard equation of an ellipse that has center (h, k) and major axis of length $2a$ is as follows. The equation is $\frac{(x - h)^2}{a^2} + \frac{(y - k)^2}{b^2} = 1$ when the major axis is parallel to the x-axis.

The equation is $\frac{(x - h)^2}{b^2} + \frac{(y - k)^2}{a^2} = 1$ when the major axis is parallel to the y-axis. For an ellipse, $b^2 = a^2 - c^2$. (281)

END statement An END statement indicates that a computer program is finished. It is the last statement in a BASIC program. (582)

E notation E notation is the computer equivalent of scientific notation. (583)

equation A statement of equality between two mathematical expressions is called an equation. (13)

expansion by minors Expansion by minors is a method that can be used to find the value of any third or higher order determinant. (112)

exponent An exponent is a numeral written to the right and above a number indicating how many times the number is used as a factor. (3)

exponential equation An equation in which the variables appear as exponents is called an exponential equation. (392)

Fibonacci sequence A fibonacci sequence is a special sequence often found in nature. It is named after its discoverer, Leonardo Fibonacci. (433)

flow chart A flow chart is a diagram used to organize and plan a computer program. (594)

FOIL FOIL is a method used to multiply binomials. The product of 2 binomials is the sum of the products of
  F the first terms
  O the outer terms
  I the inner terms
  L the last terms. (155)

formula A mathematical sentence about the relationships among certain quantities is called a formula. (4)

FOR-NEXT loop A FOR-NEXT loop instructs the computer to perform a certain task a prescribed number of times. (591)

frequency distribution A frequency distribution shows how data are spread out. (497)

function A function is a relation in which each element of the domain is paired with exactly one element of the range. (44)

geometric means The terms between any two nonconsecutive terms of a geometric sequence are called geometric means. (417)

geometric sequence A geometric sequence is a sequence in which each term after the first is the product of the preceding term and the common ratio. (416)

geometric series The indicated sum of the terms of a geometric sequence is called a geometric series. (421)

GO TO statement A GO TO statement is a BASIC statement that returns the computer to a particular step in a program. (587)

greatest integer The greatest integer of x is written $[x]$ and means the greatest integer *not* greater than x. (61)

histogram A histogram is a bar graph that shows a frequency distribution. (497)

hyperbola A hyperbola is the set of all points in the plane such that the absolute value of the difference of the distances from two given points, called the foci, is constant. The standard equation of a hyperbola that has center (h, k) and a horizontal transverse axis of length $2a$ is $\dfrac{(x - h)^2}{a^2} - \dfrac{(y - k)^2}{b^2} = 1$. The equation is $\dfrac{(y - k)^2}{a^2} - \dfrac{(x - h)^2}{b^2} = 1$ when the transverse axis is vertical. For the hyperbola, $b^2 = c^2 - a^2$. (288)

hypotenuse The hypotenuse is the side opposite the right angle in a right triangle. (551)

identity function An identity function is a linear function described by $y = x$ or $f(x) = x$. (60)

identity matrix for multiplication The identity matrix, I, for multiplication is a square matrix with a 1 for every element of the principal diagonal and a 0 in all other positions. (125)

IF-THEN statement An IF-THEN statement instructs a computer to make a comparison and tells the computer what to do next, based on the results of the comparison. (588)

imaginary number An imaginary number is a complex number of the form $a + bi$, where $b \neq 0$. (202)

imaginary unit The imaginary unit i is defined by $i^2 = -1$. (202)

inclusive events Two events are inclusive if the outcomes of the events may be the same. The probability of two inclusive events, A and B, occurring is found as follows.
$P(A \text{ or } B) = P(A) + P(B) - P(A \text{ and } B)$ (470)

inconsistent system An inconsistent system is a system of equations where the graph of the equations is parallel lines. There is no solution to this system of equations. (81)

independent events Two events are independent if the outcome of one event does not affect the outcome of the other event. The probability of two independent events, A and B, occurring is found as follows.
$P(A \text{ and } B) = P(A) \cdot P(B)$ (466)

index of summation An index of summation is a variable used with the summation symbol (Σ). (427)

infinite geometric series An infinite geometric series is the indicated sum of the terms of an infinite geometric sequence. (424)

integers (Z) The set of numbers $\{. . . , -3, -2, -1, 0, 1, 2, 3, . . .\}$. (8)

internal functions in BASIC The internal functions in BASIC perform prescribed tasks. They are ABS(X), SQR(X), INT(X), RND(X), SIN(X), COS(X), and TAN(X). (603)

interpolation Interpolation is a method for approximating values that are between given consecutive entries in a table, such as a table of logarithms or a table of trigonometric values. (389, 555)

inverse functions Two polynomial functions f and g are inverse functions if and only if both their compositions are the identity function. That is,
$$[f \circ g](x) = [g \circ f](x) = x. \quad (332)$$

inverse matrix For a matrix A, with a nonzero determinant, the inverse matrix, A^{-1}, of A is that matrix with the property
$$A \cdot A^{-1} = A^{-1} \cdot A = I \quad (125)$$

inverse variation A rational equation in two variables of the form $y = \dfrac{k}{x}$, where k is a constant, is called an inverse variation. The constant k is called the constant of variation, and y is said to vary inversely as x. (364)

irrational numbers (I) Irrational numbers are real numbers that cannot be written as terminating or repeating decimals. (8)

iteration An iteration method involves a repeated series of operations. (210)

latus rectum A latus rectum is the line segment through the focus of a parabola perpendicular to its axis of symmetry with endpoints on the parabola. (275)

Laws of Cosines Let triangle ABC be any triangle with a, b, and c representing the measures of sides opposite angles with measurements A, B, and C, respectively. Then the following equations are true.
$$a^2 = b^2 + c^2 - 2bc \cos A$$
$$b^2 = a^2 + c^2 - 2ac \cos B$$
$$c^2 = a^2 + b^2 - 2ab \cos C \quad (568)$$

Law of Sines Let triangle ABC be any triangle with a, b, and c representing the measures of sides opposite angles with measurements A, B, and C, respectively. Then the following equations are true.
$$\frac{\sin A}{a} = \frac{\sin B}{b} = \frac{\sin C}{c} \quad (565)$$

LET statement A LET statement is a BASIC statement that assigns a value to a variable. (585)

like terms Two monomials that are the same or differ only by their coefficients are called like terms. (11, 145)

linear equation A linear equation is an equation whose graph is a straight line. (48)

linear function A linear function can be defined by $f(x) = mx + b$ where m and b are real numbers. Any function whose ordered pairs satisfy a linear equation in two variables is a linear function. (50)

linear permutation The arrangement of n objects in a certain linear order is called a linear permutation. The number of linear permutations of n objects, taken r at a time, is defined as follows.
$$P(n, r) = \frac{n!}{(n - r)!} \quad (452)$$

linear programming Linear programming is a method for finding the maximum or the minimum value of a function in two variables subject to given conditions on the variables. (93)

line graph A line graph shows trends or changes. (485)

logarithm Suppose $b > 0$ and $b \neq 1$. Then for $n > 0$, there is a number p such that $\log_b n = p$ if and only if $b^p = n$. (375)

major axis The major axis of an ellipse is the segment with endpoints at the vertices of the ellipse. (282)

mantissa The mantissa is the logarithm of a number between 1 and 10. (385)

mapping A mapping illustrates how each element in the domain of a relation is paired with an element in the range. (43)

matrix A matrix is a rectangular arrangement of terms in rows and columns enclosed in brackets or large parentheses. (117)

matrix equation The matrix equation form of a system of equations is an equation of the form $AX = C$. A is the coefficient matrix for the system. X is the column matrix consisting of the variables of the system. C is the column matrix consisting of the constant terms of the system. (130)

mean The mean of a set of data is the sum of all the values divided by the number of values. (490)

median The median of a set of data is the middle value. If there are two middle values, it is the value halfway between. (490)

midpoint The midpoint of a line segment with endpoints (x_1, y_1) and (x_2, y_2) has coordinates $\left(\dfrac{x_1 + x_2}{2}, \dfrac{y_1 + y_2}{2}\right)$. (272)

minor A minor is the determinant formed when the row and column containing the element are deleted. (112)

minor axis The minor axis of an ellipse is the shorter axis. (282)

mode The mode of a set of data is the most frequent value. (490)

monomial A monomial is an expression that is a number, a variable, or the product of a number and one or more variables. (145)

multiplicative identity One is the multiplicative identity. The product of any number and 1 is identical to the original number. (10)

multiplicative inverses If the product of two numbers is 1, they are called multiplicative inverses or reciprocals of each other. (10)

mutually exclusive events Two events are mutually exclusive if their outcomes can never be the same. The probability of two mutually exclusive events, A and B, occurring is found as follows.
$$P(A \text{ or } B) = P(A) + P(B) \quad (469)$$

negative integer exponents For any number a, except $a = 0$, and for any positive integer n, $a^{-n} = \dfrac{1}{a^n}$. (149)

n factorial If n is a positive integer, the expression $n!$ (n factorial) is defined as follows.
$$n! = n(n - 1)(n - 2) \cdots (1) \quad (439)$$

normal distribution Normal distributions have bell-shaped, symmetric graphs. About 68% of the items are within one standard deviation from the mean. About 95% of the items are within two standard deviations from the mean. About 99% of the items are within three standard deviations from the mean. (497)

nth root For any numbers a and b, and any positive integer n, if $a^n = b$, then a is an nth root of b. (181)

nth term The nth term of an arithmetic sequence with the first term a_1 and common difference d is given by the following equation.
$$a_n = a_1 + (n - 1)d \quad (408)$$

octant Three mutually perpendicular planes separate space into eight regions, each called an octant. (108)

odds The odds of the successful outcome of an event are expressed as the ratio of the number of ways it can succeed to the number of ways it can fail.

Odds = the ratio of s to f or $\frac{s}{f}$ (463)

ordered triple 1. The solution to an equation in three variables is called an ordered triple. (105) 2. Each point in space corresponds to three numbers called an ordered triple. (108)

origin The origin is the point on the coordinate plane whose coordinates are (0, 0). (41)

parabola 1. The general shape of the graph of a quadratic function is called a parabola. (246) 2. A parabola is the set of all points that are the same distance from a given point and a given line. The point is called the focus. The line is called the directrix. The standard equation of a parabola with vertex at (h, k) is $y = a(x - h)^2 + k$ when the directrix is horizontal. The equation is $x = a(y - k)^2 + h$ when the directrix is vertical. (274)

parallel lines In a plane, lines with the same slope are called parallel lines. Also, vertical lines are parallel. (77)

period For a function f, the least positive value of a for which $f(x) = f(x + a)$ is the period of the function. For functions of the form $y = a \sin b\theta$ and $y = a \cos b\theta$, the period is $\frac{2\pi}{|b|}$. (516, 520)

periodic function A function f is called periodic if there is a number a such that $f(x) = f(x + a)$. (516)

permutation A permutation is the arrangement of things in a certain order. (452)

perpendicular lines Two nonvertical lines are perpendicular if and only if the product of their slopes is -1. Any vertical line is perpendicular to any horizontal line. (78)

pictograph A pictograph shows how specific quantities compare to one another. (485)

polynomial A polynomial is a monomial or the sum or difference of monomials. (114)

polynomial function A polynomial equation in the form $p(x) = a_n x^n + a_{n-1} x^{n-1} + \cdots a_1 x + a_0$ is a polynomial function. The coefficients $a_0, a_1, a_2, \ldots, a_{n-1}, a_n$ are real numbers and n is a nonnegative integer. (308)

prediction equation The equation of the line suggested by the dots on a scatter diagram is a prediction equation. (501)

principal diagonal The principal diagonal of a matrix is the diagonal extending from the upper left corner to the lower right corner of the matrix. (125)

principal values The values in the domain of the functions like Cosine, Sine, and Tangent are the principal values. (542)

PRINT statement A PRINT statement is a BASIC statement that directs the computer to print out data or messages. (582)

probability If an event can succeed in s ways and fail in f ways, then the probabilities of success $P(s)$ and of failure $P(f)$ are as follows.

$$P(s) = \frac{s}{s + f} \quad P(f) = \frac{f}{s + f} \quad (462)$$

pure imaginary number For any positive real number b, $\sqrt{-(b^2)} = \sqrt{b^2}\sqrt{-1}$ or bi where i is a number whose square is -1. bi is called a pure imaginary number. (202)

quadrants Two perpendicular number lines separate the plane into four parts called quadrants. (41)

quadratic equation Any equation that can be written in the form $ax^2 + bx + c = 0$, where a, b, and c are complex numbers and $a \neq 0$, is a quadratic equation. (217)

quadratic form For any numbers a, b, and c, except $a = 0$, an equation that may be written as $a[f(x)]^2 + b[f(x)] + c = 0$, where $f(x)$ is some expression in x, is in quadratic form. (235)

quadratic formula The solutions of a quadratic equation of the form $ax^2 + bx + c = 0$ with $a \neq 0$ are given by the quadratic formula.
$$x = \frac{-b \pm \sqrt{b^2 - 4ac}}{2a} \quad (223)$$

quadratic function A quadratic function is a function described by an equation of the form $f(x) = ax^2 + bx + c$ where $a \neq 0$. (243)

radian A radian is an angle that intercepts an arc whose length is 1 unit. (512)

radical equations Radical equations are equations containing variables in the radicands. (199)

radical sign A radical sign, $\sqrt{}$, indicates a square root. (181)

radius *See* circle.

range **1.** The range is a set of all second coordinates of the ordered pairs of a relation. (43) **2.** The range of a set of data is the difference between the greatest and least values in the set. (493)

rational algebraic expression A rational algebraic expression can be expressed as the quotient of two polynomials. (343)

rational equation A rational equation is an equation that contains one or more rational expressions. (354)

rational exponents For any nonzero num-

ber b, and any integers m and n, $n > 1$
$$b^{\frac{m}{n}} = \sqrt[n]{b^m} = (\sqrt[n]{b})^m.$$
except when $\sqrt[n]{b}$ does not represent a real number. (195)

rational numbers (Q) Rational numbers are numbers that can be expressed in the form $\frac{a}{b}$, where a and b are integers. (8)

rationalizing the denominator Rationalizing the denominator is changing the form of a rational expression to one without radicals in the denominator. (190, 207)

READ statement A READ statement is a BASIC statement that instructs the computer to input the indicated data. (582)

real numbers (R) Irrational numbers together with rational numbers form the set of real numbers. (8)

reciprocal *See* multiplicative inverse.

recursive formula A recursive formula depends on knowing one or more previous terms. (430)

relation A relation is a set of ordered pairs. (43)

relative maximum or minimum A relative maximum or minimum is a point that represents the maximum or minimum respectively for a certain interval. (328)

root A root is a solution of an equation. (226)

row matrix A row matrix is a matrix containing only one row. (120)

row operations on matrices The row operations on matrices are as follows.
1. Interchange any two rows.
2. Replace any row with a nonzero multiple of that row.
3. Replace any row with the sum of that row and another row. (118)

RUN RUN is a BASIC command that instructs the computer to execute the program. (583)

scatter diagram A scatter diagram shows visually the nature of a relationship, both shape and closeness. (501)

scientific notation A number is expressed in scientific notation when it is in the form $a \times 10^n$ where $1 \le a < 10$ and n is an integer. (151)

secant Let θ stand for the measurement of an angle in standard position on the unit circle. Then the following equation holds whenever it is defined.

$$\sec \theta = \frac{1}{\cos \theta} \quad (522)$$

sequence A sequence is a set of numbers in a specific order. (407)

series The indicated sum of the terms of a sequence is called a series. (411)

sigma notation The Σ symbol is used to indicate a sum of a series. (427)

signed minor The signed minor of an element of a matrix is the minor for that element multiplied by its sign. (128)

simplified expression An expression is simplified when:
1. It has no negative exponents.
2. It has no fractional exponents in the denominator.
3. It is not a complex fraction.
4. The index of any remaining radical is as small as possible. (197)

sine Let θ stand for the measurement of an angle in standard position on the unit circle. Let (x, y) represent the point where the terminal side intersects the unit circle. Then the following equation holds.

$$\sin \theta = y \quad (514)$$

slope The slope of a line described by $f(x) = mx + b$ is m. Slope is also given by the following expression.

$$m = \frac{y_2 - y_1}{x_2 - x_1} \quad (52)$$

slope-intercept form The equation $y = mx + b$ is in slope-intercept form. The slope is m and the y-intercept is b. (57)

solution set A solution set is the set of all replacements for variables that make an open sentence true. (13)

solving a right triangle Solving a right triangle means finding all the measures of the sides and angles. (558)

square matrix A matrix that has the same number of rows as columns is called a square matrix. (125)

square root For any numbers a and b, if $a^2 = b$, then a is a square root of b. (181)

standard deviation From a set of data with n values, if x_i represents a value such that $1 \le i \le n$, and $\bar{x}$ represents the mean, then the standard deviation is

$$\sqrt{\frac{\sum_{i=1}^{n} (x_i - \bar{x})^2}{n}}. \quad (493)$$

standard form The standard form of a linear equation is $ax + by = c$ where a, b, and c are real numbers and a and b are not both zero. (48)

subscripted variables Subscripted variables are used where there is a great amount of data. The subscripts provide labels for the different variables. (600)

sum of a geometric series The sum, S_n, of the first n terms of a geometric series is given by the following formula.

$$S_n = \frac{a_1 - a_1 r^n}{1 - r} \text{ where } r \ne 1 \quad (421)$$

sum of an arithmetic series The sum, S_n, of the first n terms of an arithmetic series is given by the following formula.

$$S_n = \frac{n}{2}(a_1 + a_n) \quad (412)$$

sum of an infinite geometric series The sum of an infinite geometric series is given by the formula

$$S = \frac{a_1}{1 - r} \text{ where } -1 < r < 1. \quad (425)$$

synthetic division A shortcut method used to divide polynomials by binomials is called synthetic division. (172)

synthetic substitution Synthetic substitution is the process of using the Remainder Theorem and synthetic division to find the value of a function. (311)

tangent Let θ stand for the measurement of an angle in standard position on the unit circle. Then the following equation holds whenever it is defined.

$$\tan \theta = \frac{\sin \theta}{\cos \theta} \quad (522)$$

term 1. Each monomial in a polynomial is called a term. (114) **2.** A term is each number in a sequence. (407)

trace A trace is the line formed by the intersection of a plane with one of the three coordinate planes. (109)

transpose The transpose of any matrix is the matrix formed by interchanging the rows and the columns of the original matrix. (127)

transverse axis The line segment of a hyperbola of length $2a$ that has its endpoints at the vertices is called the transverse axis. (287)

trichotomy property For any two numbers a and b, one of the following statements is true.

$$a < b, a = b, a > b \quad (25)$$

trinomial A polynomial with three unlike terms is called a trinomial. (154)

unit circle A unit circle has a radius of 1 unit. (512)

variable A variable is a symbol that represents an unknown quantity. (3)

vertical line test If any vertical line drawn on the graph of a relation passes through no more than one point of that graph, then the relation is a function. (45)

whole numbers (W) The set of numbers $\{0, 1, 2, 3, \ldots\}$. (8)

x-axis The horizontal number line in a plane is called the *x-axis*. (41)

x-intercept An *x*-intercept is the value of x when the value of the function or y is zero. (54)

y-axis The vertical number line in a plane is called the *y*-axis. (41)

y-intercept A *y*-intercept is the value of a function when x is 0. (54)

zero exponent For any number a, except $a = 0$, $a^0 = 1$. (148)

zero of function For any polynomial function $f(x)$, if $f(a) = 0$, then a is a zero of the function. (315)

Selected Answers

CHAPTER 1 EQUATIONS AND INEQUALITIES

1-1 Page 5
Exploratory **1.** 7 **3.** -44 **5.** 13 **7.** 21 **9.** 21
11. 0 *Written* **1.** 41 **3.** 14 **5.** 6 **7.** 60 **9.** 10
11. 22 **13.** 4 **15.** $-3\frac{2}{3}$ **17.** 148 **19.** $-\frac{19}{2}$
21. -7.9 **23.** $\frac{5}{4}$ **25.** 94 **27.** -72 **29.** -7.2 **31.** $\frac{3}{7}$
33. 272.16 **35.** $180 **37.** $300 **39.** $17,400 **41.** 128
43. 100 **45.** 93.6 **47.** $53\frac{1}{4}$

1-2 Page 9
Exploratory **1.** Z, Q, R **3.** Q, R **5.** Q, R **7.** I, R
9. W, Z, Q, R **11.** Z, Q, R *Written* **1.** 1; W, Z, Q, R
3. -9; Z, Q, R **5.** -24; Z, Q, R **7.** 1; W, Z, Q, R
9. 5; W, Z, Q, R **11.** -90; Z, Q, R **13.** 0; W, Z, Q, R
15. $\sqrt{3}$; I, R **17.** true **19.** false **21.** true **23.** true

1-3 Page 11
Exploratory **1.** associative, + **3.** distributive
5. additive inverse **7.** commutative, + **9.** multiplicative
inverse *Written* 1. commutative, $\times$ **3.** distributive
5. commutative, + **7.** commutative, + **9.** distributive
11. additive identity **13.** multiplicative inverse
15. additive identity **17.** commutative, +
19. multiplicative inverse **21.** 20 **23.** $2x + 17y$
25. $31a + 10b$ **27.** $12 + 20a$ **29.** $\frac{2}{3}a + 2\frac{1}{2}b$
31. $4.4m - 2.9n$ **33.** 0, additive identity **35.** 1,
multiplicative identity

1-4 Page 15
Exploratory **1.** reflexive **3.** subtraction
5. transitive **7.** symmetric **9.** substitution
11. symmetric **13.** reflexive *Written* **1.** symmetric
3. transitive **5.** reflexive **7.** substitution
9. distributive **11.** division **13. a.** distributive
b. substitution **c.** divison **15.** 7.5 **17.** 14 **19.** $\frac{20}{21}$
21. $\frac{35}{8}$ **23.** 7 **25.** -12 **27.** 12 **29.** $-\frac{1}{6}$ **31.** $\frac{3}{10}$
33. 8 **35.** 2.1 **37.** 3 **39.** $\frac{1}{2}$ **41.** 11 **43.** -4
45. 10 **47.** -3 **49.** -4

1-5 Page 19
Exploratory **1.** $4x$ **3.** $2x + 11$ **5.** $2(x + 7)$
7. $2x + 7$ **9.** $12 - x^2$ **11.** $\frac{1}{5}(4 + x)$ **13.** $8(x + x^2)$
15. $(x + 11)^2$ *Written* **1.** 118 **3.** 26 **5.** 85%
7. 18 years **9.** 19 years, 43 years **11.** 88% **13.** 5

15. 8 adults, 12 students **17.** 24 m, 36 m **19.** 3 hours
21. 43 mph

1-6 Page 23
Exploratory **1.** 5 **3.** 10 **5.** 36 **7.** 5 **9.** 0 **11.** 0
13. -2 **15.** 11 **17.** 1 **19.** $-2, -1, 0$ **21.** -1
Written **1.** 31, -53 **3.** 16, -6 **5.** 5, -19
7. 14, -8 **9.** 6, -13 **11.** $-3\frac{2}{3}, 8\frac{1}{3}$ **13.** 5.5, -10.5
15. 26, 11 **17.** $-4\frac{1}{3}, 2\frac{2}{3}$ **19.** 3, -3.8 **21.** 10.5, 3.5
23. $-\frac{10}{21}, -\frac{20}{7}$ **25.** no solutions **27.** $\frac{2}{3}, \frac{7}{3}$ **29.** no
solutions **31.** 4 **33.** 1,5 **35.** no solutions **37.** 1,3
39. $-1\frac{1}{3}$, 10 **41.** $\frac{5}{2}, -\frac{3}{2}$

1-7 Page 27
Written **1.** $\{x \mid x > 12\}$ **3.** $\{n \mid n \geq 7\}$ **5.** $\{r \mid r > 3.2\}$
7. $\{x \mid x > -12\}$ **9.** $\{y \mid y > 17.6\}$ **11.** $\{x \mid x \geq 6\}$
13. $\{x \mid x > 4.5\}$ **15.** $\{w \mid w \geq 5\}$ **17.** $\{z \mid z \leq 3\}$
19. $\{t \mid t < 3.25\}$ **21.** $\{x \mid x > 2.25\}$ **23.** $\left\{x \mid x \geq \frac{3}{7}\right\}$
25. $\{r \mid r \geq 5\}$ **27.** $\{x \mid x \leq 2\}$ **29.** $\{m \mid m \geq 1\}$
31. $\{b \mid b > 2\}$ **33.** $\{x \mid x \geq 232\}$ **35.** $\left\{x \mid x < \frac{2}{3}\right\}$
37. $\{x \mid x \leq -1.425\}$ **39.** $\left\{w \mid w \leq \frac{4}{3}\right\}$ **41.** $\left\{x \mid x > \frac{40}{7}\right\}$
43. $\{x \mid -1 < x < 3\}$ **45.** $\emptyset$

1-8 Page 30
Exploratory **1.** true **3.** false **5.** true **7.** $c \geq 30$
9. $s \leq 48$ **11.** $v \geq \$0.99$, or $v \geq 99¢$ **13.** $-3 < x$ and
$x < 2$ **15.** $1 < 3y$ and $3y \leq 13$ **17.** $5 \leq 3 - 2g$ and
$3 - 2g < 1$ **19.** $-2 < x < 10$ **21.** $-2 \leq x \leq 10$
23. $-5 \leq m \leq 5$ *Written* **1.** $60.37 or less
3. 21.25 **5.** $2,400 **7.** $513\frac{2}{3}$ **9.** 81 **11.** 4 more
13. at least 4 gallons **15.** $-2 < y < 7$ **17.** $x < 5$ or
$x > -1$ (all reals) **19.** $3 < x < 6$ **21.** $x < -2$ or
$x \geq 1$

1-9 Page 34
Exploratory **1.** $|x| < 3$ **3.** $|x| > 6$ **5.** $|x| > 3$
7. $|x| \leq 4$ **9.** $|x| < 6$ **11.** $|x| < 2$ *Written*
1. $\{x \mid -9 < x < 9\}$ **3.** $\{x \mid x > 2$ or $x < -4\}$
5. $\{x \mid -4 \leq x \leq 12\}$ **7.** $\{x \mid x \leq -3$ or $x \geq 3\}$
9. $\{x \mid x > 7$ or $x < -7\}$ **11.** $\{x \mid -13 \leq x \leq 13\}$ **13.** $\emptyset$
15. $\{x \mid x < -20$ or $x > 14\}$ **17.** $\{x \mid -30 < x < 54\}$
19. $\{x \mid -9 \leq x \leq 18\}$ **21.** $\left\{x \mid x \geq \frac{15}{4}$ or $x \leq -\frac{9}{4}\right\}$
23. $\{x \mid -17.6 < x < 14.8\}$ **25.** $\emptyset$ **27.** $\{x \mid -1 \leq x \leq 6\}$
29. $\{x \mid x \geq 0\}$ **31.** all reals **33.** $\{x \mid -1 \leq x \leq 1\}$
35. $\{x \mid -2 \leq x \leq 2\}$

Chapter Review   Page 37

1. 92 3. $70\frac{1}{3}$ 5. $\frac{13}{12}$ 7. Q, R 9. W, Z, Q, R
11. commutative 13. additive identity 15. 402
17. $-3p + 13q$ 19. substitution 21. symmetric
23. $-\frac{33}{13}$ 25. $\frac{8}{3}$ 27. $\frac{56}{5}$ 29. length 21 m, width 11 m
31. 12 more days 33. 11, 26 35. $-2.5, 5.5$
37. $\left\{x \mid x \geq -\frac{1}{5}\right\}$ 39. 15 gallons 41. $\frac{5}{3} < y \leq 5$
43. all reals 45. $\left\{x \mid -\frac{9}{2} \leq x \leq -\frac{1}{2}\right\}$

CHAPTER 2   LINEAR RELATIONS AND FUNCTIONS

2-1   Page 41
Exploratory 1. I 3. III 5. none   *Written*
13. $(-5, 1)$ 15. $(1, 3)$ 17. $(-3, -3)$

2-2   Page 46
Exploratory 1. domain = {1, 3, 4}, range = {1, 3, 4};
yes 3. domain = {−17, 4, 8}, range = {−2, 3, 4, 8};
no 5. domain = {−3, −2, 2, 4}, range = {−3, −2,
2, 4}; yes 7. domain = {−3, 5}, range = {−3, 5}; yes
9. {(8, 3), (−1,3), (2,3)}; yes 11. {(15, 15), (15, 30),
(15, 45), (15, 60)}; no   *Written* 1. {(−3, 3), (−2, 2),
(−1, 1), (0, 0), (1, 1), (2, 2), (3, 3)}; domain = {−3, −2,
−1, 0, 1, 2, 3}, range = {3, 2, 1, 0} 3. {(2, y) such that
y is any real number}; domain = {2}, range = {all
reals} 5. yes 7. no 9. no 11. no 13. $\frac{7}{10}$ 15. $-\frac{7}{3}$
17. $-\frac{7}{2}$ 19. $-\frac{14}{3}$ 21. $\frac{7}{a-2}$ 23. $\frac{7}{3a-2}$ 25. 0
27. $-\frac{15}{2}$ 29. $4t^3 + 2t^2 + t - 7$ 31. $\frac{20}{3}$ 33. $-\frac{19}{15}$
35. $\frac{a(a+7)}{a+4}$

2-3   Page 50
Exploratory 1. no 3. yes 5. yes 7. yes 9. no
11. yes 13. no 15. yes   *Written* 1. $2x - y = 6$
3. $x = 5$ 5. $5x - 8y = -8$ 7. $3x - y = 0$

9. 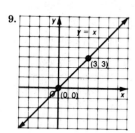 15.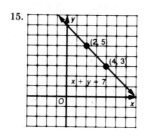

2-4   Page 55
Exploratory 1. 1, 2, −2 3. −4, 4, 1, 5. 0, 2, none
7. 2, −4, 2   *Written* 1. $-\frac{5}{2}$ 3. $\frac{2}{11}$ 5. $\frac{5}{2}$ 7. 8

9. 0 11. undefined 13. $-9, \frac{9}{5}$ 15. $1, -\frac{1}{7}$ 17. $-5,$
$-\frac{15}{2}$ 19. -2, none 21. $-2, 2$ 23. $\frac{5}{2}, 5$ 25. $-6, 4$
27. $\frac{7}{2}, 7$ 29. $-4, 6$ 43. 1 45. -8 47. 9 49. 23

2-5   Page 58
Exploratory 1. $y = 5x - 3$ 3. $y = -x + 4$ 5. $y =$
$\frac{2}{3}x - 7$ 7. $y = 2.5x$ 9. $y = 0$ 11. $-4, 6$ 13. $1, -8$
15. $\frac{1}{3}, 0$ 17. $-1, 0$ 19. $y = -\frac{2}{5}x + 2$ 21. $y = -\frac{2}{3}x +$
$\frac{4}{3}$ 23. $y = x - 2$ *Written* 1. 2, 15 3. $\frac{5}{3}, -0.2$
5. undefined, none 7. 2, -4 9. $\frac{3}{5}, -\frac{3}{7}$
11. $y = \frac{3}{4}x - 7$ 13. $y = -\frac{4}{5}x - \frac{7}{5}$ 15. $y = 5x$
17. $y = \frac{2}{5}x - \frac{3}{5}$ 19. $x = 6$ 21. $y = \frac{3}{2}x$
23. $y = -\frac{2}{3}x + 4$ 25. $y = \frac{3}{4}x - \frac{1}{4}$ 27. $y = 0$
29. $2x - y = 2$ 31. $3x + y = 11$ 33. $2x + 3y = 9$
35. $x - y = -3$ 37. $5x + y = 5$ 39. $x = -1$
41. $x + 9y = 9$ 43. $x - y = -1$ 45. $x = 0$

2-6   Page 62
Exploratory 1. A 3. D 5. A 7. A 9. G 11. D
13. G 15. A 17. A 19. G 21. C 23. A
Written

9. 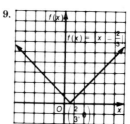 11.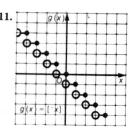

13. 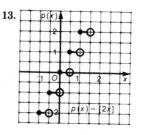 17.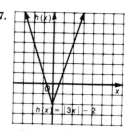

19. 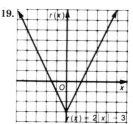 21.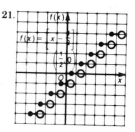

$\frac{5}{3}$; $2x = -5$, $3z - 2x = 5$, $3z = 5$ **23.** $x = \frac{8}{3}$, no y-intercept, no z-intercept; $3x = 8$, $3x = 8$, no yz-trace

11. 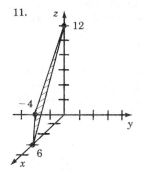 **13.**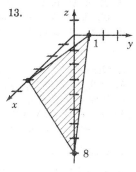

17. 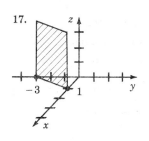 **23.**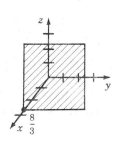

25. $3x - 6y + 4z = 12$ **27.** $-2x + 6y + z = 6$
29. $12x + 4y + 3z = -12$ **31.** $12x + 2y - 3z = 6$
33. $x + 12y + 16z = 4$ **35.** $21x + 6y - 28z = 14$
37. $3x - 5y + 2z = 8$ **39.** $4x - 2y - 3z = 12$
41. $5x - 4y + 7z = 20$ **43.** $x + 5y + 3z = 1$
45. $2x + y = 4$ **47.** $3x - 4y = 12$

4-3 Page 115
Exploratory **1.** 31 **3.** 6 *Written* **1.** -33 **3.** 29
5. -111 **7.** 5125 **9.** $(3, 6, -2)$ **11.** $(3, 1, 6)$ **13.** 0
15. $\left(6, -\frac{1}{2}, 2\right)$ **17.** $\left(\frac{4}{3}, 0, -\frac{1}{2}\right)$
19. $\left(\frac{1}{2}, \frac{2}{3}, \frac{1}{4}\right)$ **21.** 3 pennies, 5 nickels, 8 dimes

4-4 Page 119
Written **1.** $(2, -3)$ **3.** $(1, 1)$ **5.** $\left(\frac{1}{4}, -\frac{1}{2}\right)$
7. $(-1, 2, -3)$ **9.** $(5, 6, 7)$ **11.** $(-4, 1, 3)$
13. $\left(-3, \frac{1}{3}, 1\right)$ **15.** $\left(\frac{3}{4}, -\frac{2}{3}, \frac{1}{2}\right)$ **17.** $x = 1$, $y = 2$, $z = 3$, $w = 4$

4-5 Page 122
Exploratory **1.** $\begin{bmatrix} 12 & 3 \\ -6 & 9 \end{bmatrix}$ **3.** $\begin{bmatrix} \frac{5}{2} & -2 & \frac{\sqrt{2}}{2} \end{bmatrix}$ **5.** $\begin{bmatrix} 6 \\ -8 \\ 2 \end{bmatrix}$
7. $\begin{bmatrix} 6 & -2 \\ 0 & 7 \end{bmatrix}$ **9.** $\begin{bmatrix} 2 & -5 & 6 & -13 \end{bmatrix}$ **11.** $M_{3 \times 3}$
13. $M_{4 \times 5}$ **15.** $M_{3 \times 2}$ *Written* **1.** $M_{5 \times 7}$ **3.** $M_{4 \times 4}$

25. The graph of $y = [2x]$ jumps by ones at intervals of $\frac{1}{2}$ unit. The graph of $y = 2[x]$ jumps by twos at intervals of one unit. **27.** The graph of $y = |x - 3|$ is like $y = |x|$ moved 3 units *to the right*. The graph of $y = |x| - 3$ is like $y = |x|$ moved 3 units *down*. **29.** The graph of $y = |2x + 5|$ is like $y = |2x|$ moved 2.5 units *to the left*. The graph of $y = |2x| + 5$ is like $y = |2x|$ moved 2.5 units *up*. **31.** The graphs of $y = |ax|$ and $y = a|x|$ are identical if $a \geq 0$. The graph of $y = a|x|$ opens down if $a < 0$.

2-7 Page 65
Exploratory **1.** $s = 10r$ **3.** 4.8 inches **5.** 45 inches
7. \$92 **9.** 1.75 hours **11.** $\frac{2}{3}$, 1, $1\frac{1}{3}$, $1\frac{2}{3}$, $3\frac{1}{3}$, 5, $6\frac{2}{3}$, $8\frac{1}{3}$,
10, $13\frac{1}{3}$, $16\frac{2}{3}$, 20 *Written* **1.** $p = 550y + 47{,}000$
3. $d = 6000 - 75x$ **5.** $c = 0.18t + 161$
7. $c = 1.25n$; \$5.00, \$6.25, \$7.50 **9.** $c = 0.36 + 0.34m$; \$2.40, \$3.08, \$3.76, \$5.46, \$7.16, \$10.56, \$15.66, \$20.76

2-8 Page 68
Exploratory **1.** all three **3.** $(0, 0)$, $(2, -3)$ **5.** none
7. $(2, -3)$

Written

3. 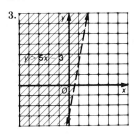 **11.**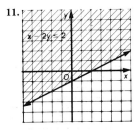

21. 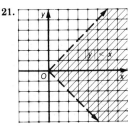 **23.**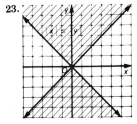

Chapter Review **Page 71** **5.** domain = $\{1, 2, 3, 4, 5\}$; range = $\{-4.5, -3.5, 4.5\}$; yes **7.** no **9.** no
11. -29 **13.** no **15.** yes **21.** $-\frac{3}{7}$, $\frac{2}{7}$, $\frac{2}{3}$ **23.** $\frac{1}{2}$, $-\frac{15}{2}$,
15 **25.** -3 **27.** 2 **29.** 6 **33.** $y = 5x - 7$ **35.** $y = -\frac{6}{7}x - \frac{18}{7}$ **37.** $4x - y = 22$ **39.** $3x - y = 6$
47. $c = 4.50 + p$

45. 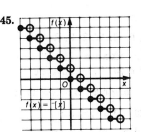 **51.**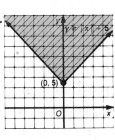

CHAPTER 3   SYSTEMS OF EQUATIONS AND INEQUALITIES

3-1   Page 79
Exploratory **1.** 4 **3.** $\frac{3}{2}$ **5.** $\frac{8}{9}$ **7.** $-\frac{1}{2}$ **9.** $-\frac{3}{8}$
11. $-\frac{8}{3}$ *Written* **1.** parallel **3.** parallel
5. parallel **7.** neither **9.** neither **11.** $y = \frac{1}{3}x$
13. $y = 3x$ **15.** $y = -x + \frac{5}{6}$ **17.** $y = \frac{3}{2}x - \frac{23}{2}$
19. $y = \frac{1}{3}x + \frac{2}{3}$ **21.** $y = \frac{5}{3}x + \frac{5}{3}$ **23.** $y = -\frac{1}{2}x - 4$
25. $y = \frac{2}{3}x - 2$ **27.** $y = -\frac{1}{15}x - \frac{23}{5}$ **29.** $-\frac{3}{4}$ **31.** 4
33. A line connecting $(-6, 5)$ and $(-2, 7)$ has slope $\frac{1}{2}$.
A line connecting $(5, 3)$ and $(1, 1)$ has slope $\frac{1}{2}$. These two lines are parallel since their slopes are the same. A line connecting $(-6, 5)$ and $(1, 1)$ has slope $-\frac{4}{7}$. A line connecting $(-2, 7)$ and $(5, 3)$ has slope $-\frac{4}{7}$. These two lines are parallel since their slopes are the same.
35. $(-1, 11)$ and $(7, 15)$; $(7, -5)$ and $(15, -1)$; $(5, 9)$ and $(9, 1)$

3-2   Page 82
Exploratory **1.** $(-3, 6)$ **3.** $(5, 2)$ **5.** $(2, -4)$
7. $(-3, 6)$ *Written* **1.** $(3, 1)$; consistent and independent **3.** no solutions; inconsistent **5.** $\{(x, y) \mid x + 2y = 5\}$; consistent and dependent **7.** $(2, -6)$; consistent and independent **9.** $(8, 6)$; consistent and independent **11.** no solutions; inconsistent
13. $\left(-\frac{4}{3}, -\frac{14}{3}\right)$; consistent and independent **15.** $\{(x, y) \mid 2x + 3y = 5\}$; consistent and dependent **17.** no solutions; inconsistent **19.** $(1, -2)$; consistent and independent **21.** $\{(x, y) \mid 9x - 5 = 7y\}$; consistent and dependent **23.** $a = 3$, $b = 8$ **25.** $r = 3$, $s = 9$

3-3   Page 85
Written **1.** $(-3, -9)$ **3.** $\left(\frac{4}{3}, \frac{2}{3}\right)$ **5.** $(-9, -7)$
7. $(2, 1)$ **9.** $(-1, 2)$ **11.** $(-4, -4)$ **13.** $(12, 2)$
15. $(5.25, 0.75)$ **17.** $\left(-1, \frac{2}{3}\right)$ **19.** $(-4, 6)$

21. $(-1, 2)$ 23. $\left(-\frac{64}{5}, \frac{31}{5}\right)$ 25. $(10, 25)$
27. $(-6, -8)$ 29. $(0.75, 0.5)$ 31. $(-3, 6)$
33. $(-3, 4)$ 35. $(2, -3)$ 37. $(4.1, -3.2)$
39. $(-1.1, -3.4)$ 41. 27, 15 43. width = 15 cm, length = 28 cm

3-4 Page 88
Exploratory 1. 14 3. 0 5. 1 7. 14

9. $\dfrac{\begin{vmatrix}5 & 2\\3 & -1\end{vmatrix}}{\begin{vmatrix}3 & 2\\4 & -1\end{vmatrix}}, \dfrac{\begin{vmatrix}3 & 5\\4 & 3\end{vmatrix}}{\begin{vmatrix}3 & 2\\4 & -1\end{vmatrix}}$ 11. $\dfrac{\begin{vmatrix}16 & -4\\21 & -5\end{vmatrix}}{\begin{vmatrix}2 & -4\\3 & -5\end{vmatrix}}, \dfrac{\begin{vmatrix}2 & 16\\3 & 21\end{vmatrix}}{\begin{vmatrix}2 & -4\\3 & -5\end{vmatrix}}$

13. $\dfrac{\begin{vmatrix}-8 & 1\\-14 & -2\end{vmatrix}}{\begin{vmatrix}3 & 1\\4 & -2\end{vmatrix}}, \dfrac{\begin{vmatrix}3 & -8\\4 & -14\end{vmatrix}}{\begin{vmatrix}3 & 1\\4 & -2\end{vmatrix}}$ *Written* 1. 72

3. -32 5. -18 7. 343 9. $(3, -4)$ 11. $\left(\frac{7}{4}, \frac{13}{4}\right)$
13. $\left(2, \frac{13}{8}\right)$ 15. $\left(-\frac{3}{7}, -\frac{3}{7}\right)$ 17. $\left(\frac{1}{2}, -2\right)$
19. $\left(-\frac{1}{3}, -6\right)$ 21. Division by zero is undefined.
23. x and y will equal some value divided by 0.

3-5 Page 91
Exploratory 1. yes 3. yes *Written*

1. 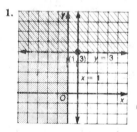 3.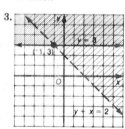

7. 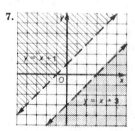 11.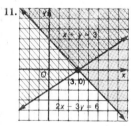

3-6 Page 94
Exploratory 1. 13 3. -4 5. -10 7. 3.9 9. 18
11. -33 13. 31 15. 0.6 17. max.: $f(4, 6) = 10$;
min.: $f(0, 0) = 0$ 19. max.: $f(5, 0) = 2\frac{1}{2}$; min.:
$f(0, 6) = -6$ 21. max.: $f(0, 0) = 0$; min.: $f(4, 6) =$

4-7 Page 132
Exploratory 1. $\begin{aligned}3x + y &= 13\\ 4x - 2y &= 24\end{aligned}$

3. $\begin{aligned}2x - 11y &= 3\\ x + 2y &= 9\end{aligned}$ 5. $\begin{aligned}x - 2y &= -8\\ 3x + y + 2z &= 9\\ 4x - 3y + 3z &= 1\end{aligned}$

7. $\begin{aligned}x + y + 2z &= 5\\ 3x - 6y + 4z &= -17\\ 4x - 5y - 2z &= 4\end{aligned}$ 9. $\begin{bmatrix}2 & -1\\3 & 2\end{bmatrix}\begin{bmatrix}x\\y\end{bmatrix} = \begin{bmatrix}11\\-1\end{bmatrix}$

11. $\begin{bmatrix}2 & 5\\3 & 4\end{bmatrix}\begin{bmatrix}x\\y\end{bmatrix} = \begin{bmatrix}1\\12\end{bmatrix}$ 13. $\begin{bmatrix}1 & 1 & -1\\2 & 3 & -4\\1 & -6 & 1\end{bmatrix}\begin{bmatrix}x\\y\\z\end{bmatrix} = \begin{bmatrix}2\\-1\\1\end{bmatrix}$

Written 1. $(5, -2)$ 3. $(7, 1)$ 5. $(-2, 3, 6)$ 7. $(5, 4, -2)$ 9. $(3, -5)$ 11. $(8, -3)$ 13. $(4, 1, 3)$ 15. $\left(\frac{3}{4}, \frac{1}{2}\right)$
17. $\left(\frac{1}{3}, 3, -5\right)$ 19. $\left(\frac{1}{3}, -\frac{1}{2}, \frac{2}{3}\right)$ 21. $\left(\frac{3}{4}, \frac{2}{3}\right)$
23. $\left(\frac{3}{2}, 4, -1\right)$ 25. $\left(-\frac{5}{3}, -\frac{5}{6}, \frac{5}{2}\right)$

4-8 Page 135
Exploratory 1. $r + b - 14 = 2m$ 3. $a + 2b - 80 = c$ 5. $a + b - 62 = c$ *Written* 1. 843
3. Streak 23; Dreamette 21; Cruiser 11 5. 12 cm, 14 cm, 19 cm 7. Mark 29, Laurie 26, Peggy 24
9. apples 27¢, bananas 19¢, oranges 14¢ 11. 491
13. 52, 61, 67

Chapter Review Page 139 1. $(-4, 2, 1)$ 3. 2
5. 7 7. $x = 6, y = -4, z = 3; 2x - 3y = 12, x + 2z = 6, -3y + 4z = 12$ 9. $x = \frac{6}{5}, y = -3, z = 2; 5x - 2y = 6, 5x + 3z = 6, -2y + 3z = 6$ 11. -50
13. $(2, -3, 4)$ 15. $(4, -3)$ 17. $\begin{bmatrix}12 & 3 & -6\\6 & -9 & 12\end{bmatrix}$
19. $\begin{bmatrix}10\\10\end{bmatrix}$ 21. $\frac{1}{11}\begin{bmatrix}1 & 2\\-4 & 3\end{bmatrix}$ 23. $-\frac{1}{8}\begin{bmatrix}10 & -6 & -6\\-6 & 2 & 2\\-7 & 5 & 1\end{bmatrix}$
25. $(3, -2, 2)$ 27. Alan 50, Jim 55, Les 52

CHAPTER 5 POLYNOMIALS

5-1 Page 147
Exploratory 1. yes, 7 3. no 5. yes, $\frac{11}{7}$ 7. no 9. 3
11. 9 13. 0 15. 5 *Written* 1. $8m$ 3. $5d^3$
5. $39x^2 - 3y^2$ 7. y^{12} 9. 2^7 11. 8^{14} 13. y^{10}
15. $81a^4$ 17. $20m^3k^5$ 19. $5625x^8y^{10}z^4$ 21. $\frac{16}{15}c^4d^2f$
23. $-162r^8s^8t^{17}$ 25. $2r^3k^2m^2$ 27. $9m^4n^3p^2$ 29. $-a^7b^3$
31. $x = 6$ 33. $x = 4$

5-2 Page 150
Exploratory 1. r^3 3. 1 5. $\frac{5}{y^3}$ 7. $\frac{1}{8}$ 9. y^4 11. 36
Written 1. $\frac{1}{m^5}$ 3. $3n^5$ 5. $2n^2$ 7. $\frac{y^7}{x^3}$ 9. $\frac{5}{b^3}$ 11. $\frac{1}{5b^2}$

13. $\frac{1}{3x^7}$ 15. $4b^2c^3$ 17. 2 19. $\frac{9}{t^5}$ 21. $\frac{d^2}{5c^3}$ 23. n^4m^2
25. 243 27. x^2 29. $\frac{1}{(x + 4)^4}$ 31. $\frac{(x + 3)^2}{5}$ 33. $\frac{1}{x^3y^2}$
35. $\frac{b^3x^4}{5^3y}$ 37. $2mn$ 39. $\frac{12}{m^2}$ 41. $-\frac{r^4s^9}{3}$ 43. $4r^{14}$
45. $\frac{1}{m} + m - \frac{1}{m^4}$ 47. 2 49. $\frac{-c^2}{c + 1}$

5-3 Page 152
Exploratory 1. 4 3. $\frac{729}{b^6}$ 5. 10,000 7. $\frac{1}{125}$ 9. 1
11. $\frac{64}{k^3}$ 13. 2.1×10^{-3} 15. 8.104×10^2 17. 9×10^9
19. 7.21×10^{-7} 21. 6,000 23. 0.00057
25. 3,210,000 27. 0.0427 *Written* 1. $\frac{b^7}{128}$ 3. $\frac{1}{xk}$
5. $\frac{4}{9y^4}$ 7. $\frac{4}{9}$ 9. $a^2 + 2ab + b^2$ 11. $\frac{32}{d^{15}f^6}$ 13. 29
15. $\frac{z^2}{xy}$ 17. $5.832 \times 10^9; 5{,}832{,}000{,}000$ 19. $5 \times 10^0;$
21. $8.6 \times 10^1; 86$ 23. $3.27 \times 10^{-4}; 0.000327$
25. $3.1 \times 10^7; 31{,}000{,}000$ 27. 2.592×10^{10} km/day
29. 1.9663×10^6 31. 15.4 cm 33. $\frac{y - 7}{y + 3}$

5-4 Page 156
Exploratory 1. 2 3. 8 5. 5 7. 3 9. 9
11. $(a + b)^2 = (a + b)(a + b) = a^2 + ab + ab + b^2 = a^2 + 2ab + b^2$ 13. $(a + b)(a - b) = a^2 - ab + ab - b^2 = a^2 - b^2$ *Written* 1. $16x + 2y$ 3. $-9x - y - 2z$ 5. $4m^2 + m + 1$ 7. $5x^2 + 1$ 9. $3a - b$
11. $r^2 - r + 6$ 13. $-3x^2 - 3x + 14$ 15. $7x^4 - 2x^3 + 7x^2 - 2x + 1$ 17. $m^7 + 3m^5 - 3m^4 + m^3 - 2m^2 - 18$
19. $4gf^3 - 4bhf$ 21. $15m^3n^3 - 30m^4n^3 + 15m^5n^6$
23. $-68b^5d^4 - 187b^6d^5 - 85b^4d^6$ 25. $a^4 + a + \frac{1}{a^2}$
27. $xy^3 + y + \frac{1}{x}$ 29. $m^2 - 2m - 35$ 31. $y^4 + y^3 + 5y^2 + 5y$ 33. $6x^2 + 31x + 35$ 35. $6x^2 - xy - 15y^2$
37. $m^2 + 8m + 16$ 39. $y^2 - 4y + 4$ 41. $y^2 - 25$
43. $x^2 - 6xy + 9y^2$ 45. $16m^2 - 24mn + 9n^2$
47. $1 + 8r + 16r^2$ 49. $16a^2 - 4b^2$ 51. $x^6 - y^2$
53. $2x^3 - 9x^2 - 7x + 24$ 55. $a^3 + b^3$ 57. $2t^3 + 9t^2 - 19t - 40$ 59. $p^3 + 4p^2 - 5p$ 61. $6x^3 - 7x^2 - 7x + 6$
63. $2a^3 - 5a^2b - 4ab^2 + 12b^3$ 65. $2k^3 - 11k^2 + 21k + 63$ 67. $z^3 + z^3r + z^2r^2 + zr + zr^2 + r^3$
69. $y^3 - 3y^2 - 16y + 48$ 71. $15r^4 - 6r^3 - 13r^2 - 2r + 10r^2d - 4rd - 12d - 6$

5-5 Page 161
Exploratory 1. $6(a + b)$ 3. $a(b + c)$
5. $(r + 3)(r - 3)$ 7. $(10 - m)(10 + m)$
9. $2(x^2 + 3y + 4b)$ 11. $3(a^2 + 2a + 3y)$
13. $(5a - b)(5a + b)$ 15. $5xy(x - 2y)$
17. $4m(2m + a + 4y)$ 19. $(x + 2)(x^2 - 2x + 4)$
21. $(r - 1)(r^2 + r + 1)$ *Written* 1. $(b - 12)(b + 12)$
3. $(1 + r)(1 - r + r^2)$ 5. $(2 - x)(4 + 2x + x^2)$
7. $3(d - 4)(d + 4)$ 9. $(3 + x)(9 - 3x + x^2)$
11. $(2 + x)(4 - 2x + x^2)$ 13. $(2a - 3)(2a + 3)$

15. $(3y - 8)(3y + 8)$ 17. $(2b - 3x)(4b^2 + 6bx + 9x^2)$
19. $ab(1 - a)(1 + a + a^2)$ 21. $(r^2 + s^2)(r - s)(r + s)$
23. $(4y - 1)(16y^2 + 4y + 1) \cdot$
$(y^4 - 5y^2 + 25)$ 27. $(1 - 2m^2)(1 + 2m^2 + 4m^4)$
29. $(a + b - m)(a + b + m)$

5-6   Page 164
Exploratory 1. $(y + 3)^2$ 3. $(k - 4)^2$ 5. $(a + 2)(a + 3)$
7. $(y + 3)(y + 7)$ 9. $(3b^2 + d)(c - 1)$
11. $(ab + 5d)(c - d)$ *Written* 1. $(a + 5)(a + 7)$
3. $(f - 9)^2$ 5. $(k + 6)^2$ 7. $(3y + 2)(y + 1)$
9. $(2z - 7)(2z - 3)$ 11. $(a + 2b)^2$ 13. $(p - 2b)^2$
15. $(2r - 5s)^2$ 17. $2(2k + 3)(k + 5)$
19. $4(h + 6)(h - 4)$ 21. $2y(y + 3)(y - 7)$
23. $(9d + 4)(2d - 3)$ 25. $(a^n - 8)(a^n + 8)$
27. $(m + n + b)(m + n - b)$

5-7   Page 167
Exploratory 1. $(y + 4k)(3y - 2)$ 3. $(a - c)(y - b)$
5. $(a - 2)(a + b)$ 7. $(2x^2 + 1)(x - 3)$
9. $\left(x + y - \frac{1}{2}\right)\left(x + y + \frac{1}{2}\right)$
11. $(m - k + 3)(m + k - 3)$
13. $(k - 3)(k + 3)(k + 4)$ 15. $(x - y)(x + y - 4)$
Written 1. $(3y - 2)(y + 4k)$ 3. $(a - c)(y - b)$
5. $(a - 2)(a + b)$ 7. $(2x^2 + 1)(x - 3)$
9. $(x + y - r)(x + y + r)$ 11. $(m - k + 3)(m + k - 3)$
13. $(k - 3)(k + 3)(k + 4)$ 15. $(x - y)(x + y - 4)$
17. $(a - b + 4)(a + b - 4)$ 19. $(2a - 1)(b + m)$
21. $(x + 3 - a)(x + 3 + a)$
23. $\left(a - \frac{1}{2} - y\right)\left(a - \frac{1}{2} + y\right)$ 25. $x(x - z)(x + y)$
27. $3(2x - 3)(3x + 1)$ 29. $(b - y - p)(b + y + p)$
31. $(b + m)(2a + b - m)$ 33. $(2a + 3)(4a^2 - 6a + 9)$
35. $3r(1 - 3r)(1 + 3r + 9r^2)$ 37. $(x + y)(x - y)^2$
39. $(x - 3)(x + 3)(x - 2)(x + 2)$ 41. $(r - p)(r + p)^2$
43. $(2x + 7y)(2a - 5b)$ 45. $(4a - 3)(2x - 3)$
47. $a(a - 2b)(a^2 - 10ab + 4b^2)$
49. $y(x + 2)(x - 4)(x - 1)$
51. $(2x + 3y + z)(2x + 3y - z)$

5-8   Page 171
Exploratory 1. $\frac{1}{7}$ 3. g^3 5. 1 7. $4a^2b^3$ 9. $3xy^3$
11. $-a^2b + a - \frac{2}{b}$ *Written* 1. $6p^3q + 4p + 5q^2$
3. $2k^2 - 3py + 4p^2y$ 5. $5r + \frac{23}{3}s + \frac{2s^2}{r}$ 7. $x - 15$
9. $3y - 1$ 11. $4a + 3 - \frac{2}{2a + 7}$ 13. $4y + 5 + \frac{3}{7y - 3}$
15. $a - 12$ 17. $a - 2b$ 19. $2z - 4$ 21. $-a - 10 +$
$\frac{44}{6 - a}$ 23. $8x - 44 + \frac{231}{x + 5}$ 25. $7m - 8 + \frac{3}{8m - 7}$
27. $2y^2 + 5y + 2$ 29. $3a^2 - 2a + 3$ 31. $m^2 +$
$m + 1$ 33. $y^2 - 6y + 9 - \frac{1}{y - 3}$ 35. $2a^2 - 3a - 2$
37. $m + 3$ 39. $x^2 - 2x + 8 - \frac{20}{x + 2}$ 41. $x^2 +$

$2x + 2$ 43. $a^2 - a - 1$ 45. yes 47. $a + 1, a - 1$
49. Both are 15.

5-9   Page 174
Exploratory 1. b 3. c *Written* 1. $2x^2 + x +$
$5 + \frac{6}{x - 2}$ 3. $2a^2 - a - 1 + \frac{4}{a + 1}$ 5. $x^3 + x - 1$
7. $6k^2 - k - 2$ 9. $2b^2 - 5b - 3$ 11. $y^3 - 11y^2 +$
$31y - 21$ 13. $2x^3 + x^2 + 3x - 1 + \frac{5}{x - 3}$ 15. $y^3 +$
$3y^2 - 16y + 55 - \frac{166}{y + 3}$ 17. $2x^3 + x^2 - 2x + \frac{3}{2x - 1}$
19. $2x^2 - 8x + 1 + \frac{5}{3x - 2}$ 21. $x^4 - 2x^3 + 4x^2 -$
$8x + 16$

Chapter Review   Page 178
1. y^{11} 3. x^6 5. $114a^4b^4$ 7. a^4 9. $\frac{n}{2}$ 11. 1 13. $\frac{x^2}{4}$
15. $\frac{3x^2}{2}$ 17. 0.0001592 19. $b^3 + 15b^2 - 3b - 2$
21. $4a^2 + 23a - 35$ 23. $y^3 + 4y^2 - 16y + 35$
25. $2m^3 + 15m^2 + 34m + 21$ 27. $(y - 5)(y + 5)$
29. $(m + 2)(m^2 - 2m + 4)$
31. $(2m - 3)(4m^2 + 6m + 9)$ 33. $(x - 2)(x - 5)$
35. $(3p - 5t)^2$ 37. $(5b + a)(b - 4a)$
39. $(7b - 5)(3b + 4)$ 41. $(x - 2y)(x + 1)$
43. $(a + b - 4)(a - b + 4)$
45. $2y^2 - 7y + 4 + \frac{3}{4y + 3}$ 47. Since the remainder
upon division is -20, $x + 1$ is not a factor of $2x^3 +$
$x^2 - 11x - 30$. 49. $2m^2 + 5m + 12 + \frac{49}{m - 4}$
51. Since the remainder upon division is 0, $2x + 1$ is a
factor of $2x^3 - 11x^2 + 12x + 9$.

CHAPTER 6   ROOTS

6-1   Page 183
Exploratory 1. 49 3. 27 5. 16 7. 169 9. $100,000$
11. -12 13. 2 15. $-|y|$ 17. -4 19. $4|a|b^2$
21. $|x + 3|$ 23. $2,601$ 25. 2.621 27. $148,877$
Written 1. -9 3. 15 5. 3 7. -1 9. 0.7
11. $11|n|$ 13. $9s^2$ 15. 24 17. $8|a|b^2$ 19. $-2bm$
21. $4a^2b$ 23. $|3p + q|$ 25. $z + a$ 27. $2m - 3$
29. $|x + 3|$ 31. $|3x + 1|$ 33. $|2x + 3y|$ 35. 9.110
37. 24.01 39. 2.008 41. $110,592$

6-2   Page 186
Exploratory 1. $2\sqrt{2}$ 3. $5|x|\sqrt{2}$ 5. $2\sqrt[3]{2}$ 7. $2\sqrt[4]{3}$
9. $|b|\sqrt{b}$ 11. $|a|\sqrt[4]{a}$ 13. $r\sqrt[5]{r^2}$ 15. $3\sqrt{5}$
17. $3\sqrt[4]{2}$ 19. $5 - \sqrt{15}$ *Written* 1. $15\sqrt{6}$
3. $2\sqrt[3]{3}$ 5. $9\sqrt{2}$ 7. $-4\sqrt[3]{3}$ 9. $33\sqrt{2}$ 11. $2\sqrt[4]{7}$
13. $48\sqrt{7}$ 15. 22 17. $3\sqrt{2} - 2\sqrt{3}$ 19. $7\sqrt{2} +$
$7\sqrt{3}$ 21. 14 23. $2ab^2\sqrt[3]{ab}$ 25. $5rp^2\sqrt{2r}$
27. $xy\sqrt[3]{3xy}$ 29. $3x^2z^2\sqrt{5}$ 31. $5mb^2\sqrt[4]{m}$
33. $6rs\sqrt[3]{4r^2s}$ 35. $6a^2b\sqrt[4]{4b}$ 37. $b\sqrt{b} + ab$

6-3   Page 188

Exploratory 1. $-\sqrt{7}$ 3. $-7\sqrt[4]{5}$ 5. $3\sqrt[3]{x}$ 7. $5\sqrt[5]{3}$
9. $3\sqrt{3}$ 11. 0 13. $17 + 7\sqrt{5}$ 15. $b^2 - 2b\sqrt{2a} + 2a$ 17. 34 19. $19 + 8\sqrt{3}$ 21. $m^2 + 2m\sqrt{y} + y$
Written 1. $8\sqrt{2} - 8$ 3. $5\sqrt{5} - 10\sqrt{2}$ 5. $-7\sqrt{7}$
7. $11\sqrt[3]{5b}$ 9. $3\sqrt[3]{2a}$ 11. $7\sqrt[3]{2} + 6\sqrt[3]{150}$ 13. $14\sqrt{6} + 2\sqrt[3]{3}$ 15. $5\sqrt{2}$ 17. $15\sqrt[6]{2}$ 19. $(1 + |x|)\sqrt[4]{x^2}$
21. $3|yz|\sqrt[4]{z^2}$ 23. $|z| + z^2 + z^4$ 25. $17 + 8\sqrt{2}$
27. $25 - 5\sqrt{2} + 5\sqrt{6} - 2\sqrt{3}$ 29. $49 - 11p$
31. $1 + \sqrt{15}$ 33. $4 - 2\sqrt{3}$ 35. $3a\sqrt{5} - 3\sqrt{ab} + \sqrt{30ab} - b\sqrt{6}$ 37. $16\sqrt[3]{3} - 12$ 39. $x^3 - 3$
41. $8 + k$ 43. $(a + 2\sqrt{5})^2$ 45. $r(r - \sqrt{2})(r + \sqrt{2})$

6-4   Page 191

Exploratory 1. $\sqrt{2}$ 3. $\sqrt[3]{3y}$ 5. $\frac{\sqrt{5}}{2}$ 7. $\frac{\sqrt[3]{5}}{2}$ 9. $\frac{\sqrt{3}}{\sqrt{3}}$
11. $\frac{\sqrt{a}}{\sqrt{a}}$ 13. $\frac{\sqrt[4]{2}}{\sqrt[3]{2}}$ 15. $\frac{\sqrt[6]{3}}{\sqrt[3]{3}}$ 17. $1 - \sqrt{3}$ 19. $1 + \sqrt{2}$
21. $3 - \sqrt{5}$ 23. $5 - 3\sqrt{3}$ 25. $2\sqrt{2} + 3$ 27. $\sqrt{2} + 5\sqrt{3}$ *Written* 1. $\sqrt{5}$ 3. $\sqrt{7}$ 5. $\sqrt[3]{9}$ 7. $\frac{\sqrt{5}}{2}$
9. $\frac{2\sqrt{2}}{3}$ 11. $\frac{\sqrt[6]{5}}{2}$ 13. $\frac{3\sqrt[3]{2}}{5}$ 15. $\frac{\sqrt[4]{5}}{2}$ 17. $\frac{\sqrt{3}}{3}$
19. $\frac{\sqrt{2m}}{m}$ 21. $\frac{\sqrt{15a}}{6a}$ 23. $\frac{\sqrt[3]{15p}}{3p}$ 25. $\frac{\sqrt[4]{54}}{3}$ 27. $\frac{3 - \sqrt{5}}{4}$
29. $\frac{3 + \sqrt{5}}{2}$ 31. $\frac{5 + 4\sqrt{2}}{7}$ 33. $\frac{19 - 11\sqrt{3}}{-2}$
35. $\frac{\sqrt{x^2 - 1}}{x - 1}$ 37. $\frac{16\sqrt{10}}{5}$ 39. 2.72 seconds 41. 7 inches

6-5   Page 196

Exploratory 1. 8 3. $\frac{1}{2}$ 5. $\frac{1}{2}$ 7. 32 9. 4 11. 3
13. 36 15. 6 17. $\sqrt{6}$ 19. $\sqrt[3]{9}$ *Written* 1. $21^{\frac{1}{2}}$
3. $32^{\frac{1}{6}}$ 5. $y^{\frac{1}{3}}$ 7. $2mr^2$ 9. $27^{\frac{1}{4}}$ 11. $n^{\frac{2}{3}}$ 13. 2
15. $\sqrt[6]{6}$ 17. $ab^2\sqrt{ab}$ 19. $2x^2\sqrt[3]{4x}$ 21. $\sqrt[3]{5p^2q}$
23. $r^2\sqrt[4]{r^2q^3}$ 25. $\sqrt[6]{x^2y^3}$ 27. $25\sqrt[6]{b^2c}$ 29. $\sqrt{3}$
31. $\sqrt{2}$ 33. 11 35. 12 37. $\frac{7}{4}$ 39. 36 41. 0.25
43. 0.3 45. $2\sqrt[12]{2^{11}}$ 47. $3\sqrt[6]{3}$

6-6   Page 198

Exploratory 1. $\frac{3^{\frac{1}{2}}}{3^{\frac{3}{2}}}$ 3. $\frac{4^{\frac{1}{2}}}{4^{\frac{2}{2}}}$ 5. $\frac{y^{\frac{1}{3}}}{y^{\frac{2}{3}}}$ 7. $\frac{p^{\frac{1}{2}}}{p^{\frac{2}{2}}}$ 9. $\frac{m^{\frac{1}{2}} - p}{m^{\frac{1}{2}} - p}$
11. $\frac{t^{\frac{2}{3}} - s^{\frac{1}{2}}}{t^{\frac{3}{3}} - s^{\frac{2}{2}}}$ *Written* 1. $2 \cdot 3^{\frac{1}{2}}$ 3. 2 5. $\frac{y^{\frac{3}{3}}}{y}$ 7. $\frac{p^{\frac{3}{2}}}{p^2}$
9. $\frac{m^{\frac{3}{2}} - mp + m^{\frac{1}{2}}p - p^2}{m - p^2}$ 11. $\frac{2(t^{\frac{2}{3}} - s^{\frac{1}{2}})}{t^3 - s}$ 13. $\frac{y^3}{y}$ 15. $\frac{b^{\frac{3}{4}}}{b}$
17. $3 \cdot 5^{\frac{1}{3}}$ 19. $\frac{rm^{\frac{1}{2}}b^{\frac{1}{2}}}{b^2}$ 21. $\frac{b^2 + 3}{b}$ 23. $3x^{\frac{5}{3}} + 4x^{\frac{8}{3}}$
25. $r^{\frac{1}{6}}$ 27. $\frac{r^2 - 2r^{\frac{3}{2}}}{r - 4}$ 29. $\frac{a - 2a^{\frac{1}{2}}b^{\frac{1}{2}} + b}{a - b}$ 31. $\frac{r^{\frac{1}{2}}s}{1 + r}$

33. $\frac{1}{b - 1}$ 35. $3xy^3$ 37. $\frac{25x^{21}}{y^8}$ 39. $\frac{3x^{\frac{1}{3}}y - 2x}{xy}$
41. $-\frac{16}{9} \cdot 2^{\frac{1}{6}}$ 43. $\frac{x^{\frac{2}{3}} + x^{\frac{1}{3}}y^{\frac{1}{3}} + y^{\frac{2}{3}}}{x - y}$ 45. $\frac{a^{\frac{4}{3}} + a^{\frac{2}{3}}b^{\frac{2}{3}} + b^{\frac{4}{3}}}{a^2 - b^2}$

6-7   Page 201

Exploratory 1. 4 3. 64 5. 1 7. 29 9. $\frac{7}{2}(\sqrt{3} + 1)$
11. $1 + \sqrt{3}$ *Written* 1. $-\sqrt{3}$ 3. $\frac{12 - 4\sqrt{2}}{7}$
5. $\frac{-15 - 5\sqrt{3}}{6}$ 7. $\frac{26 + 13\sqrt{11}}{-7}$ 9. 54 11. 7 13. $40\frac{1}{2}$
15. 23 17. 3 19. 23 21. -13 23. 8 25. no solution 27. 5 29. $\frac{541}{100}$ 31. no solution
33. no solution 35. 1 37. no solution 39. $\pm \sqrt{y^2 - s^2}$ if $y \geq s$ 41. $\frac{2mM}{r^3}$ if $r \neq 0$ 43. $\frac{T}{4v^2 - 1}$ if $4v^2 - 1 \neq 0$

6-8   Page 203

Exploratory 1. $6i$ 3. $4i\sqrt{2}$ 5. -3 7. $5i$ 9. $6i$
11. -1 *Written* 1. $9i$ 3. $5i\sqrt{2}$ 5. $\frac{2}{3}i$ 7. $\frac{i\sqrt{3}}{3}$
9. i 11. $-i$ 13. $-i$ 15. -1 17. -4 19. $-7\sqrt{2}$
21. -3 23. $-3i\sqrt{3}$ 25. 24 27. $-216i$ 29. $-18i$
31. $\pm 4i$ 33. $\pm 13i$ 35. $\pm i\sqrt{3}$ 37. $\pm 2i$ 39. $\pm 5i$
41. $\pm i\frac{\sqrt{5}}{2}$

6-9   Page 205

Exploratory 1. $8 + 11i$ 3. 3 5. 10 7. $20 + 12i$
9. $-10 + 10i$ 11. $14 + 5i$ 13. $x = 5, y = -6$
15. $x = 7, y = 2$ 17. $x = 3, y = 0$ *Written*
1. $7 + 7i$ 3. $6 + 4i$ 5. $2 - i\sqrt{7} - i\sqrt{2}$ 7. $8 - 15i$
9. $5 - 3i\sqrt{3}$ 11. $-21 - 2i$ 13. $13 - 13i$
15. $32 - 24i$ 17. $37 + 2i\sqrt{2}$ 19. $5 + 12i$ 21. 3
23. 7 25. $20 + 15i$ 27. $148 - 222i$ 29. $109 - 37i$
31. $x = 2, y = 3$ 33. $x = -1, y = -3$ 35. $x = 3, y = 1$ 37. $-a - bi$

6-10   Page 208

Exploratory 1. $2 - i$ 3. $5 + 4i$ 5. $-4i$ 7. $5i$
9. 6 11. $5 + 6i$ 13. $(3 + 2i)\frac{3 - 2i}{13} = \frac{9 - 4i^2}{13} = \frac{9 + 4}{13} = \frac{13}{13} = 1$ 15. $(6 + 8i)\frac{3 - 4i}{50} = \frac{18 - 24i + 24i - 32i^2}{50} = \frac{18 + 32}{50} = \frac{50}{50} = 1$ *Written*
1. 58 3. 85 5. 13 7. 4 9. $\frac{5 + i}{2}$ 11. $\frac{5 + i}{13}$
13. $\frac{5 - 3i}{2}$ 15. $\frac{6 + 5i}{3}$ 17. $\frac{12 + 3i}{17}$ 19. $\frac{4\sqrt{3} - 8i}{7}$
21. $\frac{1 + 4i\sqrt{3}}{7}$ 23. $\frac{2 - 3i\sqrt{5}}{7}$ 25. $\frac{16 + 63i}{50}$ 27. $\frac{-1 - i}{2}$
29. $\frac{3 - i}{10}$ 31. $\frac{7 + 3i}{58}$ 33. $\frac{1 - 3i}{4}$ 35. $3 + 2i$

Chapter Review   Page 212

1. $7|a|$ **3.** $2xy^2$ **5.** 3.391 **7.** 941.192 **9.** $2\sqrt[3]{6a^2}$
11. $-45\sqrt{30}$ **13.** $5\sqrt{2}+2\sqrt{5}$ **15.** $2\sqrt[3]{6}+3$
17. $2xy^2\sqrt[3]{9}$ **19.** $60+6\sqrt{5}+10\sqrt{2}+\sqrt{10}$
21. $\sqrt{5}$ **23.** $\sqrt[3]{4}$ **25.** 36 **27.** 0.04 **29.** $|x|y^{\frac{3}{4}}$
31. $2w^2r$ **33.** $\sqrt[4]{3}$ **35.** $\dfrac{z^{\frac{2}{3}}}{z}$ **37.** $\dfrac{z^{\frac{2}{3}}}{z-1}$ **39.** 1 **41.** 4
43. $-i$ **45.** $-30i$ **47.** $6, 16i, 73$ **49.** $\dfrac{-3-7i}{2}$

CHAPTER 7   QUADRATIC EQUATIONS

7-1   Page 218

Exploratory   **1.** yes   **3.** yes   **5.** no   **7.** no   **9.** yes
11. $3, -7$ **13.** $1, 8$ **15.** $0, -4$ **17.** $-\dfrac{5}{2}, 1$
Written   **1.** $-2, -4$ **3.** $4, 5$ **5.** $-5, 2$ **7.** -2
9. $0, -3$ **11.** $4, -1$ **13.** $-6, 5$
15. $-\dfrac{3}{2}, -1$ **17.** $-\dfrac{3}{2}, 3$ **19.** $0, \dfrac{5}{3}$ **21.** $-\dfrac{3}{2}, -\dfrac{2}{3}$
23. $-\dfrac{1}{4}, 3$ **25.** $-8, 5$ **27.** $\dfrac{2}{3}, 4$ **29.** $-\dfrac{1}{4}, \dfrac{5}{3}$
31. $\dfrac{5}{6}, -\dfrac{3}{2}$ **33.** $-\dfrac{3}{4}, 4$ **35.** $\dfrac{3}{2}$ **37.** $\dfrac{11}{4}, -\dfrac{11}{4}$
39. $0, 3, -3$ **41.** $0, -\dfrac{6}{7}, \dfrac{2}{5}$ **43.** $0, \dfrac{3}{5}$

7-2   Page 221

Exploratory   **1.** yes   **3.** no   **5.** yes   **7.** 9   **9.** 100
11. 36   **13.** $\dfrac{9}{4}$ **15.** $\dfrac{121}{4}$ **17.** $\dfrac{1}{4}$ *Written*   **1.** 9   **3.** $\dfrac{1}{16}$
5. $\dfrac{1}{4}$ **7.** $\dfrac{9}{4}$ **9.** $\dfrac{49}{4}$ **11.** 625   **13.** $6, -4$ **15.** $-11, 8$
17. $3, 5$ **19.** $-10, 2$ **21.** $3, 4$ **23.** $6, -14$ **25.** $-8, 5$
27. $4 \pm \sqrt{2}$ **29.** $\dfrac{7 \pm \sqrt{29}}{2}$ **31.** $\dfrac{5 \pm \sqrt{65}}{2}$ **33.** $-\dfrac{1}{3}, -2$
35. $-\dfrac{3}{2}, \dfrac{1}{3}$ **37.** $\dfrac{3}{2}, -7$ **39.** $\dfrac{5}{3}, -3$ **41.** $2 \pm \dfrac{2}{3}\sqrt{6}$
43. $\dfrac{-a \pm \sqrt{a^2-4a}}{2}$

7-3   Page 225

Exploratory   **1.** $5, -3, 7$ **3.** $1, 2, -1$ **5.** $3, -2, 7$
Written   **1.** $6, -5$ **3.** $-5, 3$ **5.** $6, 4$ **7.** $4, 1$ **9.** $4,$
$-\dfrac{5}{3}$ **11.** $\dfrac{5}{3}, -\dfrac{3}{2}$ **13.** $\dfrac{1}{7}, -\dfrac{5}{2}$ **15.** $\dfrac{1}{4}, -\dfrac{2}{5}$ **17.** $\dfrac{-4 \pm i\sqrt{14}}{6}$
19. $\dfrac{5 \pm i\sqrt{7}}{4}$ **21.** $\dfrac{-1 \pm i\sqrt{5}}{2}$ **23.** $\dfrac{1 \pm \sqrt{57}}{14}$ **25.** $0, \dfrac{24}{7}$
27. $\dfrac{3 \pm i\sqrt{15}}{3}$ **29.** $1 \pm i\sqrt{3}, -2$ **31.** $-2 \pm 2i\sqrt{3}, 4$
33. $\dfrac{-1 \pm i\sqrt{3}}{2}, 1$

7-4   Page 227

Exploratory   **1.** 33   **3.** 1   **5.** 0   **7.** 81   **9.** 1   **11.** -16
Written   **1.** 144; 2 real; rational; $7, -5$ **3.** 0; 1 real;
rational; 2   **5.** 12; 2 real; irrational; $2 \pm \sqrt{3}$ **7.** 16; 2
real; rational; $-\dfrac{3}{2}, -\dfrac{1}{2}$ **9.** 73; 2 real; irrational;

$\dfrac{-11 \pm \sqrt{73}}{6}$ **11.** -16; 2 imaginary; $1 \pm 2i$ **13.** 89; 2
real; irrational; $\dfrac{-9 \pm \sqrt{89}}{2}$ **15.** 36; 2 real; rational; 0, 6
17. -144; 2 imaginary; $\dfrac{2 \pm 3i}{2}$ **19.** 289; 2 real;
rational; $6, \dfrac{1}{3}$ **21.** -3; 2 imaginary; $\dfrac{1 \pm i\sqrt{3}}{2}$ **23.** 21;
2 real; irrational; $\dfrac{-1 \pm \sqrt{21}}{2}$

7-5   Page 230

Exploratory   **1.** $-7, -4$ **3.** $3, 5$ **5.** $-\dfrac{7}{3}, -3$ **7.** $\dfrac{3}{5}, 0$
9. $0, -\dfrac{3}{5}$ **11.** $\dfrac{2}{3}, \dfrac{11}{3}$ **13.** $\dfrac{1}{4}, \dfrac{1}{3}$ **15.** $\dfrac{1}{15}, -\dfrac{4}{15}$
Written   **1.** $-6; -7; -7, 1$ **3.** $\dfrac{5}{2}; -\dfrac{3}{2}; 3, -\dfrac{1}{2}$ **5.** $3; 1;$
$\dfrac{3 \pm \sqrt{5}}{2}$ **7.** $-\dfrac{21}{4}; -\dfrac{9}{2}, \dfrac{3}{4}, -6$ **9.** $3; \dfrac{5}{2}; \dfrac{3 \pm i}{2}$ **11.** $0; -\dfrac{1}{9};$
$\pm\dfrac{1}{3}$ **13.** $\dfrac{7}{2}; -\dfrac{15}{2}, 5, -\dfrac{3}{2}$ **15.** $\dfrac{2}{15}, -\dfrac{8}{15}, \dfrac{4}{5}, -\dfrac{2}{3}$ **17.** $-25;$
$156; -13, -12$ **19.** $\dfrac{7}{3}; 1; \dfrac{7 \pm \sqrt{13}}{6}$ **21.** $-\dfrac{19}{12}; \dfrac{1}{3}; -\dfrac{1}{4},$
$-\dfrac{4}{3}$ **23.** $x^2 - 3x - 10 = 0$ **25.** $x^2 - x - 6 = 0$
27. $x^2 + 13x + 36 = 0$ **29.** $3x^2 - 17x + 10 = 0$
31. $4x^2 + 13x - 12 = 0$ **33.** $25x^2 - 4 = 0$
35. $6x^2 - 5x + 1 = 0$ **37.** $x^2 + 4\sqrt{2}x - 10 = 0$
39. $x^2 - 10x + 23 = 0$ **41.** $x^2 + 36 = 0$
43. $x^2 - 10x + 28 = 0$ **45.** $8x^2 - 20x + 17 = 0$
47. 4   **49.** -5 **51.** 35

7-6   Page 233

Exploratory   **1.** 26, 27 or $-27, -26$ **3.** 37, 39 or
$-39, -37$ **5.** 15, 17   **7.** 11, 12 or $-12, -11$ **9.** 10
meters   **11.** 18 feet by 24 feet   **13.** 10, 11 or $-11,$
-10 **15.** 8 or -9 **17.** $\dfrac{2}{3}$ or $\dfrac{1}{3}$ **19.** 3 or $\dfrac{1}{3}$ **21.** 2
meters   **23.** $\dfrac{6}{5}$ or $-\dfrac{5}{6}$ **25.** 6 cm by 4 cm   **27.** 7 or 3
29. 0 or 7   **31.** 4 meters

7-7   Page 237

Exploratory   **1.** yes   **3.** no   **5.** yes   **7.** 8   **9.** 25
11. $\dfrac{1}{5}$ **13.** 4   **15.** $\dfrac{1}{13}$ *Written*   **1.** $1(x^{\frac{2}{3}})^2 - 7(x^{\frac{2}{3}}) +$
$12 = 0$ **3.** $1(x^{\frac{1}{2}})^2 - 10(x^{\frac{1}{2}}) + 25 = 0$ **5.** $1(x^{\frac{1}{4}})^2 -$
$8(x^{\frac{1}{4}}) + 15 = 0$ **7.** $1(r^{\frac{1}{3}})^2 - 5(r^{\frac{1}{3}}) + 6 = 0$
9. $1(a^{-\frac{1}{3}})^2 - 11(a^{-\frac{1}{3}}) + 28 = 0$ **11.** $\pm 2, \pm 1$
13. $\pm 4, \pm 3$ **15.** $\pm\sqrt{5}, \pm i\sqrt{5}$ **17.** $\pm\sqrt{3}, \pm i\sqrt{3}$
19. $0, 5, -5$ **21.** $\pm i\sqrt{3}, \pm i\sqrt{6}$ **23.** $\pm 2, \pm\sqrt{2}$
25. 64, 1   **27.** 1   **29.** $0, 4, -2 \pm 2i\sqrt{3}$ **31.** $2, -1,$
$-1 \pm i\sqrt{3}, \dfrac{1 \pm i\sqrt{3}}{2}$ **33.** $2, \sqrt[3]{2}, -1 \pm i\sqrt{3}$
35. 4096, 16   **37.** 8, 1000   **39.** 25, 36   **41.** 8
43. $\dfrac{1}{343}, \dfrac{1}{27}$ **45.** $\dfrac{1}{9}, \dfrac{1}{4}$

1. $-\dfrac{3}{2}, \dfrac{1}{3}$ **3.** $-\dfrac{3}{2}, -1$ **5.** $-\dfrac{6}{5}, \dfrac{1}{3}$ **7.** 49 **9.** 15, 5

11. $-\dfrac{7}{2}, 3$ **13.** $2, \dfrac{5}{3}$ **15.** $\dfrac{\pm 3\sqrt{2}}{2}$ **17.** 1200; 2 real;

irrational; $\dfrac{10 \pm 5\sqrt{3}}{2}$ **19.** 0; 1 real; rational; 4 **21.** 12;

-45; 15, -3 **23.** 0; $-\dfrac{11}{3}$; $\dfrac{\pm\sqrt{33}}{3}$ **25.** $x^2 + 2x -$

$24 = 0$ **27.** $x^2 - 10x + 34 = 0$ **29.** 32 or -12
31. 3.5 feet (24.5 is not a reasonable answer.)
33. $\pm 3, \pm\sqrt{3}$ **35.** no solutions **37.** 64, 125

CHAPTER 8   QUADRATIC RELATIONS AND FUNCTIONS

8-1   Page 244

Exploratory **1.** yes **3.** no **5.** yes **7.** yes **9.** no
11. x^2; $3x$; $-\dfrac{1}{4}$ **13.** x^2; $-3x$; $-\dfrac{1}{4}$ **15.** $3a^2$; 0; -2
17. x^2; $3x$; 0 **19.** x^2; $6x$; 9   *Written* **1.** $f(x) = x^2 -$
$4x + 4$ **3.** $f(x) = 9x^2 + 12x + 4$ **5.** $f(x) = 32x^2 +$
$16x + 2$ **7.** $f(x) = 3x^2 - 24x + 42$ **9.** $f(x) = 45x^2 -$
$60x + 24$ **11.** $f(x) = 20x^2 - 20x + 13$ **13.** $A = \pi r^2$
15. $x =$ one of the numbers; product $= 40x - x^2$
17. $x =$ the lesser number; product $= 64x + x^2$
19. $x =$ length of rectangle; area $= 10x - x^2$
21. $x =$ first integer; $x(x + 1) = (x + 1)^2 - 9$
23. $p =$ number of $1.00 price increases; $I = 2400 +$
$140p - 20p^2$ **25.** $x =$ length of side; area $=$
$120x - 2x^2$

8-2   Page 248

Exploratory **1.** -144; -64; -1; -1; -64; -144
Written

1.

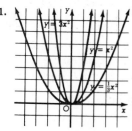

7. $(0, 0)$; $x = 0$; up **9.** $(0, 0)$;
$x = 0$; down **11.** $(0, 0)$; $x = 0$; down **13.** $(0, 0)$;
$x = 0$; down **15.** $(0, 0)$; $x = 0$; up **17.** $\dfrac{1}{2}$ **19.** 1

21. -2 **23.** -4 **25.** 3 **27.** $\dfrac{2}{3}$ **29.** $f(x) = -\dfrac{1}{4}x^2$

8-3   Page 251

Exploratory **1.** $(0, 0)$; $x = 0$; up **3.** $(3, 0)$; $x = 3$; up
5. $(-4, 0)$; $x = -4$; down **7.** $(-3, 0)$; $x = -3$; up
9. $(-2, 0)$; $x = -2$; down **11.** $(2, 0)$; $x = 2$; up
Written **1.** $f(x) = (x - 1)^2$; $(1, 0)$; $x = 1$; up

3. $f(x) = \dfrac{2}{5}(x + 2)^2$; $(-2, 0)$; $x = -2$; up
5. $f(x) = 6(x + 5)^2$; $(-5, 0)$; $x = -5$; up **7.** $f(x) =$
$-9(x - 1)^2$; $(1, 0)$; $x = 1$; down **9.** $f(x) = 4\left(x - \dfrac{11}{2}\right)^2$;
$\left(\dfrac{11}{2}, 0\right)$; $x = \dfrac{11}{2}$; up **11.** $f(x) = 5(x - 3)^2$; $(3, 0)$; $x = 3$;
up **13.** $f(x) = 8\left(x + \dfrac{3}{2}\right)^2$; $\left(-\dfrac{3}{2}, 0\right)$; $x = -\dfrac{3}{2}$; up
15. $f(x) = 9\left(x - \dfrac{10}{3}\right)^2$; $\left(\dfrac{10}{3}, 0\right)$; $x = \dfrac{10}{3}$; up

17.

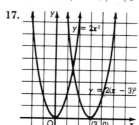

23. $f(x) = (x - 3)^2$

25. $f(x) = -\dfrac{1}{4}\left(x + \dfrac{3}{4}\right)^2$

31. $x = 0$; $f(x) = \dfrac{1}{8}x^2$

33. $x = -2$; $f(x) = (x + 2)^2$ **35.** $x = -4$; $f(x) =$
$3(x + 4)^2$

8-4   Page 255

Exploratory **1.** $(0, 0)$; $x = 0$; up **3.** $(8, 0)$; $x = 8$; up
5. $(0, 6)$; $x = 0$; down **7.** $(-3, -1)$; $x = -3$; up
9. $\left(1, \dfrac{1}{3}\right)$; $x = 1$; up **11.** $\left(-2, -\dfrac{4}{3}\right)$; $x = -2$; down
Written

7.

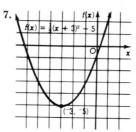

11.

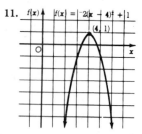

8-5   Page 257

Exploratory **1.** $40 + 10x$ **3.** income $= (40 +$
$10x)(50{,}000 - 5000x)$ **5.** 70¢ **7.** $x(300 - 2x) - (20x$
$+ 1000)$ or $-2x^2 + 280x - 1000$ *Written* **1.** -18,
18 **3.** $\dfrac{37}{2}, \dfrac{37}{2}$ **5.** $-10, 10$ **7.** 10 cm by 10 cm; 100 cm^2
9. length $= 60$ m; width $= 30$ m **11.** $11.50 **13.** 300
ft; 2.5 sec **15.** length $= 300$ m; width $= 200$ m
17. 18 cm **19.** $3.50

8-6   Page 261

Exploratory **1.** $y = (x + 2)^2$ **3.** $y = (x + 4)^2 + 1$
5. $y = 3(x - 4)^2 - 44$ **7.** $y = \left(x + \dfrac{3}{2}\right)^2 - \dfrac{13}{4}$ **9.** $y =$
$2\left(x + \dfrac{3}{2}\right)^2 - \dfrac{19}{2}$

Written 7.

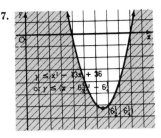

$x \le x^2 - 13x + 36$
or $y \le \left(x - 6\frac{1}{2}\right)^2 - 6\frac{1}{4}$

$\left(6\frac{1}{2}, 6\frac{1}{4}\right)$

8-7 Page 264

Exploratory 1. one > 0 and one < 0 3. both > 0 or both < 0 5. both ≥ 0 or both ≤ 0 7. one ≤ 0 and one ≥ 0 9. both ≥ 0 or both ≤ 0 **Written**
1. $\{x \mid x > 2 \text{ or } x < -3\}$ 3. $\{p \mid p \ge 4 \text{ or } p \le -6\}$
5. $\left\{b \mid -\frac{3}{2} < b < 2\right\}$ 7. $\{x \mid 0 \le x \le 4\}$
9. $\{t \mid -6 \le t \le 6\}$ 11. $\{r \mid -9 \le r \le -3\}$
13. $\left\{c \mid -\frac{1}{2} < c < 3\right\}$ 15. all reals
17. $\left\{t \mid \frac{-1 - \sqrt{10}}{2} < t < \frac{-1 + \sqrt{10}}{2}\right\}$
19. $\{x \mid -4 < x < 1 \text{ or } x > 3\}$
21. $\{x \mid x \le -4 \text{ or } -2 \le x \le 8\}$
23. $\{x \mid x \le -3 \text{ or } -2 \le x \le 1 \text{ or } x \ge 2\}$

Chapter Review **Page 266**
1. $x^2, 2x, 5$ 3. 0, 0, 16 5. $f(x) = 3x^2 + 12x + 5$
7. $f(x) = -2x^2 + 12x - 9$ 13. $\frac{1}{12}$ 15. $\frac{1}{4}$ 17. (3, 0);
$x = 3$; up 19. (4, 0); $x = 4$; up 21. (−8, 0); $x = -8$; up 23. (2, −3); $x = 2$; up 25. (−1, −2); $x = -1$; down 27. (1, 7); $x = 1$; up 29. 32 and 32
33. $\{x \mid -2 < x < 4\}$

CHAPTER 9 CONICS

9-1 Page 273

Exploratory 1. 2 3. 9 5. 11 7. 16 9. 31.1
11. $22\frac{7}{10}$ **Written** 1. $2\sqrt{53}$ 3. $\sqrt{58}$ 5. $\sqrt{53}$
7. $\frac{\sqrt{4594}}{15}$ 9. $\frac{\sqrt{5}}{10}$ 11. $\sqrt{16.85}$ 13. 1 15. $5\sqrt{3}$
17. 3 or 11 19. 7.1 or 13.1 21. $\left(\frac{3}{2}, -\frac{5}{2}\right)$
23. $\left(\frac{2}{3}, -\frac{3}{4}\right)$ 25. $\frac{3 + \sqrt{2}}{2}, \frac{3 - \sqrt{2}}{2}$ 27. $2\sqrt{106}$ and $2\sqrt{146}$ 29. $AB = \sqrt{4 + 16}$ or $\sqrt{20}$; $AC = \sqrt{16 + 4}$ or $\sqrt{20}$; Thus, $\triangle ABC$ is isosceles.
31. midpoint of hypotenuse $= \left(\frac{4 + 0}{2}, \frac{1 + 7}{2}\right) = (2, 4)$

  distance from (2, 4) to $D = \sqrt{4 + 9} = \sqrt{13}$
  distance from (2, 4) to $E = \sqrt{4 + 9} = \sqrt{13}$
  distance from (2, 4) to $F = \sqrt{4 + 9} = \sqrt{13}$
35. (−4, 14)

9-2 Page 276

Exploratory 1. 4 3. 16 5. $\frac{9}{4}$ 7. $\frac{49}{4}$ 9. $y = \frac{1}{10}x^2$
11. $y = (x - 3)^2 + 24$ 13. $y = 3(x - 4)^2 + 2$
15. $x = \frac{1}{6}y^2$ 17. $x = (y + 4)^2 + 4$ 19. $x = \frac{1}{4}(y - 1)^2 - \frac{13}{4}$ **Written** 1. (0, 0); $x = 0$; $\left(0, \frac{3}{2}\right)$; $y = -\frac{3}{2}$; up; 6 3. (−2, 3); $x = -2$; $\left(-2, 3\frac{1}{4}\right)$; $y = 2\frac{3}{4}$; up; 1 5. (8, −1); $x = 8$; $\left(8, -\frac{7}{8}\right)$; $y = -\frac{9}{8}$; up; $\frac{1}{2}$
7. (0, 1); $x = 0$; $\left(0, \frac{5}{4}\right)$; $y = \frac{3}{4}$; up; 1 9. (2, −3); $y = -3$; (3, −3); $x = 1$; right; 4 11. (3, 24); $x = 3$; $\left(3, 24\frac{1}{4}\right)$; $y = 23\frac{3}{4}$; up; 1 13. (−24, 7); $y = 7$; $\left(-23\frac{3}{4}, 7\right)$; $x = -24\frac{1}{4}$; right; 1 15. $\left(-\frac{13}{4}, 1\right)$; $y = 1$; $\left(-\frac{9}{4}, 1\right)$; $y = -\frac{17}{4}$; right; 4 17. (4, 2); $x = 4$; $\left(4, 2\frac{1}{12}\right)$; $y = 1\frac{11}{12}$; up; $\frac{1}{3}$ 19. $y = -\frac{1}{4}(x - 2)^2 + 5$
21. $y = -\frac{1}{8}(x - 8)^2 + 2$ 23. $y = \frac{1}{16}(x - 5)^2 + 1$
25. $x = \frac{1}{10}(y + 1)^2 + \frac{1}{2}$ 27. $x = -\frac{1}{2}(y - 4)^2 + \frac{1}{2}$
29. $x = -\frac{1}{8}(y + 1)^2 + 5$ 31. $y = -\frac{1}{6}(x + 7)^2 + 4$

9-3 Page 279

Exploratory 1. circle 3. parabola 5. circle 7. (0, 0); 4 9. (2, 0); 3 11. (10, −10); 10 13. $\left(-4, \frac{1}{2}\right)$; $\sqrt{6}$
15. (−5, 2); $\frac{\sqrt{3}}{2}$ **Written** 1. (2, 0); 3 3. (0, 8); 8
5. (0, 0); 8 7. (2, 5); 4 9. (−8, 3); 5 11. (−1, −9); 6
13. (6, 8); 4 15. (−4, 3); 5 17. (2, 0); $\sqrt{13}$
19. $\left(-\frac{3}{2}, -1\right)$; $\frac{\sqrt{141}}{6}$ 21. $\left(-\frac{9}{2}, 5\right)$; 7 23. (−1, −2); $\sqrt{14}$ 25. (−1, 0); $\sqrt{11}$ 27. $(x - 6)^2 + (y - 2)^2 = 25$ 29. $x^2 + (y - 3)^2 = 4$ 31. $(x + 6)^2 + (y - 2)^2 = \frac{1}{16}$ 33. $(x - 1)^2 + (y - 5)^2 = 26$
35. $(x - 2)^2 + (y - 2)^2 = 9$ 37. $(x + 3)^2 + (y - 8)^2 = 64$

9-4 Page 284

Exploratory 1. (0, 0); H 3. (0, 0); V 5. (0, 5); H
7. (2, −5); H 9. (−2, 3); V 11. $(\pm\sqrt{15}, 0)$
13. $(0, \pm\sqrt{26})$ 15. (1, 0), (−7, 0) **Written**
1. (0, 0); (0, $\pm\sqrt{21}$); 10, 4 3. (0, 0); (±4, 0); 10, 6
5. (0, 0); ($\pm\sqrt{7}$, 0); 8, 6 7. (0, 0); ($\pm\sqrt{5}$, 0); 6, 4
9. (0, 0); ($\pm3\sqrt{5}$, 0); 18, 12 11. (0, 0); (0, $\pm\sqrt{6}$); 6, $2\sqrt{3}$ 13. (−2, −3); (−2, $-3 \pm 2\sqrt{5}$); $4\sqrt{10}$, $4\sqrt{5}$
15. (−2, 3); (−2 $\pm \sqrt{3}$, 3); $2\sqrt{5}$, $2\sqrt{2}$ 17. (2, 3); (2 $\pm \sqrt{7}$, 3); 8, 6 19. (2, 2); (4, 2), (0, 2); $2\sqrt{7}$, $2\sqrt{3}$

21. $(-1, 3)$; $(2, 3)$, $(-4, 3)$; $10, 8$ **23.** $\dfrac{x^2}{169} + \dfrac{y^2}{25} = 1$

25. $\dfrac{(x + 2)^2}{16} + \dfrac{(y - 3)^2}{36} = 1$ **27.** $\dfrac{(x - 1)^2}{25} + \dfrac{(y - 4)^2}{9} = 1$

9-5   Page 290

Exploratory **1.** ellipse **3.** hyperbola **5.** hyperbola
7. ellipse   *Written* **1.** $(\pm 3, 0)$; $(\pm \sqrt{34}, 0)$; $\pm \dfrac{5}{3}$

3. $(\pm 6, 0)$; $(\pm \sqrt{37}, 0)$; $\pm \dfrac{1}{6}$ **5.** $(0, \pm 9)$; $(0, \pm \sqrt{106})$;

$\pm \dfrac{9}{5}$ **7.** $(\pm 2, 0)$; $(\pm \sqrt{13}, 0)$; $\pm \dfrac{3}{2}$ **9.** $(\pm 9, 0)$;

$(\pm \sqrt{117}, 0)$; $\pm \dfrac{2}{3}$ **11.** $(\pm 3, 0)$; $(\pm 5, 0)$; $\pm \dfrac{4}{3}$

13. $(\pm 2, 0)$; $(\pm \sqrt{29}, 0)$; $\pm \dfrac{5}{2}$ **15.** $(\pm \sqrt{2}, 0)$; $(\pm \sqrt{3}, 0)$;

$\pm \dfrac{\sqrt{2}}{2}$ **17.** $(0, \pm 6)$; $(0, \pm 3\sqrt{5})$; ± 2 **19.** $(0, -3)$,

$(-12, -3)$, $(-6 \pm 3\sqrt{5}, -3)$; $\pm \dfrac{1}{2}$ **21.** $(-2, 0)$,

$(-2, 8)$; $(-2, -1)$, $(-2, 9)$; $\pm \dfrac{4}{3}$ **23.** $(4 \pm 2\sqrt{5}, -2)$;

$(4 \pm 3\sqrt{5}, -2)$; $\pm \dfrac{\sqrt{5}}{2}$ **25.** $(1, -3 \pm 2\sqrt{6})$;

$(1, -3 \pm 4\sqrt{2})$; $\pm \sqrt{3}$ **27.** $\dfrac{x^2}{1} - \dfrac{y^2}{16} = 1$

29. $\dfrac{(y - 2)^2}{36} - \dfrac{(x + 2)^2}{64} = 1$ **31.** $2, 1, \dfrac{1}{2}, \dfrac{1}{4}, -2, -\dfrac{1}{2}, -\dfrac{1}{4}$

33. $\{y \mid y \text{ is real}, y \neq 0\}$ **35.** $\dfrac{(x - 1)^2}{9} - \dfrac{(y + 2)^2}{25} = 1$

9-6   Page 293

Exploratory **1.** circle **3.** ellipse **5.** parabola
7. hyperbola   *Written* **1.** $y = \dfrac{1}{8}x^2$; parabola

3. $x^2 + y^2 = 27$; circle **5.** $\dfrac{x^2}{4} + \dfrac{(y + 1)^2}{3} = 1$; ellipse

7. $\dfrac{y^2}{16} - \dfrac{x^2}{8} = 1$; hyperbola **9.** $x^2 + (y - 4)^2 = 5$;

circle **11.** $y = -1\left(x - \dfrac{1}{2}\right)^2 + \dfrac{9}{4}$; parabola

13. $\dfrac{(x - 3)^2}{25} + \dfrac{(y - 1)^2}{9} = 1$; ellipse **15.** $\dfrac{(y + 4)^2}{2} -$

$\dfrac{(x + 1)^2}{6} = 1$; hyperbola **17.** $y = -3x, y = 3x$,

intersecting lines **19.** $y = 0, y = 1$, parallel lines

9-7   Page 296

Written **1.** $(2, \pm 2\sqrt{3})$ **3.** $(4, 12)$, $(-1, -3)$
5. $(3, 0)$, $(-5, -4)$ **7.** $(0, -1)$, $(-3, 2)$ **9.** $(\pm 5.2, 6)$
11. no solutions **13.** no solutions **15.** $(-2, 0)$, $(2, 4)$
17. $(3, 3)$, $(-1, -1)$ **19.** $(3, 7)$, $(8, 4)$ **21.** $(\pm 1, 5)$,
$(\pm 1, -5)$ **23.** $(\pm 2, \sqrt{3})$, $(\pm 2, -\sqrt{3})$ **25.** no
solutions **27.** no solutions **29.** $(\pm 8, 0)$

9-8   Page 300

Written **1.** $(2, \pm 2\sqrt{3})$ **3.** $(2, 2)$, $(-2, -2)$ **5.** $(3, 0)$,
$(-5, -4)$ **7.** $(-3, 2)$, $(0, -1)$ **9.** $(\pm 3\sqrt{3}, 6)$ **11.** no
solutions **13.** no solutions **15.** $(-2, 0)$, $(2, 4)$

17. $(6, 9)$, $(2, 1)$ **19.** $(3, 7)$, $(8, 4)$ **21.** $(1, \pm 5)$,
$(-1, \pm 5)$ **23.** $(2, \pm \sqrt{3})$, $(-2, \pm \sqrt{3})$ **25.** no
solutions **27.** no solutions **47.** $(0, \sqrt{2})$, $(-2, -2)$

Chapter Review   Page 304

1. $2\sqrt{53}$ **3.** $\sqrt{16.85}$ **5.** $\left(1, \dfrac{3}{2}\right)$ **7.** $(0.25, 0.5)$ **9.** $(0,$
$0)$; $x = 0$; $(0, 1)$; $y = -1$; up; 4 **11.** $(4, 8)$; $y = 8$; $(3,$
$8)$; $x = 5$; left; 4 **13.** $(3, -7)$; 9 **15.** $(0, 0)$;
$(0, \pm 2\sqrt{2})$; 8, $4\sqrt{2}$ **17.** $(0, 0)$; $(\pm \sqrt{7}, 0)$; 8, 6

19. $(1, -6 \pm 2\sqrt{5})$; $(1, -6 \pm 3\sqrt{5})$; $\pm \dfrac{2\sqrt{5}}{5}$

21. parabola **23.** ellipse **25.** $(-1.6, 2.6)$, $(2.6, -1.6)$
27. $(-2, 0)$, $(2, 4)$

CHAPTER 10   POLYNOMIAL FUNCTIONS

10-1   Page 308

Exploratory **1.** no **3.** no **5.** no **7.** yes **9.** no
11. yes   *Written* **1.** 4 **3.** 1 **5.** -4 **7.** $-\dfrac{11}{2}$
9. $\dfrac{19}{3}$ **11.** -5 **13.** -6 **15.** 28 **17.** 2

19. 13 **21.** 144 **23.** 35 **25.** -12 **27.** 74 **29.** $5x +$
$5h - 10$ **31.** $x^2 + 2hx + h^2 - 7x - 7h + 4$ **33.** x^3
$+ 3hx^2 + 3h^2x + h^3 + 4x + 4h$ **35.** $x^3 + 3hx^2 +$
$3h^2x + h^3 - 4x^2 - 8hx - 4h^2$ **37.** $9x + 6$ **39.** $3x^3 -$
$9x^2 + 9x - 3$ **41.** $5x^2 - 10x + \dfrac{5}{2}$ **43.** $-5x - 12$

45. $-x^2 + x + 2$ **47.** $-\dfrac{4}{5}x^3 - \dfrac{77}{10}x^2 - \dfrac{51}{5}x - \dfrac{19}{10}$

49. $\dfrac{(x + 2)^2}{6}$ **51.** $\dfrac{2(x + 2)^2}{3(x - 2)^2}$

10-2   Page 312

Exploratory **1.** $x^2 - 3x + 1 = (x - 1)(x - 2) - 1$
3. $x^3 - 8x^2 + 2x - 1 = (x^2 - 9x + 11)(x + 1) - 12$
5. $x^5 + x^4 + 2x - 1 = (x^4 + 3x^3 + 6x^2 + 12x + 26) \cdot$
$(x - 2) + 51$ **7.** $x^5 + 32 = (x^4 - 2x^3 + 4x^2 - 8x +$
$16)(x + 2) + 0$ *Written* **1.** $2x^3 + 8x^2 - 3x - 1 =$
$(2x^2 + 12x + 21)(x - 2) + 41$ **3.** $x^4 - 16 = (x^3 +$
$2x^2 + 4x + 8)(x - 2) + 0$ **5.** $4x^4 + 3x^3 - 2x^2 + x +$
$1 = (4x^3 + 7x^2 + 5x + 6)(x - 1) + 7$ **7.** $3x^3 + 2x^2 -$
$4x - 1 = \left(3x^2 + \dfrac{1}{2}x - \dfrac{17}{4}\right)\left(x + \dfrac{1}{2}\right) + \dfrac{9}{8}$ **9.** $37, 7$

11. $-46, -31$ **13.** $314, 79$ **15.** $461, -94$ **17.** $x + 2,$
$x - 2$

19. $x + 1, x + 2$ **21.** $x - 1, x + 2$ **23.** $x - 2, x^2 +$
$2x + 4$ **25.** $x - 1, x + 1, x^2 + 1$ **27.** -17 **29.** $\dfrac{25}{2}$

31. 5

10-3   Page 318

Exploratory **1.** $\pm 1, \pm 2$ **3.** $\pm 1, \pm 2, \pm 3, \pm 6$ **5.** $\pm 1,$
$\pm 2, \pm 4, \pm 8$ **7.** ± 1 **9.** $\pm 1, \pm 2, \pm 4, \pm 5, \pm 10, \pm 20$
11. $\pm 1, \pm \dfrac{1}{2}, \pm \dfrac{1}{3}, \pm \dfrac{1}{6}$ **13.** $\pm 1, \pm 2, \pm 4, \pm \dfrac{1}{3}, \pm \dfrac{2}{3}, \pm \dfrac{4}{3}$

15. $3, -5, -\frac{5}{2}$ **17.** $3, 3, -2, \frac{1}{2}, \frac{2}{3}$ **19.** $\frac{2}{3}, 5, -1$

Written **1.** $-2, -4, 7$ **3.** $3, 3, -\frac{1}{2}$ **5.** 3 **7.** $-2, -4$

9. $1, -1$ **11.** $\frac{1}{2}, \frac{1}{4}$ **13.** $-1, -2, 5$ **15.** -6 **17.** $0,$

$-\frac{1}{3}, \frac{1}{2}, -\frac{1}{2}$ **19.** $2, -2$ **21.** height $= 2$ m, width $= 4$

m, length $= 9$ m

10-4 Page 321
Exploratory **1.** 3 or 1; 1 **3.** 4, 2, or 0; 0 **5.** 2 or 0; 2
or 0 **7.** 5, 3, or 1; 1 **9.** 1; 3 or 1 *Written* **1.** 2 or
0; 2 or 0; 4, 2, or 0 **3.** 1; 0; 2 **5.** 2 or 0; 1; 4 or 2
7. 2 or 0; 1; 4 or 2 **9.** 3 or 1; 1; 12 or 10 **11.** $3 + i,$
$3 - i, 4$ **13.** $1 + 2i, 1 - 2i, -4$ **15.** $-2 + 3i,$
$-2 - 3i, -2$ **17.** $x^3 - 4x^2 + 6x - 4$ **19.** $x^3 - 3x^2$
$+ 4x - 12$ **21.** $x^4 + 2x^3 + 7x^2 + 30x + 50$ **23.** It
has no positive real roots and only one negative real
root. Thus, there must be two complex roots.

10-5 Page 324
Written **1.** -1.3 **3.** 0.6 **5.** $1.6, -1.3, -2.4$ **7.** 1.4
9. -0.8 **11.** $0.1, 2.5$ **13.** $1, 0.8, -1.4$ **15.** -1
17. -2.4

10-6 Page 328
Written

3.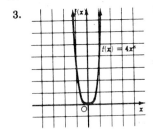

7.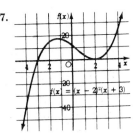

11.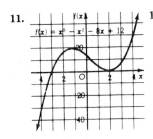

17.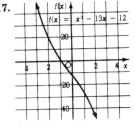

10-7 Page 331
Exploratory **1.** $-1, -5, -3$ **3.** $1, 9, 1$ **5.** $4, 4, 2$
7. $10, 10, -6$ **9.** $30, -34, 2$ **11.** $4, 9, 3$ *Written*
1. $4, 4$ **3.** $63, 27$ **5.** $129, 360$ **7.** $2x - 5, 2x - 2$
9. $4x^2 - 4x + 4, 2x^2 + 5$ **11.** $-x^4 + 2x^2 - 9, x^4 +$
$16x^2 + 63$ **13.** $-1, -1$ **15.** $50, 2$ **17.** $-7, 9$ **19.** 9
21. 8 **23.** 12 **25.** -9 **27.** $\frac{9}{4}$ **29.** $6 + 4\sqrt{2}$ **31.** $9x^2$

33. $9x^2 - 18x + 9$ **35.** $\{(3, 6), (4, 4), (6, 6), (7, -8)\}$;
does not exist **37.** $\{(1, -8), (-1, -2), (5, -8), (9, -3)\}$;
does not exist

10-8 Page 334
Exploratory **1.** $\{(1, 3), (4, 2), (5, 1)\}$; yes **3.** $\{(8, 3),$
$(-2, 4), (-3, 5)\}$; yes **5.** $\{(1, -3), (4, 2), (8, 7)\}$; yes
Written **1.** $y = \frac{1}{2}x$ **3.** $f^{-1}(x) = -\frac{1}{6}x - \frac{5}{6}$
5. $x = 3$ **7.** $f^{-1}(x) = 0$ **9.** $y = \pm\sqrt{x}$ **21.** yes

11. 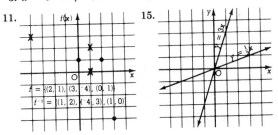 **15.**

23. yes **25.** no **27.** yes **29.** yes **31.** yes **33.** no
35. 3 **37.** a **39.** $a + 1$

Chapter Review   Page 338
1. -13 **3.** $m^2 + 7m + 3$ **5.** 2 **7.** -94 **9.** $(x + 2) \cdot$
$(x - 1)(x + 1)$ **11.** $(x + 2)(x - 1)^2$ **13.** $1, 1, \frac{3}{2}, \frac{3}{2}$

15. $5, \frac{1}{3}, \frac{3}{2}$ **17.** 3 or 1; 1; 2 or 0 **19.** 1; 0; 2 **21.** $2 +$
$i, 2 - i, 3$ **23.** $-1, 0.7$ **25.** 1.6 **29.** $324, 1249, 4x^4$
31. $1, 4, |2|x - 3| + 1|$ **35.** no

CHAPTER 11
RATIONAL POLYNOMIAL EXPRESSIONS

11-1   Page 344
Exploratory **1.** $24; \frac{1}{3}$ **3.** $3; \frac{11}{101}$ **5.** $13x; \frac{1}{3x}$ **7.** $2x^2;$

$\frac{17}{21x^3}$ **9.** $2a; \frac{19a}{21b}$ **11.** $3x^2y^2; -\frac{y^3}{6x^3}$ **13.** $4x^5y; -2xy^2$

15. $x^4y^2; 16y^2$ **17.** $m + 5; \frac{1}{2}$ *Written* **1.** $\frac{6}{7}$

3. $\frac{x^2}{4yz}$ **5.** $3b$ **7.** $-\frac{yz}{12x}$ **9.** $\frac{9abc^2}{2}$ **11.** $-\frac{7}{54c}$ **13.** cd^2x

15. $\frac{5x^3}{3y^2}$ **17.** $\frac{x}{y + 2}$ **19.** $\frac{x - 3}{2}$ **21.** 4 **23.** x

25. $a + b; \frac{1}{a - b}$ **27.** $8 - x; \frac{x^2}{2}$ **29.** $y + 3; \frac{y - 3}{y + 3}$

31. $x + 4; \frac{2x}{x - 3}$ **33.** $x + 4; \frac{x - 5}{x + 3}$ **35.** $a + 1; \frac{a + 1}{2a + 1}$

37. $-y(x + y)$ **39.** -1 **41.** $\frac{5(a - b)}{2}$ **43.** $\frac{12}{x - 1}$

45. -1 **47.** $\frac{(3m - 1)(2 - m)}{30}$ **49.** $\frac{x(x + 4)}{2y(x - 3)}$ **51.** $\frac{x - 2}{x + 2}$

53. $(x + 1)^2(x - 5)$ **55.** $(a - b)^2$ **57.** $\dfrac{w - 3}{w - 4}$

11-2   Page 347

Exploratory **1.** $\dfrac{8}{3}$ **3.** $\dfrac{9y}{7x}$ **5.** $\dfrac{1}{16}$ **7.** $\dfrac{2}{x + y}$ **9.** $\dfrac{(x - 3)^2}{(x + 4)^2}$

11. $x - y$ **13.** $\dfrac{3}{8} \cdot \dfrac{2}{1}$ **15.** $\dfrac{a^2}{b^2} \cdot \dfrac{a^2}{b^2}$ **17.** $\dfrac{3m}{m + 1} \cdot \dfrac{1}{m - 2}$

Written **1.** $\dfrac{a^2}{14}$ **3.** $\dfrac{ab}{x + y}$ **5.** $\dfrac{a^2 - b^2}{a^2 + ab + b^2}$

7. $\dfrac{x^2 + 2x - 3}{3x + 3}$ **9.** $-\dfrac{y + w}{y}$ **11.** $\dfrac{a}{2}$ **13.** $-\dfrac{x}{3}$ **15.** $\dfrac{c}{2b}$

17. $\dfrac{ac^4d}{b}$ **19.** $b(x + y)$ **21.** $\dfrac{1}{2}$ **23.** $3(a + b)$

25. $\dfrac{2(x - 1)}{3(x + 2)}$ **27.** $\dfrac{2(a + 5)}{(a - 2)(a + 2)}$ **29.** $2(x + y)$

31. $\dfrac{a(a + 2)}{a + 1}$ **33.** $\dfrac{2y(y - 2)}{3(y + 2)}$ **35.** -1 **37.** 1

39. $\dfrac{x(x + 2)}{3(x + 3)(x - 1)}$

11-3   Page 352

Exploratory **1.** 756 **3.** 2000 **5.** $14a^2b$ **7.** $x(x - 2) \cdot$
$(x + 2)$ **9.** $(x + 1)^2(x - 3)(x + 3)$ **11.** $xy(x - 8) \cdot$
$(y - 8)$ **Written** **1.** $\dfrac{31}{12a}$ **3.** $\dfrac{5 + 7a}{a}$ **5.** $\dfrac{x}{y - x}$

7. $\dfrac{-12x + 21xy - 4y}{6x^2y}$ **9.** $\dfrac{3(x - 1)}{2(x - 3)(x + 3)}$

11. $\dfrac{5a - 13}{(a - 2)(a - 3)}$ **13.** $\dfrac{3(2x + 11)}{(x - 5)(x + 5)}$ **15.** $\dfrac{7x + 38}{2(x - 7)(x + 4)}$

17. $\dfrac{7y + 11}{(y - 5)(y + 1)(y + 3)}$ **19.** 0 **21.** $\dfrac{2x^2 + x - 4}{(x - 1)(x - 2)}$

23. $\dfrac{110a - 423}{90a}$ **25.** $\dfrac{13}{y - 8}$ **27.** $\dfrac{y + 4}{y - 8}$ **29.** $\dfrac{x(x - 9)}{(x + 3)(x - 3)}$

31. $\dfrac{6}{y - 4}$ **33.** $\dfrac{2x^2 + 7x - 2}{(x + 1)^2}$ **35.** $\dfrac{3(3m^2 - 14m + 27)}{(m + 3)(m - 3)^2}$

37. $\dfrac{3}{10}$ **39.** y **41.** $\dfrac{2(x + 5)}{x^2(2x + 1)}$ **43.** $\dfrac{a + 7}{a + 2}$

45. $\dfrac{m^2 + 6m + 20}{4m - 1}$ **47.** $\dfrac{2x^2 - x + 2}{4}$ **49.** $\dfrac{y^2 - 3y - 7}{2y - 6}$

51. $\dfrac{n - 1}{n + 2}$ **53.** $\dfrac{2}{2x - 5}$ **55.** $\dfrac{3x^2 + 7x + 2}{(x + 5)(x - 5)(x - 2)}$

57. $\dfrac{7x^3 + 16x^2 + 24x + 10}{x(2x - 1)(2x + 1)(x + 2)}$

11-4   Page 355

Exploratory **1.** $2x; x \neq 0$ **3.** $10y; y \neq 0$ **5.** $x^2; x \neq 0$
7. $(x - 3)(x - 2); x \neq 3, x \neq 2$ **9.** $6(m - 5); m \neq 5$
11. $7(2 + m); m \neq -2$ **Written** **1.** $0; 3$

3. none; $-3, \dfrac{1}{6}$ **5.** none; 2 **7.** none; 4 **9.** none; 5

11. none; 54 **13.** $0; -6, 1$ **15.** $\pm 1, -2; 0$

17. $0; 2, 6$ **19.** $1; 3$ **21.** $1; 10$ **23.** $0; 5$ **25.** $0, 1; \dfrac{2}{3}$

27. $\pm\dfrac{2}{3}; -2$ **29.** $\pm 4; -6, -2$ **31.** $3; 11$ **33.** $0; \dfrac{5}{3}$

35. $0, -2; -17$ **37.** $1, 3, -2; \dfrac{1}{7}$ **39.** $\pm 3; \dfrac{3}{2}$

41. $\pm 5; -6, 2$ **43.** $2, -4; \dfrac{7}{3}$

11-5   Page 359

Written **1.** $2\dfrac{2}{9}$ hours **3.** $25\dfrac{1}{5}$ hours **5.** 20 days

7. $\dfrac{7}{13}$ **9.** 19 **11.** 3 km/h **13.** 52 km/h **15.** $3\dfrac{3}{4}$

17. $\$1800$ at 6% **19.** $1\dfrac{2}{7}$ hours

21. $5:27$ plus 16 seconds

11-6   Page 362

Exploratory **1.** $x = 1, y = 0$ **3.** $x = 3, y = 0$
5. $x = 6, y = 0$ **7.** $x = 1, x = -5, y = 0$ **9.** $x = 1,$
$x = 4, y = 0$ **Written** Equations for asymptotes
are given. **1.** $x = 4, y = 1$ **3.** $x = -1, y = 1$
5. $x = 2, y = 1$ **7.** $x = 3, y = 0$ **9.** $x = 6, y = 0$
11. $x = 1, y = 4$ **13.** $x = 4, y = 0$ **15.** $x = -3,$
$x = 1, y = 0$ **17.** $x = -2, x = 2, y = 0$

11-7   Page 365

Exploratory **1.** direct; $\dfrac{1}{4}$ **3.** direct; -4 **5.** direct; 5

7. direct; $\dfrac{4}{3}$ **9.** inverse; 9 **11.** direct; 4 **Written**

1. 36 **3.** 1.125 **5.** $\dfrac{84}{11}$ **7.** $\dfrac{121}{10}$ **9.** 24 **11.** 118.5 km

13. $11\dfrac{2}{3}$ kg **15.** $3\dfrac{23}{55}$ hours **17.** 42 pounds **19.** $\$6880$

21. $2\dfrac{2}{3}$ hours **23.** $\dfrac{343}{81}$

Chapter Review   **Page 367**

1. $\dfrac{5a}{16}$ **3.** $\dfrac{2y^2}{y - 3}$ **5.** $\dfrac{ay - 2a - 3y + 6}{a - x}$ **7.** a^2

9. $(y + 3)(y - 6)$ **11.** $\dfrac{5y(x + y)}{2x}$ **13.** $\dfrac{28a - 27b}{12ab}$

15. $\dfrac{7(x - 4)}{x - 5}$ **17.** $\dfrac{18}{y - 2}$ **19.** $\dfrac{25b + 16}{24b}$ **21.** $\dfrac{a(a + 2)}{3a^2 + 1}$

23. 31 **25.** 0 **27.** $8\dfrac{4}{7}$ hours **33.** $-\dfrac{5}{3}$

CHAPTER 12   EXPONENTIAL AND LOGARITHMIC FUNCTIONS

12-1   Page 374

Exploratory **1.** 1.6 **3.** 0.8 **5.** 2.6 **7.** $2^{4\sqrt{5}}$ **9.** 2^3
11. 3 **13.** -5 **15.** -2 **Written** **1.** 64 **3.** $5^{4\sqrt{3}}$
5. $2^{3\sqrt{7}}$ **7.** $2^{3\sqrt{3} + 4\sqrt{5}}$ **9.** $y^{4\sqrt{5}}$ **11.** y^9 **13.** m^2p^2
15. $x^{2\sqrt{3}} + 2x^{\sqrt{3}}y^{\sqrt{2}} + y^{2\sqrt{2}}$ **17.** 3 **19.** -2 **21.** 2
23. -22 **25.** -7 **27.** -9 **33.** The graphs are
reflections over the y-axis.

12-2   Page 376

Exploratory **1.** $\log_3 27 = 3$ **3.** $\log_2\left(\dfrac{1}{8}\right) = -3$

5. $\log_{10} 1000 = 3$ **7.** $4^3 = 64$ **9.** $9^{\frac{3}{2}} = 27$ **11.** $10^{-1} = $
0.1 **13.** 2 **15.** -3 **Written** **1.** $\log_3 81 = 4$
3. $\log_5 125 = 3$ **5.** $\log_4\left(\dfrac{1}{16}\right) = -2$ **7.** $\log_2\left(\dfrac{1}{16}\right) = $
-4 **9.** $\log_3\sqrt{3} = \dfrac{1}{2}$ **11.** $\log_{36} 216 = \dfrac{3}{2}$ **13.** $2^5 = 32$

15. $11^2 = 121$ **17.** $5^0 = 1$ **19.** $\left(\dfrac{1}{2}\right)^{-4} = 16$

21. $10^{-1} = \dfrac{1}{10}$ **23.** $\left(\dfrac{1}{3}\right)^{-4} = 81$ **25.** 3 **27.** 2

29. -3 **31.** $\dfrac{3}{2}$ **33.** -3 **35.** 7 **37.** 36 **39.** -4

41. 3 **43.** $\dfrac{1}{25}$ **45.** $\dfrac{1}{2}$ **47.** 3 **49.** 64 **51.** $\dfrac{1}{16}$ **53.** 6

55. 7

12-3   Page 378

Exploratory **1.** 2 **3.** 2 **5.** 4 **7.** 5 **9.** 4 **11.** 1
Written **1.** 3 **3.** 7 **5.** 5 **7.** 7 **9.** 1 **11.** 2.5
13. ± 8 **15.** 1 or -10
21. $\log_4 4 + \log_4 16 \overset{?}{=} \log_4 64$
$\qquad\qquad 1 + 2 \overset{?}{=} 3$
$\qquad\qquad 3 = 3$
23. $\log_2 32 - \log_2 4 \overset{?}{=} \log_2 8$
$\qquad\qquad 5 - 2 = 3$
25. $\log_3 27 \overset{?}{=} 3\log_3 3$ **27.** $\dfrac{1}{2}\log_3 81 \overset{?}{=} \log_3 9$
$\qquad 3 \overset{?}{=} 3(1)$ $\qquad\qquad \dfrac{1}{2}(4) \overset{?}{=} 2$
$\qquad 3 = 3$ $\qquad\qquad 2 = 2$
29. $\log_2 8 \cdot \log_8 2 \overset{?}{=} 1$ **31.** $\log_{10}[\log_3(\log_4 64)] \overset{?}{=} 0$
$\qquad 3 \cdot \dfrac{1}{3} \overset{?}{=} 1$ $\qquad\qquad \log_{10}(\log_3 3) \overset{?}{=} 0$
$\qquad\qquad 1 = 1$ $\qquad\qquad \log_{10} 1 \overset{?}{=} 0$
$\qquad\qquad\qquad\qquad\qquad 0 = 0$
33. $\log_3 81 \overset{?}{=} \dfrac{4}{3}\log_2 8$ **35.** 6, -5 **37.** 9
$\qquad 4 \overset{?}{=} \dfrac{4}{3}(3)$
$\qquad 4 = 4$

12-4   Page 384

Exploratory **1.** 21 **3.** 3 **5.** 72 **7.** $\log_3 x + \log_3 y$
9. $4\log_2 m + \log_2 y$ **11.** $\dfrac{1}{2}\log_b x - \log_b p$ **13.** $\log_3 5 +$
$\dfrac{1}{3}\log_3 a$ **15.** $\log_2 a + \dfrac{1}{2}\log_2 x$ **17.** 2 *Written*
1. 1.3222 **3.** 1.4313 **5.** 1.4771 **7.** 2.3222 **9.** 2.8451
11. 0.5229 **13.** 2 **15.** 24 **17.** 343 **19.** 6 **21.** 14
23. 3 **25.** 2 **27.** 6 **29.** 3 **31.** 5 **33.** $\dfrac{1}{3}$ **35.** $\dfrac{y}{3} + 1$
37. $\dfrac{x^4}{2}$

12-5   Page 386

Exploratory **1.** 2 **3.** 1.6839 **5.** 0.6839 $- 3$
7. 483,000 **9.** 1; 1.6767 **11.** 0; 0.6637 **13.** -1;
0.3201 $- 1$ **15.** 1; 1.7404 **17.** 1; 35.70 **19.** -2;
0.0688 **21.** 4; 39,400 **23.** -1; 0.618 *Written*
1. 1.7649 **3.** 0.9814 **5.** 3.8704 **7.** 0.3243 $- 3$
9. 0.5855 $- 2$ **11.** 4.7973 **13.** 12.3 **15.** 9080
17. 0.09 **19.** 0.159 **21.** 521,000 **23.** 0.00463

12-6   Page 390

Exploratory **1.** 7.41, 7.42 **3.** 0.000746, 0.000747
5. 4.17, 4.18 **7.** 9,520, 9,530 *Written* **1.** 0.7220

3. 1.4398 **5.** 0.2905 $- 1$ **7.** 0.4980 $- 3$ **9.** 3.698
11. 2.5177 **13.** 0.6748 $- 2$ **15.** 0.6996 **17.** 1.9035
19. 6.3320 **21.** 0.2193 $- 1$ **23.** 3,553 **25.** 601.4
27. 0.004143 **29.** 0.002754 **31.** 16,493 **33.** 0.004762
35. 0.07563 **37.** 394,273 **39.** 2,612 **41.** 0.0003705

12-7   Page 395

Exploratory **1.** $\dfrac{\log 55}{\log 3}$ **3.** $\dfrac{\log 74}{2\log 7}$ **5.** $\dfrac{\log 144}{\log 6}$ **7.** $\dfrac{\log 12}{\log 3}$

9. $\dfrac{-1}{\log 2}$ **11.** $\dfrac{\frac{1}{2}\log 13}{\log 3}$ or $\dfrac{\log 13}{2\log 3}$ *Written* **1.** 3.6479
3. 1.1059 **5.** 2.7736 **7.** 2.2619 **9.** -3.3222
11. 1.1674 **13.** 1.771 **15.** 2.230 **17.** 1.338
19. 2.387 **21.** 3.9839 **23.** 3.8394 **25.** 4.8363
27. 2.8446 **29.** 38.619 **31.** 3.1501 **33.** -2.1507
35. 2.4527 **37.** 3.2598 **39.** 2.9169 **41.** 794.8771
43. 18.4 years **45.** no

12-8   Page 399

Exploratory **1.** 1.3863 **3.** 13.7 years *Written*
1. -0.0770 **3.** 2.9407 hours **5.** 3.0778 years
7. 28.7823 years; 57.5646 years **9.** 8.155%
11. 12.5429 hours **13.** 229.07 days **15.** 9%

Chapter Review   Page 403

1. -1 **3.** $-\dfrac{7}{4}$ **5.** 81 **7.** $\log_7 343 = 3$ **9.** $\log_4 1 = 0$

11. $4^3 = 64$ **13.** $6^{-2} = \dfrac{1}{36}$ **15.** 3 **17.** $\dfrac{1}{4}$ **19.** 7

21. 3 **23.** 3 **25.** 7 **27.** 8 **29.** $-4, 3$ **31.** 0.243
33. 0.6021 $- 3$ **35.** 48 **37.** 3 **39.** 14 **41.** 4
43. 0.4232 **45.** 0.8904 $- 2$ **47.** 5.45 **49.** 0.0276
51. 0.5334 **53.** 0.6139 $- 2$ **55.** 2.165 **57.** 11.82
59. 5.7286 **61.** 1.7426 **63.** 4.2448 **65.** 69.23
67. 6.7471 years

CHAPTER 13   SEQUENCES AND SERIES

13-1   Page 409

Exploratory **1.** 4, 7, 10, 13, 16 **3.** 16, 14, 12, 10, 8
5. $\dfrac{3}{4}, \dfrac{1}{2}, \dfrac{1}{4}, 0, -\dfrac{1}{4}$ **7.** 2.3, 3.9, 5.5, 7.1, 8.7 **9.** $-\dfrac{1}{3}, -1,$
$-\dfrac{5}{3}, -\dfrac{7}{3}, -3$ **11.** $-4.2, -5.5, -6.8, -8.1, -9.4$
13. 17, 21, 25, 29 **15.** $-13, -18, -23, -28$ **17.** $\dfrac{7}{2}, \dfrac{9}{2},$
$\dfrac{11}{2}, \dfrac{13}{2}$ **19.** $-\dfrac{11}{4}, -\dfrac{13}{4}, -\dfrac{15}{4}, -\dfrac{17}{4}$ **21.** 6.84, 9.14, 11.44,
13.74 *Written* **1.** 46 **3.** -241 **5.** $\dfrac{11}{2}$ **7.** 416
9. 379 **11.** $\sqrt{3} - 10\sqrt{2}$ **13.** 27 **15.** 97 **17.** 9
19. 19 **21.** 8 **23.** 70, 85, 100 **25.** $-\dfrac{38}{5}, -\dfrac{26}{5}, -\dfrac{14}{5},$
$-\dfrac{2}{5}$ **27.** $-13, 1, 8, 22$ **29.** 168 **31.** 54 **33.** 304
35. $18,100

Exploratory 1. 116 3. 10,100 5. 375 7. 240
9. 5050 **Written** 1. 632.5 3. 702 5. 135
7. 1210 9. 287 11. −420 13. 735 15. −220
17. 387 19. $\frac{45}{2}$ 21. 6, 36, 66 23. 1, 5, 9 25. 2500
27. 231 29. 1065

Exploratory 1. yes, 5 3. yes, $\frac{3}{2}$ 5. no 7. 135, 405
9. $\frac{1}{3}$, 1 **Written** 1. 54, 162 3. 67.5, 101.25
5. 1, 3 7. $\frac{3}{2}$, 3, 6, 12 9. 12, 6, 3, $\frac{3}{2}$ 11. $a_4 = 56$
13. $a_5 = 32$ 15. $a_6 = -4$ 17. 6, 12, 24 or −6, 12,
−24 19. 4, 2, 1, $\frac{1}{2}$ 21. 10, 20, 40 or −10, 20, −40
23. −3, 6, 24, −48 25. ≈65.6% 27. \$10,486

Exploratory 1. 9; −2; 144; 5 3. 20; $-\frac{1}{4}$; $\frac{5}{64}$; 5 5. 2;
4; 512; 5 7. ±4; ±3; −972; 6 9. −364 11. 15$\frac{3}{4}$
13. 1111 **Written** 1. 93$\frac{18}{25}$ 3. 114,681 5. 732
7. 165 9. 1441 11. $\frac{63}{8}$ 13. $\frac{781}{5}$ 15. $\frac{189}{32}$ 17. ≈5.99
19. $\frac{32}{63}$ 21. 4 23. 2 25. $\frac{196820}{27}$ 27. 127

Exploratory 1. $\frac{1}{2}$; $\frac{2}{3}$; $\frac{3}{2}$ 3. 1; $-\frac{1}{3}$; $\frac{3}{4}$ 5. 1; $\frac{3}{2}$; no sum
7. $\frac{7}{10} + \frac{7}{100} + \frac{7}{1000} + \cdots = \frac{7}{9}$ 9. $\frac{73}{100} + \frac{73}{10,000} +$
$\frac{73}{1,000,000} + \cdots = \frac{73}{99}$ 11. $\frac{152}{1000} + \frac{152}{1,000,000} +$
$\cdots = \frac{152}{999}$ 13. $\frac{93}{100} + \frac{93}{10,000} + \frac{93}{1,000,000} + \cdots =$
$\frac{31}{33}$ **Written** 1. 72 3. 4 5. 27 7. $\frac{9}{5}$ 9. 9 11. 8
13. no sum 15. $\frac{100}{11}$ 17. 1 19. $\frac{31}{99}$ 21. $\frac{410}{999}$ 23. $\frac{41}{90}$
25. 4 + 3 + $\frac{9}{4}$ 27. 9 + (−3) + 1 29. 220 cm
31. 800 feet 33. $\frac{400\sqrt{3}}{3}$

Exploratory 1. j; 4; 3 + 4 + 5 + 6 3. r; 3; 0 +
1 + 2 5. i; 5; 0 + 2 + 4 + 6 + 8 7. p; 4; 6 + 7 +
8 + 9

Written 1. 13 + 20 + 27 + 34 + 41 = 135 3. 5 +
7 + 9 + 11 + 13 = 45 5. 5 + 7 + 9 + 11 + 13 =
45 7. 2 + 4 + 6 + 8 + 10 + 12 + 14 = 56 9. 9 +
8 + 7 + 6 + 5 + 4 + 3 + 2 + 1 = 45 11. 10 +
11 + 12 + 13 + 14 = 60 13. 256 + 1024 + 4096 +

16,384 + 65,536 = 87,296 15. $-12 + 6 + (-3) + \frac{3}{2}$
$= -7\frac{1}{2}$ 17. 650 19. 2540 21. 5555 23. $\frac{255}{8}$
25. $\sum_{n=1}^{5} (3n + 4)$ 27. $\sum_{n=1}^{5} (-4n + 19)$
29. $\sum_{n=1}^{13} (2n - 1)$ 31. $\sum_{n=1}^{6} 2^{4-n}$ 33. $\sum_{n=1}^{6} 243\left(-\frac{2}{3}\right)^{n-1}$
35. $\sum_{n=1}^{5} n^2$ 37. yes

Exploratory 1. 99, 120 3. 80, 99 5. 8, 7, 6, 5
7. −2, −6, −18, −54 9. −4, −4, 4, 4 11. 3, 1, 4, 5
13. $a_n = 2n$ 15. $a_n = \frac{n + 1}{n}$ 17. $a_{n+1} = \frac{1}{3} a_n, a_1 = 1$
19. $a_{n+1} = \left(-\frac{1}{2}\right) a_n, a_1 = 1$ **Written** 1. 29, 33, 37
3. $\frac{17}{10}, \frac{19}{11}, \frac{21}{12}$ 5. $\frac{1}{4}, \frac{2}{9}, \frac{1}{5}$ 7. −16, 18, −20 9. 81, 100,
121 11. 7, 12, 17, 22, 27, 32 13. 1, 2, 3, 5, 8, 13
15. 5, 11, 6, −5, −11, −6 17. $a_{n+1} = a_n + 5, a_1 = 4$;
$a_n = 5n - 1$ 19. $a_{n+1} = \frac{1}{2} a_n, a_1 = \frac{3}{2}; a_n = \frac{3}{2^n}$
21. $a_{n+1} = \frac{1}{5} a_n, a_1 = \frac{7}{2}; a_n = \frac{7}{2(5)^{n-1}}$ 23. $\sum_{n=1}^{5} \frac{3n}{n + 2}$
25. $\sum_{n=1}^{5} 2n(2n + 3)$ 27. $\sum_{n=1}^{5} 6\left(-\frac{1}{3}\right)^{n-1}$ 29. $\sum_{n=1}^{6} \frac{(-1)^{n+1}}{2n - 1}$

Written 1. 1404, 4212 3. 2.875 5. 31, 43 7. 91,
140 9. 18, 29, 47 11. 1, 1, 2, 3, 5, 8, 13, 21, 34, 55,
89, 144, 233, 377, 610, 987, 1597, 2584, 4181, 6765
13. 0.6928 15. $L_n = F_{n+1} + F_{n-1}$ for $n \geq 2$

Exploratory 1. 5040 3. 3,628,800 5. 90 7. 120
9. 5; $4rs^3$ 11. 8; $-35k^4m^3$ 13. 6; $-80x^2$ **Written**
1. $x^4 + 4x^3m + 6x^2m^2 + 4xm^3 + m^4$ 3. $y^7 + 7y^6p +$
$21y^5p^2 + 35y^4p^3 + 35y^3p^4 + 21y^2p^5 + 7yp^6 + p^7$
5. $b^5 - 5b^4z + 10b^3z^2 - 10b^2z^3 + 5bz^4 - z^5$
7. $32m^5 + 80m^4y + 80m^3y^2 + 40m^2y^3 + 10my^4 + y^5$
9. $64b^6 + 192b^5x + 240b^4x^2 + 160b^3x^3 + 60b^2x^4 +$
$12bx^5 + x^6$ 11. $243x^5 - 810x^4y + 1080x^3y^2 -$
$720x^2y^3 + 240xy^4 - 32y^5$ 13. $32y^5 + 80y^4 + 80y^3 +$
$40y^2 + 10y + 1$ 15. $\frac{1}{729} y^6 + \frac{2}{27} y^5 + \frac{5}{3} y^4 + 20y^3 +$
$135y^2 + 486y + 729$ 17. $145,152x^6y^3$ 19. $3360x^6$
21. $2,088,281,250a^4b^7$ 23. \$17,715.61

Chapter Review Page 444
1. 6, 14, 22, 30, 38 3. 234 5. 22 7. 43 boxes
9. 990 11. 2 13. 567 15. 726 17. 95.8 feet 19. $\frac{3}{2}$
21. $\frac{8}{45}$ 23. 495 25. $\sum_{k=1}^{6} (k + 1)k$ 27. $160x^3y^3$

14-1   Page 451

Exploratory **1.** independent **3.** dependent **5.** independent *Written* **1.** 3125 **3.** 90 **5.** 60 **7.** 16 **9.** 720 **11.** 840 **13.** 5040 **15.** 480

14-2   Page 454

Exploratory **1.** false **3.** false **5.** true **7.** true **9.** true *Written* **1.** 720 **3.** 3 **5.** 60 **7.** 34,650 **9.** 2520 **11.** 90,720 **13.** 6 **15.** 72 **17.** 27,720 **19.** 151,200 **21.** 56 **23.** 126 **25.** 42 **27.** 8

14-3   Page 458

Exploratory **1.** reflective, circular **3.** not reflective, circular **5.** not reflective, linear **7.** not reflective, circular **9.** not reflective, linear **11.** not reflective, circular *Written* **1.** 39,600 **3.** 840 **5.** 30 **7.** 6720 **9.** 311,040 **11.** 60 **13.** 9 **15.** $\frac{1}{504}$ **17.** 120 **19.** 72 **21.** 720 **23.** 19,380 **25.** 19,380

14-4   Page 461

Exploratory **1.** combination **3.** combination **5.** permutation **7.** combination *Written* **1.** 56 **3.** 21 **5.** 11 **7.** 30 **9.** 792 **11.** 126 **13.** 351 **15.** 5148 **17.** 6 **19.** 0 **21.** 4320 **23.** 56 **25.** 1680

14-5   Page 464

Exploratory **1.** 1 to 1 **3.** 1 to 6 **5.** 7 to 8 **7.** $\frac{3}{7}$ **9.** $\frac{6}{11}$ **11.** $\frac{5}{16}$ **13.** $\frac{1}{7}$ *Written* **1.** $\frac{1}{16}$ **3.** $\frac{1}{56}$ **5.** $\frac{1}{4}$ **7.** $\frac{1}{19}$ **9.** $\frac{9}{38}$ **11.** $\frac{5}{39}$ **13.** $\frac{4}{7}$ **15.** $\frac{2}{7}$ **17.** $\frac{9}{170}$ **19.** $\frac{18}{85}$ **21.** 33 to 108,257

14-6   Page 467

Exploratory **1.** dependent **3.** independent *Written* **1.** $\frac{1}{28}$ **3.** $\frac{25}{81}$ **5.** $\frac{1}{26}$ **7.** $\frac{3}{13}$ **9.** $\frac{1}{32}$ **11.** $\frac{1}{94,109,400}$ **13.** $\frac{9}{49}$ **15.** $\frac{1}{8}$ **17.** $\frac{5}{48}$ **19.** $\frac{1}{36}$ **21.** $\frac{1}{36}$ **23.** $\frac{1}{6}$

14-7   Page 471

Exploratory **1.** inclusive **3.** exclusive **5.** inclusive **7.** inclusive *Written* **1.** $\frac{1}{4}$ **3.** $\frac{9}{91}$ **5.** $\frac{183}{221}$ **7.** $\frac{2}{3}$ **9.** $\frac{2}{11}$ **11.** $\frac{14}{33}$ **13.** $\frac{12}{221}$ **15.** $\frac{55}{221}$ **17.** $\frac{7}{16}$ **19.** $\frac{35}{64}$ **21.** $\frac{29}{3003}$ **23.** $\frac{160}{429}$ **25.** $\frac{1}{525}$ **27.** $\frac{3}{5}$

14-8   Page 474

Exploratory **1.** binomial; $\frac{3}{8}$ **3.** not binomial **5.** binomial; $\frac{4}{81}$ **7.** not binomial **9.** not binomial

Written **1.** $\frac{1}{16}$ **3.** $\frac{5}{16}$ **5.** $\frac{23}{648}$ **7.** $\frac{1}{81}$ **9.** $\frac{11}{27}$ **11.** $\frac{193}{512}$ **13.** $\frac{32}{625}$ **15.** $\frac{821}{3125}$ **17.** $\frac{1}{8}$ **19.** $\frac{3}{8}$ **21.** $\frac{419,904}{1,953,125}$ **23.** $\frac{1,623,424}{9,765,625}$ **25.** 0.0037881 **27.** 0.8891293

Chapter Review   Page 478

1. 125 **3.** 1,625,702,400 **5.** 112 **7.** 5040 **9.** 1485 **11.** $\frac{1}{13}$ **13.** $\frac{3}{91}$ **15.** $\frac{4}{13}$ **17.** $\frac{1}{4}$

15-1   Page 482

Exploratory **1.** $52,057,000,000 **3.** $3,131,000,000 **5.** $63,664,000,000 **7.** 7,499; 20,348; −2,569; −10,251; 18,037; −884 *Written* **3.** 12 **5.** 33.3 million **7.** 14.4% **9.** General Motors Corporation **11.** 1970 **13.** 6,377,600 **15.** 27 **17.** 46 **21.** 16

15-2   Page 487

Exploratory **1.** 18.2% **3.** 7.4% **5.** 1970 **7.** Health & Hospitals

15-3   Page 492

Exploratory **1.** 3 **3.** 1 **5.** 43 **7.** 2.1 **9.** 12 **11.** none **13.** 1 **15.** none **17.** 2.1 **19.** 12, 13 **21.** 3 **23.** 1.8 **25.** 30.6 **27.** about 3.4 **29.** about 12.3 *Written* **1.** 4; 6; about 3.7 **3.** 18,590.5; none; about 18,939 **5.** $4.25; $3.75 and $4.25; $4.85

15-4   Page 494

Exploratory **1.** 10 **3.** 22 **5.** 48 **7.** 150 **9.** 34 *Written* **1.** 3.6 **3.** 6.3 **5.** 13.6 **7.** 50 **9.** 7.0 **11.** 90 **13.** 200 **15.** 27 **17.** 22 **19.** 22.1 **21.** 6.7 **23.** 8 **25.** about 4.9 **27.** about 1.6 **29.** A

15-5   Page 499

Exploratory **1.** 340 **3.** 495 **5.** 170 **7.** 1360 **9.** 1980 **11.** 680 **13.** 10,880 **15.** 15,840 **17.** 5440 *Written* **1.** 6800 **3.** 5000 **5.** 250 **7.** 68% **9.** 47.5% **11.** 50% **13.** 0.5% **15.** 50% **17.** 2.5%

15-6   Page 503

Exploratory **1.** 1.0 **3.** 3.0 **5.** 5.0 **7.** 6.5 **9.** 160 **11.** 130 **13.** 110 **15.** 80 *Written* **1.** 400 **3.** $y = 400x + 2,000,000$ **5.** $8,000,000 **7.** $-\frac{1}{10}$ **9.** $y = -\frac{1}{10}x + 28$ **11.** 3 **15.** $10,666 **19.** 75

Chapter Review   Page 507

1. $14,958 **3.** +$1051 **5.** +$1947 **7.** +$1365 **11.** 25 plants per plot **13.** 17 plants per plot **15.** 1600 **17.** $\frac{19}{20}$ **19.** $y = \frac{19}{20}x - 95$

CHAPTER 16 TRIGONOMETRIC FUNCTIONS AND IDENTITIES

16-1 Page 513

Exploratory **1.** III **3.** I **5.** I **7.** IV **9.** II **11.** I **13.** IV **15.** III **17.** III **19.** III **21.** IV **23.** II

Written **1.** $\frac{\pi}{2}$ **3.** $-\frac{\pi}{4}$ **5.** $\frac{5\pi}{2}$ **7.** $\frac{5\pi}{6}$ **9.** $\frac{\pi}{4}$ **11.** $\frac{11\pi}{6}$ **13.** $\frac{3\pi}{2}$ **15.** π **17.** $\frac{9\pi}{4}$ **19.** $-\frac{7\pi}{4}$ **21.** 180° **23.** 45° **25.** 540° **27.** −480° **29.** 30° **31.** −45° **33.** 330° **35.** $\frac{900°}{\pi}$ **37.** 990° **39.** $\frac{1170°}{\pi}$

16-2 Page 517

Exploratory **1.** − **3.** − **5.** − **7.** + **9.** + **11.** + ***Written*** **1.** 60° **3.** 300° **5.** π **7.** $\frac{\pi}{2}$ **9.** $\frac{7\pi}{4}$ **11.** 120° **13.** $\frac{\pi}{3}$ **15.** $\frac{3\pi}{4}$ **17.** 120° **19.** $\frac{10\pi}{9}$ **21.** $\frac{\pi}{4}$ **23.** $\frac{4\pi}{3}$ **25.** 240° **27.** 320° **29.** $-\frac{\sqrt{3}}{2}$ **31.** $\frac{1}{2}$ **33.** $-\frac{\sqrt{2}}{2}$ **35.** −1 **37.** $\frac{\sqrt{3}}{2}$ **39.** $\frac{\sqrt{2}}{2}$ **41.** $-\frac{\sqrt{3}}{2}$ **43.** $\frac{\sqrt{3}}{2}$ **45.** $\frac{1}{2}$ **47.** $-\frac{\sqrt{3}}{2}$ **49.** $\frac{1}{2}$ **51.** 1 **53.** 1

16-3 Page 521

Exploratory **1.** 1, 2π **3.** $\frac{2}{3}$, 2π **5.** 6, 3π **7.** 4, $\frac{8\pi}{3}$ **9.** 5, 2π **11.** 1, $\frac{2\pi}{3}$ **13.** 4, 4π **15.** 3, 3π **17.** $\frac{1}{2}$, $\frac{8\pi}{3}$ **19.** 6, π

Written

7.
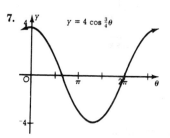
$y = 4 \cos \frac{3}{4}\theta$

11.
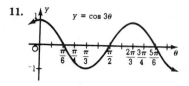
$y = \cos 3\theta$

15.
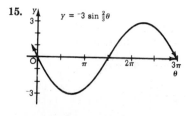
$y = {}^-3 \sin \frac{2}{3}\theta$

17.
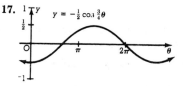
$y = -\frac{1}{2}\cos \frac{3}{4}\theta$

16-4 Page 523

Exploratory **1.** 2π **3.** π **5.** $\frac{\pi}{3}$ **7.** $\frac{8\pi}{3}$ **9.** π **11.** 3π ***Written*** **1.** I, increasing; II, decreasing; III, decreasing; IV, increasing; none **3.** I, increasing; II, increasing; III, increasing; IV, increasing; 90°, 270° **5.** I, increasing; II, increasing; III, decreasing; IV, decreasing; 90°, 270° **7.** 2 **9.** −1 **11.** $-\sqrt{3}$ **13.** 2 **15.** −2 **17.** −2 **19.** −1 **21.** −2 **23.** undefined **25.** 1 **27.** $\frac{\sqrt{3}}{3}$ **29.** 0 **31.** $-\frac{\sqrt{3}}{3}$ **33.** 1

37.
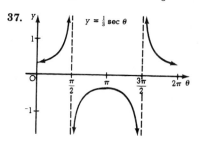
$y = \frac{1}{3}\sec \theta$

43.
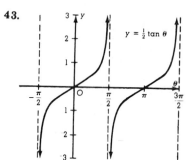
$y = \frac{1}{2}\tan \theta$

16-5 Page 527

Exploratory **1.** yes **3.** yes **5.** yes ***Written*** **1.** $\frac{\sqrt{3}}{2}$ **3.** $\frac{3}{5}$ **5.** $\frac{3\sqrt{5}}{5}$ **7.** $\frac{4\sqrt{17}}{17}$ **9.** $-\frac{4}{5}$ **11.** $\frac{5}{4}$ **13.** $-\frac{\sqrt{17}}{4}$ **15.** $-\frac{\sqrt{3}}{2}$ **17.** $-\frac{12}{13}$ **19.** $\frac{3}{5}$ **21.** 1 **23.** $2\sin x$ **25.** 2

27.
$$1 + \cot^2 \theta \overset{?}{=} \csc^2 \theta$$
$$\frac{\sin^2 \theta + \cos^2 \theta}{\sin^2 \theta} \overset{?}{=} \csc^2 \theta$$
$$\frac{1}{\sin^2 \theta} \overset{?}{=} \csc^2 \theta$$
$$\csc^2 \theta = \csc^2 \theta$$

29.
$$\sin x \sec x \overset{?}{=} \tan x$$
$$\sin x \cdot \frac{1}{\cos x} \overset{?}{=} \tan x$$
$$\frac{\sin x}{\cos x} \overset{?}{=} \tan x$$
$$\tan x = \tan x$$

31. $\pm\frac{\sqrt{15}}{4}$ **33.** $\frac{1}{9}$

Exploratory   1. 1   3. $\csc^2 \theta$ 5. 1   7. $\cos \theta$ 9. $\cot^2 x$

Written   1. $\tan \beta \, (\cot \beta + \tan \beta) \stackrel{?}{=} \sec^2 \beta$

$$\tan \beta \left(\frac{1}{\tan \beta} + \tan \beta \right) \stackrel{?}{=} \sec^2 \beta$$

$$1 + \tan^2 \beta \stackrel{?}{=} \sec^2 \beta$$

$$\sec^2 \beta = \sec^2 \beta$$

3. $\csc x \sec x \stackrel{?}{=} \cot x + \tan x$

$$\frac{1}{\sin x} \cdot \frac{1}{\cos x} \stackrel{?}{=} \frac{\cos x}{\sin x} + \frac{\sin x}{\cos x}$$

$$\frac{1}{\sin x} \cdot \frac{1}{\cos x} \stackrel{?}{=} \frac{\cos^2 x + \sin^2 x}{\sin x \cos x}$$

$$\frac{1}{\sin x \cos x} = \frac{1}{\sin x \cos x}$$

5. $$\frac{\sec \theta}{\sin \theta} - \frac{\sin \theta}{\cos \theta} \stackrel{?}{=} \cot \theta$$

$$\frac{1}{\cos \theta \sin \theta} - \frac{\sin \theta}{\cos \theta} \stackrel{?}{=} \cot \theta$$

$$\frac{1 - \sin^2 \theta}{\cos\theta \sin \theta} \stackrel{?}{=} \cot \theta$$

$$\frac{\cos^2 \theta}{\cos \theta \sin \theta} \stackrel{?}{=} \cot \theta$$

$$\frac{\cos \theta}{\sin \theta} \stackrel{?}{=} \cot \theta$$

$$\cot \theta = \cot \theta$$

7. $$\frac{\sin \alpha}{1 - \cos \alpha} + \frac{1 - \cos \alpha}{\sin \alpha} \stackrel{?}{=} 2 \csc \alpha$$

$$\frac{\sin^2 \alpha + (1 - \cos \alpha)}{(1 - \cos \alpha)(\sin \alpha)} \stackrel{?}{=} \frac{2}{\sin \alpha}$$

$$\frac{\sin^2 \alpha + 1 - 2 \cos \alpha + \cos^2 \alpha}{(1 - \cos \alpha) \sin \alpha} \stackrel{?}{=} \frac{2}{\sin \alpha}$$

$$\frac{2 - 2 \cos \alpha}{(1 - \cos \alpha) \sin \alpha} \stackrel{?}{=} \frac{2}{\sin \alpha}$$

$$\frac{2(1 - \cos \alpha)}{(1 - \cos \alpha) \sin \alpha} \stackrel{?}{=} \frac{2}{\sin \alpha}$$

$$\frac{2}{\sin \alpha} = \frac{2}{\sin \alpha}$$

9. $$\frac{\cos^2 x}{1 - \sin x} \stackrel{?}{=} 1 + \sin x$$

$$\frac{\cos^2 x}{1 - \sin x} \cdot \frac{1 + \sin x}{1 + \sin x} \stackrel{?}{=} 1 + \sin x$$

$$\frac{\cos^2 x \, (1 + \sin x)}{1 - \sin^2 x} \stackrel{?}{=} 1 + \sin x$$

$$\frac{\cos^2 x \, (1 + \sin x)}{\cos^2 x} \stackrel{?}{=} 1 + \sin x$$

$$1 + \sin x = 1 + \sin x$$

11. $$\frac{\sin \theta}{\sec \theta} \stackrel{?}{=} \frac{1}{\tan \theta + \cot \theta}$$

$$\frac{\sin \theta}{\frac{1}{\cos \theta}} \stackrel{?}{=} \frac{1}{\frac{\sin \theta}{\cos \theta} + \frac{\cos \theta}{\sin \theta}}$$

$$\sin \theta \cdot \cos \theta \stackrel{?}{=} \frac{1}{\frac{\sin^2 \theta + \cos^2 \theta}{\cos \theta \cdot \sin \theta}}$$

$$\sin \theta \cdot \cos \theta \stackrel{?}{=} \frac{1}{\frac{1}{\cos \theta \cdot \sin \theta}}$$

$$\sin \theta \cdot \cos \theta = \cos \theta \cdot \sin \theta$$

15. $$\cos^2 x + \tan^2 x \cos^2 x \stackrel{?}{=} 1$$

$$\cos^2 x + \frac{\sin^2 x}{\cos^2 x} \cdot \cos^2 x \stackrel{?}{=} 1$$

$$\cos^2 x + \sin^2 x \stackrel{?}{=} 1$$

$$1 = 1$$

17. $$\frac{1 + \tan^2 \theta}{\csc^2 \theta} \stackrel{?}{=} \tan^2 \theta$$

$$\frac{\sec^2 \theta}{\csc^2 \theta} \stackrel{?}{=} \tan^2 \theta$$

$$\frac{\frac{1}{\cos^2 \theta}}{\frac{1}{\sin^2 \theta}} \stackrel{?}{=} \tan^2 \theta$$

$$\frac{1}{\cos^2 \theta} \cdot \frac{\sin^2 \theta}{1} \stackrel{?}{=} \tan^2 \theta$$

$$\frac{\sin^2 \theta}{\cos^2 \theta} \stackrel{?}{=} \tan^2 \theta$$

$$\tan^2 \theta = \tan^2 \theta$$

21. $$\cos^4 x - \sin^4 x \stackrel{?}{=} \cos^2 x - \sin^2 x$$

$$(\cos^2 x + \sin^2 x)(\cos^2 x - \sin^2 x) \stackrel{?}{=} \cos^2 x - \sin^2 x$$

$$1(\cos^2 x - \sin^2 x) \stackrel{?}{=} \cos^2 x - \sin^2 x$$

$$\cos^2 x - \sin^2 x = \cos^2 x - \sin^2 x$$

23. $$\frac{\tan^2 x}{\sec x - 1} \stackrel{?}{=} 1 + \frac{1}{\cos x}$$

$$\frac{\tan^2 x(\sec x + 1)}{(\sec x - 1)(\sec x + 1)} \stackrel{?}{=} 1 + \frac{1}{\cos x}$$

$$\frac{\tan^2 x(\sec x + 1)}{\tan^2 x} \stackrel{?}{=} 1 + \frac{1}{\cos x}$$

$$\frac{1}{\cos x} + 1 = 1 + \frac{1}{\cos x}$$

25. $$\frac{1 + \sin x}{\sin x} \stackrel{?}{=} \frac{\cot^2 x}{\csc x - 1}$$

$$\frac{1 + \sin x}{\sin x} \stackrel{?}{=} \frac{\csc^2 x - 1}{\csc x - 1}$$

$$\frac{1 + \sin x}{\sin x} \stackrel{?}{=} \frac{(\csc x - 1)(\csc x + 1)}{\csc x - 1}$$

$$\frac{1 + \sin x}{\sin x} \stackrel{?}{=} \csc x + 1$$

$$\frac{1 + \sin x}{\sin x} \stackrel{?}{=} \frac{1}{\sin x} + 1$$

$$\frac{1 + \sin x}{\sin x} = \frac{1 + \sin x}{\sin x}$$

Exploratory   1. $45° + 60°$ 3. $-135° - 30°$
5. $30° + 45°$ 7. $225° + 60°$ *Written*

1. $\dfrac{\sqrt{6} + \sqrt{2}}{4}$ 3. $\dfrac{-\sqrt{2} - \sqrt{6}}{4}$ 5. $\dfrac{-\sqrt{6} - \sqrt{2}}{4}$

7. $\dfrac{\sqrt{6} + \sqrt{2}}{4}$ 9. $\dfrac{-\sqrt{6} - \sqrt{2}}{4}$

11. $\sin(270° - \theta) = \sin 270° \cos \theta - \cos 270° \sin \theta$
$$= -1 \cdot \cos \theta - 0 \cdot \sin \theta$$
$$= -\cos \theta$$

13. $\sin(180° + \theta) = \sin 180° \cos \theta + \cos 180° \sin \theta$
$$= 0 - 1 \cdot \sin \theta$$
$$= -\sin \theta$$

15. $\sin(90° + \theta) = \sin 90° \cos \theta + \cos 90° \sin \theta$
$$= 1 \cdot \cos \theta + 0$$
$$= \cos \theta$$

17. $\dfrac{\sqrt{3}}{2}$ **19.** $\dfrac{1}{2}$ **29.** $-2 - \sqrt{3}$ **31.** $-2 + \sqrt{3}$

33. $\sqrt{3}$ **35.** $-2 - \sqrt{3}$ **37.** $-2 + \sqrt{3}$ **39.** $-\tan \theta$

41. $\dfrac{\tan \alpha - \tan \beta}{1 + \tan \alpha \tan \beta}$

16-8   Page 538

Exploratory **1.** I or II **3.** I or II **5.** I **7.** II **9.** I or II **11.** I or II **13.** I **15.** II   ***Written*** **1.** $\dfrac{\sqrt{3}}{2}; \dfrac{1}{2};$ $\dfrac{\sqrt{2 - \sqrt{3}}}{2}; \dfrac{\sqrt{2 + \sqrt{3}}}{2}$ **3.** $\dfrac{4}{9}\sqrt{5}; -\dfrac{1}{9}; \dfrac{\sqrt{30}}{6}; -\dfrac{\sqrt{6}}{6}$

5. $-\dfrac{120}{169}, \dfrac{119}{169}; \dfrac{5\sqrt{26}}{26}, \dfrac{\sqrt{26}}{26};$ **7.** $-\dfrac{3\sqrt{7}}{8}; -\dfrac{1}{8}; \dfrac{\sqrt{8 - 2\sqrt{7}}}{4};$ $\dfrac{-\sqrt{8 + 2\sqrt{7}}}{4}$ **9.** $-\dfrac{\sqrt{15}}{8}; -\dfrac{7}{8}; \dfrac{\sqrt{10}}{4}, \dfrac{\sqrt{6}}{4};$ **11.** $-\dfrac{3\sqrt{55}}{32}; \dfrac{23}{32};$ $\dfrac{\sqrt{8 - \sqrt{55}}}{4}; \dfrac{-\sqrt{8 + \sqrt{55}}}{4}$ **13.** $\dfrac{\sqrt{15}}{8}; \dfrac{7}{8}; \dfrac{\sqrt{8 + 2\sqrt{15}}}{4};$ $\dfrac{-\sqrt{8 - 2\sqrt{15}}}{4}$

15. $\cos^2 2x + 4 \sin^2 x \cos^2 x \overset{?}{=} 1$
$$\cos^2 2x + \sin^2 2x \overset{?}{=} 1$$
$$1 = 1$$

17.
$$\sin^4 x - \cos^4 x \overset{?}{=} 2 \sin^2 x - 1$$
$$(\sin^2 x - \cos^2 x)(\sin^2 x + \cos^2 x) \overset{?}{=} 2 \sin^2 x - 1$$
$$(\sin^2 x - \cos^2 x) \cdot 1 \overset{?}{=} 2 \sin^2 x - 1$$
$$[\sin^2 x - (1 - \sin^2 x)] \cdot 1 \overset{?}{=} 2 \sin^2 x - 1$$
$$\sin^2 x - 1 + \sin^2 x \overset{?}{=} 2 \sin^2 x - 1$$
$$2 \sin^2 x - 1 = 2 \sin^2 x - 1$$

19. $\sin^2 \theta \overset{?}{=} \dfrac{1}{2}(1 - \cos 2\theta)$

$$\sin^2 \theta \overset{?}{=} \dfrac{1}{2}[1 - (1 - 2\sin^2 \theta)]$$

$$\sin^2 \theta \overset{?}{=} \dfrac{1}{2}[2 \sin^2 \theta]$$

$$\sin^2 \theta = \sin^2 \theta$$

16-9   Page 541

Exploratory **1.** 1 **3.** 2 **5.** 2 **7.** 4 **9.** 4 **11.** 0
Written **1.** 45°, 135°, 225°, 315° **3.** 0°, 180°, 210°, 330° **5.** 30°, 90°, 150°, 270° **7.** 0°, 90°, 270° **9.** 30°, 150° **11.** $0° + n \cdot 120°$ where n is any integer **13.** $45° + n \cdot 180°$ where n is any integer **15.** $120° + n \cdot 360°$ where n is any integer, $240° + n \cdot 360°$ where

n is any integer **17.** $90° + n \cdot 360°$ where n is any integer, $180° + n \cdot 360°$ where n is any integer **19.** $0° + n \cdot 360°$ where n is any integer, $60° + n \cdot 360°$ where n is any integer, $300° + n \cdot 360°$ where n is any integer

16-10   Page 544

Exploratory **1.** $\dfrac{1}{2}$ **3.** $-60°$ **5.** undefined **7.** 1 **9.** 150° **11.** 45° **13.** undefined **15.** 60° **17.** $\dfrac{\sqrt{2}}{2}$ **19.** $-90°$ **21.** 90° **23.** 0   ***Written*** **1.** $\dfrac{1}{2}$ **3.** 90° **5.** $\dfrac{1}{2}$ **7.** $\dfrac{1}{2}$ **9.** $\dfrac{5}{12}$ **11.** $\dfrac{24}{25}$ **13.** $\dfrac{\sqrt{3}}{2}$ **15.** $\dfrac{\sqrt{2}}{2}$ **17.** $-\dfrac{4}{3}$ **19.** $\dfrac{1}{2}$ **21.** $\dfrac{\sqrt{2}}{2}$ **23.** $-\dfrac{1}{2}$ **25.** $\dfrac{1}{2}$ **27.** $\dfrac{\sqrt{3}}{2}$ **29.** $\dfrac{\sqrt{2}}{2}$

Chapter Review   Page 547

1. $\dfrac{2\pi}{3}$ **3.** $\dfrac{3\pi}{2}$ **5.** 60° **7.** $\left(\dfrac{240}{\pi}\right)°$ **9.** 205° **11.** 180° **13.** $\dfrac{2\pi}{3}$ **15.** $\dfrac{16\pi}{9}$ **17.** $\dfrac{\sqrt{3}}{2}$ **19.** -1 **21.** $-\dfrac{1}{2}$ **23.** $-\dfrac{\sqrt{2}}{2}$ **25.** 1 **27.** 1; 2π **29.** 4; π **31.** $\dfrac{2\sqrt{3}}{3}$ **33.** $-\dfrac{1}{2}$ **35.** $\sqrt{3}$ **37.** 2 **39.** $-\dfrac{4}{5}$ **41.** $\dfrac{\sqrt{17}}{4}$ **43.** 0 **45.** $\dfrac{2\sqrt{3}}{3}$

47.
$$\dfrac{\sin \theta}{\tan \theta} + \dfrac{\cos \theta}{\cot \theta} \overset{?}{=} \cos \theta + \sin \theta$$
$$\dfrac{\sin \theta}{\frac{\sin \theta}{\cos \theta}} + \dfrac{\cos \theta}{\frac{\cos \theta}{\sin \theta}} \overset{?}{=} \cos \theta + \sin \theta$$
$$\sin \theta \cdot \dfrac{\cos \theta}{\sin \theta} + \cos \theta \cdot \dfrac{\sin \theta}{\cos \theta} \overset{?}{=} \cos \theta + \sin \theta$$
$$\cos \theta + \sin \theta = \cos \theta \sin \theta$$

49. $\tan x + \cot x \overset{?}{=} \sec x \csc x$
$$\dfrac{\sin x}{\cos x} + \dfrac{\cos x}{\sin x} \overset{?}{=} \sec x \csc x$$
$$\dfrac{\sin^2 x + \cos^2 x}{\cos x \sin x} \overset{?}{=} \sec x \csc x$$
$$\dfrac{1}{\cos x \sin x} \overset{?}{=} \sec x \csc x$$
$$\dfrac{1}{\cos x} \cdot \dfrac{1}{\sin x} \overset{?}{=} \sec x \csc x$$
$$\sec x \csc x = \sec x \csc x$$

51. $-\dfrac{1}{2}$ **53.** $\dfrac{(\sqrt{2} + \sqrt{6})}{4}$ **57.** $\dfrac{7}{8}$ **59.** 0° **61.** 270° **63.** 15°, 75°, 195°, 255° **65.** 30° **67.** 60° **69.** 0

CHAPTER 17   TRIANGLE TRIGONOMETRY
17-1   Page 553

Exploratory **1.** $\sin A = \dfrac{5}{13}; \sin B = \dfrac{12}{13}$ **3.** $\sin A =$

$\frac{3\sqrt{13}}{13}$; $\sin B = \frac{2\sqrt{13}}{13}$ **5.** $\cos A = \frac{\sqrt{5}}{5}$; $\cos B = \frac{2\sqrt{5}}{5}$

7. $\tan A = \frac{5}{12}$; $\tan B = \frac{12}{5}$ **9.** $\tan A = \frac{3}{2}$; $\tan B = \frac{2}{3}$

Written **1.** 0.8000 **3.** 1.3333 **5.** 0.8000 **7.** 0.4706
9. 0.8824 **11.** 0.5333 **13.** 0.3492 **15.** 0.9370
17. 0.3727 **19.** 1.3333 **21.** 2.8636 **23.** 2.1250
25. $\sin A = 0.9428$; $\cos A = 0.3333$; $\tan A = 2.8284$
27. $\sin A = 0.4545$; $\cos A = 0.8907$; $\tan A = 0.5103$

29. $-\frac{\sqrt{3}}{2}$ **31.** $\frac{\sqrt{3}}{2}$ **33.** $-\frac{1}{2}$ **35.** $2 + \sqrt{3}$

17-2   Page 556

Exploratory **1.** 0.6691 **3.** 0.9272 **5.** 343.8 **7.** 1.171
9. 0.4488 **11.** 0.9605 **13.** 0.9511 **15.** 0.4592
Written **1.** 0.7880 **3.** 0.9272 **5.** 0.2812 **7.** 4.511
9. 0.5125 **11.** 50.54 **13.** 1.809 **15.** -2.616
17. -0.2518 **19.** 0.9228 **21.** 59°7′ **23.** 19°13′
25. 44°00′ **27.** 12°32′ **29.** 53°55′ **31.** 45°5′
33. 40°42′ **35.** 35°51′

17-3   Page 559

Exploratory **1.** $\sin 15° = \frac{a}{37}$ **3.** $\sin 49°13′ = \frac{10}{c}$

5. $\cos 16° = \frac{13}{c}$ **7.** $7^2 + b^2 = 16^2$ **9.** $\tan A = \frac{7}{12}$

Written **1.** $c = \sqrt{53}$, $A = 15°57′$, $B = 74°04′$ **3.** $b = 5$, $A = 67°23′$, $B = 22°37′$ **5.** $a = \sqrt{133}$, $A = 62°31′$, $B = 27°29′$ **7.** $a = 3.86$, $b = 13.46$, $B = 74°$
9. $B = 52°45′$, $c = 13.82$, $a = 8.36$ **11.** $A = 47°50′$, $c = 12.14$, $b = 8.15$ **13.** $A = 77°$, $a = 5.85$, $b = 1.35$
15. $B = 13°$, $a = 181.92$, $c = 186.71$ **17.** $A = 57°$, $c = 39.35$, $b = 21.43$ **19.** $B = 34°5′$, $a = 13.25$, $b = 8.97$ **21.** $B = 45°$, $b = 7$, $a = 7$ **23.** $B = 75°$, $a = 6.47$, $b = 24.15$

17-4   Page 562

Written **1.** 64.35 m **3.** 1119.36 ft **5.** 7.42 ft
7. 22.07 m **9.** 9°36′ **11.** 22°48′ **13.** $x = 63°26′$, $y = 26°34′$, $z = 63°26′$ **15.** 100 ft, 300 ft **17.** 102.25 ft
19. 4.05 cm **21.** 164.92 km

17-5   Page 566

Exploratory **1.** area $= \left(\frac{1}{2}\right)(10)(17)(\sin 46°)$ **3.** area

$= \left(\frac{1}{2}\right)(15)(30)(\sin 90°)$ **5.** $\frac{\sin 50°}{14} = \frac{\sin B}{10}$ **7.** $\frac{\sin 53°}{a} =$

$\frac{\sin 61°}{2.8}$ *Written* **1.** 55.152 **3.** 27.531 **5.** 37.001
7. 63.2089 **9.** $C = 74°$, $b = 8.8904$, $c = 10.19$
11. $B = 60°19′$, $C = 36°31′$, $c = 47.95$ **13.** $A = 52°$, $b = 100.17$, $c = 90.40$ **15.** $B = 52°53′$, $A = 62°27′$, $a = 16.68$ **17.** $A = 24°24′$, $a = 5.54$, $c = 11.74$
19. 93.13 cm **21.** 536.19 ft **23.** 424.26 mi
25. 109.63 ft

17-6   Page 570

Exploratory **1.** Law of Cosines **3.** Law of Cosines
5. Law of Cosines **7.** Law of Cosines **9.** Law of
Cosines   *Written* **1.** $A = 46°37′$, $B = 73°50′$, $C = 59°33′$ **3.** $A = 44°25′$, $B = 57°07′$, $C = 78°28′$
5. $b = 17.92$, $A = 54°42′$, $C = 78°18′$ **7.** $C = 81°$, $a = 9.11$, $b = 12.15$ **9.** $A = 29°58′$, $B = 110°15′$, $C = 39°47′$ **11.** $P = 1434.26$ ft; $A = 86,804.28$ ft^2
13. 228.38 mi; 19°53′ **15.** 183.03 mi **17.** 35°41′
19. 2033 kilometers

17-7   Page 574

Exploratory **1.** no triangle **3.** 1 triangle **5.** 1
triangle   *Written* **1.** 1; $B = 90°$, $C = 53°08′$, $c = 8$
3. none **5.** 1; $A = 44°46′$, $B = 37°14′$, $b = 54.99$
7. none **9.** none **11.** none **13.** none **15.** none

Chapter Review   Page 577

1. 0.6000 **3.** 0.8000 **5.** 0.7500 **7.** 1.6667 **9.** 0.7500
11. $\sqrt{3}$ **13.** 0.9397 **15.** 0.8192 **17.** 1.0724
19. 68°00′ **21.** 23°30′ **23.** 19°10′ **25.** $B = 65°$, $a = 2.54$, $b = 5.44$ **27.** $A = 5°$, $b = 70.98$, $c = 71.25$
29. $c = 3.16$, $A = 18°26′$, $B = 71°34′$ **31.** $a = 7.14$, $A = 45°34′$, $B = 44°26′$ **33.** 55.53 m **35.** 38°39′
37. $c = 11.65$, $C = 63°11′$, $B = 66°49′$ **39.** $A = 51°$, $a = 70.22$, $c = 89.69$ **41.** $a = 4.36$, $B = 23°24′$, $C = 96°35′$ **43.** $c = 4.54$, $A = 58°05′$, $B = 81°55′$ **45.** no solution **47.** $B = 35°08′$, $C = 98°52′$, $c = 13.74$

Index

A

Absolute value, 21
  inequalities, 33
Addition
  associative property, 10
  commutative property, 10
  complex numbers, 204
  identity property, 10
  inequalities, properties, 25
  inverse property, 10
  matrices, 121, 601
  probabilities, 469
  property for equations, 14
  rational expressions, 350
Additive identity, 10
Additive inverses, 10
Agnesi, Maria, 468
Algebraic expressions, 4
Amplitude, 520
Angles
  coterminal, 511
  depression, 561
  elevation, 561
  radian, 512
  sides, 511
  standard position, 511
Antilogarithm, 386
Applications, 32, 51, 83, 133,
  158, 206, 231, 262, 277, 314,
  357, 380, 415, 465, 500, 525,
  571
  See also Problem Solving,
  Formulas
Arccosine, 543
Arcsine, 543
Arctangent, 543
Area
  elipses, 293
Arithmetic means, 409
Arithmetic sequence, 407
  common difference, 407
  *n*th term, 408
Arithmetic series, 411
  sum, 412
Arrangements, probability
  and, 452
Associative properties, 10
Asymptotes, 361

hyperbola, 287
Augmented matrices, 117
Axis of symmetry, 246

B

Bar graph, 485, 489
Base, exponent, 3
Bases, change of, 393
BASIC
  See also Computer Programs
  Data statement, 582
  DIM statement, 597, 600
  END statement, 582
  E notation, 583
  flow charts, 594
  FOR-NEXT statements, 591
  GO TO statement, 587
  IF-THEN statement, 587
  internal functions, 603
  LET statement, 585
  loops, 587, 591
  matrices, 600
  order of operations, 583
  PRINT statement, 582, 589
  program, 582
  programming exercises,
  606–609
  READ statement, 582
  RUN command, 583
  subscripted variables, 597
  string variables, 586
  variables, 585
Bernoulli, Jacob, 484
Binomial expansions, 439, 472,
  473
Binomials, 154
  conjugates, 188
  factoring, 159
  FOIL rule, 155
Binomial theorem, 439
Binomial trials, 473
Boundary, 67, 260
Bounds, of zeros, 322

C

Calculators, 6, 9, 16, 24, 47,
  56, 95, 116, 153, 161, 175,
  184, 189, 192, 196, 225, 245,
  280, 293, 313, 345, 374, 387,
  400, 435, 464, 496, 524, 531,
  557
Center
  circle, 278
  ellipse, 282
  hyperbola, 287
Central tendency, 490
Chapter Review, 37, 71, 102,
  139, 178, 212, 240, 266, 304,
  338, 367, 403, 444, 478, 506,
  547, 577
Chapter Summary, 36, 70, 101,
  138, 177, 211, 239, 266, 302,
  337, 367, 402, 443, 477, 505,
  546, 576
Chapter Test, 39, 73, 103, 141,
  179, 213, 241, 267, 305, 339,
  369, 405, 445, 479, 507, 549,
  579
Characteristic, 385
Circle graphs, 486, 489
Circles, 278
  center, 278
  equation, 278
  unit, 512
Circular permutations, 455
Closure, 12
Coefficient, 145
Combinations, 459
  formula, 459
Common difference, 407
Common logarithms, 385
Common ratio, 416
Commutative properties, 10
Completeness property, 8
Completing the square, 220
Complex conjugates theorem,
  319
Complex fractions, 346
Complex numbers, 204
  conjugates, 207
  division, 207
  properties, 209

Normal distribution, 497
nth root, 181
  properties, 182
nth term
  arithmetic sequence, 408
  geometric sequence, 416
Numbers
  complex, 204
  imaginary, 202
  integers, 8
  irrational, 8
  perfect, 227
  rational, 8
  real, 8
  whole, 8
Number line, distance, 271

O

Octants, 108
Odds, 463
  application, 465
Open sentences, 13
Operation symbols, 3
Ordered pairs, 41
Ordered triples, 105, 108
Order of operations, 3
  BASIC, 583

P

Parabolas, 246, 274
  axis of symmetry, 246, 274
  directrix, 274
  focus, 274
  graphs
    $y = a(x - h)^2$, 250
    $y = a(x - h)^2 + k$, 253
  latus rectum, 275
  maximum or minimum
    values, 256
  problem solving, 256
  vertex, 246, 274
Parallel lines, 77
Pascal, Blaise, 442
Pascal's triangle, 439, 442
Perfect numbers, 227
Periodic function, 516
  application, 525
Permutations, 452
  circular, 455

linear, 452
  reflections, 457
  repetitions, 453
Perpendicular lines, 78
Pictograph, 485
Plane,
  equation, 108
  intersecting, 114
Polynomials, 154
  approximating zeros, 323
  complex conjugates theorem,
    319
  depressed, 312
  Descartes' rule of signs, 320
  division, 169
  factoring, 159–167
  factor theorem, 311
  function, 308
  fundamental theorem of
    algebra, 319
  graphs, 326
  in one variable, 307
  location principle, 323
  rational zero theorem, 316
  remainder theorem, 310
  synthetic division, 172
  zeros, 315
Power property, logarithms,
  383
Powers
  of binomials, 439
  computation using
    logarithms, 396
  division, 148
  multiplication, 146
  of a product, 146
  of a quotient, 151
  raising to a power, 146
  zero, 148
Prediction equation, 501
Principal values, 542
PRINT statement, 582, 589
Probability, 449–479
  binomial trials, 473
  dependent events, 466
  inclusive events, 470
  independent events, 466
  mutually exclusive events,
    469
  success and failure, 462
Problem solving
  equations, 17
  exponential equations, 397
  figures and drawings, 560
  four-step plan, 17–18
  guess and check, 219

identify necessary
    information, 168
  inequalities, 28
  interpolation, 391
  linear functions, 64
  linear programming, 93
  logarithms, 397
  make a table, 297
  parabolas, 256
  patterns, 63
  quadratic equations, 232
  rational equations, 358
  right triangles, 561
  sequences, 420
  simpler problem, 92
  three variables, 134
  work backwards, 535
Product property
  logarithms, 381
Properties
  associative, 10
  commutative, 10
  completeness, 8
  complex numbers, 209
  distributive, 11
  equality, 13–14
  equality of exponential
    functions, 373
  identity, 10
  inverse, 10
  inverse functions, 332
  logarithmic functions, 377
  logarithms, 381
  nth root, 182
  powers, 146, 148, 151
  radicals, 185, 190
  trichotomy, 25
  zero product, 217
Proportion, variation, 363
Pure imaginary number, 202
Pythagorean theorem, 271

Q

Quadrants, 41
Quadratic equations, 217
  completing the square, 220
  problem solving, 232
  sum and product of
    solutions, 228
  zero product property, 217
Quadratic expression, 307
Quadratic form, 235
  solving equations, 235